Methods of
QUANTITATIVE INORGANIC ANALYSIS

Methods of

QUANTITATIVE INORGANIC ANALYSIS

An Encyclopedia of Gravimetric, Titrimetric and Colorimetric Methods

by **KAZUNOBU KODAMA**
Nagoya Municipal Industrial Research Institute
Nagoya, Japan

1963
INTERSCIENCE PUBLISHERS
a division of John Wiley & Sons—New York—London

Library of Congress Catalog Card Number 63–19270

Printed in Great Britain by Page Bros. (Norwich) Limited, Norwich

PREFACE

The aims and layout of this book are described in the following introductory chapter and need not be repeated here. I have attempted to collect all published methods in the field of inorganic gravimetric, titrimetric and colorimetric analysis. The attempt may not have been wholly successful, but the comprehensive data which have been compiled, for example, about 100 colorimetric procedures for iron, should be of considerable value to all analytical chemists. The coverage is complete to the end of 1957 publications, the delay in the appearance of this volume being caused by the work of checking and correction. The whole field has been concentrated and compressed into this comparatively small volume, hence it has proved essential to employ formulas and abbreviation wherever possible; the system familiar to readers of *Chemical Abstracts* has been followed.

I shall be grateful to receive information on any omissions or errors which may be noted.

I am deeply indebted to John Wiley and Sons, Springer-Verlag, D. Van Nostrand Co., Chapman and Hall Ltd., Prentice-Hall Inc., the American Chemical Society, the American Society for Testing Materials, the United States Atomic Energy Commission and Dr. F. Hecht, all of whom have given me permission to quote from their books or journals. I am also indebted to the Scientific Research Institute of Tokyo, to the Nagoya Municipal Industrial Research Institute and to other libraries of universities and institutes where the material for this book was collected.

I wish to express my thanks to Dr. O. Shimamura of Tokyo University, to Mr. T. Kanie of the Nagoya Institute, and to innumerable other analysts for valuable information, and, finally, to my wife for her work in preparing the typescript.

January, 1963 K. Kodama

CONTENTS

PART II. ORGANIC REAGENTS IN INORGANIC ANALYSIS

PART III. DETERMINATION OF ELEMENTS

Hydrogen Sulfide Group

Ag, Hg, Pb, Bi, Cu, Cd, Re; As, Sb, Sn, Ge, Mo, Se, Te; Au, Ru, Rh, Pd, Os, Ir, Pt

I. ELEMENTS FORMING SULFIDES INSOLUBLE IN ACIDS AND ALKALI SULFIDES

Ag, Hg, Pb, Bi, Cu, Cd, Re (and Ru, Rh, Pd, Os)

II. ELEMENTS FORMING SULFIDES INSOLUBLE IN ACIDS BUT SOLUBLE IN ALKALI SULFIDES

As, Sb, Sn, Ge, Mo, Se, Te (and Au, Pt, Ir)

LIST OF ABBREVIATIONS USED

abs.	absolute
Ac.	acetyl (AcH acetaldehyde; AcOH acetic acid)
a.c.	alternating current
addn.	addition
addnl.	additional
alc.	alcohol, alcoholic
alk.	alkaline (not alkali)
am.	amyl (not ammonium)
amp.	ampere(s)
amt.	amount
anhyd.	anhydrous
app.	apparatus
approx.	approximate, approximately
aq.	aqueous
atm.	atmospheric
at. wt.	atomic weight
biol.	biological
b.p.	boiling point
Bu.	butyl
Bz.	benzoyl
calc.	calculate
calcd.	calculated
calcn.	calculation
chem.	chemical
coeff.	coefficient
com.	commercial
compd.	compound (noun)
compn.	composition
conc.	concentrate (verb)
concd.	concentrated
concn.	concentration
const.	constant
contg.	containing
cor.	corrected
cryst.	crystalline
crystd.	crystallized
crystn.	crystallization
d.	density
d.c.	direct current
decomp.	decompose
decompd.	decomposed
decompn.	decomposition
deriv.	derivative
det.	determine
det.	determine
detd.	determined
detn.	determination
diam.	diameter
dil.	dilute
dild.	diluted
diln.	dilution
dissocd.	dissociated
dissocn.	dissociation
distd.	distilled
distg.	distilling
distn.	distillation
elec.	electrical
e.m.f.	elecromotive force
en.	ethylenediamine
equil.	equilibrium
equiv.	equivalent
est.	estimate
Et ethyl.	($Et_2$0 ethyl ether)
evap.	evaporate
evapd.	evaporated
evapg.	evaporating
evapn.	evaporation
expt.	experiment
exptl.	experimental
ext.	extract
extd.	extracted
extn.	extraction
F	formal (concentration)
g.	gram(s)
geol.	geological
hr.	hour(s)
in.	inches
inorg.	inorganic
insol.	insoluble
iso-Bu, iso-Pr, etc.	isobutyl, isopropyl, etc.
kg.	kilogram
l.	liter(s)
lab.	laboratory
lb.	pound(s)
m.	meter(s)
M	molar
ma.	milliampere(s)
manuf.	manufacture
max.	maximum(s)
Me	methyl (MeOH, methanol; Me_2CO acetone)
mech.	mechanical
meq.	milliequivalent
min.	minimum, minute(s)
mixt.	mixture
ml.	milliliter(s)
mm.	millimeter(s)
mμ	millimicron(s)
mol.	molecule, molecular
mol. wt.	molecular weight
m.p.	melting point

N	normal (concentration)
no.	number
org.	organic
p.d.	potential difference
petr. ether	petroleum ether
Ph.	phenyl
pn.	propylenediamine
powd.	powdered
p.p.m.	parts per million
ppt.	precipitate
pptd.	precipitated
pptg.	precipitating
pptn.	precipitation
Pr.	propyl
prep.	prepare
prepd.	prepared
prepn.	preparation
py	pyridine
qual.	qualitative
quant.	quantitative
resp.	respectively
r.p.m.	revolutions per minute
sapon.	saponification
sat.	saturate
satd.	saturated
satg.	saturating
satn.	saturation
sec.	second(s)
sep.	separate (verb)
sepd.	separated
sepg.	separating
sepn.	separation
sol.	soluble
soln.	solution
soly.	solubility
sp. gr.	specific gravity
sq. cm.	square centimeter
tech.	technical
temp.	temperature
v.	volt(s)
vol.	volume
wt.	weight

PART I

GENERAL CONSIDERATIONS

1

INTRODUCTION

This book was initially intended to provide collected data on all the methods of inorganic quantitative analysis; these procedures could then be compared and the most accurate, the most reliable and the shortest technique could be selected.

The data provided would then be available for research as well as for routine analytical purposes and much tedious literature research would not be an essential preliminary to the solution of any analytical problem which presented itself.

The field is, however, so vast that it proved essential to limit the collection to chemical (gravimetric, titrimetric and photometric) methods; physical methods (spectrochemical and X-ray analysis, polarography, radiochemical methods, etc.) are not considered. Many excellent textbooks are already available in the field of 'instrumental' analysis. The texts which deal with gravimetric, titrimetric or colorimetric analysis are less satisfactory and are seldom comprehensive.

Part I consists of an introductory description of general procedures. In Part II are enumerated and briefly described organic reagents used in inorganic analysis, for here certain difficulties may arise for inorganic analysts who are unfamiliar with organic chemistry. Where organic reagents are concerned in Part III, reference to Part II is also necessary. For example, titrimetric methods involving oxine or anthranilic acid for the determination of an element via its salts are described in Part III and these methods may not be the same as those given in Part II; the methods in Part II are generally better. Parts I and II are essential to the proper understanding of Part III.

The main emphasis of this book is placed on Part III, in which methods for the determination of individual elements are discussed in the order used in Hillebrand and Lundell's book. Each chapter deals with one element or group of elements and is divided into the following parts: Introduction, Attack, Separation, and Determination. Under Determination, selected methods are described which are suitable for macro, semi-micro or micro amounts of the element concerned. The other methods are classified as gravimetric, titrimetric or colorimetric and are normally listed according to their worth, although this arrangement is not always strictly maintained. In most cases, the methods are also listed according to the principles of their first steps. For example, the gravimetric method for silver and hydrochloric acid is described in the same place as the titrimetric, nephelometric and colorimetric methods based on the precipitation of silver halides or pseudohalides.

For the sake of brevity, theoretical discussions and details of apparatus are omitted; material which is readily available in other books is merely cited. The number of references has been kept to a minimum by selecting some well-known standard books (see below). References which appear in Part III are usually omitted in Part II. Many abbreviations are used in the description of the analytical procedures; all of these should be familiar to readers of *Chemical Abstracts*; they are listed on p. xiii. Inorganic reagents are represented by their chemical formulae and the number of molecules of water of crystallization is usually ignored; the purest commercial grade of reagent should generally be used. The trivial names of organic compounds are used throughout the book. Where several names exist for a particular compound, only one name is chosen although it may differ from that of original reference; alternative names are listed in Part II. However, despite the abbreviations, sufficient information has been given in many cases to make recourse to the original literature unnecessary. The temperature data which are given for drying, heating or igniting precipitates are of Japanese origin; Duval's data are shown in parentheses whenever they differ.

This book has been compiled from the texts listed below and from many different journals. The ground is covered to the end of 1957.

Bibliography

HILLEBRAND, W. F. and LUNDELL, G. E. F., *Applied Inorganic Analysis* (1929). 2nd ed. revised by LUNDELL, G. E. F., BRIGHT, H. A. and HOFFMAN, J. I., Wiley, New York (1953). This is the authoritative text on inorganic analytical chemistry. The revision of the methods of determination of individual elements in the second edition is not very satisfactory. The majority of the methods are also cited in the following two books.

Scott, W. W., *Standard Methods of Chemical Analysis*, 5th ed. by Furman, N. H., Vols. I–II, Van Nostrand, New York (1939/40). This was written by more than twenty authorities and the treatment is uneven.

Kimura, K., *Inorganic Quantitative Analysis*, Kyoritsu Shuppan, Tokyo (1949).

Fresenius, F. and Jander, G., *Handbuch der analytischen Chemie*, Teil III, Bd. Ia, IIa (1940), IIb (1945), IVb (1950), Vaα (1957), Vaγ (1951), VIIaα (1950), VIIIa (1949), Springer, Berlin. These texts are comprehensive but some are now out-of-date. The following volumes were not available to the author: Bd. IIIaβ/IIIb, 2. Aufl. (1956), Vaβ (1953), Vb (1957), VIaα (1953), VIIIbβ (1953).

Schoeller, W. R. and Powell, A. R., *The Analysis of Minerals and Ores of the Rarer Elements*, 3rd ed. by Powell, A. R., Griffin, London (1955). This is an excellent text except for colorimetric analysis.

Hecht, F. and Donau, J., *Anorganische Microgewichtsanalyse*, Springer, Wien (1940). This is valuable for microanalytical techniques.

Schoeller, W. R., *The Analytical Chemistry of Tantalum and Niobium. The Analysis of their Minerals and the Application of Tannin in Gravimetric Analysis*, Chapman & Hall, London (1937).

Pigott, E. C., *Ferrous Analysis. Modern Practice and Theory*, 2nd ed., Chapman & Hall, London (1953). Several excellent methods are described.

A.S.T.M. *1956 Book of A.S.T.M. Methods for Chemical Analysis of Metals*, Am. Soc. for Testing Materials, Philadelphia.

Welcher, F. J., *Organic Analytical Reagents*, Vols. I–IV, Van Nostrand, New York (1947/48). This is the standard comprehensive work on organic reagents. Much detail is given but no attempt at criticism is made.

Sandell, E. B., *Colorimetric Determination of Traces of Metals*, 2nd ed., Interscience, New York (1950).

Yoe, J. H., *Photometric Chemical Analysis*, Vol, I, Colorimetry, Wiley, New York (1928).

The above texts have been selected as standard and nearly all the methods of determination included in them are cited in the present book.

The following books have also been referred to.

Treadwell, W. D., *Tabellen und Vorschriften zur quantitativen Analyse*, Deuticke, Leipzig-Wien (1938); 2. Aufl. (1947).

Treadwell, F. P. and Hall, W. T., *Analytical Chemistry*, Vol. II, Quantitative Analysis, 9th ed., Wiley, New York (1942).

Mellor, J. W. and Thompson, H. V., *A Treatise on Quantitative Inorganic Analysis*, 2nd ed., Griffin, London (1938). Numerous early references are cited, but the treatment of rarer elements is not satisfactory.

Willard, H. H. and Diehl, H., *Advanced Quantitative Analysis*, Van Nostrand, New York (1943).

Kolthoff, I. M. and Sandell, E. B., *Textbook of Quantitative Inorganic Analysis*, Macmillan, New York (1950).

van Tongeren, W., *Gravimetric Analysis*, Centen, Amsterdam (1937).

Kolthoff, I. M., Stenger, V. A. and Belcher, R., *Volumetric Analysis*, Vols. I–III, Interscience, New York (1942/57).

Belcher, R. and Wilson, C. L., *New Methods in Analytical Chemistry*, Chapman & Hall, London (1955).

A.O.A.C., *Official Methods of the Association of Official Agricultural Chemists*, 7th ed., Washington (1950). 8th ed. (1955).

Washington, H. S., *The Chemical Analysis of Rocks*, 4th ed., Wiley, New York (1930).

Groves, A. W., *Silicate Analysis*, 2nd ed., Allen & Unwin, London (1951).

Chemists of the U.S. Steel Corporation, *Sampling and Analysis of Carbon and Alloy Steels*, Reinhold, New York (1938).

Tawara, K., *et al.*, *Tekko Kagaku-Bunseki Zensho*, Part I–II, Nikkan-Kogyo, Tokyo (1952/53).

Lundell, G. E. F., Hoffman, J. I. and Bright, H. A., *Chemical Analysis of Iron and Steel*, Wiley, New York (1931).

Snell, F. P. and Snell, C. T., *Colorimetric Methods of Analysis*, Vol. II, Van Nostrand, New York (1949).

Allport, N. L., *Colorimetric Analysis*, Chapman & Hall, London (1945). 2nd ed. Vol. I (1957) was not available. The references given are limited.

Rüdisule, A. *Nachweis, Bestimmung und Trennung der chemischen Elemente*, Bd. 1–9 (1913+), *Nachtrag* (1937), Drechsel, Bern.

Berl, E. and Lunge, G., *Chemisch-technische Untersuchungsmethoden*, 8. Aufl., Bd. I–V (1931/34). *Ergänzungswerk* von J. D'Ans, Teil I–III (1939/40), Springer, Berlin.

Gmelins Handbuch der anorganischen Chemie, 8. Aufl., Verlag Chemie, Weinheim.

Shibata, Y., *Muki-Kagaku-Zensho*, Maruzen, Tokyo (1944+).

Böttger, W., *Physikalische Methoden der analytischen Chemie*, Bd. I–III, Akad. Verlagsges., Leipzig (1935). Bd. II, 2. Aufl. (1949) was not available.

Berl, W. G., *Physical Methods in Chemical Analysis*, Vols. I–III, Academic Press, New York (1950/56).

Willard, H. H., *et al.*, *Instrumental Methods of Analysis*, Van Nostrand, New York (1952).

Lingane, J. J., *Electroanalytical Chemistry*, Interscience, New York (1953).

Milton, R. F. and Waters, W. A., *Methods of Quantitative Micro-Analysis*, Arnold, London (1949). About half this text is devoted to inorganic analysis.

The following books were not available for reference.

Duval, C., *Traité de micro-analyse minérale*, Tome I–III (1954/56). Presses scientifiques internationales, Paris.

Delahay, P., *Instrumental Analysis*, Macmillan, New York (1957).

Harley, J. H. and Wiberly, S. E., *Instrumental Analysis*, Wiley, New York (1954).

Charlot, G. and Bezier, D., *Modern Methods of Quantitative Inorganic Analysis*, Tr. by Murray, R. C., Wiley, New York (1957).

Proske, O., *et al.*, *Analyse der Metalle*, Bd. I–III (1949/56), Springer, Berlin.

Ginsberg, H., *Leichtmetallanalyse*, Gruyter, Berlin (1955).

Lange, B., *Kolorimetrische Analyse*, 5. Aufl., Verlag Chemie, Weinheim (1956).

Kortüm, G., *Kolorimetrie, Photometrie und Spektrometrie*, Springer, Berlin (1955).

Am. Public Health Association, *Standard Methods for Examination of Water, Sewage, and Industrial Wastes*, 10th ed., New York (1955).

For theory, etc. the following books should be consulted.

LUNDELL, G. E. F. and HOFFMAN, J. I., *Outlines of Methods of Chemical Analysis* (1938); 2nd ed., Wiley, New York (1951).

SMITH, T. B., *Analytical Processes, A Physico-Chemical Interpretation*, 2nd ed., Arnold, London (1940).

HAMILTON, L. F. and SIMPSON, S. G., *Calculations of Analytical Chemistry*, 4th ed., McGraw-Hill, New York (1954).

Kagaku-Zikken-Gaku, Part I, Vols. IX–X, Kawade, Tokyo (1942).

Zikken-Kagaku-Koza, Vol. XV, Maruzen, Tokyo (1957+).

Other important texts are listed below.

KIRK, P. L., *Quantitative Ultramicroanalysis*, Wiley, New York (1951).

ROSIN, J., *Reagent Chemicals and Standards*, 3rd ed., Van Nostrand, New York (1955).

STROUTS, C. R. N., *et al.*, *Analytical Chemistry*, Vols. I–II Clarendon, Oxford (1955).

YOE, J. H. and KOCH, Jr., H. J. (editors), *Trace Analysis*, Wiley, New York (1957).

The recent titles of *Die chemische Analyse* edited by MARGOSCHES, B. M. and BÖTTGER, W. (Enke, Stuttgart) are listed below.

Bd. 4–5. SCHLEICHER, A., *Elektroanalytische Schnellmethoden*, 3. Aufl. (1947).

Bd. 26. JANDER, G. and PFUNDT, O., *Leitfähigkeitstitrationen und Leitfähigkeitsmessungen* (1934).

Bd. 30. LIESCHE, O., *Rechenverfahren und Rechenhilfsmittel mit Anwendungen auf die analytischen Chemie* (1932).

Bd. 31. WEIHRICH, R. und WINKEL, A., *Die chemische Analyse in der Stahlindustrie*, 4 Aufl. (1954).

Bd. 33. JANDER, G., ed., *Neuere massanalytishe Methoden*, 4. Aufl. (1956).

Bd. 34. BERG. R., *Die analytische Verwendung von o-Oxychinolin*, ('*Oxin*'), 2. Aufl. (1938).

Bd. 35. WINKLER, L. W., *Auswählte Untersuchungsverfahren für das chemische Laboratorium*, Neue Folge (1936).

Bd. 36. WOGRINZ, A., *Analytische Chemie der Edelmetalle* (1936).

Bd. 37. PRODINGER, W., *Organische Fällungsmittel in der quantitativen Analyse*, 4. Aufl. (1957).

Bd. 38. KURTENACKER, A., *Analytische Chemie der Sauerstoffsäuren des Schwefels* (1938).

Bd. 39. BAYER, F., *Gasanalyse*, 2. Aufl. (1941).

Bd. 40. WEBER, K., *Inhibitorwirkungen* (1938).

Bd. 41. BRENNECKE, E., *Schwefelwasserstoff als Reagens in der quantitativen Analyse* (1939).

Bd. 42. MIKA, J., *Die exakten Methoden der Mikromassanalyse* (1939).

Bd. 43. MORITZ, H., *Spektrochemische Betriebsanalyse*, 2. Aufl. (1956).

Bd. 44. GERICKE, S., *Analytische Chemie der Düngmittel* (1949).

Bd. 45. SCHWARZENBACH, G., *Die komplexometrische Titration*, 2. Aufl. (1956).

2

GENERAL PROCEDURES

1. THE SAMPLE

The method of sampling depends on the object of the analysis. It is essential that the sample should be representative of the whole, e.g. in the analysis of rocks or ores. In mineral analysis, foreign matter should be removed as far as possible (see, e.g., Scott, p. 1300, Schoeller and Powell, p. 1, A.S.T.M., p. 57). Although details cannot be given here, it must be stressed that the method of sampling is just as important as the analytical method; for if the sample is taken wrongly, erroneous conclusions may be drawn.

The sample should generally be ground to an impalpable powder. Scattering or contamination (especially from sieves) must be avoided, and the sample must be stored with suitable precautions because the finer the powder, the greater its hygrosco icity, etc.

Samples may be divided into four groups (Lundell and Hoffman).

Rocks and refractories. Rocks contain Si, Al, Fe, Ca, Mg, Na, K, H, O as major constituents; Mn, Ti as minor constituents; and Cu, Co, Ni, Zn, V, Cr, Zr, Sr, Ba, Li, S, Cl, F, C, N as traces. Refractories contain the same major constituents as rocks but the proportions may differ; they also contain Pb, Bi, Cu, Cd, As, Sb, Sn, Mo, Se, Au, Co, Ni, Zn, U, Cr, rare earths, Ti, Zr, P, S, F, B, some of which may occasionally be major constituents. Glass is the most complicated of these materials.

Iron and its alloys. Fe, Mn, C, Si, P, S are usually present; Cu, Co, Ni, Cr, Mo, V, Ti, W, Al are often added as alloying components, and U, Zr, Nb, Ta, Ce, Se, B are occasionally added; As, Sb, Sn, N, O, H may be present as impurities.

Non-ferrous metals and their alloys. Alloys containing Cu, Pb, Sn, Zn, Ni, Bi, Ag, Au, Pt, Al, Mg, Ti, Ta as the base metal are often used. Cu, Pb, Sn, Sb, Ni, Fe, Mn, Zn, Al, P are commonly found; Bi, Cd, Ag, Au, Pt, Pd, Cr, Ti, Mg, Si are often found; and Hg, As, Te, Ru, Rh, Os, Ir, Co, V, Be, Ta, Ca, Sr, Ba, Na, Li, S, C are rarely found.

Minerals, ores and chemicals. The variety of these is such that preliminary identification of all their components is essential. Total analysis is normally needed for minerals; ores and chemicals must be analyzed for both their wanted and unwanted components.

2. THE ATTACK

Weigh out 0·5–1 g of sample and treat with suitable reagents to obtain an aqueous solution. See Lundell and Hoffman (1938) p. 24, and the appropriate chapters of this book for the reagents most suited to a given sample. The materials attacked by the different reagents are listed below.

2.1. H_2O

Some inorganic salts.

2.2. Acids

Preferably use HCl and evap. to remove excess; $HClO_4$ is now often used.

(1) HCl. Used for carbonates and oxides of Ba, Ca, Fe, Mn, Mg, Sn, Ti, U, Zn. Used with some oxidant (HNO_3, $KClO_3$, etc.) for Al, Sb, Bi, Cu alloys; for ferro-alloys of Cr, Co, Ni, Ti, Si; and for sulfides of of Cu, Co, Pb, Mo, U, Zn. Used under pressure for some silicates and Pt metals (q.v.).

(2) HNO_3. Used for alloys of Bi, Cd, Co, Cu, Pb, Mn; for Si–Mn and ferro-alloys of Mn, P, Ti; for ores of Cu, Cd, Mo, Co, Ni.

As *aqua regia* for Au, Hg, V, Pt metals and alloys, and ores of Cd, Hg, Rh, W. Used with Br_2 for detn. of S in sulfides of Pb, Ni, Fe, Sb, As.

(3) H_2SO_4 (usually 1:5). Used for ores of Al, Be, Mn, Pb, Th, rare earths, Ti, U; for some steels, non-ferrous alloys and metals.

(4) HF (+ H_2SO_4, HCl, HNO_3, $HClO_4$, etc.). Used for silicates (detn. of Fe^{2+}, alkali metals) and alloys or ores of Cu, Nb, Ta, W. HF + HNO_3 + H_2O (5:5:200) is used for Sb–Sn.

The following method is useful in silicate analysis.[1] Add HF or NH_4HF_2, heat, add $H_2C_2O_4$, heat to dull red, add HCl + H_2O, evap. nearly to dryness, add EtOH + Schaffgotsch's soln. (satd. $(NH_4)_2CO_3$ in 180 ml. NH_4OH + 800 ml. H_2O + 900 ml. EtOH), filter. Add HCl to filtrate, evap. to dryness and det. alkali metals; det. Fe, etc., in ppt., and SiO_2 by difference.

Steels are readily dissolved by HF + 30% H_2O_2: oxidize C with $HClO_4$ and add $H_2C_2O_4$ for Fe–W and Fe–Mn–Si. Only Fe–Cr is difficult to dissolve.[2]

(5) 46–48% HBr + Br_2 (10:1). To 0·5 g. Fe–Mo or Fe–Si (especially if Si exceeds 17%), add 10 ml. reagent, cover, heat till no more Br_2 evolves; add 150 ml. hot H_2O, decant, add 5 ml. HNO_3 and, after 2 min., 50 ml. H_2O; filter through paper, wash with 4% HCl, hot H_2O, etc. This is suitable for Si detn.[3] and for Sb or Sn alloys (A.S.T.M.).

(6) HI (d. 1·70).[4] Used for qual. analysis of HgS, SnO_2, Ag halides, sulfates of Pb, Ca, Sr, Ba, Cr, anhyd. $CrCl_3$ and CaF_2.

(7) $HClO_4$ (usually 72%).[5] Advantages are that dil. solns. are not reduced even by strong reductants (org. compds., nascent H_2, electrolytic or catalytic reduction, N_2H_4, NH_2OH, Devarda's alloy, Na–Hg, H_3PO_2, $Na_2S_2O_4$, etc.) at low temp., but are reduced by prolonged heating with Ti^{3+}; most of its metal salts are sol. in H_2O and in many org. solvents (EtOH, Me_2CO); the concd. acid oxidizes Cr and V to their highest valency states, and decomp. org. compds. Its disadvantage is that explosions may occur when the concd. acid is heated with org. compds. such as EtOH.

$HClO_4$ is better than earlier methods for dissoln. of steels in detns. of Cr, V, Si, P, W, etc., and in removal of Cr, for dissoln. of W and its carbides, and for destruction of organic material. Wet combustion with $HClO_4$ is used in the detn. of inorg. components in biological materials and coals, and for the destruction of org. reagents. The method is: heat with dil. $HClO_4$ or $HClO_4$ + HNO_3 and H_2SO_4 up to ca. 200°C; pretreat easily oxidized materials with HNO_3 and evap. nearly to dryness; for compds. which are difficult to oxidize, e.g. leathers, add 25 mg. $K_2Cr_2O_7$; or add 0·2 ml. 0·01*N* OsO_4 or 30 mg. NH_4VO_3 as catalyst in the detn. of Cr.

Com. $HClO_4$ may contain 0·2–0·4 mg. Cr/l.[6] To purify, cool to −5 to −10°C, filter, heat to 200°C, cool, distil at ca. 100°C below 7 mm. Hg pressure.[7] Constant boiling $HClO_4$, b.p. 203°C, is 72·4%; above 85%, explosions may occur but $HClO_4$ is safe below 72%. The walls of fume cupboards in which $HClO_4$ has been used should be washed down occasionally.

The percentage of elements volatilized when heated at 200–220°C with mixed acids is listed in Table 1.[8] Ag, Pb, Cu, Cd, Pt, Pd, Ir, Rh, Fe, Ni, Co, Zn, U, Ga, In, Al, Be, Th, rare earths, Zr, Ti, Nb, Ta, group IV, Mg, group V, and W are not volatilized.

When org. compds. are decompd. with HNO_3 + H_2SO_4 + $HClO_4$, traces of metals may be lost after HNO_3 has evapd.[9]

If much Al is present in the decompn. of silicates with HF + $HClO_4$, F cannot be completely removed by fuming and must be steam-distilled at 140–150°C.[10]

TABLE 1. Percentage of Elements Volatilized with Mixed Acids at 200–220°C

Element	HCl + $HClO_4$	HBr + $HClO_4$	HCl + H_3PO_4 + $HClO_4$	HBr + H_3PO_4 + $HClO_4$	HCl + H_2SO_4	HBr + H_2SO_4	HF + $HClO_4$
Au	1	0·5	0·5	0·5	0·5	0·5	0
$Hg^{+,2+}$	75	75	75	75	75	90	0
B	20	20	10	10	50	10	100
Tl	1	1	1	1	0·1	1	—
Si	0	0	0	0	0	0	100
Ge	50	70	10	90	90	95	<10
Sn^{2+}	99·8	100	0	99·8	1	100	0
Sn^{4+}	100	100	0	100	30	100	0
P	1	1	1	1	1	1	—
As^{3+}	30	100	30	100	100	100	100
As^{5+}	5	100	5	100	5	100	100
Sb^{3+}	2	99·8	2	99·8	33	99·8	<10
Sb^{5+}	2	99·8	0	99·8	2	98	<10
Bi	0·1	1	0	1	0	1	0
V	0·5	2	0	0	0	0	—
Cr^{3+}	99·7	40	99·8	40	0	0	indefinite
Mo	3	12	0	0	5	4	0
Se^{4+}	4	2–5	2–5	2–5	30	100	indefinite
Se^{6+}	4	5	5	5	20	100	indefinite
Te^{4+}	0·5	0·5	0·1	0·5	0·1	10	—
Te^{6+}	0·1	0·5	0·5	1	0·1	10	—
Mn	0·1	0·02	0·02	0·02	0·02	0·02	<3
Re	100	100	80	100	90	100	indefinite
Os	100	100	100	100	0	0	—
Ru	99·5	100	100	100	0	0	—

(8) H_3PO_4. Used alone or with other acids for steels, silicates,[11] and ilmenite sands.[12]

2.3. Alkalies

35% NaOH or KOH is used for Al and its alloys.

2.4. Fluxes

If the sample is not attacked by any of the above treatments, mix it with 6–20 times its weight of a suitable flux in a crucible and cover with the flux. Heat slowly, fuse until clear and cool while rotating or inclining the crucible until the melt has solidified; then cool to room temperature. The solidified mass usually detaches easily from the crucible; if not, add a little H_2O and heat, or allow the melt to solidify round a platinum wire and heat momentarily over a strong flame.

Fluxes are classified as acid (for metal oxides) and alkaline (for silicates, metal oxides).

(a) Acid fluxes. (*i*) $NaHSO_4$ or $KHSO_4$. These are preferably heated to form pyrosulfate. To 1 g. sample in a quartz or Pt crucible, add at least 10 g. flux, heat very slowly; excessive heating should be avoided; if necessary, add some H_2SO_4 and reheat. Used for ores of Al, Sb, Cu, Cr, Co, Fe, Mn, Ni, Rh, Ta, Ti, W, ferro-alloys of Cr, Mo, W, Th phosphates, basic metal oxides and slags.

(*ii*) KHF_2 (or $NH_4F + H_2SO_4$, $CaF_2 + H_2SO_4$, $NaF + KHSO_4$). Used for minerals of Zr, Nb, rare earths. $NaBF_4$ is used for beryl (see Chapter 44).

(*iii*) B_2O_3 or H_3BO_3. Used sometimes for SiO_2 detn. in minerals contg. F, or for alkali metal detn. in alumina.

(*iv*) $ZnCl_2$. Used for detns. of Cu, Mg, Fe^{2+}, Ni, K in silicates, for Nb, Ta, and for identification purposes.[13]

(b) Alkaline fluxes. (*i*) Na_2CO_3, m.p. 849°C. Mix 1 g. sample with 4–8 g. flux in a Pt crucible; heat at 1000–1100°C for 15–20 min., cool and add H_2O (+ some EtOH if Mn yields a green color). Used for silicates, silver halides, Pb and Ba sulfates, etc.

When gas heating is used, traces of Fe are lost. It is better to fuse in an elect. muffle; heat the SiO_2 obtained at 1200°C, treat with HF + H_2SO_4 and reheat. Pretreat the crucible by heating at 1200°C and wash with hot HCl.[14]

The amt. of flux can be reduced.[15] Mix 0·5 g. sample with 0·5 g. Na_2CO_3 (+ 0·05 g. KNO_3 when Fe^{2+} or much Pb is present), cover with 0·5 g. flux and fuse at 1200°C for 15 min.; add 20 ml. HCl (1:1), evap. to dryness, add 5 ml. HCl and 15 ml. warm water; warm, filter through paper and wash with 2% HCl. Most minerals, rocks and refractories (except fused alumina) are attacked.

For Sb, As, Cr, Fe, Mo, V, Zr minerals or silicates contg. some sulfide, fuse with 10 g. $Na_2CO_3 + KNO_3$ (or $KClO_3$, MgO, ZnO) (1:1 or 3:2) at 600–700°C for 15–20 min.

K_2CO_3, m.p. 909°C, is better for Nb, Ta, W minerals. Dehydrate just before use. The mixture with Na_2CO_3 has a lower m.p.

(*ii*) NaOH, m.p. 318°C. Fuse 5 g. flux in a Fe, Ag, or Ni crucible (preferably inserted through an asbestos plate), add the sample gradually, and heat for 20–30 min. at 400–500°C. Used for oxide minerals of Sb, Sn, Zn and Zr minerals, Cr minerals (+ KNO_3), TiO_2 and titanite, bauxite, monazite, wolframite, carborundum, Fe–W (+ KNO_3), Pt metals and alloys, and silicates such as cordierite or vesuvianite which are scarcely attacked by other methods.

KOH, m.p. 360°C, is used for Zr minerals (+ KF). 3 g. KOH + 2 g. KNO_3 + 1 g. K_2CO_3 attacks most materials.[16]

(*iii*) Na_2O_2. Mix the sample in a Pt crucible thinly lined with fused Na_2CO_3 with 4 times its weight of flux, cover with flux, heat at 480 ± 20°C, cool, dissolve in 50–100 ml. H_2O. Used for chrome refractory, bauxite, flint clay, zircon, chromite, wolframite, scheelite, rutile, magnetite, garnet, cassiterite, tantalite, titanite, beryl, ilmenite sand, glass basalt, rhyolite, trachyte and andesite. Os–Ir requires repeated treatment.[17]

Zirconium crucibles are useful for these fusions.[18]

Fusion at 600–700°C in a Fe, Ni or Ag crucible is used for minerals of Sb, As, Sn, Cr, Mo, Ni, V, U, and for Cr detn. in some alloys and steels (Hillebrand and Lundell, p. 701).

The explosion method with sugar carbon is usually reserved for detn. of S in organic materials (Hillebrand and Lundell, p. 702).

(*iv*) Borax, m.p. 742°C. Sometimes used for Zr minerals and for oxides of Al, Fe, Ti. Mix 0·5 g. Nb or Ta mineral with 5 g. fused borax, fuse for 1 hr. (Ti minerals) or 2 hr. (Nb, Ta minerals); cool, add HF (1:4), warm, filter (rare earths); add 6 ml. H_2SO_4 (1:1) + 10 ml. HCl, evap. to fumes (Ti, Nb, Ta).[19]

Na_2CO_3 + borax (1:1) is used for refractories.

(*v*) $NaNH_2$. Proposed for silicates but of no practical value.

(*vi*) Other fluxes. 5 g. Na_2CO_3 + S (1:1) is used at 300–400°C for 0·1 g. cassiterite in a porcelain crucible; alternatives are 2·5–3 g. CaO + 0·15–0·16 g. C at 900°C, or 5 g. KCN at white heat. Anhyd. $Na_2S_2O_3$ fusion is used for oxide minerals of As, Sb or Sn.

$Na_2CO_3 + SiO_2$ has been used for CaF_2, $K_2CO_3 + KBF_4$ for zircon, and $CaCO_3 + NH_4Cl$ for alkali metals. $PbCO_3$, Bi_2O_3 and many others have been proposed (see Mellor and Thompson (1938), p. 139).

2.5 Heating in gases

Heating in chlorine or chlorides (CCl_4, S_2Cl_2) is used in the analysis of Pt metals, Nb, Ta, W (q.v.). HCl is used in Fe^{2+} detns. and for alumina.

Hydrogen is used at 800°C for SnO_2 and at 1000°C for wolframite or barite. Oxygen is used at 500–1000°C for org. compds. and at 1400°C for S in steels. HCl + HNO_3 may be used for sulfides.

2.6. Organic compounds

(a) Ashing. $Ca(OH)_2$, $Mg(OAc)_2$, etc., are usually added when volatile elements are detd. (see Chapters 28, 60, and 61).

(b) Wet combustion. $HClO_4$, $H_3PO_4 + K_2Cr_2O_7$ (for S), $H_2SO_4 + CrO_3$ or $H_3PO_4 + KIO_3$ (for C), HNO_3 in a sealed tube (Carius method), fuming $H_2SO_4 + H_2O_2$ have been recommended.

(c) Fusion methods. For fusion with Mg, see Chapters 25, 26, and 57. The Parr bomb method with Na_2O_2 is useful for halogens and S, and fusion with Na or K in a sealed tube or bomb at 400–950°C for F.

3. GROUP SEPARATION BY CLASSICAL METHODS

After the aqueous solution has been prepared, the elements are separated into groups. The usual grouping reagents are HCl (acid group and group I), H_2S in acidic solution (group II), NH_4OH and $(NH_4)_2S$ (group III), $(NH_4)_2C_2O_4$ and $(NH_4)_2HPO_4$ (group IV and Mg). The remaining elements are found in group V (alkali metals) and among the anions.

The general groups of elements are shown in Table 2 and the grouping of elements in representative samples is given in Table 3 (Lundell and Hoffman).

TABLE 2. Grouping of Elements

Sample. Prep. HCl soln., evap.[a]

- *Acid Group*
  Si, Nb, Ta, W ; Ag
  Pb, Tl ; Th, Ti, Zr, Hf ;
  Ba, Sr, Ca ; P, S, Cl, Br, I
- *Volatilization* (complete or partial)
  Hg, Re ; As, Sb, Sn, Ge, Se, Te ;
  Au, Ru, Os ; Si, P, S, Br, I, F,
  B, C, N ; rare gases
- H_2S
  - *H_2S group*
    (Ag), Hg, Pb, Bi, Cu, Cd, Re ;
    As, Sb, Sn, Ge, Mo, Se, Te ;
    Au, Pt metals.
    Fe, Co, Ni, Zn, V, Tl, In
    W
  - Oxidize, NH_4OH
    - *NH_4OH group*
      Fe, U, In, Ga; Al, Be, Cr, Th, Sc,
      rare earths, Zr, Hf, Ti, Nb, Ta
      Co, Zn, V ; P
      Si, W
    - $(NH_4)_2S$
      - *$(NH_4)_2S$ group*
        Ni, Co, Zn, Mn, Tl
        V
        W
      - $(NH_4)_2C_2O_4$
        - *$(NH_4)_2C_2O_4$ group*
          Ca, Sr
          Ba, Mg, Li
        - $(NH_4)_2HPO_4$
          - *$(NH_4)_2HPO_4$ group*
            Mg, Ba
            Ca, Sr
          - Elements still in soln.
            Li, Na, K, Rb, Cs ; V ; Br, I
            Si, W

Elements in bold type are pptd. completely or partly when present alone.
Elements in ordinary type are not pptd. when alone, but may be found when other elements are present.
Elements in italic type are pptd. incompletely in the proper group and appear in other groups.

[a] F, B, org. compds. should be removed. Detn. of volatile elements needs special operations.

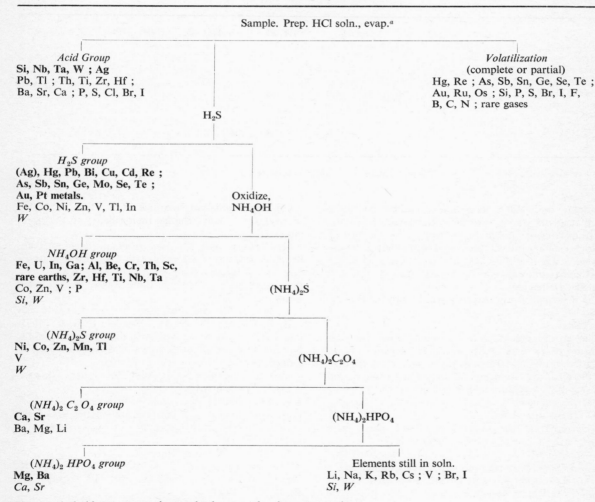

TABLE 3. Grouping of Elements in Representative Samples

(A) Rocks

	Acid	H_2S	NH_4OH	$(NH_4)_2C_2O_4$	$(NH_4)_2HPO_4$	Others
Major	Si	—	Al, Fe	Ca	Mg	Na, K, H, O
Minor {small	—	—	Ti, P[a]	—	—	
Minor {trace	—	Cu	Zr, Cr, V[a]	Sr	Ba	Li, C, N, S, Cl, F
Rare	Ta, Nb, W	Mo, Sn, Pt Ag, Pb, Au	Be, Th, U, rare earths	—	—	B, He

[a] Usually found in this group.

(B) General

	Acid	H_2S	NH_4OH	$(NH_4)_2S$	$(NH_4)_2C_2O_4$	$(NH_4)_2HPO_4$	Alkalies
Rocks	+++	—	+++	+	+++	+++	+++
Refractories	+++	++	+++	++	+++	+++	+++
Steels	++	++	+++	+++	—	—	—
Non-ferrous metals and alloys	++	+++	++	++	—	++	—
Minerals, ores, chemicals	different with samples						

+++ Generally present; ++ minor—trace; + trace if present; — rare.

H_2SeO_3 and KIO_3 are among other inorganic group reagents which have been suggested. The ideal of group reagents would be to have a specific reagent for each element but, despite the development of many organic reagents, this has not yet been achieved; dimethylglyoxime appears to be the nearest approach to a specific reagent.

The principal group reagents are described below.

3.1. Acids

The group precipitated by direct treatment or digestion of the fused mass with acids depends on the acid used. Si, W, Nb, Ta generally appear in the residue, but W remains in solution when H_3PO_4 is present, and Nb, Ta may precipitate incompletely in the presence of certain elements.

(1) HCl is often used.

Procedure. Treat the sample or fused mass with water, add HCl, evap. to dryness and leave for 1 hr. on a steam-bath or in air at 110°C, moisten with HCl and add water; filter through paper (see Chapter 55).

Si (traces pass into the filtrate even after double evapn.; they may be recovered from the group III ppt.), Nb, Ta, W ppt.

Interferences are Ag, B, F, Ba, Sr, (Ca), Ti, Zr, Hf, Th, Tl^+, Pb, C, P, S, Cl, Br, I, Au, Pt (partly as metal), Os. Obviously certain of these elements ppt. when present together, e.g. AgCl, $PbSO_4$, $Th_3(PO_4)_4$.

Ge, As^{3+} (and Au) volatilize. Se^{4+}, Te^{4+}, V^{4+}, Tl^+ (partly), Cr^{3+}, Mn^{2+} change their valency to the states indicated.

(2) H_2SO_4 is generally used in metallurgical analysis. Sepn. of SiO_2 is better than with HCl. Care must be taken to avoid spattering.

Procedure. Evap. to white fumes, cool slightly, add water, etc.

Si, Nb, Ta, W, Ba, Pb ppt.

B, F, Ca, Sr, Ti, Zr, Hf, Th, Ag, P, S, Cl, Br, I interfere. Ge, Sn, Sb hydrolyze in dil. acid soln. Cr, Fe, Ni and Al form almost insol. anhyd. sulfates on prolonged heating or on evapn. to dryness.

Halogens vaporize and P, Au, Os, Re partly vaporize.

(3) $HClO_4$ (cf. p. 7).

Procedure. Add $HClO_4$, evap. to fumes, boil for 10–15 min., cool, add H_2O, filter through paper and wash with HCl (1:1). (The ppt. may explode on ignition if not washed with HCl).

Si, Nb, Ta, W, Sn, Sb ppt.

Interferences are B, F, C (possible explosion), K, Rb, Cs, Ba, Ti, Zr, Hf, Th, V, Mo, Mn, Ag, Ge, Pb, Bi, P, S, Cl, Br, I.

Re, Os, Ru, halogens and Cr (+ HCl) vaporize. Cr^{6+} changes valency.

(4) HNO_3 is used for Sn or Sb detn. rather than for SiO_2 detn.; it is used for SiO_2 only when P must be detd. simultaneously.

TABLE 4. Elements Precipitated in Strongly Acidic Solution with H_2S (Lundell and Hoffman)

	Normality of HCl					Normality of H_2SO_4					Color
	0·2	0·5	1	3	6	0·5	3	6	18	36	
Ag	++	++	++	O	O	++	++	++	++	++	black
Hg^{2+}	++	++	++	++	++	++	++	++	++	++	black
Pb	++	O	O	OO	—	OO	—	—	—	—	black
Bi	++	++	++	—	—	++	++	++	++	O	black
Cu	++	++	++	++	O	++	++	++	++	O	black
Cd	++	+	O	—	—	++	O	—	—	—	yellow
Re	O	O	O	O	O	OO	O	O	+	O	brown-black
As^{3+}	++	++	++	++	++	++	++	++	++	++	yellow
As^{5+}	O	O	O	O	++	O	O	O	++	++	yellow
Sb^{3+}	++	++	++	+	—	++	++	++	—	—	orange-yellow
Sb^{5+}	++	++	++	+	OO	++	++	++	++	++	orange-yellow
Sn^{2+}	++	++	++	O	—	++	++	++	—	—	orange-black
Sn^{4+}	++	++	++	++	++	++	++	++	++	O	yellow
Ge	OO	O	O	O	++	OO	O	++	+	O	white
Mo	+	O	O	O	OO	+	O	OO	OO	OO	dark brown
Se^{4+}	++	++	++	++	++	++	++	++	++	++	orange-yellow
Se^{6+}	OO	O	O	O	O	—	—	—	—	—	orange-yellow
Te^{4+}	++	++	++	++	++	++	++	++	++	++	black
Te^{6+}	—	—	—	—	O	OO	OO	OO	OO	OO	black
Au	++	++	++	++	++	++	++	++	++	++	brown-black
Ru	O	O	O	O	O	+	O	O	O	O	brown-black
Rh	O	O	O	O	O	O	O	O	O	O	brown-black
Pd	++	++	++	+	O	++	++	++	++	++	brown-black
Os	O	O	O	O	—	OO	OO	O	O	O	black
Ir	O	O	O	O	O	O	O	O	O	O	black
Pt	O	O	O	O	O	OO	O	O	OO	—	brown-black
In	OO	—	—	—	—	—	—	—	—	—	

NOTE: ++ pptn. complete; + nearly complete; O incomplete; OO very incomplete; — no ppt.

Procedure. Add HNO_3, evap. to dryness, add warm HNO_3, heat, add hot H_2O; filter through paper, wash with hot H_2O.

Si, Nb, Ta, W, Ti, V, Mo, Ge, Sn, Sb ppt. Au, Ir, Pd partly ppt.

B, F, Ba, Zr, Hf, Th, Ag, P, As, S, Cl, Br, I interfere. Fe causes incomplete sepn. of Sn.

Os, Ru, halogens volatilize; Au volatilizes partly if HCl is present.

(5) HF is used in the analysis of rare earths, Nb, Ta minerals, and for the separation of rare earths, Th, Sc, U^{4+}, Ca, (Pb, Zr, Fe) from Nb, Ta, Ti, Zr, U^{6+}, Sn, Fe, Al, Be, etc.

3.2. H_2S and its substitutes[20]

About a third of the elements can be precipitated as sulfides at various pH values.

Substitutes for H_2S have been suggested. H_2S is generated when a mixture containing paraffin wax, S and siliceous earth and asbestos (25:50:25) is heated to 50°C.[21] Acetone satd. with H_2S,[22] thioacetamide,[23] and other organic materials (see Chapter 8, Section 2.3) are convenient.

(a) Elements pptd. in strongly acidic soln. of pH less than 1. These elements are shown in Table 4; they can be divided into 2 groups:

Cu group: (Ag), Hg, Pb, Bi, Cu, Cd, Re, (Ru, Rh, Pd, Os), ((Ga, In, Tl)).

As group: As, Sb, Sn, Ge, Mo, Se, Te, (Au, Pt, Ir), ((W,V)).

The order of pptn. with decrease in the HCl concn. is As, Mo, Ag, Cu, Sb, Bi, Hg, Au, Pt, Sn, Cd, Pb.

Procedure. Add 2·4 ml. HCl or 1·5 ml. H_2SO_4/40 ml. soln. Heat, pass H_2S through for 10–15 min. at 70–90°C; add 60 ml. H_2O, pass more H_2S, stopper and leave for 15 min.; filter through paper and wash with H_2S water containing a little acid.

NOTES. (1) Ag is usually sepd. previously with HCl.

(2) Not all the elements of group II ppt. by the above method (see Table 4). Some, e.g. As, are better treated in more concd. acid. Mo (q.v.) ppts. better from H_2SO_4 soln. With Pb, add 1 drop of NH_4OH while passing H_2S.

Pt ppts. well from concd. H_2SO_4; pptn. is complete on passing H_2S into the hot, dil. acid soln. for 1 hr. HCl soln. should be used for Rh and Ir; complete pptn. requires 2–3 hr. Complete pptn. of Os and Ru is difficult. Pb, Cd and Sn^{4+} ppt. incompletely when much Cl^- is present.

(3) Copptn. occurs with (Si, Nb, Ta, W), Fe, Co, Ni, Zn, V, Tl, In, Ga. Especial trouble is found in combinations of Cu, Cd or Hg with Zn, (Fe); Cu, As, Sb, Hg, Sn, or Pb with Tl; Sn^{4+} with Fe (in HCl soln.) or Co; Sn^{2+} with Ni; Cu, Sn or Cd with Hg (see below); and Pt with Fe. A study of Mn, Ni, Zn and Tl has been made with radioactive tracers.[24] Copptn. of Fe, Ni, Co, Zn, Tl can be prevented by using more concd. acid soln; that of W, V is avoided by addn. of tartaric acid.

(4) Sepn. within group II can be done in several ways.

(*i*) *Sepn. with alkali metal sulfides*. Used for the sepn. of the Cu group from the As group.

Sulfide ppts. can be extracted with the sulfide soln; this is rarely used in quant. analysis. Treatment with H_2S or sulfide soln. in alk. soln. can be used when the ppt. is small. Pouring the slightly acidic soln. into an excess of the sulfide soln. is preferred when the ppt. is large.

The dissoln. of different metallic sulfides depends on the sulfide soln. which is added. HgS is insol. in $(NH_4)_2S$ and alkali metal polysulfides but sol. in Na_2S or K_2S + NaOH or KOH; HgS can be sepd. from Cu, Pb, Cd or from As, Sb, Sn by boiling the filtrate with NH_4NO_3. CuS is insol. in Na_2S or K_2S and is only very slightly sol. in $(NH_4)_2S$; it is quite sol. in $R_2S + R_2S_x$. Bi_2S_3 is insol. in $(NH_4)_2S$, $(NH_4)_2S_x$, NaHS or KHS, but is appreciably sol. in Na_2S, K_2S, Na_2S_x, or K_2S_x in admixture with NaOH or KOH.

(*ii*) *Sepn. by complex formation*. HF (5 ml. HF + 5 ml. HCl/300 ml. soln.) can be used for the sepn. of As^{3+}, Sb^{3+}, Pb, Cu from Sn, Ge. It is very suitable for sepn. of Sb^{3+} from Sn^{4+} and of Sn^{2+} from Sn^{4+}; sepn. of As^{3+}, Sb^{3+}, from As^{5+} and Sb^{5+} is possible.

$H_2C_2O_4$ is used for the sepn. of As, Sb from Sn.[25] To the soln. add 10 ml. 20% tartaric acid, then add 10% K_2CO_3 until neutral to phenolphthalein. Add 10 ml. in excess and 5 ml. 3% H_2O_2, evap. to 80 ml., neutralize with HCl, add dropwise 10 g. $H_2C_2O_4$ dissolved in H_2O. Boil, pass H_2S through for 20 min. adding H_2O as required, dil. to 200 ml. with hot H_2O, pass H_2S for 10 min., cool to below 90°C, pass H_2S for 10 min., filter through paper and wash with 50 ml. 1% $H_2C_2O_4$ and then 50 ml hot H_2O.

CN^- in alk. soln. is used for the sepn. of Ag, Cu from Hg, Pb, Bi, Cd.

EDTA is used for the sepn. of Cu, Cd from Pb.

(*iii*) *Sepn. by other methods.*

Hg from Cd: use H_2S and 45 ml. HCl/100 ml. soln.

Hg from Pb, Bi: use H_2S and 40–50 ml. HCl/100 ml. soln.

Hg from As, Bi, Pb: boil the mixed sulfides with dil. HNO_3. Cu, Cd, Sn interfere; some PbS is oxidized to $PbSO_4$.

Cu from Cd, Ni, Zn: add $Na_2S_2O_3$ to the acid soln. and boil (see Chapter 22); incomplete sepn. is obtained when dil. H_2SO_4 is added to the mixed sulfides and boiled.

Cd from Sb: use 18 ml. HCl/100 ml. soln.; boil, add H_2S, dil. to 200 ml., add H_2S.

Cd from Zn: use 4–5N H_2SO_4 or HCl soln.; add $(NH_4)_2SO_4$ or NH_4Cl and H_2S.

As from Sb, Cd, Bi, Pb, Sn: use 10N HCl soln. and H_2S; Ge, Mo, Se, Te, Hg interfere.

(5) As group sulfides are dissolved by treatment with NaOH + Cl_2 (or H_2O_2, K_2CO_4) followed by acid.

(b) Elements pptd. in weakly acidic soln. at pH 2–3. Zn (at a final acidity of 0·01N H_2SO_4), In (at 0·025N), Tl and Ga are pptd. Buffer should be added to maintain the correct pH. The Zn detn. is noteworthy.

(c) Elements pptd. in nearly neutral soln. at pH 5–6. Used for sepn. of Ni, Co, (Fe) from Mn; pyridine soln. appears preferable.

Procedure. To the weakly acidic soln. add Na_2CO_3 until alk., then AcOH until acid; add 5 g. NaOAc/1 g. Ni + Co, dil. to 200 ml. with H_2O, heat to 80°C and pass H_2S. Alternatively, add Na_2CO_3 to give a ppt. and HCl until just clear; add 5 ml. buffer (25 ml. 1:4 HCl + pyridine until neutral to methyl red), boil, add 10 ml. 20% pyridine and pass H_2S[26].

(d) Elements pptd. in alk. soln. When H_2S or $(NH_4)_2S$ is added to an ammoniacal soln. of the metals, the Cu group and group III elements ppt.; sepn. of the Cu group, Fe, Ni, Co, Mn and Zn from the As group, group IV, etc., is thus possible.

Procedure. Add NH_4Cl and NH_4OH until the soln. is neutral, add 2 ml. in excess, dil. to 100 ml. with H_2O, cool, pass H_2S, add 2 ml. NH_4OH and dil.; stopper, leave for 5–12 hr., filter through paper and wash with 2% NH_4Cl contg. H_2S.

Sepn. of Cu, Pb, Fe, Zn, etc. from Sn and Al is possible with Na_2S. After groups I and II have been sepd., Fe, Ni, Co, Mn, Zn, Al, U, Tl, In, etc. can be sepd. from group IV, Mg, etc. After this, when CO_3^{2-}, PO_4^{3-}, F^-, group IV and Mg are absent, the important sepn. in group III (i.e. sepn. of Fe, Ni, Co, Zn, Cu and Tl^+ from PO_4^{3-}, Al, Be, V, Cr, Ti, Zr, Nb, Ta, rare earths and U) is done in presence of tartrate. Note that pptn. of Mn and In is incomplete.

Procedure. To 100 ml. soln. add at least a 3-fold excess of tartaric acid, make alk. with NH_4OH, neutralize with 1:1 HCl, add 2 ml. HCl in excess, pass H_2S, add NH_4OH, pass H_2S and complete as above.

When groups I and II and the NH_4OH ppt. have been removed, Mn, Co, Zn and Tl can be sepd. from group IV, Mg, etc.

3.3. NH_4OH and its substitutes

Many elements precipitate in faintly acidic or alkaline solutions. The degree of precipitation depends on the pH, the reagents, and the other ions present. The precipitation pH of many elements are shown in Fig. 1.[27] Many reagents have been used; precipitation from homogeneous solution with urea gives readily filterable precipitates.

(a) NH_4OH (pH 6·5–7·5). Fe^{3+}, Al, Tl^{3+}, In, Ga, U, Be, Th, Sc, Ti, Zr, Hf, Nb, Ta ppt. completely; pptn. of some rare earths is incomplete.

Procedure. Add 2–3 g. NH_4Cl/100 ml. slightly acidic soln., boil and add dil. NH_4OH until yellow to methyl red or methyl orange; filter through Whatman No. 41 paper, wash with 2% NH_4NO_3 or NH_4Cl.

NOTES. (1) B, F^- and polyhydroxy compounds interfere. SiO_2, Sb, Se, Te, As, V, P, W, Mo coppt.; pptn. is usually

complete when a 10-fold amount of Fe^{3+} is present and this serves for the concn. of these elements. Group IV, Mg (with excess PO_4^{3-}, CO_3^{2-} or F^-), Zn (with much Cr), Co, Cu and Mn (on long boiling) also coppt.; pptn. of Mn is complete when H_2O_2 or Br_2 is added.
(2) Addn. of filter pulp after neutralization favors complete pptn. and filtration. The longer hydroxides are boiled, the more difficult they are to dissolve, hence filters should be ignited and added to the main ppt. Repptn. must be done.
(3) When EDTA is added, only Be, Ti and U^{6+} ppt. (see Chapters 44 and 50).

(b) Basic acetate and similar methods. (*i*) NaOAc (pH 5·6). Fe, Ti, Zr, Hf, Th, Al, Ga, In, Tl, Sn, Bi, Pd ppt.

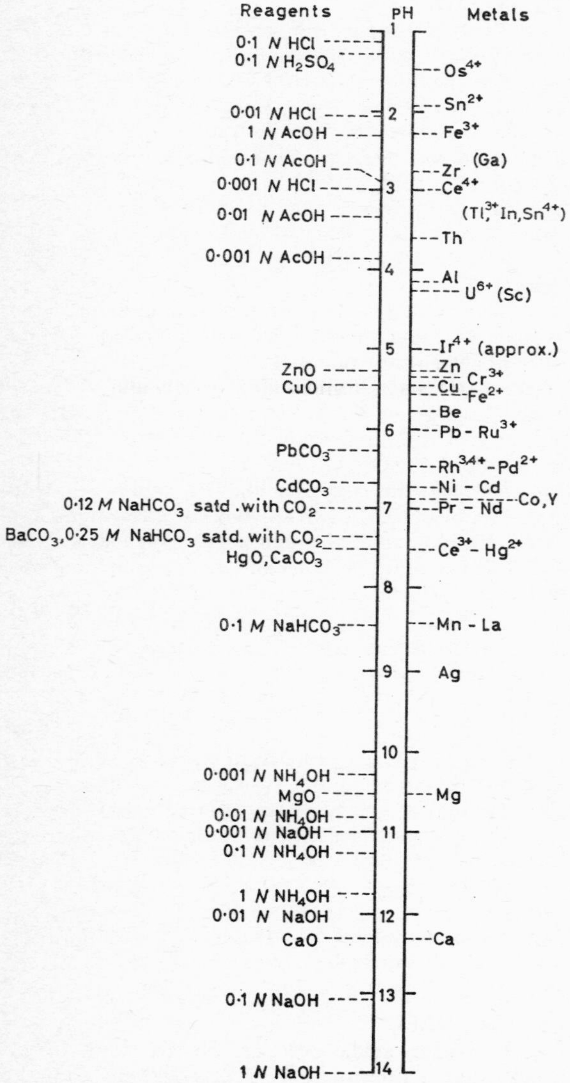

FIG. 1. Precipitation pHs of metal hydroxides and reagents for pH control.

completely, and U, Cr, rare earths, Ru, Os, Hg incompletely. It is useful for sepn. of much Fe from Ni, Co, Zn, Mn, Cu, and for removal of PO_4^{3-}.
Procedure. To 100 ml. HCl-contg. soln., add 1:3 NH_4OH to give a red color and dil. $(NH_4)_2CO_3$ dropwise with constant stirring until the ppt. dissolves slowly; dil. to 400 ml. with hot H_2O, boil (no pptn. below 70°C), add 2–5 g. NaOAc in 10–25 ml. H_2O dropwise, and boil for 3 min.; filter through Whatman No. 41 paper, wash with hot 1% NaOAc, add HCl, etc.

NaOAc or NH_4OAc can also be used with KCl but pptn. of Al is incomplete (Hillebrand and Lundell, p. 80, 81).

(*ii*) Urea + $(NH_4)_2SO_4$.[28] Add dil. NH_4OH to a soln. contg. 0·1 g. Al until turbid, add dil. HCl until clear and then add 1–2 drops more; add 4 g. urea, 1 g. $(NH_4)_2SO_4$, 20 g. NH_4Cl, and dil. to 500 ml. with H_2O; boil gently for 2 hr., digest for 1 hr. on a hot plate, filter through paper, wash, add HCl, NH_4OH, etc.

(*iii*) Succinic acid + urea (pH 4·4).[28] To an HCl-soln. contg. 0·1 g. Al/100 ml., add 2 ml. 10% $NaHSO_3$, 2 ml. phenylhydrazine and 300 ml. reagent soln. (10 g. urea, 5 g. NH_4Cl and 5 g. succinic acid/1.); add NH_4OH till just alk. to methyl orange, boil for 40 min., add paper pulp, filter through paper, wash with 1% NH_4-succinate, etc. Al is sepd. from 1 g. of group IV, Mg, Mn and Cd by 1 pptn., from 0·1 g. Ni or Co by 1 pptn. or from 1 g. by repptn., from 1 g. Zn by repptn., and from Fe^{2+}; for copper, add 4 g. $NH_2OH{\cdot}HCl$ + 10 ml. 2*N* NH_4HSO_3 to the boiling HCl soln.

(*iv*) HCOOH + urea[29] is useful for Th and Fe (q.v.).

(*v*) NH_4-benzoate (pH 6·3).[30] Used for sepn. of Fe, Al, Cr, Ti, Zr, Ce^{4+}, Bi and Sn from Ni, Co, Zn, Mn, V^{4+}, V^{5+}, Fe^{2+}, Ce^{3+}, group IV, Mg, Cd and Hg. Add NH_4OH to 100 ml. soln. till turbid, add 1 ml. AcOH, more than 1 g. NH_4Cl, and for each 65 mg. Al or 125 mg. Fe or Cr, add 20 ml. reagent (10% NH_4-benzoate + 1 mg. thymol/1.); heat for 5 min. (Al, Fe) or 20 min. (Cr), filter through paper, wash with a soln. contg. 100 ml. reagent + 20 ml. AcOH/1., and reppt. Acidify the filtrates, evap. and filter to remove benzoic acid.

(c) Carbonates. (*i*) $NaHCO_3$ (8%). Used in ferrous analysis and for sepn. of Be from Al. Al, Cr, Ti, Zr, Nb, Ta, Ti ppt. completely, and Fe^{3+}, U, Cu, Sn, P, V almost completely; the former group can thus be sepd. from much Fe^{2+} and Mn. Co, Ni, W ppt. incompletely. *Procedure*. To 200 ml. H_2SO_4-contg. soln., slowly add reagent soln. and add more (4 ml. for up to 5% Cr in steel, 6 ml. for more than 5% Cr) after pptn. begins; add filter pulp, boil for 1 min., filter through paper, wash 4–5 times with 0·1% $NaHCO_3$.

Traces of Mn may ppt.; treat with aqua regia and H_2SO_4, evap. to fumes, add H_2O and Na_2O_2, boil, dissolve in HNO_3, add $NaNO_2$, etc. (colorimetry),

(*ii*) Carbonate suspensions. $BaCO_3$ (pH 7·25, freshly prepd. from 90 g. $BaCl_2$ + 36 g. Na_2CO_3/1.) permits sepn. of Fe^{3+}, Al, Ti, Zr, Cr, U, (P, V) from Fe^{2+},

Ni, Co, Zn, Mn on shaking. In the cold Be ppts. completely, the Ce group slowly and the Y group very slowly; on heating Be ppts. incompletely and the Ce and Y groups completely.

$PbCO_3$ (pH 6.2) is used for the sepn. of Th, Zr, Ce^{4+}, Fe^{3+} from Ce^{3+}, La, Nd, Pr, Sm, and the Y group. UO_2^{2+}, Cr^{3+} and Al ppt. incompletely.

$CdCO_3$ (pH 6·5) is used for the sepn. of Cr, V from Fe^{2+}. SO_4^{2-} does not interfere.

$CaCO_3$ (pH 7·4) is rarely used owing to its grain coarseness.

(*iii*) Hydrazine carbonate (prepd. by passing CO_2 through 10% $N_2H_4{\cdot}H_2O$ for 3–4 hr. at 0°C, leaving for 2 hr. and removing CO_2 under reduced press) is useful for sepns. of Fe from Co, Ni, and of Al from Zn; it is the best method for Al detn.[31]

Procedure. To 30–45 ml. soln. add the reagent until the soln. is blue to bromothymol blue; leave for 30 min., place on a steam-bath for 50–80 min. (till no more NH_3 evolves) adding H_2O as required, filter through paper and wash with hot H_2O.

Guanidine carbonate (carbamidine or iminourea carbonate) $(NH{:}C(NH_2)_2)H_2CO_3$ is also used for sepn. of Be from Al[32] (see Chapters 44 and 50).

(d) Other inorganic reagents. (*i*) ZnO (pH 5·5) . Fe^{3+}, V^{4+}, U^{4+}, Ga, In, Tl^{3+}, Al, Cr, Ce^{3+}, Ti, Zr, Hf, Th, Nb, Ta, W, P, Sn^{4+}, As, Bi, Te^{6+} ppt. completely; Be, rare earths, V^{5+}, U^{6+}, Ni, Ag, Hg, Pb, Cu, Sb, Sn^{2+}, Mo, Ge, Se, Au, Pt metals ppt. incompletely. Fe, Cr are sepd. from Co, Mn, Ni (when Cu, Mo are absent) in ferrous analysis. See also Chapter 35.

(*ii*) HgO (pH 6) is used for sepn. of Fe, Al, Cr from Mn. Pptn. of Zn, Co, Ni, Be, Ce^{3+}, La is incomplete.

(*iii*) $Na_2S_2O_3$ ppts. Ti, Th, Al, Zr completely, the Y group, Cr, Fe, V incompletely and the Ce group not at all. When Zr is present, Ti ppts. incompletely unless phenylhydrazine is added.

(*iv*) KCNO is used for sepn. of Al, In from Mn, Zn, Ni, Co (+KCN). See Chapter 41.

(*v*) NH_4NO_2 or $NaNO_2$ (pH 4·6–6·0) is used in the detn. of Be (q.v.). Al, Fe, Cr, etc. ppt. with $NaNO_2$ + NaN_3.

(*vi*) KIO_3 + KI or $KBrO_3$ + KBr (pH 7·5). Sn, Bi, Fe, Ni, Co, Mn, Al, Cr ppt. completely.

(e) Organic bases. Many org. bases have been suggested;[33] some of these are described below.

(*i*) Urea is used to regulate pH in many cases in pptn. from homogeneous soln. See above and also Chapters 46 and 52.

(*ii*) Phenylhydrazine is used for sepn. of Al, Ti, Zr, Th, Cr, (P, V) from Fe, Mn, etc. Be, Ce^{4+} ppt. incompletely. Ni, Co, Zn, Cd, Hg, form difficultly sol. salts.

Procedure. To the acid soln. (preferably sulfate) add methyl orange, NH_4OH to give a turbidity and HCl to clear it; dil. to 100–200 ml. with H_2O, heat, add 5–20 drops satd. NH_4HSO_3 (if deep red, add HCl) and neutralize with NH_4OH. Add 6–7 drops 1:1 HCl, 1–3 ml. reagent, and stir. The soln. should be alk. to methyl orange but acid to litmus. Filter through paper and wash with a soln. obtained by treating 2–3 ml. reagent with satd. SO_2 soln. until the ppt. which appears just dissolves, adding reagent until there is no SO_2 odor and diluting 5–10 ml. of this soln. to 100 ml.

(*iii*) Hexamine (pH 5·5).[34] Fe^{3+}, Al, Cr, Th, Ti, U, Zr are sepd. from Ni, Mn, Mg, etc; Co and Zn require repptn. Ce, La, Nd, Pr, Y do not ppt. in the cold but ppt. slightly on heating (see Chapter 46). It is also used in the detn of Te.

Procedure. Add 10% hexamine to 30 ml. soln. contg. NH_4Cl till pptn. is complete; leave for 3 hr., filter through paper and wash with 1% reagent + 1% NH_4NO_3.

(*iv*) Pyridine[35] is used for sepn. of Fe, Al, Cr, Ti, Zr, U from Mn, Cu, Ni, Co. See also Chapter 30, p. 224.

Procedure. To 0·1 g. R_2O_3/100 ml. soln. add 3 g. NH_4Cl, boil, add 10–15 ml. 20% pyridine, boil, etc.

(*v*) Satd. aniline soln. (pH 4·45–4·50) is used for sepn. of Al from Mn, Ni, Co; Zn requires repptn. See also Chapter 30, p. 224.

Procedure. Add reagent soln. to 20 ml. soln. till pptn. is complete and add at least 40 ml. in excess; leave for at least 30 min., filter through paper, wash with 1% reagent, etc.

p-Chloroaniline is used for sepn. of Be from Ti (see Chapter 44) and dimethylaniline for detn. of Te. *o*-Phenetidine is not satisfactory.

(f) Separations in strongly alkaline solution. (*i*) NaOH is used for sepn. of Cu or Fe, Co, Mn, Ti, Zr, Hf, Th, rare earths, Cr, U, In from Al, Be, P, V, Ge, Ga, W, Mo, As, Sn, Pb, Zn, SO_4^{2-}.

Procedure. Heat the slightly acidic soln. and pour into an equal vol. of hot 10% NaOH, boil for a few min., cool for 15–30 min., filter through paper (washed with hot 5% NaOH + some $NaSO_4$) and wash in the same way. Add HCl, NH_4OH, etc.

NOTES. (1) When less than 5 mg. Be or Al is present or when the Fe/Al ratio is large, sepn. is incomplete; it is also affected by large amt. of PO_4^{3-} (see Chapters 43 and 44). Some Al ppts. when Ni or Mg is present; Ti, Zr, Th ppt. completely only if a 10-fold amt. of Fe is present. U passes into the filtrate when CO_3^{2-} or VO_3^{-} is present; pptn. of Nb, Ta is incomplete. Pt vessels are preferable.
(2) With NaOH + Na_2CO_3, group IV ppts. but U passes into the filtrate; with NaOH + H_2O_2 or Na_2O_2, Ni ppts. and Cr, V go into the filtrate (U is dissolved if Na_2CO_3 is added). With NaOH + Br_2, Ni, Co ppt.
(3) KOH + H_2O_2 in the cold is used for the sepn. of Ti from Fe.

(*ii*) Fusion with Na_2CO_3 and extn. with H_2O serves to sep. Fe, Ti, Zr, rare earths from (Al), Cr, V, P; U, SiO_2 ppt. partly.

3.4. $(NH_4)_2HPO_4$

(a) In strongly acidic soln. Zr, Hf are detd. in 1:9 H_2SO_4 soln. Copptn. of Ti is avoided by addn. of H_2O_2 and that of Th, Sn, Bi by repptn.; Nb, Ta copptn. cannot be prevented.

The detn. of Bi in 1:75 HNO_3 is very satisfactory.

(b) In weakly acidic or weakly alk. soln. Al, Be, Zn, U are detd.; Fe interferes.

(c) In NH_4OH (1:20) soln. Mg, Mn are detd.; Be, group IV, Th, rare earths, Sn, Pb, Bi, In, ppt. completely; Fe, Al, Ti, Zr, Nb, Ta, U, Tl, Hg, Sb, Rh, Pt ppt. incompletely. When tartrate or citrate is added, Mg, Mn, Ca, rare earths, Th, Pb, Au ppt. completely and U, Be, Sr, Ba, Hg, In incompletely.

3.5. Organic reagents

$H_2C_2O_4$ and ether extraction have long been used as org. reagents in inorg. analysis. Cupferron, thionalide, dithizone, oxine, anthranilic acid, oximes, arsonic acids, tannin, etc. are widely used as group or specific reagents. These compds. are most important for lateral sepns. after vertical sepns. by the reagents listed above. Details are given in Part II.

4. OTHER METHODS OF SEPARATION

Ion exchange chromatography with exchange resins, cellulose (see Part II), active alumina (see Chapters 52 and 58) or silica gel (see Chapters 27 and 39) is regularly used in modern analysis. Paper chromatography can also be applied.[36]

Distillation and Volatilization are excellent for sepns. of volatile elements (see Table 2, cf. Table 1). Micro diffusion methods are sometimes useful.[37]

References

1. Flaschka, H., *Z. anal. Chem.*, **129**, 326 (1949).
2. Kawamura, K., *Japan Analyst*, **2**, 347, 415 (1953).
3. Cotton, J. B., *Analyst*, **66**, 286 (1941).
4. Caley, E. R. and Burford, H. G., *Ind. Eng. Chem., Anal. Ed.*, **8**, 63 (1936).
5. Smith, G. F., *Mixed Perchloric, Sulfuric and Phosphoric acids and their Applications in Analysis*, (1935); *Perchloric Acid*, 4th ed. (1940); *Further Applications in the Use of Perchloric Acid in Analysis*, (1942), G. F. Smith Co., Columbus.
6. Barard, D., *Ann. chim. anal. app.*, (3) **17**, 257 (1935).
7. Smith, G. F., *et al., Ind. Eng. Chem., Anal. Ed.*, **3**, 52, 55, 48 (1931).
8. Hoffman, J. I. and Lundell, G. E. F., *J. Research Natl. Bur. Standards*, **22**, 465 (1939); for HF + $HClO_4$, see Chapman, F. W., Jr., *et al., Anal. Chem.*, **21**, 700 (1949).
9. Lecoq, H., *Bull. soc. roy. sci. Liege*, **11**, 318 (1942).
10. Willard, H. H., *et al., Ind. Eng. Chem., Anal. Ed.*, **14**, 234 (1942).
11. Talvitie, N. A., *Anal. Chem.*, **23**, 623 (1951).
12. Morimoto, T., *et al., Tetsu to Hagane*, **39**, 626 (1953).
13. Feigl, F. and Caldas, A., *Mikrochim. Acta*, 1310 (1956).
14. Shell, H. R., *Anal. Chem.*, **26**, 591 (1954).
15. Hoffman, J. I., *J. Research Natl. Bur. Standards*, **25**, 379 (1940).
16. Yoshida, Y., *J. Chem. Soc. Japan.* **63**, 439, 446, 615, 622 (1942).
17. Seelye, F. T. and Rafter, T. A., *Nature*, **165**, 317 (1950); Rafter, *Analyst*, **75**, 485 (1950).
18. Petretic, G. J., *Anal. Chem.*, **23**, 1183 (1951).
19. Jefferey, P. G., *Analyst*, **82**, 67 (1957).
20. Brennecke, E., *Schwefelwasserstoff als Reagens in der quantitativen Analyse, Chem. Anal.*, **41** (1939); Kato, T., *J. Chem. Soc. Japan*, **54**, 889 (1933); **55**, 213, 293, 331, 337, 345, 1152 (1934); **56**, 210 (1935); **58**, 598, 972, 977 (1937).
21. Palasciano, L., *Z. anal. Chem.*, **111**, 263 (1937/38).
22. Welcher, **I**, p. 401.
23. Baker, H. H., *Anal. Chem.*, **21**, 192 (1949); Swift, E. H. and Butler, A., *ibid.*, **28**, 146 (1956).
24. Alimarin, I. P., *et al., Primenenie Mechenykh Atomiv v Anal. Khim., Akad. Nauk S.S.S.R., Inst. Geokhim. i Anal. Khim.*, 13 (1955).
25. Winkler, P. E., *Bull. soc. chim. Belges*, **42**, 503 (1933).
26. Ostroumov, E. A., *Ind. Eng. Chem., Anal. Ed.*, **10**, 693 (1938); Ostroumov and Maslenikova, G. S., *ibid.*, 695.
27. Gilchrist, R., *J. Research Natl. Bur. Standards*, **30**, 89 (1943); Oka, Y., *J. Chem. Soc. Japan*, **61**, 311 (1941); Britton, H. T. S., *Hydrogen Ions*, 4th ed., Vols. I–II Chapman & Hall, London (1955–56); Hillebrand and Lundell, p. 76.
28. Willard, H. H., and Tang, N. K., *Ind. Eng. Chem., Anal. Ed.*, **9**, 357 (1937); Boyle, A. K. and Musser, D. F., *ibid.*, **15**, 621 (1943); also see Hillebrand and Lundell p. 82 for Na-succinate method.
29. Willard and Sheldon, J. L., *Anal. Chem.*, **20**, 1162 (1950).
30. Kolthoff, I. M. *et al., J. Am. Chem. Soc.*, **56**, 812 (1934); Lehrman, L. and Kramer, J., *ibid.*, 2648; Welcher, **II**, p. 23.
31. Kozu, T., *J. Chem. Soc. Japan*, **54**, 682 (1933).
32. Welcher, **II**, p. 388.
33. Yoe and Sarver, *Organic Analytical Reagents*, p. 58 *et seq.* (1941).
34. Kozu, T., *J. Chem. Soc. Japan*, **56**, 22, 562, 683 (1935); Welcher, **III**, p. 124.
35. Ostroumov, E. A., *Z. anal. Chem.*, **106**, 170 (1936); Welcher, **III**, p. 15.
36. Anderson, J. R. A. and Lederer, M., *Anal. Chim. Acta*, **5**, 321, 396 (1951); Lacourt, L., *Mikrochim. Acta*, 269 (1957); Pollard, F. H. and McOmie, J. F. W., *Chromatographic Methods in Inorganic Analysis*, Butterworths, London (1954); Lederer, E. and Lederer, M., *Chromatography*, 2nd ed., Elsevier, Amsterdam (1957); Smith, O. C., *Inorganic Chromatography*, D. van Nostrand, New York (1953).
37. Conway, E. J., *Microdiffusion Analysis and Volumetric Error*, Crosley-Lockwood, London (1947).

3

GRAVIMETRY

Gravimetric methods form a fundamental part of quantitative analysis; they are usually the most accurate methods available but they are time-consuming. In general, the precipitate is formed in aqueous solution, separated from the mother liquor, washed, heated or ignited to constant weight and weighed as a compound of definite composition.

In special cases the method may involve separation from a fused mass (fire assay) or absorption of a gas in some absorbent (e.g. detn. of CO_2 or H_2O).

1. FORMATION OF PRECIPITATES

The ppt. is usually formed by dropwise addn. of a slight excess of reagent to the hot, stirred sample soln.; when the ppt. is fine, it is aged for some hr. on a steam-bath or at room temp. It should preferably be repptd.

The reagent should be specific and should not interfere in the detn. of other elements in the filtrate; it should be easily removed from the ppt. by washing or heating. The conversion factor should be small. Inorg. reagents are usually less specific than org. reagents but the latter are more difficult to remove from the ppt. and cause more trouble in later detns. in the filtrate.

Precipitation from homogeneous solution generally gives a purer and more readily filterable ppt.[1]

2. SEPARATION OF PRECIPITATES

2.1. Filtration

The various methods are listed below.

(a) Filter paper. The size and type of paper chosen depends on the quantity and quality of the ppt.; the vol. of mother liquor is unimportant. Quant. paper should be used for sepns. as well as detns. Paper often contains impurities and absorbs metallic ions and should not be used in colorimetric detns. of traces of metals.

The ppt. is usually filtered after it has settled; rapid settling and filtration are favored by the addn. of filter paper pulp to the soln. before or after pptn.

The various types of filter paper are listed along with their uses in Table 5.

A pad of filter paper pulp on a Witt plate in an ordinary filter funnel allows rapid filtration. The depth and fineness of the pulp are prepd. according to the type of ppt.

(b) Glass filters. These are often used for filtration of ppts. from org. reagents. They are graded from No. 0 (coarse) to No. 4 (fine), are easily heated to constant weight and can be heated to 250°C (heating above 150°C and cooling should be done slowly). They should not be used with concd. alkalies.

TABLE 5. Types of Filter Paper and their Uses

Whatman	Schleicher and Schüll	Toyo	Uses
1	595	1	Qual.
2	597	2	Qual., fine ppt.
30		3	Quant., a little more ash
41	589 black band	5A	Quant., rapid, hydroxides, etc.
40	589 white band	5B	Quant., general use
42	589 blue band	5C	Quant., fine ppt.
44	590	6	Quant., general use, little ash
54	575	4	Hardened, suction

(c) Munroe crucibles. These consist of a Pt sponge filter pad in a Pt funnel; they can be used for any ppt. and at any temp. but are troublesome to prep.

(d) Porcelain filters. These can be heated to higher temps. than glass filters but are slightly hygroscopic.

(e) Quartz filters. These are better than glass or porcelain filters but are more expensive.

(f) Gooch filters. These are porcelain filter crucibles with asbestos filter pads. Water (1–2 mg.) may be retained even after drying at 110°C. They absorb alkalies and may be attacked by acids. Glass fiber pads may replace the asbestos.

(g) Alundum filters. These are seldom used.

Filters (d), (e), (f) and (g) should not be used for ppts. which are difficultly sol. in acids, e.g. Al_2O_3, Cr_2O_3, SiO_2, SnO_2, or for gelatinous ppts. The solvents used to remove ppts. from these filters can be found in Mellor and Thompson (1938), pp. 773–774.

(h) Collodion membranes. These can be used for the sepn. of very fine colloidal ppts.; they are not used in quantitative work.

2.2. Centrifugation

A centrifuge is often used for the sepn. of small or fine ppts.; it has also been applied for sepn. immediately before a gravimetric finish.[2]

2.3. Washing

The ppt. is washed 7–10 times with suitable liquids. It should not be washed more than necessary; repptn. must be done if the amt. of impurity is large. Washing with EtOH or Me_2CO followed by Et_2O is sometimes used to remove reagent and H_2O, and to facilitate drying.

3. HEATING OF PRECIPITATES

The ppt. must be heated or ignited to a compd. of definite compn.; the temp. required for the various ppts. is differently recommended.[3] The data given in Part III are mainly of Japanese origin; Duval's data are given in parentheses when they differ from the Japanese values.

The ppt. should be heated electrically; if gas heating is used, some compds. may absorb CO_2 and H_2O, and basic compds. may absorb SO_3 (0·1–2 mg. SO_3 is absorbed by varying amts. of CaO, MgO, NiO, CuO, ZnO, Fe_2O_3, Al_2O_3 and KCl).[4]

4. COOLING, WEIGHING AND THE CONVERSION FACTOR

The hot ppt. is cooled in a desiccator, which should be small so that a min. amt. of air is present. If the ppt. is at all hygroscopic, the desiccant must be powerful. An ideal desiccant absorbs moisture quickly and has a large capacity; it should be easy to regenerate and the amt. of residual moisture should be small. The capacity for absorption of CO_2 is sometimes important. The types of desiccant and the comparative values for residual moisture are listed in Table 6.

The ppt. should be weighed rapidly and until const. wt. is obtained, i.e. a variation of less than 0·3 mg. on the macro scale.

Four figures are usually given for the factor; but it is pointless to use a value which is much more accurate than the accuracy attainable with the analytical method.

TABLE 6. Types of Desiccant

Desiccant	Residual moisture in mg./l. at 25–30°C	Remarks
P_2O_5	0·0001	Surface becomes glazed and capacity drops rapidly. Unregeneratable. Most powerful. Excellent in small desiccator.
BaO	0·0007	Nearly ideal. Useful at higher temp. than P_2O_5. Absorbs CO_2. Unregeneratable.
Anhydr. $Mg(ClO_4)_2$ (Anhydrone)	0·002	Excellent. Regeneratable at less than 250°C at 0·1 mm. Hg. Not usable with NH_3.
H_2SO_4	0·003	Inconvenient. Capacity drops gradually. Not suitable for high temp. or for CaO.
CaO	0·003	Slow absorption.
$CaSO_4$	0·005	Slow absorption. Low capacity.
Alumina	0·005	Small capacity. Regeneratable at 175°C for 6–7 hr.
KOH	0·005 ?	
Silica gel	0·03	
$Mg(ClO_4)_2.2\text{-}3H_2O$ (Dehydrite)	0·03	
Anhydr. $CaCl_2$	0·36	Unsuitable for CaO.
NaOH	0·80	
Anhydr. $Ba(ClO_4)_2$	0·82	
$ZnCl_2$	0·98	
Granular $CaCl_2$	1·5	
Anhydr. $CuSO_4$	2·8	

References

1. GORDON, L., SALUTSKY, M. L., and WILLARD, H. H., *Precipitation from Homogeneous Solution*, Wiley, New York (1959).
2. BECK, G., *Anal. Chim. Acta*, **4**, 245 (1950).
3. ISHIMARU, S., *Kagaku-Zikken-Gaku*, X, 97 (1942); DUVAL, C., *Inorganic Thermogravimetric Analysis*, Elsevier, Amsterdam (1953).
4. IEVIŅŠ, A., *Z. anal. Chem.*, **102**, 412 (1935).

4

ELECTROLYTIC DEPOSITION

Some elements, e.g. Cu or Pb, can be determined more accurately and separated more advantageously by electrolytic deposition[1] than by other methods. This is particularly true when controlled cathode potentials are used. Electrolysis at a Hg cathode is often utilized in steel analysis and internal electrolysis is sometimes convenient, e.g. in routine sepn. of Ag, Cu, Bi from Pb.

In practice the current density should be chosen correctly; if it is too low, the deposit is coarse, and if too high, the deposit is spongy. High temps. and stirring favor better deposition and shorter times. Addn. of gelatine or a depolarizer is also useful. Metals can be sepd. from each other if their potential difference is greater than 0·35 v. for univalent ions, or 0·2 v. for divalent ions; otherwise, the conditions must be controlled by addn. of complexing agents, temp. adjustment, etc. The electrodeposition potentials of several metals in different media with Pt electrodes are listed in Table 7.[2] Any metal can be completely deposited by electrolysis at a voltage 0·2 v. lower than that listed.

Details of controlled cathode potential electrolysis can be found in any of the cited references. Coulometric analysis[3] is described under titrimetry in the appropriate places in Part III.

The elements deposited under specific conditions are listed below (Lundell and Hoffman).

(1) On cathode from mineral acid soln. Cu, Rh, Pd, Ag, Cd, Sb, Re, Pt, Au, Hg, Pb, Bi, Po deposit. Detn. of Cu is very satisfactory. Ag, Hg, Cu, Pb can be sepd. from Sn, Sb, Mo, W in HNO_3 + HF soln.

(2) On cathode from org. acid soln. Fe, Cu, Zn, Cd, In, Sn, Te, Bi deposit.

(3) On cathode from alk. soln. Cu, Ni, Co, Zn, Pd, Ag, Cd deposit. Ni, Co can be detd. N_2H_4 or NH_2OH is added to prevent corrosion of the Pt electrode by electrolysis in alk. soln.

(4) On cathode from cyanide soln. Co, Ni, Cu, Zn, Ag, Hg, Cd, In, Au deposit.

(5) On cathode from alk. sulfide soln. Sn, Sb, Au, Hg deposit.

(6) On cathode as hydrated oxide from acidic soln. Mo, Re, U deposit.

TABLE 7. Electrodeposition Potentials[a]

Metal ions	Supporting electrolytes: 0·3*M* HCl, 0·14*M* $NH_2OH.HCl$	0·2*M* H_2SO_4	0·7*M* HNO_3	0·4*M* Na_2Tart, 0·1*M* NaHTart	1·2*M* NH_4OH, 0·2*M* NH_4Cl	0·4*M* KCN, 0·2*M* KOH
Au	+0·60	+0·70	+0·70	(+0·50)	—	−1·00
Hg	+0·15	+0·40	+0·40	(+0·25)	−0·05	−0·80
Ag	—	+0·40	+0·40	(+0·30)	−0·05	−0·80
Cu	−0·15	−0·05	−0·05	−0·30	−0·45	−1·55
Bi	−0·15	−0·08	−0·05	−0·35	—	(−1·70)
Sb	−0·20	−0·33	(−0·03)	−0·75	—	−1·25
Sn	−0·50	—	—	—	—	—
Pb	−0·55	—	+1·70[b]	−0·50	—	—
Cd	−0·80	−0·80	—	−0·90	−0·90	−1·20
Zn	—	—	—	−1·10	−1·40	−1·50
Ni	—	—	—	—	−0·90	—
Co	—	—	—	—	−0·85	—

[a] ±0·03 v. *vs.* S.C.E.; values in parentheses not quant.; 0·1 g. metal ion/200 ml.

[b] Anodic potential.

(7) Into Hg cathode from feebly acidic soln. (usually $0{\cdot}3N$ or 1% v/v H_2SO_4). Fe, Co, Ni, Zn, Cr, Ag, Hg, Bi, Cu, Cd, Sn, Mo, Ge, Ga, In, Tl, Re, Au, Rh, Pd, Ir, Pt pass completely into the Hg; Os, Pb, As, Te, Se pass incompletely into Hg but are completely sepd.; Ru, Sb, La, Nd sep. incompletely; sepn. of Mn is almost complete when H_3PO_4 is added. With a magnetic cathode cell, no film forms on the Hg surface and 99·6% Mn can be sepd. by adding 30% H_2O_2.[4] Mn is also almost completely sepd. at pH 2·4–4·7 but reductants and $(NH_4)_2SO_4$ interfere unless some Ni is added.[5] Sepns. in detns. of Al, Ti, V in steels and of Fe, Co, Ni in Al, Ti, Zr are important.

The apparatus has been described[4, 6] and the method reviewed.[7]

For micro work,[8] use an Ag plate (1·5 × 2 cm.) with a Pt wire, and electrolyze in $Hg_2(NO_3)_2$ soln. contg. 5–7 ml. 0·5–1·0N H_2SO_4 at 1 amp. for 45 min. and at 0·5 amp. for 15 min.

(8) On anode as hydrated oxide from acidic soln. Pb, Mn, Co, Tl deposit. Pb can be detd. satisfactorily.

References

1. SAND, H. J. S., *Electrochemistry and Electrochemical Analysis*, Vols. I–III, Blackie, London (1940); SCHLEICHER, A., *Elektroanalytische Schnellmethoden*, 3. Aufl. (1947); DIEHL, H., *Electrochemical Analysis with Graded Cathode Potential Control*, G. F. Smith, Columbus (1948); LINGANE, J. J., *Electroanalytical Chemistry* (1953); ASHLEY, S. E. Q., *Anal. Chem.*, **21**, 70 (1949); **24**, 91 (1952); DEFORD, D. D., *ibid.*, **26**, 135 (1954); **28**, 660 (1956).
2. TANAKA, M., *Japan Analyst*, **6**, 341, 409, 413, 477, 483, 617 (1957).
3. LINGANE, J. J. *Electroanalytical Chemistry*, p. 347 *et seq.* (1953).
4. CENTER, E. J., *et al.*, *Anal. Chem.*, **23**, 1134 (1951).
5. MCDUFFIE, B., and HAZLEGROVE, L. S., *Anal. Chem.*, **24**, 826 (1952).
6. JOHNSON, H. O., *et al.*, *Anal. Chem.*, **19**, 481 (1947); PARKS, T. D., *ibid.*, **20**, 148 (1948); AYLWARD, G. H. and WOOLDRIDGE, H. V., *Analyst*, **78**, 386 (1953).
7. MAXWELL, J. A. and GRAHAM, R. P., *Chem. Revs.*, **46**, 471 (1950).
8. HAHN, R. B., *Anal. Chem.*, **25**, 1749 (1953).

5

TITRIMETRY

1. INTRODUCTION[1]

Titrimetric analysis is convenient but errors of less than 0·1% can be achieved only when great care is taken; the largest errors are found with very dilute solutions and visual indicators.

To obtain the most accurate results, the temp. of titration should be within 2°C of the temp. of the standardization. The temp. correction for the standardization is simple; the correction for each titration can be found from Fig. 2.[2] Weight burets can be used to avoid temp. effects and other volumetric errors but the normal advantage of speed is then lost.

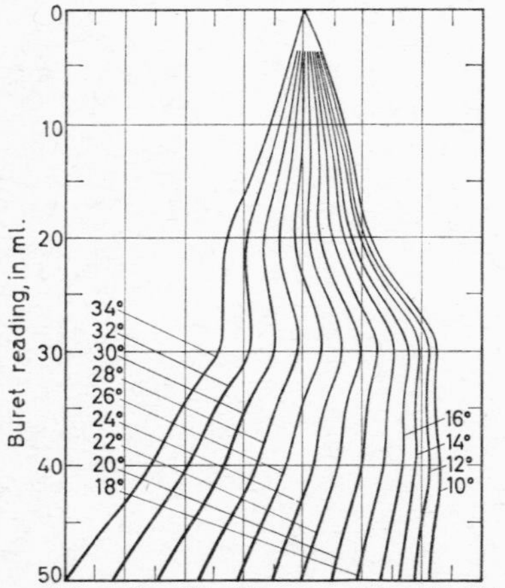

FIG. 2. Chart for determining the combined correction for buret errors and for deviations from 20°C in temperature of the 'average' solution.

The standards used must be pure and of large equivalent weight; they must be strictly protected from moisture. In very accurate work, rational atomic weights (values in air) should be used but this is unnecessary in routine work.

Under the usual macro conditions, more than 25 ml. of standard soln. and of titrant should be used to avoid errors in volume measurement. Blanks must be detd. under the conditions of the actual titrations. The use of a 'titration thief' helps to avoid overtitration.

Titrimetric analysis can be divided into three categories:

(1) neutralization titrations,

(2) titrations involving precipitation or complex-formation,

(3) oxidation–reduction titrations (redox titrations).

2. NEUTRALIZATION TITRATIONS

Apart from straightforward acid–base titrations, neutralization titrations are used in the detn. of H_3BO_3, NH_3, CO_2, F as H_2SiF_6, P as phosphomolybdate, Mg or P as $MgNH_4PO_4$, Re as $HReO_4$, S as the benzidine salt, and Sb, Be, Al by hydrolysis.

2.1. Primary standards

(The figures given in brackets represent the no. of g. necessary to prep. 1 l. of 0·1*N* soln.)

(a) Standards for acids. (*1*) $KHCO_3$ (10·007) is not hygroscopic and must not be heated. Powder and dry for 4 hr. over H_2SO_4 under CO_2. Use with phenol red indicator as given below.

(*2*) Na_2CO_3 (5·298). Dry pure Na_2CO_3 at 300°C (*in vacuo*); or heat $NaHCO_3$ at 300°C for 1·5 hr. (heating can be done in boiling $PhNO_2$ vapor and then *in vacuo*).

Dissolve the compd. in previously boiled and cooled H_2O, and titrate in the cold to methyl orange, or hot to phenol red indicator. In accurate work, titrate until the soln. is red to methyl orange, add 1 drop aq. Br_2, boil for some min., cool and titrate with 0·01*N* NaOH to methyl red or bromothymol blue.

(*3*) $Na_2C_2O_4$ (6·699). To purify, dissolve in a 32-fold, or greater, excess of H_2O, add NaOH till slightly alk., let stand, filter and evap. to 1/10 of its vol.; filter, powder, wash, recrystallize (until no SO_4^{2-} is present and the soln. is neutral to phenolphthalein), and dry at 240°C. Fuse a weighed sample in a Pt crucible until just molten (to convert to Na_2CO_3) and titrate as above.

(*4*) Borax (19·061). To purify, heat 15 g. in 50 ml. H_2O at less than 55°C, cool, filter, wash twice each with H_2O, EtOH and Et_2O, and let dry for 12–18 hr. on a glass plate. Store in a hygrostat. Titrate to methyl red and use a comparison soln. $K_2B_4O_7{\cdot}4H_2O$ can also be used.[3]

(*5*) Tl_2CO_3 (see p. 33). Titrate at boiling point to bromocresol purple.

(*6*) KIO_3 (3·566). Titrate 100 mg. KIO_3 + 150 mg. KI + 800 mg. $Na_2S_2O_3$ to methyl yellow or methyl orange.

(*7*) Yellow HgO (10·830). Pour 1 l. aq. 10% $HgCl_2$ into 650 ml. 1·5*N* NaOH, filter, wash and dry in the dark *in vacuo* over H_2SO_4. Weigh 1 g., add 20 g. KBr/25 ml. soln., heat under protection from a soda-lime guard tube, cool and titrate first to phenolphthalein and then to methyl orange.

(*8*) BrCN (see p. 33).

(*9*) Tris(hydroxymethyl)aminomethane (2-hydroxy-2-amino-1,3-propanediol or trimethylolaminomethane) (12·112) is easily synthesized and an excellent standard.[4]

(*10*) 4-Aminopyridine (9·412). Recrystallize from C_6H_6 or toluene and dry for 2 hr. at 105°C (m.p. 161°C.) Titrate to methyl red.[5]

(*11*) Diphenylguanidine (21·117) is satisfactory.[6]

(*12*) Ag or $AgNO_3$ is accurate for HCl standardization but inconvenient.[7]

(b) Standards for alkalies. (*1*) $H_2C_2O_4{\cdot}2H_2O$ (6·299). Dissolve in 1:1 EtOH + Et_2O, filter, evap., dissolve in warm H_2O, cool while stirring, filter, recrystallize and dry on a tile. Titrate to phenolphthalein. Purification as ethyl oxalate is also used. KHC_2O_4 and $KHC_2O_4{\cdot}H_2C_2O_4{\cdot}2H_2O$ have been suggested.

(*2*) KH-phthalate (20·406). Add a slight excess of K_2CO_3 to sublimed phthalic acid, recrystallize and dry at 125°C. Titrate to phenolphthalein or thymol blue.

(*3*) Benzoic acid (12·200). Recrystallize twice from EtOH and once from H_2O, sublime *in vacuo*, fuse at 140°C in a Pt dish, powder; dissolve in EtOH and titrate to phenolphthalein.

o-Chlorobenzoic and 2,4,6-trinitrobenzoic acids have been proposed.[8]

(*4*) $KH(IO_3)_2$ (38·985). To prepare, add 110 g. $KClO_3$ to 400 ml. hot H_2O contg. 40 ml. HCl, add 100 g. powdered I_2 slowly, warm, boil for some min., filter, cool while stirring and recrystallize three times from H_2O. Dry at 120°C. Titrate to methyl orange and then to phenolphthalein.

(*5*) H_2SO_4 (const. boiling or freezing) gives errors of ±0·01%.[9]

(*6*) Other standards which have been suggested are const. boiling HCl, $HClO_4$,[10] sulfamic acid,[11] α-furoic acid (pyromucic acid),[12] salicylic acid,[13] adipic acid,[14] succinic acid or anhydride, maleic acid, fumaric acid, malic acid, picric acid, KH-tartrate, pyridinium perchlorate, *p*-nitrobenzoic acid, hydrazinium sulfate, borax + mannitol, $K_2Cr_2O_7$, $3CdSO_4{\cdot}8H_2O$ (electrolysis), and biguanide sulfate.[15]

2.2. Neutralization indicators[16]

In addn. to the usual single pH indicators, mixed and screened indicators (Table 8)[17] are often used in neutralization titrations. Universal indicators (Table 9) are useful for pH measurements but are never used in accurate titrations. It is sometimes convenient to use fluorescent indicators (for details, see ref. 16), turbidity indicators (e.g. isonitrosoacetyl-*p*-aminoazobenzene, pH 11·0; isonitrosoacetyl-*p*-toluazobenzene, pH 11·5; $Hg_3[Cr(SCN)_6]_2$, pH 4·0), or adsorption indicators (e.g. fluorescein + $SnCl_2$; eosin or uranin + traces of Bi^{3+} or Pb^{2+}).

Visual indicators must be chosen so that the color change at the end-point coincides with the equivalence point of the titration, which depends on the type and strength of the acid and base.

(a) Strong acid–strong base. Any indicator is suitable for 1*N* solns. With more dilute solns., titrate acids at the b.p. with bases to phenol red, cresol red, bromothymol blue or rosolic acid; for the reverse titration, use methyl red or phenol red.

(b) Weak acid–strong base. With 1*N* solns., phenolphthalein is accurate when K exceeds 10^{-6}, and thymolphthalein when K lies between 10^{-6} and 3×10^{-8}; nitramine or tropeolin OO gives errors of ±5% when $K = 5 \times 10^{-6}$ and a comparison soln. is used. With 0·1*N* solns., thymolphthalein gives errors of ±1·2% when K is less than 5×10^{-8}, and of ±0·5% when K exceeds 10^{-8} and a comparison soln. is used. With 0·01*N* solns., phenolphthalein or thymol blue gives errors of ±0·2% when K exceeds 3×10^{-6} and ±5% when K is less than 10^{-7}; a comparison soln. of the correct pH (±0·1) must be used.

Acids in a mixture can be titrated separately if K_1/K_2 exceeds 10^4.

Particular applications are:

(*i*) H_3PO_4, H_3AsO_4. Titrate as a monobasic acid (pH 4·35) to methyl orange, methyl yellow or bromophenol blue using a 0·05*M* KH_2PO_4 comparison soln.; as a dibasic acid (pH 9·6) to thymolphthalein, phenolphthalein (in half-saturated NaCl) or thymol blue using a 0·05*M* Na_2HPO_4 comparison soln.; or as a tribasic acid to phenolphthalein or thymol blue in presence of concd. $CaCl_2$.

(*ii*) $H_4P_2O_7$. Titrate as a dibasic acid (pH 4·25) to methyl orange, methyl yellow or bromophenol blue; or as a tetrabasic acid in presence of $CaCl_2$ as above.

(*iii*) HF. Titrate to phenolphthalein, thymol blue, phenol red or neutral red. If H_2SiF_6 is also present, titrate both acids at b.p. to phenolphthalein and, in another aliquot, titrate H_2SiF_6 alone to phenolphthalein after adding 1 g. NaCl + some 4*N* HCl, evapg., adding H_2O and re-evapg.

(*iv*) H_2SO_3. Titrate as a monobasic acid (pH 4·4) to methyl orange, methyl yellow or bromophenol blue; or as a dibasic acid to phenolphthalein or thymol blue after addn. of $HgCl_2$ or $BaCl_2$.

(*v*) H_2CO_3. Titrate as a monobasic acid (pH 8·25) to

TABLE 8. Mixed and Screened Indicators

Indicator[a]	Solvent	Ratio	pH	Color change acid	alk.	Remarks
Methyl yellow + Methylene blue	EtOH	1 : 1	3·25	blue-violet	green	Excellent, keep in dark
As above		5 : 3	3·8	blue-violet	green	
Hexamethoxy red + Methyl green	EtOH	1 : 1	4·0	violet	green	Blue-violet at 4·0, keep in dark
Methyl orange + 0·25% Indigocarmine	H_2O	1 : 1	4·1	violet	green	
Methyl orange + Aniline blue	H_2O	1 : 1	4·3	violet	green	Artificial light, keep in dark
0·02% Methyl orange + Na–Bromocresol green	H_2O	1 : 1	4·3	orange	blue-green	Yellow at 3·5, green-yellow at 4·05
Methyl orange + Xylene cyanol FF (1 g. + 1·4 g./500 ml. 50% EtOH)		1 : 1	3·8–4·0	red	green	
0·2% Bromocresol green + 0·2% Methyl red	EtOH	4 : 1	4·2–4·7	yellow	blue	Good for carbonate titrations
Bromocresol green + 0·02% Methyl red	EtOH	1 : 1	4·8	pale pink	pale blue-grey	Excellent for carbonate titrations
Bromocresol blue + 0·2% Methyl red	EtOH	3 : 1	5·1	wine-red	green	Very sharp, excellent
Methylene blue + 0·2% Methyl red	EtOH	1 : 1	5·4	purple	green	Dirty blue at 5·4, keep in dark
Na–Bromocresol green + Alizarin S	H_2O	1 : 1	5·6	violet	yellow-green	Red-brown at 5·6
Na–Chlorophenol red + Aniline blue	H_2O	1 : 1	5·8	green	violet	
Na–Chlorophenol red + Na–Bromocresol green	H_2O	1 : 1	6·1	yellow-green	blue-violet	Blue-green at 5·4, blue at 5·8, pale violet-blue at 6·0
Na–Bromothymol blue + Na–Bromocresol purple	H_2O	1 : 1	6·7	yellow	blue-violet	Yellow-violet at 6·2, violet at 6·6
Na–Bromothymol blue + Azolitmin	H_2O	2 : 1	6·9	violet	blue	
Neutral red + Methylene blue	EtOH	1 : 1	7·0	violet-blue	green	Excellent, keep in dark
Neutral red + Bromothymol blue	EtOH	1 : 1	7·2	rose	green	
Cyanine + Phenol red	50% EtOH	2 : 1	7·3	yellow	violet	Orange at 7·2, decolorizes
Na–Bromothymol blue + Na–Phenol red	H_2O	1 : 1	7·5	yellow	violet	Dirty green at 7·2, pale violet at 7·4, excellent
Neutral red + Tetrabromophenol blue	H_2O	5 : 3	8·0			
Na–Cresol red + Na–Thymol blue	H_2O	1 : 3	8·3	yellow	violet	Pink at 8·2, excellent
α-Naphtholphthalein + Cresol red	EtOH	2 : 1	8·3	pale rose	violet	Pale violet at 8·2
α-Naphtholphthalein + phenolphthalein	EtOH	1 : 3	8·9	pale rose	violet	Pale green at 8·2
Methyl green + phenolphthalein	EtOH	2 : 1	8·9	green	violet	Pale blue at 8·8, keep in dark
Thymol blue + phenolphthalein	50% EtOH	1 : 3	9·0	yellow	violet	Green at 9·0, excellent
α-Naphtholphthalein + phenolphthalein	50% EtOH	1 : 2	9·6	pale rose	violet	Green at 9·0
Thymolphthalein + phenolphthalein	EtOH	1 : 1	9·9	colorless	violet	Pink at 9·6
0·2% Nile blue + phenolphthalein	EtOH	2 : 1	10·0	blue	red	Violet at 10·0, excellent
Thymolphthalein + Salicyl yellow	EtOH	2 : 1	10·2	yellow	violet	
0·2% Nile blue + Salicyl yellow	EtOH	2 : 1	10·8	green	red-brown	

[a] Unless otherwise stated, 0·1% soln. of each indicator is used.

TABLE 9. Universal Indicators[a]

	Kolthoff	Van Urk No. 2	Van der Brug	Čuta and Kámen	Bergen	Kato
EtOH %	95	70	75	95	100	80
pH range	3–12	2–12	2–10	1·2–12·7	2–10	3–13
Thymol blue	—	—	5	—	100	20
Pentamethoxy red	—	—	—	50	—	—
Tropeolin OO	—	70	—	—	—	—
Methyl yellow	18·8	—	—	—	60	—
Methyl orange	—	100	—	—	—	—
Methyl red	6·3	80	25	2·2	40	50
Bromothymol blue	25·0	400	60	10	80	60
α–Naphtholphthalein	—	500	—	—	—	—
Cresolphthalein	—	400	—	—	—	—
Phenolphthalein	25·0	500	60	3·55	20	60
Thymolphthalein	25·0	—	—	—	—	—
Salicyl yellow	—	150	—	—	—	50
Trinitrobenzene	—	—	—	112·5	—	—

[a]See WOODS, J. T. and MELLON, M. G., *J. Phys. Chem.*, **45**, 313 (1941); KATO, T., *Analysis & Reagents* (*Japan*), **2**, 146 (1947); *Technol. Repts. Tohoku Univ.*, **17**, 148 (1953); also see DUBSKY, J. V. and LANGER, A., *Z. anal. Chem.*, **106**, 187 (1936); SMITH, *Analytical Processes, Physico-chemical Interpretation*, p. 448 (1940) (other four indicators).

NOTES. (1) Indicators, mg./100 ml., color change,

pH	1	2	3	4	5	6	7
Color	(pink-red)	rose	red-orange	orange-red	orange	yellow	yellow-green

pH	8	9	10	11	12	13
Color	green-blue	blue-green	violet	(purple)	(red-brown)	brown-green

(2) Thymolphthalein + Tropeolin O (4 : 1) is convenient for pH 9–13, changing through yellow–green–blue–violet.

(3) Mix aq. 0·05*M* $Fe(NH_4)_2(SO_4)_2$ and 0·15*M* tiron and filter; pH 2·6 greenish-blue, pH 4·0–5·1 dark blue, pH 6·3 deep violet (SEN, B., *et al.*, *Sci. and Culture* (*Calcutta*), **22**, 457 (1957)).

phenolphthalein or thymol blue; or as a dibasic acid to these indicators after addn. of $BaCl_2$.

(*vi*) CrO_3. Titrate in satd. NaCl soln. to these indicators adding $BaCl_2$ near the end-point.

(*vii*) H_3BO_3. Neutralize any strong acid present to methyl yellow, add mannitol, invert sugar or glycerol, and titrate to phenolphthalein, thymol blue or α-naphtholphthalein (see Chapter 61). If polyalcohols are not added, use tropeolin O or nitramine and a comparison soln. (0·05*M* Na_2CO_3) if the soln. is less than 1*M*.

(*viii*) HCN, H_3AsO_3 (monobasic). Titrate to nitramine or tropeolin O.

(*ix*) HCOOH, AcOH and homologs. Titrate to phenolphthalein, thymol blue, phenol red, or neutral red; titrate higher fatty acids in EtOH solns.

(*x*) $H_2C_2O_4$ and homologs. Titrate as above, or add 4–5 g. $CaCl_2$/25 ml. 0·1*N* soln. and titrate to methyl yellow.

(c) Weak base–strong acid. With 1*N* solns., methyl yellow is accurate when K exceeds 10^{-7}; tropeolin OO or thymol blue gives errors of ±0·5% when K exceeds 5×10^{-10} and a comparison soln. is used. With 0·1*N* solns., methyl yellow or methyl orange gives errors of ±0·2% when K exceeds 10^{-6} and of ±0·5% when K exceeds 10^{-8} and a comparison soln. is used. With 0·01*N* solns., methyl red gives errors of ±0·2% when K exceeds 3×10^{-6} with H_2O as the comparison soln.; with methyl red or bromocresol green, the error is ±0·5% when K exceeds 10^{-7} and a comparison soln. is used.

In practice, NH_4OH is titrated to methyl red, bromocresol green, methyl orange, bromophenol blue or methyl yellow. Several salts of strong bases and weak acids can be titrated as follows. Borates and sulfides are titrated to any of these five indicators. Carbonates are titrated to any of the last three indicators; for titration to HCO_3^- (pH 8·35), use thymol blue or phenolphthalein and a comparison soln., or thymol blue + cresol red (6:1) titrated to a pink color (see Chapter 62, p. 460). Phosphates are titrated to methyl orange, methyl yellow or bromophenol blue to form the primary salt. For Ca-phosphate, add a known excess of acid, boil, cool, titrate with 0·1*N* NaOH to methyl yellow, using a KH_2PO_4 comparison soln., add $K_2C_2O_4$ in excess, and titrate with 0·1*N* NaOH to thymolphthalein.

(d) Weak acid–weak base. Such titrations are never used if they can be avoided (but see under Conductometric Titration). Several org. acids can be titrated with NH_4OH as follows; the equivalence pH values are given in parentheses. AcOH (7·0), phthalic (7·2) and citric (7·4) acids are titrated to phenol red or neutral red; formic, lactic (6·5), succinic and benzoic (6·7) acids to bromothymol blue or chlorophenol red; oxalic acid (6·9) to bromothymol blue or phenol red; salicylic acid (6·3) to bromothymol blue or methyl red; and tartaric acid (6·65) to bromothymol blue.

3. TITRATIONS INVOLVING PRECIPITATION OR COMPLEX-FORMATION: ARGENTIMETRY AND MERCURIMETRY

Argentimetry can be utilized for the determination of most elements which form chlorides or thiocyanate complexes, as well as of ions which react directly with Ag^+ itself. The reaction of Ag^+ and CN^- is also used in the detn. of Ni and Co. Mercurimetry has become more popular since the introduction of diphenylcarbazone indicator. Other methods involving precipitation or complex formation are more specialized and cannot be discussed generally. Chelatometry is dealt with below (Section 4).

3.1. Primary standards

(The figs. given in parentheses show the no. of g. required for 1 l. of 0·1*N* soln.)

(1) NaCl (5·844). Pass HCl gas into satd. NaCl soln., filter, wash with H_2O and dry at 500–600°C in an elect. muffle.

(2) KCl (7·453). Recrystallize three times from H_2O and dry at 500–600°C.

(3) KBr (11·898). Recrystallize $KBrO_3$ from H_2O, heat to 500–600°C and powder.

(4) $AgNO_3$ (16·987). Powder and dry at 110° and then 220–250°C.

(5) Ag (10·788). Treat $AgNO_3$ soln. with HCO_2NH_4, heat, filter, wash and fuse in a CaO boat.

(6) Hg (10·630). Dissolve in HNO_3, boil and dil.; it is more convenient than Ag for SCN^- standardization.

(7) HgO (10·830). (See Section 2.1a).

3.2. Indicators

Adsorption indicators and their uses are listed in Table 10.[18] During titrations, solns. must be stirred vigorously; the pH of the soln., the temperature, the concn. of the required ion, and the other ions present (especially multivalent ions which promote coagulation of the ppt. and thus cause premature end-points) are important. Addn. of surface-active agents is beneficial.[19]

Other indicators for these titrations are listed in Table 11.

4. TITRATIONS INVOLVING PRECIPITATION AND COMPLEX FORMATION: CHELATOMETRY (COMPLEXIMETRY)[20]

Although chelatometry originated only in 1945, it has been developed so rapidly that it requires treatment separately from other complex-formation methods. Much the most important reagent of the aminopolycarboxylic acid type is EDTA (ethylenediaminetetraacetic acid) which is generally used as its sodium salt. The other reagents, nitrilotriacetic acid (NTA), 1,2-diaminocyclohexanetetraacetic acid (CyDTA) and ethyleneglycol bis(β-aminoethyl)tetraacetic acid (EG TA), have been less studied.

4.1. Reagents

(a) EDTA-Na_2. Dissolve 10 g. in 100 ml. H_2O, add EtOH to give a turbidity, filter, add an equal vol. of EtOH, filter and wash with Me_2CO and Et_2O. If dried at 80°C, use 3·723 g./l. for 0·01*M* solns.; if at 140°C, use 3·363 g./l.

For Ca titration, use 4 g. EDTA + 0·1 g. $MgCl_2 \cdot 6H_2O$/l. For Ba titration, use 28 g. EDTA + 2·6 g. $MgCl_2 \cdot 6H_2O$ + 1·9 g. $CaCl_2 \cdot 2H_2O$ + 7·9 ml. 50% NaOH/l. (0·05*M*) or 7·0 g. EDTA + 0·8 g. $ZnCl_2$ + 1·0 g. $MgCl_2 \cdot 6H_2O$ + some 50% NaOH/l. (0·01*M*). The Zn or Mg chelate can also be used separately in substitution titrations. For stability constants of the metal complexes, see Chapter 8, Section 1.6.

(b) NTA. Dissolve 19·11 g. NTA + 7·5 g. NaOH in 200 ml. hot H_2O, neutralize with 0·1*N* NaOH to methyl red and dilute with H_2O to 1 l.

(c) CyDTA. This forms the most stable complexes (cf. Chapter 8, Section 1.6) so that Pb, Zn, Cd, Ni and Fe^{3+} can be titrated in acidic solns.; the titrant must be added slowly. KCN masks Cu, Hg but not Mn, Co, Ni, Fe^{2+} or Fe^{3+}.

(d) Primary standards. $CaCO_3$ (mol. wt. 100·09), Zn (65·38), Hg (200·6), $HgCl_2$ (276·52), Ca acid malate (414·286), $MgSO_4 \cdot 7H_2O$ (246·50, store over $MgSO_4 \cdot 7H_2O$ + H_2O (5:1)), $Znpy_2(SCN)_2$, $Zn(NH_4)_2(SO_4)_2 \cdot 6H_2O$, $Cdpy_2(SCN)_2$, $Cd(NH_4)_2(SO_4)_2$, Cd(*o*-$NH_2C_6H_4CO_2)_2$, Ni, PbO, $Pb(NO_3)_2$ and $PbCl_2$ have been suggested.

4.2. Indicators

(For structures, see Part II).

(a) For general use. (*i*) Eriochrome black T is sol. in H_2O, EtOH but unstable in soln.; 0·5 g. + 4·5 g. $NH_2OH \cdot HCl$ in 100 ml. abs. MeOH or EtOH is stable for 3 months; also used are mixtures contg. 0·2 g. + 15 ml. triethanolamine + 5 ml. EtOH, 0·5 g. + 0·125 g. methyl yellow + 100 ml. diethanolamine, 0·1 g. + 10 g. NaCl. Use 2–4 drops or ca. 10 mg./100 ml. test soln. The color is wine-red below pH 6·3, blue up to pH 11·5, and orange above pH 11·5.

At pH 10, titrate with EDTA to the change from wine-red to blue after adding 2 ml. buffer (70 g. NH_4Cl + 570 ml. NH_3/l.)/100 ml. test soln. The following ions can be titrated: Mg (above 10 μg.), Ca (add 1 ml. 0·1*M* Mg–EDTA), F^- (via Ca), Zn, Na (via Zn), Cd, In (at b.p.), Mn (add tartrate, ascorbic acid and heat). Fe^{3+}, Ni, Co, Cu, etc., can be masked by addn. of drops of 5% KCN, or by Na_2S, BAL, etc. (see below). Ba, Sr are titrated directly with the mixed standard soln. (above). Co, Ni (hence Pd and CN^-), Pd, Pb, rare earths, Ga, In, Al, Mg (in detns. of PO_4^{3-} and AsO_4^{3-}) are detd. with excess EDTA and back-titration

14. WELCHER, **II**, p. 22.
15. RÁY, A. K., *Z. anal. Chem.*, **156**, 18 (1957).
16. KOLTHOFF, I. M., *Acid–Base Indicators*, Macmillan, London (1937); TOMÍČEK, O., *Chemical Indicators*, Butterworths, London (1950); BRENNECKE, E., Beseitigung der Titrierfehlers bei acidi- und alkali-metrische Titrationen, *Chem. Anal.*, **33**, 1 (1937).
17. KOLTHOFF, Vol. 2, p. 58; HÄHNEL, S., *Svensk Kem. Tidskr.*, **47**, 4 (1935).
18. FAJANS, K., Adsorptionsindikatoren für Fällungstitrationen, *Chem. Anal.*, **33**, 161 (1937); UZUMASA, Y., *Kagaku-Zikken-Gaku*, **X** 391 (1942).
19. NOGAMI, H., *et al.*, *J. Pharm. Soc. Japan*, **74**, 1402 (1954).
20. SCHWARZENBACH, G., Die komplexometrische Titration, *Chem. Anal.*, **45** (1956); *Complexometric Titrations*, Methuen, London (1956); UENO, K., *Chelatometry*, Nankodo, Tokyo (1956); PŘIBIL, R., *Komplexony v chemické Analyse* (1953); *Komplexometrické Titrace*, Prague (1955); WELCHER, F. J., *Ethylene-diamine Tetraacetic Acid*, D. van Nostrand, New York (1957); BARNARD, A. J., JR., *et al.*, *Chemist Analyst*, **45**, 86, 111 (1956); **46**, 18, 46, 76, 106 (1957); VERMA, M. R. and THERATTIL, K. J., *J. Sci. Ind. Research* (*India*), **15A**, *Suppl. No.* 9, 1–41 (1956).
21. CHENG, K. L., *Chemist Analyst*, **45**, 79 (1956).
22. BODEŠÍNSKÝ, B., *Chem. listy*, **51**, 726 (1957).
23. WEHBER, P., *Z. anal. Chem.*, **153**, 253 (1956).
24. KÖRBL, J. and PŘIBIL, R., *Chemist Analyst*, **45**, 102 (1956); *Chem. listy*, **50**, 1440 (1956); **51**, 726 (1957).
25. KÖRBL, J. and PŘIBIL, R., *Chem. listy*, **51**, 1061 (1957).
26. FRITZ, J. S., *et al.*, *Anal. Chem.*, **29**, 821 (1957).
27. LATIMER, W. M., *The Oxidation States of Elements and their Potentials in Aqueous Solutions*, 2nd ed. pp. 340–5, Prentice-Hall, New York (1952); LUNDELL and HOFFMAN (1938).
28. ISHIMARU, S., *Kagaku-Zikken-Gaku*, **X**, 1 (1942); STEPHEN, W. I., *Ind. Chemist*, **29**, 31, 79, 128, 169 (1953).
29. HILLEBRAND and LUNDELL, 100 (108).
30. WALDEN, G. H., JR., *et al.*, *J. Am. Chem. Soc.*, **56**, 350 (1934); FRYLING, CH. F. and TOOLEY, G. H., *J. Am. Chem. Soc.*, **58**, 826 (1936); COLE, S. S. and KUMINS, C. A., *Bull. Am. Ceram. Soc.*, **20**, 329 (1941); SMITH, G. F. and CAGLE, F. W., *Anal. Chem.*, **20**, 183 (1948); HILLEBRAND and LUNDELL, (112).
31. COOKE, W. D., *et al.*, *Anal. Chem.*, **22**, 654 (1950); MCNABB, W. M., *ibid.* **23**, 1325 (1951); SILL, C. W. and PETERSON, H. E., *ibid.* **24**, 1175 (1952).
32. PFEFFER, P., *Notizbl. hess. Landesamtes Bodenforsch. Wiesbaden*, **83**, 292 (1955).
33. YOSHIMURA, C., *J. Chem. Soc. Japan*, **72**, 701 (1951); **73**, 702 (1952); **74**, 116, 325, 544, 747, 818 (1953); **76**, 411 (many references) (1955); STEPHEN, *Ind. Chemist*, **28**, 13, 55, 107 (1952).
34. SMITH, G. F. and WILCOX, C. S., *Ind. Eng. Chem., Anal. Ed.*, **9**, 419 (1937).
35. TANAKA, M., *Bull. Chem. Soc. Japan*, **26**, 299 (1953); **27**, 10 (1954); MURAKAMI, Y., *ibid.* **26**, 348 (1953); KIMURA, K. and MURAKAMI, Y., *Mikrochemie*, **36/37**, 727 (1951); LINGANE, J. J. and DAVIS, D. G., *Anal. Chim. Acta*, **15**, 201 (1956).
36. DE BEER, E. J. and HJORT, A. M., *Ind. Eng. Chem., Anal. Ed.*, **7**, 120 (1935).
37. YASUDA, S. K. and LAMBERT, J. L., *Chemist Analyst*, **45**, 50 (1956).
38. VAVRINECZ, G., *Magyar Kém. Folyóirat*, **42**, 1 (1936).
39. KOLB, J. J., *Ind. Eng. Chem., Anal. Ed.*, **16**, 38 (1944).
40. BUEHRER, T. F. and MASON, C. M., *Ind. Eng. Chem., Anal. Ed.*, **1**, 68 (1929).
41. MACNEVIN, W. M. and KRIEGE, O. H., *Anal. Chem.*, **25**, 767 (1953).
42. LUDEKENS, W. L. W. and DA SILVA, N. R., *Research* (*London*), **9**, S31 (1956).
43. MØLLER, M., *Z. anal. Chem.*, **99**, 351 (1934).
44. BERRY, A. J., *Analyst*, **64**, 27 (1939); JENSEN, E. and NILSSEN, B., *Ind. Eng. Chem., Anal. Ed.*, **11**, 508 (1939).
45. STAMM, H., *Chem. Anal.*, **33**, 49 (1937); ISSA, I. M. and ISSA, R. M., *Chemist Analyst*, **44**, 99 (1955) (many references).
46. FURMAN, N. H., *Chem. Anal.*, **33**, 23 (1937); PETZOLD, W., *Die Cerimetrie and die Anwendung Ferroine als massanalytische Redoxindikatoren*, Verlag Chemie, Weinheim (1955); YOUNG, P., *Anal. Chem.*, **24**, 152 (1952).
47. SMITH, G. F., *Anal. Chem.*, **27**, 1142 (1955).
48. SINGH, B. and SINGH, S., *Anal. Chim. Acta*, **14**, 109 (1956).
49. WATSON, J. P., *Analyst*, **76**, 177 (1951).
50. UBBELOHDE, A. R. J. P., *J. Chem. Soc.*, 1505 (1935); TANINO, K., *Repts. Sci. Research Inst.*, **32**, 20, 24 (1956); IKEGAMI, T., *J. Chem. Soc. Japan, Ind. Chem. Sect.*, **52**, 173 (1949); SAITO, K. and SATO, R., *ibid.*, **55**, 59 (1952).
51. TSUBAKI, I., *J. Chem. Soc. Japan*, **66**, 10 (1945); **71**, 454 (1950); SINGH, B. and SINGH, R., *Anal. Chim. Acta*, **10**, 408 (1954); **11**, 412 (1954); RAO, K. B., *et al.*, *Z. anal. Chem.*, **156**, 180 (1957).
52. RAO, K. B. and RAO, G. G., *Z. anal. Chem.*, **157**, 96, 100 (1957).
53. KIBOKU, M., *Japan Analyst*, **5**, 503 (1956); **6**, 11, 356, 491 (1957).
54. BECK, G., *Mikrochemie ver. Mikrochim. Acta*, **35**, 169 (1950); **36/37**, 245 (1951); **38**, 1, 152 (1951); *Mikrochim. Acta*, 977 (1956); KEYWORTH, D. A. and STONE, K. G., *Anal. Chem.*, **27**, 833 (1955); JENŠOVSKÝ, L., *Chem. listy*, **50**, 1103 (1956).
55. BRICKER, C. E. and LOEFFLER, L. J., *Anal. Chem.*, **27**, 315, 1419 (1955).
56. BECK, M. T., *Acta Chim. Acad. Sci. Hung.*, **5**, 209 (1955).
57. ERDEY, L. and BUZÁS, I., *Acta Chim. Acad. Sci. Hung.* **6**, 77 (1955).
58. LATIMER, W. M., *The Oxidation States of Elements and their Potentials in Aqueous Solutions*, 2nd. ed., pp. 56, 62, 67, Prentice-Hall, New York (1952); LUNDELL and HOFFMAN (1938).
59. LUNDELL and HOFFMAN, 151 (1938).
60. LANG, R., *Chem. Anal.*, **33**, 60 (1937); JAMIESON, G. S., *Volumetric Iodate Methods*, Chem. Catalog Co., New York (1926); SMITH, G. F., *Analytical Applications of Periodic Acid and Iodic Acid and their Salts*, G. F. Smith, Columbus (1950).
61. LANG, R., *Chem. Anal.*, **33**, 86 (1937); SZEBELLÉDY, L. and MADIS, W., *Z. anal. Chem.*, **114**, 116, 197, 249, 253, 343, 347, 350 (1938).
62. SMITH, G. F. and BLISS, H. H., *J. Am. Chem. Soc.*, **53**, 2091, 4291 (1931).
63. MODIANO, J. and PARIAUD, J. C., *Compt. rend.*, **241**, 500 (1955).
64. SINGH, B. and SOOD, K. C., *Anal. Chim. Acta*, **13**, 301, 305 (1955); for details see KOLTHOFF and BELCHER, *Volumetric Analysis*, Vol. III, 639 (1957).

65. Singh, B. and Singh, R., *Anal. Chim. Acta*, **10**, 81, 569 (1954); Singh, B. and Sood, K. C., *ibid.*, **11**, 313, 319 (1954); Singh, A., *J. Indian Chem. Soc.*, **32**, 544 (1955); Paul, R. C. and Singh, A., *ibid.*, **32**, 599 (1955).

66. Goldstone, N. I. and Jacobs, M. B., *Ind. Eng. Chem., Anal. Ed.*, **16**, 206 (1944); also see Erdey, L. and Buzás, I., *Acta Chim. Acad. Sci. Hung.*, **6**, 93, 115 (1955).

67. Kulwarskaja, R. M., *Z. anal. Chem.*, **89**, 199 (1932).

68. Jackson, D. T. and Parsons, J. L., *Ind. Eng. Chem., Anal. Ed.*, **9**, 14 (1937); Levi, G. R., *ibid.*, 250; Brown, E. G., *Anal. Chim. Acta*, **7**, 494 (1952).

69. Gengrinovich, A. I., *et al.*, *Trudy Komissii Anal. Khim., Akad. Nauk S.S.S.R.*, **5**, 237 (1954); Fialkov, Ya. A. and Kagan, F. E., *Ukrain. Khim. Zhur.*, **18**, 55, 64 (1952); Kagan, F. E., *ibid.*, **22**, 94 (1956).

70. Gengrinovich, A. I., *et al.*, *Trudy Komissii Anal. Khim., Akad. Nauk S.S.S.R.*, **5**, 237 (1954); Čihalik, J., *et al.*, *Chem. listy*, **49**, 693, 1167, 1176 (1955); **51**, 264, 272 (1957).

71. Škramovský, S., *Chem. listy*, **48**, 1335 (1954); **49**, 141 (1955).

72. Syrokomskiĭ, V. S., *et al.*, *Zavodskaya Lab.*, **16**, 131, 273, 1041 (1950); Singh, B., *et al.*, *J. Indian Chem. Soc.*, **29**, 34, 537 (1952); **30**, 143 (1953); **32**, 736 (1955); *Anal. Chim. Acta*, **9**, 22 (1953); Simon, V., *Chem. listy*, **49**, 1727 (1955).

73. Brennecke, E., *Chem. Anal.*, **33**, 108 (1937); Muraki, I., *J. Chem. Soc. Japan*, **71**, 407 (1950); **76**, 201 (1955); *Bull. Osaka Ind. Research Inst.*, **1**, 925 (1950); **4**, 132 (many references) (1953); Stolyarov, K. P. and Pogodaeva, V. G., *Vestnik Leningrad. Univ.*, **11** (10), *Ser. Fis. i Khim.*, (2) 87 (1956).

74. Lingane, J. J. and Pecsok, R. L., *Anal. Chem.*, **20**, 425 (1948).

75. Singh, B., *et al.*, *Anal. Chim. Acta*, **14**, 213, 508, 568 (1956); **15**, 277 (1956).

76. Szabó, Z. G. and Sugár, E., *Anal. Chim. Acta*, **6**, 293 (1952); *Anal. Chem.*, **22**, 361 (1950).

77. Troberg, B., *Z. anal. Chem.*, **91**, 161 (1932); Müller, E. and Tänzler, K. H., *ibid.*, **89**, 339 (1932); Ryabchikov, D. I. and Nersesova, S. V., *Izvest. Sektora Platiny i Drug. Blagorod. Metal., Inst. Obshcheĭ i Neorg. Khim., Akad. Nauk S.S.S.R.*, **18**, 102 (1945).

78. Tsubaki, I., *J. Chem. Soc. Japan*, **67**, 67 (1946); *Tetsu to Hagane*, **33**, 2 (1947); **37**, (3) 28 (1951); *Japan Analyst*, **3**, 137 (1954); Issa, I. M. and El Sherif, I. M., *Anal. Chim. Acta*, **14**, 466 (1956).

79. Tsubaki, *J. Chem. Soc. Japan*, **67**, 68 (1946); Banerjee, P. C., *J. Indian Chem. Soc.*, **12**, 198 (1935); **19**, 35 (1942) Maass, K., *Z. anal. Chem.*, **97**, 241 (1934); Ellis, C. M. and Vogel, A. I., *Analyst*, **81**, 693 (1956).

80. Syrokomskiĭ, V. S. and Zhukova, K. N., *Zavodskaya Lab.*, **11**, 754 (1945).

81. Uzel, R. and Přibil, R., *Collection Czechoslov. Chem. Communs.*, **10**, 330 (1938).

82. Tourky, A. R., *et al.*, *Anal. Chim. Acta*, **10**, 168 (1954); **16**, 81 (1957); *Rec. trav. chim.*, **75**, 22 (1956); Issa, I. M. and Daess, A. M., *Chemist Analyst*, **44**, 89 (1955).

83. Tourky, *et al.*, *Analyst*, **73**, 258, 262, 266 (1948).

84. Gapchenko, M. V., *Zavodskaya Lab.*, **10**, 245 (1941).

85. Belcher, R., *et al.*, *Anal. Chem.*, **26**, 1025 (1954); Shults, II, W. D., *et al.*, *ibid.*, **27**, 1750 (1955); Tourky, A. R., *et al.*, *Rec. trav. chim.*, **75**, 22 (1956); Issa, I. M. *et al.*, *Anal. Chim. Acta*, **14**, 466, 474 (1956).

86. Edwards, K. W. and Kern, D. M., *Anal. Chem.*, **28**, 1876 (1956).

87. Belcher, R. and West, T. S., *Anal. Chim. Acta*, **5**, 260, 268, 360, 364, 472 (1951); **7**, 470 (1952); Burriel, F. M., *et al.*, *ibid.*, **10**, 301 (1954); **11**, 214 (1954); *Anales real soc. españ. fís y quím.* (*Madrid*), **47B**, 257 (1951); **49B**, 45 (1953); **50B**, 303 (1954).

88. Zýka, J. and Vulterin, J., *Collection Czechoslov. Chem. Communs.*, **20**, 804 (1955); *Chem. listy*, **48** 1745, 1754, 1762, 1768 (1954).

89. Erdey, L., *et al.*, *Magyar Kém. Folyóirat*, **56**, 262 (1950); **58**, 295 (1952); *Acta Chim. Acad. Sci. Hung.*, **4**, 195, 325 (1954); **5**, 235 (1955); Rao, G. G. and Rao, N. N., *Z. anal. Chem.*, **147**, 338 (1955); Yoshimura, C. and Fujitani, T., *J. Chem. Soc. Japan*, **76**, 304 (1955).

90. Simon, V. and Zýka, J., *Chem. listy*, **49**, 1646 (1955); **50**, 360 (1956); Berka, A. and Simon, V., *ibid.*, **50**, 829 (1956).

91. Kolthoff, I. M. and Furman, N. H., *Potentiometric titration*, 2nd ed., Wiley, New York (1932); Mika, I., Die exakten Methoden der Mikromassanalyse, *Chem. Anal.*, **42** (1939); Müller, G., *Die elektrometrische Massanalyse*, 7. Aufl., Steinkop, Dresden (1944); Berl, W. G., *Physical Methods in Chemical Analysis*, Vol. II, p. 105 (1951), (Laitinen, H. A.); Kolthoff, I. M. and Laitinen, H. A., *pH and Electro-Titrations*, Wiley, New York (1941).

92. Furman, N. H., *Ind. Eng. Chem., Anal. Ed.*, **2**, 213 (1930); **14**, 367 (1942); *Anal. Chem.*, **22**, 33 (1950); **23**, 21 (1951); **26**, 84 (1954); Reilley, C. N., *ibid.*, **28**, 671 (1956).

93. Kolthoff, I. M. and Lingane, J. J., *Polarography*, (1952), Interscience, New York, p. 887 *et seq.*; Kolthoff, I. M., *Anal. Chem.* **26**, 1685 (1954); Laitinen, H. A., *ibid.*, **21**, 66 (1949); **24**, 46 (1952); **26**, 666 (1956).

94. Kolthoff, I. M., *Konduktometrische Titrationen*, Steinkopf, Dresden (1923); Jander, G. and Pfundt, O., *Leitfähigkeitstitrationen und Leitfähigkeitsmessungen*, *Chem. Anal.*, **26** (1934); Britton, H. T. S., *Conductometric Analysis*, Chapman and Hall, London (1934); Berl, W. G., *Physical Methods in Chemical Analysis*, Vol. II, p. 51 (1951), (Britton, H. T. S.).

95. Delahay, P., *New Instrumental Methods in Electrochemistry*, p. 319, Interscience, New York (1952); Kruse, K. and Huber, R., *Hochfrequenztitration*, Verlag Chemie, Weinheim (1957).

96. Goddu, R. F. and Hume, D. N., *Anal. Chem.*, **26**, 1314, 1740 (1954); Underwood, A. L., *J. Chem. Educ.*, **31**, 394 (1954).

97. Bobtelsky, M., *Anal. Chim. Acta*, **13**, 172 (1955).

6

OPTICAL METHODS

Colorimetry is very suitable for the determination of small concentrations of ions. As little as $10^{-5}\%$ of a constituent can be determined, whereas it is difficult and generally inaccurate to determine concentrations below 0·01% by volumetric or gravimetric analysis.

Modern colorimetric analysis, in the wider sense including absorptiometry, has been developed extensively since the introduction of commercial spectrophotometers and the general recognition of the value of organic reagents.[1] Recently, it has become possible to determine macro amounts by differential methods.[2] About 40% of the analytical literature in 1955 was devoted to colorimetry as against 11% in 1929–30.[3] The references given below[4] and in Chapter 1 should be consulted for details of experimental methods.

Fluorimetry[5] is more sensitive than colorimetry. Measurements can be made in the solvent phase (e.g. oxine, morin for detn. of Al, Be, Ga) or in the solid phase (see Chapter 39).

Turbidimetry and *nephelometry*[6] are basically similar. In turbidimetry, the amount of light absorbed by a suspension is measured; in nephelometry, the amount scattered is measured. The former technique is useful when the suspension is colored. In this text, these methods are classified as colorimetry when the suspension is colored and as nephelometry when it is not.

Flame photometry[7] is especially useful for the determination of alkali and alk. earth metals, where other microanalytical methods are troublesome or not available. The method has recently been extended to other determinations. Interference from other ions present should be taken into account. The addition of alcohols or extraction of organic complexes may increase sensitivity.

Infra-red spectrometry is rarely used (see Chapter 58).

It is not feasible to give details of the techniques of these methods here. For the technique may vary considerably depending on the instrument available; manufacturers normally supply plentiful advice with the instrument. Indications of the applications of these methods for the analysis of elements and groups are best given under the element concerned in the later chapters.

References

1. Mellon, M. G., A Century of Colorimetry, *Anal. Chem.*, **24**, 924 (1952); Yoe, J. H., Colorimetric Analysis with Organic Reagents, *ibid.*, **29**, 1246 (1957).
2. Hiskey, C. F., *et al.*, *Anal. Chem.*, **21**, 1440 (1949); **22**, 1464 (1950); **23**, 506, 1196 (1951); Bastian, R., *ibid.*, **23**, 580 (1951); **25**, 259 (1953).
3. Mellon, M. G., *Anal. Chem.*, **24**, 924 (1952); Fisher, R. B., *et al.*, *ibid.*, **28**, 9A (1956).
4. Mellon, M. G., editor, *Analytical Absorption Spectrophotometry*, Wiley, New York (1957); Hershenson, H. M., *Ultraviolet and Visible Absorption Spectra, Index for* 1930–1954, Academic Press, New York (1956).
5. Radley, J. A. and Grant, J., *Fluorescence Analysis in Ultra-Violet Light*, 4th ed., Van Nostrand, New York (1954); Danckwortt, P. W. and Eisenbrand, J., *Lumineszenzanalyse in filtrierten ultravioletten Licht*, 6. Aufl., Akad. Verlagsges., Leipzig (1956); White, C. E., *Ind. Eng. Chem., Anal. Ed.*, **11**, 63 (1939); *Anal. Chem.*, **21**, 104 (1949); **22**, 69 (1950); **24**, 85 (1952) **26**, 129 (1954); **28**, 621 (1956).
6. Yoe, J. H. and Kleinmann, H., *Photometric Analysis*, Vol. II, Wiley, New York (1929).
7. A.S.T.M., *Symposium of Flame Photometry* (1951); Mavrodineanu, R. and Boiteux, H., *L'analyse spectrale quantitative par la flamme*, Tom. I–II, Masson, Paris (1954); Herrmann, R., *Flammenphotometrie*, Springer, Berlin, (1956); Burriel, F. and Ramirez-Muñoz, J., *Flame Photometry*, Elsevier, Amsterdam (1957); Japan Soc. Anal. Chem. & Spectroscop. Soc. Japan, *Flame Photometric Analysis* (1954); Otozai, K. and Fukushima, S., Collected References, *Japan Analyst*, **6**, 670 (1957).

PART II

ORGANIC REAGENTS IN INORGANIC ANALYSIS

7

INTRODUCTION

Organic reagents have played a large part in the expansion of inorganic analysis during the past 20 years. Although several reagents, e.g. 1-nitroso-2-naphthol, were discovered in the nineteenth century, it was not until the 1930's that the field was developed to any great extent.

In gravimetric analysis, organic reagents have simplified the determination of micro amounts of elements, for the precipitates are often voluminous and the factors very favorable. Organic reagents are generally more specific than inorganic precipitants. In titrimetric analysis, great improvements have been made by the introduction of reversible organic indicators, e.g. ferroin in cerate titrations and the diphenylamines in dichromate titrations. Many elements can be determined by precipitation as their oxinates or anthranilates and subsequent titration with bromate. However, organic reagents have had by far the greatest influence in colorimetric analysis.

More than 1000 organic reagents have now been suggested in the literature and their classification and identification pose numerous problems; most texts classify them alphabetically or according to the method of Beilstein. In this text, the reagents are classified as far as possible by their reactions; some inevitably appear in several chapters. The term organic reagent is here used in its conventional sense, i.e. to designate reagents which give precipitation or color reactions with inorganic materials. Of course, organic solvents for extraction purposes, etc., and organic titrimetric standards and indicators properly belong to the class of organic reagents, but the list would then become impossibly long; accordingly, only a few of these are mentioned.

Quite generally in this Part, the reagents are given their trivial names, one name being given to one reagent. The sensitivity in one drop (0·05 ml.) is indicated by μg.

Chapter 8 covers reagents which mainly form inner complexes. This is the most important class. Compounds containing both N and —OH groups, e.g. oxines, oximes, nitroso compounds, cupferron, etc., are particularly noteworthy; they are specific for elements in b-subgroups of the periodic table and many are very useful for determinations of Fe, Cu, etc. Reagents containing N and —COOH groups show similar tendencies whereas urea derivatives lie between the above compounds and those forming addition complexes (see below).

Reagents containing S as the active group are specific for elements of the hydrogen sulfide group; many are important in colorimetric analysis. Those which also contain N, e.g. dithizone, thionalide, etc., have very varied applications.

The N-containing compounds described in Chapter 9 form the so-called addition complexes. *o*-Phenanthroline and its analogs are very useful in the colorimetric analysis of Fe, Cu, and as indicators in redox titrations. An important reaction described in this chapter involves precipitation of halogen complexes of metals.

Hydroxy compounds are listed in Chapter 10. Those which form colored complexes with Ti or Fe have long been applied colorimetrically, while tartaric acid is often used as a masking agent. Compounds which form boric acid esters are important. Higher analogs are mentioned in Chapter 12. Organic acids which form difficultly soluble salts are described in Chapter 11; many note-worthy reagents for alkali metals, Th and Zr, are given here.

Among reagents which form adsorption complexes (Chapter 12) tannin is indispensable in the analysis of Group III elements. The compounds discussed in the section dealing with anthraquinone and phthalein derivatives and in the intermediate sections generally form lakes with hydroxide precipitates; their action may be regarded as a weighting effect for the hydroxy compounds mentioned in Chapter 9. Many of these compounds form colored esters with boric acid. Adsorption indicators are of course important in titrimetry. Ion-exchange resins are a useful adjunct to many types of analysis (Chapter 13).

Reagents which precipitate anionic groups are listed in Chapter 14. The mechanisms of redox reactions are so varied that exact classification is difficult; the borderlines between the groups in Chapter 15 are not always very clear. Organic redox indicators are also described in Chapter 15.

Various kinds of solvents are used in inorganic analysis, but only those which provide the so-called ion-association systems are mentioned in Chapter 16. Chapter 17 lists miscellaneous reagents which cannot be conveniently classified in any of the above groups.

Bibliography

WELCHER, F. J., *Organic Analytical Reagents*, Vols I–IV, Van Nostrand, New York (1947/48); a virtually complete collection of the reagents recommended until 1947, classified according to the organic system; syntheses and uses are described in detail and the references are comprehensive. This book has been constantly referred to for this Part.

YOE, J. H. and SARVER, L. A., *Organic Analytical Reagents*, Wiley, New York (1941).

MELLAN, I. *Organic Reagents in Inorganic Analysis*, Blakiston, Philadelphia (1941).

The Merck Index, 5th Ed., New York (1940).

FEIGL, F., *Spot Tests*, Vol. I, 4th Ed., Elsevier, Amsterdam (1954).

FEIGL, F., *Chemistry of Specific, Selective and Sensitive Reactions*, Academic Press, New York (1949); many profound suggestions about the reaction mechanisms of organic reagents are made.

SANDELL, E. B., *Colorimetric Determination of Traces of Metals*, 2nd Ed., Interscience, New York (1950).

FLAGG, J. F., *Organic Reagents used in Gravimetric and Volumetric Analysis*, Interscience, New York (1948).

NAITO, T., *Analysis by Organic Reagents*, Hirokawa, Tokyo (1944).

KURODA, K., *Chemical Analysis by Specific Reagents*, Kawade, Tokyo (1948).

KOZU, T., *Organic Reagents for Metal Analysis*, Kaniya, Kyoto (1941).

PRODINGER, E., Organische Fällungsmittel in der quantitativen Analyse, *Chem. Anal.*, **37**, 3. Aufl. (1939); English trans. by HOLMES, S. (1940); 4. Aufl. (1957).

Hopkins and Williams, Ltd., *Organic Reagents for Metals*, 5th Ed., Vol. I (1955).

BERNOT, J., *Réactifs organiques en analyse minérale*, Dunod, Paris (1947).

VON STEIN, P., *Organic Reagents in Inorganic Analysis*, Chem. Publ. Co., New York (1942).

International Commission on New Analytical Reactions and Reagents, *Tables of Reagents for Inorganic Analysis*, 4th Rept. (1950).

8

REAGENTS FORMING INNER COMPLEXES

1. COMPOUNDS CONTAINING N AND —OH, —COOH, =CO, —CHO

1.1. Oxine[1]

(8- or *o*-hydroxyquinoline, 8-quinolinol, quinophenol) (I). [Colorless, but usually yellow because of some H_2O; m.p. 75°C; sol. in EtOH, AcOH, NH_4OH, many organic solvents.]

Oxine forms insol. complexes of type (II) with many metals under the conditions listed in Table 15. There are

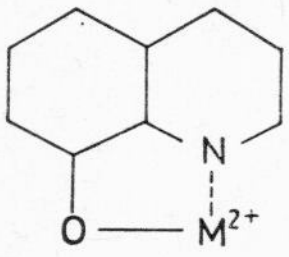

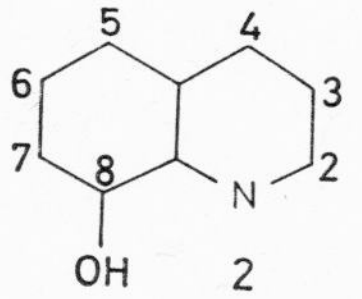

(I)

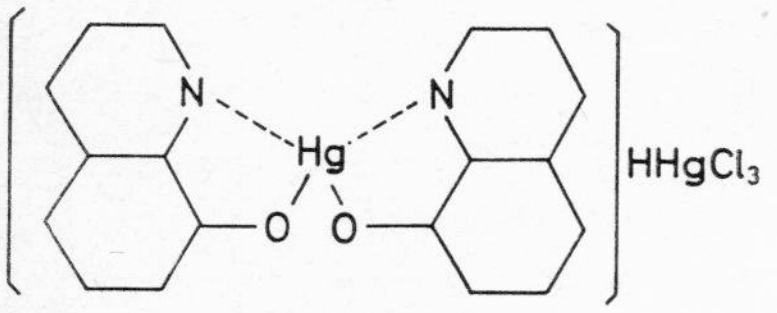

(III)

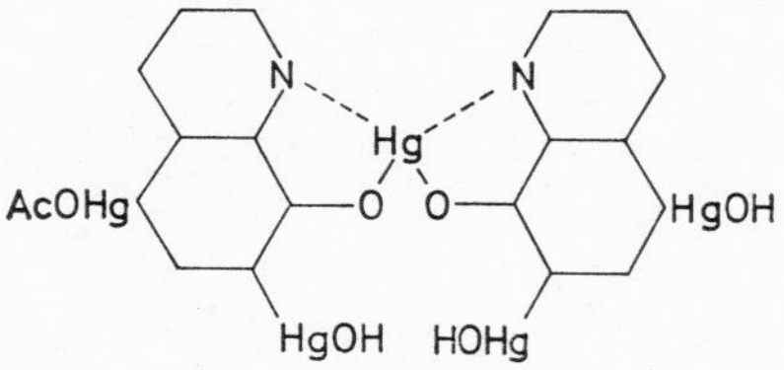

(IV)

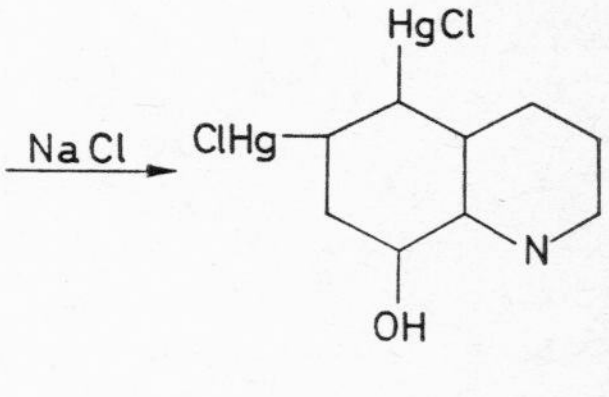

(V)

several exceptions. Hg forms a yellow ppt. of type (III) from $HgCl_2$ soln.; it is sol. in NaCl soln. A red-brown ppt. of type (IV) forms from $Hg(NO_3)_2$ or $Hg(OAc)_2$ soln.; it converts to type (V) with NaCl.[2] $[HgC_9H_6NO(OH)_2]Hg_2$ ppts. from mineral acid soln.[3] Fe^{2+} (for absorption spectra see ref. 4) gives a brown-red ppt. of $Fe(C_9H_6ON)_2$ from boiling aq. soln. $[Fe(C_9H_6ON)_3]H$ (brown-black) ppts. from cold soln. but hot H_2O or dil. acids convert it to $Fe(C_9H_6ON)_2$; the pure ppt. is prepd. from alc. and forms $[Fe(C_9H_6ON)_3]K$ with KOH.[5] Be ppts. as $Be_2O(C_9H_6ON)_2{\cdot}2H_2O$ (see Chapter 44) and Ti as $TiO(C_9H_6ON)_2{\cdot}2H_2O$. $Th(C_9H_6ON)_4{\cdot}C_9H_7ON{\cdot}xH_2O$ gives $Th(C_9H_6ON)_4$ at 150–160°C. $Sc(C_9H_6ON)_3{\cdot}C_9H_7ON$, $UO_2(C_9H_6ON)_2{\cdot}C_9H_7ON$ (similarly Pu), $WO_2(C_9H_6ON)_2$, $MoO_2(C_9H_6ON)_2$ and V (see below) are also ppted. Other complexes are of the type $M^{2+}(C_9H_6ON)_3\ M^+$, where M^{2+} = Mg, Zn, Cd, Co, Ni, Mn and M^+ = H, NH_4, K, Na.[5] Li, Na, K, Ag, Tl^+, Cr^{3+} complexes and $Nd(C_9H_6ON)_4{\cdot}H_2O$[6] are also formed.

Oxine also yields difficultly sol. salts with complex metallic cyanides, thiocyanates or halides and with heteropoly acids. $C_9H_7ON{\cdot}HBiI_4$ ppts. from HNO_3 or H_2SO_4 soln. contg. KI and is detd. titrimetrically, or colorimetrically after soln. in AmOAc, Me_2CO, etc. Bi also forms a type II complex which is better for gravimetric or titrimetric purposes. P is detd. gravimetrically or titrimetrically as $(C_9H_7ON)_3{\cdot}H_7[P(Mo_2O_7)_6]{\cdot}2H_2O$ and Si gravimetrically as $(C_9H_7ON)_4{\cdot}H_4(SiMo_{12}O_{40})$; Ge behaves similarly to Si.

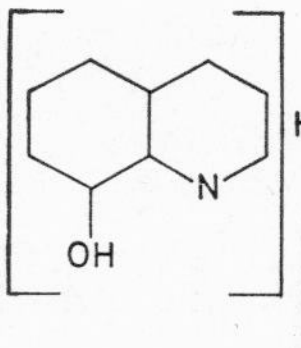

(VI)

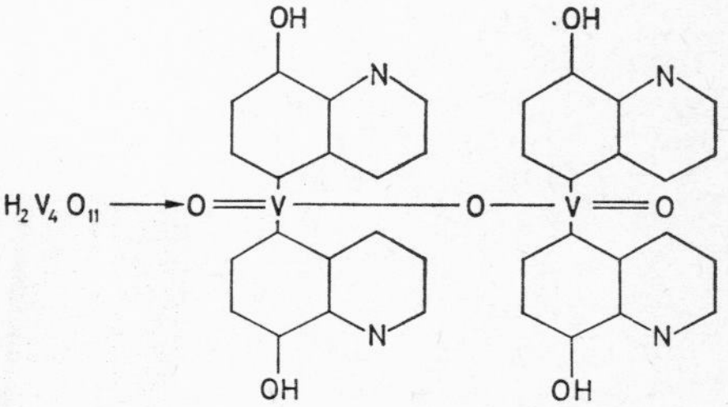

(VII)

Meta-, ortho-, pyro- or polyvanadates yield from AcOH soln. a yellow ppt. (VI) which becomes black (VII) on heating and cooling (see Chapter 38). W (red to yellow) and Mo may give similar reactions. A ppt. of uncertain compn. forms from dil. acidic solns. of $ReCl_6^{2-}$.

TABLE 15. Oxinates

Metal	Conditions and sensitivity			Optimum pH ($CHCl_3$ extn.)	Remarks
	AcOH + NH_4OAc	NH_4OAc + $(NH_4)_2$-tart.	NaOH + Na_2-tart.		
Cu	* 1·6	* 2	* 3·7	5·3–14·5 (2·8–14·0)	410 mμ; also C_6H_6 extn. at pH 2·8–12, 2–30 μg.
Ag	++ (20)	+ (3·0)	—		
Au	+ 6	+	—		
Be	—	(oo) 1·6	—	8·2 ± 0·2	
Mg	—	* 2	* 3·7	9·4–12·6 (10·2)	$CHCl_3$ extn. from soln. + butyl cellosolve; see text
Ca	—	+ 10	+	9·2–13	
Sr	—	+	—	(11·28)	Extn. with 1*M* oxine/$CHCl_3$
Ba	—	+	—		
Zn	* 1	* 4	++ 7	4·6–13·4	Extn. incomplete, see text
Cd	* 2	* 4	++ 9	5·7–14·5	Extn. incomplete, see text
Hg^+	+ 16	+ 10	—		Red-brown
Hg^{2+}	+ 50	+ 50	—		Red-brown
Al	* 3	* 6	—	4·4–9·8 (4·5–10·7)	Also C_6H_6 extn. at pH 4·6–9·6, 4–40 μg
Ga	—	* 2		3·6–11 (3·0–11·7)	392·5 mμ
In	* 2	+	—	2·5–3·0? (>4·0)	400 mμ
Tl	—	—		4·0–8·0 (>4·0)	Extn. incomplete
Sc	*			6·5–8·5	
Y	++ (5·8)	++		(9·55)	$Y(Ox)_2X$ at pH 8·6–8·8
La	++ 2	++ (1·8)		>7·1?	
Ce^{3+}	++ (4·9)	* 0·59		>9·4? (9·9–10·5?)	Grey-green, 505 mμ
Ce^{4+}				(9·9–10·6)	Purple, 480 mμ
Pm				(9·3–9·6)	$Pm(OX)_3$ or $Pm(OX)_3(HOx)$
Ti	* 3	* 10	—	4·8–8·6 (4·0–9·0), (3·8–5·4 + H_2O_2)	Orange-yellow with H_2O_2, 425 mμ
Zr	+ 1·6	++ (1·6)	—	acetate buffer	Cl^-, SO_4^{2-} interfere
Sn^{2+}	—	+	—		
Sn^{4+}	+	+	—	(2·5–5·5)	Incomplete?
Pb	+ 10	+ (11)	—	8·5–12·3 (8·2–11·0)	

TABLE 15—*contd.*

Metal	Conditions and sensitivity: AcOH + NH_4OAc	NH$_4$OAc + $(NH_4)_2$-tart.	NaOH + Na_2-tart.	Optimum pH ($CHCl_3$ extn.)	Remarks
V	+ 1·6	—	—	2·0–5·3 (3·2–5·1)	AmOH or AmOAc extn. at pH 3·5–4·2, 10–150 μg
Nb	++	*		1*N* NH_4OH + citrate (2·8–10·5)	
Ta	++	++			
Sb	+	+		6–7	
Bi	* 3	* 4·5	+ (27)	4·8–10·5 (4·0–5·2)	
Po				(3·4–4·0)	1 : 1 complex, 73·6% extn.
Cr	+ 20	+ 40	—		
Mo	* 1	+ (2100)	—	3·6–7·3 (2·0–5·6)	Orange-yellow
W	* 2	+	—	5·0–5·6 (3·0–4·3)	Extn. incomplete?
Th	* 6	++ 2·3	+ (5)	4·4–8·8 (7·5–9·5)	
U^{6+}	* 4	++ 5	—	5·7–9·8? (7·0–9·0)	Red-brown, 420 mμ
Pu	*			3·5–9	AmOAc extn. of Pu^{6+} at pH 4–8, of Pu^{4+} at ca. 8
Mn	(oo) 3	++ 6	—	5·9–10·0 (7·2–12·5? + $Fe(CN)_6^{3-}$)	Dirty yellow
Re	+ 80	—	—		
Fe^{2+}	+	+	+		Red, see text
Fe^{3+}	* 1	* 4	—	2·8–11·2 (2·5–12·5)	Green-black, 470 or 570 mμ; C_6H_6 extn. at pH 2·8–12·0, 1–30 μg
Co	* 3	+ 18	+ (21)	4·4–14·5 (7·3–8·2)	420 mμ; C_6H_6 extn. at pH 5·7–9·5; colorimetry is impossible
Ni	* 3	+ 5	+ (38)	4·6–14·5 (5·5–8·8)	Brown; C_6H_6 extn. at pH 3·9–5·2, 20–120 μg
Ru	+	+		(acetate buffer)	
Rh	+	+			
Pd	* 2	++ (5)	+ (5)	(dil. HCl)	
Os	+	+			
Ir	+	+			
Pt	+ (890)	+ (250)	—		

* weighable as oxinate; (oo) must be ignited; + + pptn. complete; + pptn. almost complete; — no pptn. Sensitivity by *Berg* and (*Shiba*); the color of ppt. is pale green-yellow, and λ_{max} = 395 mμ unless otherwise indicated.

Metals can be detected with fused oxine, a dark color being caused by 0·05 μg. Fe_2O_3 or 0·5 μg. V_2O_5; 2 μg V_2O_5 are detectable in presence of 75 mg. MoO_3 or 14 mg. WO_3.[7]

Rare earths can be detected after paper chromatography;[8] 0·08 μg. NH_2OH/ml. Na_2CO_3 soln. can be detected by the formation of green indoxine.

Methods of determination. *Reagent.* Use freshly prepd. 2–4% oxine in EtOH, Me_2CO or MeOH soln. for gravimetry or titrimetry, and 0·01–1% in $CHCl_3$ for colorimetry; a 10% soln. is said to favor extn. of alk. earths.[9]

Oxine acetate soln. is stable; dissolve 3–4 g. oxine in the min. amt. of AcOH, add NH_4OH until turbid, and clear with AcOH.

Procedures. Adjust the soln. to a suitable pH (Table 15), heat to 60–70°C and add reagent until the soln. is yellow (for AcOH soln.) or yellow-orange (for NH_3 soln.); boil for some min., allow to cool for small amts., filter on paper or sintered glass and wash with hot H_2O.

If a ppt. appears in the filtrate, heat to ensure that it dissolves. To remove the reagent from the filtrate, ext. with Et_2O or $CHCl_3$ after adjusting the pH to 5–10, or evap. with occasional addn. of NH_4OH.

For gravimetry, heat to constant weight at a suitable temp.; sometimes different temps. are recommended by different authors.[10] Alternatively, cover with 1–3 g. $H_2C_2O_4$ and ignite to the oxide.

For titrimetry, the bromate method is most often used. Dissolve the ppt. in 12·5% HCl, add H_2O to give a final HCl concn. of less than 5%, 0·5–1 g. KBr, 1–2 drops methyl red, and 0·01–0·1*N* $KBrO_3$ until yellow followed by 1–2 ml. in excess. Then add a small excess of standard As_2O_3 soln., 0·025–0·2 ml. 1% *p*-ethoxychrysoidine or brilliant carmoisine, and $KBrO_3$ soln. to the colorless end-point.[11] Coulometric[12] and iodometric finishes are also possible.

Alternative finishes are as follows:

(*i*) Oxidize with 0·05*N* $(NH_4)_2Ce(NO_3)_6$ in 2*M* $HClO_4$; this is suitable for traces of Mg because 59·7 equivs. of Ce^{4+} are required whereas only 8 equivs. of BrO_3^- are needed.[13] $Ce(SO_4)_2$ is not recommended.[14]

(*ii*) Dissolve in hot 10% H_2SO_4 and titrate with $KMnO_4$; this is unsuitable for macro amts. but the results are good for 8-hydroxyquinaldine.[15]

(*iii*) Det. excess oxine in the filtrate; Mg, Fe, Al can be detd. But oxine may volatilize.

(*iv*) 'Filtration method': titrate a known amt. of reagent with the sample soln. until a small filtered portion gives no turbidity with the sample; macro amts. of Mg, Zn, Al, P, Fe can be detd.

(*v*) Titrate the acid liberated when the reagent is added to a neutral sample soln., with 0·1*N* NaOH and phenol red or α-naphtholphthalein indicator; Mg, Cu, Zn can be detd.

(*vi*) Titrate directly with oxine soln. using diazobenzene sulfonic acid as external indicator. Alternatively use an amperometric end-point.

For colorimetry, the extn. method is preferable. Ext. the metal complex with $CHCl_3$ from the soln. at the optimum pH given in Table 15; compare the color (Al, V, Ce, U, etc.) or measure the ultraviolet fluorescence (Ga, In, Al). The distribution coefficient of oxine between $CHCl_3$ and H_2O is 720 at 18°C between pH 5 and 9; it is much lower outside that pH range.

Alternative colorimetric methods are as follows:

(*i*) Reduction of Folin–Denis reagent. The accuracy is ±5% for 5–50 μg. Mg, Bi, Al, Zn; Au, Cu cannot be detd.

(*ii*) Dissolve the ppt. in acid and couple with sulfanilic acid by means of $NaNO_2$; the accuracy is ±7% for 10–100 μg. Mg or 25–200 μg. Al.

(*iii*) Convert the metal complex to the Fe^{3+} complex; compare the color or ext. with $CHCl_3$ and dil. with BuOH; the accuracy is ±1 μg. for 20–50 μg. Mg.

(*iv*) Dissolve the ppt. in HCl and measure the absorption at 365 or 252 mμ.

Azotometry can be used for detn. of Al, Bi, Ca, Cd, Co, Cr, Cu, Fe, La, Mg, Mn, Ni, Pb, Th, Ti, U, Zn (10–200 μg./ml.); the ppt. is dissolved, $KBrO_3$, KBr, KI, N_2H_4 are added and the N_2 released is measured.[16]

Separations. (*i*) *By pH control and masking agents.* (See Table 15). Cu is sepd. from other elements in feebly mineral acid soln.

In AcOH soln. Cu is sepd. from Cd; Mg, Ca, Mn from other elements; and Be from Fe, Al, Cu, etc. Hg is sepd. from other elements if KCN is added, Fe, Ti from Al if malonate is present, and Mo, W, U, V, (Ti) from other elements if EDTA is present.[17]

Mn, Mg are sepd. from Ca, Sr, Ba, Na, K in NH_4OH and $(NH_4)_2$-tartrate soln. In NaOH and Na_2-tartrate soln. Cu, Mg, Zn, Cd are sepd. from other elements (these 4 elements have been termed the 'oxine group'). Mg, Al, Zn, Fe, Mn, Ni, Co, Cu, Bi, Ti, U, V, Mo, W are sepd. from P.[18]

(*ii*) *By extn. with org. solvents.* This is useful for colorimetry. Fe, Al, Bi, Co, Ni, Cu, In, Ga, V are sepd. from Ca, Mg, W, Mo, Cr, P. See Table 15 for the optimum pH values; different recommendations have been made.[19] Fe, Cu, Mo, Ni can be masked with cyanide, Fe^{2+} with phenanthroline, and Th, Zr with sulfobenzenearsonic acid. If EDTA is added to the soln. above pH 8, Mo, W, Ti (pH 7·9–9·0) are extd. completely on shaking 3 times; over 95% Cu, V are extd. if Ca^{2+} is added, but Fe^{3+}, Al, Co, Mn^{2+}, Ni are not extd.[20] Pb, Pm, Y, Po complexes have been studied with radioactive tracers.[21]

Mg can be extd. from neutral (to congo red) soln. contg. 50% (v/v) butyl cellosolve. Mg, Zn, Cd can also be extd. on addn. of $BuNH_2$, the absorption max. wavelength increasing by 10–20 mμ; aromatic amines are unsatisfactory.[22]

Extn. of the ppt. with EtOH allows sepn. of Al, Zn, Mn, Cu from Mg, and extn. with EtOH + NH_4OH, sepn. of Al, Fe, etc. from Mg.

1.2. Derivatives and analogs of oxine

(*1*) *Chloroxine* (5,7-dichloro-8-hydroxyquinoline, m.p. 108°C) has been studied. *Bromoxine* (5,7-dibromo-8-hydroxyquinoline, m.p. 195°C) is also useful. [White crystals, sol. in concd. mineral acids, Me_2CO, Et_2O, C_6H_6, CS_2, sparingly sol. in EtOH, insol. in H_2O]. As 1% solns. in Me_2CO, these reagents give a ppt. with Fe^{3+} (green), V^{3+} (brown) and Cu (yellow-green) from 0·05*N* HNO_3 soln. contg. 25% Me_2CO; with Ti (orange-yellow) from *N* acid soln.; with Ga from slightly acidic soln. (chloroxine permits extn. with $CHCl_3$ at pH 2–9); and with Mo, W, phosphomolybdate, etc., from neutral soln.

Fe and Cu ppt. from acidic soln. contg. tartaric or citric acid, but Ti does not; only Cu ppts. from acidic soln. contg. $H_2C_2O_4$. Only Sb^{5+} ppts. as $Sb(C_9H_4ONCl_2 \text{ (or } Br_2))_2Cl_3$ from concd. HCl soln. (see Chapter 26). Cu, Sb, Fe, Ti, Al, Ga, Ge can be detd. gravimetrically and U colorimetrically. Rare earths can be extd. and Nd, Er detd. colorimetrically by extn. with $CHCl_3$ from alk. soln. (see Chapter 48: Nd and Er). La, Th, U can be extd.[23]

Bromoxine or *iodoxine* (the di-iodo analog) ppts. Sb^{3+}, Cd, Cu, Bi, Hg^+, Hg^{2+}, Pb, Fe^{2+}, Fe^{3+}, Cr^{3+} below pH 4 and Al, Zn, Co, Mn, Ni, V^{4+}, V^{2+} above pH 4; V can be detd.[24] Iodoxine is suitable for gravimetric detn. of Cu and colorimetric detn. of Fe, U, Th; the colors of the Cu, Ni, Co, Fe, U^{6+}, Pd, Th, Zr, Ti, V^{3+}, Pb iodoxinates are darker than those of the oxinates.[25]

(*2*) *8-Hydroxyquinaldine* (2-methyl-8-hydroxyquinoline, 2-methyloxine, m.p. 74°C).[26] The reactions are similar to those of oxine but Al does not ppt. Zn can be sepd. from Mg, Al, and Al from Fe, Cu, Cd, Mn, Sn, Sb, Pb, Ni, Co, Zn (by $CHCl_3$ extn. at pH 9·2); Mg can be sepd. from Al. Be can be detd. gravimetrically, titrimetrically or colorimetrically, Ga, In, Be fluorimetrically, and Cu, Fe, Cr, Ti, Ga, In colorimetrically. The soly. products are: Cu, 4×10^{-26}; Zn, 10^{-26}; Cd, $2{\cdot}5 \times 10^{-20}$; Mn, $4{\cdot}5 \times 10^{-19}$; Co, $1{\cdot}4 \times 10^{-22}$; Ni, $6{\cdot}2 \times 10^{-21}$.

Other methyl derivs. ppt. Al. The *5-methyl deriv.* ppts. Pd quantitatively but the *7-methyl compd.* is usually the most sensitive of the monomethyl derivs.[27] The *7-allyl deriv.* is similar to oxine,[28] while the *2-phenyl deriv.* ppts. only Hg from dil. HNO_3 soln.[29] Cu, Mg can be detd. with the *dimethyl compd.*[30]

7-Chloromethyloxine ppts. Fe^{3+}, V^{4+} at pH 1·0 and Fe^{3+}, Co, Ni, Cu, Zn, Cd, Mn, Bi, V, U, Ag, Pb at pH 4·6.[31] The *5- or 6-trifluoromethyl deriv.* reacts with metals but the corresponding 7-deriv. does not.[32]

(*3*) *Ferron* (7-iodo-8-hydroxyquinoline-5-sulfonic acid, loretin, yatren, mixiod, m.p. 285°C) [Yellow-brown crystals, sol. in H_2O]. This is used as a 0·2% soln. for the colorimetric detn. of Fe^{3+} (extn. with Bu_3N, AmOH), Al (370 mμ), F^- (via Al) and H_2O_2 (via Fe^{2+}).[33] V also gives a color. Th and Ca can be detd. gravimetrically. The corresponding *Cl and Br compds.* behave similarly.

8-Hydroxyquinoline-5-sulfonic acid is used for the colorimetric detn. of Fe^{3+} in acid solns. (the black-green color changes through brown to red on addn. of alkali) and of V (brown); Cu gives a yellow color. The stability of the complexes is in the order, Cu, Ni, Co, Zn, Pb, Cd, Mn, Ca, Sr, Ba.[34] La, Pr, Nd and Sm can be sepd. with the 5- or 7-sulfonic acid in conjunction with electrolysis and carbonate and glucose pptns.[35] Sm, Gd can be sepd. from Eu in a similar way by electrolysis in AcOH medium, $H_2[Eu(C_9H_5NOSO_3)_2]\cdot 4H_2O$ being pptd.[36] Ce can be sepd. from La in Na_2CO_3 soln.[36]

The *7-nitro compound* is used for the colorimetric detn. of Fe^{3+}.

8-Hydroxyquinoline-disulfonic acid is readily synthesized and water-soluble; 0·1 μg Fe^{3+} yields the blue-green 2:3 complex at pH 2 (see Chapter 33).

(*4*) *Indoxine* (quinolinequinone-(5,8)-[8-hydroxyquinolyl-5-imide]) (VIII). This is red in acid and green in alk. soln.; it is used titrimetrically for detns. of Cu, Ag, Hg, Ni and colorimetrically for Zn.

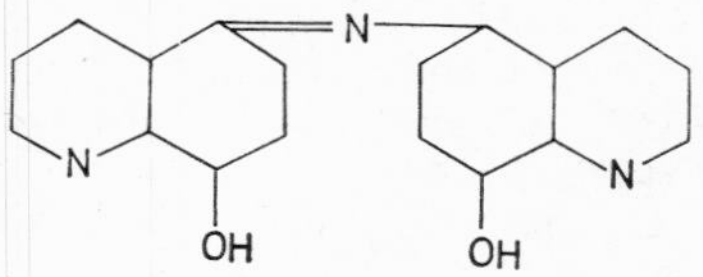

(VIII)

(*5*) *Azo derivs.*[37] These are more specific for Pd and Hg. *Naphthazoxine* (5-(4-sulfo-1-naphthylazo)-8-hydroxyquinoline) gives an orange-red color with 2 μg. Pd, pink with Hg, and green with Cu or Cr. *5-p-Acetaminophenylazo-8-hydroxyquinoline* is used to detect Mg (blue), Ag and Hg (change of color on Cl^- addn.) *8-Hydroxyquinoline-azo-*p*-nitrobenzoic acid* can be used gravimetrically for Zn.

Stilboxine (4,4′-di(8-hydroxy-5-quinolylazo)-stilbene-3,3′-disulfonic acid) and *naphthylazoxine* are indicators for Hg^{2+}—I^- and chelatometric titrations respectively.

(*6*) *Kairin A* (*N*-ethyl-8-hydroxytetrahydroquinoline hydrochloride) serves as a spot test for down to 0·005 μg. As^{3+} in HCl + $FeCl_3$ medium. *Thalline sulfonate* (6-methoxy-1,2,3,4-tetrahydroquinoline sulfonate) reacts with 0·3 μg. Fe^{3+}, 1 μg. Ag, 0·7 μg. $AuCl_4^-$, $PtCl_6^{2-}$, and CrO_4^{2-} to give green colors, and with $Cr_2O_7^{2-}$, MnO_4^- and IO_4^- to give red colors.[38]

(*7*) *5-Hydroxyquinoline-8-carboxylic acid* gives a blue-black color with 1 μg. Ru^{3+} in 50 ml. of hot soln. below pH 1·3 (colorimetric) and a green color, unstable to acid, with Fe^{2+} in hot or cold soln.

8-Hydroxyquinoline-2-carboxylic acid (*8-hydroxyquinaldinic acid*) ppts. Mg (red), Ag (grey), Pd (black), Ce^{4+} (yellow), Au^{3+} (purple), Zn (yellow), Pb and UO_2^{2+} (orange) at pH 5·3, but ppts. Ni (white), Mg (orange) and Pd only at pH 13·1 in tartrate soln. Colors are formed with Fe^{2+}, Fe^{3+} (green-black), Cu^{2+} (green-yellow), Ru^{3+} (brown), Cr^{3+} (brown-yellow), Co, Ga, Sb^{3+} (yellow), Al, Zn, Mn, In, Ca, Pt (pale yellow) at pH 5·3, and with Cr^{3+} (green), Ca (green-yellow) and the other metals at pH 8·35 in tartrate soln.[39]

(*8*) *4-Hydroxybenzothiazole* (IX) is difficult to synthesize but can replace oxine in detns. of Cu, Ni, Co, Zn. These metal complexes are insol. in $CHCl_3$; the Al and Mg complexes are more sol. in H_2O than the oxinates. Ti, Mo, W, V do not ppt.

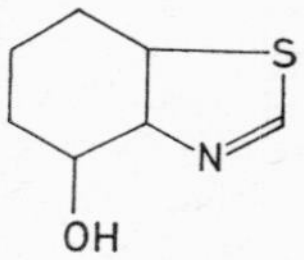

(IX)

(*9*) *2-(*o*-Hydroxyphenyl)-benzoxazole* (X)[40] [m.p. 124°C, sol. in EtOH, strong fluorescence] is an excellent gravimetric reagent for Cu at pH 3·5–14·0 and for Cd at pH 9·0–14·0; colorimetric or titrimetric detn. of Cd is possible. Ni, Co, Fe, Bi, Cr, Mn, Zn do not ppt. in tartrate soln.

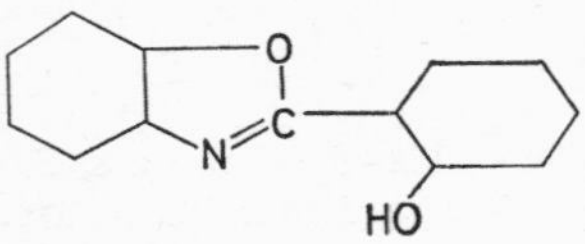

(X)

*2-(*o*-Hydroxyphenyl)-benzimidazole* (XI)[41] [m.p. 242°C, sol. in EtOH, strong fluorescence] ppts. Hg from citrate soln. (gravimetric and titrimetric detn.); Fe is also pptd. *2-(*o*-Hydroxyphenyl)-benzothiazole* is used fluorimetrically for Be at pH 4·5–5; only Cu, Zn

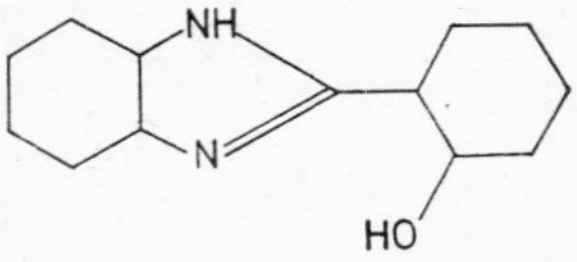

(XI)

interfere if tartrate is added (see Chapter 44). *Benzothiazoline, pyridine, quinoline, imidazole and isoquinoline derivs.* are less specific than those mentioned above.[42]

(*10*) *Alizarin blue* (XII) is a very sensitive gravimetric reagent for Cu (0·025 μg.).

(*11*) *5,8-Dihydroxyquinoxaline* (XIII)[43] gives colors with Ga, In, Mo, Pb, Tl^{3+}, V^{5+}, W, Ag and Au^{3+}; it ppts. Cd, Co, Cu, Fe^{2+}, Ni, Zn and Ti. At pH 3·5–5 the reagent is specific for Cu (1 μg./ml.). *Hemipyocyanine* (XIV) reacts with Ag (blue), Hg^{2+} (red), Hg^{+}, Cu (dark

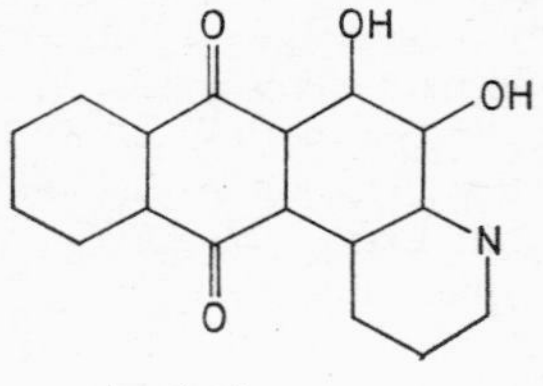

(XII)

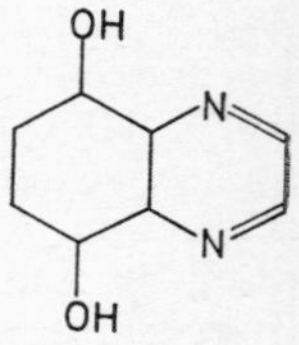

(XIII)

violet), Cd (blue-black), Pb (brownish), Fe^{2+} (brown-black), Fe^{3+} (brown), Co (dark grey), Ni, Mn (purple), Zn (red), and Cr^{3+} (red).[44] *10-Hydroxybenzo-[h]-quinoline* (XV) has been prepd.[45]

(*12*) *Other derivatives. 5-Nitrosooxine* ppts. Cu, Zn incompletely; Al, Ga, In, Mg do not ppt.[46] *7-Allyl-5-nitrosooxine* ppts. Mg at pH 5·3; Cu also ppts., pL (− log limiting concn. in g.-equiv./l.) being 6·2–6·4.[28] *5-Methyl-7-nitrosooxine* ppts. Hg^{2+} (pL 5·5), Al, Cd, Ce^{4+}, Co, Cr^{3+}, Fe^{2+}, Fe^{3+}, Ga, Pb, Hg^{+}, Ni, Tl, V^{5+} (pL 4·2–4·8), Zn (pL 5·3), Cu^{2+}, Ce^{3+} (pL 3·2) at pH

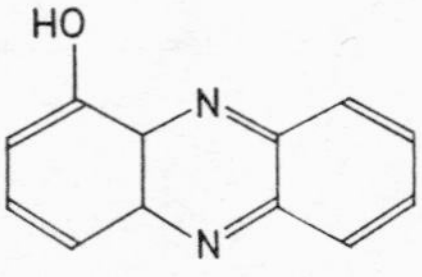

(XIV)

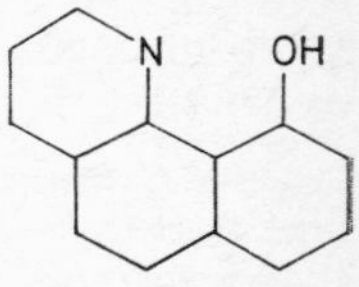

(XV)

5·3; Al, Fe, Ga, Pb, V do not ppt. at pH 13·1[47] (cf. nitrosonaphthol). *Hydroxyoxine* is not a useful reagent. *8-Hydroxyquinoline*-N-*oxide* forms complexes with Cu (green-yellow), Mn and Fe^{3+} but not with Fe^{2+}, Ni, Co or Zn.[48]

The complexes of Ag, Zn, Cd, Ni, Cu with *8-mercaptoquinoline* differ from the oxinates, e.g. the Cu complex possesses double nuclei with a Cl bridge.[49]

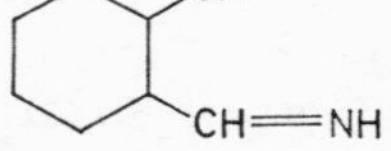

(XVI)

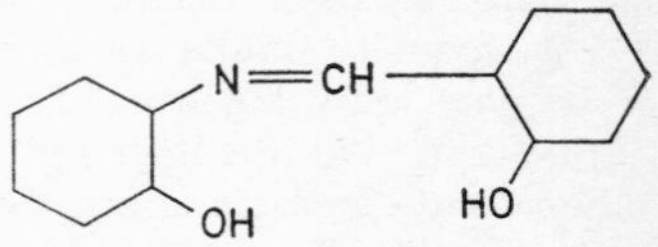

(XVII)

1.3. Salicylimine and its analogs

(*1*) *Salicylimine* (salicylalamine, salicylaldimine) (XVI)[50] ppts. Cu, Ni, Pd, Fe, Co, Hg, Zn, Cd, Re; Cu ($CHCl_3$ extn. is possible) and Ni are detd. gravimetrically. *Disalicylalethylenediamine* ppts. Cu (Chapter 22), from tartrate-contg. soln. at pH 4·6. Its *sulfo deriv.* permits colorimetric detn. of Fe (violet-red).

Disalicylalpropylenediamine is suitable for detn. of Cu and Ni, the complexes being sol. in org. solvents. For other analogs, see ref 51.

Salicylamide permits colorimetric detn. of U at pH 6·6–7·2 (yellow).

(*2*) o-(*Salicylideneamino*)-*phenol* (XVII)[52] gives a green fluorescence with Ga and Al (Chapters 42 and 43) at pH 5. o-(*2-Hydroxynaphthylmethyleneamino*)-*phenol* and the *semicarbazone and semioxamazone of salicylaldehyde* have been examined.[53] Zn (Chapter 36) can be detd. fluorimetrically with *salicylaldehyde acetylhydrazone*.[54]

1.4. α-Dioximes[55]

α-Dioximes of satd. allyl or alicyclic compds. ppt. Ni and Pd selectively. Aliphatic derivs. give a red color with Fe^{2+} and aromatic derivs. a violet color. A weighting effect is shown by the decreasing pH of pptn. of Ni as the chain length increases.[56] The β-form does not react; the γ-form gives a colored 1:1 complex with Ni. Unsatd. derivs., e.g. *o*-benzoquinonedioxime, are not specific. One oxime group may be replaced by another N-contg. group which can form coordination linkages, e.g. in iminodiacetylmonoxime or nitrosoguanidine.

(*1*) *Dimethylglyoxime* (biacetyldioxime, 2,3-butanedionedioxime) (XVIII) [m.p. 235–237°C decomp., sol.

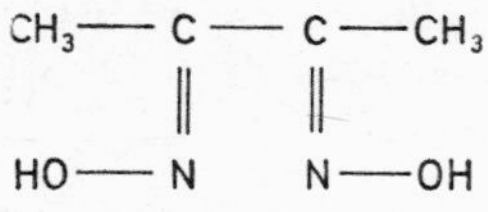

(XVIII)

in EtOH, Et_2O, insol. in H_2O]. This is commonly used as a 1% soln. in EtOH.

(*i*) In slightly mineral acidic soln. Ni forms a red polymer which becomes the yellow monomer on extn. with AmOH or $CHCl_3$.[57] Pd can be detd. by pptn. from 1*M* H_2SO_4 or HCl; the yellow complex can be extd. with C_6H_6, $CHCl_3$, etc. Bi, Au (partial reduction to metal) and Pt also ppt.; Co (0·5 μg., brown) and Re (with $SnCl_2$) give colors.

(*ii*) Ni is detd. in presence of Co, Mn, Zn in solns. contg. AcOH and NaOAc.

(*iii*) Ammoniacal soln. contg. citrate is suitable for detns. of Ni and Pb and for colorimetry of Fe^{2+} (for absorption spectra, see ref. 4). Ammoniacal media with additives are used in several colorimetric detns. Co gives a red color (0·25 μg./ml.) if benzidine, tolidine or *o*-dianisidine is added; if S^{2-} is added, the color is dark red which changes to green-blue on H_2O_2 addn. Pyridine soln. is suitable for colorimetric detn. of Fe^{2+} (extn.); Cu is detd. if IO_4^- or $S_2O_8^{2-}$ + Ag^+ is added.

Ni can be detd. colorimetrically by the red 1:2 or violet 1:4 (more sensitive) complex formed in solns. contg. NaOH and $S_2O_8^{2-}$, I_2 or Br_2. In NaOH + Sn^{2+} media, Ni forms a green, and Co a violet, complex.

V (*2* μg.) and Sn (0·04 μg.) can be detected via Fe^{3+}, and Ag detd. colorimetrically via Ni^{2+} + KCN + dimethylglyoxime.

The metal complexes of dimethylglyoxime and of its *O*-monomethyl ether have been studied.[58] *Diethylaminobutanedionedioxime* has no advantage for the colorimetric detn. of Fe.

(*2*) α-*Benzildioxime* (α-diphenylglyoxime) [m.p. 237°C, sparingly sol. in EtOH, insol. in H_2O] is more specific for Ni than dimethylglyoxime. Re can be detd. colorimetically (pink-red) if $SnCl_2$ is added. The β and γ compds. are suitable for detection of Pd and Ni respectively.

α-*Furildioxime* [m.p. 166–168°C, sol. in EtOH, Et_2O and hot H_2O] is suitable for the gravimetric detn. of Pd and for colorimetric detns. of Ni (at pH 7·5–8·3 with *o*-$C_6H_4Cl_2$ extn.) and Re. The synthesized compd. contains only 50% of the α-form. For the structure of the Pd complex, see ref. 59. *Methylbenzoylglyoxime* is used gravimetrically for Pd (micro) and *phenylglyoxime* for Ni. For the reaction of phenylglyoxime and derivs. with Fe^{2+} see ref. 60; the complexes are orange and become purple on pyridine addn.

(*3*) *Heptoxime* (1,2-cycloheptanedionedioxime) is excellent for detn. of Ni; the ppt. formed above pH 2·7 is extd. with $CHCl_3$.[61] For synthesis, see ref. 62.

Nioxime (1,2-cyclohexanedionedioxime) [m.p. 189–190°C] is useful gravimetrically for Pd and colorimetrically for Fe and Ni; pptn. of Ni and sepn. of Ni from Fe are incomplete. For synthesis, see ref. 63. The *4-methyl deriv.* is the best reagent for Ni, pptg. it at pH 3. *4-Isopropyl* and other homologs are also available.[64] Heptoxime, nioxime and their homologs are water-sol.

(*4*) *Diaminoglyoxime* (oxalenediamidoxime, niccolox) [m.p. 199°C decomp.] is easily prepd.; Ni (Fe, Co interfere) and Pd can be detd. and Cu and Hg^{2+} also

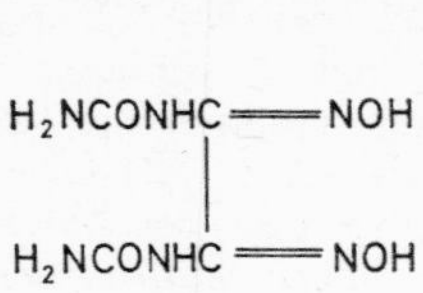

(XIX)

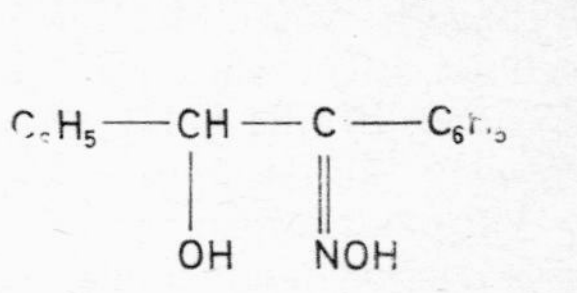

(XX)

react. *Dicarbamidoglyoxime* (oxalenediuramidoxime) (XIX) also ppts. Ni; the reagent decomps. to diaminoglyoxime and urea in NH_4OH soln.[65]

1.5. Cupron and salicylaldoxime analogs

(*1*) *Cupron* (α-benzoinoxime)[66] (XX) [m.p. 152°C, sol. in EtOH, Et_2O, Me_2CO, insol. in H_2O; β-form, m.p. 99°C] is used as a 2–4% soln. in EtOH. Its Cu complex is monobasic (XXI) when pptd. from acidic soln. and dibasic (XXII) from alk. soln.; the β-form does not ppt. with Cu but gives a brown color.

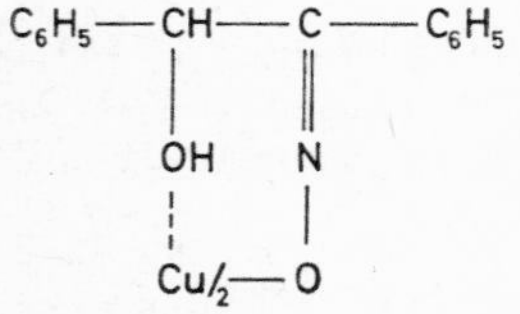

(XXI)

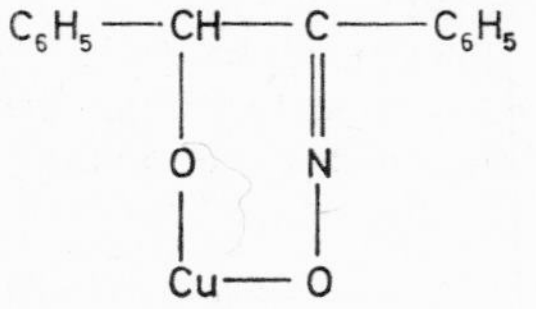

(XXII)

Cu is detd. in tartrate-contg. NH_4OH soln.; the ppt. is sol. in org. solvents (even 0·1 μg. gives a green color). With mineral acid solns. Pd, Mo ($CHCl_3$ extn.) and W ppt. completely; Cu, Cr^{6+}, Ni, Nb, Ta, V^{5+}, Au, UO_2^{2+} ppt. incompletely. Mo can be pptd. as a sort of heteropoly acid.

Various derivs. have been tested.[66]

(*2*) *Salicylaldoxime* (XXIII)[67] [m.p. 63°C, sol. in EtOH]. The reagent is prepd. by dissolving 1 g. in 5 ml. cold EtOH, pouring into 95 ml. H_2O at 30°C and filtering before use.

Pd is detd. gravimetrically in feebly mineral acid soln. or colorimetrically by C_6H_6 extn.; V is incompletely

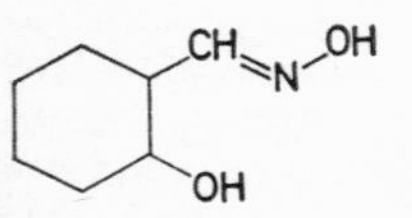

(XXIII)

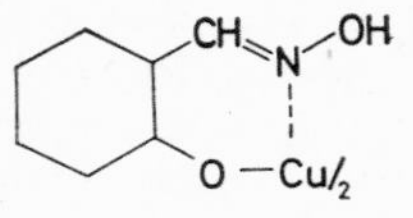

(XXIV)

pptd. Cu (0·5 μg) is detd. gravimetrically or colorimetrically above pH 2·6; the yellow-green ppt. (XXIV) can be extd. with *n*-AmOH at pH 3·5–9·5. Fe^{3+} gives an orange-red color. In neutral or acetate-buffered solns. ppts. are formed with Ni (pH 7–8, green), Co (orange-brown), Mn (green), Zn (pH 7·4–8·2, pale yellow), Cd (white), Pb (above pH 9, yellow), Ag (yellow), Bi (pH 9–11, yellow), Hg^{2+} (yellow) and Fe^{2+} (brown); all the ppts. except Pb are sol. in NH_4OH.

Various derivs. react similarly, e.g. p-*homosalicylaldoxime* (*p*-methylsalicylaldoxime), *5-nitrosalicylaldoxime* and p-*hydroxybenzaldoxime*. o-*Hydroxyacetophenoneoxime* can be used for the gravimetric detn. of Cu and Ni; Ag, Fe^{2+}, Ce^{3+}, Ni, Mn, Ti, Pd, V^{5+}, Hg, Pb, Cu, Cd, Zn also form ppts. while Fe^{3+}, Co, U^{6+}, Mo give colors. *Resorcylaldoxime* (2,4-dihydroxybenzaldoxime) is used colorimetrically for Fe^{3+} (purple) and gravimetrically for Ni (green) and Cu (greenish). *Resacetophenoneoxime* (2,4-dihydroxyacetophenoneoxime) serves similarly for Fe^{3+} (and U) and for Ni (and Cu). *Quinacetophenoneoxime* (the 2,5-isomer) is similar.

3- or 5-Methylsalicylaldoxime does not ppt. Cu, Zn or V. *β-Naphtholaldoxime* ppts. Cu, Ni (below pH 1·2), Co (above pH 3·8), Zn (above pH 4·8) but its soly. is small.[68] *2-Propionyl-1-naphtholoxime* (XXV) ppts. Cu

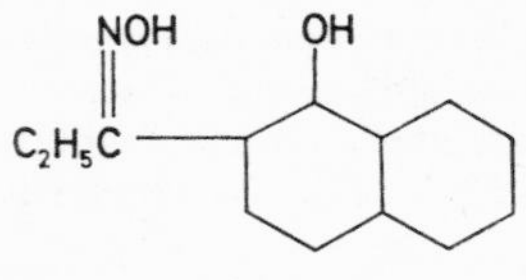

(XXV)

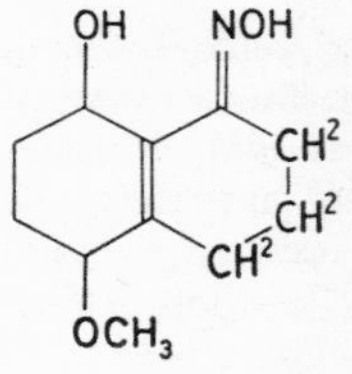

(XXVI)

at pH 2 and Ni at pH 3.[69] *3-* or *5-Oximinomethylsalicyclic acid* forms ppts. or colors with Cu, Ti, Zr, Co, Fe, U.[70] Various other derivs. and homologs have been described.[67]

(*3*) *8-Hydroxy-5-methoxytetraloneoxime* (XXVI) ppts. Cu, Ni, Co; the Cu and Ni complexes can be extd. with $CHCl_3$ for colorimetry. For other analogs, see ref. 71.

1.6. Oximes contg. additional N atoms

(*1*) *β-Isatoxime* (isatin-β-oxime) (XXVII) forms ppts. with Ag (red), Pb (yellow), Fe^{3+} (green), Ni (yellow-green), Co (brown), Cu^{2+} (green), Cu^{+} (orange), Hg^{+}, Hg^{2+} (yellow-orange) and UO_2^{2+} (yellow) in acetate-buffered solns.; U can be detd. gravimetrically.

α-(or *2-*)*Isatoxime* ppts. Hg^{2+}, Cu, UO_2^{2+} from acidic

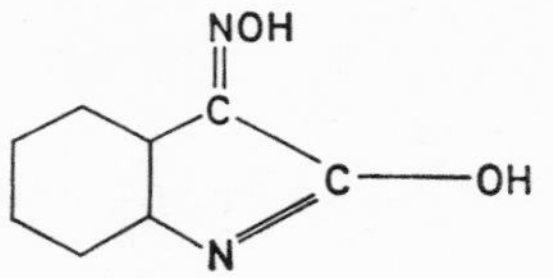

(XXVII)

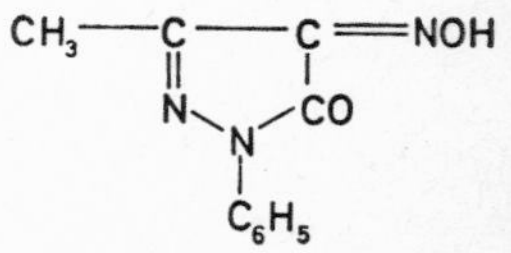

(XXVIII)

media, Pb, Ag, Zn, Bi from 10% NaOAc, and Ba, Tl, Cd, Pb, Ni, Co from alk. media.[72] The *methyl ether deriv.* is an excellent colorimetric reagent for Cu at pH 5–7 in tartrate solns.; if Hg is complexed as the iodide and $CHCl_3$ extn. is used, the method is specific.[73]

4-Isonitroso-N-phenyl-3-methylpyrazolone-5 (XXVIII) forms orange or yellow ppts. with Ag, Hg, Pb, Cu, Zn, green ppts. with Ni, Mn, and a purple ppt. with UO_2^{2+} in AcOH-contg. soln.; it gives green and red colors with Fe^{2+} and Fe^{3+} resp. *Isonitroso-3-phenylpyrazolone* is used gravimetrically for Cu.

Violuric acid (5-isonitrosobarbituric acid, 5-nitroso-2,4,6-trihydroxypyrimidine) (XXIX) reacts with Pd (gravimetric detn.), Tl, Cd, Zn, Pb, Ba, Sr, Ca, Mg, Be, Na, Li to give reddish ppts., and Ag, Fe^{2+} (colorimetric detn.), NH_4^+, Cs, Rb, K to give green or blue ppts.; the *Zn salt* reacts with Cu (3 μg.) and Hg.[74]

Isonitrosomalonylguanidine serves for colorimetric detn. of Co and Fe (blue). *2-Pyrrole-α-aldoxime* ppts. Cu (green). *5,8-Quinolinedionedioxime* ppts. Cu, Fe, Co, Ni in acetate-buffered soln. but the ppt. is difficult to filter and explodes on heating; the reagent is 10 times as sensitive as oxine.[75]

(*2*) *Amidoximes.*[76] *Homoveratric acid* (3,4-dimethoxyphenylacetic acid) *amidoxime* ppts. Cu (green) and Hg^{2+} (yellow); it forms colors with Fe^{2+} (reddish) and

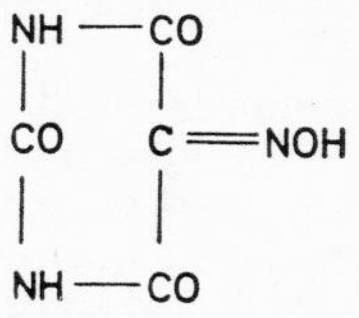

(XXIX)

Ni (violet if H_2O_2 is added). *Formamide oxime* ppts. Hg^{2+} (yellow) and Hg^{+} (grey). *α-Hydroxyisobutyric acid amidoxime* ($(CH_3)_2C(OH)C(NH_2)NOH$) ppts. Hg^{+} (white); the ppt. turns brown on addn. of NH_3.

Salicylamidoxime resembles salicylaldoxime forming red to yellow colors with U (pH 7·9–9·1), Fe^{3+} (pH 8·3–10), Pd, Ti (acidic soln., sol. in AmOH); Cu (green) and Ni (violet) are detd. gravimetrically.[77]

Succinamide dioxime ($(CH_2C(NOH)NH_2)_2$) ppts. Ag, Hg^{2+}, Cd, Pb, Co in NH_4OH soln.; colors are formed with Cu^{2+} (greenish), Fe^{2+} (pink), Fe^{3+} (brownish), UO_2^{2+} (yellow, changing to brownish on NH_4OH addn.).[78]

Malonamic amidoxime ($NH_2COCH_2C(NH_2)NOH$) ppts. Ag, Hg, Pb, Cu, Fe^{3+}, Ni.[79] *Phthalimidoxime* ppts. Ni, Co, Cu.[80]

(*3*) *Diacetylmonoxime* p-*nitrophenylhydrazone* gives a violet color with Co (1 μg.) in NH_4OH soln.[81]

1.7. Hydroxamic acids

Benzohydroxamic acid ($C_6H_5C(OH)NOH$) is suitable for colorimetric detns. of U in feebly acidic soln. (0·5 μg., orange), Fe in acidic soln. (purple) and V in strongly acidic soln. (blue, hexanol extn.; in feebly acidic and neutral or alk. soln., the colors are resp. red and purple). Mo (1 μg.) ppts. from NH_4OH soln. and Cu, Zn, Co, Ni, Ag, Hg^{2+}, Fe^{2+}, Cr in acetate-buffered soln.[82] The N-*phenyl deriv.* is used for La extn. with $CHCl_3$ at pH 4·5 for sepn. from Th and U.[83]

Salicylhydroxamic acid is used colorimetrically for U (0·25 μg., also gravimetric), V and Mo.[84] *Salicylaldehyde aminoacetohydroxamic acid* (salicylaldehyde glycinehydroxamic acid) is a colorimetric reagent for Fe^{3+} (p. 256). *Oxalohydroxamic acid* (HOOCC(OH)NOH) ppts. U (0·25 μg.), Zr, Th, Ca, which can be detd. colorimetrically by dissolving the ppt. in HCl and converting it to the Fe^{3+} complex.[85] *Formohydroxamic acid* is easily made and is used for colorimetric detn. of Fe.[86]

1.8. Miscellaneous oximes

(*1*) *Formaldoxime* is suitable for colorimetric detns. of Mn (0·08 μg./ml., red), Ni (the greenish color becomes brown) and V^{4+} (yellow); Cu (violet) and Fe (purple, unstable) also form colors.

Diisonitrosoacetone, *isonitrosoacetylacetone* and *ethy α-isonitrosoacetylacetate* form blue colors with Fe^{2+} which can be extd. with org. solvents and measured. *Diacetylmonoxime* is used for the colorimetry of Co, as is *α-benzilmonoxime* which also gives a color with Fe^{2+}; the β-form does not react. *α-Furilmonoxime* is suitable for Fe^{2+} colorimetry on addn. of pyridine.

Isonitrosoacetophenone (oximinoacetophenone) gives a blue color with Fe^{2+} (0·03 mg./l.) and yellow to brown colors with Ag, Pb, Cd, Co, Mn, Zn. *Isonitrosodibenzoylmethane* yields colors with Fe^{2+} (C_6H_6 extn.), Cu, Fe^{3+}, Co, Ni.[87] For other aliphatic monoximes, which usually show colors with Fe^{2+}, see ref. 88.

(*2*) *Isonitrosodimedone* (isonitrosodimethylcyclohexanedione, isonitrosodimethyldihydroresorcinol) (XXX)

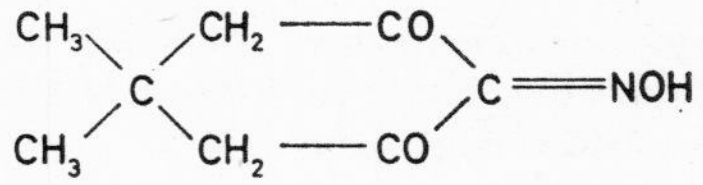

(XXX)

ppts. Co, which is used colorimetrically or gravimetrically, and forms colors with Fe^{3+} (detn.), Cu and Ni.[89]

(*3*) *Phenanthraquinonemonoxime* forms green ppts. with Tl, Cr^{3+}, Fe^{2+} and yellow to brown ppts. with Pb, Hg^{+}, Hg^{2+}, Cu, Ni, Co, Ag.

(*4*) *Isonitrosothiocamphor* (XXXI) ppts. Co and Cu but not Ni (see p. 271).

1.9. Nitroso compounds

Nitrosophenols[90] tend to be more specific for Co and Pd.

(*1*) *α-Nitroso-β-naphthol* (1-nitroso-2-naphthol, 1,2-naphthoquinone-1-oxime) [Dark brown, m.p. 109°C; sol. in EtOH, Et_2O, C_6H_6, CS_2, AcOH, alkalies; insol.

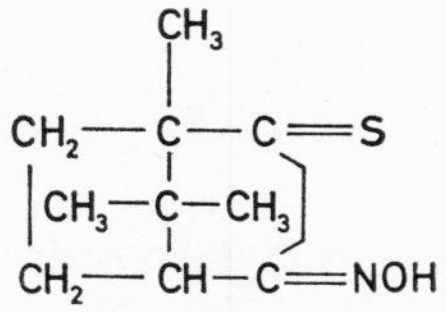

(XXXI)

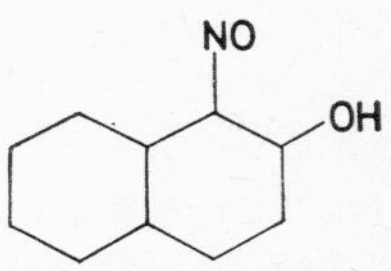

(XXXII)

in H_2O]. The reagent is prepd. by dissolving 1–4 g. in 50–100 ml. AcOH, pouring into 100 ml. H_2O and filtering after a few days.

The structure differs in strongly acidic (XXXII) and

in feebly acidic or alk. solns. (XXXIII), the structure of the complexes in the latter media being of the type (XXXIV). $[Co(C_{10}H_6NO{\cdot}O)_3]H$ and its Na and K salts have been prepd.[91]

The compd. is useful for colorimetric and gravimetric detns. of Co below pH 8·74 (0·04 μg.), Pd below pH 11·82 (hence detn. of CN^-) and Rh at pH 4·8–5·6. It also ppts. Fe^{2+} (alk. soln.; for absorption spectra,

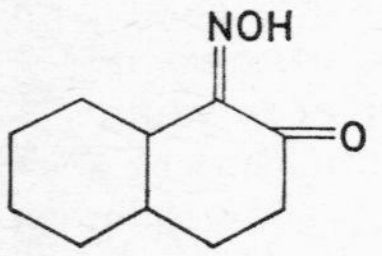

(XXXIII)

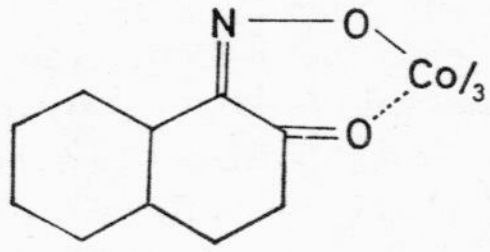

(XXXIV)

see ref. 4), Fe^{3+} (pH 0·95–2), Ag, Au, Bi, Cu (pH 3·96–13·2), Sn, Sb, Cr, Mo (feebly AcOH soln.), W, U (pH 4·05–9·38), Ti, Zr, V (pH 2·05–3·21), Nb, Ta. The Pd, Co and Fe^{3+} complexes can be extd. with $CHCl_3$.

β-Nitroso-α-naphthol [Yellow, m.p. 161–163°C; more sol. in H_2O than the *α-β* compound] forms red to violet ppts. with Co, Zr (0·2 μg.) and Pd.

(*2*) o-*Nitrosophenol* (quinone-monoxime) [Yellow, m.p. 126°C decomp., sol. in H_2O, Et_2O, dil. alkalies]. In acidic soln., the complexes formed with Co, Pd, Fe^{3+} can be extd. with petr. ether but those with Fe^{2+}, Cu^{2+}, Hg^{2+}, Ni, Zn cannot; possibly an NP–M–X complex is sol. in H_2O while an NP–M–NP complex is sol. in petr. ether. For derivs., see ref. 92 and for complex structures, see ref. 93.

o-*Nitrosocresol* and *4-nitrosoresorcinol* are more sensitive; *2,4-dinitrosoresorcinol* and *2,4-dinitrosoorcinol* are sensitive for Cu, Co, Ni but are inconvenient for colorimetry.

m-*Methoxy*-o-*nitrosophenol* (*o*-Nitrosoresorcinol monomethyl ether, coniferron)[94] [Orange-yellow, m.p. 158–159°C] is stable, more sensitive to Co and less sensitive to interferences than nitroso-R salt, and more sensitive to Fe^{2+} than *o*-phenanthroline. Co and Fe^{2+} are detd. colorimetrically. The complexes formed with Co (pH 1·5–10), Pd (pH 3–4), Fe^{3+} (pH 2–4) can be extd. with org. solvents; those with Fe^{2+}, Cu and Ni cannot.

3-Nitrososalicylic acid reacts with Co (sol. in petr. ether), Ni and Cu (insol. in petr. ether); Co and Ni can be detd. simultaneously.

(*3*) *Nitroso-R salt* (1-nitroso-2-naphthol-3,6-disulfonic acid, Na salt) forms colored complexes with Co, Fe^{2+}, Ni, and ppts. with Pb, Ag, Ba (insol. in HCl, Et_2O), Ca (sol. in HCl). See Chapters 33 and 35.

2-Nitrosochromotropic acid and the *2,7-dinitroso* analog form colors with Cu (purple) and Co (blue). *2-Nitroso-1-naphthol-4-sulfonic acid* forms colors with Fe^{2+} (green) at pH 5, Co (red) at pH 7–8, Cu, Ag and Ni; Ni can be detd. *1-Nitroso-2-hydroxy-3-naphthoic acid* is suitable for gravimetric detn. of Pd, Co and U. p-*Nitrosophenylazochromotropic acid* forms a colored complex with Co.

(*4*) *2-Isonitroso-1-ketotetralin* (2-nitroso-3,4-dihydro-1-naphthol) is similar to α-nitroso-β-naphthol. *Nitrosophenolphthalein* reacts with Cu, Ni, Co, Zn, Mn, Fe, Hg, Pb.

(*5*) *Nitrosamines.* p-*Nitrosodimethylaniline* [m.p. 85°C], the *diethyl homolog* [m.p. 84°C] and p-*nitrosodiphenylamine* [m.p. 143°C, sol. in EtOH, Et_2O, $CHCl_3$] form red complexes with Pd which can be extd. with Et_2O, $CHCl_3$; this provides an excellent detn. The color with Pt deepens on heating and can be measured. The dimethyl compd. gives a deep green with Ru and a red color with Ir and is used colorimetrically; the diethyl and diphenyl compounds give progressively weaker colors with Ru and Ir (q.v.).

α-Nitroso-β-naphthylamine and the *β-α* compd. are used gravimetrically for Cu, Co and Ni. *Nitrosoguanidine* forms a colored ppt. with Ni, etc. similar to that of dimethylglyoxime.

1.10. Cupferron and its analogs[95]

(*1*) *Cupferron* (ammonium nitrosophenylhydroxylamine) (XXXV) [Pale yellow, m.p. 163–164°C; sol. in EtOH, H_2O; stabilized by addn. of a little solid

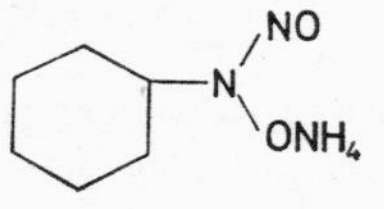

(XXXV)

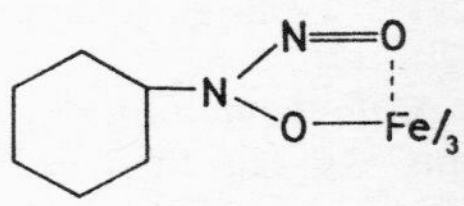

(XXXVI)

$(NH_4)_2CO_3$]. The reagent is used as a 5% aq. soln. stabilized with 0·05 g. phenacetin/100 ml. if necessary.

The reactions are listed in Table 16; the complexes are usually of type (XXXVI) but with Mg, Zn, Cd, Mn, Co, Ni they are of the type $M^{2+}[(C_6H_5NONO)_3]$. For extn. data, see ref. 96, and for the Ce complex, see ref. 97.

The reagent is important in many detns. and for many sepns. Fe^{3+}, Ti, Zr, V, U^{4+} can be sepd. from Al, Cr, U^{6+}, Fe^{2+}, Zn, PO_4^{3-}, tartrate, etc.; V from W in HF soln.; Bi from Ag, Hg, Pb, Cd, As, Sb, Cr, Mn, Ni, Co; Sn from As, Pb, Sb^{5+}, Zn; Ga from Al, Cr, In; Ti from Nb, Ta (q.v.); and Ti (q.v.) from Zr, Th, Fe^{3+}, Al, Cr, rare earths, Pb, Cu, Cd, Bi, Sb, Zn, Mn, Ni, Co, Ca, etc., As^{3+}, As^{5+}, V, Mo, W and B in solns. of pH 4·3–7·0 contg. EDTA. Hf can be detd. colorimetrically. *Procedure for detns.* Cool the soln., preferably to 5°C, add filter pulp and an excess of reagent (as indicated by a transient white ppt.). Filter under suction, wash, heat very slowly and finally ignite. HNO_3 and oxidants interfere.

TABLE 16. Cupferrates

Metal	Pptn.			Extn. with reagent/solvent
	Acidic	Feebly acidic	Neutral	
Cu		++ grey, sol. in NH_4OH		HCl (1 : 9), $CHCl_3$ ++; H_2SO_4 (1 : 99–1 : 7) +
Ag	o		+	
Be		$H_2C_2O_4$ ++		
Zn			+	neutral +
Hg	Hg^+, 0·5*N*, ++	Hg^{2+} +		neutral, C_6H_6, $CHCl_3$ +
Al		HCOOH, AcOH ++	+	pH 2–5, $CHCl_3$, o
Ga	H_2SO_4(1 : 12), ++			2*N* H_2SO_4, $CHCl_3$ ++
In	HCl (1 : 18), +			dil. acid, C_6H_6, $CHCl_3$ +
Tl	o			
Ce	Ce^{4+} ++, Ce^{3+}, etc. o		Ce^{3+} ++, pale brown	Ce^{4+}, 0·1–0·15 *N* H_2SO_4, AmOAc ++
Ti	H_2SO_4 (1 : 49–1 : 19) + H_2-Tart, ++ yellow			HCl (1 : 9), $CHCl_3$, Et_2O, EtOAc ++
Zr	H_2SO_4 (1 : 19–2 : 3), ++ white			H_2SO_4 (1 : 9), EtOAc ++
Sn	1·5*N*, ++			Sn^{4+}, HCl (1 : 9), EtOAc ++; Sn^{2+}, 1·5*N* acid C_6H_6, $CHCl_3$ ++
Pb	o	AcOH, +		
V	V^{4+} brown, V^{5+} black-brown, HCl or H_2SO_4 (1 : 99) ++[a]		$V^{4+,5+}$ +, V^{3+} ++, black-brown	V^{5+}, HCl (1 : 9), EtOAc; H_2SO_4 (1 : 9), Et_2O for minute amt. ++
Nb	H_2SO_4 (1 : 9) + H_2-Tart or $H_2C_2O_4$, ++			$CHCl_3$ +
Ta	As above			
Pa				1–4*N* acid, C_6H_6, Et_2O, $CHCl_3$ ++
Sb^{3+}	o	+		Sb^3, H_2SO_4 (1 : 9), $CHCl_3$ + +
Bi	++			HCl or H_2SO_4, PhMe or MeCOEt ++
Cr		+		
Mo	o			HCl (2 : 9) ++; H_2SO_4 (1 : 49–2 : 9), $CHCl_3$, 4 μg. remains
W	H_2SO_4 (1 : 19–1 : 4) o; + HF none			HCl (1 : 9), EtOAc o
Th	o	AcOH, ++		HCl (1 : 9), EtOAc o
U	U^{4+} H_2SO_4 (1 : 24–1 : 12) + NH_2OH ++		U^{6+} ++	U^{4+}, H_2SO_4 (1 : 9) + $NH_2OH.HCl$ + Et_2O ++, Hg–Zn when traces, no extn. with $CHCl_3$; U^{6+}, $CHCl_3$, 1 mg. extd.; neutral, Et_2O o
Mn			o	
Fe	Fe^{3+}, HCl or H_2SO_4 (1 : 4) ++, red-brown, insol. in NH_4OH	Fe^{2+} +		Fe^{3+}, H_2SO_4 (1 : 9), $CHCl_3$, Et_2O, EtOAc ++
Ni			o	neutral, $CHCl_3$, etc. o
Co		AcOH, ++		dil. AcOH, Et_2O or EtOAc o
Pd	o			

[a] Ppt. sol. in Me_2CO, yellow-brown, rapidly changes to green (colorimetric detn.). ++ complete; + incomplete; o partial

(2) *Neocupferron* (ammonium α-naphthylnitrosohydroxylamine) reacts with many metals in a very similar way to cupferron; the ppts. are generally less soluble and more bulky. The *2-fluorenyl analog* and neocupferron itself are more sensitive to Fe and Cu than cupferron and are used gravimetrically. The p-*xylyl analog* is used colorimetrically with $CHCl_3$ extn. for Ti (298 mμ) and Th (307 mμ).[98]

Ammonium ar-α- or *-β-nitrosohydroxyaminotetrahydronaphthalene* is used gravimetrically for Fe in 10% HCl soln. (α-, 0·3 μg./ml.; β-, 0·1 μg./ml.), or colorimetrically after $CHCl_3$ extn. Cu (5 μg./ml.) is detd. similarly in 30% AcOH soln.

(3) *Various derivs. contg. other radicals* in place of the —NO group in cupferron have been tested.[99] N-*Benzoyl*-N-*phenylhydroxylamine* (—COC_6H_5) [m.p. 121–122°C, slightly sol. in H_2O, sol. in NH_4OH, EtOH, C_6H_6, Et_2O] is useful for sepns. of Cu from Pb, Hg;

Ti from Al; and Ta from Nb, Ti, Zr. It forms ppts. with Sn (gravimetric detn.), Ti, Zr, V^{5+} (C_6H_6 extn. and colorimetry), Mo, W, Fe (pH 3–5·5), Al (pH 3·6–6·4) and Cr. Th (pH 2), U^{6+} (pH 3·5) and La (pH 7) can be extd. with 0·1*M* solns. in $CHCl_3$.[100]

The N-*furoyl deriv.* and various aliph. derivs. are of little interest.[101] If the —$CSNH_2$ group replaces the nitroso group, the compd. becomes H_2O-sol., but if the —$CSNHC_6H_5$ group replaces it, there is no reaction with Ti or Zr. The —$CSNHCH_2CH{:}CH_2$ group makes a more specific reagent; only Ag, Hg^+, Hg^{2+}, Sn^{2+} and Sn^{4+} ppt.[100]

(*4*) *3-Hydroxy-1,3-diphenyltriazine* (*N*-phenyl-*N*-phenylazohydroxylamine) (XXXVII) [Pale yellow,

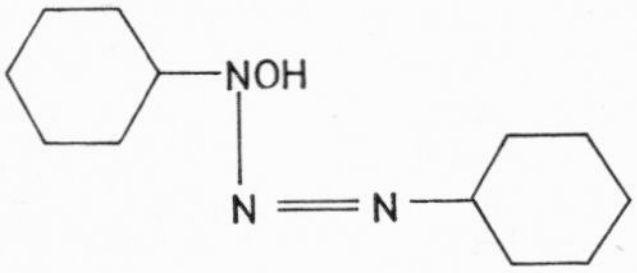

(XXXVII)

m.p. 119·5–120°C, sol. in EtOH] is used gravimetrically for Cu and Pd at pH 3 or below; Fe, V, Ti, Mo ppt. but the complexes decomp. on heating in acidic soln. The reagent also decomps. Ni can be detd. gravimetrically at pH 4·4–7·0. *3-Hydroxy-1-*p*-chlorophenyl-3-phenyltriazine* ppts. Ti at pH 2·3; the ppt. is weighed.

1.11. Quinaldic acid and its analogs

For a general discussion of compds. contg. N and —COOH, see ref. 102.

(*1*) *α-Quinaldic acid* (quinaldinic acid, quinoline-2-carboxylic acid) (XXXVIII) [Yellow, m.p. 155–156°C, sol. in hot H_2O, alkalies]. The reagent is used as the Na-salt (5·636 g./150 ml.).

Cu is detd. gravimetrically in H_2SO_4 or AcOH solns. at pH 1·5–7, Cd at pH 3·7–7·2, Zn in neutral or dil. AcOH solns., and Th in dil. AcOH soln. Pb, Ni, Co, Fe^{3+}, U, Ag, Al, Cr, Hg, Mn ppt. in neutral soln. Fe^{2+} forms a readily sol. red ppt. in the cold which

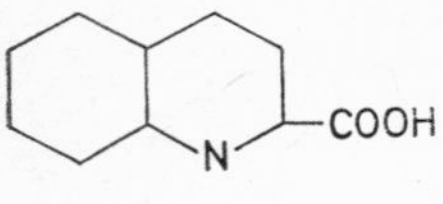

(XXXVIII)

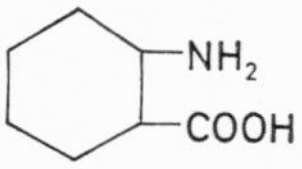

(XXXIX)

changes to an insol. violet form; recent study has shown that the red form is the 1:3 complex while the violet form in presence of CN^- is a 1:2 complex contg. varying amts. of CN^-.[103] The sepn. of Cu and Cd is nearly complete, 0·05% Cd appearing in the Cu ppt. and 0·3% Cu in the Cd ppt. (see pp. 179 and 186).

5-Nitroquinaldic acid ppts. Ag, Hg, Pb, Cu, Fe, Co, Ni, Mn; Zn can be detd. colorimetrically; Sn^{2+} gives an orange color in acid soln.

Quinoline-8-carboxylic acid reacts with Ag (pH 5·3–7·7), Cu (pH 1·8–3·8), Cd (pH 5·7–7·7), Fe^{2+}, Hg^{2+} and Tl^+; Cu and Fe have been detd. The *5-nitro deriv.* reacts with Ag (pH 2·1–5·3), Cu (pH 1·4–3·4), Cd (pH 4·0–5·6), Fe^{2+}, Ni, Co, Pb, Bi and Zn; Ag and Cu are detd. gravimetrically.

5,6-Benzoquinaldic acid ppts. Cu at pH 0·82–9·4, Hg at pH 4–6·5, and Cd, Fe^{2+}, Ni, Co, Zn, Mn, Ag, Pb, Bi, Al, Be, Th, Zr, Ti, U, V, W, Cr, Mo at about pH 3; most of these metals can be detd. gravimetrically. The Fe^{2+} complex if CN^- is added is of the type $[Fe(BQ)_2(CN)_2]\,M_2$ and is used colorimetrically.[104]

(*2*) *α-Picolinic acid* (pyridine-2-carboxylic acid) and *quinolinic acid* (pyridine-2,3-dicarboxylic acid) react with Ag in Na_2CO_3 soln. contg. $S_2O_8^{2-}$. The former can be used for Fe colorimetry and to mask Fe in the colorimetric detn. of Al with oxine in $CHCl_3$.[105] *Benzothiazole-2-carboxylic acid* is easily prepd. and useful for Fe colorimetry. *Cinchophene* (atophan, phenylcinchoninic acid, 2-phenylquinoline-4-carboxylic acid) ppts. Rh, Pd, Os, Pt, Ir, Au and Fe^{3+}.[106]

(*3*) *Quinoline-8-sulfonic acid* forms complexes with Cu, Zn, Cd, Mn, Co, Ni of the type $[MA_2(C_9H_6NSO_3)_2]$ where A = H_2O, $PhNH_2$, *o*- or *p*-toluidine, α-naphthylamine or *o*-phenanthroline; combinations of Zn with toluidine and Mn with *p*-toluidine or α-naphthylamine are unsatisfactory.[107]

1.12. Anthranilic acid and its derivatives

Anthranilic acid (*o*-aminobenzoic acid) (XXXIX) [white-pink, m.p. 145°C, sol. in EtOH, Et_2O] forms ppts. in neutral or feebly acidic solns. with Ag (0·24 μg.), Cu (0·013 μg., pH 1·4–2·8), Mn, Zn, Pb, Hg^{2+} (0·06 μg.), Cd (pH 4·2–5·2), Pd (0·015 μg.), Ni (pH 3·6–4·5) and Co (pH 4·1–5·1). The red ppt. with Ce^{4+}

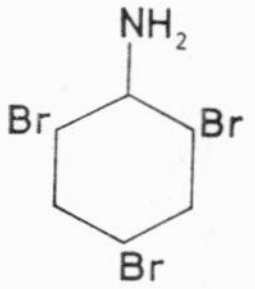

(XL)

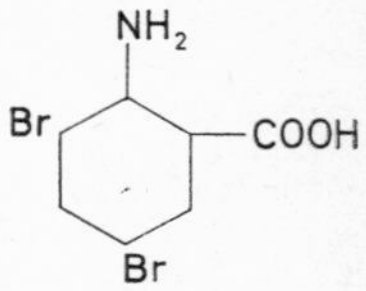

(XLI)

turns brown with NH_4OH and the pink soln. obtained with HNO_3 can be used colorimetrically.

Procedures. (*i*) Reagent. Dissolve 3 g. in 22 ml. *N* NaOH, filter, dil. to 100 ml. with H_2O; if not acidic, add more reagent. Store in a brown bottle and discard if discolored.

(*ii*) Gravimetry. Filter the ppt. obtained at the above pH values through sintered glass, wash with a diluted (1:15 or 20) reagent soln. and then with EtOH; heat at a suitable temp. and weigh.

(*iii*) Titrimetry. Tribromination to (XL)[108] is better than dibromination to (XLI).[109] Dissolve the ppt. in 4*N*

HCl, add an excess of $KBrO_3$–KBr soln., leave for 30 min. and back-titrate iodometrically; the soln. must be above 1·5*N* in HCl at the end-point. With Cu, back-titrate with As^{3+} soln. rather than iodometrically. The ppts. can also be detd. by titration with $Ce(ClO_4)_4$ and nitroferroin indicator or colorimetrically by coupling with *N*-(1-naphthyl)-ethylenediamine-HCl.[110]

5-Bromoanthranilic acid can be used in the same way as anthranilic acid; the *3,5-dibromo deriv.* is used for the gravimetric detn. of Ag, Cu, Ni.[111] The *5-sulfo deriv.* is used in Fe^{3+} colorimetry. *3-Amino-2-naphthoic acid* gives ppts. which filter badly. m- or p-*Aminobenzoic acid* can be used to detect Cu.

α-Naphthylphthalanilic acid is the best phthalanilic acid for the detn. of Pd (p. 244). p-*Aminosalicylic acid* is used for colorimetric detns. of Fe. *Isonicotinic acid hydrazide* (isoniazid) ppts. Cu at pH 4·3–4·4, Hg^{2+} at pH 4·8–6, and Cd at pH 4·4–4·5.[112]

1.13. Aminopolycarboxylic acids[113]

These acids form very stable complexes with many metal ions.

(*1*) *EDTA* (ethylenediaminetetraacetic acid, ethylenedinitrilotetraacetic acid, complexone II, enta, versene) $[CH_2N(CH_2CO_2H)_2]_2$. It is commonly used as the disodium dihydrate salt (versenate, complexone III, sequestrene, trilon B, nullgapon, etc.). The stability constants of the metal complexes are listed in Table 17.

The reagent is widely used in titrimetry (see Chapter 5, Section 4) and in ion exchange sepns. (q.v). It can be

TABLE 17. Logarithm of Stability Constants of Metal-EDTA and other Complexes

Metal	EDTA	NTA	UDT	CyDTA	DTPA	EGTA
Li	2·79	3·28	5·40			
Na	1·66	2·15	3·32			
Mg	(8·69)	5·41	8·84	10·32	9·02	5·4
Ca	10·70	6·41	8·77	12·50	11·10	10·7
Sr	8·63	4·98	7·65		9·68	8·1
Ba	7·76	4·82	6·78	7·99	8·63	8·0
Cu^{2+}	18·80	12·7		21·30	21·03	
Zn	16·50	10·4	3·2	18·67	18·14	
Cd	16·46	9·5	5·7	19·23	18·93	
Hg^{2+}	21·86	11·8		(24·30)		23·8
Al	16·13	7·10		17·63		
Sc	23·1					
Y	18·09			19·15		
La	15·50	10·3	10	16·26		
Ce	15·98	>10	~10	16·76		
Pr	16·40			17·31		
Nd	16·61			17·68		
Sm	17·14			18·38		
Eu	17·35			18·62		
Gd	17·37			18·77		
Tb	17·93			19·50		
Dy	18·30			19·69		
Ho	18·74					
Er	18·85			20·68		
Tm	19·32			20·96		
Yb	19·51			21·12		
Lu	19·83			21·51		
Ga	20·27			22·91		
In	24·95					
Pb	18·04			19·68		
V^{2+}	12·70					
V^{3+}	25·9					
V^{4+}	18·70			19·40		
Cr^{3+}		7·10				
Mn^{2+}	13·49	7·4	4·0	16·78	15·11	
Fe^{2+}	(14·33)	8·8			16·66	
Fe^{3+}	(25·1)	15·9				
Co	16·31	10·6	3·2	18·92	19·00	
Ni	18·62	11·3	3·3		20·21	
Th	23·2					

used gravimetrically for Mg and colorimetrically for Cu, Ni, Fe, Cr, Co, Mn^{3+}, Pd, Ir, Bi; for absorption spectra, see ref. 114. It is also widely used as a masking agent. Fe^{3+}, Cu^{2+} do not oxidize KI if EDTA is added.

(*2*) *HEEDTA* (*N*-hydroxyethylethylenediaminetri-acetic acid, entol, versenol) has been used for colorimetry of Fe, and *CyDTA* (1,2-diaminocyclohexane-*N,N,N′,N′*-tetraacetic acid, hexamethylenediamine-tetraacetic acid, DCTA, HexaVer)[115, 116] for colorimetry of Mn^{3+}. *Benzhydrylaminediacetic acid* ($(C_6H_5)_2CHN(CH_2CO_2H)_2$),[116] *DTPA* (diethylenetriaminepentaacetic acid),[117] *EGTA* (ethyleneglycol bis-(β-aminoethyl)-*N,N′*-tetraacetic acid)[118] and others have also been synthesized. These compds. are finding increasing use for titrimetric and masking purposes, as are *NTA* (nitrilotriacetic acid, triglycine, complexone I, trilon A), *hydrazinodiacetic acid* and *uramildiacetic acid* (UDT).

1.14. Miscellaneous compounds contg. N and —COOH groups

(*1*) *Zincon* (*o*-[α-(2-hydroxy-5-sulfophenylazo)]-benzilidenehydrazinobenzoic acid, 2-carboxy-2′-hydroxy-5′-sulfoformazylbenzene) (XLII) can be used in the

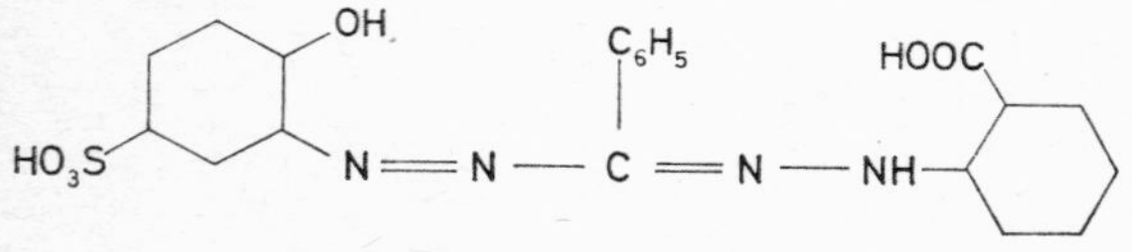

(XLII)

colorimetric detn. of Cu above pH 5·2, Zn at pH 8·5–9·5 and Hg^{2+}; the sensitivity for Cu and Zn is similar to that of dithizone. Fe, Co and Ni also react. It can serve as an indicator in some EDTA titrations.

(*2*) *Formazylcarboxylic acid* ($C_6H_5N{:}NC(COOH){:}NNHC_6H_5$) ppts. Ag in neutral or feebly AcOH soln., but not Pb, Hg or Cu.[119]

(*3*) *Pyruvic acid phenylhydrazone* ($CH_3C({:}NNHC_6H_5)COOH$) gives a violet color with Hg^{2+} which turns brownish on solvent extn.[120]

(*4*) *Sodium diethylcarbamate* ($(C_2H_5)_2NCOONa$) gives characteristic crystals with Hg, Cd, Pb, Co, Mn, Zn, Sr.

(*5*) *Phenylalanine* ($C_6H_5CH_2CHNH_2COOH$) gives a green ppt. with Ce^{4+} which turns brown with NH_4OH. *Norleucine* (α-amino-*n*-caproic acid) ppts. Cu (1 μg.), Hg and Zn. *Glycine* and *phenylglycine* also react with Cu. N,N-*Dihydroxyethylglycine* masks Fe, no ppt. being formed above pH 11.[121]

(*6*) *Penicillin G* ppts. Fe in acetate-buffered soln. (gravimetric detn.).

(*7*) p-*Sulfamoylbenzoate* ($H_2NSO_2C_6H_4COOH$) ppts. Ag (0·5 μg./ml.) in NaOH soln.[122]

1.15. Urea derivs. contg. the ═CO group

(*1*) *s-Diphenylcarbazide* (1,5-diphenylcarbohydrazide) ($CO(NHNHC_6H_5)_2$) [m.p. 169–170°C, sol. in EtOH, Me_2CO, slightly sol. in H_2O]. The alc. soln. is stabilized by the addn. of phthalic or thioglycolic acid; abs. EtOAc or Me_2CO solns. are stable for months. Blue to violet complexes are formed with Cd, Mg, Ag, Pb, Co, Ni, Zn in feebly acid solns.; the reagent is oxidized to the carbazone by Hg^{2+}, Cu^{2+}, Fe^{3+}, again forming blue to violet complexes. CrO_4^{2-} also oxidizes it, the 2:3 complex of Cr^{3+} with diphenylcarbazone being formed; this is used colorimetrically.[123] Colors are also formed with MnO_4^- and Mn^{3+}; Cl^- (0·3 μg.), Pb, ClO_3^- (0·05 μg.) and IO_4^- can be detected.

Diphenylcarbazone ($C_6H_5N{:}NCONHNHC_6H_5$) [Orange, m.p. 150°C decomp., sol. in EtOH] gives red to violet colors with Hg (0·1 μg.), Ag, Cu, Pb, Fe^{2+}, Cd, Zn, Co, Au, Pt, As, CrO_4^{2-} (colorimetric detn.), V and MnO_4^-. It is more sensitive than the carbazide and is used as an indicator in mercurimetry.

Di-1- or *-2-naphthylcarbazone* forms blue to violet colors with Hg, Cu, Cd; *2,2′-*, *3,3′-* or *4,4′-dinitrodiphenylcarbazide* gives a brown color with Cd (0·5 μg.) which turns bluish with HCHO, and a violet color with CrO_4^{2-} (0·15 μg.), while their *carbazones* give colors with Hg, Cu, Cd, Fe. For other derivs. and analogs, see ref. 124. *Diphenylcarbazide disodium disulfonate* has been used as a mercurimetric indicator.

(*2*) *Cryogenin* (*m*-benzaminosemicarbazide) ($H_2NCOC_6H_4NHNHCONH_2$) [m.p. 172°C, sol. in EtOH, Me_2CO, Et_2O, $CHCl_3$, slightly sol. in H_2O] ppts. Cu (colorimetric detn.), Pb, Hg and Sr; Fe, Zn, Mn, CrO_4^{2-}, $Cr_2O_7^{2-}$, Co, Ni and Ag also react. *Phenylsemicarbazide* and *diphenylsemicarbazide* react similarly.

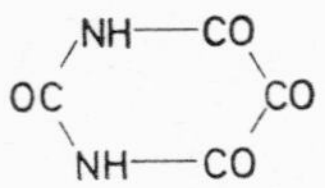

(XLIII)

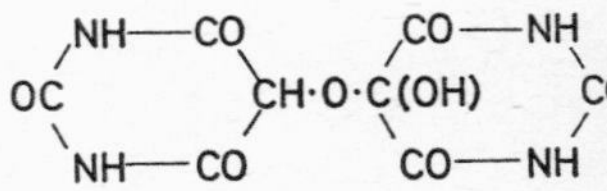

(XLIV)

(*3*) *Dicyanodiamidine sulfate*[125] (guanylurea sulfate, Grossman's reagent) ($[H_2NC({:}NH)NHCONH_2]_2H_2SO_4 \cdot 2H_2O$) [Sol. in H_2O]. In alk. soln. $Cu(C_2H_5N_4O)_2$ and the Ni, Ag and Pd complexes ppt.; the Ag and Pd ppts. are sol. in NH_4OH. V ppts. in neutral soln.; Co ppts. in NH_4OH soln. contg. sucrose. *Alloxan* (mesoxalylurea) (XLIII) gives a red-grey complex with Cd and yellow to red complexes with Mg, Fe^{3+}, Co, Ni, Mn, Zn which darken on addn. of NaOH. *Alloxantin* (uroxin) (XLIV) is used colorimetrically for Fe^{3+} (blue).

(*4*) *Murexide* (ammonium purpurate) (XLV) is used colorimetrically for Ca; Sc and other metals react.[126] It is used as an indicator for EDTA titrations and for titrations of Ni and F^- with CN^- and Ce^{3+} resp. The corresponding Zn salt forms colors with Hg and Ag.

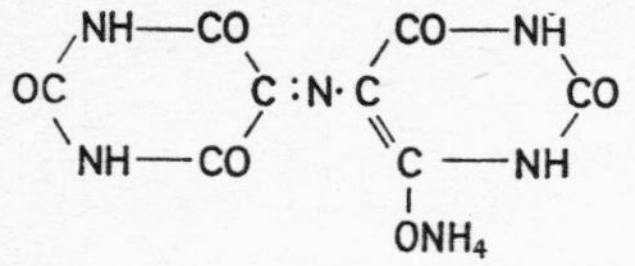

(XLV)

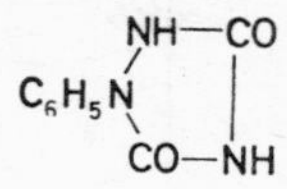

(XLVI)

(*5*) *1-Phenylurazole* (XLVI) reacts with Hg and Ag in acetate-buffered soln. *Diphenylhydantoin* (XLVII) permits detns. of Cu as $Cu(C_{15}H_{11}N_2O_2)_2$ and of Ni. *Uric acid* (XLVIII) reacts with Sn^{4+} (but not Sn^{2+}),

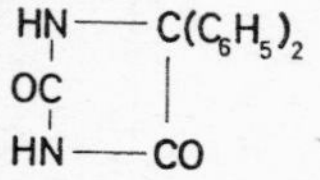

(XLVII)

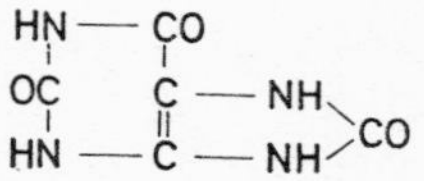

(XLVIII)

WO_4^{2-}, Zn, Tl in alk. soln. *Cyanuric acid* ($(HNCO)_3$) gives characteristic crystals with Mn^{2+} if NH_3 is added.

1.16. Miscellaneous compounds

(*1*) *Cuprizone* (bis-(cyclohexanone)oxalyldihydrazone) (XLIX) is used colorimetrically for Cu at pH 7–10 and

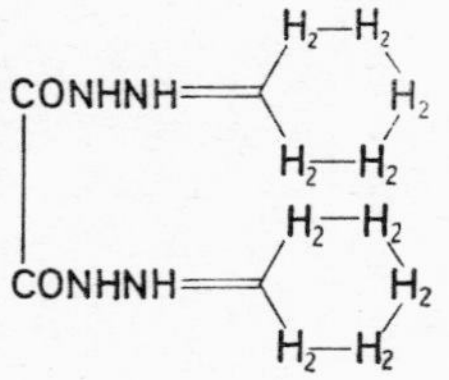

(XLIX)

is twice as sensitive as diethyldithiocarbamate.[127] *Oxalic acid dihydrazide* can be used similarly if NH_4OH and acetaldehyde are added.

(*2*) *1,2-Diaminodihydroxyquinone* gives a violet color with Hg (1 μg.); if PO_4^{3-} is added and the soln. is filtered, there are no interferences.[128] p-*Dimethylaminophenyliminocamphor* (L) gives violet colors with

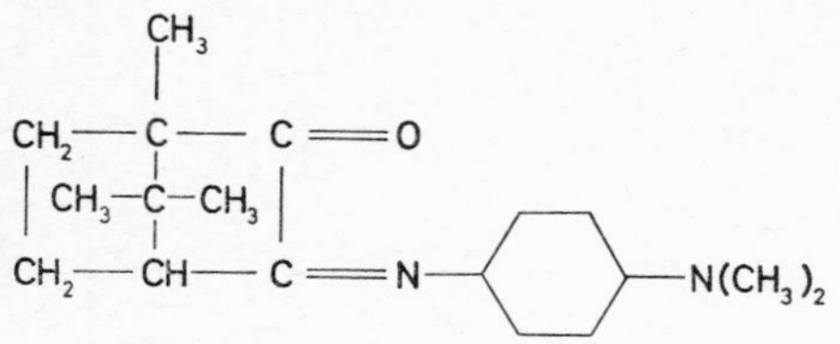

(L)

Hg, Bi and Ag as does the *ethyl analog*. *Urobilin* (stercobilin) gives pink colors with Hg (1 μg.), Zn (1 μg.), Cu, Au and Ag which can be extd. with $CHCl_3$ and fluoresce under UV light.

(*3*) *Ephedrine* gives yellowish colors with Au (LI), Ir, Os^{8+} and Pd. *Isatine* gives characteristic crystals with Ag and Cd in NH_4OH soln.

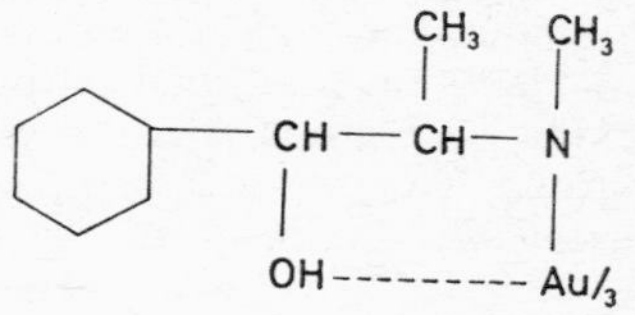

(LI)

(*4*) *2,4-Dinitro-α-naphthol* (the Na or NH_4 salt is Martius or Manchester yellow) ppts. Tl (0·04 μg.) and Co (0·5 μg.). *2-Nitro-1,3-indanedione* (LII) ppts. Fe^{2+}, Ag, Pb, Hg, Cu and Co.[129]

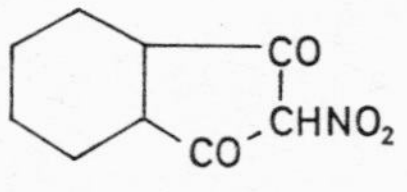

(LII)

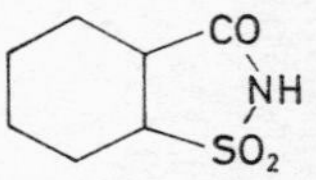

(LIII)

(*5*) *Saccharin* (LIII) ppts. Tl (20 μg./ml.).

(*6*) *Succinimide* and iso-$PrNH_2$ form a violet complex with Co.[130]

(*7*) p-*Aminoacetophenone* is used for gravimetric detn. of Pd (0·5 μg.) in dil. HCl solns.

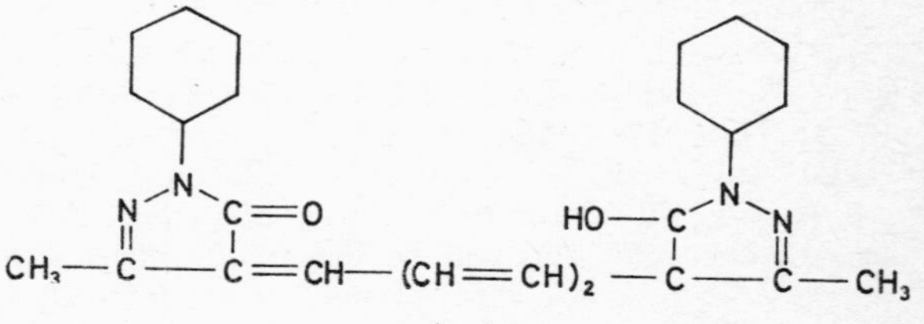

(LIV)

(*8*) *Zolon red* (LIV) is sparingly sol. in H_2O but sol. in org. solvents and alkalies; it is a very sensitive reagent for Ag and Cu^+ (blue).[131]

2. COMPOUNDS CONTAINING S

2.1. Rhodanine and its derivs.[132]

Metals replace the H of the imino group.

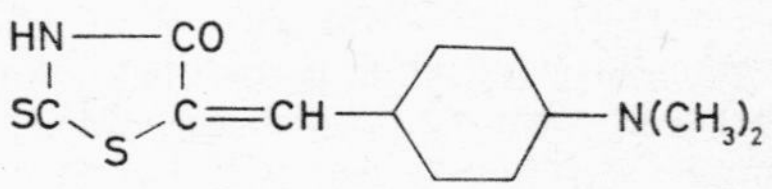

(LV)

(*1*) p-*Dimethylaminobenzilidenerhodanine* (*p*-dimethylaminobenzalrhodanine) (LV) [Red, m.p. 200°C decomp., sparingly sol. in EtOH, Et_2O, insol. in H_2O.] Ag (0·02 μg.) Hg (0·33 μg.) and Au (0·1 μg.) have been detd. colorimetrically in slightly acidic soln., giving reddish ppts.; Cu^+ (0·8 μg.), Pd (0·004 μg.), Pt also ppt. while Cu^{2+}, Co, Fe, Ni give colors. The *ethyl analog* behaves similarly.

(*2*) *Rhodanine* ppts. Ag (detn.), Hg, Cu, Au, Pd, Pt. The compd. obtained by substitution of the ring S by O behaves similarly but that obtained by replacement of S by O in the =CS group does not. Substituents in the $=CH_2$ group have no advantage, except that o-*benzaldehyde-sulfonic acid-rhodanine* is sol. in H_2O.

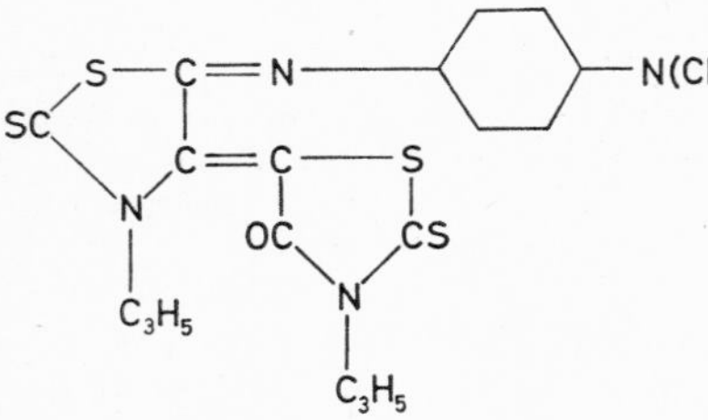

(LVI)

Isonitrosorhodanine is used gravimetrically for Ag and *5-isonitroso-*N*-allylrhodanine* is specific for Ag (1 part in 5 × 10^3). *4,5-Dehydro-4′,5′-bis-*N*-allylrhodanyl-5-*p*-dimethylaminoanil* (LVI) gives violet colors with Ag (1 part in 10^4), Cu^{2+} and Hg^{2+}.

2.2. Thiourea and its derivs.[133]

Metals replace the H of the amino or imino group.

(*1*) *Thiourea* (thiocarbamide) (H_2NCSNH_2) [m.p. 171°C, sol. in H_2O, EtOH] is used colorimetrically for Bi, Sb, Sn^{4+}, Ru (3 μg./ml.), Os (10 μg./ml., $Os(NH_2CSNH_2)_6Cl_3.H_2O$), Pd, Re (in HCl soln. contg. $SnCl_2$); Ag, Hg, Pb, Fe, Ni and Cr also give colors. Se, Te ppt. from acidic soln. and can be detd. colorimetrically; Pb ppts. from HNO_3 soln. Cd ppts. as a double complex salt on addn. of Reinecke's salt. Cu can be masked.

(*2*) *Phenylthiourea* (phenylthiocarbamide) [m.p. 154°C, sparingly sol. in H_2O] forms ppts. with Ag (10 μg./ml.), Hg^+ (20 μg.), Hg^{2+} (1 mg.), Cu^+ (10 μg.), Au^{3+}, Pd and Pt (each 10 μg.); the Pd complex can be detd. gravimetrically or extd. with AmOAc from HCl soln. and thus sepd. from many elements.

Methylthiourea (methylthiocarbamide) is used to detect Bi. *Allylthiourea* (thiosinamine, rhodalline) reacts with Ru in acidic soln., Cd and U in alk. soln. *2-Naphthylthiourea* gives white or reddish colors or ppts. in NH_4OH soln. with Ag (also in acid soln.), Pb (black on heating), Cd, Co, Ni and Zn; Hg forms a white ppt. in acid soln. and Bi a yellow ppt.; Cu gives a blue color in AcOH soln. and a white ppt. in H_2SO_4 soln.[134] *s-Methylthiourea* (2-methyl-2-thiopseudourea) *sulfate* ppts. Cu, Ni and Co as methylmercaptides from NH_4OH solns.; the ppts. can be weighed; Co and Ni can be detd. colorimetrically. *s-Diphenylthiourea* (thiocarbanilide) ppts. Re and forms colors with Os (10

TABLE 18. Reactions between Thiourea Derivatives and Pt Metals or Re in dil. HCl soln.

Reagent	Os^{6+} (+Sn^{2+})	Ru	Pt cold	Pt hot	Pd cold	Pd hot	Rh cold	Rh hot	Ir cold	Ir hot	Re
Thiosemicarbazide	yellow-brown + (yellow)	pale blue – (green-violet 435, 575)	—	—	—	—	yellow –	pale yellow —	—	pale yellow +	(yellow)
2,4-Diphenylthiosemicarbazide	orange++	purple++ 565	yellow-brown ++	green-yellow++	—	deep yellow++	—	deep yellow++	—	rose++	red++
1,4-Diphenylthiosemicarbazide	violet++ 520	blue-violet++	—	green++	deep yellow++	yellow+	—	yellow+	—	rose++	
4-Phenylthiosemicarbazide	yellow++	purple+ (515)	yellow+	brown++	—	orange –	—	yellow+	yellow –	yellow –	(yellow)
Diphenylthiourea	red++	blue++ (630, 650)	—	yellow++	yellow++	yellow+	—	yellow++	—	yellow++	(—)
o,o′-Ditolylthiourea	red++ 490 (violet)	blue++ (620)	—	yellow++	yellow++	yellow++	—	yellow++ (orange)	—	yellow++	(—)
p,p′-Ditolylthiourea	rose++(violet)	blue++(630)	yellow++	yellow++	yellow++	yellow++	—	orange++	—	yellow+	(—)
N,N′-Bis-dimethylaminophenylthiourea	orange –	blue-green –	—	yellow++	—	yellow –	—	orange –	—	yellow –	
Thiobarbituric acid	(yellow)	(red 570)	(yellow)		(red ppt.)		(yellow)		(—)		(yellow)

++ extractable; + difficult to extract; – unextractable; — no reaction; the figs. indicate max. absorption wavelength.

In parentheses are data by Knight *et al.* (Os^{8+} + EtOH soln.).

μg./ml.) and Ru (30 μg./ml.) which can be extd. with Et_2O.

The reactions between thiourea derivs. and the Pt metals are summarized in Table 18;[135] diphenylthiourea is the best reagent for Ru and 1,4-diphenylthiosemicarbazide for Os.

(*3*) *Dithiocarbamidohydrazine* ($NH_2CSNHNHCSNH_2$) ppts. Bi, Cu^{2+}, Cu^{+} and Cd.[136] *1,6-Diallyl-2-5 dithiobiurea* (bis-(allylthiocarbamoyl)-hydrazine), the diallyl deriv., has been used gravimetrically for Ag at pH 4·7–5·1, Hg at pH 3–3·5, Cu at pH 2·5–3·5, Pb at pH 5–6, Ni at pH 8–9 and Zn at pH 7·8–8·6; it is also

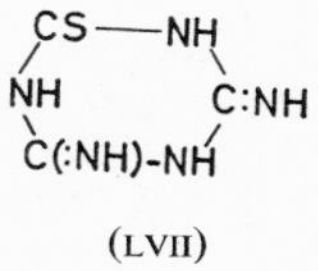

(LVII)

used colorimetrically for Bi and as indicator in titrations of PO_4^{3-} with $BiOClO_4$ (hence in detns. of Mg, Be, etc.).[137] *Guanidylthiourea* is used colorimetrically for Ag. *Thioammeline* (LVII) ppts. Cu at pH 3–3·5 and seps. it from Cd, Zn, Ni.[138]

(*4*) *2-Mercaptobenzimidazole* (phenylenethiourea) (LVIII) [m.p. 292–293°C sol. in hot H_2O, EtOH] ppts.

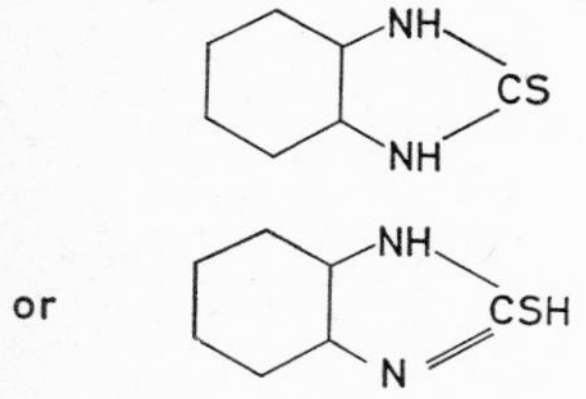

(LVIII)

$BiY_3 \cdot 3HA$ (where HA = H_2SO_4, HCl or HNO_3), Pb(OH)Y, Cd(OH)Y·NH_3, Cd(OH)Y, Ag, Hg and Au.

(*5*) *Phenylthiosemicarbazide* ($C_6H_5NHNHCSNH_2$) reacts with Ru and Os in acidic soln., Hg, Ag, Cu^{+}, Cu^{2+}, Ni, Co, Au, Pd and Pt in NaOH soln.; Ru (purple) and Cu^{+} (blue) can be detd. colorimetrically; Pt is detd. gravimetrically in Na_2CO_3 soln. *2,4-Diphenyl thiosemicarbazide* is used colorimetrically for Re in H_2SO_4 soln., the red color being extd. with $CHCl_3$. *Thiosemicarbazide* (aminothiourea) ppts. Ag, Cu^{2+}, Os, Ru, Pt (in feebly acidic or alk. soln.; AmOAc extn.) and Pd (green alk. color turns brown on heating). See also Table 18.

Acetone- or *benzaldehyde-thiosemicarbazone* ppts. Ag and Cu; Cd is detd. gravimetrically with *salicylaldehyde thiosemicarbazone*. *Biacetyloxime thiosemicarbazone* forms colors with Mn (purple in NH_4OH). For *3-thiosemicarbazones* of *isatin* and its derivs. see ref. 139. *Resorcylaldehyde thiosemicarbazone* and some derivs. ppt. Ag, Hg and Cu; they provide sensitive colorimetric detns. for Co.[140] Pd is detd. gravimetrically with p-*ethylsulfonylbenzalthiosemicarbazone*.

(*6*) *Thiobarbituric acid* (LIX) reacts with Ru, Rh (gravimetric detn.), Pd, Cu and Ag.[141] The p-*dimethylaminobenzilidene* deriv. gives a purple color with Ag (0·02 μg.), Hg, Cu, Pd (0·002 μg.), Pt, Ir and Au (0·01 μg.).[142] The *5-ethyl-5,2′-methylbutyl deriv.* gives a green

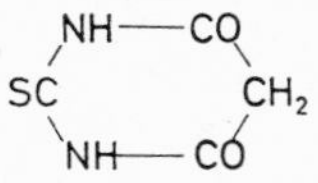

(LIX)

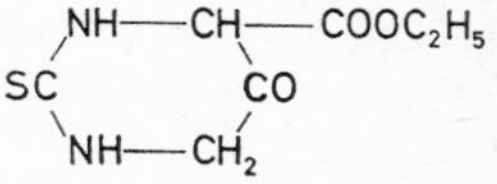

(LX)

color with Cu. *Trithiobarbituric acid* is sensitive to Ag and Cu.[142]

Dimethyldithiohydantoin ppts. Cu (20 μg./ml.). *Diphenylthiovioluric acid* is used to det. Cu gravimetrically at pH 7·2–8·0 and Fe^{2+}, Fe^{3+} colorimetrically at pH 4·9–5·6.[143] For *thiohydantoin derivs.*, see ref. 144.

(*7*) *2-Thio-5-keto-4-carbethoxy-1,3-dihydropyrimidine* (LX) forms reddish ppts. in acid solns. with Ag (1:2 complex approx., colorimetric detn.), Hg, Au and Pd (1:1 complex); Cd, NH_4^+, Cu, Fe^{2+}, Pb, Zn, Mn, Sn also react.

Bis-(dimethylaminostyryl)-thiopyrimidone (LXI) ppts. Ag, Hg (0·01 μg.), Au and Pd in slightly acidic soln.

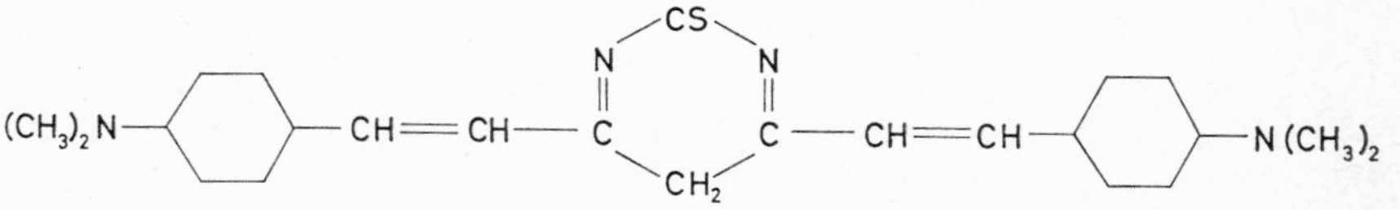

(LXI)

2.3. Dithizone and its analogs

(*1*) *Dithizone*[145] (diphenylthiocarbazone, phenylazothionoformic acid) (LXII) [Violet-black or brown-black; sol. in EtOH, $CHCl_3$, CCl_4, NH_4OH; sparingly

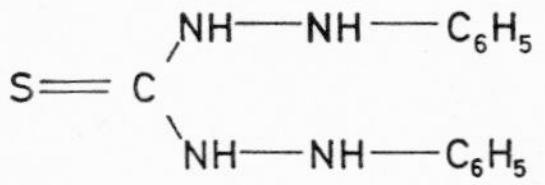

(LXII)

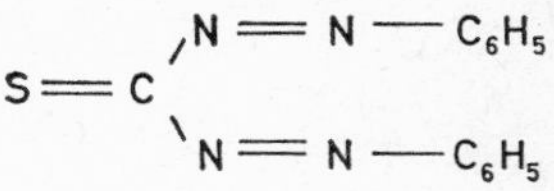

(LXIII)

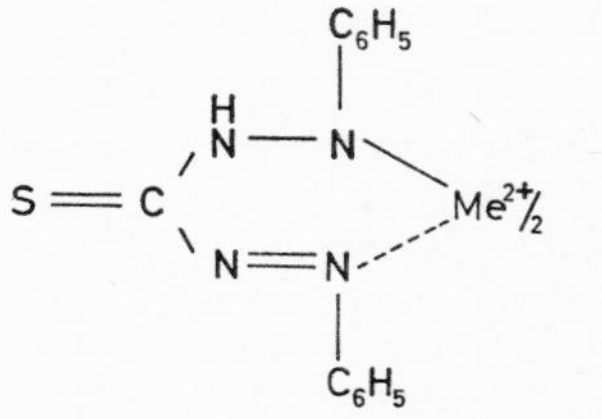

(LXIV)

TABLE 19. Dithizonates

Metal	Complex	Color	λ_{max} in mμ in CCl_4 ($\epsilon \times 10^{-4}$)	pH for extn.	Remarks	*o*-Tolyl-analog	*p*-Tolyl-analog
(Dithizone)			620 (3·46) 289, 450			628 (3·80) 460	628 (4·64) 458
Cu^+	K	brown		dil. mineral acid (ca. 0·1*N*)			
Cu^+	E	violet		basic	Only slightly sol. in CCl_4		
Cu^{2+}	K	violet-red	548	dil. mineral acid		538	554
Cu^{2+}	E	yellow-brown		basic	Also in slightly acid soln. if Cu in excess of Dz		
Ag	K	yellow	460	dil. mineral acid		456	474
Ag	E	red-violet		basic	Slightly sol. in $CHCl_3$ (red)		
Au		yellow-brown		dil. mineral acid	Red → orange → yellow, flocs in CCl_4; sol. in $CHCl_3$		
Zn	K	purple-red	535 (9·26)	neutral–weakly basic	Extn. complete in weakly acidic soln. if Dz in excess of Zn	525	546 (9·84)
Cd	K	red	520 (8·42)	basic	Stable to 1*N* NaOH	515	530 (9·93)
Hg^+	K	orange		dil. mineral acid			
Hg^+	E	purple-red		basic			
Hg^{2+}	K	orange-yellow	490 (7·0)	mineral acid	Also in weakly alk. soln. with excess of Dz	486 (5·07)	500 (8·03)
Hg^{2+}	E	violet-red	526 (3·2)	basic	Also in slightly acid soln. if Hg in excess		
In		red	510	5–6 (CCl_4) 8·3–9·6 ($CHCl_3$)			
Tl^+	K	red	500	9–12 (CCl_4)			
Tl^{3+}	K	yellow-red		3–4 (CCl_4)	Incomplete, oxidation		
Sn^{2+}	K	red	508	$>$4 (6–9 in CCl_4)	Unstable		
Pb	K	cinnabar-red	525 (6·86)	8·5–11 ($CHCl_3$)		500	537 (6·97)
Bi	K	orange-yellow	505	$>$2 (CCl_4)		476	—
Bi	E	orange-red		basic			
Te			430	1			
Po				0–5			
Mn	K	violet-brown ($CHCl_3$)		ca. 11	Unstable, brown flocs.		
Fe^{2+}	K	violet-red		$>$7 (CCl_4)	Fe^{3+} does not form complex, but oxidizes Dz in alk. soln. especially in presence of CN^-		
Co	K	violet	560	8–9 (CCl_4)	Ext. stable to dil. mineral acid		
Co	E?	brownish		strongly basic	Decompn. product?		
Ni	K	brownish		weakly basic	Ext. stable to dil. mineral acid, grey from strongly basic soln.		
Pd	K	brown ($CHCl_3$)		dil. mineral acid	Extn. is slow		
Pd	E	red-violet		dil. mineral acid	Excess Pd		
Pt	K?	yellow		25% v/v HCl			

sol. in H_2O and dil. mineral acids]. Dithizone forms colored complexes with many metals (Table 19); the complexes are in the keto form (LXIV) in acidic soln. and in the enol form (LXV) in alk. soln. or when insufficient dithizone is present. All the complexes listed, except the enol form of the silver complex, are sol. in CCl_4. The Pb, ^{146}Po and ^{147}Te complexes have been studied with radioactive tracers; extn. of the Te complex is nearly complete at pH 1 and decreases with increasing pH.

Dithizone is sensitive to oxidation and the commercial product needs purification to remove diphenylthiocarbodiazone (LXIII); oxidation can be prevented by $NH_2OH \cdot HCl$ addn. A reagent soln. in CCl_4 or $CHCl_3$ is normally used; both dithizone and the metal complexes are more sol. in $CHCl_3$. With a C_6H_6 soln., Pb (p. 160) is completely extd. with one portion instead of

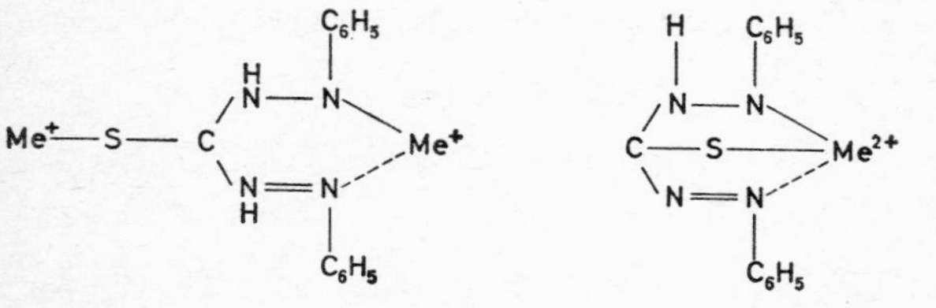

(LXV)

the 2–3 needed with $CHCl_3$ or CCl_4. A reagent soln. in Me_2CO is stable and suitable for field analysis;[148] a methyl cellosolve soln. has been used;[149] the metal complex colors differ in these media.

Sepns. with the reagent in CCl_4 or $CHCl_3$ are as follows. In dil. mineral acid solns. Pd, Au, Hg^{2+}, Ag and Cu are extd. If much Zn is present, the little extd. can be removed by washing with dil. acid. The greater the acidity, the slower the reaction. Extn. can be made from a soln. of higher pH and the extract shaken with dil. acid, e.g. if a CCl_4 phase contg. Cu, Pb and Zn complexes is shaken with 0·05*N* acid, only Cu remains in the CCl_4 phase. If the dil. acid soln. contains SCN^-, Hg, Au and Cd are extd.; if CN^- is also added, Hg and Cu are extd. If Br^- or I^- are added, Pb, Au and Cu are extd. Ag can be sepd. from Cu and Hg by extn. from 0·03*N* HCl soln. contg. 20% NaCl; Ag is extd. also if the soln. is dild. 10 times.

In feebly acidic soln. (pH 3), Bi is extd.; if CN^- is added, Pb, Hg, Ag and Cu are extd. At pH 5, Pd, Sn^{2+}, Zn are extd. (while Cd, Co, Ni are incompletely extd.) if $S_2O_3^{2-}$ is added. At pH 4–5 in presence of $S_2O_3^{2-}$ and CN^-, Sn^{2+} and Zn are extd. Diethyldithiocarbamate can replace $S_2O_3^{2-}$, and cuprethol can be used in the sepn. of Zn (q.v.) from Pb, Cu, Cd, Co, Hg, Ag at pH 5·5–6. EDTA in dil. acid soln. masks Pb, Zn, Bi, Cd, Ni, Co, Tl and some Cu, but not Hg or Ag (q.v.).

In feebly alk. soln. Pb and Zn are extd. If the alk. soln. contains CN^-, Pb, Sn^{2+}, Tl^+ and Bi are extd. Cd is sepd. from Pb and Zn in 1*N* NaOH contg. citrate.

Procedures. (*i*) Colorimetric method. Ext. the metal dithizonate with a standard reagent soln. (usually below 0·001% w/v) and measure the absorbance of the excess reagent (620 or 450 mμ) or of the complex (Table 19). Simultaneous detn. of 2 metals is possible. Titration or differential extn. methods can be used (see Chapter 20, p. 160).

In an alternative method, the metal dithizonate is sepd. as above and the excess reagent is removed by shaking with dil. alkali (simplest from CCl_4); this procedure is more troublesome and gives larger errors than the above. Hg dithizonate in $CHCl_3$ can be sepd. from dithizone which is adsorbed on an alumina column (see Chapter 19). The dithizone color can also be compared after the metal dithizonate has been shaken with dimercaptopropanol (see Chapter 19, p. 151).

Contamination from vessels and reagents may be important, e.g. H_2SO_4 may contain Pb. Some Pb (p. 160) may be lost owing to adsorption on glass from alk. soln. Oxidants must be avoided. Dithizone and its complexes are sensitive to light.

(*ii*) Detection method. Fuse the sample with 0·025% dithizone in naphthalene. The colors obtained are usually reddish. Bi, Cd (0·02 μg.), Hg (0·01 μg.), Sn (0·004 μg.), Ag (0·02 μg.), Zn, Co, Sb, Mn, Ce, Mg, Cu, Fe and Pb react.[150]

The chromatographic detection of Pd (0·005 μg., blue-green) lying between Ni (purple) and Co (violet) is possible.[151]

Pd, Zn, Cd, Co and Cu in sea water can be concd. by means of a dithizone-treated cellulose acetate column.[152]

Dithizone has been used as an indicator in EDTA titrations and in Zn^{2+}–$Fe(CN)_6^{4-}$ titrations, etc.

(*2*) o-*Ditolylthiocarbazone* is more resistant to oxidation and less sol. in alkalies than dithizone. The colors of most of the metal complexes are darker but the reagent is inferior to dithizone for the detn. of Pb, Hg and Zn.[153] Ag and Hg react with the *o*- or *p*-tolyl analog above pH 1; Cu is sepd. from other metals at pH 2–4·5. See Table 19 for the absorption max. in CCl_4.[154]

The properties of *di-2,4-dimethylphenylthiocarbazone*[155] lie between those of dithizone and *di-β-naphthylthiocarbazone*. The naphthyl analog is more sensitive than dithizone and the Pb, Hg and Bi complexes are much more pink in color. Zn is extd. at pH 10–11; a CCl_4 soln. is better than $CHCl_3$ which cannot be extd. with NH_4OH. The absorption max. for the CCl_4 reagent are: reagent, 665 ($\epsilon = 40\,000$) or 465 mμ; Bi, pH 7·2, 540 mμ ($\epsilon = 170\,000$); Ni, pH 8·0, 540 mμ ($\epsilon = 90\,000$). For synthesis and purification of the reagent, see ref. 156.

Other analogs of dithizone have no advantage.[157] *Di-*(p*-diphenyl*)*-thiocarbazone* is sensitive to arsenicals.[158]

(*3*) *Diphenylthiocarbazide* (thiodiphenylcarbazide) reacts with Bi, Pb, Co, Ni, Cd, Ag and Hg; Cu gives a white ppt. in neutral soln. which turns red with alkali, violet with AcOH and blue with HCl.

Thiocarbohydrazide is used gravimetrically or colorimetrically for Mo (p. 218). For its reactions, and derivs., see ref. 159.

2.4. Thiazole derivatives and analogs

(*1*) *2-Mercaptobenzothiazole* (2-benzothiazolethiol, *o*-thiocarbamidothiophenol, captax) (LXVI) [Pale

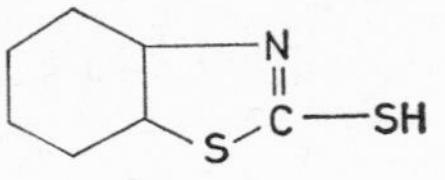

(LXVI)

yellow, m.p. 170°C, sol. in hot EtOH, NH_4OH, insol. in H_2O, acids]. Ppts. are formed in acid or alk. soln. with Cu which is reduced to Cu^+ (orange, LXVII), and

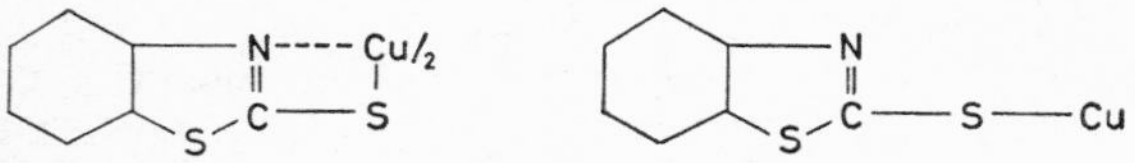

(LXVII)

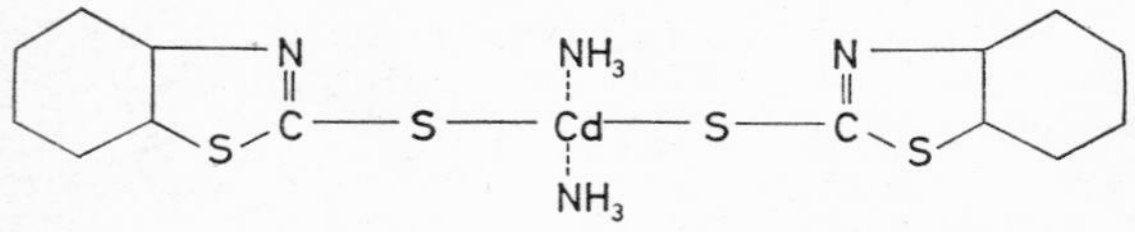

(LXVIII)

in ammoniacal solns. with Cd (white, LXVIII, the normal salt being formed at 110°C), Pb (yellow normal and white basic salts; LXIX and LXX), Tl (which is reduced to Tl^+), Co (green), Zn (white) and Bi, Ag, Au, Pt, Pd, Ni (all yellow or brown). Au, Al and Th ppt. in neutral soln.; Hg ppts. in KOH soln. contg. KI. The

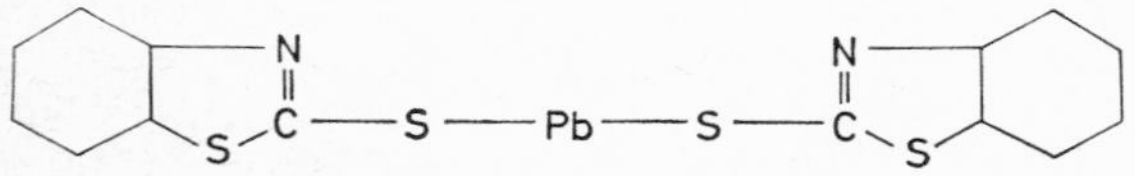

(LXIX)

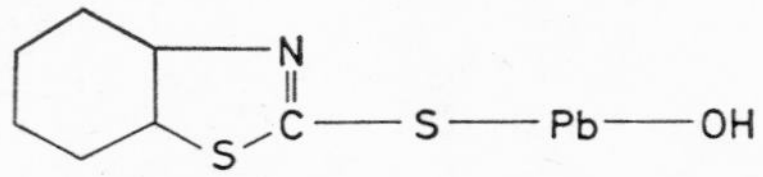

(LXX)

reagent is useful for the sepn. of Cu from Cd and for Bi and Hg detns. (pp. 179, 168, 154).

2-Mercaptobenzothiazole and *2-mercaptobenzoxazole* (LXXI) ppt. Rh (gravimetric detn.), Pt and Pd but not

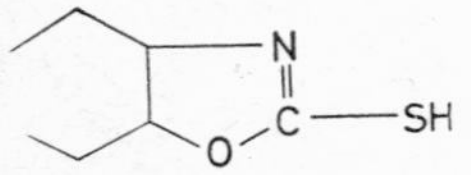

(LXXI)

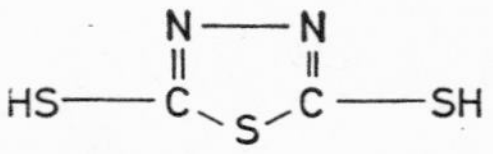

(LXXII)

Ir in acidic solns.; [160] in KOH soln. Rh and Pd ppt. but Pt does not.[161] *2-Mercapto-4,5-dimethylthiazole* is used colorimetrically for Rh and *2-phenylbenzothiazole* gravimetrically for Os (p 239).

2-Aminobenzothiazole (benzothiazolonimide) ppts. Ag and Hg; *2-acetamino-6-aminobenzothiazole* gives a red color with Ir. *Bi-* or *Sb-2-mercaptothiazoline* ppts. I^- (p. 446). For *thiazole-styryl dyes*, see Welcher, Vol. III, p. 560.

(*2*) *Bismuthiol* (2,5-dimercapto-1,3,4-thiodiazole) (LXXII)[162] forms ppts. with Cu (0·02 μg.) and Pb in acid soln.; Bi ppts. in alk. soln.

Bismuthiol II (bismuthon, mercaptophenyldithiodiazolone, 5-mercapto-3-phenyl-2-thio-1,3,4-thiodiazole-2-one) (LXXIII)[162, 163] is used for gravimetric detn. of

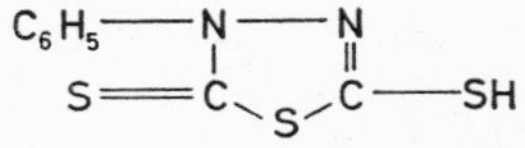

(LXXIII)

Ag at pH 8 or up to 0·2*N* HNO_3 or 1*N* H_2SO_4; Ag is sepd. from Os, Ir, Ru, Rh at pH 5–9 in solns. contg. EDTA or $Na_2S_2O_3$, from Au at pH 8–9 with $Na_2S_2O_3$ added, and from Pd at pH 6 with CN^- present. Bi can be detd. gravimetrically if the soln. is below 0·3, 0·5 or 1*N* in HNO_3, HCl or H_2SO_4 resp. Pb, Hg, Cu, Pd (pH 8 up to 0·1*N* acid) can be detd. gravimetrically; Au, Cd, Zn, Sn, Sb, As, Fe, Ni, Pt, Ir^{4+}, Ru, Os^{4+}, Rh and Tl (pH 1–13) also ppt. Os, Ru, Rh and Ir do not ppt. if EDTA is added. Pd and Pt ppt. in neutral soln. contg. $S_2O_3^{2-}$ but Pd is sepd. from Pt at pH 6–8 from tartrate-contg. soln. or in neutral soln. if CN^- is added.

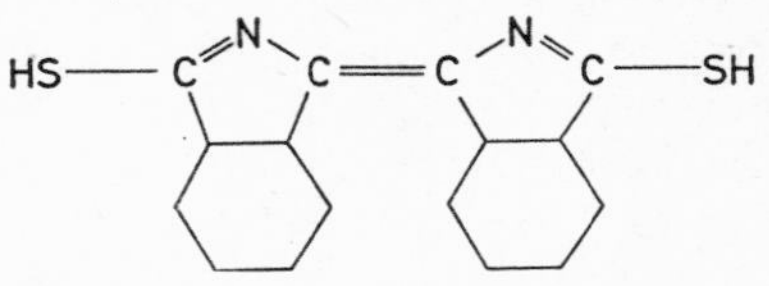

(LXXIV)

(*3*) *Dithio-β-isoindigo* (LXXIV) forms a red Ag complex which is sol. in BuOH and permits sepn. from Pb.

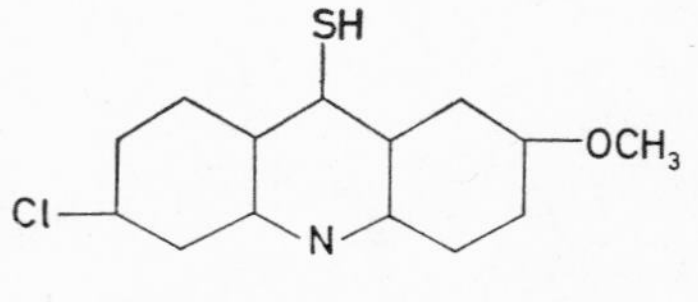

(LXXV)

(*4*) *2-Chloro-7-methoxy-5-thiolacridine* (LXXV) ppts. Cu, Hg and other elements of groups II and III in neutral soln. (see p. 154 and 180).

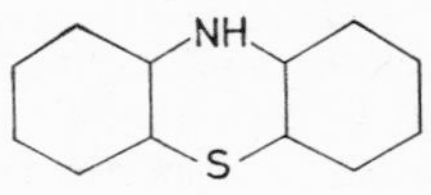

(LXXVI)

(*5*) *Phenothiazine* (LXXVI)[164] reacts with Ag (3 μg.; 0·54 μg. if diphenylcarbazide is added), Fe (0·15 μg.) and Pd.

(*6*) *Thiazolidinones* contg. various substituents have been examined, e.g. for Cu and Ag.[165]

2.5. Miscellaneous compds. contg. S and N

(*1*) *4-Amino-4′-hydroxydiphenyl sulfide* ($H_2NC_6H_4S$-C_6H_4OH) reacts with Pd^{2+} and V^{2+}.

(*2*) *4,4′-Bis-(dimethylamino)-thiobenzophenone* (thio-Michler's ketone)[166] is prepd. by the action of H_2S on auramine. It is used colorimetrically for Hg^{2+} (blue-green) and forms orange or purple colors with Ag, Cu^+, Au, Pt and Pd, the sensitivity being about 1 p.p.m.

(*3*) *Thiosalicylidene-ethylenediamine*[167] is prepd. by treating the condensation product of *o*-chlorobenzaldehyde and ethylenediamine with NaHS. The ppts. formed with Co, Tl^+ (slightly sol. in $CHCl_3$), Bi, Cu, Ag, Hg (most stable) and Pd are yellow, red or brown and can be extd. with $CHCl_3$ from HCl or NH_3 solns. The similar ppts. with Ni, In, Te^{4+}, Sn^{2+}, Cd, Pb, Au^{3+}, Pt^{2+}, Pt^{4+} can be extd. from HCl soln; the Sb^{3+} ppt. is insol. in $CHCl_3$ and the Zn ppt. is unstable.

2.6. Thioglycolic acid and its derivatives

(*1*) *Thionalide* (thioglycolic acid β-aminonaphthalide) (LXXVII)[168] [m.p. 111–112°C, sol. in many solvents]

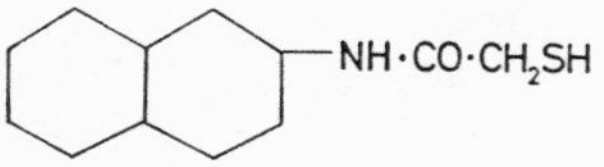

(LXXVII)

forms ppts. with metals of the sulfide group (LXXVIII).

(*i*) In mineral acid soln. below 2*N*, the following metals react; the figures in parentheses indicate the sensitivity in μg./ml. Cu (0·1), Ag (0·2), Au (0·4), Bi (0·1), Pt (0·1), Pd (0·1) and Ir form yellow ppts.; Hg^{2+} (0·06), Sn^{2+}, Sn^{4+} (0·08; no ppt. if H_3PO_4 is added), As (0·02), Sb^{3+} (0·02) form white ppts.; Ru, Os

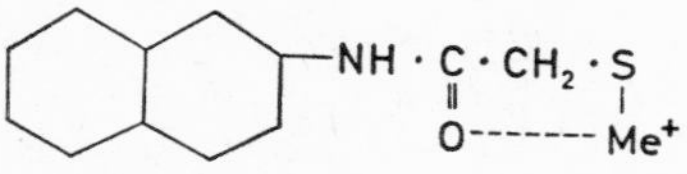

(LXXVIII)

(1:3 complex) and Rh form brown ppts. Nearly all these metals can be detd. gravimetrically.

(*ii*) In NaOH solns. below 1*N* contg. tartrate, Cu (0·5), Au (5), Hg (1), Cd (0·4) and Tl (0·1) ppt.; Mn and Fe^{2+} ppt. incompletely and Ag is reduced. If the soln. also contains KCN, Tl (0·1) ppts. and Hg, Bi, Pb (above 5 mg.) ppt. incompletely. The reagent is then nearly specific for Tl. In Na_2CO_3 soln. contg. KCN and tartrate, Au (5), Sn (4), Sb (0·5), Bi (0·4), Pb (0·1) and Tl (0·1) ppt.; Ag is again reduced.

Thionalide is superior to H_2S for this group of elements for several reasons. It is much more sensitive; the ppts. have a definite compn. and can be weighed directly after drying; the conversion factors are favorable; there is less copptn. than with H_2S; and selectivity can be improved by suitable choice of conditions. Several alternative finishes are available (see below). Finally, the excess reagent can be readily removed by adding 5–10% I_2 in KI or EtOH to the soln. at 70–80°C, cooling, filtering and washing with H_2O until the filtrate gives no starch reaction.

Disadvantages of thionalide are the low soly. in mineral acids and the pptn. of dithionalide (LXXIX)

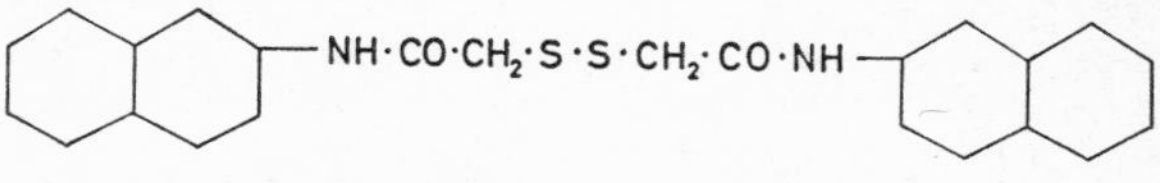

(LXXIX)

by oxidants; addn. of $NH_2OH{\cdot}H_2SO_4$ or $N_2H_4{\cdot}H_2SO_4$ avoids this effect; dil. HNO_3 does not interfere in any case.

Reagent. Use 1% in EtOH for general purposes, 1% in AcOH for acid solns. and 5% in Me_2CO for alk. solns.; each of these is stable for several days.

Procedure. Adjust the soln. to suitable conditions as indicated above. Boil, add excess reagent, leave for 30 min., filter through a No. 4 sintered crucible and wash the ppt.

(*a*) Weigh after drying, usually at 105°C, or after ignition.

(*b*) Volumetric methods. For iodometry, dissolve the ppt. in AcOH, add dil. H_2SO_4 and excess I_2 and back-titrate with $S_2O_3^{2-}$ soln. to starch indicator or potentiometrically. Alternative potentiometric finishes consist of adding excess KOH and H_2O_2 and back-titrating with HCl, or excess $Cr_2O_7^{2-}$ and back-titrating with Fe^{2+} soln. A 'filtration' titration with 1% reagent in AcOH is also possible.

(*c*) Nephelometry. To 15 ml. of neutral or slightly acid soln., add 5 drops 2*N* H_2SO_4, boil, add 30 drops 1% reagent in AcOH, leave for several hr. and compare with standards. 0·01 μg. Cu, 0·005 μg. Hg and 0·001 μg. Ag can be detd.

(*d*) Colorimetry. Wash the ppt. with H_2O and dissolve in pyridine; for Tl, wash with *N* H_2SO_4 and dissolve in EtOH. Add Folin–Denis reagent and measure the color produced.

(*2*) o-(*Mercaptoacetamido*)-p-*nitrophenol*[169] forms ppts. with Ag, Hg^+, Hg^{2+}, Cu^{2+}, As^{3+}, As^{5+}, Pd, Pt, Au, Se at pH 1–2, with Bi at pH 2, with Cd, Pb at pH 3, with Co, Ni in NH_4OH soln., and with Tl in CN^--contg. KOH soln. Ag and Hg^{2+} are detd. gravimetrically and Co colorimetrically. The sensitivities vary from 1 part in 10^4 to 10^5, being highest for Cu, Ni and lowest for As^{5+} and Pb.

p-*Mercaptoacetamidoacetanilide* ppts. Ag, Cu, Hg, Se, Au, Pt, Rh in acid soln. and Ni, Co, Bi, Tl, Pb in alk. soln.; Ag, Cu, Hg are detd.[170] *Mercaptoacetanilide* has properties between those of thionalide and thioglycolic acid. *Thioglycolanilides* of 10 aromatic amines have been studied; they pptd. Ag, Hg, Pb, Cu, Cd, Bi, Sn, Zn, Co, Ni. Co can be detd. gravimetrically or colorimetrically with *derivs. of* o- *and* m-*aminobenzoic acid.*[171] Nine analogs have been tested.[172]

(*3*) *Thioglycolic acid* (mercaptoacetic acid) ($HSCH_2$-COOH) [b.p. 104–106°C, sol. in H_2O, EtOH, Et_2O] forms yellow to orange colors with Ag, Pb, Bi, Au, Pd (0·05 μg.), Se (alk. soln.), Co, Mn, Mo (colorimetric detn.), UO_2^{2+}, CN^-, NO_2^- (20 μg., colorimetric detn., *S*-nitrosothioglycolic acid is formed). The color is blue with W and Fe^{3+} (acid soln., fading), pink with Ni and Fe^{2+} (alk. soln., detn.) and black with Hg^+. Hg^{2+} (acid soln.), Cu and Ni (alk. soln.) ppt.

Thiodiglycolic acid ($S(CH_2COOH)_2$) reacts with Ag, Hg, Pb, Cu and Ba. The Ba-salt of *isonitrosothioglycolic acid* gives a blue color with Fe^{3+} (3 μg.).

(*4*) *β-Isothioureidopropionic acid* ($HN_2C(:NH)SCH_2$-CH_2COOH) is hydrolyzed to β-mercaptopropionic acid in NH_4OH soln.; both reagents form a black ppt. with Ni, which is sol. in excess NH_4OH or in acid (a reddish color forms and disappears on NH_4OH addn.); the color is caused by a Ni-β-mercaptopropionic acid complex;[173] Ni and Co (q.v.) can be detd. Fe also reacts but Ag, Au, Bi, Cr, Cu, Hg^{2+}, Mn, Pb, Pt, Rh, Sn, Th, Ti and Zr do not.

Mercaptosuccinic acid (thiomalic acid) reacts with Mo (the test can be made specific), Co (0·9 μg./ml., colorimetry), UO_2^{2+} (alk. soln.), Ag, Pb, Hg, Tl, Cu^+ (alk. soln.).[174]

2.7. Miscellaneous carboxylic acids contg. S

(*1*) *Phenylthiohydantoic acid* (LXXX) [m.p. 163°C, sol. in hot H_2O, hot EtOH] ppts. Co (sepn. from Ni), Cu, Ag, Cd, Hg, Tl, Pb, Sb, Bi, Se, Te completely from

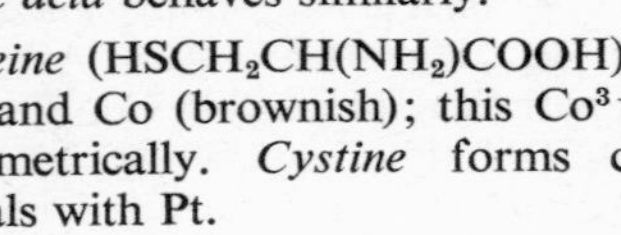

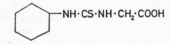

(LXXX)

NH_4OH solns. contg. tartrate; Fe, Ni, Ru, Rh, Pd, Os, In, Sn ppt. partly; Ir, Pt, Au, Zn, Ge ppt. only from concd. solns. or on long standing. *β-Naphthylthiohydantoic acid* behaves similarly.

(*2*) *l-Cysteine* ($HSCH_2CH(NH_2)COOH$) reacts with Fe (purple) and Co (brownish); this Co^{3+} complex is detd. colorimetrically. *Cystine* forms characteristic yellow crystals with Pt.

2.8. Thioacid derivatives

(*1*) *Potassium thiocarbonate* forms colors with Co, Ni (detn.), Cd, Tl, Pd, Os (20 μg./ml.), Hg, Bi, Cu, some of which can be extd. with Et_2O.

(*2*) *Ammonium thioacetate* ppts. Pb in HCl solns.; the blue Co complex is extd. with AmOH. *Thioacetic acid* reacts with Fe or Bi. These and *thioformamide* are said to be a superior substitute for H_2S in acidic solns. The pptn. of metal sulfides by hydrolysis of *thioacetamide* is a very complicated reaction.[175]

(*3*) *Potassium dithiooxalate* ($(CSOK)_2$) gives yellow complexes with Hg^{2+}, Bi (darkens on boiling), Cd, Sb (turns brown), Sn^{4+}, Zn, Mn^{2+}; reddish complexes with Ag, Pb (both turn black), Sn^{2+}, Fe, Pt, Co; brown or black complexes with Hg^+, Pd, Cu (green with excess reagent, black on boiling); the pink Ni complex retains its color on boiling and can be detd. colorimetrically. *Oxanilic acid thioamide* ($C_6H_5NHCOCSNH_2$) completely ppts. Cu in NaOAc, Ni in NH_4OH, and Co in feebly acid solns.

(*4*) *Potassium xanthate* (ethylxanthogenate, xanthogenate, ethyldithiocarbonate) ($C_2H_5OCS_2K$) forms a red complex with Mo (0·04 μg.) which can be extd. with Et_2O, $CHCl_3$ for sepn. from Re; Cu (0·03 μg.), Co, Ni, Pb, Fe, Mn and Zn also react. At pH 4, Ni, Cu, Co, Mo, Bi, Pb, Sn^{2+}, Fe^{3+}, Zn, Hg^{2+}, As^{3+}, Sb^{3+} and Cr^{6+} are completely extd. with CCl_4; at pH 7, extn. of Ni, Co and Fe^{3+} is complete and that of Bi and Zn partial; at pH 9 only Co extn. is complete and that of Ni partial.[176]

Higher analogs are slightly more sensitive, e.g. Mo or Cu (0·5 μg./ml.) reacts with *cetyl-* or *myricylxanthate*. *Viscose* (cellulose xanthate) gives red or brown complexes with Pb (1 μg.), Bi (0·5 μg.), Cu (0·25 μg.), Co (1 μg.), etc.

Xanthogenamide ($C_2H_5OCSNH_2$) reacts with Cu.

(*5*) *Sodium diethyldithiocarbamate* (cupral) ($(C_2H_5)_2$-NCS_2Na)[177] is a particularly useful reagent for Cu detns. although it reacts with many other elements (Table 20). The order of stability of the complexes is: Hg^{2+}, Pd, Ag, Cu, Tl^{3+}, Ni, Bi, Pb, Co^{3+}, Co^{2+}, Cd, Tl^+, Sn^{2+}, Zn, In, Sb^{3+}, As^{3+}, Fe^{3+}, Te^{4+}, Mn^{3+}, Mn^{2+}; for the Po complex, see ref. 21.

At pH ca. 14 in NaOH soln. contg. CN^- and tartrate or EDTA, only Pb and Tl ppt. If CN^- and EDTA are not added, Co^{3+}, Ni, Cu, Ag, Au, Cd, Hg, Tl, Pb and Pt-metals ppt. At pH ca. 9 in tartrate-contg. NH_4OH soln., these metals and Mn^{2+}, Mn^{3+}, Fe^{2+}, Fe^{3+}, Co^{2+}, Zn, In, Sn^{2+}, Sb^{3+}, Bi and Te^{4+} ppt. At pH ca. 5 in tartrate-contg. AcOH soln., V^{4+}, V^{5+}, Nb, Cr^{3+}, Mo^{6+}, U^{6+}, Ga, Sn^{4+}, As^{3+} and Se^{6+} ppt.; As^{5+}, Sb^{5+} and Fe^{3+} ppt. incompletely from hot feebly acid or alk. solns.

The Pb salt is used colorimetrically for Cu; the Cu salt is specific colorimetrically for Hg^{2+}, if Ag and Hg^+ are removed with HCl, Au with $H_2C_2O_4$ and Pd with dimethylglyoxime. A soln. of the Ag salt in pyridine is an excellent reagent for As as arsine.

Diethylammonium diethyldithiocarbamate in $CHCl_3$ serves to sep. by extn. Sn^{2+}, Cu, Bi, Hg, Sb^{3+}, As^{3+}, Cd, In, Se, Te, Pd, Cr from Sn^{4+}, Sb^{5+}, As^{5+}, Fe^{2+},

TABLE 20. Diethyldithiocarbamates

Metal	pH	Interferences (pH)	Absorbancy (ϵ, μg./25 ml. in 5 cm. cell for colorimetry)	Remarks
Cu	4–11++ (1–3·5)	CN^- (8–11, or if much), (BO_2^-)	Max. 436 mμ (ϵ = 13 000, <20), 600 mμ (<200); min. 365 mμ (ϵ = 1180)	In pH >10 soln. contg. EDTA, Bi, Au, Pd, Pt, Os, Tl, etc. do not interfere
Ag	4–11++	CN^- (<7, or if much)		Sepn. and nephelometry
Au	4–11 o	CN^- (8–11)	330–700 mμ rapid increase <380 mμ, max. 410 mμ (ϵ = 1970) etc.	Interference in other metal detns.
Zn	8–11++	CN^- (8–11, or if much), EDTA (5–11), much NH_4^+, PO_4^{3-}	<360 mμ	Sepn. and nephelometry
Cd	4–11++ (3)	EDTA (>8)	<360 mμ	At pH 11 in KCN soln., Cd, Bi, Tl, Pb are sepd. from Zn, etc.
Hg	4–11++	CN^- (extn. o)	<400 mμ	Sepn. and nephelometry
Ga	<5·5 o?	EDTA	ultraviolet, remarkable near 300–320 mμ	No practical value
In	4–10++	EDTA (7–11) PO_4^{3-} (extn. o)	considerable <360 mμ, max. 305 mμ	Sepn. and gravimetry; colorimetry by converting to Cu-salt?
Tl^+	4–11++	EDTA (8–11)	Considerable <390 mμ	Sepn. and nephelometry. Extn. from KCN-contg. soln. at pH 11
Tl^{3+}	4–11++		<550 mμ, max. 426 mμ (ϵ = 1330, <600), min. 402 mμ (ϵ = 1160)	Sepn. in pH 11+KCN+EDTA soln.; only Tl, Bi extd.
Sn	4–5·8	EDTA (<5, o)	<600 mμ, const. near 400 mμ (30–300)	
Pb	4–11++	EDTA (>7), (PO_4^{3-}, BO_2^-)	remarkable <410 mμ	Sepn. and nephelometry. In KCN soln. at pH 10, Pb, Bi, Cd, Tl, are sepd. from other metals. Conversion to Cu-salt
As	4–5·8++		<400 mμ	Sepn.
Sb	8·2–9·5++		<450 mμ, nearly const. at 350 mμ (ϵ = 3370, 10–120)	Sepn. at pH 9·2 in KCN soln.; Bi, Te Tl^{3+}, much Cu, Hg, As, Se interfere. Conversion to Cu-salt?
Bi	4–11++ (1–10)		<500 mμ, max. 366 mμ (ϵ = 8620, 5–100), min. 345 mμ (ϵ = 7530)	Sepn. (see Tl)
V	4–5·9++	EDTA (5–6, o)	remarkable <580 mμ, 400 mμ (5–50)	Sepn.
Nb	4–5·5, o $Tart^{2-}$	EDTA	<370 mμ?	
Se	4–6·2 (3)		slow increase <500 mμ, considerable <380 mμ	Sepn.; nephelometry?
Te	4–8·8++ (5*N* H^+ –3·3)		<530 mμ, max. 428 mμ (ϵ = 3160, 10–150), min. 410 mμ (ϵ = 2990)	Sepn. from much Se. In KCN + tartrate soln., Bi, Sb, Tl, much Cu, Hg interfere
Po	1 (93%)		1 : 1 complex	
Cr^{6+}	(0–6)			pH 4, 500 μg. Cr, 100 mg. reagent/5 ml., blue-green ppt.
Mo				pH 4, 100 mg. reagent/5 ml. purple color
W				pH 4, 1 mg. W, 100 mg. reagent/5 ml., white ppt. → clear
U^{6+}	(6·5–8·5)		yellow color at pH 4–8, const. increase <620 mμ; colorimetry at 400 mμ	Extd. with AmOH, Et_2O, but not with CCl_4
Mn	6–9++ shake with air (Mn^{3+})	EDTA, PO_4^{3-}	<800 mμ, max. 505 mμ (ϵ = 3710, only Fe interfered), 355 mμ (ϵ = 9520), min. 405 mμ	Bi, Cd, In, Pb, Sb, Te, Tl, (Fe, Hg) interfered in KCN-contg. soln. at pH 8–9
Re				concd. HCl soln., EtOAc extn.?
Fe	4–9·8++ (0–10)	CN^- (o), EDTA (>6), much tartrate, $P_2O_7^{4-}$ (>9), PO_4^{3-}, BO_2^-	<800 mμ, max. 600 mμ (ϵ = 2050), 515 mμ (ϵ = 2490), min. 595, 495 mμ.; colorimetry at 600–480 and 335–350 (ϵ_{340} = 12 700)	No practical value

TABLE 20—*contd.*

Metal	pH	Interferences (pH)	Absorbancy (ϵ, μg./25 ml. in 5 cm. cell for colorimetry)	Remarks
Ni	4–11++ (0–10)	CN^- (8–11), EDTA (>5·5)	small >470 mμ rapid increase <400 mμ, max. 393 mμ (ϵ = 6110), 326 mμ (ϵ = 34 200), min. 370 mμ, const. at 430–435 mμ (ϵ = 1770), colorimetry at 430–435 (10–100) 326 (0·3–5), 393 (3–30)	At pH 11 Ag, Bi, Cd, Co, Cu, Hg, Pb, Pd, Tl, Zn, (Au, Os, Pt) extd.; at 326 all interfere; at 393 or 430 Au, Bi, Cu, Os, Co interfere; simultaneous detn. with Cu, Co possible
Co	4–11++ shake with air (6–8)	CN^- (8–11), EDTA (>6)	<800 mμ, max. 650 mμ (ϵ = 549), 367 (ϵ = 15 700), 323 (ϵ = 23 300); min. 564, 355, 305 mμ. Colorimetry at 650 (40–400), 480 (25–250), 367 (1–15), 323 (0·5–10)	At 323 all extd. metals interfere; at 367 Cd, Zn do not; at 480 and 650, only Au, Os, Ni, Cu interfere
Ru^{3+}	6–11, 12 hr. o	CN^- (o)	800–300 mμ, rapid increase <500 mμ, max. 575 mμ	
Rh	as Ru		<600 mμ, considerable between 440–300, rapid increase at shorter wavelength	
Pd	4–11++	CN^- (8–11)	small >510 mμ, weak between 510–390, max. 305 mμ (ϵ = 54 800), const. 345–350 (ϵ = 7130). Colorimetry at 305 (0·5–8), 348 (5–60)	At pH 11 in EDTA soln., Ag, Bi, Hg, Tl^{3+}, (Au, Os, Pt) extd.; at 305 all interfere; at 436 or 348 Cu has little effect
Os	4–11 o 7–9 3 hr.+	CN^-	<680 mμ	
Ir	4 days, yellow ppt.	CN^-	<600 mμ	
Pt	4–11 o	CN^-	<500 mμ, const. between 410–390, max. 355, min. 327 mμ	

++ pptn. or extn. complete; + nearly complete; o incomplete. The pH data in parentheses are not Bode's.

PO_4^{3-}; Fe^{3+} and Mo are incompletely extd. This is very useful for isolation of Sn, Sb or As: Cu, etc., are extd., N_2H_4 added, and Sb^{3+}, As^{3+} are extd.; thioglycolic acid is then added and Sn^{2+} is extd. (see Chapters 21, 25, 27). The *butyl* analog is used for colorimetric Cu detn. after extn. of the mercaptobenzothiazole complex with AmOH (see Chapter 22, p. 180).[178]

Cuprethol (diethanolammonium *N,N*-hydroxyethyldithiocarbamate or bis-(2-hydroxyethyl)-dithiocarbamate) gives a brown color with Cu (colorimetric detn.), a green color with Fe^{2+}, and Hg can be detd. titrimetrically; it masks Pb, Cu, Cd, Hg and Ag (see Chapter 36). *Ammonium* o-*aminophenyldithiocarbamate* is used colorimetrically for Cr. These reagents are readily prepd.

(LXXXI)

Ammonium phenyldithiocarbamate or *phenylhydrazinedithiocarbamate* reacts with Cu, Co, Ni, Bi, Hg^+, Ag; the Cu complex is extd. with CCl_4 but that of Ni is not.[179]

Zinc dibenzyldithiocarbamate (arazate) is an excellent colorimetric reagent for Cu.

Ammonium dithiocarbamate forms yellow, reddish or brown ppts. with Ag, Cu, Pb, Bi, Sn, Sb, Fe, Ni, Mn, white ppts. with Zn, Al, and green with Co; the color of the aq. phase is violet with Cu, yellow with Pb and red with Ni.

(*6*) *Piperidine pentamethylenedithiocarbamate* (piperidinium piperidyldithioformate) (LXXXI) ppts. Cu (yellowish, colorimetric detn.) and Mn. *Sodium pentamethylenedithiocarbamate* is used gravimetrically for Pb and *tetramethylenedithiocarbamate* (pyrrolidine

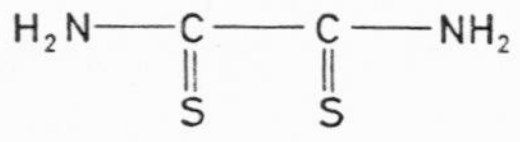

(LXXXII)

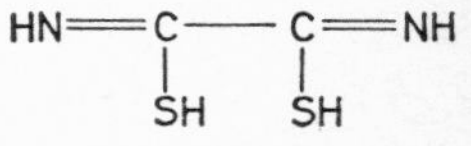

(LXXXIII)

dithiocarbamate) for detn. of Sn. *Dimine* (cyclohexylethylaminedithiocarbamate) is used gravimetrically for Cu and Fe; many other metals are pptd.

(*7*) *Rubeanic acid* (dithiooxamide) (LXXXII) [Red, sol. in EtOH; *hydrorubeanic acid* (LXXXIII) is an isomer]. This acid forms ppts. in NH_4OH soln. with Cu

(0·006 μg./ml.), Co (0·01 μg./ml., pH 6·5–7·2) and Ni (0·04 μg./ml., pH 9·5–10·5) which are green to violet in color, stable to acids and can be used colorimetrically; the Co and Ni ppts. are sol. in pyridine. In acidic soln. it forms ppts. with Ru (0·2 μg./ml.), Pd (0·05 μg./ml., pH 4·2–7·0, colorimetric detn.), Ag (0·05 μg./ml., pH 4·0–4·6), Au, Pt (PtS ?), Cd and Zn (as sulfides). *Diphenylrubeanic acid* reacts similarly (see Chapter 22).

(*8*) *Phenylhydrazine phenylthiocarbazinate* (C_6H_5-NHNHCSSNHNHC$_6H_5$) ppts. Hg, etc.

(*9*) *Thiobenzamide* ppts. Hg^{2+} (p. 154); Cu (0·5 μg.) can be detd. colorimetrically (see p. 176); Ag, Au, Pd, Ir also react.

(*10*) *Tetraethylthiuram disulfide* ($(C_2H_5)_2$NCSSSCSN$(C_2H_5)_2$) permits colorimetric detn. of Cu in acidic soln.; Se also ppts. The Cu salt is used in colorimetric detns. of Ag and Hg.

(*11*) *Dithiophosphoric acid ester* ($(RO)_2PS_2H$) reacts with Mo, etc. in dil. HCl solns.[180] For the titrimetric detns. of Cu with *Ni-diethyldithiophosphate*, see p. 181.

2.9. Thiols

(*1*) *Dithiol* (4-methyl-1,2-dimercaptobenzene, toluene-3,4-dithiol) forms yellow ppts. in acid solns. with Ag, Hg, Pb, Cd, As, Sb, red ppts. with Sn^{2+} (0·1 μg., colorimetric detn.), Bi, Mo, and black ppts. with Cu and Co. Mo and W can be detd. colorimetrically (green and blue, resp.).

For synthesis, see ref. 181. *Diacetyl-* or *dibenzyl-3,4-toluenedithiol* or the Zn salt are more stable.[182] *1,2-Dimercaptobenzene* behaves similarly to dithiol. *4-Chloro-1,2-dimercaptobenzene* forms a ppt. with Sn^{2+} which is less sol. than the dithiol ppt.

Thiophenol ppts. Au, Pt and Pd (gravimetric detn.). o-*Mercapto*-p-*cresol* (3-mercapto-4-hydroxytoluene) distinguishes Re (brown) from Mo (pink-brown) by extn. with a mixture of $CHCl_3$ and iso-BuOH from 6*N* HCl soln. On extn. with *2-thiopyrogallol* in iso-BuOH, Mo, W and Pt give violet, pink and orange colors resp.[183]

(*2*) *Thiosalicylic acid* (*o*-mercaptobenzoic acid) reacts with Fe^{3+}, Fe^{2+}, Ti, Cu, Co, Ni; the Fe^{3+} complex is red in acid and green in NH_4OH soln. *5-Mercaptosalicylic acid* (2-hydroxy-5-mercaptobenzoic acid) is sensitive to Fe (1 p.p.m.) and Pd (0·5 p.p.m.).

(*3*) *2,3-Dimercaptopropanol* (BAL, dimercaprol, dikaptol) forms ppts. with Ag, Hg, Cd, Cu, Co, As, Sb, Sn, Pb, Bi, which are sol. in NH_4OH. It is used to mask Hg, Cd, Pb, Bi and other elements in many chelatometric titrations; Ni, Mn, Fe and Al cannot be masked.[184]

Ethylene disulfide (HSCH:CHSH) reacts with Cu and Ni, and *dodecylmercaptan* with Pd and Pb.[185]

(*4*) *8-Mercaptoquinoline*, see under Oxine analogs.

2.10. Miscellaneous Compounds

(*1*) *Dithiane* (LXXXIV) forms the ppt. $HgCl_2 \cdot C_4H_8S_2$ (see p. 154). *Thiophene* behaves similarly.

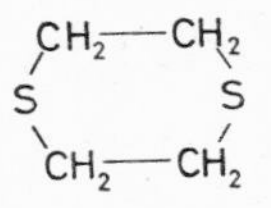

(LXXXIV)

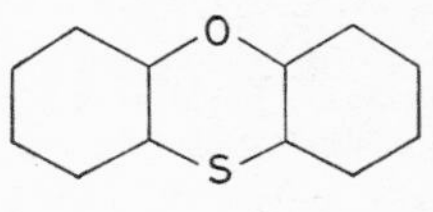

(LXXXV)

(*2*) *Phenoxthin* (LXXXV) ppts. Au (red) and Pd (0·01 μg.) as $PdCl_2(C_{12}H_8OS)_2$.

(*3*) *2-Naphthol sulfide* (2,2′-dihydroxydinaphthyl sulfide) ppts. Cu (red) in NH_4OH solns.[186]

(*4*) *4-* or *5-Phenyl-1,2-dithiol-3-thione* (LXXXVI) or its *4-methyl-5-phenyl deriv.* reacts with Cu (0·4 μg.), Ag, Au, Hg, Sn, Pt and Pd.[187]

(*5*) *Thiocarbine* (uncertain compn.) forms red, violet or brown complexes with Pb, Bi, Cu, Pd in NH_4OH soln.; the Pb complex does not change color with 1% NaOH or KCN but becomes colorless on addn. of 10% NaOH; the Bi complex becomes colorless with

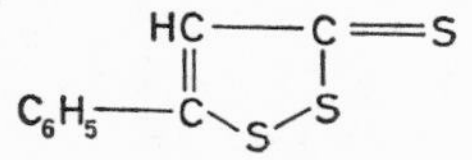

(LXXXVI)

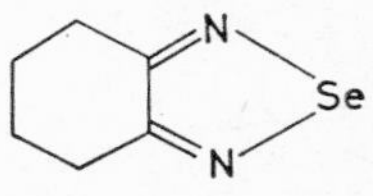

(LXXXVII)

1% NaOH but the Cu and Pd complexes bleach only with KCN. The supernates of the Ag, Hg and Cd complexes are yellow but are bleached by KCN.

(*6*) *1-Thiocyano-2,4-dinitrobenzene* forms an orange ppt. of 2,2′,4,4′-tetranitrodiphenyldisulfide on boiling with Ag in NH_4OH soln.[188]

(*7*) *Piazselenol* (LXXXVII) is specific for Pd (2 μg./ml.) forming the yellowish ppt., $PdCl_2 \cdot [Se(N_2C_6H_4)]_2$, which can be weighed.

(*8*) *Triselenomethylene* (?) (prepd. by heating H_2Se and HCHO) gives a yellow complex with Ge (0·5 p.p.m.).

References

1. Hollingshead R. G. W., *Oxine and its Derivatives*, Vols. I–IV, Butterworths, London (1954/56); Berg, R., *Oxin, Chem. Anal.*, **34** (1938); Feigl, 181 (1949); Berg, R., *Z. anorg. Chem.*, **204**, 208 (1932); Shiba, Y., *Repts. Govt. Ind. Research Inst. Tokyo*, **27**, (8), 12 (1932); Ishimaru, S., *J. Chem. Soc. Japan*, **55**, 288 (1934); Johnston, W. D., and Freiser, H., *Anal. Chem.*, **24**, 602 (1952).
2. Nagase, Y., *Analysis and Reagents* (*Japan*), **2**, 163 (1947).
3. Feigl, 185 (1949).
4. Sone, K., *Bull. Chem. Soc. Japan*, **25**, 1 (1952).

5. IINUMA, H., *Research Repts., Fac. Eng., Gifu Univ.*, **2**, 74 (1952).
6. NAKATSUKA, Y., *et al.*, *Acta Chim. Taiwan*, **1**, 25 (1948).
7. FEIGL, F., and BAUMFELD, I. *Anal. Chim. Acta*, **3**, 15 (1949); WEST, P. W., and GRANATELLI, L., *Anal. Chem.*, **24**, 870 (1952).
8. POLLARD, F. H., *et al.*, *J. Chem. Soc.*, 4730 (1953).
9. DYRSSEN, D., *Svensk Kem. Tidskr.*, **67**, 311 (1955).
10. HOLLINGSHEAD, R. G. W., *Oxine and its Derivatives*, Vols. I–IV, p. 600, Butterworths, London (1954/56).
11. POETHKE, W., *Pharm. Zentralhalle*, **86**, 2 (1947). Better than the method by SCHULEK, E. and CLAUDER, O., *Z. anal. Chem.*, **108**, 385 (1937).
12. CARSON, W. N., *Anal. Chem.*, **22**, 1565 (1950).
13. SMITH, G. F., and WILLARD, H. H., *A.S.T.M. Bull.*, (108), 33 (1941).
14. GERBER, L., *et al.*, *Ind. Eng. Chem., Anal. Ed.*, **14**, 658 (1942).
15. PHILLIPS, J. P., and O'HARA, F. J., *Anal. Chem.*, **23**, 535 (1951).
16. TAKIURA, K., *et al.*, *J. Pharm. Soc. Japan*, **75**, 724 (1955).
17. PŘIBIL, R., *et al.*, *Collection Czechoslov. Chem. Communs.*, **15**, 120 (1950); **16**, 69 (1951).
18. ISHIMARU, S., *J. Chem. Soc. Japan*, **55**, 732 (1934); **56** 62 (1935).
19. MOELLER, T., *Ind. Eng. Chem., Anal. Ed.*, **15**, 346 (1943); GENTRY, C. H. R., and SHERRINGTON, L. G., *Analyst*, **71**, 432 (1946); **75**, 17 (1950); SUDO, E., *J. Chem. Soc. Japan*, **72**, 718, 817 (1951).
20. TAYLOR, R. P., and FURMAN, N. H., *Anal. Chem.*, **27**, 309 (1955).
21. ISHIMORI, T., *Bull. Chem. Soc. Japan*, **27**, 139 (1954); **28**, 203 (1955); ISHIMORI and TATEDA, A., *J. Chem. Soc. Japan*, **78**, 78 (1957).
22. UMLAND, F., and HOFFMAN, W., *Angew. Chem.*, **68**, 704 (1956).
23. DYRSSEN, D., *Acta Chem. Scand.*, **10**, 341 (1956).
24. ALIMARIN, I. P., and KRYUKOV, V. G., *Zhur. Anal. Khim*, **10**, 56 (1955).
25. MUKHERJEE, A. K., and BANERJEE, B., *Naturwissenschaften*, **42**, 416 (1955).
26. MERRITT, L. L., and WALKER, J. K., *Ind. Eng. Chem., Anal. Ed.*, **16**, 387 (1944); PHILLIPS, J. P., *et al.*, *Anal. Chem.*, **24**, 1033 (1952).
27. IRVING, H., *et al.*, *J. Chem. Soc.*, 1489 (1949).
28. HOLLINGSHEAD, *Research*, **8**, *Suppl. No. 2*, S59 (1955).
29. BOCQUET, G., and PÂRIS, R. A., *Anal. Chim. Acta*, **14**, 201 (1956).
30. BERGES, L. S., *Anales real soc. españ. fís y quím.* (*Madrid*), **49B**, 529, 535 (1953); also see HOLLINGSHEAD, R. G. W., *Oxine and its Derivatives*, Vols. I–IV, p. 806, Butterworths, London (1954/56).
31. FERNANDO, Q., *et al.*, *Anal. Chim. Acta*, **14**, 297 (1956).
32. BELCHER, R., *et al.*, *J. Chem. Soc.*, 376 (1955).
33. MUSHA, S., *et al.*, *J. Chem. Soc. Japan*, **72**, 995 (1951); **73**, 363 (1952).
34. NÄSÄNEN, R., and UUSITALO, E., *Acta Chem. Scand.*, **8**, 112 (1954).
35. NAKATSUKA, Y., *et al.*, *Acta Chim. Taiwan*, **1**, 37 (1948).
36. CHANG, T. HS., *J. Chinese Chem. Soc.*, (II) **2**, 63 (1955); **3**, 23 (1956).
37. For details see WELCHER, **I**, 344; HOLLINGSHEAD, R. G. W., *Oxine and Its Derivatives*, Vols. I–IV, p. 946, Butterworths, London (1954/56).
38. BATALIN, A. KH., *Trudy Komissii Anal. Khim., Akad Nauk S.S.S.R.*, **3**, 208 (1951).
39. HOLLINGSHEAD, R. G. W., *Oxine and Its Derivatives*, Vols. I–IV, p. 900, Butterworths, London (1954/56).
40. WALTER, J. L. and FREISER, H, *Anal. Chem.*, **24**, 984, 1985 (1952); EVCIM, N. and REBER, L. A., *ibid.*, **26**, 936 (1954).
41. WALTER and FREISER, *Anal. Chem.*, **25**, 127 (1953).
42. CHARLES, R. G. and FREISER, *Anal. Chim. Acta*, **11**, 1 (1954); JOHNSTON, W. D. and FREISER, *ibid.*, 301.
43. KAWAI, S. *et al.*, *Japan Analyst*, **5**, 165 (1956).
44. AKIYAMA, T. *et al.*, *Bull. Kyoto Coll. Pharm.*, (4), 16 (1956).
45. YOSHINO, T., *J. Chem. Soc. Japan*, **78**, 108, 112 (1957).
46. IRVING, H. *et al.*, *Analyst*, **80**, 260 (1955).
47. HOLLINGSHEAD, *Anal. Chim. Acta*, **12**, 201 (1955).
48. MURASE, I., *J. Chem. Soc. Japan*, **75**, 1180 (1954).
49. IINUMA, H. *et al.*, *Acta Chim. Taiwan*, **1**, 13 (1948).
50. FEIGL, 345 (1949).
51. TERENT'EV, A. P. *et al.*, *Zhur. Anal. Khim.*, **7**, 120 (1952).
52. HOLZBECHER, Z., *Chem. listy*, **47**, 680 (1953).
53. HOLZBECHER, Z., *Sbornik Celostátni Pracovni Konf. Anal. Chemiků*, **1**, 166 (1952).
54. HOLZBECHER, Z., *Chem. listy*, **49**, 166 (1955).
55. HOOKER, D. T. and BANKS, C. V., *Preparation, Properties and Analytical Applications of some Substituted Alicyclic vic-Dioximes* (1956); DIEHL, H., *Applications of the Dioximes to Analytical Chemistry* (1940), G. F. Smith Chem. Co., Columbus; VOTER, R. C. and BANKS, *Anal. Chem.*, **21**, 1320 (1949); WELCHER, **III**, 157; FEIGL, 270 (1949).
56. PESHKOVA, V. M., *Zhur. Anal. Khim.*, **10**, 86 (1955).
57. YAMAZAKI, K. and MATSUMOTO, C., *J. Chem. Soc. Japan*, **76**, 736 (1955).
58. CHARLES, R. G. and FREISER, H., *Anal. Chim. Acta*, **11**, 101 (1954).
59. SHINRA, K. and ISHIKAWA, K., *J. Chem. Soc. Japan*, **74**, 271, 353 (1953); YAMAZAKI, Y. *et al.*, *ibid.*, **78**, 126 (1957).
60. YAMAZAKI, K. and MATSUMOTO, C., *J. Chem. Soc. Japan*, **78**, 837 (1957).
61. VOTER and BANKS, *Anal. Chem.*, **21**, 1320 (1949); FERGUSON, R. C. *et al.*, *Mikrochemie ver. Mikrochim. Acta*, **38**, 11 (1951); FERGUSON and BANKS, *Anal. Chem.*, **23**, 1486 (1951).
62. VAN DER HAAR, R. W. *et al.*, *J. Org. Chem.*, **14**, 836 (1949).
63. RAUH, E. G. *et al.*, *J. Org. Chem.*, **10**, 199 (1945).
64. HOOKER, D. T. and BANKS, *Anal. Chem.*, **26**, 1666 (1954); **28**, 79 (1956); *U.S. Atomic Energy Comm.*, **ISC**-230 (1951); **ISC**-597 (1955).
65. OKÁČ, A. and GRUBER, J., *Collection Czechoslov. Chem. Communs.*, **15**, 26 (1950); SHINRA, K. and SHIMURA, K., *J. Chem. Soc. Japan*, **74**, 355 (1953).
66. FEIGL, 266 (1949); FEIGL *et al.*, *Ber.*, **58**, B2294 (1924); WELCHER, **III**, 237.
67. FEIGL, 198 (1949); EPHRAIM, F., *Ber.*, **65**, B1210, 1215 (1931); FLAGG, J. F. and FURMAN, N. H., *Ind. Eng. Chem., Anal. Ed.*, **12**, 529 (1949); WELCHER, **III**, 252.
68. ENDO, J. and MASHIMA, M., *J. Chem. Soc. Japan*, **73**, 386 (1952); **74**, 564, 622 (1953).
69. MERCHANT, R. N. and PISHAWIKAR, D. G., *Sci. and Culture* (*Calcutta*), **21**, 536 (1956).
70. RÂY, A. K. and RÂY, P., *Sci. and Culture* (*Calcutta*), **21**, 547 (1956).
71. MOMOSE, T. and OKURA, Y., *Japan Analyst*, **5**, 332 (1956).

72. HOVORKA, V. and DIVIŠ, L., *Collection Czechoslov. Chem. Communs.*, **14**, 116 (1949); **15**, 589 (1950).
73. DIVIŠ, L. and ŠKODA, L., *Chem. listy*, **46**, 663 (1952); **48**, 535 (1954).
74. WANG, K., *J. Chinese Chem. Soc.*, **17**, 163 (1950).
75. DUCKWALL, A. L. *et al.*, *Trans. Ky. Acad. Sci.*, **16**, 20 (1955).
76. KURAŠ, M. and RŮŽIČKA, E., *Chem. listy*, **44**, 41 (1950).
77. BANDYOPADHAYAY, D. and RÂY, P., *Sci. and Culture* (*Calcutta*), **19**, 466 (1954); *J. Indian Chem. Soc.*, **33**, 21 (1951).
78. KURAŠ, M. and RŮŽIČKA, E., *Chem. listy*, **48**, 1257 (1954).
79. KURAŠ, M. and RŮŽIČKA, E., *Chem. listy*, **49**, 1897 (1955).
80. OKÁČ, A. and HORÁK, J., *Chem. listy*, **50**, 1496 (1956).
81. FEIGL, F. and GOLDSTEIN, D., *Analyst*, **81**, 709 (1956).
82. SINGH, M. M. and DAS GUPTA, A. K., *J. Sci. Ind. Research* (*India*), **8B**, 186 (1949); **11B**, 268 (1952); MUSANTE, C., *Gazz. chim. ital.*, **78**, 536 (1948).
83. DYRSSEN, D., *Acta Chem. Scand.*, **10**, 353 (1956).
84. BHADURI, A. S., *Sci. and Culture* (*Calcutta*), **18**, 95 (1952); BHADURI and RÂY, P., *ibid.*, 97.
85. DAS GUPTA and GUPTA, J., *J. Sci. and Ind. Research* (*India*), **9B**, 237 (1950); DHAR, S. K. and DAS GUPTA, *ibid.*, **11B**, 500, 520 (1952); **12B**, 518 (1953).
86. VONESCH, E. E. *et al.*, *Anales asoc. quím. Argentina*, **41**, 162 (1953).
87. VLÁČIL, F. and HOVORKA, V., *Chem. listy*, **45**, 439 (1951).
88. WELCHER, **III**, 339–354; FEIGL, 209 (1949).
89. SHOME, S. C., *Anal. Chem.*, **20**, 1205 (1948); *Anal. Chim. Acta*, **3**, 679 (1949); GUHA-SIRCAR, S. S. and BHATTACHARJEE, S. C., *J. Indian Chem. Soc.*, **18**, 155 (1941).
90. FEIGL, 252 (1949).
91. IINUMA, H., *Research Repts., Fac. Eng., Gifu Univ.*, **1**, 35 (1951).
92. CRONHEIM, G., *J. Org. Chem.*, **12**, 7, 20 (1947).
93. SHIMURA, H., *J. Chem. Soc. Japan*, **76**, 867, 870 (1955).
94. TORII, T., *J. Chem. Soc. Japan*, **76**, 328, 333, 675, 680, 707, 825 (1955); *Japan Analyst*, **4**, 177 (1955).
95. SMITH, G. F., *Cupferron and Neocupferron*, G. F. Smith Chem. Co., Columbus (1938); FEIGL, 262 (1949).
96. FURMAN, N. H. *et al.*, *Anal. Chem.*, **21**, 1325 (1949).
97. HAGIWARA, Z., *Techn. Repts. Tohoku Univ.*, **18**, 32 (1953); **19**, 73 (1954).
98. ELVING, P. J. and OLSEN, E. C., *J. Am. Chem. Soc.*, **78**, 4206 (1956).
99. SHOME, S. C., *Current Sci.*, **13**, 257 (1944); *Analyst*, **75**, 27 (1950); *Anal. Chem.*, **23**, 1186 (1951).
100. DYRSSEN, D., *Acta Chem. Scand.*, **10**, 353 (1956).
101. LUTWICK, G. D. and RYAN, D. E., *Can. J. Chem.*, **32**, 949 (1954); ARMOUR, C. A. and RYAN, *ibid.*, **35**, 1454 (1957).
102. FEIGL, 215 (1949).
103. SHINRA, K. and YOSHIKAWA, K., *J. Chem. Soc. Japan*, **74**, 644 (1953).
104. MALLICK, A. K. and MAJUMDAR, A. K., *Sci. and Culture* (*Calcutta*), **14**, 477 (1949); *J. Indian Chem. Soc.*, **29**, 255, (1952); MAJUMDAR and DE, A. K., *ibid.*, **30**, 123, 401 (1953); MAJUMDAR and SEN, B., *Anal. Chim. Acta*, **9**, 529 (1953).
105. MAJUMDAR, A. K. and SEN, B., *Anal. Chim. Acta*, **8**, 369, 384 (1953); **9**, 536 (1953).
106. CASTAGNOU, R. *et al.*, *Bull. trav. soc. pharm. Bordeaux*, **88**, 184 (1950).
107. NAKATSUKA, Y. *et al.*, *Acta Chim. Taiwan*, **1**, 1 (1948).
108. SHENNAN, R. J. *et al.*, *Analyst*, **61**, 395 (1936); DAY, A. R. and TAGGART, W. T., *Ind. Eng. Chem.*, **20**, 545 (1928); also see CIMERMAN, C. and SELZER, M., *Anal. Chim. Acta*, **9**, 26 (1953).
109. FUNK, H. and DITT, M., *Chem.-Ztg.*, **57**, 334 (1933).
110. HOLMES, F. and CRIMMIN, W. R. C., *Anal. Chim. Acta*, **13**, 135 (1955).
111. BHATKI, K. S. and KABADI, M. B., *Sci. and Culture* (*Calcutta*), **18**, 548 (1953).
112. AKIYAMA, T. *et al.*, *Japan Analyst*, **5**, 701 (1956).
113. SCHWARZENBACH, G. *et al.*, *Helv. Chim. Acta*, **30**, 1307 (1947); **31**, 456, 1029 (1948); **32**, 1175, 1682 (1949); MARTELL, A. E. *et al.*, *J. Am. Chem. Soc.*, **72**, 3743, 5357 (1950); **74**, 5052, 5057, 6021, 6228 (1952); **75**, 2185, 2888, 4814 (1953); **76**, 215 (1954).
114. PLUMB, R. C. *et al.*, *J. Phys. and Colloid Chem.*, **54**, 1208 (1950).
115. PŘIBIL, R., *Chem. listy*, **49**, 179 (1955).
116. LASTOVSKIĬ, R. P. *et al.*, *Zhur. Anal. Khim.*, **10**, 128 (1955).
117. WÄNNINEN, E., *Suomen Kemistilehti*, **28B**, (9) 146 (1955).
118. SCHMID, R. W. and REILLEY, C. N., *Anal. Chem.*, **29**, 264 (1957).
119. KUL'BERG, L. M. and LEDNEVA, A. M., *Zhur. Anal. Khim.*, **2**, 131 (1947).
120. HOLZBECHER, Z., *Chem. listy*, **45**, 442 (1951).
121. ROBERTSON, J. H. and BYRN, E. E., *Anal. Chem.*, **26**, 1854 (1954).
122. CIUHANDU, GH. *et al.*, *Acad. rep. populare Romîne, Studii cercetări chim.*, **5**, (1) 79 (1957).
123. PFLAUM, R. T. and HOWICH, L. C., *J. Am. Chem. Soc.*, **78**, 4862 (1956); DAS SARMA, B. and RAY, J. N., *Sci. and Culture* (*Calcutta*), **21**, 477 (1956); also see BOSE, M., *Anal. Chim. Acta*, **10**, 201, 209 (1954).
124. KRUMHOLZ, P. and HÖNEL, F., *Mikrochim. Acta*, **2** 177 (1937); WELCHER, **III**, 448, 461.
125. FEIGL, 205 (1949).
126. BECK, G., *Anal. Chim. Acta*, **1**, 69 (1947).
127. WETLESEN, C. W. and GRAN, G., *Svensk Pappenstidn.*, **55**, 212 (1952); ALLEN, M. and LLEWELYN, F. W. M., *Ann. Rept. East Malling Research Sta. Kent*, 461 (1954).
128. NAZARENKO, V. A., *Zhur. Anal. Khim*, **1**, 322 (1946).
129. MACHANOVA, M. *et al.*, *Latvijas PSR Zinātņu Akad. Vēstis*, (5) 113 (1954).
130. WELCHER, F. J. and BUEHLER, J. A., *Proc. Indiana Acad. Sci.*, **65**, 89 (1955).
131. GEHAUF, B. and GOLDENSON, J., *Anal. Chem.*, **27**, 420 (1955).
132. DUBSKÝ, J. V., *Chem. Obzor*, **8**, 71 (1933); SCOTT, A. W. and ROBBINS, T. E., *Ind. Eng. Chem., Anal. Ed.*, **14**, 206 (1942); WELCHER, **III**, 415; FEIGL, 328 (1949).
133. YOE, J. H. and OVERHOLSER, L. G., *Ind. Eng. Chem., Anal. Ed.*, **14**, 435 (1942); BARDODĚJ, Z. and VEJDELĚK, Z. J., *Chem. listy*, **45**, 38 (1951); SANDELL, 528.
134. BHATKI, K. S. and KABADI, M. B., *Sci. and Culture* (*Calcutta*), **18**, 548 (1953).
135. GEILMANN, W. and NEEB, R., *Z. anal. Chem.*, **152**, 96 (1956); KNIGHT, S. B. *et al.*, *Anal. Chem.*, **29**, 571 (1957).
136. GUPTA, J. and CHAKRABARTTY, B., *J. Sci. and Ind. Research* (*India*), **8B**, 133 (1949).
137. GUPTA, J. and SARMA, K. P. S., *J. Indian Chem. Soc.*, **28**, 89 (1951); DUTT, N. K. and SARMA, *Sci. and Culture* (*Calcutta*), **21**, 333 (1956).
138. BANDYOPADHAYAY, D., *J. Indian Chem. Soc.*, **32**, 651 (1955).

139. Hovorka, V. and Holzbecher, Z., *Collection Czechoslov. Chem. Communs.*, **14**, 248 (1949); **15**, 275, 281 (1950).
140. Guha-Sircar, S. S. and Satpathy, S., *J. Indian Chem. Soc.*, **31**, 450 (1954); Mitra, G. N. and Guha-Sircar, *ibid.*, **32**, 435 (1955).
141. Currah, J. E. *et al.*, *Ind. Eng. Chem.*, *Anal. Ed.*, **18**, 120 (1946); Allen, W. F. and Beamish, F. E., *Anal. Chem.*, **22**, 451 (1950).
142. Pavolini, T. and Grambarin, F., *Anal. Chim. Acta*, **3**, 27 (1949).
143. Singh, R. P., *Current Sci.*, **25**, 59 (1956).
144. Turkevich, N. M., *Zhur. Anal. Khim.*, **11**, 180 (1956).
145. Sandell, *Colorimetric Determination of Metals*, 2nd ed., p. 87, Interscience, New York, (1950); Welcher, **III**, 461; Feigl, 241 (1949); Fischer, H., *Angew. Chem.*, **47**, 685 (1934); **50**, 919 (1937); *Mikrochemie*, **30**, 38, 307 (1942/43); Irving, H. *et al.*, *J. Chem. Soc.*, 537, 541, 1841, 1847 (1949); 356 (1952); Cooper, S. S. and Sullivan, M. K., *Anal. Chem.*, **23**, 613 (1951); Iwantscheff, G., *Angew. Chem.*, **69**, 472 (1957).
146. Ishimori, T., *Bull. Chem. Soc. Japan*, **27**, 139, 520 (1954).
147. Mabuchi, H., *Bull. Chem. Soc. Japan*, **29**, 842 (1956).
148. Warren, H. V. *et al.*, *Econ. Geol.*, **48**, 306 (1953).
149. Vallee, B. L., *Anal. Chem.*, **25**, 517 (1953); **26**, 914 (1954).
150. Carlton, J. K. and Bradbury, W. C., *Anal. Chem.*, **26**, 1226 (1954).
151. Ashizawa, T., *Repts. Balneol. Lab., Okayama Univ.*, **6**, 20 (1952).
152. Carritt, D. E., *Anal. Chem.*, **25**, 1927 (1953).
153. Suprunovich, I. B. and Shamshin, D. L., *Zhur. Anal. Khim.*, **1**, 198 (1946).
154. Takei, S. and Shibuya, K., *Japan Analyst*, **5**, 695 (1956); **6**, 630 (1957).
155. Oesper, R. E. and Klingenberg, J. J., *J. Org. Chem.*, **13**, 309 (1948).
156. Cooper, S. S. and Kofron, V. K., *Anal. Chem.*, **21**, 1135 (1949); Hubbard, D. M., *ibid.*, **28**, 1802 (1956); Grzhegorzhevskiĭ, A. S., *Zhur. Anal. Khim.*, **9**, 109 (1954).
157. Hubbard and Scott, E. W., *J. Am. Chem. Soc.*, **65**, 2390 (1943).
158. Tarbell, D. S. and Bumett, J. F., *J. Am. Chem. Soc.*, **69**, 263 (1947).
159. Buu-Hoi, Ng. Ph., *et al.*, *Bull. soc. chim. France*, 647 (1955).
160. Haines, R. L. and Ryan, D. E., *Can. J. Research*, **27B**, 72 (1949); Ryan, D. E., *Anal. Chem.*, **22**, 599 (1950).
161. Ubaldini, I., *Gazz. chim. ital.*, **78**, 293 (1948); Ubaldini, I. and Nebbia, L., *Ann. chim. applicata*, **38**, 241 (1948).
162. Dubský, J. V., *Z. anal. Chem.*, **98**, 184 (1934); **96**, 412 (1934).
163. Majumdar, A. K. *et al.*, *Z. anal. Chem.*, **154**, 262 (1957); **155**, 1, 7, 81, 86, 166 (1957); **156**, 103 (1957).
164. Duval, R., *Anal. Chim. Acta*, **3**, 21 (1949).
165. Patnaik, B. K., *J. Indian Chem. Soc.*, **34**, 75 (1957).
166. Gehauf, B. and Goldenson, J., *Anal. Chem.*, **22**, 498 (1950); Yuasa, T. and Aoki, F., *Japan Analyst*, **2**, 305 (1953).
167. Beck, G., *Mikrochemie ver. Mikrochim Acta*, **33**, 188 (1947).
168. Berg, R., *Z. anal. Chem.*, **115**, 204 (1938/39); Umemura, T., *J. Chem. Soc. Japan*, **61**, 25 (1940); Welcher, **IV**, 165.
169. Buscaróns, F. and Artigas, J., *Anales real soc. españ. fís. y quím.* (*Madrid*), **48B**, 140 (1952); **49B**, 375 (1953).
170. Buscaróns, F. and Capitán, F., *Anales real soc. españ. fís. y quím.* (*Madrid*), **46B**, 453, 569 (1950).
171. Misra, R. N. and Guha-Sircar, S. S., *J. Indian Chem. Soc.*, **32**, 127 (1955); **33**, 523 (1956).
172. Swain, R. C. *et al.*, *J. Indian Chem. Soc.*, **32**, 529 (1955).
173. Uhlig, L. J. and Freiser, H., *Anal. Chem.*, **23**, 1014 (1951).
174. Catoggio, J. A., *Anales direc. nacl. quím.* (*Buenos Aires*), **7**, 40 (1954).
175. Swift, E. H. and Butler, E. A., *Anal. Chem.*, **28**, 146 (1956); **29**, 419 (1957).
176. Pilipenko, A. T. and Uliko, N. V., *Zhur. Anal. Khim.*, **10**, 299 (1955).
177. Bode, H., *Z. anal. Chem.*, **142**, 414 (1954); **143**, 182 (1954); **144**, 165 (1955); **157**, 414 (1957); Wickbold, R., *ibid.*, **152**, 259, 262, 266, 338, 342 (1956); **153**, 21, 24 (1956); Lacoste, R. J. *et al.*, *Anal. Chem.*, **23**, 871 (1951); Welcher, **IV**, 82.
178. Sag, G., *Bull. soc. chim. France*, 30 (1949).
179. T'ien, P. Sh. and Wang, K., *Sci. Sinica* (*Peking*), **5**, 657 (1957).
180. Busev, A. I., *Doklady Akad. Nauk S.S.S.R.*, **66**, 1093 (1949).
181. Kojima, M., *Japan Analyst*, **6**, 34 (1957).
182. Clark, R. E., *Analyst*, **82**, 177 (1957).
183. Dziomko, V. M. and Cherepakhin, A. I., *Versoyuz. Zaochnyĭ Politekh. Inst., Sbornik Stateĭ*, (9) 65, (11) 37 (1955).
184. Přibil, R. and Roubal, Z., *Chem. listy*, **48**, 818 (1954).
185. Ziegler, M. and Glemser, O., *Z. anal. Chem.*, **149**, 101 (1956).
186. Airan, J. W. and Wagle, D. S., *J. Univ. Bombay*, **22**, *Pt.* 3, *Sci., No.* 34A, 71 (1953).
187. Voronkov, M. G. and Tsiper, F. P., *Zhur. Anal. Khim.*, **6**, 331 (1951).
188. Bürger, K., *Mikrochim. Acta*, 310 (1957).

9

NITROGEN COMPOUNDS

1. *o*-PHENANTHROLINE AND ITS ANALOGS[1]

(*1*) *o-Phenanthroline* (α,α′- or 1,10-phenanthroline) (I) [Monohydrate, m.p. 99–100°C] forms a red 1:3 complex with Fe^{2+} (ferroin) and is one of the best colorimetric reagents for Fe; the perchlorate can be extd. with $PhNO_2$; ferroin is a valuable redox indicator (see Chapter 15, Section 4). Cu^+ forms an orange 1:2

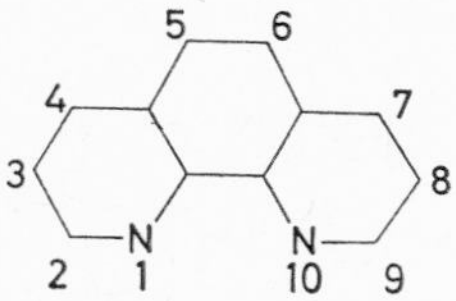

(I)

complex at pH 8·3 which can be extd. with octanol, Ru^{2+} a yellow 1:3 complex and Mn^{3+} a yellow complex; these metals and Cd (in UV light) can be detd. colorimetrically. Pd is detd. gravimetrically as $PdCl_2 \cdot C_{12}H_8N_2$. Mo yields a colored complex if $SnCl_2$ is added. Cu^+ gives a brownish ppt. if SCN^- is added and a blue ppt. if I^- is added.

Ferroin ppts. ClO_4^-, $S_2O_8^{2-}$, IO_4^-, phosphomolybdic and phosphotungstic acids and complex metal halides (e.g. in titration of Hg^{2+} (q.v.) with Br^-), and its oxidized form (ferriin) can be used colorimetrically for V^{4+}, U^{4+}, etc. The Zn complex ion forms ppts. with MoO_4^{2-} ($10^{-4}M$), SCN^- ($2{\cdot}5 \times 10^{-3}M$), $Fe(CN)_6^{3-}$ ($2{\cdot}5 \times 10^{-4}M$), VO_3^- ($10^{-4}M$), I^-, WO_4^{2-} ($0{\cdot}1M$), CN^-, CNO^-, $Cr_2O_7^{2-}$, $Fe(CN)_6^{4-}$ ($0{\cdot}4M$), ClO_4^- ($0{\cdot}8M$).[2]

Many derivs. have been prepd., those with alkyl or aryl groups in the 2,9- or 4,7-positions being especially useful (Table 21).[1, 3] *Bathophenanthroline* (4,7-diphenyl-1,10-phenanthroline) is very sensitive for Fe and *neocuproine* (the 2,9-dimethyl deriv.) for Cu; *bathocuproine* (2,9-dimethyl-4,7-diphenyl deriv.) is the best reagent for Cu. These complexes are more easily extd. with org. solvents such as AmOH, $C_2H_2Cl_2$, etc., than the *o*-phenanthroline complexes.

The *5-nitro* and the *3,5,6,8-tetramethyl derivs.* are used colorimetrically for Fe; the *4,7-dihydroxy deriv.* reacts with Fe in strongly alk. soln.

(*2*) *2,2′- or α,α′-Dipyridyl* (2-(2-pyridyl)-pyridine, 2,2′-bipyridine) [m.p. 69–70°C, sol. in EtOH, Et_2O, C_6H_6, sparingly sol. in H_2O]. The red Fe^{2+} complex is less stable than that of *o*-phenanthroline but can be used colorimetrically; the sensitivity limit is 0·03 μg. The brownish color of the Cu^+ complex is also measurable; Mo^{4+} (0·4 μg.) forms a purple complex. Cu^+ forms orange or red ppts. in presence of SCN^- or I^- resp. The Fe-dipyridyl ion ppts. Nb, Ta (0·2 μg.), HgI_4^{2-}, CdI_4^{2-} (0·05 μg Cd), ClO_4^-, etc.

Cuproine (2,2′-diquinolyl, biquinolyl, 2-(2′-quinolyl)-quinoline) is used colorimetrically for Cu^+ (purple) with AmOH extn. $CuCl_2$ (orange), $CuSO_4$ (green), $CoCl_2$ (green) and Fe^{2+} also react. *Bilepidine* (4,4′-dimethylcuproine) is more sensitive. For various derivs. see Table 21.

(*3*) *1-(2-Pyridyl)-isoquinoline* and its *3,4-dinitro deriv.* give colored complexes with Fe^{2+} (585, 586 mμ) but *1,1′-biisoquinoline* does not.[4] *2-(2′-Pyridyl)-benzimidazole* gives a red 1:6 complex with Fe^{2+} at pH 5·7 which can be extd. with $CHCl_3$ or AmOH and measured at 490 mμ; Fe^{3+}, Cu^+, Cu^{2+} and Hg also react. *2-(2′-Pyridyl)-imidazoline* forms a purple Fe^{2+} complex (560 mμ) at pH 9·0 but *2-(2′-pyridyl)-benzoxazole* does not.[5]

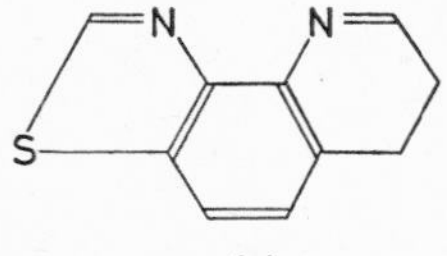

(II)

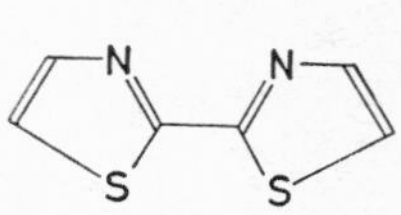

(III)

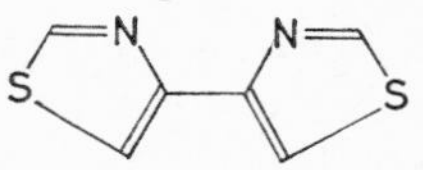

(IV)

Quinthiazole (II) gives a yellow color with Fe^{2+} (1 p.p.m.); *2,2′-bithiazoline* (III) reacts only on heating and *4,4′-bithiazoline* (IV) does not react.[6] *2-(2′-Pyridyl)-pyrrole* reacts with Fe, Cu and many other metals; *2-(2′-pyridyl)-quinoline* ppts. Au and Pt.

TABLE 21. Cuprous and Ferrous Complexes of *o*-Phenanthroline Derivatives and Analogs

Reagent	Cu^+ λ_{max} (mμ)	Cu^+ ε	Fe^{2+} λ_{max} (mμ)	Fe^{2+} ε
o-Phenanthroline	435	7250	510	11 100
2,9-Dimethyl-*o*-phenanthroline	454	7950	—	—
2,9-Diphenyl-*o*-phenanthroline	441	3620	—	—
4,7-Diphenyl-*o*-phenanthroline	—	—	535	22 400
4-Ethyl-*o*-phenanthroline	437	8060	514	13 200
5-Ethyl-*o*-phenanthroline	442	7960	518	12 420
4,6-Diethyl-*o*-phenanthroline	443	8410	518	13 700
4,7-Diethyl-*o*-phenanthroline	438	8670	515	15 020
4,7-Diphenoxy-*o*-phenanthroline	425	8020	500	14 660
5,6-Dimethoxy-*o*-phenanthroline	441	7500	515	11 960
4,7-Dimethoxy-*o*-phenanthroline	UV	—	500	12 270
4,7-Dihydroxy-*o*-phenanthroline	—	—	520	14 800
5-Amino-*o*-phenanthroline	UV	—	524	12 060
5,6-(2-Pyrido)-*o*-phenanthroline	UV	—	518	12 670
5,6-(Cyclohexeno)-*o*-phenanthroline	446	6970	524	12 660
2,9-Dimethyl-4,7-diphenyl-*o*-phenanthroline	479	14 200	—	—
4,7-Bis(4-dimethylamino-1-methylbutylamino)-*o*-phenanthroline	—	—	510	19 200
4-(3-Diethylaminopropylamino)-*o*-phenanthroline	—	—	543	12 600
4,7-Bis(3-diethylaminopropylamino)-*o*-phenanthroline	—	—	510	18 800
2,2′-Dipyridyl	435	4550	522	8650
4,4′-Dimethyl-2,2′-dipyridyl	433	5210	526	8470
4,4′-Diphenyl-2,2′-dipyridyl	455	6570	386	21 360
			552	21 280
4,4′-Diamino-2,2′-dipyridyl	463	9600	379	13 640
			569	8135
4,4′,6,6′-Tetramethyl-2,2′-dipyridyl	450	6800	—	—
2,2′-Diquinolyl	540	5409	—	—
	(358)	(52 000)		
4,4′-Dimethyl-2,2′-diquinolyl	550	7020	—	—
4,4′-Diphenyl-2,2′-diquinolyl	?	9020	—	—
2,2′,2″-Tripyridyl	444	1420	552	12 500
	506	1240		
4′-Phenyl-2,2′,2″-tripyridyl	452	2630	560	22 185
	517	2690 } Cu^{2+}		
4,4″-Dimethyl-4′-phenyl-2,2′,2″-tripyridyl	457	2440	575	26 360
	519	2514		
4,4′,4″-Triphenyl-2,2′,2″-tripyridyl[a]	466	3050	383	21 100
	528	3120	583	30 200
6,4′,6″-Triphenyl-2,2′,2″-tripyridyl	423	4520	—	—
	567	3180		

[a] Co 466, 528 mμ, ε = 3052, 3120. UV, ultraviolet region.

(4) 2,2′,2″-Tripyridyl (terpyridyl, 2,6-bis(2-pyridyl)-pyridine, 2,6-di-2′-pyridylpyridine) is used colorimetrically for Fe^{2+} (red); if ethylenediamine is added, Cu, Co, Ni, Zn do not interefere. The orange Co complex is detd. colorimetrically after $PhNO_2$ extn. of the perchlorate (ε = 2900).

Terosite (2,6-bis(4-phenyl-2-pyridyl)-4-phenylpyridine) is the most sensitive reagent for Fe; *tersole* (2,6-bis(4-methylpyridyl)-4-phenylpyridine) and *terosine* (2,6-bis(2-pyridyl)-4-phenylpyridine) re next n order of sensitivity (see Table 21). The complexes of these reagents with Fe and Co can be extd. with *n*-hexanol.

2. MISCELLANEOUS NITROGEN COMPOUNDS

(*1*) *Pyridine* (py) forms complex ppts. with many metals if SCN^- is present. $Cupy_2(SCN)_2$ is sol. in $CHCl_3$ or PhCl; Cu is detd. gravimetrically or colorimetrically. Ppts. of $Cdpy_2(SCN)_2$, $Cdpy_4(SCN)_2$ (white), $Copy_4(SCN)_2$ (pink; blue with HNO_3) and similar complexes of Ni, Zn, Fe^{3+}, Mn, UO_2^{2+}, Cr and Ca are formed. Cu forms similar complexes if the SCN^- is replaced by OCN^- (colorimetry; Co, Ni, Zn also ppt.). $[Cupy_2]^{2+}$ salts of benzoate, MnO_4^- or $S_2O_5^{2-}$ also ppt. Ag (0·05 μg.) forms a red color with py and $S_2O_8^{2-}$ (Ag^{2+}). Some of these complexes can be detd.

α-Picoline (2-methylpyridine) with OCN^- forms crystals with Co and Fe; with CH_3I it forms a Bi ppt. (orange). *2-Aminopyridine* (α-pyridylamine) in presence of I^- ppts. Cu, Co and Zn; with I^- or Br^- it forms characteristic crystals with Sb (orange), Bi (scarlet) and Au (orange). *Coramine* (pyridine-β-carboxylic acid diethylamide) forms crystals with Cu or Co and SCN^-. *Piperidine* (hexahydropyridine) with SCN^- ppts. Sn^{4+} (0·1 μg., white); in presence of Na nitroprusside, Co (0·05 μg.) forms a green complex (other group III elements do not interfere). *α-Phenylpyridine* ppts. H_2PtCl_6.

(*2*) *Quinoline* forms complex salts with Bi (0·3 μg.), Cu if SCN^- is added; with Sn^{2+} (1·5 μg.), Cd (0·15 μg.), Sb (0·2 μg.), Fe (0·3 μg.), Bi (0·2 μg.), Cu (0·05 μg.) if I^- is added; Cr with $C_2O_4^{2-}$ forms $[Cr(C_2O_4)_2]$ (C_9H_7N). *Isoquinoline* (2-benzazine) ppts. Cu (pH 3), Zn (above pH 4), Cd, Co and Ni if SCN^- is added. With SCN^- present, *β-naphthoquinoline* ppts. Hg, Bi, Cd, Ni, Co, Zn, U and Fe^{3+}. With I^-, it ppts. Cd, Hg, Bi, Cu, Pb, Ag, Sn; Cd (9·4 μg./ml.) is detd. gravimetrically as $(C_{13}H_9N)_2H_2CdI_4$ from H_2SO_4 solns. *α-Naphthoquinoline* with I^- ppts. Bi and Cd but is inferior to the β-compd.

Quinaldine (2-methylquinoline) with I^- ppts. Bi, as does *8-nitroquinoline*. *6-Nitroquinoline* ppts. $Pd(C_9H_6O_2N_2)_2$ (the compn. is doubtful[7]) but not the other Pt metals. *1-(2-Quinolyl)-4-allylthiosemicarbazide* forms a green ppt. with Cd in presence of I^- but does not ppt. Cu. *8-Aminoquinoline* ppts. Cu if Br^- is added (gravimetric detn.). For oxine and its analogs, see p. 45.

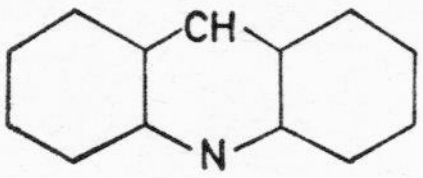

(V)

(*3*) *Acridine* (V) with SCN^- ppts. Co (5 μg.) as $Co(C_{13}H_9N)_2(SCN)_3$, which is used for concn. and sepn. from Fe^{2+}, V^{4+}, Zn and Mo. Fe^{3+} (0·1 μg.), Zn (0·01), Cu (0·1), Hg (0·5), Bi (2), Cd (10), UO_2^{2+} (2),

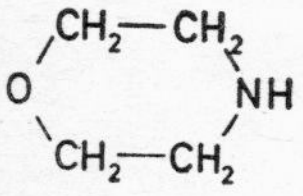

(VI)

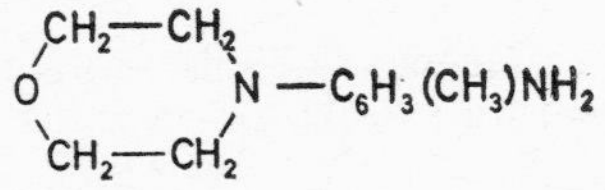

(VII)

Ni, In, Au, Pt, Ir, Pd, Rh form similar ppts. With I^- acridine ppts. Ag (0·4 μg.), Cd and Bi. ***Trypaflavine*** (acriflavine) reacts with Hg and Pd^{2+}.

m- or p-*Phenanthroline* ppts. Bi, Hg, Cd and Co in presence of SCN^- or I^-.

(*4*) *Morpholine* (VI) ppts. Cu and Zn. p-*Amino-3-methylphenylmorpholine* (VII) forms colors with Au, Cr, V, Os, Cu, Fe, Pt and Ag.

(*5*) *Antipyrine* (phenazone, 1,5-dimethyl-2-phenyl-3-pyrazolone) (VIII) with SCN^- forms ppts. with Co, Cu, Fe, Zn and Ni which can be extd. with EtOAc, C_6H_6 or AmOH and detd. colorimetrically. In presence of I^-, Sb^{3+}, Bi and Hg ppt. and are detd. similarly; with Br^-, Cd ppts. but Cu does not. See also hexamine. *1-Phenyl-3-methylpyrazolone* reacts with Ag, Cu, Fe

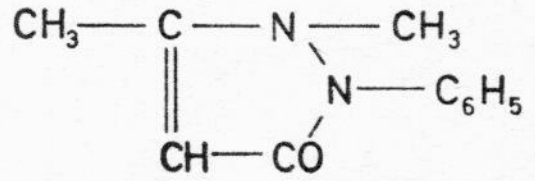

(VIII)

and Co. *Bromopyrine* ppts. Cd (p. 188) as $[C_{11}H_{11}ON_2Br]$ H_2CdBr_4. *Diantipyrinyl-(o-hydroxyphenyl)-methane* with Br^- also ppts. Cd (but not Cu, Zn or Fe) whence Cd is detd. gravimetrically or titrimetrically; a yellow complex forms with Ti. *Diantipyrinylmethane* with Br^- ppts. Cd (detn.) and Bi. In presence of SCN^-, it ppts. Co and Zn (nephelometry), while *tetramethyldiaminodiphenylantipyrinylcarbinol* ppts. Zn, Cu, Cd, Bi, Sb, Co, and *2-furyldiantipyrinylmethane* ppts. Fe (colorimetry). *Isopropylantipyrine* with I^- ppts. Sn^{2+}.

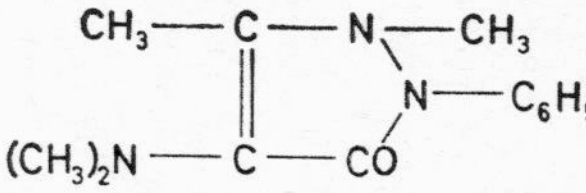

(IX)

Pyramidone (aminopyrine, 4-dimethylaminoantipyrine) (IX) is used colorimetrically for Fe in acid solns. In presence of SCN^- it forms complex ppts. with Co, Cu, Ni, etc. With I^- addn. Cd, Hg, Bi, Cu, Pb, Sb ppt.; with CN^-, Cu ppts.

3,5-Dimethylpyrazole (X) forms a blue ppt. with Co $(Co(C_5H_7N_2)_2)$ in NH_4OH soln., as do *glyoxaline*

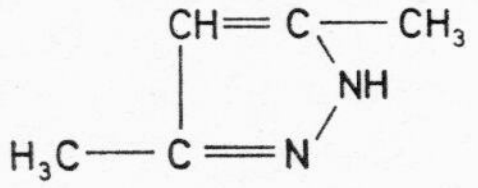

(X)

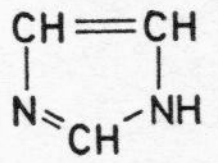

(XI)

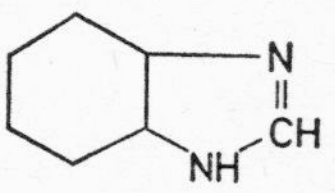

(XII)

(imidazole) (XI) and *benzimidazole* (XII). Benzimidazole also reacts with Ag, Hg, Cu, Cd and Zn but only slowly with Ni; Co and Ag are detd. gravimetrically.

The *2-methyl* and *2-phenyl derivs.* ppt. Ag and Hg. *1-Methyl-2-mercaptoimidazole* yields a red ppt. with Fe and SCN^-.

2-Methylbenzothiazole ppts. Bi, Hg, Sb, Cu and Fe if I^- is added.

Benzotriazole (silvone, azimidobenzene) ppts. Cu (pH 7–8·5), Ag, Pd, Ni, Cd, Zn, Co and Fe^{2+}; Cu, Ag (p. 147) and Pd are detd. gravimetrically. The *5-bromo deriv.* also ppts. Ag in feebly acid soln. and can be weighed.

Hydrazinophthalazine (XIII) and *dihydrazinophthalazine* are used colorimetrically for Fe^{3+} and V.

2-Amino-6-methyl-4-hydrazinopyrimidine (XIV) and

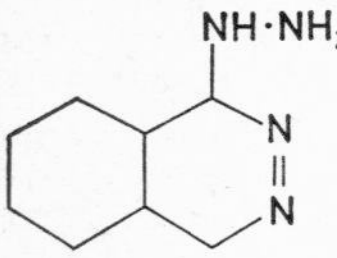

(XIII)

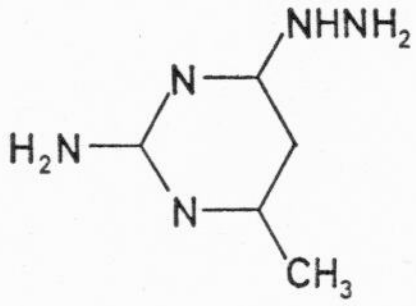

(XIV)

its analogs[8] form violet or red complexes with Ag, Cu, Cd, Mn^{2+}, Fe^{3+} (all 0·05 μg.), Al (5 μg.) and Fe^{2+} (0·5 μg.), yellowish complexes with Co, Ni, Cr^{3+} (all 0·01 μg.) and white with Hg (5 μg.).

2,3-Diaminophenazine (XV) ppts. Cu^+ and Hg, and forms colored complexes with Bi, Pb and Cd. $\alpha,\beta,\gamma,\delta$-

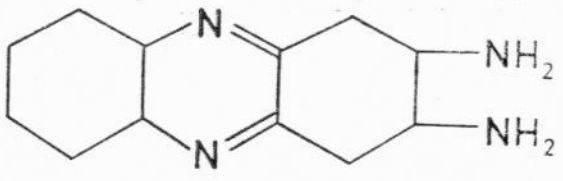

(XV)

Tetraphenylporphine reacts with Zn (colorimetry) and Cu.

(*6*) *Alkaloids. Atropine sulfate* ($(C_{17}H_{23}O_3N)_2.H_2SO_4$) forms yellow crystals with Au, as do *theobromine* ($C_7H_8O_2N_4$) (also with Ru), *hyoscine* ($C_{17}H_{21}O_4N$) and *hyoscyamine* ($C_{17}H_{23}O_3N$); the Pt metals do not ppt. with the last 2 reagents.

Strychnine ($C_{21}H_{22}O_2N_2$), *quinine* (methoxycinchonine) and *quinidine* form complexes with Os, V, Co, Cr, Fe. *Cinchonidine* ($C_{19}H_{22}ON_2$) forms yellowish ppts. with Pt, Os, Ir, Pd and Au, as does *espartine* (sparteine, lupinidine) ($C_{15}H_{26}N_2$). *Morphine* ($C_{17}H_{19}O_3N{\cdot}H_2O$) forms an orange complex with Ti in H_2SO_4 soln. and a brown complex with Ce in NH_4OH soln. *Narcotine* ($C_{22}H_{23}O_7N$) forms a brown complex with Ti; if $FeSO_4$ and $SnCl_2$ are added, Au, Hg and Pt react.

Many of the alkaloids form complex salts if Br^-, I^- or SCN^- is present with the metal. With Br^- addn., *brucine* ($C_{23}H_{26}O_2N_2$) ppts. Cd (gravimetric detn.) but not Zn and Cu, *cocaine* ($C_{17}H_{21}O_4N$) ppts. Bi (0·5 μg.) and Cu, and quinine ppts. Cd. With I^-, brucine ppts. Cd (titrimetric detn.); quinine ppts. Cd, Hg, Pb, Cu, Bi, Sb, Sn, Pt, Pd; *caffeine* (theine, 1,3,7-trimethylxanthine) ($C_8H_{10}O_2N_4.H_2O$) ppts. Bi (p. 167), Ag, Hg^+, Cu, Au; *cinchonine* ($C_{19}H_{22}ON_2$) ppts. Bi (0·14 μg, gravimetric detn.), Hg, Pb; cocaine ppts. Pb (0·01 μg., nephelometry), Ag, Au, Ge; morphine and *veratrine* ($C_{32}H_{49}O_9N$) ppt. Sb; and strychnine ppts. Sb and Hg. With SCN^- addn., espartine ppts. Co, Fe (0·01 μg.), V, Zn, Cd, Cu; narcotine ppts. Pb, Hg, Cu, Cd, Co, Ni, Fe^{2+}, Zn; and cinchonine ppts. Mo (p. 217) if $SnCl_2$ is also added. *Epinephrine* (adrenarin) forms colored complexes with Fe^{2+} and Fe^{3+} in presence of oleic acid.

(*7*) *Aniline* in presence of SCN^- forms white or green ppts. with Cu, Cd, Ni; with Co-dimethylglyoxime it forms $Co[O_2N_2C_2(CH_3)_2](C_6H_5NH_2)BiI_4$ with a detection limit of 10 μg. Bi/ml.[9] o-, m- or p-*Toluidine* (2-aminotoluene, 2-methylaniline) ppts. Ni and Cu if SCN^- is added; the Ni ppt. may be $[Ni(NH_3)_4]$-$[C_6H_4CH_3NH_2.HSCN]_4(SCN)_2$. Co ppts. if dimethylglyoxime is present. N,N-*Dimethylaniline* forms a green ppt. with Ni; the *ethyl homolog* gives colors with Cu, Co and Ni. α-*Naphthylamine* ppts. Au, and Hg and Cu if SCN^- is added. *1-Naphthylamine-4,6,8-trisulfonic acid* forms a 1:2 purple complex with Os^{6+} at pH 1·5 which can be detd. colorimetrically; the complex is blue at pH 5 and green at above pH 10. 28 homologs have been tested.[10] p-*Thiocyanoaniline* is used gravimetrically for Pd (q.v.).

(*8*) p-*Aminobenzophenone* with Br^- ppts. Pd (p. 244). *Auramine* (4,4′-bisdimethylaminobenzophenoneimide) ppts. Pd (but not Bi or Cu) in citric acid solns. p-*Aminoacetophenone* is used for gravimetric detn. of Pd. (0.5 μg.) in dil. HCL solns.

(*9*) *Benzidine* (*p,p*′-dianiline, 4,4′-diaminodiphenyl) forms reddish or yellowish ppts. with Cu (alk. soln.), Ag, Pt; if CN^- is added, Cu (0·6 μg., blue) and Pd ppt.; if SCN^-, OCN^- or Br^- is added, Cu forms resp. violet (XVI),[11] red and brown ppts. *Benzidine sulfonic acid* and SCN^- form a blue ppt. with Cu.[12]

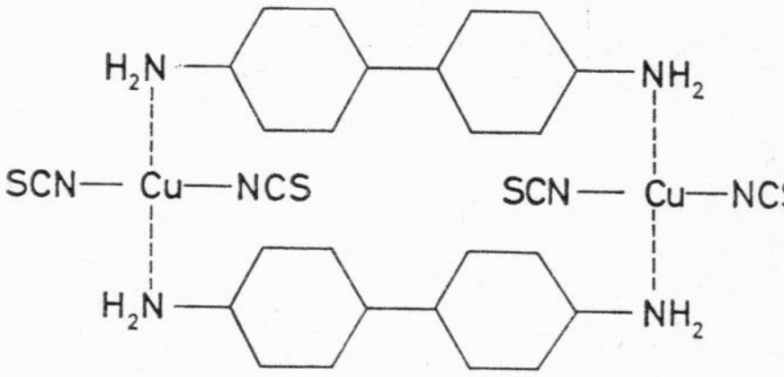

(XVI)

o-*Tolidine* (4,4′-bis-*o*-toluidine, 3,3′-dimethylbenzidine) forms a green ppt. with Cu and complexes with Co, Hg and Au; blue ppts. are formed with Cu on

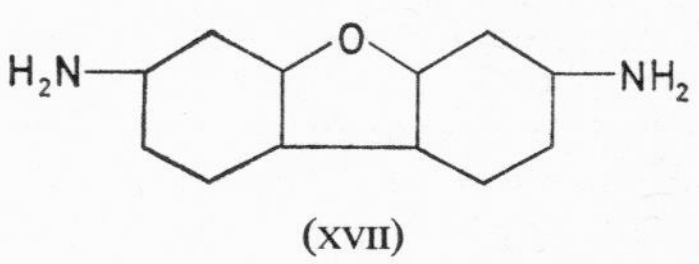

(XVII)

addn. of SCN^- (0·03 μg. Cu), CN^- or OCN^-; Co ppts. in presence of dimethylglyoxime. o-*Dianisidine* (bis-*o*-anisidine, 3,3′-dimethoxybenzidine, 4,4′-diamino-3,3′-dimethoxydiphenyl) forms violet ppts. with Cu if CN^-, SCN^- or OCN^- is added. *2,7-Diaminodibenzofuran* (XVII) and *2,7-diaminofluorene* (XVIII) behave in the same way with Cu, the ppts. being bluer than those with dianisidine; 2,7-diaminofluorene also ppts. Cd, Zn and Cu without addns.

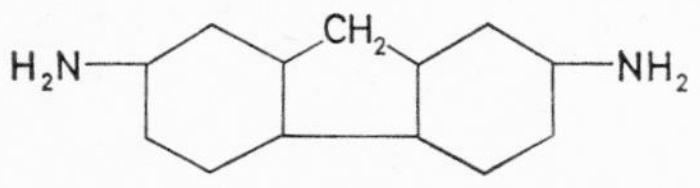

(XVIII)

(*10*) m-*Phenylenediamine* (1,3-diaminobenzene) forms red colors with Cu (green on NH_4OH addn.) and Fe; U and V ppt. the *o*-deriv. gives blue crystals with Ni. The *p*-deriv. ppts. Ag (NH_4OH), Cd and Zn (neutral); with SCN^- addn. blue ppts. of Cu, Fe (sol. in HCl), Ni and Zn are formed; on addn. of Cu^{2+} and I^-, Hg is pptd. as $Cu[C_6H_4(NH_2)_2]_2HgI_4$ and thus detd. gravimetrically.

1,3,4-Toluylenediamine ppts. Ni (blue-green). N,N-*Diphenyl*-p-*phenylenediamine* is used colorimetrically for Cu. N,N,N′,N′-*Tetramethyl*-p-*phenylenediamine* ppts. Cu, Hg^+, Hg^{2+}, Fe^{3+} and Ag.

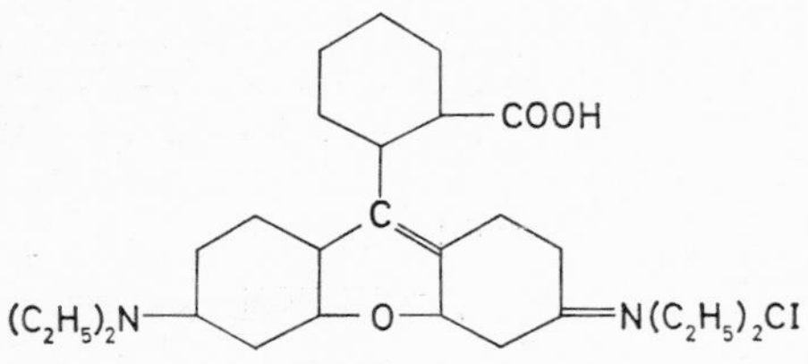

(XIX)

(*11*) *Rhodamine B* (tetraethylrhodamine, Colour Index 749) (XIX) [Purple, sol. in H_2O, EtOH] in presence of Cl^- forms a blue-violet complex with Sb^{5+} (0·5 μg.) which can be extd. with C_6H_6 or EtOAc; the complex with Au (1 μg.) is extd. with iso-Pr_2O, and the Tl^{3+} complex with $CHCl_3$; if SCN^- is added, Zn forms a green complex which is extd. with Et_2O; Ga, Bi and Hg also forms complexes in Cl^--contg. soln.; Sb, Au, Ga, Tl and Zn can be detd. colorimetrically.

Brilliant green in HCl solns. forms complexes with Sb^{5+} (50 μg.), Tl^{3+} and Au (0·5 mg.) which are extd. with AmOAc or toluene; Sb and Tl are detd. colorimetrically. *Crystal violet* behaves similarly with Tl^{3+}, as does *malachite green*. *Methyl violet* in Cl^--contg. soln. reacts with Sb^{5+} and Tl^{3+}; in I^--contg. soln. with Cu, Cd, Hg, Bi; in SCN^--contg. soln. with Zn; Sb, Tl, Hg and Zn are detd. colorimetrically. *Methylene blue* ppts. Zn with SCN^- (gravimetric detn.) and Sb with Cl^-. *Fuchsine* is used colorimetrically for Sb^{5+}; Au ppts. as $3AuCl_3$:1Fs or $2AuCl_3$:1Fs which is not reduced by H_3PO_2. Pd decolorizes the reagent at pH 2–4 (0·005 μg.); at high concns. a brown ppt. (XX) appears.[11]

(*12*) Various azo dyes such as p-*dimethyl*- or p-*diethylaminoazobenzene*, *phenylaminophenylazobenzene*, *and dimethyl- or diethylaminophenylazodiphenyl* react with Sb^{5+} in presence of Cl^-.[13] *Methyl orange* forms yellow crystals with Mg, Ni, Pb, Cr, U, and violet or black crystals with Co, Ce and Al; methyl orange and *methyl red* ppt. Zn in presence of SCN^-. p-*Diaminoazobenzene* forms a red ppt. with Cu (0·2 μg.) which is extd. by $CHCl_3$. p-*Aminobenzeneazodimethylaniline* ppts. Pt.

(*13*) *Hexamine* (hexamethylenetetramine, hexa, urotropin, methenamine) (XXI) [Sol. in H_2O, EtOH,

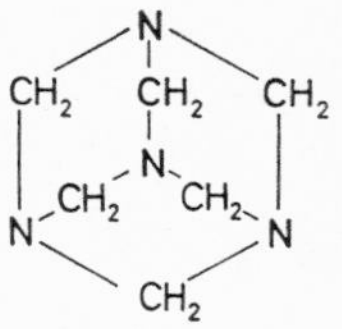

(XXI)

$CHCl_3$] forms characteristic white or yellow crystals with Ag, Pb, Hg, Cd, Sb, As, Bi, Sn, Au, Ir, Pt, Os, Pd. In presence of Na nitroprusside, Co, Ca, Li, Mg, Mo form characteristic crystals. In presence of SCN^-, Co, Ni, Cu, In, Fe, V, Zn ppt. In presence of I^-, Sb, Bi, Pd and Mg ppt.; Pt can be sepd. from Pd as $[(CH_2)_6N_4]$-H_2PtI_6 and detd. gravimetrically. If allyl iodide or antipyrine is also added, Cd is pptd. as $[(CH_2)_6N_4$·$C_3H_5I]_2CdI_2$ or Bi as $[(C_{11}H_{11}N_2OCH_2)_3N]_2$·$3HBiI_4$ resp. With NH_4-benzoate, $Cu_3(C_6H_5CO_2)_6$·$(CH_2)_6N_4$ ppts. With $Fe(CN)_6^{3-}$, $2Li_3Fe(CN)_6$·$K_3Fe(CN)_6$·$5[(CH_2)_6$-N_4·$6H_2O]$ ppts.; with $Fe(CN)_6^{4-}$, $3[MgCaFe(CN)_6]$·4 $[(CH_2)_6N_4]$·$40H_2O$ ppts.

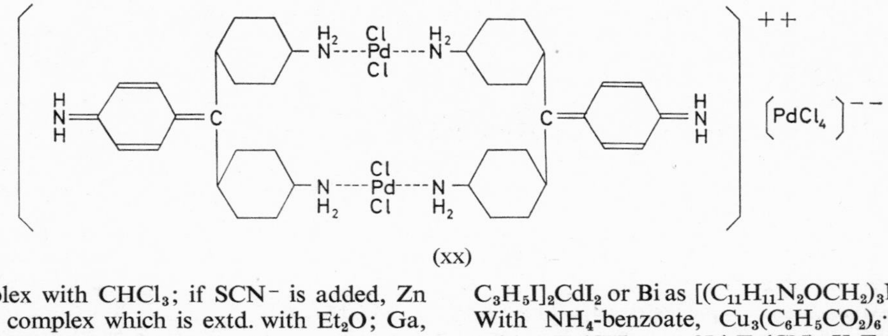

(XX)

Triethylenetetramine is used titrimetrically for Cu. *Diethylenetriamine* forms blue colors with Cu, purple with Ni and Cr and yellow with Co and Mn; Ni, Co are detd. colorimetrically. 3-*Dimethylaminopropylamine* is used colorimetrically for Cu.

(*14*) *Biguanide* (diguanide, guanylguanidine) (NH-$[C(NH)NH_2]_2$) ppts. Cu and Ni (titrimetric detn.); Cu or Hg can be detd. by pptn. of $Cu(C_2H_7N_5)_2HgI_4$. *Ethylenebiguanide* ppts. Cu and Ni. o-*Phenylenebiguanide* forms yellow, red or brown colors with Ag, Hg^{2+}, Cu, Bi, Sb^{3+}, Zn, Co^{2+}, Co^{3+} and Ni. *Potassium dicyanoguanidine* ($KC_3N_5H_2$) reacts with Fe^{3+}, Cu, Ag, Hg^+, Pd, Pt and Au.[14] *Nitroaminoguanidine* (HNC-$(NHNO_2)NHNH_2$) forms a ppt. with Ni in NH_4OH and a blue soln. on addn. of NaOH (specific for Ni).

(*15*) *Ethylenediamine* (en) forms white or yellow ppts. with Cu, Hg^{2+}, Ni and U. Co is detd. colorimetrically in alk. soln. $S_2O_3^{2-}$ (0·04 mg.) forms violet $[Ni(en)_2]S_2O_3$. $[Cu(en)_2]Hg$(or Cd)I_4, $Ag(SCN)_2[Co(en)_2(SCN)_2]$, $[Pd(en)_2]HgI_4$, $[Co(en)_2(SCN)_2]BiI_4$, $[Co(en)_3(SCN)_2]$-$(BiI_4)I$, and $[Cr(en)_3]SbS_4 \cdot 2H_2O$ can be used as weighing forms (see the metal required).

Propylenediamine (pn) $(CH_3CH(NH_2)CH_2NH_2)$ gives colors with Cu, Au, Fe, etc. It forms complex salts of the above type with Cu and Ag or Hg (q.v.). *Triethylenediamine* with I^- forms a red Bi ppt. *Piperazine* (diethylenediamine) (XXII) behaves likewise with Bi,

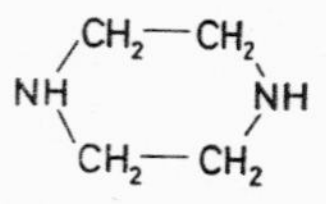

(XXII)

and also ppts. Pb (0·05 μg.), Tl, Sb, Sn, Au (0·5 μg.); with SCN^- or Br^- and MoO_4^{2-} present, Co, Cu, Zn, Fe, In and Au ppt.; Mo, W and V form crystals (orange, yellow and black, resp.) in presence of pyrogallol and AcOH.

(*16*) *Methylamine* ppts. Bi if I^- is added; Ag forms crystals and Ni gives a blue color on heating. In presence of I^-, *diethylamine* ppts. Sn, Sb, *diethylaminoethanol capryl ester* ppts. Cd (sensitive),[15] *tetraacetylammonium hydroxide* ppts. Bi (sol. in C_6H_6), *tetramethylammonium chloride* ppts. Ge, and *tetraethylammonium chloride* ppts. Sb and Bi. The last compd. also ppts. Au; the corresponding I^- salt forms crystals with Sb and Bi (white and yellow resp.) but if the soln. also contains I^-, Sb^{5+} and Bi (0·26 μg.) form reddish ppts.; the corresponding Br^- salt is used to detect Pt metals and ppts. Tl if I^- is added.

Phenyltrimethylammonium iodide (trimethylphenylammonium iodide) in presence of I^- ppts. Cd (as $[C_6H_5(CH_3)_3N]_2CdI_4$), Cu, Bi, Pb, Ag, Sb and Hg; Cd and Bi are detd. gravimetrically. A mixture of the basic salt and carbonate forms characteristic crystals with Cu, Cd, Ni, Co, Mn and Zn. *Phenylbenzyldimethylammonium chloride* ppts. Pt (2 μg.) and is used gravimetrically. *Pinacyanol iodide* (photosensitizer) ppts. Ag and Hg (0·01 μg, blue)[16] if I^- is added.

Dibenzylamine ppts. Co and Fe in presence of SCN^-. *Tributylamine* behaves similarly; here the ppts. can be extd. and detd. colorimetrically. Co forms a blue complex in presence of OCN^-. *Butylamine* favors solvent extn. of Mg, Zn or Cd oxinate (see oxine).

(*17*) *Ethanolamine* (2-aminoethanol) forms colored complexes with Au, Ag, Co, Cu, Ni, Mn. *Triethanolamine* forms colors with Cu (blue), Ni (purple, blue on heating), Co, Fe and Mn (green, colorimetry); Bi, Sb and V ppt. in presence of I^-, Cu ppts. in presence of BO_2^-. See also Chapter 5, Section 4.3. *Iodisan* (hexamethyldiaminoisopropanol iodide) $([(CH_3)_2NC(CH_3)I]_2$-CHOH) ppts. Cd but not Zn.

Betaine $\overline{OCH_2N(CH_3)_3O}$ ppts. Au. In HBr soln. Au is detd. gravimetrically with N-(N-*bromo*-C-*tetradecylbetainyl*)-C-*tetradecylbetaine*.

Choline $(HOCH_2CH_2N(CH_3)_3OH)$ forms a green color with Co if $Fe(CN)_6^{3-}$ is added (colorimetric detn.). *Oxamide* $(CONH_2)_2$ forms a yellow color with Ni in alk. soln. *Urea* (carbamide) ppts. Sb and Sn in presence of I^-.

(*18*) m-*Nitrobenzoic acid hydrazide* ppts. Pd and A in acid solns.; Hg^{2+}, Cu, Fe, Ni, Au, Mo, Pt, Pd and Os ppt. in neutral soln.

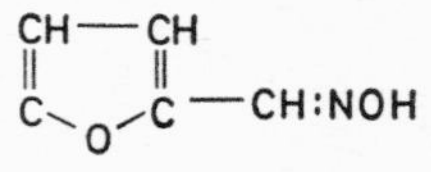

(XXIII)

β-Furfuraldoxime (XXIII) ppts. Au, Ag, Hg^+, Pb, Ce^{4+}; the ppt. $PdCl_2 \cdot (C_5H_5O_2N)_2$ is used gravimetrically or colorimetrically but $Pd(NO_3)_2$ does not ppt. and $PdSO_4$ ppts. incompletely.

References

1. SMITH, G. F., *Anal. Chem.*, **26**, 1534 (1954); FEIGL, 319 (1949); WELCHER, **III**, 64.
2. KRUSE, J. M. and BRANDT, W. W., *Anal. Chem.*, **24**, 1306 (1952).
3. WILKINS, D. H., *et al.*, *Anal. Chem.*, **27**, 1574 (1955); *Anal. Chim. Acta*, **8**, 46 (1953); **9**, 338 (1953); SCHILT, A. A. and SMITH, *ibid.*, **16**, 401 (1957).
4. IRVING, H. M. and HAMPTON, A., *J. Chem. Soc.*, 430 (1955).
5. WALTER, J., and FREISER, H., *Anal. Chem.*, **25**, 518 (1953); **26**, 217 (1954).
6. ERLENMEYER, H. and SCHMID, E. H., *Helv. Chim. Acta*, **22**, 1369 (1939).
7. FEIGL, 284 (1949).

8. SHIHO, D. and TAKABAYASHI, N., *J. Chem. Soc. Japan*, **76**, 877 (1955).
9. GUSEV, S. I., *J. Applied Chem. U.S.S.R.*, **18**, 247 (1945).
10. STEELE, E. L. and YOE, J. H. *Anal. Chem.*, **29**, 1622 (1957); WINGFIELD, H. C. and YOE, J. H., *Anal. Chim. Acta*, **14**, 446 (1956).
11. FEIGL, F., *Anal. Chem.*, **21**, 1303 (1949).
12. BUSCARÓNS, F. and NIETO, F., *Anal. Chim. Acta*, **14**, 401 (1956).
13. BÉVILLARD, P., *Compt. rend.*, **236**, 711 (1953); **238**, 2087 (1954).
14. DRANEY, J. J., *et al.*, *Mikrochemie ver. Mikrochim. Acta*, **35**, 238 (1950).
15. BOUILLOUX, G., *Bull. soc. chim. France*, 547 (1957).
16. VASIL'EVA, E. V., *Zhur. Anal. Khim.*, **2**, 167 (1947).

10

HYDROXY COMPOUNDS

1. COMPOUNDS FORMING COMPLEXES MAINLY WITH Fe, Ti OR Cu

1.1. Aromatic compounds

For reactions with Ti, see ref. 1.

(*1*) *5-Phenylsalicylic acid* (4-hydroxydiphenyl-3-carboxylic acid) reacts in acidic soln. with Fe^{3+} to give a violet complex which is used colorimetrically (and indirectly for F^- detn.). UO_2^{2+} gives a pink color; in alk. soln. Cu forms a green complex.

Salicylic acid (*o*-hydroxybenzoic acid) forms a red complex with Ti and yellow with W in acid soln.; UO_2^{2+}, Cu, Fe^{3+} and V give red or violet colors in neutral soln.; Ce^{4+} forms a black ppt. which turns grey with NH_4OH. Ti, UO_2^{2+} and Fe^{3+} (hence F^-) are detd. colorimetrically. Ti and Al are sepd. from Zr, Th, and partly from Nb, Ta, by pouring the sample soln. into hot 10% NH_4-salicylate.

Sulfosalicylic acid (salicylsulfonic acid) forms a violet complex with Fe^{3+} in acid soln. (colorimetry) and a yellow complex in alk. soln. Ti, Nb and Be also react, the Be complex showing an absorption peak at 317 mμ at pH 9·2–10·8; they are detd. colorimetrically. The acid is used to sep. Ti from Fe. *Acetylsalicylic acid* (aspirin) forms a reddish complex with Mn (0·1 μg./ml.) if NH_4OH and H_2O_2 are added. *5-Nitrosalicylic* or *3,5-dinitrosalicylic acid* serves for Fe colorimetry below pH 5·8.

Thymol (3-hydroxy-4-isopropyltoluene) is used colorimetrically for Ti in H_2SO_4 soln. Cu forms reddish colors with *α-naphthol* on boiling in 0·1*N* HCl, with *β-naphthol* in NH_4OH soln. and with *phenol.* These 3 phenolic compds. turn purple if heated with WO_4^{2-} in H_2SO_4. GeO_4^{2-} gives a pink color (blue light) if phthalic acid is also added.

R Salt (2-naphthol-3,6-disulfonic acid, Na salt) is used colorimetrically for U at pH 4·2. *Naphtholtrisulfonic acid* gives a blue complex with Fe^{3+}.

(*2*) *Resorcinol* (1,3-dihydroxybenzene) in NH_4OH solns. forms colors with Pb, Cu, Cd, Fe (blue supernate), Ni, Mn (both bluish), Co (violet) and Pt (red). Zn (10 μg./ml.) forms a yellow color which turns blue on heating and red on acidifying (colorimetry). Ce, La, Th and Zr also react.

Pyrocatechol (catechol, pyrocatechuic acid, 1,2-dihydroxybenzene) forms a reddish 1:1 complex with Ti in weakly acidic to 80% H_2SO_4 solns. Fe^{3+} forms a green 1:2 complex in acid soln. and a red 1:3 complex in NH_4OH soln., where Co and Ce^{4+} also form reddish colors. In tartaric acid-contg. soln. Sb ppts.; in $(NH_4)_2C_2O_4$ soln. Nb and Ta react, Ta being detd. colorimetrically; BuOH extn. permits sepn. of Ta and Ti from Nb. Mo, V and W give orange crystals; those of V and W turn more yellow in color on addn. of aniline or benzylamine.

Hydroquinone gives a red color with Ti in acidic soln. and blue with Cu in NaOH soln.; W and Ta are detd. colorimetrically in H_2SO_4 soln., Ta forming a 1:2 complex.

Tiron (tiferron, Na-pyrocatecholdisulfonate, 1,2-dihydroxybenzene-3,5-disulfonate) forms in feebly acidic solns. a blue color with Fe^{3+} (0·05 μg., the color is violet in neutral and red in alk. soln.; it is not bleached by F^- or PO_4^{3-}), a purple color with V^{4+} and yellow colors with Ti, Nb, Ce, MoO_4^{2-}, OsO_4^{2-} and UO_2^{2+}; all but V and Os are detd. colorimetrically. Tiron also serves as an indicator and masking agent in chelatometric titrations (p. 30).

Chromotropic acid (1,8-dihydroxynaphthalene-3,6-disulfonic acid) forms colored complexes with many metals: green with Fe^{3+} at pH 1·6–6·2, reddish with Cu at pH 5–11, yellow with Hg^{2+} at pH 3–6, reddish with UO_2^{2+} at pH 4–10, red with Nb; the colors formed with WO_4^{2-}, MoO_4^{2-} and VO^- are yellow at pH values of 4·3–6, 4–7 and 0–6 resp., and red at pH 6·2–10, 7·9–10·5 and 8–10 resp. In strong acid solns. Ti forms a violet 1:1 complex with an absorption peak at 530 mμ; the color lightens as the pH increases, being yellow at pH 5·1–9 (1:2 complex); at pH 0·8–3·8 the red 1:2–1:4 complex shows a peak at 470 mμ. B is detd. colorimetrically. Ag is pptd. as a yellow complex at pH 0–6 and a brown complex at pH 8–10.[2] *Dinitrosochromotropic acid* is used colorimetrically for Th at pH 2·5–3·4.

β-Resorcylic acid (2,4-dihydroxybenzoic acid) reacts with Fe, U and Cd in NH_4OH soln. *Protocatechuic acid* (the 3,4-compd.) forms a green-blue complex with Fe^{2+} and Fe^{3+} at pH 3 which becomes red at pH 8·5.

Resacetophenone (2,4-dihydroxyacetophenone) reacts with Fe^{3+}, Cu (gravimetric detn.), Hg, Mn and Al. *Protocatechuic aldehyde* forms a green-violet color with Fe^{3+} in acid soln.; the reddish color in alk soln. is used colorimetrically; Mo also reacts. *Vanillin* (4-hydroxy-3-methoxybenzaldehyde) gives a bluish complex with Fe^{3+}. *2,5-Dihydroxy-1,4-benzoquinone* reacts with Sc (40 μg./3 ml.), Th and the Y group but not with the Ce group.[3]

2,4-Dinitroresorcinol forms a brown complex with Cu (4 μg.), green-blue with Fe^{3+} and green with Fe^{2+} (0·2 μg./ml.).

Chloranilic acid is used colorimetrically for Mo, forming the 1:1 complex.

(*3*) *Pyrogallol* (1,2,3-trihydroxybenzene, pyrogallic acid) ppts. Sb (gravimetric detn.), Bi, Fe^{2+}, Fe^{3+}, Os^{8+}, Th in acidic soln.; it forms a blue complex with V, yellow with Ti (weakly acidic, 1:4 complex; 80% H_2SO_4, 2:3 complex) and with Ta ($C_2O_4^{2-}$ addn.), and orange with Mo. In NH_4OH soln. it yields red, violet and yellow complexes with Ti, Ce^{4+} and Nb ($C_2O_4^{2-}$ addn.) resp. If formanilide is added (*pyrogallol aldehyde*), Ti and Zr ppt.; if SO_3^{2-} is added, Cu forms a red color. The *tribromo* compd. ppts. Bi (8 μg./ml.).

Hydroxyhydroquinone (1,2,4-trihydroxybenzene) ppts. Fe^{3+}, Fe^{2+}, Ce^{4+} but not Sb or Bi. *Phloroglucinol* (1,3,5-trihydroxybenzene) reacts with Fe and Hg (20 μg./ml.).

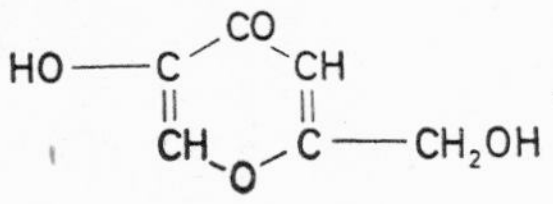

(I)

Gallic acid (3,4,5-trihydroxybenzoic acid) in acidic solns. ppts. Bi (gravimetric detn.), Sb, Hg, Ag, Sn, and forms yellow complexes with Ti (80% H_2SO_4, 1:4 complex), Nb, Ta, Mo (colorimetry), and bluish complexes with Fe^{3+} and V. In NH_4OH soln. Ce^{4+}, Th and Pb react. *Pyrogallolcarboxylic acid* reacts with Ti and *pyrogallolsulfonic acid* with Fe, Nb, Ta, Bi and Ce.

(*4*) *Kojic acid* (I) and *phenylpyruvate* are used colorimetrically for Fe^{3+}; the former also reacts with Cu. *Meconic acid* (II) forms a red 1:2 Fe^{3+} complex and a

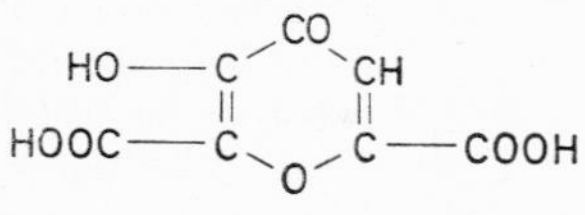

(II)

V^{4+} complex (0·1 μg.). *Citrinin* reacts with Fe^{3+} (2·5 μg.);[4] *benzoin* ($C_6H_5CHOHCOC_6H_5$) gives a green fluorescence with Zn. *5,7-Dihydroxy-4-methylcoumarin* forms a red complex with Cu in NH_4OH soln.[5] *Resoflavine* (Colour Index 1015) reacts with Ti.

1.2. Aliphatic compounds

(*1*) *Dihydroxymaleic acid* is used colorimetrically for Ti. *Acetonedicarboxylic acid* ppts. Hg (1 μg., HCl soln.) and Mn^{2+} and forms a pink color with Fe^{2+}; the *ethyl ester* is used colorimetrically for Cu.

(*2*) *Glycerol* (glycerine) gives a yellow color with Fe; if NaOCl is added, Cu and Co form brownish colors.

(*3*) *Tartaric*, *citric* and *tartronic acids* are often used as masking agents, e.g. for Fe, Al, Ti, Zr.

(*4*) *Ascorbic acid* is used colorimetrically for Ti (hence for F^-) and U^{6+} (p. 302).

2. β-DIKETONES

(*1*) *Acetylacetone* (2,4-pentanedione) [b.p. 139°C, sol. in H_2O (0·17 g./ml.), Et_2O, etc.] forms complexes with many metals (Table 22);[6] the complexes are sol. in org. solvents as well as in the reagent itself. Acetylacetone reacts with Tl to give a yellow color or an orange ppt. if CS_2 in C_6H_6 is added (III).

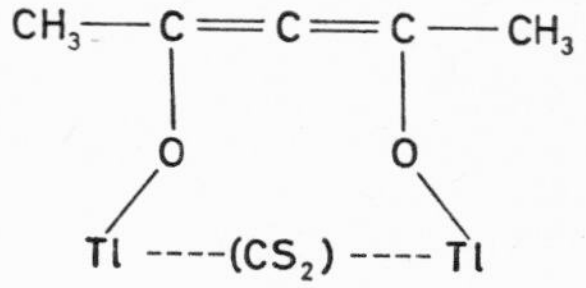

(III)

(*2*) *Benzoylacetone* ($C_6H_5COCH_2COCH_3$) ppts. Cu and forms colors with Co and Ni in neutral soln.

Dibenzoylmethane (benzoylacetophenone) (C_6H_5-$COCH_2COC_6H_5$) [m.p. 76–78°C, sol. in EtOH, C_6H_6, etc., insol. in H_2O] is used colorimetrically for U; Co and Ni also react; Fe forms a red 1:1 complex (ϵ = 1060 at 505 mμ[7]); Pu^{4+} can be extd. *2-Acetoacetylpyridine* is a better reagent for U but *2-furoylbenzoylmethane* is most sensitive.[8] For other analogs, see refs. 8 and 9.

The affinity of these compds. for Cu is roughly proportional to the percentage of the enolic form (which

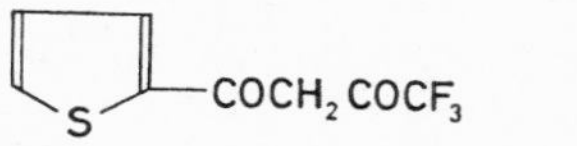

(IV)

is given in parentheses) in the following order: dibenzoylmethane (100) > acetylacetone (80·4) ≫ acetonedicarboxylic acid ester (16·8) > acetoacetic ester (7·4).[10]

(*3*) *2-Thenoyltrifluoroacetone* (TTA, 1-(2-thienyl)-4,4,4-trifluoro-1,3-butanedione) (IV) [m.p. 42·5–43·2°C] forms complexes with many metals (Table 22) but is mainly used in sepns. of actinide metals. In addn. to those mentioned, Os^{3+} and Ru^{3+} form reddish complexes and Th and Zr ppt. Tl^+ forms a yellowish complex if CS_2 is added. For other analogs, see ref. 11.

Th is sepd. from Ra, Ac, etc. by extn. with 0·25*M* reagent in C_6H_6 from HNO_3 soln. (pH 2·5) or with

TABLE 22. Acetylacetonates and Thenoyltrifluoroacetonates[a]

Metal	Acetylacetone Reagent	Acetylacetone Reagent in $CHCl_3$	TTA Reagent in C_6H_6
Cu	pH 2–6, 86%, 345 mμ, + EDTA, 10%	pH 0·5–2·7, 10–87%	pH 3·4 (0·02)[b], blue, 500 mμ
Be	pH 2–3, 100%	pH 5–10, 100%, + EDTA selective (C_6H_6)	pH 6–7 (0·02), 380 mμ
Zn	pH 5·5–7, 70%	pH 4·0–6·0, 10–60%	
Al	pH > 4, 92%	pH 0·95–4·4, 10–90%	pH 5·5 (0·02)
Ce	Ce^{3+}, pH > 4		Ce^{4+}, 1*N* H_2SO_4 (0·5*M* in xylene)
Ga	pH > 2·5, 95%	pH 0·3–1·5, 10–99%	
In	pH > 2·8, 100%		
Ti		pH 0–1·6, 10–76%	
Zr	pH 2–3, 73%	pH 0·9–2·3, 10–70%	2*M* $HClO_4$ (0·02 or 0·5*M* in xylene), 2–10*N* HNO_3, 1·3–8 *N*HCl
Pb	pH > 4, 5%; pH > 9, 80%, 347 mμ		pH > 4 (0·25)
V^{3+}		pH 2·4, 100%	
V^{4+}	pH 2·5, 73%	pH 0–2·1, 10–70%	
Bi	pH < 1, 10%, pH > 1, 0%; + EDTA, ca. 0%		pH > 2 (0·25)
Cr^{3+} (complex)		pH −0·3 (2*N* acid)–2·0, 99–99·5%	
Cr^{3+} (hydrated ion)		pH 0–6·0, 0%	
Mo		pH −0·8 (6*N* acid)–2·0, 96–98%	
W		pH 0–4·5, 0%	
Mn	pH ca. 4	pH 5·5–6·5, 10–20%	yellow
Fe^{2+}		pH 0–2·5, 0%	
Fe^{3+}	pH 1·5, red	pH −0·3 (2*N* acid)–1·5, 10–99·9%	pH 2–3 (0·02), red, colorimetric detn.
Co^{2+}	pH 0·3–2, 100%	pH 0–6·0, 0%	
Co^{3+}		pH −0·3 (2*N* acid)–2·0, 95–99·5%	
Ni		pH 0–6·6, 0%	green
Th		pH > 5·8 (C_6H_6)	pH > 0·8 (0·25)
U^{6+}	pH 4–7, 365 mμ	+ EDTA, sepn. from Bi (C_6H_6)	pH > 3·0 (0·2), yellow
Np^{4+}			0·5*M* H^+ (0·15)
Pu^{4+}		pH 2–10 (C_6H_6)	0·5*M* H^+ (0·15)

[a] The percentages given indicate the completeness of the extn.
[b] The figures in parentheses indicate the molarity of the TTA soln.

reagent in CCl_4 from $HClO_4$ soln. (pH 2), and by stripping with 6*M* HCl.[12] Zr is sepd. from Hf by extn. with 0·02*M* reagent in C_6H_6 from 2*M* $HClO_4$;[13] alternatively, Zr is extd. with 0·5*M* reagent in xylene from 2–10*M* HNO_3 or 1·3–8*M* HCl (2*M* for micro and 6*M* for macro amts.) by shaking for over 10 min.[14] Ce is sepd. from other rare earths with 0·5*M* TTA in xylene from solns. contg. $K_2Cr_2O_7$ and $NaBrO_3$ and *N* H_2SO_4 and by stripping with 10*M* H_2SO_4.[15] Np, Pu,[16] Am and Cm, etc.[17] can be extd.

2-Furoyltrifluoroacetone is used for extn. of Pu and gravimetric detn. of Pd.

(*4*) *Dipivaloylmethane* ($(CH_3)_3CCOCH_2COC(CH_3)_3$) permits sepn. of Li from Na and K by extn. with 0·1*N* reagent in Et_2O (see alkali metals).

3. COMPOUNDS FORMING ESTERS WITH BORIC OR GERMANIC ACID[18]

(*1*) *Methanol* forms a volatile ester with boric acid in presence of a dehydrating agent; it is used for the sepn. or flame photometric detn. (0·01 μg.) of B. *Ethanol* is less satisfactory.

(*2*) *Mannitol* (*d*-mannite) allows the titration of boric, germanic, vanadic and telluric acids as strong acids; this is one of the most reliable methods for B detn. *Sorbitol* is the most sensitive reagent for B (0·003 μg./ml.) if NaCl is added.[19] *Glycerol, invert sugar, sucrose, fructose and Ca-gluconate*[20] have also been used for B detn. Fructose is preferable to mannitol for Ge detn. (p. 211). For a study of the reaction of B with polyhydric alcohols, see ref. 21.

(*3*) *Resacetophenone* gives fluorescence with BO_2^- in EtOH and with Ge in AcOH if H_3PO_4 is added (see Chapters 28 and 61).

(*4*) *Propylene glycol* is used in the titration of tellurate.

(*5*) *Alizarin*, see Chapter 12, p. 92.

References

1. SOMMER, L., *Chem. listy*, **50**, 1702, 1711, 1729 (1956); **51**, 875 (1957); SHNAĬDERMAN, S. YA., *Ukrain. Khim. Zhur.*, **23**, 92 (1957).
2. SHNAĬDERMAN, S. YA. and MOVCHAN, N. P., *Ukrain. Khim. Zhur.*, **19**, 429 (1953).
3. POKRAS, L. and KILPATRICK, M., *Anal. Chem.*, **25**, 1270 (1953).
4. LIANG, S. C., *Sci. Record* (*China*), **2**, 72, 373 (1949).
5. OKÁČ, A. and HORAK, J., *Chem. listy*, **49**, 1402 (1955).
6. STEINBACH, J. F. and FREISER, H., *Anal. Chem.*, **25**, 881 (1953); **26**, 375 (1954); MCKAVENEY, J. P. and FREISER, H., *ibid.*, **29**, 290 (1957); KRISHEN, A. and FREISER, H., *ibid.*, **29**, 288 (1957).
7. LIBERTI, A. and COLLOTTI, G., *Ricerca Sci.*, **24**, 384 (1953).
8. YAMANE, Y., *J. Pharm. Soc. Japan*, **77**, 386, 391, 396, 400 (1957).
9. MUSANTE, C., *Gazz. chim. ital.*, **76**, 123 (1946).
10. MOORE, T. S. and YOUNG, M. W., *J. Chem. Soc.*, 2694 (1932).
11. KINGDON, K. W. and MELLON, M. G., *Anal. Chem.*, **28**, 860 (1956).
12. MEINKE, W. W. and ANDERSON, R. E., *Anal. Chem.*, **24**, 708 (1952); MENIS, O., *et al.*, *ibid.*, **29**, 1426 (1957).
13. HUFFMAN, E. H. and BEAUFAIT, JR., L. F., *J. Am. Chem. Soc.*, **71**, 3179 (1949).
14. MOORE, F. L., *Anal. Chem.*, **28**, 997 (1956).
15. SMITH, G. W. and MOORE, F. L., *Anal. Chem.*, **29**, 448 (1957).
16. MOORE, F. L., *Anal. Chem.*, **29**, 941, 1767 (1957).
17. MAGNUSSON, L. B. and ANDERSON, M. L., *J. Am. Chem. Soc.*, **76**, 6207 (1954).
18. FEIGL, 354 (1949).
19. BURKHALTER, T. S., *et al.*, *Anal. Chem.*, **26**, 1851 (1954); **28**, 1186 (1956).
20. OEHME, F., *Chem. Tech.*, **3**, 171, 178 (1951).
21. KINOSHITA, Y., *et al.*, *Nagoya Shiritsu Daigaku Yakugakubu Kiyo*, **5**, 32 (1957).

11

ACIDS FORMING SPARINGLY SOLUBLE SALTS

1. WITH MAINLY GROUP IV AND V ELEMENTS

1.1. With mainly Group V elements

(*1*) *Sodium or lithium tetraphenylboron* (Kalignost) ppts. K, NH_4^+, Rb and Cs and is used gravimetrically, titrimetrically or colorimetrically (see the elements concerned). The K salt is less sol. than AgCl. Certain alkaloids are also pptd. For a bibliography, see ref. 1.

(*2*) *Picric acid and its derivatives.*[2] (*i*) *Hexyl* (dipicrylamine, hexanitrodiphenylamine, NH_4-salt, aurantia, imperial yellow) (I) [Yellow, insol. in H_2O]. This is

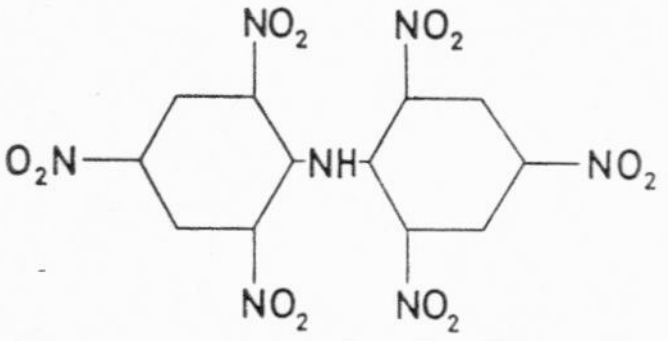

(I)

used as a 0·2–0·5*N* soln. of the Na or Mg salt. It ppts. K (3 μg.), Rb, Cs, Tl^+ completely and NH_4^+, Ba, Pb, Hg, Zr incompletely.

Dixylopicrylamine is occasionally preferable[3] while *α-hexyl* (picryl-2,4-dinitro-α-naphthylamine) is generally preferable; *dihexyl* (1,3-dipicryl-4,6-dinitrophenylenediamine) is less satisfactory.[4] *Tetranitroacridone* seems promising.[5] *2,4-Dinitronaphthosultam* (II), *thiohexyl*

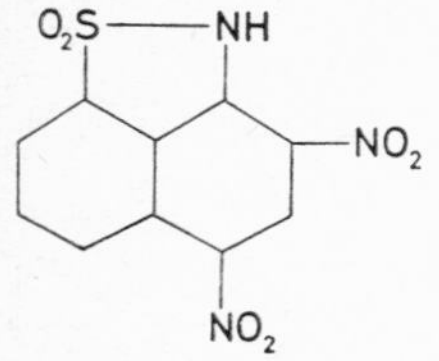

(II)

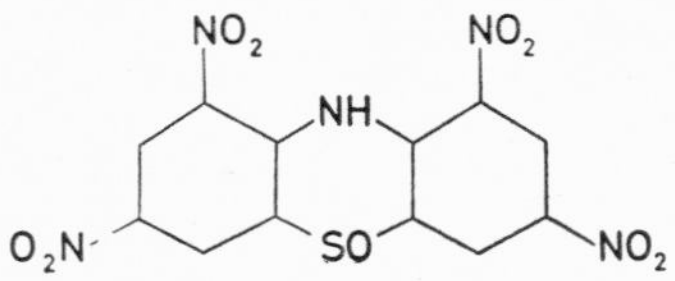

(III)

(tetranitrophenothiazine-5-oxide) (III) and *tetranitrophenothiazine-5-dioxide* have been tested.[6]

(*ii*) *Picric acid* (2,4,6-trinitrophenol, carbazotic acid) forms ppts. or crystals with Ag (20 μg.), Hg^{2+} (0·2 μg.), Pb, Cu (0·05 μg.), Bi, Cd (1 μg.), Au (0·2 μg.), Ni (0·1 μg.), Co (0·3 μg.), Zn, Ba, Mg, K, NH_4^+ and Na; K and Bi are detd. gravimetrically.

Dimethylpicric acid forms more insol. salts than picric acid with K, NH_4^+, Sr and Ba. *Na-ethylmethylpicrate* (3-ethyl-5-methyltrinitrophenol) is used gravimetrically for Ba. *Methylpropylpicric acid* ppts. Ba, Ce, Pb, Ag but not Sr or Ca.[7] *2,4,6-Trinitroresorcinol* (styphnic acid), *2,4,6-trinitro-*m*-cresol* and *2,4-* or *2,6-dinitrophenol* form crystalline needles with K and NH_4^+; o- or p-*nitrophenol* forms needles also with Mg. *NH_4-picrate* and 2,4-dinitrophenol are used to sep. Th from rare earths in pH 4·8–5·2 solns.[8]

(*iii*) *4,6-Dinitrobenzofuroxan* forms a yellow ppt. with K.[9]

(*3*) *Aromatic nitro or azo sulfonic acids.* (*i*) *Naphthol yellow S* (Na-flavianate, 2,4-dinitro-1-naphthol-7-sulfonate) ppts. K (0·4 mg./ml.), NH_4^+, Rb, Ag, Tl, Hg^+, Pb, Cu^{2+}, Fe^{2+}, Co, Ni, Zn, Mn and Mg; in acidic soln. it is specific for Zr (5 μg./ml.) in group III. *1,5-Dinitro-2-naphthol-7-sulfonate* behaves similarly. *3,4-Dihydroxyazobenzene-4′-sulfonic acid* ppts. K, Rb, Cs and Th.

(*ii*) *6-Chloro-5-nitrotoluene-3-sulfonate* (Na-salt) has sparingly sol. K, Rb and Ba salts; the *bromo deriv.* is inferior, as both the K and Na salts are less sol.

(*iii*) *Na-chrysamminate* (2,4,5,7-tetranitro-1,8-dihydroxyanthraquinone) ppts. Ca (0·3 μg.), Sr and Mg.

(*4*) *Miscellaneous compounds. Dilituric acid* (5-nitrobarbituric acid, nitromalonylurea) (IV) is used gravimetrically for K and Cd. For violuric acid, see

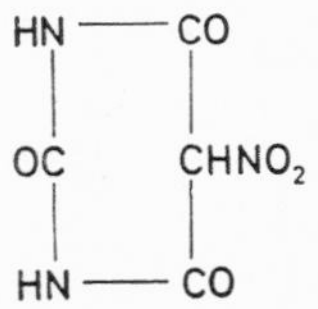

(IV)

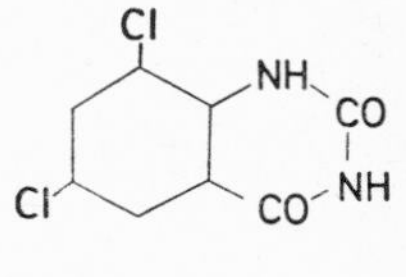

(V)

Chapter 8, Section 1.6. *6,8-Dichlorobenzoyleneurea* (V) has a sparingly sol. Na salt.

Eiconogen (Na-salt) and *naphthalene-α-sulfonic acid* give a sparingly sol. K salt. Na is detd. with *Mg-1,8-naphthylaminesulfonate* (1-amino-8-naphthalenesulfonate) either gravimetrically or titrimetrically; the soly. of the salts formed in g./l. are as follows: Na, 6·3; NH_4^+, 18·6; Li, 22·9; K, 25·3; Rb, 49·4; Mg, 111.[10]

Hymolal ($CH_2(CH_2)_nOSO_3Na$) ppts. K (8 μg.). *Locain* (locaonic acid, a glucoside) ppts. K, Ba and Pb. *γ-Methyldicyanodihydroxyhydropyridine* (VI) gives sparingly sol. K (0·6 mg.) and Na salts in acidic soln.

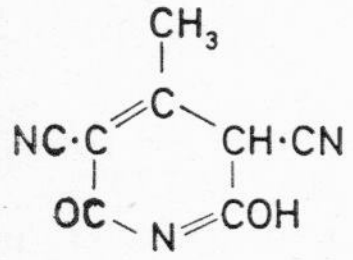

(VI)

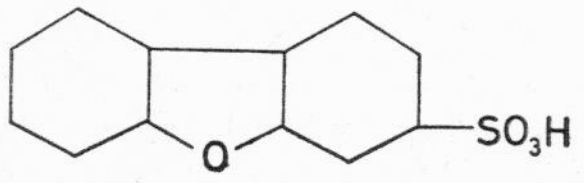

(VII)

Dibenzofuran-2-sulfonic acid (VII) has sparingly sol. alkali metal salts.[11]

α-Methoxyphenylacetic acid is more selective for Na (1:3300).[12] *5-Oxo-4-oximino-3-phenylisoxazoline* ppts. Na (red) and K (yellow).

2′-Hydroxy-4′-nitrochalcone ($C_6H_5COCH:CHC_6H_3(OH)(NO_2)$) ppts. Ca but not Ba or Sr.[13]

1.2. Polyhydroxy acids

(*1*) *Tartaric acid.* K acid tartrate ppts. from EtOH soln.; the soly. increases in the order K < Rb < Cs. Sr and Ba can be detected. Sc is detd. gravimetrically with $(NH_4)_2$-tartrate; if Ba is added, $Ba_2GeC_8H_8O_{14}\cdot 2H_2O$ and $Ba_5B_2C_{12}H_8O_{24}\cdot 4H_2O$ ppt. (see the elements concerned). *Racemic acid* is used gravimetrically for Ca. *Mesotartaric acid* masks Zr in the colorimetric detn. of Th with thoron.

Dihydroxytartaric acid forms sparingly sol. salts with Na and Li; lanthanides also ppt.[14] The *osazone of sodium dihydroxytartrate* ppts. Ca (0·1 μg.), Sr and Ba.

(*2*) *Saccharic acid* ($HOOC(CHOH)_4COOH$) ppts. Mg.

(*3*) *Rhodizonic acid* (dioxydiquinone, 1,2-dihydroxyquinoyl) (VIII). For a general discussion of aromatic

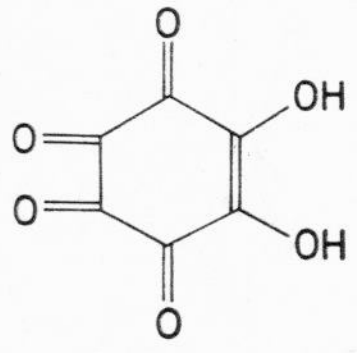

(VIII)

polyhydroxy acids, see ref. 15. The violet-black Na-salt of the acid gives an orange soln. which is used as the reagent; it becomes colorless on acidification. In neutral soln. reddish brown ppts. are formed with Hg^+, Cd, Bi, Fe^{2+}, Zn, UO_2^{2+}, Ba (0·25 μg.) and Sr (4 μg.); the ppts. are brown with Tl^+, violet with Pb (10 μg.) and orange with Cu and Hg^{2+}. In acidic soln. Sn^{2+} forms a violet ppt. and Hg^+ (fading), Tl^+, Pb, Cd and Ba reddish or brown ppts; Fe^{3+} gives a blue-green color. Dimethylamine-HCl causes the Ba color to change to bright red and the Sr color to violet.[16]

Tetrahydroxyquinone (tetrahydroxybenzoquinone) reacts similarly but is slightly less sensitive for Ba. Both these compds. are used as indicators in the titration of SO_4^{2-} with Ba^{2+}.

Triquinoyl (cyclohexanehexone) gives an orange color with Ba on heating.

Resorcinol gives a sparingly sol. salt with Na.

(*4*) *Chloranilic acid* (2,5-dichloro-3,6-dihydroxy-*p*-benzoquinone) forms ppts. with Ca, Sr, Ba, Fe, Zn, Hg^{2+}, La, Th; Ca is detd. gravimetrically and Ca and Sr colorimetrically. Several anions are detd. by exchange reactions with metal chloranilates. *Bromanilic acid* is preferable for Ca (p. 390). *Iodanilic acid hemiether* is also used colorimetrically for Ca. *Nitranilic acid* (2,5-dihydroxy-3,6-dinitroquinone) forms crystals with Na, K, NH_4^+, Ca, Ba.

5,5-Dimethylcyclohexanedione-1,3 ppts. Hg^+ (10 μg.) at pH 1·5–2.[17]

Pyrogallolcarboxylic acid ppts. Ca (colorimetric detn.), Ba and Sr.

(*5*) *2,3-Dihydroxyquinoxaline* (IX) ppts. Ba, Ca (pH 9·0–9·5) and Sr in NH_4OH soln. *Naphthylhydroxamic acid* (naphthalhydroxamic acid; *N*-hydroxynaphthal-

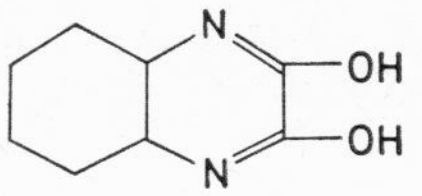

(IX)

imide) ($C_{10}H_6(CO)_2NOH$) ppts. Ca and Mg; the yellow Sr (0·1 μg./ml.) ppt. turns red-brown on heating.[18] Ca can besepd. from Mg.[19]

4,5-Benzotropolone forms a sparingly sol. Na salt.[20]

*2-Hydroxy-*1*-naphthaldehyde* is used gravimetrically for Cu, Mg and Be in NH_4OH soln.

1.3. Miscellaneous compounds

(*1*) *Picrolonic acid* (1-(*p*-nitrophenyl)-3-methyl-4-nitropyrazolone-5) (X) [Yellow–yellow-brown, m.p. 125°C decomp., sol. in EtOH, sparingly sol. in H_2O; it exists in the pseudo acid form (XI) in acidic soln]. It is used for micro-detns. of Ca (0·01 μg.) at pH 2–3, of Sr and Pb at pH 2–6·5, and of Th at pH 2–3·2. The Cu, Zn, Mn and Mg salts are also sparingly sol.; K and Na ppt. if NH_4Cl is added.

(*2*) *Oxalic acid* at pH 3–4 (acid to thymol blue) ppts. Au (as metal), Sc, Y, La, rare earths, Th, Ca, Sr completely and Ag, Bi, Cd, Cu, Pb, Sn, Ni, Co, Zn, Mn, Ta, Ba incompletely; at pH 8, Au (as metal), Bi, Sn, Fe, In, Sc, Y, La, rare earths, Nb, Ta, Ca, Sr ppt.

completely and Pb, Hg, Ni, Co, Mn, Tl, Be, Th, Ti, Zr, Hf, Li, Ba, Mg incompletely. It is used as a complexing agent in the dissoln. of bisulfate melts of Nb and Ta compds., in the detn. of Co with PbO_2, and in the detection of Mn in AcOH soln. by means of air or NaOCl oxidation.

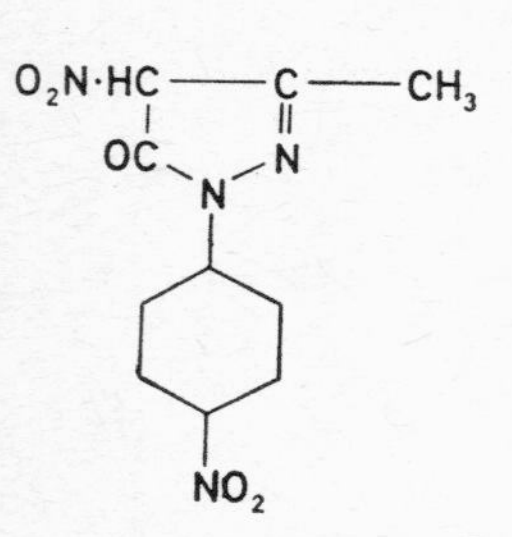

(X)

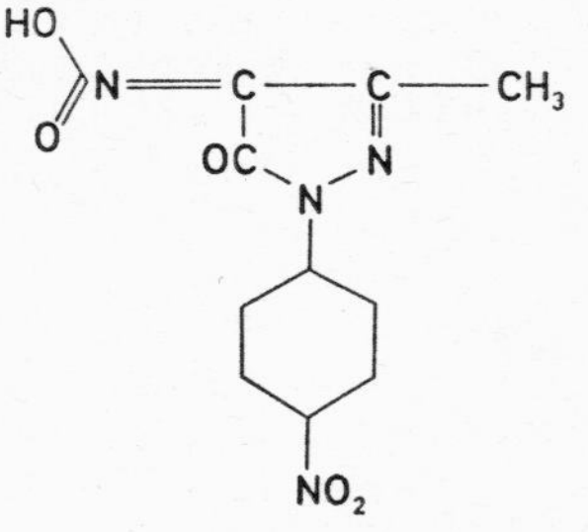

(XI)

Methyl oxalate is used for homogeneous pptn. *Malonic acid* is used to detect Ba.

(*3*) *Higher fatty acids. Oleic, stearic, palmitic, myristic acids* or their derivs., e.g. *Na-sulforicinate*, ppt. Ca, etc. and are used in the detn. of water hardness. Li is detd. nephelometrically in AmOH exts. *Na-laurylsulfate* is used titrimetrically for Ba.

Citarin (Na-anhydromethylenecitraconate) forms cryst. ppts. with Ag, Cu, Mg, Ba, Sr, Ca, Zn, Cd, Hg^{+}, Hg^{2+}, Al, Pb, Mn, Fe^{3+}, Bi and Sn.

(*4*) p-*Toluic acid* or p-*bromobenzoic acid* forms ppts. with Ca and Sr. *1-Hydroxy-2-naphthoic acid* (1-naphthol-2-carboxylic acid) forms crystals with K, NH_4^+ and Mg.

(*5*) *Sulfondiacetic acid* ($SO_2(CHCO_2H)_2$) ppts. Ba and Hg^{+}.

2. CARBOXYLIC ACIDS SELECTIVE FOR Th, Zr, ETC.

(*1*) *Tetrachlorophthalic acid* is used gravimetrically for Th at pH 1–1·2 (sepn. from rare earths) and for Zr in 2*N* HCl soln.; see Chapter 46 and Chapter 49, Zirconium.

Succinic, dibromosuccinic, phthalic and *3-nitrophthalic acids* form crystals with these metals but pptn. is incomplete; *sebacic, fumaric, adipic, 1,2-* or *1,8-naphthalic acid* ppt. them incompletely in a colloidal form; *hexahydrophthalic acid* forms no ppt.[21] Sebacic and fumaric acids had previously been widely used.

Zr (p. 355) may be detd. with phthalic acid in 0·3*N* HCl (hence detn. of F^-) or with fumaric acid in 0·25*N* HCl soln. Phthalic acid also ppts. Pb, Co, Cu and Ni.

Adipic acid is specific for Hg in the HCl group and is used gravimetrically as is *hydroxycinnamic acid*; *anthracenesuccinic acid* is used for detn. of Cd (p. 187).

(*2*) Many carboxylic acids have been used for the detn. of Th by Indian chemists. Generally, Zr is pptd. below pH 2 and Th and Fe^{3+} above pH 2; repptn. permits sepn. from rare earths, U, etc. when large amts. are present. Those acids which have been proposed are given in Table 23; a review by the authors is necessary, for it is not clear which acids are to be preferred. *2-(4-Sulfamoylphenylazo)-1,8-dihydroxynaphthalene-3,6-disulfonic acid* has also been suggested; it forms a 1:1 complex with Th and Zr and also ppts. Fe, Al and Co.[53]

(*3*) *Mandelic acid* (α-hydroxyphenylacetic or phenylglycolic acid) ($C_6H_5CHOHCOOH$) ppts. Zr in 2*M* HCl soln. permitting sepn. from Fe, Al, Ti, Th and gravimetric or colorimetric detn. (see Chapter 49, p. 355). It ppts. Cu in neutral soln.

p-*Bromomandelic acid* is preferable since the ppt. can be weighed directly after drying at 120–130°C (see Chapter 49, p. 355); other halogen-substituted mandelic acids have been tested.[54] The sepn. of rare earths has been studied.[55] m-*Azo-β-naphtholmandelic acid* is used as a spot test for Zr (0·1–10 μg.). *1-Naphthylglycolic acid* can be used gravimetrically for Zr.

Benzilic acid ($(C_6H_5)_2C(OH)COOH$) is used for Zr in 1*M* HCl; Ti interferes.[56] m-*Cresoxyacetic acid* ($CH_3C_6H_4OCH_2COOH$) is used for Zr as well as Th but SO_4^{2-} interferes.[57] Phenoxyacetic,[58] salicylic[58] and cinnamic[59] acids are used for Zr in 0·24, 0·18 and 0·1*M* HCl solns. resp.; Ti, V, Cr and Sn interfere with the last reagent. Phenoxyacetic acid also ppts. Hg.[60]

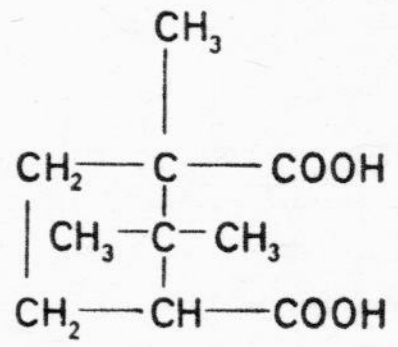

(XII)

(*4*) *Camphoric acid* (XII) ppts. Ga (p. 316) in AcOH soln. and Th at pH 4·4 (sepn. from Ce, etc.).[61]

(*5*) *2-Fluorobenzoic acid* is used colorimetrically for Fe (p. 257).

3. ARSONIC, PHOSPHONIC, SULFINIC AND SELENINIC ACIDS

3.1. Arsonic acids[62]

These are useful for Zr detns.

(*1*) *Phenylarsonic acid* (benzenearsonic acid) ($C_6H_5AsO(OH)_2$) [m.p. 158–162°C, sol. in H_2O, EtOH] ppts. Zr, Hf, Ti, Sn, Bi, Fe, Nb, Ta and U in strong mineral acid soln. and Th in acetate-buffered soln.; Zr, Bi, Sn, Nb and Ta are detd.

p-*Hydroxyphenylarsonic acid* ppts. Ti, Zr, Sn, Ce^{4+}. *Atoxyl* (Na-arsanilate, *p*-aminophenylarsonate) is used to det. Zr, Ti, Fe, Co, Cu, U and to detect Ce^{4+} (0·02 mg./ml.).

o-*Aminophenylarsonic acid* ppts. Th, Ti, etc.; for

TABLE 23. Carboxylic Acids for Detn. of Th

Acid	pH	Sepn. of	Remarks	Reference
m-Nitrobenzoic	pink to methyl orange $0{\cdot}2N$ HNO_3	Th from rare earths, Fe, U; Zr from Th	Ce^{4+}, Zr, Ti, Zn, Hg interfere, see Th	22
o-Chlorobenzoic	2·8–3·8	Th from rare earths	Sepn. from U at pH 2·6–2·8	23
Anthranilic	4·2–4·8	—	Also titrimetric detn.	24, 25
p-Aminobenzoic	4·2–4·8	—		24
5-Iodoanthranilic	4	Th from 3-fold rare earths		25
Benzoic	2·2–2·6		Also detn. of Zr	26
m-Iodobenzoic			Also 2-hydroxy-3,5-diiodobenzoic, 2,3,5-triiodobenzoic	27
p-Aminosalicylic	4–5·6	Th from 13-fold rare earths	Ignite or titrate bromometrically; also gravimetric detn. of Pd	28
p-Toluic			Also *o*-toluic or acetylsalicyclic	29
Hydroxytoluic	2·5–6·0			30
Cinnamic	2·6–2·8	Th from 50-fold rare earths		
	2–2·6	Th from 2000-fold Ce	Boiling soln.; Sn, Ti, Fe, Zr interfere	31
m-Nitrocinnamic	3·8–4·0		Weigh as salt	32
Vanillic	3·6	Th from Ce, Al, Be		33
Anisic			Also trimethylgallic; veratric is less satisfactory	34, 35
m-Hydroxybenzoic	3·5–6		More satisfactory; also stearic and pyrogallic	36
Sulfanilic	>2		Good reagent; also furoic	37
Phenoxyacetic				38
Phenylglycine-*o*-carboxylic	4·4–5·2		Also *p*-compd.	39
2,4-Dichlorophenoxy-acetic	2·8	Th from 40-fold rare earths	For Zr, use 15–20 ml. $3{\cdot}5N$ HNO_3 and 0·5 g. NH_4OAc/50 ml. soln.	40
Guaiacyloxyacetic	4·4	Th from 20-fold rare earths		40
Phenylacetic			Also phenylpropionic, 1-naphthylacetic	41, 42
Naphthionic		Th from 16-fold rare earths		43
1-Hydroxy-2-naphthoic	3·0–5		Also for Zr; also 4-bromo or nitro derivs.	44
β-Hydroxyamino-*β*-phenylpropionic	4–6	Th from 15-fold rare earths		45
Salicylic	> 4		Also 3-bromo, 5-nitro, amino, hydroxy derivs. Zr is detd. with (nitro)-salicylic, *β*- or 5-bromoresorcylic at pH 2–4; with bromo- or aminosalicylic at pH 3·2. Zr is sepd. from Th with 5-nitrosalicylic or *β*-resorcylic	46
Trichlorophenoxyacetic			Also *o*-cresoxyacetic, propionic and analogs.	47, 48
Coumaric			Also analogs	49
Diphenic	4·5–8·6	Th from 26-fold rare earths	At pH below 2, only Zr ppts.	50
m- or *p*-nitrophthalanilic	2·7–4·6		Zr also ppts. Pd can be pptd. Also analogs	51
Rhodanine-*N*-salicylic				52

the difference between the *o*-, *m*-, and *p*-compds., see ref. 63. With salicylaldehyde addn., 1 part of Sc in 2×10^8 forms a yellow ppt. p-*Butylphenylarsonic acid* is used to det. Fe^{3+}. *3-Nitro-4-phenolarsonic acid* (3-nitro-4-hydroxyphenylarsonic acid) is used gravimetrically for Sn and colorimetrically for Cd (1 μg. can be detected). m-*Nitrophenylarsonic acid* is used to detect Sn; for analogs, see ref. 63. *4-Sulfobenzenearsonic acid* acts as a masking agent for Th.[64]

(*2*) n-*Propylarsonic acid* is an excellent reagent for Zr; Ti does not interfere. *Arrhenal* (Na-methanearsonate or methylarsonate) is used to det. Zr and Ce^{4+}.

(*3*) *Thoron* (thorin, thoronol, naphtharson, APANS,

1-(*o*-arsenophenylazo)-2-naphthol-3,6-disulfonic acid) (XIII) ppts. Th, Ti, Zr, Hf, U, Be, Fe^{3+} and Li; Th (hence F^-), U, Be and Li are detd. colorimetrically. For synthesis, see ref. 65.

Neothoron (arsenazo, *o*-arsenophenylazochromotropic acid, 7-(2-arsenophenylazo)-1,8-dihydroxy-3,6-naphthalenedisulfonic acid) is red in acid and violet in

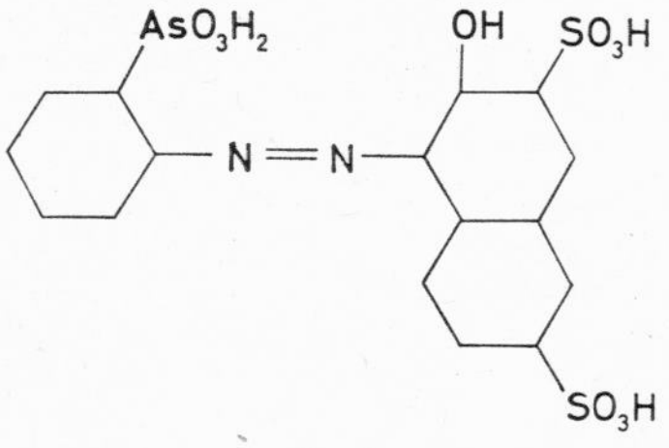

(XIII)

alk. soln. It is better for Th, giving a violet ppt. at pH 1 (see Chapter 46). It also reacts with V^{4+} (0·5 μg./ml.) when the ratio V^{4+}/V^{5+} is less than 8; if H_2O_2 is added, the violet color turns pink.

N-[*4*(o-*Arsenophenylazo*)-*1-naphthyl*]*ethylenediamine* is used colorimetrically for F^- after Th addn.

Pararsonic acid (*p*-dimethylaminoazophenylarsonic acid) ppts. Zr (0·1 μg.) and is thus used colorimetrically for F^- detn.; it also forms yellow or brown ppts. with Sn, Ce^{4+} and Ti; reddish or brown colors form with Au, Sb, Mo, W in acidic soln. *4*-(p-*Dimethylaminophenylazo*)-*diphenylarsinic acid* is used to detect Zr and F^-; for analogs, see ref. 66.

(*4*) *1-Anthraquinonearsonic acid* is sensitive to Sb.

3.2. Phosphonic and phosphinic acids

Benzenephosphonic acid[67] and *phytic acid* (C_6H_5-$[OPO(OH)_2]_6$) ppt. Th; the former is used at pH 0·5; both allow gravimetric detns. *Bis*-p-*chlorophenylphosphonic acid* and *benzenephosphinic acid* ppt. Fe^{3+}, the latter being used gravimetrically.

3.3. Sulfinic and seleninic acids[68]

(*1*) *Phenylsulfinic acid* (benzenesulfinic acid) (C_6H_5-SO_2H) ppts. Th (gravimetric detn.), Fe, Zr, Ce^{4+}, Sn, U^{4+}. The p-*bromo* or *chloro derivs*. behave similarly. *Naphthyl-1-* (*or -2-*)*sulfinic acid* is not suitable.

(*2*) *Phenylseleninic acid* ppts. Fe^{3+}, Mo, W, etc.; Mo and W are probably pptd. in the form of heteropoly acids. In acidic soln. Ti, Zr, Hf, Th, Ce, Sn, Pb, Nb, Ta, Bi are completely pptd.; in 2*N* HNO_3 media, only Zr, Sn, Ti, Nb, Ta and Ce^{4+} ppt. and the last 4 metals can be kept in soln. with H_2O_2.[69]

Phenyltellurinic acid ppts. Ag in addn. to the above metals. No pptn. occurs with selenonic or telluronic acid; for analogs, see ref. 69.

References

1. Barnard, Jr., A. J., *Chemist Analyst.*, **44**, 104 (195 ; Barnard, and Büechl, H., *ibid.* **45**, 110 (1956); **46**, 16 (1957); Mukoyama, T., *Kagaku no Ryoiki*, **10**, 105 (1956).
2. Feigl: 280 (1949).
3. Malatesta, L., *Gazz. chim. ital.*, **77**, 147 (1947).
4. Ishibashi, M. and Toei, K., *J. Chem. Soc. Japan*, **76**, 104 (1955).
5. Toei, K., *Japan Analyst*, **3**, 76 (1954).
6. Toei, K., *J. Chem. Soc. Japan*, **77**, 670, 1083, 1270 (1956).
7. Moore, C. E., *et al.*, *Anal. Chim. Acta*, **15**, 1 (1956).
8. Rao, C. L., *et al.*, *J. Indian Chem. Soc.*, **28**, 261 (1951).
9. Rathsburg, H. and Scheuerer, A., *Die Chemie*, **56**, 12 (1943).
10. Dranitskaya, R. M. and Dremlyuk, R. L., *Ukrain. Khim. Zhur.*, **22**, 821 (1956).
11. Wendland, R. T. and Smith, C. H., *J. Am. Chem. Soc.*, **71**, 1593 (1949).
12. Reeve, W. and Christoffel, I., *Anal. Chem.*, **29**, 102 (1957).
13. Almássy, Gy., *et al.*, *Magyar Kém. Folyóirat*, **60**, 373 (1954).
14. Beck, G., *Mikrochim. Acta*, 1495 (1950).
15. Feigl, 174 (1949).
16. Llacer, A. J., *Mikrochim. Acta*, 921 (1955).
17. Duval, C. and Wadier, C., *Compt. rend.*, **240**, 433 (1955).
18. Beck, G., *Mikrochemie ver. Mikrochim. Acta*, **36**/**37**, 245 (1951).
19. Flaschka, H. and Huditz, F., *Radex Rundschau*, 181 (1952).
20. Williams, G. E., *et al.*, *Proc. S. Dakota Acad. Sci.*, **31**, 199 (1952).
21. Gordon, L., *et al.*, *Anal. Chem.*, **21**, 1323 (1949).
22. Osborn, G. H., *Analyst*, **73**, 381 (1948); Venkataramaniah, M. and Rao, Bh. S. V. R., *Z. anal. Chem.*, **133**, 248 (1951).
23. Rao, B. R. L. and Rao, Bh. S. V. R., *J. Indian Chem. Soc.*, **27**, 457, 610 (1950).
24. Murthy, D. S. N. and Rao, Bh. S. V. R., *J. Indian Chem. Soc.*, **27**, 459 (1950).
25. Datta, S. K. and Banerjee, G., *J. Indian Chem. Soc.*, **31**, 779 (1954).
26. Rao, C. L. and Rao, Bh. S. V. R., *J. Sci. Ind. Research (India)*, **10B**, (7) 152, 254 (1951); Venkataramaniah, M., *et al.*, *Analyst*, **77**, 103 (1952).
27. Datta, S. K. and Banerjee, G., *J. Indian Chem. Soc.*, **32**, 167 (1955).
28. Datta, S. K. and Banerjee, G., *J. Indian Chem. Soc.*, **32**, 231 (1955); *Anal. Chim. Acta*, **13**, 23 (1955).
29. Rao, B. R. L. and Rao, Bh. S. V. R., *J. Indian Chem, Soc.*, **27**, 569 (1950).
30. Deshmukh, G. S., *Naturwissenschaften*, **42**, 69 (1955).
31. Venkateswarlu, C. and Rao, Bh. S. V. R., *Naturwissenschaften*, **42**, 636 (1955); Krishnamurty, K. V. S. and Venkateswarlu, C., *Rec. trav. chim.*, **71**, 668 (1952).
32. Verma, M. R., *et al.*, *Nature*, **178**, 324 (1956).
33. Krishnamurty, K. V. S. and Purushottam, A., *J. Indian Chem. Soc.*, **28**, 671 (1951).
34. Krishnamurty, K. V. S. and Rao, Bh. S. V. R., *J. Indian Chem. Soc.*, **28**, 261 (1951).
35. Venkataramaniah, M., *et al.*, *J. Indian Chem. Soc.*, **27**, 81 (1950).

36. DESHMUKH, G. S. and XAVIER, J., *J. Indian Chem. Soc.*, **29**, 911 (1952).
37. LAKSHMINARAYANA, D. and RAO, BH. S. V. R., *J. Indian Chem. Soc.*, **29**, 551 (1952).
38. VENKATARAMANIAH, M., *et al.*, *J. Indian Chem. Soc.*, **27**, 81 (1950).
39. DATTA, S. K. and BANERJEE, G., *J. Indian Chem. Soc.*, **31**, 149 (1954).
40. DATTA, S. K. and BANERJEE, G. *J. Indian Chem. Soc.*, **31**, 397, 773, 929 (1954); *Anal. Chim. Acta*, **12**, 323 (1955).
41. PURUSHOTTAM, A. and RAO, BH. S. V. R., *Z. anal. Chem.*, **141**, 87 (1954).
42. DATTA, S. K. and BANERJEE, G., *Anal. Chim. Acta*, **12**, 38 (1955).
43. VENKATARAMANIAH, M. and RAO, BH. S. V. R., *Analyst*, **75**, 553 (1950).
44. DATTA, S. K., *J. Indian Chem. Soc.*, **33**, 257, 394 (1956).
45. BANERJEE, G., *Z. anal. Chem.*, **147**, 348 (1955).
46. DATTA, S. K., *J. Indian Chem. Soc.*, **32**, 687 (1955).
47. DATTA, S. K., *Anal. Chim. Acta*, **14**, 39 (1956).
48. DATTA, S. K., *Naturwissenschaften*, **42**, 439 (1955).
49. VERMA, M. R., *et al.*, *Z. anal. Chem.*, **152**, 427 (1956).
50. BANERJEE, G., *Z. anal. Chem.*, **147**, 404, 409 (1955); **148**, 105 (1955).
51. DATTA, S. K., *Z. anal. Chem.*, **147**, 259, 267, 324 (1955).
52. ROUT, M. K., *J. Indian Chem. Soc.*, **33**, 683 (1956).
53. DATTA, S. K., *Z. anal. Chem.*, **153**, 89 (1956).
54. BELCHER, R., *et al.*, *Anal. Chim. Acta*, **10**, 37 (1954).
55. WEAVER, B., *Anal. Chem.*, **26**, 476 (1954).
56. KLINGENBERG, J. J., *et al.*, *Anal. Chem.*, **26**, 754 (1954); VENKATARAMANIAH, M. and RAO, BH. S. V. R., *J. Indian Chem. Soc.*, **28**, 257 (1951).
57. VENKATARAMANIAH, M. and RAO, BH. S. V. R., *Anal. Chem.*, **23**, 539 (1951); **24**, 747 (1952).
58. SASTRI, T. V. and RAO, BH. S. V. R., *J. Indian Chem. Soc.*, **28**, 530 (1951).
59. VENKATESWARLU, C. and RAO, BH. S. V. R., *J. Indian Chem. Soc.*, **28**, 354 (1951).
60. DATTA, S. K., *J. Indian Chem. Soc.*, **30**, 657 (1953).
61. MURTHY, D. S. N. and RAO, BH. S. V. R., *J. Indian Chem. Soc.*, **30**, 218 (1953).
62. FEIGL, 291 (1949); WELCHER, **IV** 49; *Org. Reactions*, **2**, 415 (1944) (synthesis).
63. PIETSCH, R., *Mikrochim. Acta*, 954, 1019 (1955).
64. MARGERUM, D. W., *et al.*, *Anal. Chem.*, **25**, 249 (1953).
65. MARGERUM, *et al.*, *Anal. Chem.*, **25**, 1219 (1953).
66. TSUJI, K., *et al.*, *J. Pharm. Soc. Japan*, **74**, 1180, 1184 (1954).
67. BANKS, C. V. and DAVIS, R. J., *Anal. Chim Acta*, **12**, 418 (1955).
68. FEIGL, 289 (1949).
69. ALIMARIN, I. P. and SOTNIKOV, V. S., *Doklady Akad. Nauk S.S.S.R.*, **113**, 105 (1957).

ADSORPTION COMPOUNDS AND MISCELLANEOUS COMPLEXES

1. TANNIN[1]

Tannin (gallotannic or tannic acid, erroneously called digallic acid) [Pale yellow–pale brown, sol. in H_2O or EtOH] dissolves in H_2O as a negative colloid; it forms adsorption compounds (which are called tannin complexes by Schoeller) with positively charged metal hydroxides or with other sols. The ppts. formed are readily filtered under gentle suction if filter paper pulp is added previously; the porous oxides obtained by ignition are easily fused with pyrosulfate. Tartrate, etc., do not interfere with the pptn. except in the case of W, but in general pptn. is affected both by the presence of complex-forming acids and by the pH of the soln. The most interesting reactions occur in oxalate solns., e.g., the sepn. of Nb and Ta.

(*1*) *Mineral acid solns.* The ppt. of W with cinchonine or antipyrine flocculates readily with tannin, permitting sepn. from U, Be, Al. Nb and Ta are pptd. by tannin in dil. H_2SO_4 soln.; they are sepd. from Ti, Zr and from V if cinchonine is added. Ti is pptd. in dil. H_2SO_4 soln. and sepd. from Fe, Al, Cr, Co, Ni, Zn, Mn, PO_4^{3-}. Ge is sepd. in dil. acid soln. from Ti, Zr, V, As, Ga, Zn, Cu, Fe, Mn. In dil. HCl soln. the order of precipitability is Ge–Zr–Sn–Ti (cf. oxalate soln. below).

(*2*) *Acetate buffer soln.* Be does not ppt. at pH 4·6 and can thus be sepd. from Al, Fe, Cr, Th, V, Ti, Zn, Sn, etc. The accuracy of the pptn. of U with NH_4OH is increased by tannin addn. when trace U is involved. Ga hydroxide is more sol. in alkali than that of Al; tannin facilitates complete pptn. and allows sepn. from Zn, Ni, Co, Mn, Cd, Be, Tl. Cu is pptd. completely by tannin. Mo forms a brown ppt. with tannin in AcOH soln.; this can be used colorimetrically for Mo, and as an external indicator in titrations of Mo, Pb, etc.

(*3*) *Tartrate soln.* In neutral soln. Al, Fe, Cr, Ga, Ti, Zr, Hf, Th, V, U, Nb, Ta ppt. completely; this is useful in trace detns. and for recovery purposes.

(*4*) *Salicylate soln.* Pptn. of Ti in NH_4OH soln. is complete on tannin addn. The reaction is similar in presence of pyrocatechol.

(*5*) *Oxalate soln.* The elements are classified into 2 groups according to the pH of pptn. The order of decreasing acidity for pptn. is as follows:

$\longleftarrow$ Group A

Sn–Ta (yellow)–Ge–Ti (red)–Nb (orange) –|–

Group B $\longrightarrow$

V(blue-black)–Fe^{3+} (purple-black)–Zr (white)–Hf–Th (white)–UO_2^{2+} (brown)–Al (white)–Cr (green).

Group A. Sn, Ta, Nb, Ge, W complexes are insol. in dil. H_2SO_4 but the Ti complex is sol. Sn, Ta, Ti, Nb, Ge complexes are insol. in weakly acidic oxalate soln. which is half-satd. with NH_4Cl. The W complex is not pptd. from solns. contg. org. acids but partial pptn. is induced by other Group A elements.

Group B. V, Fe, Zr, Th, Al, Cr complexes are sol. in weakly acidic oxalate soln. which is half-satd. with NH_4Cl, but they are insol. in ammoniacal oxalate soln. or in weakly acidic tartrate soln.

V is not present in Nb or Ta minerals, hence Group A can be sepd. from Group B by addn. of tannin to the weakly acidic oxalate soln. which has been half-satd. with NH_4Cl, after Fe has been removed with H_2S from the ammoniacal tartrate soln.

When Ti and W are absent, Ta (yellow ppt. at pH 1·9) can be sepd. from Nb (orange ppt. above pH 2·4) by adjusting the pH of the soln. while observing the color of the ppt.; the sepn. is favored by the addn. of brucine or other alkaloids (see Chapter 51).

Ge can be detd. by pptn. from an oxalate-contg. 0·07N mineral acid soln.

(*6*) *Ammoniacal soln.* (Group C). The rare earth elements, Be and Mn form white ppts.; those of Ce and Mn darken on exposure to air. The complexes are sol. in weakly acidic tartrate soln. but insol. in ammoniacal tartrate soln., the latter being useful for the detn. or recovery of traces.

2. ANTHRAQUINONE DERIVATIVES AND ANALOGS[2]

The compounds described in this and the following sections generally form colored lakes with hydroxide sols of metals in alkaline solns. and form colors with Zr, HBO_2 and H_2GeO_3 in strong acid solns.

(*1*) *Alizarin* (1,2-dihydroxyanthraquinone) (I) [Brownish yellow–orange red, m.p. 289–290°C, sol. in H_2O, EtOH, Et_2O, C_6H_6, AcOH, alkalies]. In alk. soln. alizarin forms lakes with many metals. Al (0·15 μg.) gives a purple color which varies with the conditions; the complex is not stoichiometric and may be an adsorption compd. of alizarin on the surface of the hydroxide sol.[3] In (0·05 μg.), Ga (0·03 μg.), Sb, Bi, Cu, Co, Fe^{2+}, Mn, Mg, Hg^{2+}, Pt^{2+} and Sn^{2+} also give purple colors. Cd, Sn^{4+} give orange colors, Fe^{3+}, Ti^{3+} black, Cr^{3+} (0·6 μg.) yellow, Ti, U, violet, Th purple, and Tl, CrO_4^{2-} blue. Ca, Au, Ni, Sr, Zn ppt. if the concn. exceeds 1 p.p.m.

In acidic soln. Zr (0·2 μg.) gives a red-brown color

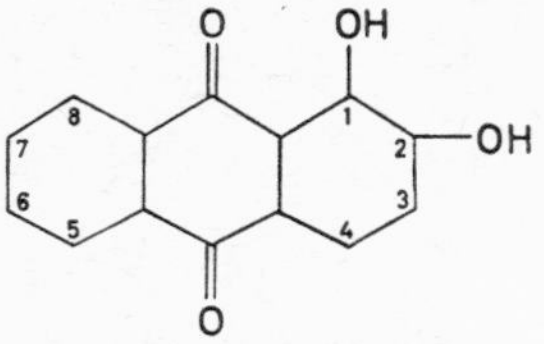

(I)

if alizarin is in excess and violet if Zr is in excess; the complex is decolorized by F^-, PO_4^{3-}, AsO_4^{3-}, SO_4^{2-}, $S_2O_3^{2-}$, $C_2O_4^{2-}$ or hydroxy organic acids. It is used colorimetrically for F^- (1 μg.). In H_2SO_4 soln. $SnCl_4$, HBO_2 and H_2GeO_3 (5 μg.) also react.

Alizarin S (alizarin red S, Na alizarin sulfonate, 1,2-dihydroxyanthraquinone-3-sulfonate) also forms lakes with many metals. Al (0·1 μg.) is detd. colorimetrically, the red lake being stable in AcOH soln.; UO_2^{2+} forms a 1:1 blue complex at pH 8·2; Ca, Cr, etc. also react in ammoniacal soln. Zr and Th (and hence F^-) are detd. colorimetrically in acid soln., while BO_2^- (1 μg. B) forms a red color. Th and Sc are sepd. from Al in dil. acid soln. Sb ppts. at pH 1·4–4·5 from 5% Na_2SO_4 soln. but As does not. Ti is detd. colorimetrically in $SnCl_2$-contg. dil. HCl soln.

Chrysazin (istizin, 1,8-dihydroxyanthraquinone) reacts with Be (10 μg.) to form a red fluorescence, with Mg (0·9 μg.) to give a red color, and with Al and Li. *Quinizarin* (1,4-dihydroxyanthraquinone) behaves similarly. *Hystazarin* (hystazine, 2,3-dihydroxyanthraquinone) forms purple lakes with Ca and Mg.

Quinizarin-2-sulfonic acid provides a satisfactory colorimetric detn. of Be (1 μg.). *1,4-Dihydroxy-5,8-dichloroanthraquinone* forms a pink color with 0·5 μg. Al, a yellow-green fluorescence with 0·1 μg., and an orange-pink fluorescence under UV light; 0·002 μg. Al can be detected by spot tests.[4] *Tetra-* or *tribromo-chrysazin* is most sensitive to B (0·001 μg.) and is used colorimetrically.[5] *1-Hydroxy-2-methylanthraquinone* forms a purple lake with Al.

(*2*) *Purpurin* (1,2,4-trihydroxyanthraquinone) [Brown-yellow, m.p. 256°C, sol. in H_2O, EtOH (yellow), alkalies (red) and Et_2O]. In H_2SO_4 soln. Zr forms an orange color (bleached by F^-) and BO_2^- (0·6 μg. B) a reddish color. Sn forms a fluorescent lake at pH 5.

Purpurin-3-sulfonic acid (alizarin red PS) is used for Al (0·5 μg.) and for F^- (via Zr). *Anthrapurpurin* (1,2,7-trihydroxyanthraquinone), *anthragallol* (1,2,3- isomer) and *flavopurpurin* (1,2,6-isomer) form orange-red colors with Sn (0·2 μg.).

(*3*) *Quinalizarin* (1,2,5,8-tetrahydroxyanthraquinone, alizarin bordeaux) [Red, m.p. > 215°C; sol. in alkali (violet), acids (yellow); sparingly sol. in EtOH, Et_2O; insol. in H_2O]. In NaOH soln. Be (0·14 μg.), Mg (0·25 μg.) and UO_2^{2+} form blue or violet lakes. At pH 5, rare earths (0·13 μg. Ce), Th (6·6 μg.), Zr, Pb, Fe, UO_2^{2+}, Ga, Ba, Sr, Ca, Zn, In, Cu, Sn, Sb, As^{3+}, Ge, Mo, Al, Be, Ti, V, Tl^{3+} give pink, blue or violet lakes; Th is detd. colorimetrically. In weakly acidic soln. Al gives a purple lake and UO_2^{2+} an orange one; in NH_4OH soln. In (0·05 μg.) gives a violet lake. In H_2SO_4 soln. the red Zr lake is bleached by F^-; BO_2^- (0·06 μg. B), Ge, Nb and Ta form colors. The Sc complex can be extd. with EtOAc or iso-AmOH.

Quinalizarin acetate (acetylquinalizarin) is used colorimetrically for Ge at pH 5; B also reacts. *Rufianic acid* (quinalizarin-3-sulfonic acid) forms a red color with BO_2^- (0·2 μg.).

Alizarin cyanine R (1,2,4,5,8-pentahydroxyanthraquinone) reacts with Zr and is the most sensitive reagent for F^- (0·01 μg./ml.). *Rufigallic acid* (rufigallol, 1,2,3,5,6,7-hexahydroxyanthraquinone) forms a deep purple color with Zr, and a pale pink color with Hf in HCl soln.

(*4*) *Carmine* (carmine red, carminic acid; the chief constituent of cochineal) (II) [Violet-brown–red, m.p. 136°C, sol. in H_2O, EtOH]. Pb (0·1 μg.) forms a

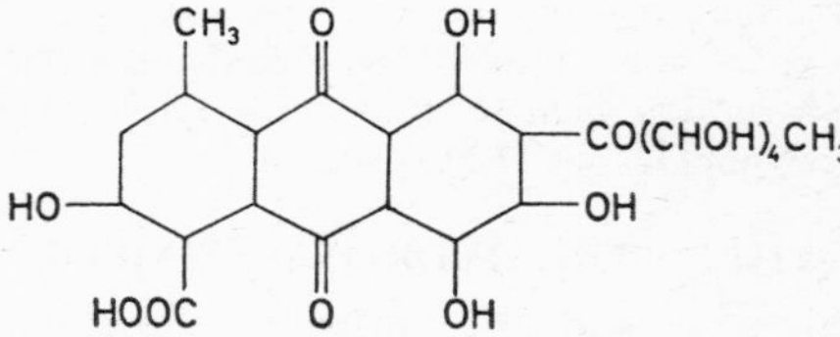

(II)

blue color in NH_4OH soln.; in acidic soln. Zr (0·5 μg.) forms a blue color, and Th and BO_2^- are detd. colorimetrically. *Cochineal* has been used fluorimetrically for Al, Mo and W.

(*5*) *1,1′-Dianthrimide* (1,1′-dianthraquinonylamine) is the best of 60 compds. tested for the detn. of BO_2^-.[6] B has also been detd. colorimetrically with *1,8-diaminochrysazin* (0·0022 μg. B/ml.), *1,5,(?)-tribromoanthrarufin* (0·0009 μg. B; most sensitive), *1,5-diaminoanthrarufin* (0·0025 μg. B), *dinitroanthrarufin*, *dinitrochrysazin* and *dicyanoquinizarin* (see Chapter 61). For anthraquinone dyes used for B, see ref. 7.

4,4′-Diamino-1,1′-dianthraquinonylamine is used colorimetrically for BO_2^-. *1,2-Diaminoanthraquinone* or its *3-sulfonic acid* reacts in NaOH soln. with Cu (0·3 μg.), Ni and Co; the bluish colors formed with Cu and Ni turn red with NH_4OH but that of Co does not.

1-Aminoanthraquinone-2-carboxylic acid reacts with Al, Mg, Zn. *1-Amino-4-hydroxyanthraquinone* reacts with Be, Li in alk. soln. and with Th at pH 2 to give a red fluorescence under UV light. *Anthraquinone-1-azo-4′-dimethylaniline* reacts with Sn (0·01 μg.), Te (0·006 μg.), Sb (0·1 μg.), UO_2^{2+}, Mo, Au, Zn, Cd, Hg,

Pb, Ir, Fe, Ge, Al. *5-Chlorobromamine acid* (5-chloro-1-amino-2-anthraquinonesulfonic acid) reacts with Zr (0·1 μg.). *Solway purple* (the sodium salt of 1-hydroxy-4-sulfo-*p*-tolylaminoanthraquinone) forms a blue color with BO_2^-, as do the unsulfonated compd.

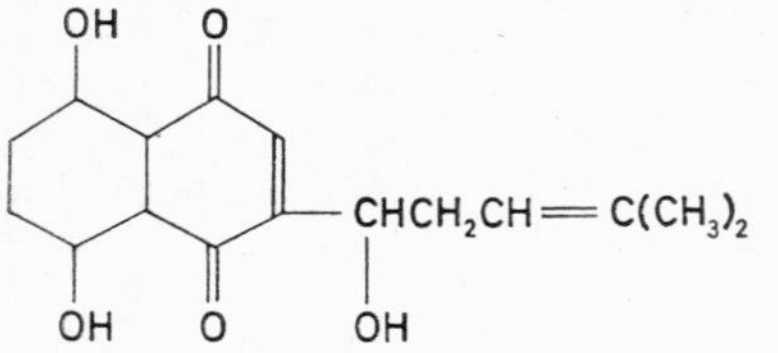

(III)

and alizarin blue;[8] the latter compds. also react with Zr and Hf (see also Chapter 8, Section 1.2).

(6) *Alkannin* (the chief constituent of alkanet) (III) reacts with many metals in neutral soln.; Al gives a purple ppt. with an orange-yellow fluorescence; Mg, Be, UO_2^{2+}, Sn^{4+}, Fe^{3+}, Ti, Cr, Hg, Bi, Mn, Sr, Ca, SiO_2 form bluish or green colors; Sn^{2+} and Pb give brown and rose colors resp.

Naphthazarine (5,8-dihydroxy-1,4-naphthoquinone) is used colorimetrically for Th and reacts also with Al, Be and Mg in the same way as alkannin. For the prepn. of these 2 reagents, see ref. 9. The reactions of *purpurogallin* have been studied.[10] *9-Hydroxynaphthacenequinone-6-sulfonic acid* forms a pink color (under blue light) with GeO_3^{2-} in H_2SO_4 soln.

3. OTHER POLYHYDROXY COMPOUNDS

(1) *Curcumin* (turmeric, turmeric yellow; chief constituent of curcuma tincture) (IV). [Orange-yellow,

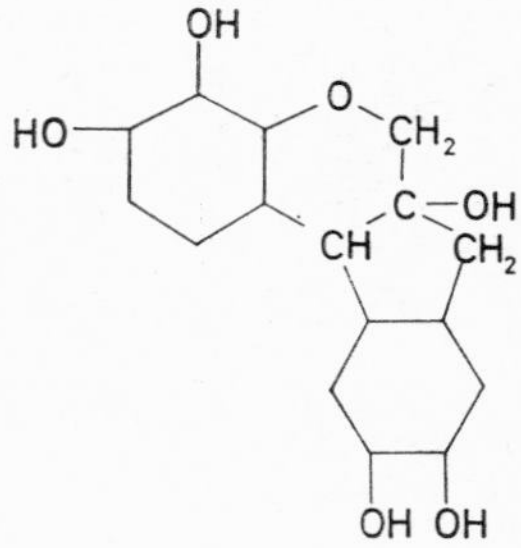

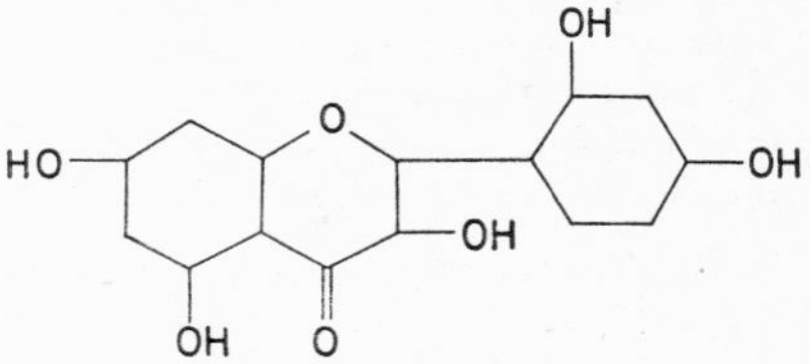

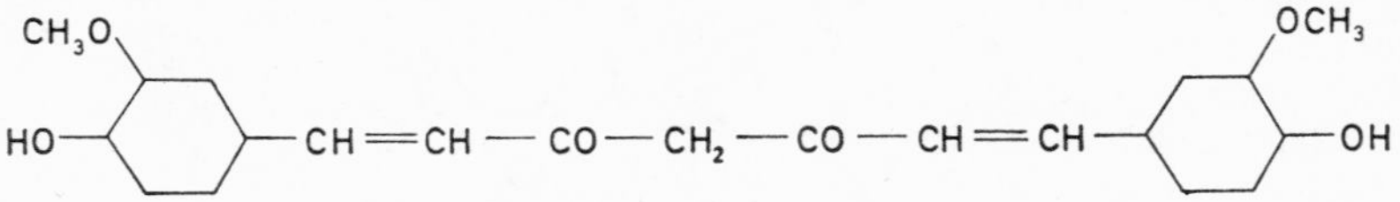

(IV)

m.p. 183°C, sol. in alkali, AcOH, EtOH; insol. in H_2O, Et_2O]. Be, Mg, U, Fe and Al form lakes, Be being detd. colorimetrically. In acidic soln. BO_2^- (0·02 μg.) causes a reddish color by formation of rosocyanine; this changes to blue-green on NaOH addn. which can be used colorimetrically. Zr, Hf, Ti, Mo, W, Nb and Ta also react in acidic soln.

(2) *Hematoxylin* (hydroxybrazilin) (V) [Colorless–yellow-brown, m.p. 140°C, sol. in caustic alkali, EtOH, Et_2O; sparingly sol. in H_2O]. Al gives a blue color in $(NH_4)_2CO_3$ + NH_4OH soln. which becomes yellow-brown on AcOH addn.; Fe, Sn, Cu and Pb form blue–purple lakes in NH_4OH soln. Al, F^-, Zr and Sn can be detd.

Hematein (the aerial oxidation product of hematoxylin in NH_4OH soln.) is used colorimetrically for

Sn, Ge (1·5 μg./ml.), Al (hence F^-) in acid soln.; it reacts with Pb in neutral soln. Y and La (p. 351) can be

(V)

detd. simultaneously. *Brazilin* forms a dark brown lake with Fe.

(3) *Morin* (3,5,7,2′,4′-pentahydroxyflavone) (VI) [m.p. 285°C, sol. in EtOH, AcOH, alkali]. In neutral or dil. AcOH solns., Al (0·2 μg.), Be, UO_2^{2+}, Ga, In, Sc, Zr,

(VI)

Th, Y, Ce, Sn^{4+} form yellow-green colors which can be extd. with AmOH and which fluoresce under UV light. Many elements can be detd. fluorimetrically but the reagent is nearly specific for Be in 1N NaOH soln.

Quercetin (2,4,3′4′-tetrahydroxyflavanol) is used colorimetrically for Al, U (3 μg.), Ge, Sn, Zr, Th; it also reacts with Fe (0·3 μg.) and Ce. Both morin and quercetin ppt. Nb and Ta.[11] *Quercitrin* (quercetinrhamnoside) reacts similarly. *Pentamethylquercetin* serves for colorimetric BO_2^- detn. *Flavanol* reacts with Zr and Sn in dil. H_2SO_4 soln. (colorimetry) and the complexes fluoresce under UV light. *Myricetin* (5,7,3′,4′,5′-pentahydroxyflavanol) forms an orange-red ppt. with Sb (3 μg./ml.) in EtOH soln. and a color with Zr in acidic soln. (colorimetry). *9-Methyl-2,3,7-trihydroxy-6-fluorone* ppts. Sb (0·2 μg.), Ge, Ce and Bi at pH 4; Bi and Pb can be sepd.;[12] Fe gives a violet color. The reaction of these reagents with Sb is similar to that of pyrogallol.[13]

(4) *Phenylfluorone* (2,6,7-trihydroxy-9-phenyl-3-fluor-

one) (VII) forms reddish colors with Ge, Ga, Ti, Sn, Sb^{3+}, Mo, Fe and Zr in dil. acidic solns.; Ge, Sn, Sb, Zr (hence F^-) can be detd. The Ge color may be due to

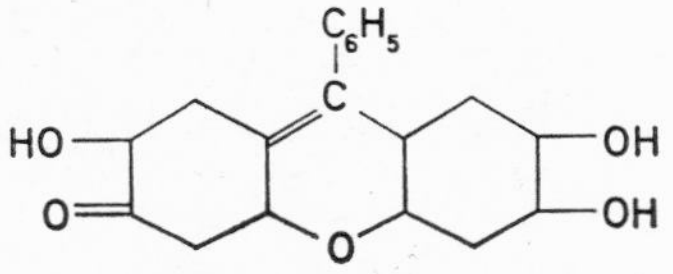

(VII)

the formation of a heteropoly acid;[13] it is not decolorized in strong acid soln. The properties of some of the complexes are described in the following table.[14]

	Ge	Sn	Ti	Zr
λ_{max} mμ	510	510	525	540
$\epsilon \times 10^{-4}$	8·5	1·2	4·7	15
Complex	2 : 1	—	2 : 1	4 : 1

Dimethylaminophenylfluorone (2,6,7-trihydroxy-9-(4-dimethylaminophenyl)fluorone) is a sensitive reagent. For other analogs and homologs, see ref. 15. For the reaction of *2,6,7-trihydroxyfluorone* with Sn and Sb, see ref. 16.

(*5*) *Gossypol* (constitution uncertain) forms pale red colors with Sb^{3+}, Sn^{4+} (0·3 μg.), Mo (0·1 μg.).[17]

(*6*) *Morellin* (an antibiotic) is used colorimetrically for Th and UO_2^{2+}.

4. AZO AND OTHER NITROGEN-CONTAINING COMPOUNDS[18]

Many complex-forming reagents, particularly *o*-hydroxyazo compounds, are considered in this section. Many of these reagents fall within the categories listed in Chapter 8 and some in those of Chapters 9 or 15; their strict classification is difficult.

4.1. *o*-Hydroxy monoazo compounds

α-Pyridyl-β-azonaphthol (1-(2′-pyridylazo)-2-naphthol, PAN) forms complexes with Bi, Cd, Cu, Pt, Sn^{2+}, U^{4+}, Hg, Th, Pb, Fe^{3+}, Ni, Zn, Ce^{4+}, rare earths, Co and Pd; most of the complexes are sol. in AmOH, those of Ni, Co, Cd and Zn being sol. in CCl_4. See also Chapter 5, Section 4.

Eriochrome black T (1-(1-hydroxy-2-naphthylazo)-4-nitro-2-naphthol-4-sulfonic acid, Solochrome black T,

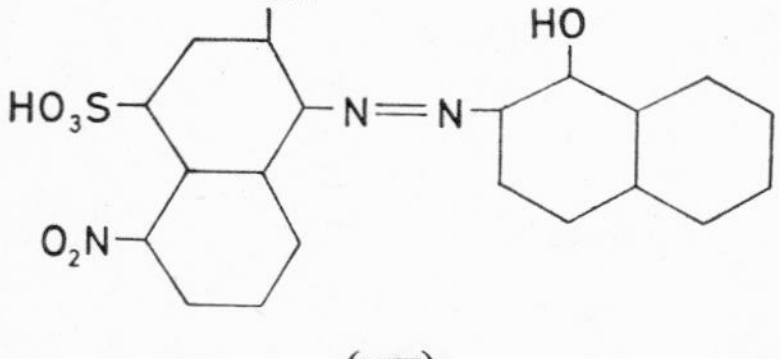

(VIII)

Colour Index 203) (VIII) forms a wine-red complex with Mg which can be detd. colorimetrically; see also Chapter 5, Section 4. For analogs, see ref. 19.

Erio OS (1-(1-hydroxynaphthaleneazo)-2-hydroxy-5-nitronaphthalene) forms red complexes with Ga, In, Ca, Mg, Zn, Cd, Co, Ni, Cu, Hg, Pb; these can be extd. with BuOH.[20] *Fast grey RA* (1-azo-2-hydroxy-naphthyl-3-nitrobenzene-5-sulfonic acid) is used colorimetrically for Zr, Cu and V. *Xylidine blue I* (Na-1-azo-2-hydroxy-3-(2,4-dimethylcarboxanilido)-naphthalene-1′-(2-hydroxybenzene-5-sulfonate), 2-naphthol-3-(2,4-dimethyl)carbanilido-1-azo-(2-hydroxybenzene-5-sul-

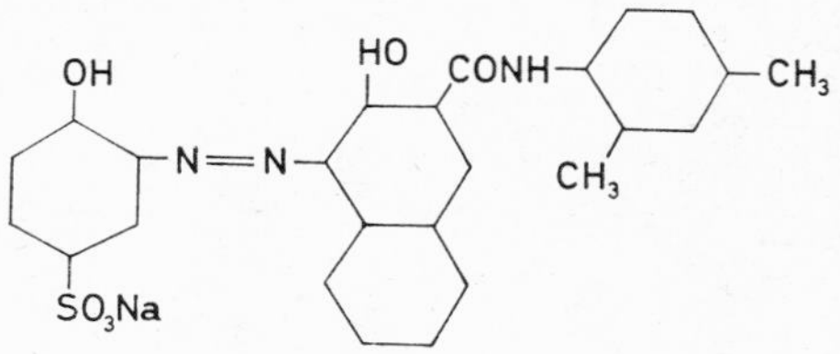

(IX)

fonate)) (IX) changes from red to blue-violet at pH 7 and to pink at pH 11–12. It forms a red complex with Mg at pH 8–11 in 60% EtOH soln. and is 10 times as sensitive for Mg as Titan yellow. For *Xylidine blue II* (2-(2-hydroxy-3-(2,4-xylylcarbamoyl)-1-naphthylazo)-phenol), see Chapter 53, p. 398.

Solochrome black 6B (eriochrome blue-black B, Colour Index 201) (X) gives a blood-red fluorescence

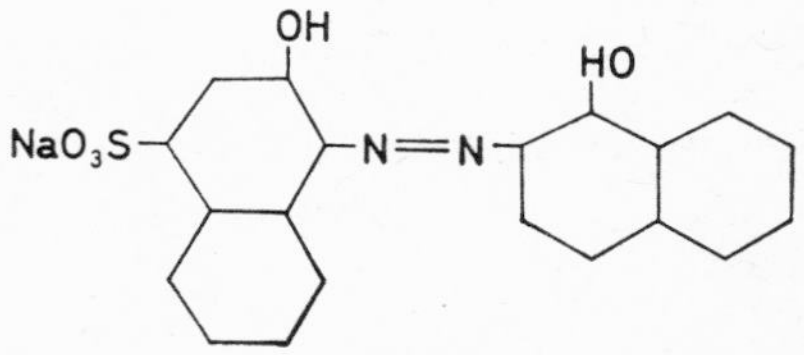

(X)

with Al (0·5 μg.) and Ga (5 μg.) under UV light ; Co (1 μg./ml.) reacts similarly in AcOH soln. if NO_2^- is added. *Solochrome red ERS* and *solochrome black WEFA* can be used fluorimetrically for Ga.

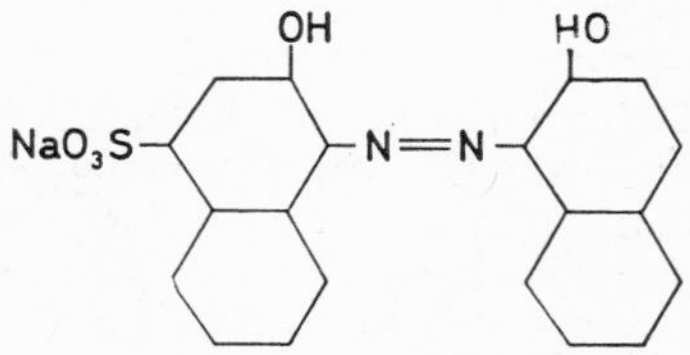

(XI)

Calcon (pontachrome blue-black R conc., chrome blue N, eriochrome blue-black R, 2,2′-dihydroxy-naphthaleneazo-4-sulfonic acid, Colour Index 202) (XI) gives an orange-red fluorescence with Be and Al; Al (and hence F^-) can be detd. See also Chapter 5, Section 4.

Plasmocorinth (Fast mordant blue B conc., sunchromine fast blue MB, 2-(5-chloro-2-hydroxyphenylazo)-1,8.dihydroxy-3,6-naphthalenedisulfonicacid) (XII) is used colorimetrically for Be and Ca. *Varnish*

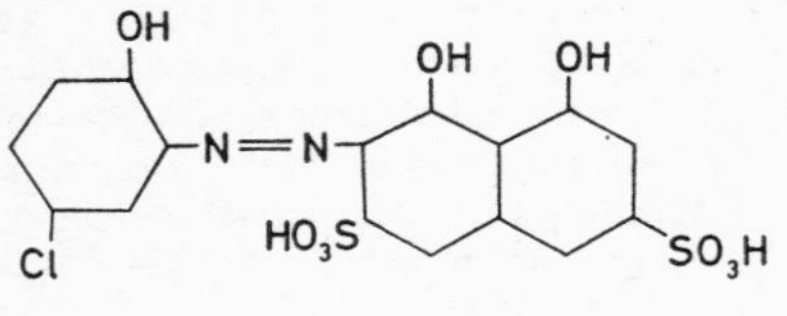

(XII)

scarlet C (azocal A, 1-(2-carboxyphenylazo)-2-hydroxynaphthalene-3,6-disulfonic acid) (XIII) can also be used colorimetrically for Ca.

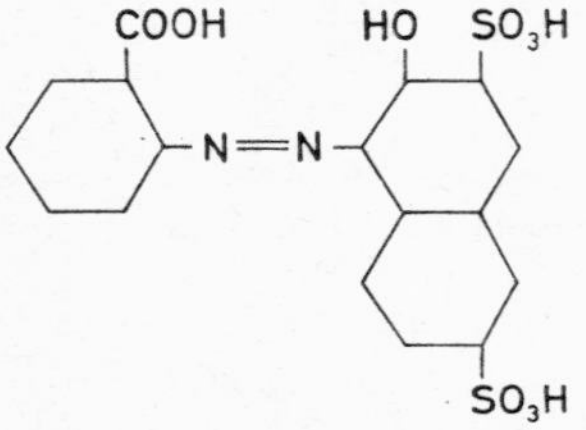

(XIII)

1-(4-Nitro-2-sulfophenylazo)-2-hydroxynaphthalene forms a pink color with Ba which permits the detn. of 1·5 μg. SO_4^{2-}/ml.; similar compds. have been described.[21]

Pontachrome violet SW (XIV) can serve for the

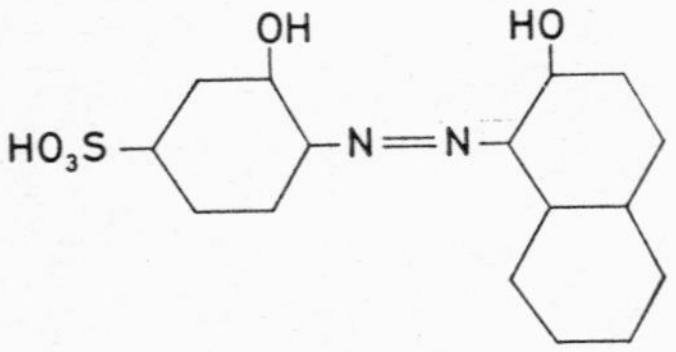

(XIV)

amperometric titration of Mg. *Beryllon I* (H acid-azo-H acid) and *beryllon II* (H acid-azo-chromotropic acid) are used colorimetrically for Be.

SPADNS (*p*-sulfophenylazochromotropic acid, 2-(*p*-sulfophenylazo)-1,8-dihydroxynaphthalene-3,6-disulfonic acid), *SNADNS* (2-(4-sulfo-1-naphthylazo)-chromotropic acid), *di-SNADNS* (2,7-bis(4-sulfo-1-naphthylazo)-chromotropic acid) and *nitroso-SNADNS* (7-(4-sulfo-1-naphthylazo)-1,8-dihydroxy-2-nitrosonaphthalene-3,6-disulfonic acid) form pink complexes with Zr and violet complexes with Th, which can be utilized colorimetrically. These compds. also serve as indicators in chelatometry and in titrations of F^- with Th or of Th with $C_2O_4^{2-}$.

Neothoron forms violet complexes with Al (colorimetry) and Be (0·02 μg.). p-*Aminophenylazochromotropic acid* gives a deep blue colour with Ca or Mg. *Chromotrope P4B* (serichrome blue R, Colour Index 180) (XV) reacts with Cr. *Amaranth* is used colorimetrically for Th (hence for F^-). *2-Hydroxy-5-methylazobenzene-4′-sulfonic acid* reacts with Zr and Th (1 p.p.m.).

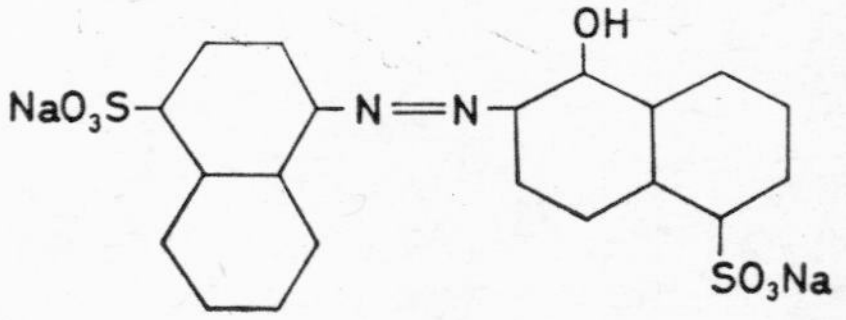

(XV)

Magneson (*p*-nitrobenzeneazoresorcinol) forms lakes with Mg (0·5 μg.), Be, Zn, Zr, Ag, Cd, Al, Ni, Co, La, Ca; the red Zn lake is bleached by CN^- addn. *Magneson II* (*p*-nitrobenzeneazo-α-naphthol) forms blue colors with Ca and Mg (0·2 μg.). *Para red* (Colour Index 44, the β-naphthol analog) forms a blue color with Mg. p-*Nitrobenzeneazoorcinol* forms brownish colors with Be (0·1 μg.) and Mg. *Chrome yellow O* (Colour Index

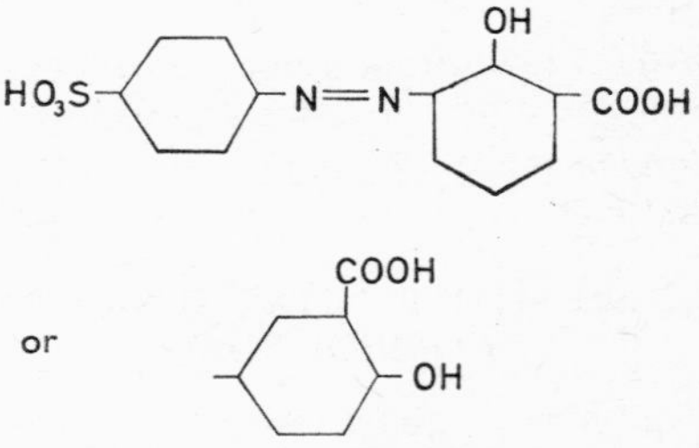

(XVI)

148) (XVI) gives a yellowish color with Fe (0·8–5 μg./ml.) which can be used colorimetrically. *Calcodur yellow 4GL* (?) forms a dark green to yellow color with Fe which can thus be detd.

Superchrome garnet Y (Colour Index 168) (XVII) and

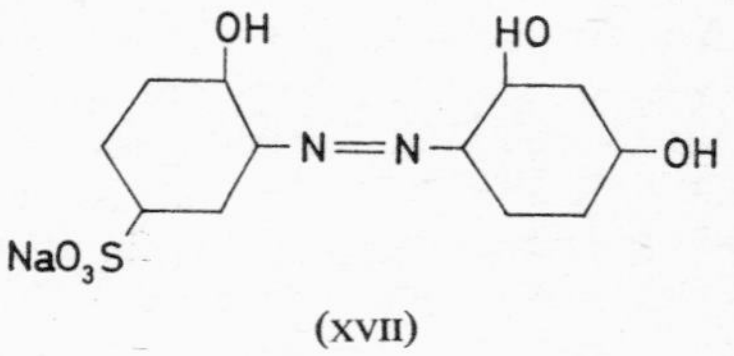

(XVII)

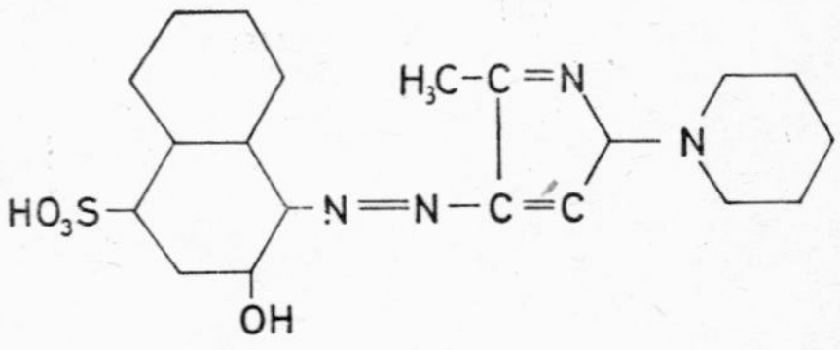

(XVIII)

eriochrome red B (Colour Index 652) (XVIII) permit colorimetric detn. of Al and thus of F^-. The latter reagent reacts with Co (0·5 μg./ml.) in AcOH soln. if NO_2^- is added.

4.2. Other azo dyes

Titan yellow (Clayton's yellow, thiazole yellow, mimosa, Colour Index 813) (XIX) serves for the colorimetric detn. of Mg (0·2 μg./ml.); Al, Cd, Ca, Co, Ni, Sn, Zn, Mn also form lakes.

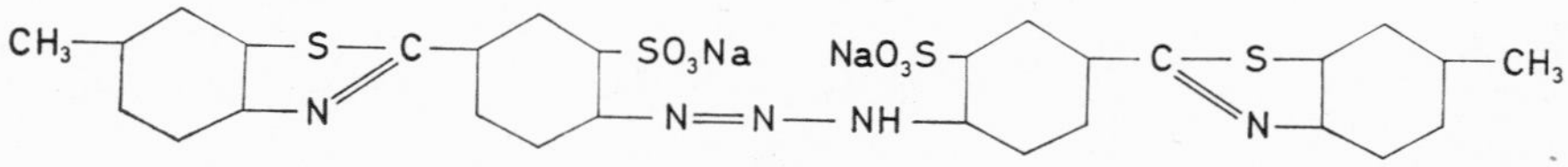

(XIX)

Cadion (*p*-nitrobenzenediazoaminoazobenzene), *cadion 2B* (4-nitronaphthalenediazoaminoazobenzene) and *cadion 3B* (benzenediazoaminobenzene-4-azonitrobenzene) yield a blue color with Mg and an orange-red color with Cd.

Tropaeolin OO (orange IV, aniline yellow, Colour Index 143) (XX) reacts with Mg, Cu, Ni, Co, Zn and

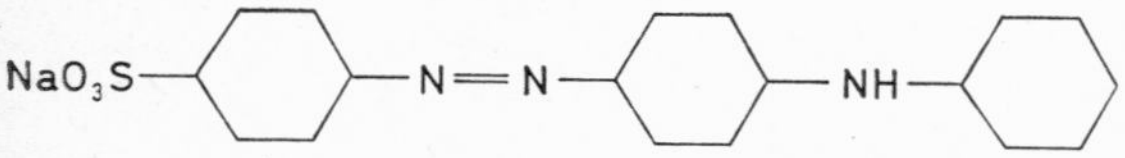

(XX)

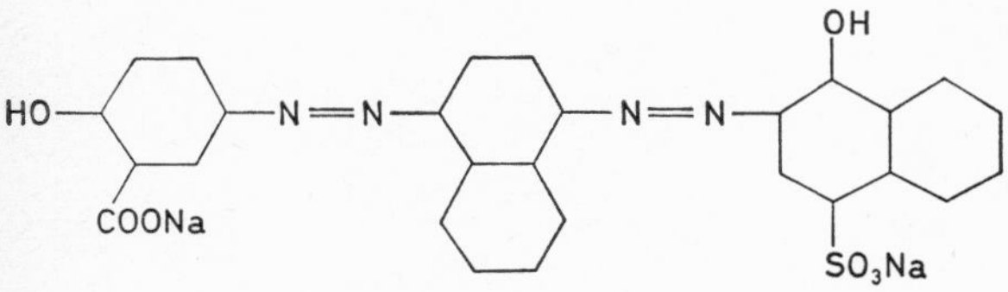

(XXI)

La. *Diamond black F* (Colour Index 299) (XXI) reacts with Mg, Cu (40 μg./ml.), Zn, Ca and Fe.

p-*Dimethylaminoazobenzenesulfonic acid* forms yellow colors with Mg and Ni and a violet-black color with Co. *Diamino bright blue FFG* (triazo dye) yields a pale blue color with Al. *Congo corinth* (Colour Index 375)

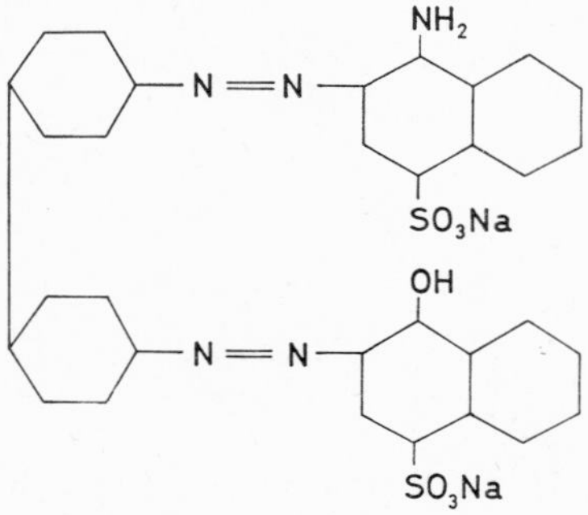

(XXII)

(XXII) reacts with Mg, Co, Ni and *azo blue* (Colour Index 463) with Mg; *benzopurpurin G* (Colour Index 502) and *Chicago blue 6B* (diamine pure blue FFG, Colour Index 518) also form blue colors with Mg.

Direct green B (Colour Index 593) reacts with Cu (1 μg./ml.) at pH 6–9. *Direct orange R* (toluylene orange R, Colour Index 446) forms an orange lake with Mg. *Benzopurpurin 4B* (Colour Index 448) forms red to brown colors with Mg, Hg^+, U and Al, but a blue shade with Hg^{2+}.

Acid alizarin yellow RC (Colour Index 343) and *acid alizarin red G* react with Cr.

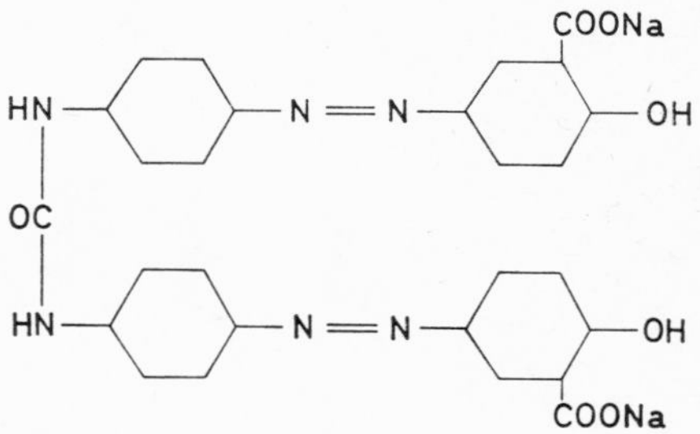

(XXIII)

Benzo fast yellow 5GL (Colour Index 346) (XXIII) reacts with Cu, being 40 times more sensitive than diethyldithiocarbamate.

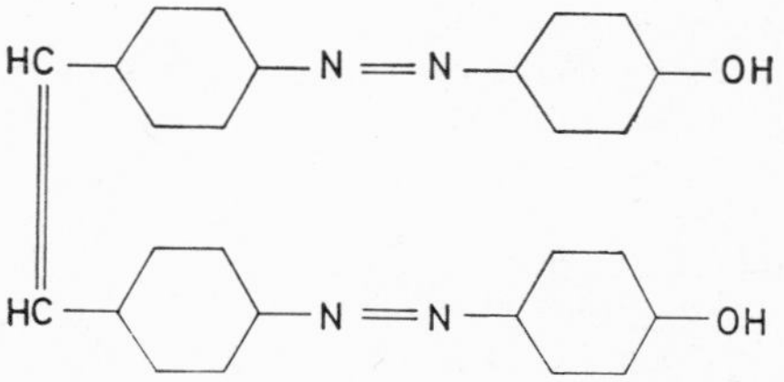

(XXIV)

Brilliant yellow (Colour Index 364) (XXIV), *stilbene purple* and *stilbene blue* react with Mg to form reddish colors; stilbene blue is particularly sensitive (0·13 μg. Mg/ml.); brilliant yellow also reacts with Co and Ni. *Stilbazo* (the 3-hydroxy deriv. of brilliant yellow) is used colorimetrically for Al.[22] *Stilbnaphthazo* (4,4′-bis-(2-hydroxy-1-naphthylazo)stilbene-2,2′-disulfonic acid) forms a bluish color with Ba.[23]

4.3. Reagents for B and Ge

Chromotrope 2B (*p*-nitrobenzeneazochromotropic

acid, Na-salt, Colour Index 45) (XXV) reacts with BO_2^- (0·08 μg. B) in H_2SO_4 and with GeO_3^{2-}. The

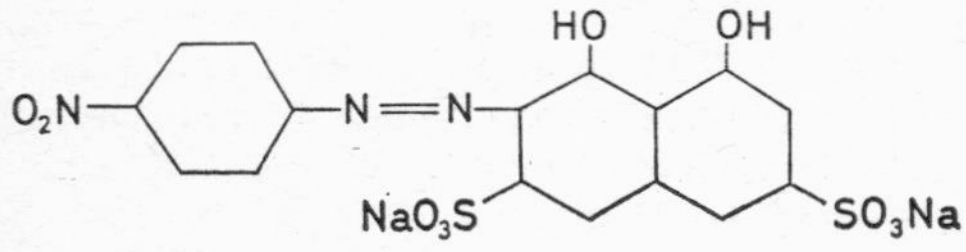

(XXV)

diphenylguanidine salt of chromotrope 2B serves for the colorimetric detn. of Th and hence of F^-. *Congo red* (Colour Index 370) (XXVI) forms a blue color with BO_2^- on heating.

3,4-Dihydroxyazobenzene can be used colorimetrically

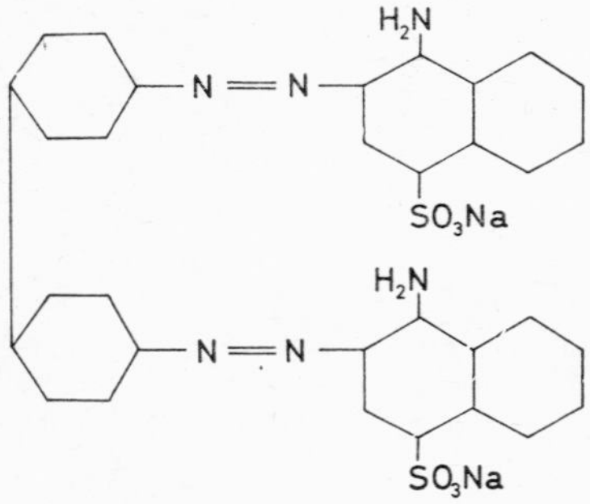

(XXVI)

or gravimetrically for Ge (40 μg./ml.). *3,4-Dihydroxyphenylazoterphenyl* forms a blue-violet ppt. with Ge (1–2 mg./l.) in dil. HCl soln. but Ag, Au, Ba, Tl, W, Sb and Mo interfere.[24]

4.4. Other reagents for Mg

1,3-Bis(3-methyl-4-nitro-5-pyrazolyl)-triazine forms a violet complex with Mg and is specific for Mg in NaOH soln.[25]

Mg also reacts with *dihydrothio-*p*-toluidinesulfonic acid*, p*-phenylenediamine* (purple in KOH soln.), p*-aminophenol* (blue in NaOH soln.) and *diphenylthiocarbazide* (3 p.p.m. Mg in NH_4OH soln.); *p*-phenylenediamine also reacts with Ba and Sr.

4.5. Gallocyanine and resorufin

Gallocyanine (XXVII) forms red to blue complexes

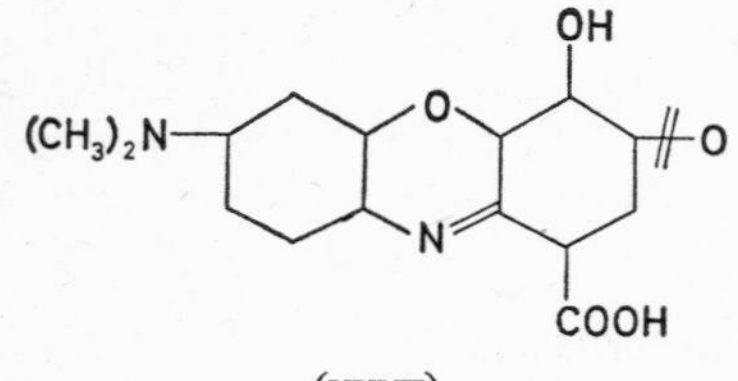

(XXVII)

with Pb (0·3 μg.) and Ge (20 μg./ml.) in NH_4OH soln. and with Zr in HCl soln.

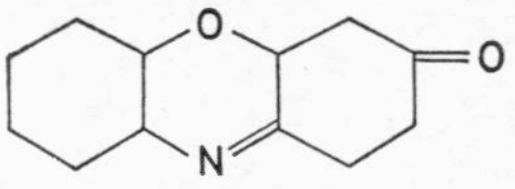

(XXVIII)

Resorufin (azoresorufin) (XXVIII) ppts. Al, Ba, Cd, Cr, Cu, Fe, Ni, Sr in alk. soln., and Mg, Pb, Ag in neutral soln.

5. PHTHALEIN ANALOGS

(*1*) *Aluminon*[26] (ammonium aurintricarboxylate) (XXIX) [Brown-red, sol. in H_2O] forms red lakes in

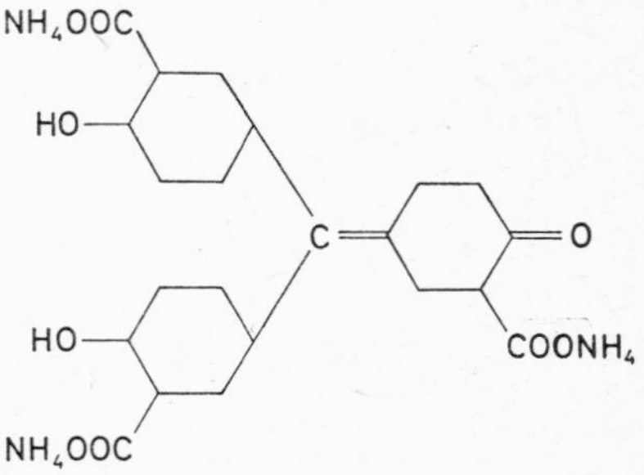

(XXIX)

alk. soln. with Al (above pH 4·5), Be, Fe, Th, Zr, Hf, Cr, Sc, Y, rare earths, Ga, In, Ca, Sr, Ba, Mg; all these, except Al and Be, are decolorized by $(NH_4)_2CO_3$. Some of the com. reagents require purification.[27]

Trihydroxyaurin forms a violet color with Ge (0·3 μg./ml.).

Alumocreson (trimethylaurintricarboxylic acid) [dark red, sol. in EtOH, slightly sol. in H_2O] forms pinkish

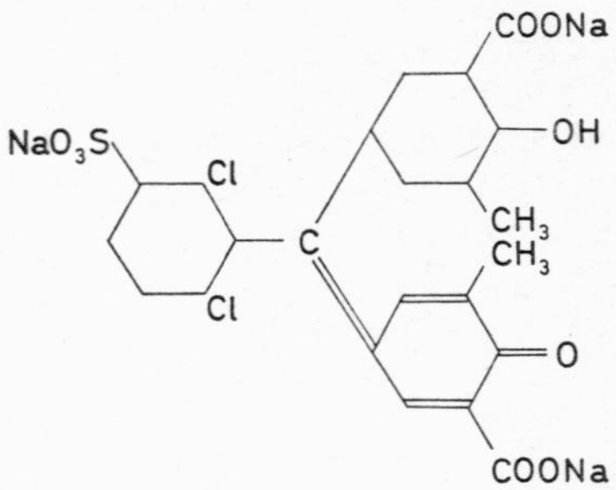

(XXX)

colors with Al (0·007 μg., colorimetry), Fe (0·002 μg.), Be (0·008 μg.), Ge (0·065 μg.), UO_2^{2+} (0·05 μg.) and Pt^{2+} (1·3 μg.): see Chapter 43, p 322.

Chrome azurol S (brilliant blue B, Colour Index 723) (XXX) is used colorimetrically for Be and Th (and thus for F^-), and as an indicator in chelatometric titrations.

(2) *Pyrocatechol violet*[28] reacts with Bi, Th, Cu, Zr, Pb, Cd, Ni, Co, Zn, Mn, Mg; Zr is detd. colorimetrically as is F^-. See Chapter 5, Section 4.2.

o-*Cresolphthalein complexan* is used colorimetrically for the alk. earths. For phthalein complexan analogs, see ref. 29. *Parafuchsine hexaacetic acid* reacts with Ag, Hg, Cd, Mo, Al, Be, Cr, V, Zn and Ca.[30]

(3) *Gallein* (pyrogallolphthalein, Colour Index 781) (XXXI) [brown-violet, sol. in EtOH, alkali and acids;

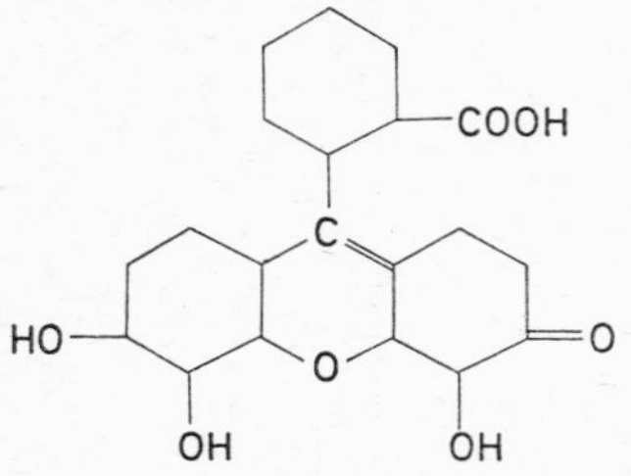

(XXXI)

pale yellow below pH 3·8 and violet above pH 13] reacts with Sb (2 μg./ml.), Sn, Pb, Ag and Fe; the Sb complex is sol. in C_6H_6 and Me_2CO while the Sn complex is decolorized by $NaNO_2$. *Thiogallein*, which is the di-SH deriv. in the *o*-position to O in the gallein ring, is more sensitive, reacting with Sb (0·4 μg./ml., sol. in CS_2 + Me_2SO), Sn and Ni.

Fluorescein (resorcinolphthalein, Colour Index 766;

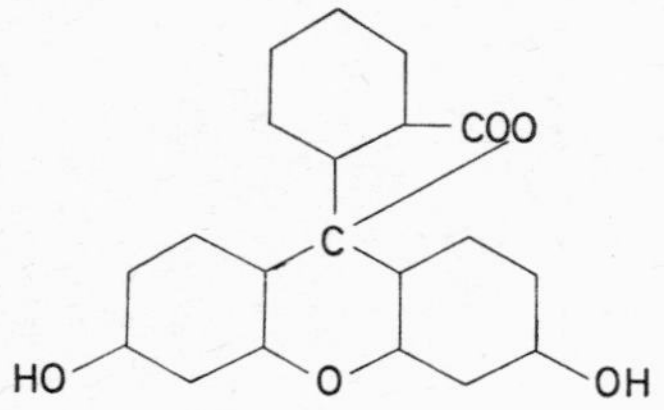

(XXXII)

uranin is the Na-salt) (XXXII) reacts with Al, Sb, Mg, Hg, Pb, Ag and BO_2^-.

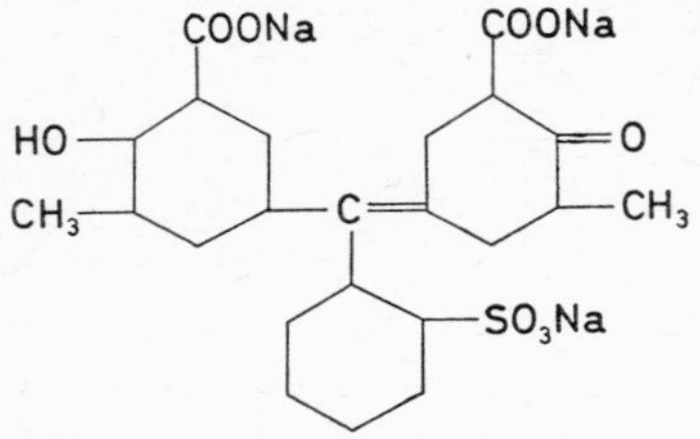

(XXXIII)

Tetrabromophenolphthalein ppts. Cu, Fe, Hg, whereas *bromophenol blue* (tetrabromophenolsulfonphthalein) reacts with Pb (2·5 μg.) and Hg (20 μg.).

(4) *Eriochrome cyanine R* (solochrome cyanine, Colour Index 722) (XXXIII) forms lakes with Al (1 μg.), Zr, Be, Ti and Tl; Al is detd. colorimetrically at pH 4·6–5·6 and Zr and F^- can also be detd. *Chromoxane cyanine RA* (?) is used colorimetrically for Al.

(5) *Naphthochrome green G* (XXXIV) reacts with Be

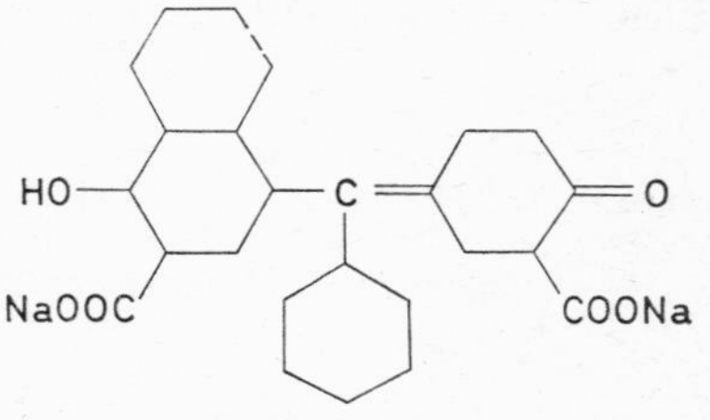

(XXXIV)

(0·2 μg.) at pH 11·5–12·3; the violet Be lake can be detd. colorimetrically. This reagent, *chrome fast pure blue* and other hydroxytriphenylmethane dyes are sensitive to Al (1 μg.).[31]

(6) *Methyl violet* (methylrosaniline, aniline violet, Colour Index 680) (XXXV) ppts. Ta (0·04 μg.). *Brilliant*

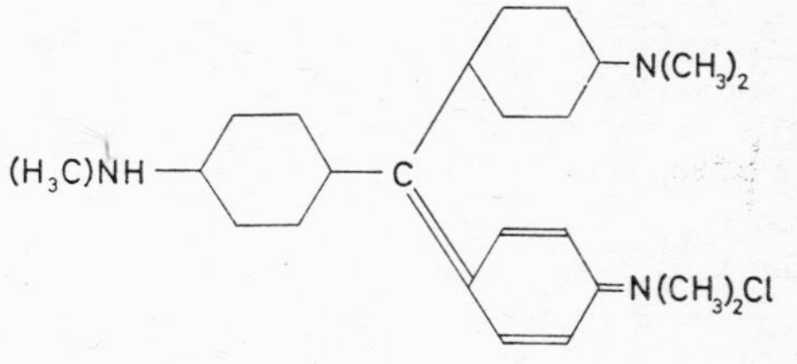

(XXXV)

green (Colour Index 662) ppts. Hg^+, Ba and Ta (0·4 μg.) in Na_2CO_3 soln. *Brilliant violet* (Colour Index 683) ppts. Ag, Hg^+ in Na_2CO_3 soln. and Sn^{2+} in NH_4OH soln. *Sunchromine pure blue B extra* forms a violet lake with Ce^{3+}.

6. ADSORPTION INDICATORS

For the usual type of adsorption indicator, see Chapter 5, Section 3.

Starch can also be regarded as an adsorption indicator: the complex formed between starch and iodine

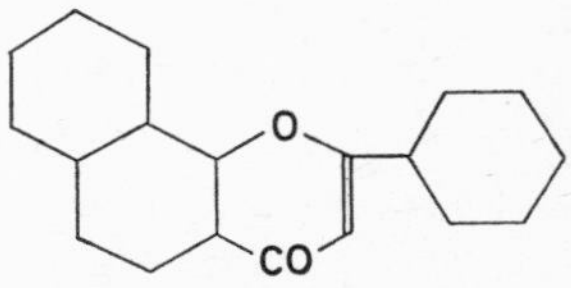

(XXXVI)

is vital in iodimetry and is often used both for the detection and colorimetric detn. of I_2 and for the detn. of oxidants which liberate I_2 from HI, e.g. NO_2^-, Fe^{3+}, Cu^{2+}. *Linear starch* is more stable than starch and is more satisfactory in colorimetric detns.[32] The *Na-salt of starch glycolic acid* is sol. in H_2O.[33] *Amylose*[34] or *glycogen* may also be substituted for ordinary starch.

α-Naphthoflavone (XXXVI) reacts with Br_2 (1 μg.) to give an orange-red color, and with I_2 to give a purple color; see also Chapter 15, Section 4. *Polyvinyl alcohol* forms a deep pink color with I_2 and is more sensitive than starch; it is also used colorimetrically for B.

References

1. SCHOELLER, *The Analytical Chemistry of Tantalum and Niobium. The Analysis of their Minerals and the Application of Tannin in Gravimetric Analysis* (1937); COLIN, L. L., *J. Chem. Met. Mining Soc. S. Africa*, **50**, 314 (1950).
2. FEIGL, F., 201 (1949); WELCHER, **IV**, 407.
3. FEIGL, F., *Anal. Chem.*, **21**, 1311 (1949).
4. KUL'BERG, L. M. and MUSTAFIN, I. S., *Doklady Akad. Nauk S.S.S.R.*, **77**, 285 (1951).
5. COGBILL, E. C. and YOE, J. H., *Anal. Chim. Acta*, **12**, 455 (1955); also see B.
6. ELLIS, G. H., *et al. Anal. Chem.*, **21**, 1345 (1949).
7. EMI, K., *et al.*, *J. Chem. Soc. Japan*, **78**, 1299 (1957).
8. TRINDER, N., *Analyst*, **73**, 494 (1948).
9. TORIBARA, T. Y. and UNDERWOOD, A. L., *Anal. Chem.*, **21**, 1357 (1949).
10. RAO, D. V. R. and GUHA-SIRCAR, S. S., *J. Proc. Inst. Chemist (India)*, **28**, 238 (1956).
11. TOMÍČEK, O. and HOLEČEK, H., *Chem. listy*, **46**, 11 (1952).
12. FIANDER, S. J., *Analyst*, **80**, 476 (1955).
13. FEIGL, F., 179 (1949).
14. SANO, H., *Bull. Chem. Soc. Japan*, **30**, 790 (1957).
15. KIMURA, K., *et al.*, *Bull. Chem. Soc. Japan*, **29**, 635, 640, 812 (1956).
16. NAZARENKO, V. A. and LEBEDEVA, N. V., *Zhur. Anal. Khim.*, **10**, 289 (1955).
17. PIZARRO, A. V., *Anal. Chim. Acta*, **5**, 529 (1951); **6**, 105 (1952).
18. WELCHER, **IV**, 332–406; KUL'BERG, L. M. and IVANOVA, Z. V., *Zhur. Obshcheĭ Khim.* **17**, 601 (1949).
19. EMI, K., *et al.*, *J. Chem. Soc. Japan*, **78**, 736, 741, 977, 979 (1957).
20. FLASCHKA, H., *Mikrochim. Acta*, 784 (1956).
21. KUZNETSOV, V. I., *Doklady Akad. Nauk S.S.S.R.*, **77**, 61 (1951).
22. KUZNETSOV, V. I., *et al.*, *Zavodskaya Lab.*, **16**, 787 (1950).
23. MARKOVA, L. D., *Ukrain. Khim. Zhur.*, **23**, 89 (1957).
24. BÉVILLARD, P., *Compt. rend.*, **233**, 1112 (1951); **239**, 59, 239 (1954); *Bull. soc. chim.*, 307 (1954).
25. SACCONI, L., *Gazz. chim. ital.*, **78**, 219 (1948).
26. MUKHERJEE, A. K. and DAY, A. K., *Z. anal. Chem.*, **152**, 424 (1956).
27. SMITH, W. H., *et al.*, *Anal. Chem.*, **21**, 1334 (1949).
28. RIBA, O., *et al.*, *Chem. listy*, **49**, 1786 (1955); **50**, 888 (1956); **51**, 1462 (1957).
29. EMI, K., *et al.*, *J. Chem. Soc. Japan*, **78**, 974 (1957).
30. LASTOVSKIĬ, R. L., *et al.*, *Zhur. Anal. Khim.*, **11**, 405 (1956).
31. FEIGL, F., *et al.*, *Anal. Chem.*, **29**, 456 (1957).
32. LAMBERT, J. L., *Anal. Chem.*, **23**, 1101, 1249, 1251 (1951).
33. PEAT, S., *et al.*, *Nature*, **159**, 810 (1947).
34. LIGETT, L. M. and DIEHL, H., *Anachem. News*, **6**, 9 (1946).

13

ION EXCHANGE RESINS AND CELLULOSE COLUMNS

1. ION EXCHANGE RESINS

1.1. General remarks

Ion exchange resins[1] (ion exchangers, resinous exchangers, exchange adsorbents, organic zeolites, organolites, ionites) are a group of extremely valuable reagents whose development is quite recent but which have become widely applied in analyses. Their spectacular applications include the separation of the lanthanide and actinide elements and the analysis of Bikini ashes.[2]

Ion exchange resins which are commercially available are listed in Table 24. They are granular, semi-transparent, brown-yellow synthetic resins; they provide a network to which are fixed either organic acids or bases. They are classified as cation exchange resins (cation exchangers, cationites) and anion exchange resins (anion exchangers, anionites). Among them are strongly acidic resins (the styrene-sulfonic acid type, e.g. Amberlite IR-120, Dowex 50, etc.) and strongly basic resins (quaternary ammonium type, e.g. Amberlite IRA-400, Dowex 2, etc.) which are most widely used in analyses.

Strongly acidic cationites. The styrene-sulfonic acid type are synthesized by copolymerization of styrene and divinylbenzene and then by sulfonation; commercial products contain 8–12% divinylbenzene and about 20% H_2O when air-dried. At 100°C they lose the bulk of the moisture. When the dried resins are immersed in H_2O, they absorb considerable amounts, generating heat and swelling, the extent of which depends on the divinylbenzene content; the smaller the content, the greater the swelling.

These resins are stable both physically and chemically; they can be used more than 2000 times, are stable to heat (100°C), and chemicals (5% NaOH, satd. Cl_2, 0·1% $KMnO_4$, 0·1*N* HNO_3, org. solvents). The exchange capacity is ca. 4–5 meq./g. or 1·4–2·3 meq./ml. resin, which corresponds to ca. 2*N* electrolyte soln.

Phenolsulfonic acid type. These are among the earliest types and are easily synthesized from phenolsulfonic acid and formaldehyde. Many similar materials have been suggested, but the acidity is weaker and the exchange capacity (ca. 2–3 meq./g.), heat-resistance and stability are less, hence they have been superseded by the resins mentioned above. Another type, the arylsulfonic resins, is synthesized from *p*-hydroxybenzilsulfonic acid and formaldehyde, and the acidity is still weaker.

Weakly acidic cationites. Carboxylic acid type resins are of two kinds; one is synthesized from methacrylic acid and divinylbenzene; the other from 1,3,5-resorcylic acid or phenoxyacetic acid and formaldehyde. The exchange capacity is very high (5–10 meq./g.), and the resins are used for purification of streptomycin or for sepn. of amino acids, vitamins, etc.

The phenol type is prepd. from polyphenols and formaldehyde; the acidity is very weak.

Sulfonated coal or gum is only very occasionally used in analysis.

Strongly basic anionites. Chloromethylation and amination (with tertiary amines) of co-polymers of styrene and divinylbenzene yields these resins which have quaternary ammonium functional groups.

Typical examples are Dowex 1 and 2, Amberlite IRA-400 and -410, etc.; the exchange capacity is ca. 3 meq./g. or 1 meq./ml. They are pale yellow to yellow; the RCl form is stable at 100°C but the ROH form should be used below 40°C. They are stable to strong acids and bases, org. solvents, dil. H_2O_2 or Cl_2, 0·1% $KMnO_4$. They adsorb all anions and are widely applicable. Aliphatic resins synthesized from vinyl chloride and styrene are also available.

Weakly basic anionites. Amination with primary or secondary amines instead of tertiary amines yields resins which have respectively secondary or tertiary amino-groups, e.g. Amberlite IR-45, Dowex 3. Another type of resin contg. primary up to tertiary amines (e.g. Wofatit M) is synthesized from *m*-phenylenediamine, etc., and polyethylenediamine and formaldehyde. The aliphatic type have a stronger basicity than the aromatic type. They adsorb ions of strong acids, but not those of weak acids, and are unstable to HNO_3.

Amphoteric resins. Weakly acidic–weakly basic types are commercially available. Strongly acidic–strongly basic types have been synthesized.[3]

TABLE 24. Ion Exchange Resins

	Cationites strong styrene	Cationites strong others	Cationites weak	Anionites strong	Anionites weak	Company	Remarks
Allassion	CS	CP		AS AZ	AW ADM	ACFI, France	
Amberlite	IR-120 IR-112* IR-119 XE-69 (IR-120) XE-66B (IR-120)	IR-1 IR-2 IR-100 IR-105 XE-111	IRC-50+ XE-64 (RH, IRC-50) XE-88 (R-NH$_4$, IRC-50) XE-97	IRA-400 IRA-401* IRA-410‡ IRA-411*‡ XE-75 (IRA-401) XE-98 (IRA-411) XE-67	IR-3 IR-4 IR-4B‡‡ IR-45** XE-114° XE-58 (IR-4B) XE-59 (IR-4B) XE-76 (IR-45)	Rohm & Haas, U.S.A.	A.G. (Analytical grade) C.G. (Chromatographic grade) Type I, 100–200; Type II, <200 mesh). Medical use (200–500 mesh)
Amberplex		C-51			A-1		Membrane
Diaion	SK # 1 # 2*	K BK		SA # 100 SA # 100* SA # 200‡ SA # 201*‡	A	Mitsubishi, Japan	Analytical grade (100–200 mesh)
Dowex	50-X1 50-X2 50-X4 50-X8 50-X12 50-X16	30		1-X1 2‡-X2 1-X2 2-X4 1-X4 2-X7·5 1-X7·52-X8 1-X8 2-X10 1-X10	3**	Dow Chem. Co., U.S.A.	Numbers after X indicate % of divinylbenzene. Various particle sizes (50–400 mesh); colloidal agglomerates and white for 50-X8 and X12
Duolite	C-25 C-25 L* C-20	C-1, C-3 C-10	CS-101+ CS-100++ C-60+++	A-40 A-42	A-1, A-2 A-3, A-7 A-70°	Chem. Process Co., U.S.A.	
Illico		C-211 C-231	C-271	A-224 A-244 A-444	A-204 A-164 A-364	Illinois Water Treatment	

Imac	C 12		C 19		A 17° A 25	Activit, Holland
Ion	X					Microchem., U.S.A.
Ionac		C-200		AD	A 300° A 293 M‡‡‡	Am. Cyanamid Co.
Lewatit	S-100 KSN	21 KS, KSB PN, CNS	24 C CNO	MN M-2	35 M, M-1* M-I H°	Bayer, Germany
Liquonex	CRW	CRM CRQ CRP		AD	AF‡‡	Liquid Conditioning, U.S.A.
Nalcite	HCR (Dowex 50)	MX (Dowex 30)		SBR (Dowex 1) SAR‡ (Dowex 2)	WBR (Dowex 3)	Natl. Al. Corp., U.S.A.
Neklolith		RH, RAH, RAE, RH 33	R, RA			R. Reichling, Germany
Orgacit		A			B	Yamada, Japan
Permionic (Nepton)		CR-51 CR-41			ARX-44	Ionics Inc., U.S.A.
Permutit	Q QX*		H 70 XAC	S-I, S-II ES	W A°	Permutit Co., U.S.A.
Wofatit		K, KS P†, D†	C R		M‡‡, N L 150°	I.G., Germany
ZeoKarb	225	215 315	216	DeAcidite FF	DeAcidite° G, H	Permutit Co., England

* low cross-linkage; ** styrene; + acrylic; ++ phenolic; +++ phosphonic; † arylsulfonic; ° medium basic; ‡ choline; ‡‡ alkylamine; ‡‡‡ melamine-guanidine.

Specific resins. A resin contg. a dipicrylamine radical as functional group can be used for concn. of K.[4]

With the resin from *m*-phenylenediglycine (C_6H_4-$(NHCH_2COOH)_2$) and HCHO, Fe, Co are adsorbed at pH 5, Ni below pH 5 and Cu above pH 5; sepns. of Co from Fe and Cu at pH 2·5 and of Cu from Fe and Co at pH 6 are possible. The anthranilic acid analog is not useful, and the *o*-aminophenol analog is similar to a carboxylic acid resin.[5] Cu can be sepd. from Ni with a resin formed from *m*-phenylenediaminetetraacetic acid and resorcinol.[6]

Polythiol styrene is specific for metals of the sulfide group and is a strong reductant.[7]

Phosphonic or phosphinic acid resins exhibit greater first dissociation consts. than the sulfonic acid type, the second consts. lying between carboxylic acid and phenolic resins; they have comparatively large exchange capacities. They are yellow in the acid form, but become dark brown and increase 50% in vol. when they adsorb alkali ions, being more selective for Na than K.[8] U is sepd. from Cu, Co, etc. with alkyl phosphate or phosphonate resins.[9]

Redox resins. Polymers of vinylhydroquinone exhibit reversible redox reactions.[10] Polyphenol formaldehyde resins are similar and can be used to remove dissolved oxygen from water.[11]

Fe adsorbed on a cationite and reduced, or Cu or Fe adsorbed on an anionite and reduced with hydrosulfite (Duolite S-10) may be used.

1.2. Experimental techniques

For many purposes com. resins are satisfactory; finer particles are washed out by stirring in a beaker and decanting.

The batch method is used only in conjunction with a column method in analysis. The *column method* is generally excellent. The column is made from small-diam. glass tubing, e.g. a buret; usually the tip is curved in a horizontal S-shape so that the liquid level cannot fall below the level of the resin. A wad of glass wool or a plate of sintered glass is placed in the conical section. The tube is filled with water and then a slurry of resin treated as above is added. No bubbles should be present at any time in the resin bed.

Conditioning. The column is first washed with Me_2CO, EtOH or Et_2O, then with H_2O to remove org. impurities, and then with fairly concd. and dil. acids; it may also be advantageous to wash with strong bases. After washing thoroughly with H_2O, the resin is converted to the desired form (see below).

Adsorption and elution. The soln. to be analyzed is adjusted to the appropriate conditions and passed through the column. The resin is washed with a suitable eluant. By proper choice of eluants, the elution curves of several ions can be sepd. Any part of the effluent whose elution curve does not overlap others can be collected, thus permitting purification of a particular substance. The column operation can be monitored in several ways:

(*1*) On the effluent, by analysis of fractions, by means of color, absorbancy,[12] radioactivity,[13] conductivity,[14] pH,[15] refractive index[16] or polarographic cell.[17]

(*2*) On the resin bed (detection of adsorption band) by radioactivity,[18] high frequency,[19] color of resin (for example Fe^{3+} forms a dark band on a strongly acidic cationite; with strongly basic anionites, Co gives a blue band while Cu forms yellow, brown or orange bands in 4, 9 or 12*M* HCl resp.[20]), pH indicator[21] or analysis of several parts of the resin bed.[22]

Regeneration. Strong acids or bases are generally used for regeneration (and for conditioning).

For strongly acidic resins, a 10-fold excess of 2–6*N* (usually 3–4*N*) HCl is used. With an unused resin, heating with 5*N* HCl on a steam-bath is recommended.

Weakly acidic resins are treated with a 5-fold excess of 1*N* HCl. Strongly basic resins are treated with a 10-fold excess of 2–3*N* NaOH. An unused resin is treated with 1*N* HCl and 0·5*N* NaOH alternately.

Weakly basic resins are treated with a 5-fold excess of 1–2*N* NaOH.

Other reagents, e.g. NaCl of the above concn., can be used instead. In any case, the type and concn. range of the reagents and the flow rate should be considered. For example, regeneration of RNa can be done with 1*N* HCl; that of RCa with 3–4*N* HCl in 10 min.; that of RFe in 30 min.; that of adsorbed Ti, Zr, Nb, Ta with $H_2C_2O_4$; and that of RAg with 1–2*N* HNO_3. The regeneration of basic resins is slower than that of acidic resins.

If the resin bed contracts very much, it must be loosened by sucking liquid up through it from the bottom or by shaking. The contraction is greater when strongly acidic resins adsorb polyvalent ions or ions which are strongly adsorbed. Weakly acidic resins contract more when in the acid form or when they are immersed in stronger electrolytes.

1.3. Factors affecting separation

The mechanism of ion exchange has been studied by means of ion exchange equilibria and ion exchange velocity. The following factors are said to affect the sepn.:

(a) Chemical factors. (*1*) Valency, ionic radius. Ions of higher valency are strongly adsorbed by strongly acidic resins from solns. of lower concn. at room temp. ($Th^{4+} > Al^{3+} > Ca^{2+} > Na^+$).

Ions of smaller ionic radius are more strongly adsorbed than others of equal valency. For example, Tl, Ag > Cs > Rb > K, NH_4^+ > Na > H^+ > Li > $(CH_3)_4N^+$; Ra > Ba > Sr > Ca > Zn ⩾ Cu ⩾ Ni ⩾ Co ⩾ Fe^{2+} ⩾ Mg, Mn, UO_2^{2+} > Be; Ac > rare earth elements > Al > Fe^{3+}.

For the strongly basic resins (Amberlite IRA-400, ROH form) similar series are found, but these are less distinct than the above: citrate > SO_4^{2-} > $C_2O_4^{2-}$ > I^- > NO_3^- > CrO_4^{2-} > Br^- > SCN^- > Cl^- > $HCOO^-$ > OH^- > F^- > AcO^-.

(*2*) pH change. The behavior of H^+ or OH^- is somewhat different, especially for weakly acidic or basic resins. It is easily understood, for example, from the law of mass action that the H^+ concn. affects the adsorption of a given ion by acidic resins. The sample should, therefore, be dissolved in a volatile acid and the acid removed by evapn. Alkali-metal ions can be sepd. from divalent and trivalent ions by eluting with 0·1*N* HCl; bivalent ions are sepd. from trivalent ions by 1*N* HCl.

The effect of pH is especially noticeable when complexing agents are used (see p. 113).

(*3*) Adsorption other than ionic. Because the effective pore size of most resins is about 5–10 Å, ions of greater radius are not adsorbed; e.g. polymetaphosphate is sepd. from PO_4^{3-}, $P_2O_7^{4-}$ by an anionite, and proteins are sepd. from amino acids. By means of resins contg. different amts. of divinylbenzene, very elaborate sepns. are possible, but these are outside the scope of inorg. analysis.

Benzene rings in the resins attract benzoic acid, salicylic acid, etc. more strongly than inorg. acids.

(*4*) Formation of complex ions. The adsorbability of an ion may be greatly changed by complex formation, especially when the sign of the charge changes (e.g. $Fe^{3+} \rightarrow FeCl_4^-$); this is very widely used in sepns.

(*5*) Type of resins. The exchange rate is faster, the greater the amt. of swelling, i.e. the smaller the cross-linking. Diffusion coefficients at a given degree of cross-linking are strongly dependent on the charge of ions for cationites, while the effect is smaller for anionites. The degree of cross-linking may also affect the selectivity for some ions.

Strong acids are sepd. from weak acids by weakly acidic resins. Ca and Mg are removed by carboxylic acid resins. Certain selective resins (see above) are useful.

(*6*) Solvents. The difference of adsorbability between ions decreases in solvents other than H_2O. In some cases, addn. of alcohols favors sepn. (see sepn. of Cu, Zn from Al by RCl, p. 111, and of alkali metals, p. 115).

(b) Physical factors. (*1*) Dilution. Differences in adsorbability decrease in more concd. solns.; this is utilized in regeneration. In 0·1*N* soln., M^+ is sepd. from M^{2+}; in 0·5*N*, M^{2+} is sepd. from M^{3+}. In very dil. soln. the sepn. of ions of different valency becomes more effective. Adsorption of polyvalent ions is favored by diln. when monovalent ions are present.

(*2*) Flow rate. Flow rates affect the exchange equilibrium; sepn. and elution are less efficient if the flow rate is too fast, especially for polyvalent ions whose diffusion velocity in the resin phase is slow. Very slow rates are required in the sepn. of similar ions such as lanthanides or actinides. Slower rates are needed for anionites rather than for cationites.

(*3*) Size of resin particles. The size should be made as uniform as possible by screening (wet screening is preferable). The effect is due to exchange velocity; the finer the resin, the sharper the elution curves. Resins of 100–300 mesh size are used for the sepn. of similar ions, but com. resins are satisfactory for simple sepns.

(*4*) Dimension of column. Long columns of small diam. are better than short columns of large diam. contg. the same amt. of resin. Usually the ratio of diam. to length is 1:10–20 and the length is 10 cm. In the sepn. of similar ions the ratio is 1:100–200.

(*5*) Temperature. High temp. favors diffusion, thus elution curves become sharper; this is utilized in the sepn. of lanthanides.

(*6*) Viscosity. High viscosity hinders exchange equilibria.

1.4. Applications in inorg. analysis

The published methods are classified as follows.

(*1*) Simple sepns. where com. resins are satisfactory; these are readily applicable in routine work.

(*2*) Concn. for which ion exchange resins are superior to evap. or pptn.

(*3*) Sepn. of similar ions. Here sepns. can be made quite easily where older methods fail or are not satisfactory, e.g. sepn. of lanthanides. Fine resins and monitoring are usually indispensable.

(*4*) Other applications. Purification, recovery, etc.

The published data collected below may not always be adequate under different conditions (e.g. the absolute or relative amt. of the ions, the type of resin, etc.).

Possibly the most useful routine sepns. are the following: the sepn. of cations from anions, especially by strong cationites, and the detn. of salt concn.; sepns. with HCl using cationites or anionites, the latter being far better; and sepn. of U by anionites.

2. SIMPLE SEPARATIONS

2.1. Cationites

(a) Sepn. of cations and anions. *Detn. of salt concn.*[23] In 1939 Samuelson and his co-workers suggested detn. of salt concn. by titrating with standard alkali the acid formed when salt solns. are passed through strongly acidic resins (RH form) and washed with H_2O. Of course, a correction for CO_2 and for any alky. of the sample is necessary.

If the liberated acids decomp., it is better to titrate with $AgNO_3$ the Cl^- obtained by passing the sample soln. through the resin (RNa or RK form), washing with H_2O, eluting the adsorbed ions with dil. HCl, evapg. the effluent to dryness, and igniting to remove NH_4-salt, if necessary. These methods are convenient and so accurate that standard solns. can be prepd.;[24] they are applicable to salts of anions with less than trivalent cations except for the following instances:

$HgCl_2$; dil. Fe^{3+} soln. (acidify); Cr^{3+} (with the green sulfate solns., some is eluted; use resins of low divinylbenzene content and add NaOAc;[25] elution is complete with thiocyanate); phosphate (PO_4^{3-} is difficult to wash out of the column; wash thoroughly and evap.; for interfering ions, see below); pyrophosphate, metaphosphate, oxalate, etc. (some Fe, Al, Cr, La, etc. is eluted); chromates, molybdates, tungstates, salts of hetero-poly acids, vanadates (acids decomp., ppt. or are adsorbed; see below); permanganates, bromates, iodates (easily reduced resins are unsuitable); sulfites, carbonates, hydroxides (add strong acids, boil, then proceed as usual); org. acids (long-chain aliphatic and aromatic acids are especially difficult to wash out; pass dil. soln. through resin bed of fine particle size; wash with alc. if necessary).

As the references for these methods are too numerous to cite completely, only a few interesting examples are given below.

(*i*) Detn. of Na, K. Pass the mixed sulfate soln. through the column, neutralize with $0{\cdot}01N$ NaOH to methyl red + methylene blue, ppt. K as tetraphenylborate, ignite to KBO_2 and titrate.[26] SiO_2 can be detd. in soda-lime glass.[26]

(*ii*) S in pyrites. Dissolve in aqua regia, evap., add H_2O, pass through column, titrate H^+, Cl^- and calc.[27]

Removal of cations. The technique is frequently and easily applied for the detn. of anions.

(*i*) S. Dissolve pyrites in aqua regia, evap. with HCl, pass through column, and weigh as $BaSO_4$.[28] Similar methods for pure iron and low-S steels,[29] Ni and Cu alloys[30] are available. Traces of SO_4^{2-} in NaCl can be titrated with alkali after evapn. of the effluent.[25] Fe^{3+} can be removed before titration of SO_4^{2-} with Ba^{2+} in presence of rhodizonate or thoron indicator (see Chapter 58, p. 435).

(*ii*) PO_4^{3-}. Pass 400–500 mg. PO_4^{3-} in $0{\cdot}1N$ HCl soln. through Amberlite IR-100 (17 cm. long) during 10 min., add H_2O, adjust to pH 4·63, and titrate to pH 8·98.[31] Many workers[30, 32] apply this method to analyses of phosphate ores, boiler water, fertilizers, etc.

With Amberlite IR-112 (RNa), the sepn. of PO_4^{3-} from NH_4^+, Mg, Ca, Ba, Ni, Co, Mn, Cu, Zn, Fe^{2+} is easy. Sepn. from Cd is possible in H_2SO_4 soln.; from Ag, Pb in HNO_3 soln.; from Cr^{3+} if fresh soln. is used and the green compd. is absent; from UO_2^{2+}, La in slightly stronger HCl soln. if the RH-form of the resin is used; and from Al by washing with $0{\cdot}01N$ HCl. Sepn. from Fe^{3+} is complete with Amberlite IR-120 if Fe^{3+}: $PO_4^{3-} < 1:10$; above this ratio, SO_2 reduction is necessary. For studies by means of radioactive tracers see ref. 33. Sepn. of SO_4^{2-} from PO_4^{3-} is possible.[34]

(*iii*) As. Sepn. from Fe and Cu is possible with Ion X (12 ml. of 60–100 mesh) if the soln. contains 2 ml. HCl per 40 ml. and the rate is 20 ml./min. Iodimetric (insecticides),[35] colorimetric (in Ni, Cu),[30] or neutralization finishes[18, 33] are available. The same precautions as for phosphate are necessary.[33]

(*iv*) SeO_3^{2-}. At pH 3 (NaOAc soln.) phenolsulfonic acid resin (RNa) permits sepn. from Fe and Zn; colorimetry or polarography has been used.[36]

(*v*) F^-. In natural water, Orgacit A or Diaion K (2 g., RNa), gives sepn. from Fe, Al, Be, Ca, etc.; colorimetry with Al^{3+}-hematoxylin is used finally.[37] For chrome-plating soln., EtOH reduction is required before passage through Diaion K (RH, 25 ml.) with an Al^{3+}-aluminon finish (see Chapter 60, p. 451).

(*vi*) SiO_2. Orgacit A (RNa, 50 ml.) is used with $0{\cdot}5N$ HNO_3 soln., before colorimetry (in Fe ores, etc.).[38]

(*vii*) B. 5 mg. H_3BO_3 and less than 10 mg. Fe, Al, Zn or NH_4^+ are sepd. at above pH 1·5 on Diaion K (40–60 mesh, 15 g. dried resin); the effluent is titrated.[39] This is simpler than distn. and has many applications.[40] See also Section 2.3.

(*viii*) CNO^-. Cations are removed with Dowex 50 (20–50 mesh, RNa) before hydrolysis of CNO^- with dil. acid to form NH_4^+; anions are removed with RH-form resin; after elution with dil. NaOH, colorimetry with Nessler's reagent is suitable.[41]

(*ix*) CN^-. Colorimetry with $PdCl_2$ and α-furildioxime is used after removal of Fe and Al.[42]

(*x*) V. Dissolve 0·5 g. steel in acid (aqua regia when Cr is present), add $HClO_4$, evap., add H_2O to give $0{\cdot}5N$ acid, followed by H_2O_2; pass through Amberlite IR-210 (20 mesh, 1 cm. diam., 30 ml., treated with 100 ml. $0{\cdot}4N$ HNO_3 contg. 1–2 drops 3% H_2O_2) and wash (with the same soln. contg. a little non-ionic surfactant); evap., add $Pb(ClO_4)$ (to sep. from Cr, Mo) and det. colorimetrically with H_2O_2.[43] Wofatit R can be used with $0{\cdot}1N$ H_2SO_4 contg. H_2O_2 for sepn. of Mo, V, W from Fe, Ti, Ni, Cu, Mn.[44]

V is completely adsorbed on $ROHSO_3H$ resin at pH 1–12 but adsorption is incomplete on $ROHSO_3Na$, $ROHSO_3NH_4$ or $RONaSO_3Na$ at pH 1, and non-existent below pH 5.[45] In these cases V is adsorbed as VO^{2+}; reduction is complete with ZeoKarb 215 or 216 and Amberlite IR-120 but incomplete with ZeoKarb 225; sepn. from PO_4^{3-} is possible.[46] Wofatit F permits sepn. from PO_4^{3-} in acid soln. contg. Na_2SO_3.[47] V is also adsorbed on Amberlite IR-100 (RH) and is eluted as a blue soln. with HCl.[48] Ce^{4+} or $KMnO_4$ titration is used (in Cr–W–V steel or Fe–V) after sepn. by means of Diaion K.[49]

Removal of anions. (*i*) Alkali metals. Use the RH form of resin for sulfate and phosphate, and the RNH_4 form for vanadate, chromate, molybdate, tungstate, phosphotungstate, etc. This is better than pptn. methods. K is detd. in fertilizers; Na and K are detd. by flame photometry after removal of SO_4^{2-} and PO_4^{3-}.[50]

(*ii*) Ca, Mg. Pass through the column, wash with H_2O, elute with acid and det. by chelatometric titration. Sepn. from Fe is possible by washing with $0{\cdot}2M$ $H_2C_2O_4$. Ca can be detd. in plant materials and Mg in natural water, etc.[51]

(*iii*) Th is sepd. from PO_4^{3-} by elution with $0{\cdot}1M$ HCl and is detd. colorimetrically with quercetin (see p. 341).

For sepn. of UO_2^{2+} from anions, see ref. 52.

(b) Sepn. of metals. *Elution with HCl or chloride.* (*i*) Natural water. Pass 200 ml. 0·01*N* to 40 ml. 0·5*N* salt soln. of pH 2·0–9·0 through Diaion K (80–120 mesh, RH, 10 ml.); titrate an aliquot with standard alkali to give $SO_4^{2-} + Cl^-$, det. Cl^- by Mohr's method and calc. SO_4^{2-}. Thoroughly wash the column, elute with 350 ml. 0·1*N* HCl, wash with H_2O and titrate with alkali (Na + K) (Na can be sepd. from K if triple the above amount of resin is used). Elute with 100–120 ml. 1*N* HCl and det. Fe, Al, Ca, Mg by the usual method (Ca, Mg are sepd. from Fe, Al by eluting with 0·5*N* HCl and using double the above amount of resin).[53]

(*ii*) Sepn. of Cd or Hg from other metals. Dissolve 1 g. non-ferrous alloy in dil. HNO_3, evap. to dryness, add HCl, evap. and repeat the treatment. Dissolve in 1*N* HCl, filter if turbid, and dil. with 1*N* HCl to 100 ml.; pipet 25 ml. (when Cd is less than 0·001%, use a larger column and pipet more or conc. with H_2S), pass through Amberlite IR-120 (50–100 mesh, RH, 1·3 × 19 cm.) at a rate of 1 ml./min., wash with 125 ml. 0·1*N* HCl and pass 200 ml. 0·5*N* HCl at 1·5 ml./min.; det. colorimetrically with dithizone. Cu and Zn in Cd are detd. similarly after sepn. of Cd as above and elution of Cu and Zn with 2*N* HCl.[54] See also Section 3.

For sepn. of Hg from other ions, pass the soln. through Dowex 50-X8 (100–200 mesh, 24 mm. × 2 in. washed with H_2O and 0·05*M* NaCl) and elute with 45–50 ml. 0·05*M* NaCl; for the cuprethol-Cu^{2+} finish, see Chapter 19, p. 155.

For sepn. of Au from Hg, use Dowex 50 and elute Au with 2*N* HCl and Hg with HCl.[55]

(*iii*) Sepn. of Ga, In, Ge from Pb, Cu, Zn, Fe, Sb.[56] The normality of HCl where the metal ions appear in the effluent with Dowex 50 (20–50 mesh, RH, 0·8 × 100 cm.) is as follows: $Sb^{3+} > 0{\cdot}1$, In $\geqslant$ 0·4, Zn, Pb $\geqslant$ 0·5, Cu $\geqslant$ 0·7, Fe $\geqslant$ 1·0, Ga $\geqslant$ 1·3. The following sepns. are possible.

Sepn. of In from other elements. Pass 0·4*N* HCl soln. through the column and elute with 2 l. 0·4*N* HCl at a rate of 10 ml./min. to sep. from Pb, Cu, Zn, Fe. With a 30 cm. column and 400–800 ml. 0·5*N* HCl, In is sepd. from Cu; with 0·2*N* HCl Sb is eluted, and with 0·4*N* HCl In is eluted.

Sepn. of Ga from other elements. 12 l. 1·0*N* HCl elutes Cu and 2 l. 1·5*N* HCl elutes Ga; 12 l. 0·8*N* HCl elutes Sb, Pb, Cu, Zn, and 2 l. 1·5*N* HCl elutes Ga; 1 l. 1*N* HCl contg. SO_2 elutes Fe, Cu, Zn, Pb (filter if turbid) and 2 l. 1·5*N* HCl elutes Ga; 0·4*N* HCl elutes In, and 1·3*N* HCl elutes Ga.

Ge, (As, Sb) are sepd. from other elements by elution with 0·1*N* HCl. HBr (0·4–0·5*N* for In elution and 0·7*N* for Ga), HNO_3 and H_2SO_4 (0·8*N* for Cu elution, 0·9*N* for Fe and 1*N* for In) cannot replace HCl.

(*iv*) Sepn. of Be from Al. Pass a soln. contg. 1·20 meq. Be, 0·51 meq. Al and 10·0 meq. Ca through Diaion K (RCa, 5 ml.); elute Be with 100 ml. 0·01*N* $CaCl_2$ and Al with 100 ml. 0·1*N* $CaCl_2$.[57]

(*v*) Other examples. Sepn. of Se from Te. Pass a feebly acidic soln. contg. 50–1000 μg. of each metal through Amberlite IR-120 (60 mesh, RH, 10 ml.), wash with 100 ml. H_2O, 100 ml. 0·3*N* HCl and 100 ml. 3*N* HCl. Se appears in the first 75 ml. effluent, Te between 125–255 ml. and heavy metals thereafter.[58]

Sepn. of Th, Nd and U. Pass through Dowex 50-X8, and elute Th with 7*N* HCl, Nd with 8*N* HCl and U with 1*N* HCl.[59]

Sepn. of U from Fe. Pass the slightly (HCl) acidic soln. through Lewatit S-100 (0·3–0·4 mm., RH, 1 × 55 cm.), wash with 100 ml. H_2O and elute with 0·8*N* HCl at 80–85 ml./hr.; discard 400 ml.; UO^{2+} appears in the 500–800 ml. fraction and Fe thereafter. This is better than $(NH_4)_2CO_3$ elution.[60]

Sepn. of Fe from Al. Pass less than 3 meq. Fe + Al in less than 0·5*N* acidic soln. through Amberlite IR-120 (50–80 mesh, 1 cm. diam., 20 ml. resin), wash with H_2O, and elute Fe^{2+} with 0·1*N* KI + 0·15*N* KCl + 2*N* HCl; Fe is detd.[61] by titrating the liberated I_2 with $Na_2S_2O_3$.

With 0·7*M* HCl at 1·2 cm./min. and Dowex 50 (fine, RH, 4·6 cm.² × 55 cm.) the order of appearance in the effluent is Hg, Cd, (Li, Na), (K, Be), Pb, (Mg, Zn, Mn).[62]

Urine analysis. Pass 2 ml. urine through a 2 g. resin column, wash with H_2O until no Cl^- appears in the effluent, and elute NH_4^+ with 200 ml. 0·1*N* HCl at 1–2 ml./min. and Mg with 60 ml. 1*N* HCl.[63]

Sepn. of As from Sb or Sn. Pass the soln. contg. 1 mg. As and 1 mg. Sn through Wofatit P (RH, 10 g.), and elute As with 0·6*N* HCl; 7·0 mg. As can be sepd. from 1·0 mg. Sb with 1*N* H_2SO_4.[64]

Elution with other halides and pseudohalides. (*i*) Sepn. of Bi from Sb, Cu, Pb. With Wofatit P (RH), 1*N* H_2SO_4 + 6% NH_4SCN elutes Bi and permits sepn. from Sb. With 8 g. resin (RK), 0·1*N* H_2SO_4 + 1% KI (pH 1·8–2·2) elutes 0·1 mg. Bi, sepg. it from 4 mg. Cu and 1·0 mg. Pb.[64]

(*ii*) Sepn. of Fe from Ti. To a soln. contg. less than 67 mg. Fe and 0·7 mg. Ti, add 50% KCN, filter, wash, dissolve the ppt. in dil. H_2SO_4 and dil. with H_2O. Pass through Diaion K (30–70 mesh, RH, 1 cm. diam., 10 g. resin), elute Fe with 200 ml. 2*N* KCN, wash with H_2O and elute Ti with 100–200 ml. 10% H_2SO_4. Use colorimetry with H_2O_2. This is suitable for the analysis of limonite.[65]

(*iii*) Sepn. of Cr from Fe, Mn, Ni. Add KSCN to the soln., boil and pass through RNa resin.[66]

Elution with org. acids. (*i*) Sepn. of Sn^{2+} from Sb^{3+}. Pass 10 mg. metal in 25 ml. of dil. HCl soln. through Amberlite IR-120 (100 mesh, RH, 6 cm. long, 10 ml. resin) and elute Sb with 0·4% tartaric acid soln. which has been adjusted to pH 1 with HCl.[67]

(*ii*) Sepn. of Ca, Mg from much Fe, Al. Dissolve 1–20 g. of steel in 6*N* H_2SO_4 + the min. amt. HNO_3 (fuse the residue with $KHSO_4$ and combine); add 20–40 ml. 20% tartaric acid followed by dil. NaOH to pH 3; cool to below 20°C, pass through 35 ml. Diaion K and wash with 100 ml. H_2O; elute Mg with 30 ml. 20% NH_4Cl and H_2O, etc.[68]

(*iii*) Sepn. of Al, Fe and Zn. Elute Fe with 200 ml. pH 2·0–2·5 soln. contg. citrate, Al with 150 ml. pH 11 soln. contg. citrate, and Zn with 2*N* HCl.[69]

(*iv*) Sepn. of Tl from Sb, Fe, Cu, Zn, Cd, Pb, Al is possible with tartaric acid or citric acid soln. In is sepd. from Zn, Pb with sulfosalicylic acid soln.[70] Be is sepd. from Cu, U, Ca, etc. with Dowex 50 (RH) by means of less than 0·02*M* sulfosalicylic or gentisic acid soln. (pH 3–4·5).[71]

Zn is sepd. from Cd (1:1000) with Dowex 50 (20–35 mesh, RNH_4) by elution with 0·25*M* $(NH_4)_3$-citrate (pH 4).[72]

(*v*) Sepn. of Mo from Fe, etc. Dissolve steel (0·1–0·5 g. when Mo $>$ 1%; 0·5–1 g. when Mo $<$ 1%) in 5 ml. 6*N* H_2SO_4, warm, add 1 g. $(NH_4)_2S_2O_8$ and boil for 10 min. (when W is present, add 10 ml. 6*N* HCl, warm, add 1–20 ml. HNO_3, boil, evap. to near dryness, add 10 ml. 6*N* H_2SO_4, evap., and add 5–10 ml. 6*N* H_2SO_4; if a ppt. remains, add 10 g. Na_3-citrate and NaOH, boil, and neutralize with H_2SO_4). Dil. with H_2O to 50 ml., add 0·1 g. $Na_2S_2O_5$, boil off SO_2, add 7 g. citric acid and 3 g. Na_3-citrate; adjust to pH 1–2, dil. to 100 ml. with H_2O, pass through Dowex 50-X12 (50–100 mesh, 20 ml.) discard the first 15 ml., pipet 10 ml., and det. by polarography.[73]

Mo can also be adsorbed from feebly acidic HCl soln. to sep. it from W. NaOH elution permits sepn. of Fe, Cu from Mo, W, Zn, Al, Sb[64, 74]; 5% $NaNH_4HPO_4$ (pH 9·0) elution can also be used.[49]

(*vi*) Analysis of fission products. Pass the less than 0·1*N* HCl soln. through Amberlite IR-100; Ru, Sb and anions appear in the effluent. Elute Zr, Hf, Nb with 0·5% $H_2C_2O_4$, elute rare earths with 5% $(NH_4)_3$-citrate at pH 3, and alk. earths with 5% $(NH_4)_3$-citrate at pH 5.[2, 75] For the sepn. of elements in each fraction, see Section 4. This is the fundamental method of analysis of fission products.

(*vii*) Impurities in $UO_2(NO_3)_2$. Adsorb on Amberlite IR-120, elute UO_2^{2+}, Fe, Cu with 0·5*N* $H_2C_2O_4$, Cd, Ni, Co, Mn with 0·1*N* HCl, and rare earths with 5% $(NH_4)_3$-citrate.[76] UO_2^{2+}, Fe, Al, Cd, Mg, Ca can be eluted with 2*N* HCl and tracer amt. of Th with 0·5*M* $H_2C_2O_4$;[77] for the detn. of Th in natural waters and rocks, see Chapter 46 (p. 340).

(*viii*) Concn. of rare earths and sepn. from 1·5 g. Th. Pass the sample soln. (pH 2–2·3 contg. an equiv. amt. of EDTA) through Dowex 50 (2·2 × 30 cm. treated with 10% $HCOONH_4$ buffer of pH 2·1), and wash with 50 ml. formate buffer and 350–400 ml. H_2O.[78]

(*ix*) Sepn. of Be from Fe, Al, Ti. Use Amberlite 120 (0·4–0·6 mm., 1·8 × 12 cm.); elute Fe, etc. with a soln. of pH 3·5 contg. 20 ml. 10% EDTA/400 ml. and 1 ml. H_2O_2, and elute Be with 3*M* HCl.[79] $H_2C_2O_4$ can also be used.[80] Ga is sepd. from Zn with RNH_4 resin and elution of Ga with a 6–10-fold amt. of tartrate soln. or a 3-fold amt. of EDTA soln. at pH 4–5; Zn is eluted with 10% HCl.[81]

(*x*) Sepn. of Tl^+ from Pb, Hg, Bi. Add 20 mg. EDTA for each 10 ml. sample soln. at pH 4, pass through Amberlite IR-120 (RNa, 2 ml., 5 cm., pH 4) and wash with 20 mg. EDTA/20 ml. H_2O and then H_2O to elute Pb, etc.; elute Tl with 50 ml. 2*N* HCl; ppt. with $[Co(NH_3)_6]Cl_3$ and det. Tl by colorimetry of Co in the ppt. with nitroso-R salt (see p. 308).

(*xi*) Sepn. of Bi from Zn, Cd, Pb. Pass the EDTA-contg. soln. at pH 1 through Amberlite IR-112 (RNH_4, 0·5 × 9 cm. or 0·4 × 23 cm.).[82]

(*xii*) Sepn. of Pb from Ba. Pass the soln. contg. 60 mg. nitrates and 0·3 g. EDTA/100 ml. at pH 4·0–4·5 through Amberlite IR-120 (RNH_4, 30 mesh, 6 ml., 9 cm.) at a rate of 1–1·5 ml./min.; elute Pb with a soln. of pH 4–4·5 contg. 0·3 g. EDTA/100 ml. and Ba with a soln. of pH 10·8 contg. 0·3 g. EDTA, 2·5 g. NH_4OAc and 5 ml. NH_4OH/100 ml.; back-titrate the excess EDTA with $MgCl_2$.[83] Alternatively, use Amberlite IR-120 (80–100 mesh, RNH_4, 5 ml., 6 cm.), and elute Pb with 200 ml. 2% NH_4OAc at pH 5·8–6·1, and Ba with 250 ml. 10% NH_4Cl or 100 ml. 5% $(NH_4)_3$-citrate neutralized to methyl red.[84]

(*xiii*) Sepn. of Cu and Ag. Pass through Dowex 50-X8 (RNH_4, 480 mesh, 5 ml.), elute Cu with 0·01*M* EDTA, and Ag with 1–2*N* NH_3 and 1–2*N* NH_4Cl.[85]

Elution with other inorg. salts. Fe, Cr and Mn are sepd. on RNa resin by eluting Fe with polyphosphate at pH 3–4 and Cr with polyphosphate at pH 7.[66] For sepn. of Fe, Al, Cr from Cu, Zn, Co, Ni, Cd, see ref. 86. Cu can be sepd. from Al, Mg[66] and Zn from Cu, Cd[87] by means of $Na_2S_2O_3$.

Be is sepd. from Cu, Ni by elution with 10% $(NH_4)_2CO_3$ and Be from Mo by elution with 5% NH_3.[88]

With the carboxylic acid resin, Amberlite IRC-50 (RNH_4, 325 mesh, 6 ml.), Cu can be sepd. from Ni, Zn by elution with 1*M* NH_3 and 1*M* NH_4Cl.[85] For sepn. of Cu from Co and of Zn from Cd, see ref. 89.

2.2. Anionites

(a) Sepn. of anions from cations. *Detn. of salt concn.* As in the case of cationites, salt concns. can be detd. by passing the sample soln. through anionites in suitable form, e.g. ROH, RCl, and titrating the effluent with acid, $AgNO_3$, etc. However, it is time-consuming to wash and regenerate anionites and it is necessary to take precautions for carbonate ions, hence the use of cationites is generally more convenient. Anionites are better, nevertheless, for phosphates owing to the interference of Fe^{3+} with cationites, for sulfites owing to decompn., for tungstates owing to pptn., and for vanadates (see cationites).

As an example is cited the detn. of S in sulfides or roasted ores.[90] To 0·5 g. sample in a Ni crucible, add 4 g. Na_2O_2 and 2 g. $Na_2C_2O_4$, mix, cover with 1 g.

Na_2O_2 and cover; insert a 0·5 cm. filter paper strip, ignite, and then add H_2O; filter; acidify with HCl, boil and dil. to a definite vol. Adjust the pH of an aliquot to 7·5 with NH_4OH or HCl using a glass electrode, pass through Amberlite IRA-400 (0·6 × 14 cm., RCl) and titrate with $AgNO_3$; the increase in Cl^- corresponds to the SO_4^{2-} present originally.

Removal of anions. Na can be detd. with zinc uranyl acetate after removal of PO_4^{3-} by the batch method with Wofatit M (RCl); K can be detd. after treatment with Amberlite IRA-400 (0·98 × 15 cm., RCl).[91] Tartrate and PO_4^{3-} can be removed by treating the weakly acidic sample soln. with resin before the qual. analysis of groups III, IV.[91] Al is sepd. from PO_4^{3-} and CrO_4^{2-} by means of Dowex 1-X8 (50–100 mesh, RCl).[92, 93]

For the sepn. of H_2O_2 from CrO_4^{2-}, add Amberlite IRA-400 (RCl) to the sample soln., stir for 10 min. and centrifuge; det. H_2O_2 colorimetrically with Ti-$(SO_4)_2$.[94]

Removal of cations. For the detn. of SiO_2 in alginate, pass the sample through 15 g. Amberlite IRA-400, wash, elute with 10 ml. 2·5*N* NaOH and det. SiO_2 colorimetrically.[95] For the sepn. of CrO_4^{2-} from much Ni, adjust the soln. to pH 12 with NH_4OH soln., and pass through guanidine resin.[96]

(b) Sepn. of anions. (See also **(c)** below). Sepn. of SiO_3^{2-} from PO_4^{3-}. Pass the neutral soln. through Orgacit B (RCl) and det. SiO_3^{2-} colorimetrically (Honda[38]).

Sepn. of F^- from SO_4^{2-} and PO_4^{3-}. Pass the soln. contg. 1 meq. of each ion through Amberlite IRA-410 or 400 (RCl, 0·6 × 12 or 25 cm.), wash with 0·1% NaCl and det. F^- in 40 ml. effluent colorimetrically with Al-Eriochrome cyanine R; this yields 96–98% recovery.[97] F^- can also be eluted with 0·1*N* NaOH from Amberlite IRA-400 (100 mesh, 0·7 × 15 cm., ROH);[97] 12·5 μg. F^- can be eluted with 0·5*N* NaOH and sepd. from 12·5 mg. P (which is eluted with 0·8*N* NaOH) from Dowex 1-X8 (100–200 mesh, ROH, 1·6 × 10·5 cm.).[98] With Amberlite IRA-400 treated with 2*N* Na_2CO_3 and H_2O, Al can be eluted with 300 ml. 0·2*N* Na_2CO_3 and sepd. from F^- which is eluted with 250 ml. 1*N* Na_2CO_3.[99]

Sepn. of $S_2O_3^{2-}$ and $S_4O_6^{2-}$. Neutralize 20 ml. sulfite pulp waste with $MgCO_3$, pass through Amberlite IRA-410 (0·12–0·38 mm., RCl, 1·25 × 8 cm.) and wash with 20 ml. H_2O; elute $S_2O_3^{2-}$ with 75 ml. 4*N* NaCl, and elute $S_4O_6^{2-}$ with 5 ml. H_2O and 30 ml. 0·3*M* Na_2SO_3.[100]

Sepn. of AcO^-, PO_4^{3-}, NO_3^- and SO_4^{2-}. Pass the soln. contg. 5 mg. of each ion through Amberlite IR-4B (RCl, 2 ml.), and elute the ions in the order given with 0·01, 0·1, 0·2*N* HCl and 0·2*N* NaOH respectively.[25]

Sepn. of AcO^- and BO_2^- from SO_4^{2-}. Pass the soln. which should be 0·5*M* in AcOH and 0·5*M* in H_2SO_4, through Dowex 1 (200–230 mesh, RSO_4, 0·48 cm.² × 15·7 cm.), and wash with H_2O at a rate of 0·3 cm./min.[101]

(c) Sepn. of metals. *Elution with HCl.* In HCl soln. several of the transition elements form chloride complexes which are adsorbed by anionites. In Table 25 the logarithms of the distribution coeffs. of metal ions are listed (Honda *et al.*[1]). (See also Fig. 11 on page 89 in Yoe and Koch: *Trace Analysis* (1957)). It is possible to sep. many ions by utilizing this phenomenon and the different degrees of stability of the complexes. The adsorbability shows a remarkable parallelism with the extractability of the chlorides or thiocyanates by ether (compare Tables 28 and 29, e.g. the sepn. of Sc from rare earths). This phenomenon has been thoroughly studied by Kraus *et al.*[102] and Jentzsch *et al.*[103]

Kraus *et al.* succeeded in obtaining the following sepns.

(*i*) Sepn. of Ni, Mn, Co, Cu, Fe^{3+}, Zn. Pass a 12*M* HCl soln. contg. 6 mg. of each ion/0·85 ml. through Dowex 1 (200–230 mesh, 0·29 cm.² × 26 cm.) and elute Ni with 10 ml. 12*M* HCl, Mn with 10 ml. 6*M* HCl, Co with 10 ml. 4*M* HCl, Cu with 10 ml. 2·5*M* HCl, Fe^{3+} with 20 ml. 0·6*M* HCl, and Zn with 0·005*M* HCl (all at a rate of 0·5 cm./min.).

(*ii*) Sepn. of Al, Ga, In, Tl. The soln. should contain 0·5*M* Al, and 0·15*M* Ga, In, Tl in 4 ml. 7*M* HCl. Pass this soln. through the resin (0·4 cm.² × 20 cm.) and elute Al with 20 ml. 7*M* HCl, In with 50 ml. 7*M* HCl and 30 ml. 12*M* HCl, Ga with 500 ml. 1*M* HCl, and Tl with 800 ml. 4*M* $HClO_4$.

(*iii*) Sepn. of V^{4+}, Ti, Fe^{3+}. Pass 1 ml. 12*M* HCl contg. 0·05*M* V, 0·018*M* Ti and 0·025*M* Fe through the resin; elute V with 20 ml. 12·1*M* HCl, Ti with 20 ml. 9·1*M* HCl, and Fe with 20 ml. 1·0*M* HCl.

(*iv*) Sepn. of Pb, Bi, Fe^{3+}. Pass 0·02 ml. 8*M* HCl soln. contg. trace amts. of Pb, Bi, and 0·05*M* Fe through the resin (0·3 cm.² × 4·7 cm.); elute Pb with 8*M* HCl, Fe with 0·5*M* HCl and Bi with 1·0*M* H_2SO_4. Alternatively, use a 1*M* HCl soln., and elute Fe with 1*M* HCl, Pb with 8*M* HCl and Bi with 1*M* H_2SO_4.

(*v*) Sepn. of Th, Pa, U. Elute Th with 10*M* HCl, Pa with 9*M* HCl and 1*M* HF, and U^{6+} with 0·1*M* HCl.

(*vi*) Other sepns. U^{4+} can be sepd. from U^{6+}: rare earths are eluted with 8*M* HCl, U^{4+} with 8*M* HCl + 0·1*M* HF, U^{6+} with 0·5*M* HCl, and Zn with 0·01*M* HCl. Sc and Y in tracer amts. are sepd. in concd. HCl. Cd and In in trace amts. can also be sepd.

Other interesting sepns. which have been obtained by other workers are:

Sepn. of RaD (Pb) RaE (Bi) and RaF (Po). The mixt. of the elements extd. from the radon tube with several drops HCl is passed through Amberlite XE-98 (65–120 mesh, 8·5 × 30 mm., treated with 2*N* HCl); RaD is eluted with 2*N* HCl, RaE with concd. HCl, and RaF with HNO_3 (1:1), all at a rate of 100 ml./2 hr.[104]

Sepn. of As^{3+} from As^{5+}, Ge. Pass through Dowex 2 (80–120 mesh, RCl, 0·92 cm.² × 13 cm.); elute As^{5+} with 8*M* HCl, As^{3+} with 1*M* HCl, and Ge with 1*M* H_2SO_4.[105]

Sepn. of S, Se, Te, Po. Pass 1 ml. 12*N* HCl contg. 4 mg. Se, 6 mg. Te, 5 × 10^{-3} μC Po and 3 mg. S (as

TABLE 25. Logarithm of Distribution Coefficient of Ions against Strong Anionites in HCl soln.

HCl *N*	12	10	8	6	4	2	1	0·1	0·01	0
Li, Na, K, Rb, Cs, Fr	—	—	—	—	—	—	—	—	—	—
Cu^{+}	>0	<1	1	>1	2	>2				
Cu^{2+}	1	1	1	1	<1	0	0	—	—	—
Ag	+	0	<1	<1	1	2	<3	3		
Au^{+}	+	+	+	+	+	—	—			
Au^{3+}	3	4	>4	5	>5	6	+	+	+	+
Be, Mg, Ca, etc.	—	—	—	—	—	—	—	—	—	—
Zn	1	>1	2	>2	>2	<3	2	1	0	—
Cd	1	>1	2	>2	>2	3	3	2	1	0
Hg^{2+}	>1	2	>2	3	>3	4	>4	+	+	—
B, Al	—	—	—	—	—	—	—	—	—	—
Sc	0	—	—	—	—	—	—	—	—	—
Ya, La, etc.	—	—	—	—	—	—	—	—	—	—
Ga	4	>4	<5	5	3	1				
In	>0	<1	<1	<1	1	1	<1	0		
Tl^{+}	+	—	—	—						
Tl^{3+}	>2	3	>3	4	>4	5				
Si	—	—	—	—	—	—	—	—	—	—
Ge	2	2	<2	<1	0	0				
Sn^{2+}	1	>1	<2	2	>2	>2	3	±	—	—
Sn^{4+}	3	<4	<4	4	<4	3	>2			
Pb	—	—	0	0	1	>1	>1	<1	0	—
Ti^{3+}	0	—	—	—	—					
Ti^{4+}	1	0	—	—	—	—	—	—	—	—
Zr	>3	>2	<1	0						
Hf	<3	2	<1	0						
P	—	—	—	—	—	—	—	—		
As^{3+}	1	1	1	<1	0	0	—			
As^{5+}	+	+	+	+	—	—	—	—		
Sb^{3+}	>1	>1	2	>2	3	>3	3	+	±	±
Sb^{5+}	>5	>5	5	4	<3	0	±	—	—	—
Bi	<2	<2	2	>2	3	<4	4	5	5	
$V^{3+, 4+}$	0	—								
V^{5+}	3	2	0							
Nb	3	3	3	2	>1	2	2			
Ta	<3	2	>1	1	1	<2	2	>2		

HCl *N*	12	10	8	6	4	2	1	0·1	0·01	0
S	—	—	—	—	—	—	—	—	—	—
Se^{4+}	+	+	1	<1	>0	0	0	—		
Te^{4+}	+	+	+	+	+	—	—			
Po	+	+	+	+	+	+	+	+	+	+
$[Cr(H_2O)_6]^{3+}$	—	—	—	—	—	—	—	—	—	—
Cr^{6+}	+	+	+	+	+	+	+	+	+	+
Mo	2	2	2	2	2	1	<1			
W	>1	<2	<2	>1	+	+	+	+	+	+
Mn^{2+}	0	0	0	0	—	—	—	—	—	—
Tc	+	>2	<3	3	3	4	4	+	+	+
Re	1	1	>1	<2	>2	3	>3	4		
Fe^{2+}	1	<1	<1	0	0	—	—	—	—	—
Fe^{3+}	>4	>4	<5	<4	>2	>1	>0	0		
Co	>1	<2	<2	<1	0	—	—	—	—	—
Ni	—	—	—	—	—	—	—	—	—	—
Ru^{4+}	>1	>1	<2	2	>2	>2				
Rh	—	—	—	—	<1	1	>1	+		
Pd	>1	>1	>1	2	>2	<3	<3	3		
Os^{4+}	>2	<2	3	>3	>3	<4	>4			
Ir^{3+}	—	—	—	0	<1	1	>1			
Ir^{4+}	>2	>2	<3	3	>3	4	+	+		
Pt^{2+}	+	+	+	+	+	+	—	—	—	—
Pt^{4+}	2	>2	<3	3	3	3	>3	4		
Ac	—	—	—	—	—	—	—	—	—	—
Th	—	—	—	—	—	—	—	—	—	—
Pa	<4	3	<3	2	<1					
U^{4+}	3	2	>1	0						
U^{6+}	3	3	<3	2	1	0	—	—	—	—
$Np^{4+, 5+}$	+	+	+	+	+					
Pu^{3+}		—	—	—						
Pu^{4+}	+	+	+	+	+					
Am^{3+}	+									
Cm^{3+}	+									
Cf^{3+}	+									
Es^{3+}	+									
Fm^{3+}	+									

NOTE. + adsorbed; ± slightly adsorbed; – not adsorbed.

SO_4^{2-}) through Dowex 1-X4 (180 mesh, 0·6 cm.^{2} × 3·8 cm. treated with 12*N* HCl); elute SO_4^{2-} with 2·5 ml. 12*N* HCl, Se (greenish band) with 3·5 ml. 6*N* HCl, Te (yellow band) with 12 ml. 2*N* HCl and Po with 1*N* $HClO_4$ or HNO_3.[106]

Sepn. of Sn, Sb, Te. Pass the 6*N* HCl soln. through Dowex 1-X2; elute Sb, Te and Sn with 3*N*, 1*N* and 0·1*N* HCl respectively.[107] High temp. (80°C) favors the sepns. of Mn from Fe and Ni from Co.[108]

Applications in routine work. (*i*) Sepn. of Zn from Al, Mg, Cu, Co, Ni, Mn^{2+}, Cr^{3+}, Fe^{3+}, Th, Zr, Ti, U^{6+}, Be, Ca. Pass the soln. contg. 5–50 mg. Zn + other metals in 2*N* HCl through Amberlite IRA-400 (100 mesh, RCl, 50 ml., 12 cm.); 50 ml. 2*N* HCl removes the other metals; 0·25*N* HNO_3 elutes Zn, Cd, 20% Sn, some Mo and a little In, Sb, Bi, Pb, Pt, W. Zn is sepd. from Sn, In, Ga, U by Et_2O extn. of $Znpy_4(SCN)_2$. Zn is detd. with oxine or EDTA. For the detn. of Zn in Al alloys, addn. of a non-ionic surfactant favors sepn. (EDTA titration). For Zn in Pb-ore see ref. 109. Zn can be sepd. from Cd by concd. HCl,[110] and from Fe, etc. before colorimetry with zincon. Ni can be sepd. with 12*N* HCl from Fe, which is eluted with 0·5*N* HCl, and Zn (eluted with 0·005*N* HCl before quinaldic acid detn.).

(*ii*) Sepn. of Zn and Cd. Pass the sample soln. contg. 100 g. NaCl/l. 0·12*N* HCl soln. through Dowex 1 (200–400 mesh, RCl, 1 in.^{2} × 10 in.; 90 g. resin for 1 g. amt., and 10 g. resin for 0·1 g. amt.) at a rate of 2–4 ml./min.; Fe, Mn, Al, Be, Ni, Cr, Cu, Ti, SO_4^{2-} appear in the effluent; a soln. contg. 20 g. NaCl/l. 2*N* NaOH elutes Zn, and H_2O and 1*N* HNO_3 elute Cd. Bi interferes; sepn. from Sb, Sn, As is possible by HBr evapn., and sepn. from Pb by H_2SO_4 evapn.[111] Cd (20 μg.) is not successfully sepd. from Cu (0·9 g.) with 1*N* HCl on Dowex 2 (80–100 mesh).[54]

(*iii*) Sepn. of In from other elements. Dissolve minerals etc. in aqua regia, add H_2SO_4, evap., and add H_2O; filter; add NH_4OH and reppt.; add 5*N* HCl and pass through Wofatit L-150 (0·08–0·15 mm., 0·75 × 65 cm. treated with 5*N* HCl) at a rate of 60 ml./hr.; wash with 4*N* HCl; In and Sn are eluted with 120–140 ml. 1*N* HCl at a rate of 30–40 ml./hr. before polarographic detn. of In.[103] For sepn. of Ga from Sn, Fe, see ref. 112.

(*iv*) Sepn. of Sb from Pb. Pass the HCl soln. contg. a little Br_2 through Dowex 1-X8 (80–120 mesh, RCl, 1·4 × 6 cm., treated with HCl contg. a little Br_2) at a rate of 1 ml./min.; 50 ml. HCl elutes Pb, 50 ml. 1*M* HNO_3 and 10 ml. H_2O elute Sn^{4+}, Fe^{3+}, Cu, Zn, and 50 ml. 1*M* NaOH elutes Sb; for detn. of Sb in Pb with rhodamine B see Chapter 26, p. 199.

(*v*) Sepn. of Sn and Pb. Pass the sample soln. prepd. as above through Dowex 1-X8 (120–200 mesh, RCl, 1 × 6 cm., treated with 8*M* HCl contg. 0·1 ml. Br_2); 50 ml. 8*M* HCl elutes Pb, and 40 ml. 1*M* HNO_3 elutes Sn; for detn. of Sn in Pb with hematein, see Chapter 27, p. 206.

(*vi*) Sepn. of Al from Fe by elution with 9*M* HCl, and from Pb by elution with 2*M* HCl is possible. For the detn. of Al with aluminon in Cu–Al, U–Al, Pb, Sn, Fe, stainless steels, see p. 321; for Al–Fe analysis, see ref. 113.

(*vii*) Sepn. of Al, Cu and Zn. Pass 30 ml. soln. contg. 65% v/v EtOH and 1·77*M* HCl through Dowex 1-X8 (80–100 mesh, RCl, 1·5 × 16 cm.); 100 ml. of the above solvents removes Al; 2*M* HCl elutes Cu, and H_2O elutes Zn. For the detn. of Al and Cu (EDTA titration or polarography) in Zn-base die-casting alloys, see ref. 114. Cu can be detd. by diethyldithiocarbamate in Al after sepn. of Al on Wofatit L-150 in 8*M* HCl soln. and elution with 2*M* HCl.[115]

(*viii*) Sepn. of Co from Ni, Mn, etc. Ash the blood sample, dissolve in 9*M* HCl and filter; ext. with iso-Pr_2O; pass through Dowex 1-X8 (50–100 mesh, 0·8 × 11·5 cm., treated with 0·01*M* HCl and 9*M* HCl); 20 ml. 9*M* HCl removes Ni, Mn, etc., and 4*M* HCl elutes Co which is detd. spectrographically,[116]

(*ix*) Sepn. of Ni, Mn, Cr from Co and from Fe. Dissolve heat-resistant alloys in aqua regia, filter and ppt. Mo and Cu with H_2S. Add HCl and H_2O, evap. and repeat. Pass through Dowex 1, elute Ni, Mn, Cr with 9*M* HCl, Co with 4*M* HCl and Fe with 1*M* HCl.[117] Sepn. of P, Fe, Co, and Zn is possible.[96] Ni can be sepd. from Co, Fe and detd. colorimetrically with dimethylglyoxime and NaOBr.[118]

Adsorption in LiCl soln. is stronger than in HCl; the adsorption of Be in 13*M* LiCl is particularly notable.[102]

Elution with other halides or thiocyanate. The use of HBr has no special advantage.[119]

(*i*) Sepn. of Bi (0·2 mg.) from Cu (50 mg.). Adjust the pH to 12 with NH_4OH, add 2–3 g. KI or 3–4 g. NH_4–SCN, and pass through guanidine resin; Cu appears in the effluent and Bi is eluted with 100 ml. 2% NaOH. Sb is adsorbed in acidic soln. contg. KI.[64]

(*ii*) Sepn. of Zn (0·75 mg.) from Cd (1 g.). Dissolve the metal in 50% HNO_3, add 2·5 ml. 50% H_2SO_4, evap., fume for 5 min., cool and add 100 ml. H_2O and 6 g. KI. Pass through DeAcidite FF (RSO_4, 80 ml., 1·5 cm., treated with 50 g. KI and 25 g. H_2SO_4/l.) at a rate of 10–12 ml./min., wash with 5% KI, collect 300 ml. effluent, pipet 5–50 ml., and apply the dithizone method.[120]

(*iii*) Sepn. of Fe from Al. Use less than 2 mg. Fe^{3+} in 1·5*M* NH_4SCN soln.; pass through Amberlite IRA-400 (1·3 × 15 cm., treated with 3*N* HCl, then with 50 ml. 0·3*M* NH_4SCN at pH 1 (HCl)), wash with the 0·3*M* NH_4SCN to remove Al and elute Fe with 3–4*N* HCl.[121]

(*iv*) Sepn. of Fe from Cr. Pass the 0·3*M* NH_4SCN soln. at pH 1 through Amberlite IRA-410 (ca. 400 mesh treated with 4*N* HCl), elute Cr with the same SCN^- soln., and elute Fe with 0·5–4*N* HCl. If much Cr is present, oxidize to Cr^{6+} with $(NH_4)_2S_2O_8$ and $AgNO_3$, pass through the resin and elute Fe with 0·5*N* HCl and Cr with 0·5*N* NaOH and then 0·5*N* HCl.[122]

Elution with sulfate. Sepn. of U^{6+} from Fe^{2+}, V^{4+}, Cl^- (0·1*M*), NO_3^- (0·01*M*), Co, Ni, Zn, Cu, Mo, Al, Mg, rare earths. Dissolve a sample contg. less than 100 mg. U in HF + HNO_3, evap. to dryness, fuse with Na_2CO_3, add H_2SO_4 to give a 5% soln., add 2 g. MnO_2 and boil; leave to cool, add 50 ml. H_2O and NaOH to give pH 1·0–1·5; filter and wash with H_2O; add 5 drops 0·1% methylene blue and 6% H_2SO_3 until the soln. is colorless; add 5 ml. in excess. Pass through Amberlite IRA-400 (40–60 mesh, 0·5 in. × 5 in., treated with 10% H_2SO_4 and H_2O) at a rate of 2 ml./min., elute Fe, etc. with H_2O and U with 50 ml. 1*M* $HClO_4$.[123]

Elution with nitrate. Sepn. of U from other metals. Pass the soln. which is satd. with NH_4NO_3 and acidified with HNO_3 through Amberlite IR-400 and wash with half-satd. NH_4NO_3.[124] Alternatively, use a soln. contg. 0·3*M* HNO_3 and 1·6*M* $Al(NO_3)_3$ with De-Acidite FF (0·2–0·3 mm., 1·5 g.); elute Fe, etc., with 6 ml. 1·6*M* $Al(NO_3)_3$, Al with 8 ml. 8*M* HCl, and U with 25 ml. 0·1*M* HCl.[125]

Sepn. of Th from rare earths. Pass the 6*N* HNO_3 soln. through Amberlite IRA-400 (RNO_3), at a rate of 1 drop/5 sec.; rare earths appear in the effluent and Th is eluted with H_2O.[126] Pb can be sepd. from Bi and from Eu in nitric acid soln.[102]

Elution with other inorg. salts. Sepn. of V from U. Pass a soln. contg. 50 mg. U_3O_8, 250 mg. V_2O_5 and 10 g. Na_2CO_3/100 ml. through 10 g. Amberlite IRA-400 (RCl); elute V with 200 ml. 10% Na_2CO_3, and U with 150 ml. 5% NaCl.[127]

Sepn. of Sn and Ge from As and Sb. Treat the sulfide ppt. with 3% Na_2S_x and use an ROH resin column; elute Sn, Ge with 0·5*N* KOH, As with 1·2*N* KOH, and Sb with 3·5*N* KOH. If the weakly basic soln. is treated with ROH resin, Sb appears in the effluent and As is eluted with 8% KOH.[128]

Sepn. of As and Se from Mo and Re. Pass the soln. contg. less than 300 mg. ReO_4^-/100 ml. through Amberlite IRA-400 ($RClO_4$, 5 g.) at a rate of 10–20 ml./min.; As, Se are not adsorbed; elute Mo with 300 ml. 1*M* $K_2C_2O_4$ at a rate of 2 ml./min., wash with 50 ml. H_2O, and elute Re with 200 ml. 1*M* $HClO_4$ at a rate of 2 ml./min.[129] This is preferable to elution of Mo with NaOH, or of Re with HCl.[130] For other studies see ref. 131.

Elution with org. acids. (*i*) Sepn. of U from other elements. Adjust to pH 4·25–5·25 with AcOH; pass through Amberlite IRA-400; other elements are not adsorbed; U is eluted with 0·8*N* HCl. This can be used for concn. of U in natural waters.[132]

(*ii*) Sepn. of Ga from Fe. Pass the soln. (pH 4) contg. 1 g. $H_2C_2O_4$/150 ml. through Permutit ES (RC_2O_4, 1·6 cm., 30 ml.); elute Fe with 0·001*N* $H_2C_2O_4$ and Ga with 1*N* NaOH.[133] For the sepn. of Fe from Al see ref. 118. With Dowex 1, Te and Sb^{5+} are eluted with 0·1*M* $H_2C_2O_4$ and Sn with 1*M* H_2SO_4.[134]

(*iii*) Sepn. of alkali metals from other metals. Add the soln. which is aq. or less than 3·5*N* in HCl, to 13 ml. Dowex 2 (0·3–0·4 mm., a mixt. of equal amts. of REDTA and ROAc) in a cylindrical separatory funnel and stir for 5 min.; add an equal vol. of EtOH and pass through a column contg. 1·1 × 7 cm. REDTA + ROAc resin and 1·1 × 5 cm. RC_2O_4 and then through a 0·9 × 20 cm. ROH column at a rate of 1 ml./min. Wash with 150 ml. 50% EtOH, add a known excess of 0·1*N* HCl, boil and titrate with NaOH to methyl red indicator; the accuracy is ±0·3% for Na and ±0·4% for K.[135] The alkali metals can be sepd. from the alk. earths[136] and in plating soln. contg. PO_4^{3-} or CN^-.[137]

(*iv*) Sepn. of Ca, Mg, Mn from Al and Fe. Pass the soln. through Dowex 2 (0·2–0·33 mm., R citrate, 1·5 × 18 cm.); wash with H_2O to remove Ca, etc., elute Al with HCl, and elute Fe with H_2O and 1*M* HCl.[138]

2.3. Combined uses

(a) Platinum metals. (*i*) Treat the soln. contg. Pd, Pt, Rh, Ir with HCl, evap. and repeat; add 20 ml. H_2O and 5 ml. NH_4OH and pass through Amberlite IR-100; elute Pt, Rh, Ir with 100 ml. 0·025*M* NH_4OH + 0·025*M* NH_4Cl, and Pd with 0·1*M* HCl. Acidify the eluate contg. Pt, etc. with HCl, pass through Dowex 2 (or Dowex 1 or Amberlite IR-4B), and elute Rh followed by Pt with the above soln.; Ir remains in the resin.[139]

(*ii*) To the chloride soln. add 1% hydroquinone until no further color change occurs; add 5 ml. 1% EDTA, boil, make alk. with NaOH, cool, adjust to pH 2·8 with 3*N* HCl and pass Cl_2 for 10 min.; pass through Dowex 50-X8 (20–50 mesh, RH, 1·4 × 50 cm.); elute Pt, Pd, Ir with 50 ml. 10% Cl_2, and Rh with 3*N* HCl (the Rh is recovered incompletely but in a pure form).[140]

(*iii*) Add HNO_3, $HClO_4$ to the soln., evap., repeat, evap. to 0·2–0·5 ml. and dil. to 10 ml. with H_2O; pass through Dowex 50; elute Pt with H_2O, Pd with 0·05–0·5*N* HCl, Rh with 2*N* HCl, and Ir with 4–6*N* HCl. The sepn. of Rh and Ir is difficult.[141]

(*iv*) Sepn. of 2·7 mg. Ir from 5·55 mg. Rh. Add aqua regia to the soln., evap. almost to dryness, add 0·3*M* HCl and thiourea, and heat for 1 hr. on a steam bath adding 0·3*M* HCl as necessary; cool and pass through Dowex 50 W-X8 (1·4 × 17·5 cm., treated with H_2O, 3*M* HCl and H_2O) at a rate of 2–3 ml./min.; elute Ir with 100 ml. 3*M* HCl, and Rh from the reddish column with 300 ml. 6*M* HCl at 74°C.[142]

(*v*) Pd^{2+} and Pt^{4+} in 0·1–12*M* HCl are strongly adsorbed by Dowex 1 (200–230 mesh); the adsorption is weaker in more concd. HCl and adsorption of Ir^{3+} is negligible.[143] Ir^{4+} is adsorbed but Rh is not.[144]

With Permutit ES (ROH), Pd, Ir and Rh are eluted with 1*N* NaOH and Pt with 2·5*N* HNO_3.[145]

Pd and Pt can be sepd. from base metals on Dowex 50 (40 mesh, RH, 4 × 60 cm.) by eluting Pd and Pt with H_2O.[146]

(b) Boron. Fuse 0·2–0·3 g. silicate with a 6-fold amt. of K_2CO_3, leach with hot H_2O and mix with 30–40 ml.

Amberlite IR45 (ROH) + Nalcite HCR (RH, 60–100 mesh); transfer to a 20 ml. resin column, wash with 250 ml. H_2O and titrate a 100 ml. aliquot.[147]

(c) Silicate analysis. Silicate (0·1 g.) can be analyzed after treatment with HF and H_2SO_4 by means of 4 columns. With Dowex 1-X8 (50–100 mesh, RCl, 1 cm., 40 ml.), Na, K, Mg, Ca, Al are eluted with 10·5*N* HCl; Ti, Mn, P with 6*N* HCl; and then Fe with 0·5*N* HCl. With Amberlite IR-120 (100–150 mesh, RH, 10 ml.) P is eluted with H_2O, Na with 0·2*N* HCl + MeOH, K with 0·5*N* HCl, and Mg, Ca, Al with 4*N* HCl. In this last fraction Dowex 50-X12 (100–120 mesh, RNH_4, 15 ml.) permits elution of Al, Mg with 1*N* NH_4OAc, Ca with 2*N* NH_4OAc, and the remainder of the Al with 4*N* HCl. With Amberlite IR-120 (100–150 mesh, RH, 5 ml.) P is eluted by H_2O, Ti with 0·8*N* H_2SO_4, and Mn with 5% H_2SO_4 in the original second fraction.[148]

3. CONCENTRATION

Even tracer amts. of ion are adsorbed completely by on exchange resins and this provides a far better method of concn. than copptn. For example, the percentages of Ba and La in the effluent were $7{\cdot}5 \times 10^{-4}$% and 0·03% resp. when 0·0041*M* Ba^{2+}, $5 \times 10^{-3}M$ La^{3+} and tracers were put through a suitable column; the corresponding figures were $3{\cdot}3 \times 10^{-3}$% and 0·14% when the concn. of Ba was reduced by 1/10.[149]

(a) Cu in milk. Add $HClO_4$ until the pH is below 3·0, filter and adjust to pH 5 with NH_4OH. Pass through Amberlite IR-100 (treated with hot 10% HCl), wash with H_2O and then with 40 ml. 6% HCl; det. Cu polarographically.[150] Fe and Cu can be detd. in wine.[151]

(b) Cu in oil. To 10 g. oil add an equal vol. of 2-propanol (add a little C_6H_6 if the phases sep.); pass through Zeo-Karb 215, wash with 80 ml. 2-propanol and H_2O; elute with 60 ml. 10% H_2SO_4 and H_2O, and use the diethyldithiocarbamate method.[152]

(c) Trace elements in plant materials. Pass 2 ml. of the solution contg. $4 \times 10^{-4}M$ Cu, Cd, Ni, Zn and Mn in 0·1*N* NH_4Cl or $(NH_4)_2HPO_4$ through Amberlite IR-100, and wash with H_2O; elute Cd with 0·1*N* HCl and Zn, Mn, Cu, Ni with 1*N* HCl; recoveries are 94% Cu, 96% Cd, 99% Ni, 95% Zn and 87% Mn.[153]

(d) Natural waters. Pass the water through a 30 ml. RH column + 30 ml. ROH column at a rate of 5 l./30 min.; Na, K, Ca, Mg, Fe^{3+} (pH 2), Cl^-, SO_4^{2-} are adsorbed.[154] Rain water can be treated similarly.[155]

F^- is adsorbed on cationite contg. Th, and eluted by 40 ml. 0·5*N* NH_4OH.[156] SO_4^{2-} is adsorbed on Amberlite IR-4B (50–100 mesh, RCl) from natural water; the resin is treated with 20 ml. 0·1*N* HCl and 0·5*N* NH_4OH.[157]

(e) Radioactive elements in urine. Coppt. with Ca-phosphate, pass through resin to remove PO_4^{3-} and elute; recovery is quant. for La, Y and 90% for Sr, Ba.[158] Y[159] and Ra[160] have been further studied.

(f) Concn. of Pb. For Zn or Cd metal or electroplating soln., coppt. Pb with $BaSO_4$ or $SrSO_4$ and heat on a steam bath with 20 ml. each of Amberlite IR-120 (RH) and Amberlite IRA-410 (ROH) wrapped in nylon cloth; elute Pb with NH_4OAc from the cationite and apply the dithizone method.[161]

(g) Concn. of H_2S group elements. Use the RS form of a weak anionite.[162]

(h) Ag, Au, Cu, Ni, Co, Zn. Use the RCN form of a strong anionite.[163] For Au, see also ref. 164.

(i) Concn. of alkali metals. Rb and Cs can be concd. in sea water.[165] 0·5 μg. Li can be sepd. from 0·5 g. Ca on Amberlite IR-100.[166]

(j) Qual. analysis. Ge is concd. on Amberlite IRA-411, Dowex 1-X1 or -X2-hematoxylin, and Al or Zr is concd. if alizarin S is added.[167] With strong anionites, Cr is retained if H_2O_2 is present; Ti requires a cationite and H_2O_2 or phenols; Fe, tiron or dipyridyl; Bi, thiourea; Cu, phenylenediamine + NH_4SCN; Ni, dimethylglyoxime + Br_2 or rubeanic acid; and Co, thiocyanate or nitroso R salt.[168] Similar methods have been proposed.[169] For RCl, RS, ROH, RCO_3 as grouping agents, see ref. 170.

For the concn. of μg. amts. of cation with Amberplex C-1 membrane, see ref. 171.

4. SEPARATION OF SIMILAR IONS

This is difficult and sometimes nearly impossible by ordinary analytical methods; it provides a singular field of application of ion exchange resins. Resins of smaller particle size (ca. 300 mesh) and very slow rates of elution are normally used; the addn. of complex-forming reagents and the monitoring of columns, as mentioned in Section 1.1, are common.

4.1. Lanthanides[172]

(a) Cationites. When rare earth elements are adsorbed on Amberlite IR-100, Dowex 50, etc. (<300 mesh) from less than 0·1*N* HCl soln. and eluted with citric acid (at pH 3 by NH_4OH addn.), they are found in the effluent in the order of their ionic radii, i.e., in the following order: Lu, Yb, Tm, Er, Ho, Y, Dy, Tb, Gd, Eu, Sm, Pm, Nd, Pr, Ce, La. Sepn. is difficult for the three combinations, Lu–Yb, Ho–Y–Dy and Gd–Eu–Sm.

The dimensions of the column should be $0{\cdot}4 \times 15$ cm., with 0·25*M* citric acid at pH 3·05 as eluant at a rate of 0·03 ml./min.,[173] for tracer amts. For mg. amts. the size should be $0{\cdot}25$ cm.$^2 \times 100$ cm., and the eluant 5% citric acid at pH 3·28 at a rate of 0·6 ml./min.[174] For 10 g. amts., 450 g. resin in a 4×60 cm. column is used.[175] Kg. amts. can be sepd.[176]

The higher the concn. of citric acid, the faster is the elution; in most cases 5% is used. The order of elution with 5% citric acid at pH 2·80 is Dy—Tb—Y, but with 0·1% citric acid at pH 2·80, it is Dy—Y—Tb. For the purification of Y and Dy, therefore, they are sepd. from other lanthanides with 0·1% citric acid at pH 5·8–6·1 and the Y and Dy are sepd. with 5% citric acid at pH 2·8.[175]

Increasing the pH hastens elution, but low pH values favor the sepn. With 0·1% citric acid, sepn. is best at pH 3·80 but at pH 4·20 or 4·40 results are nearly as satisfactory and are obtained in 1/3 of the time. Higher temps. also shorten the time required.[177]

Acetic, malic, tartaric and citric (I) acids, glycine, NTA (II) and EDTA (III) have been compared as eluants. At equal flow rates, sepn. efficiency increases up to (I) and then falls off; but at high pH and with flow rates in excess of those with (I), greater efficiencies are obtained with (II) and (III) at equal molarities. Sepn. with EDTA is enhanced when Fe^{2+} or Mn^{2+} are interpolated between Sm–Nd or Nd–Pr respectively.[178] Sepn. is better in the order of EDTA > lactic acid, glycine > malic acid ⩾ citric acid for Sm–Eu or Eu–Tb; lactic acid is best because the soly. of EDTA at the required pH is small.[179]

EDTA elution has been used with RCu- or RFe^{3+}-form resin; the RCu-form is better, and EDTA is preferred to HEEDTA.[180] The effects of di- and tri-valent ions have been studied.[181] For other studies, see ref. 182.

NTA can be used as eluant.[183] Sm, Nd, Pr are sepd. from La by using 0·5% hydrazinoacetic acid and 1·5% NH_4OAc at pH 5·5, and 1% NTA and 2% NH_4Cl at pH 7·5–8·0 respectively. TTA (5·0 g. in 45·0 ml. dioxane and 50·0 ml. H_2O adjusted to pH 4·97) permits elution of Eu and its sepn. from Y.[184] Lactic acid requires less strict pH control than citric acid.[179, 185] α-Hydroxyisobutyric acid causes increases in the difference of the relative sepn. factors.[186] Glycolic acid elution has been used.[187]

Cationites have proved valuable in several other ways, e.g. the sepn. of Tb from Gd and Eu,[188] the discovery of Pm,[189] the sepn. of Pm and Sm,[190] the isolation of Tm,[191] in various other sepns.[13, 192] and in analysis of bone[193] and Zr metal.[194]

(b) Anionites. 0·0125*M* Citric acid at pH 2·1 elutes Pm and Eu in that order from Dowex A-1 (0·08 cm.² × 14·9 cm., R-citrate).[195] Sc can be sepd. from other rare earths.[102]

4.2. Actinides

The differences in ionic radii in this group are greater than in lanthanides, hence sepn. is easier.

For example, Bk is prepd. by bombardment of ^{241}Am with ca. 35 m.e.v. He ions; it is sepd. from Am^{4+} by LaF_3 carrier, adsorbed on a cationite and sepd. from rare earths by elution with 13*M* HCl; Bk, Cm and Am are then adsorbed on Dowex 50 (0·2 × 20 cm., RNH_4) and eluted with 0·25*M* citric acid at pH 3·5 (1 drop/2 min.) to sep. them from each other. The order of adsorbability is (Pm, Am)—Cm—Sm—Eu—Gd—Bk—Yb—Y.[196]

The elution curves of Am—Cm—Bk—Cf and Eu—Gd—Tb—Dy show a fine analogy, which confirms the actinide series and is utilized for their identification.[197]

The order of adsorbability depends on the eluant. 0·25*M* Citric acid at pH 3·05 gives Lu—(Cm, Pm, Am); 6*M* HCl gives Lu—(Cm, Am, Pm)—Ce; 9*M* HCl gives (Cm, Am)—(Pm, Ce); and 13·3*M* HCl gives (Am + Cm)—Lu—Pm.[198]

As in the case of lanthanides, lactic acid is the most effective eluant. With Dowex 50-X12 (0·2 × 5–6 cm.), 0·4*M* lactic acid at pH 4·5, 85°C and a rate of 1 drop/5 min., gives the series Fm—Es—Cf—Bk—Cm—Am. With Dowex 50-X12 (0·3 × 5 cm.), elution with 20% EtOH and 12·5*M* HCl gives the series Fm—(Es—Cf)—Bk—Am—Cm; 13*M* HCl elution from Dowex 1-X8 (0·3 × 5 cm.) gives Fm—(Es, Cf)—Bk—(Cm—Am); and 1·0*M* NH_4SCN elution gives Cm—Am—Es—Fm—(Bk)—Cf.[199] In some cases only a few atoms/ml. are concerned.

Elution with lactic acid gives the full series, Pm—Am—Cm—Sm—Eu—Bk—Gd—Cf—Tb—Es—Dy—Ho.[200] Glycolic acid has been used.[18] α-Hydroxyisobutyric acid gives the order Am, Cm, Bk, Cf, Es, Fm, Md.[201] Np can be sepd. from U[202] and Pu can be purified.[203] By means of Dowex 1-X8, Am (4 g.) is sepd. from 280 g. rare earths by eluting the latter with 5*M* NH_4SCN and the former with 1*N* HCl.[204]

The SCN^- complexes of lanthanides and actinides have been studied by means of Dowex 50 and Dowex 1.[205]

4.3. Polyvalent ions such as Ti, Zr, Hf, Nb, Ta

The analysis of mixts. of these elements is difficult (see Chapter 51) and is not fully solved, but ion exchange resins allow an approach to it; anionites seem to be preferable.

(*1*) Sepn. of Zr and Hf. Use a soln. contg. 20 mg. ZrO_2 and 10 mg. HfO_2; adsorb on 600 mg. Amberlite IRA-400 (200–325 mesh, RCl), transfer to a 0·78 cm.² × 30 cm. column and elute with 0·2*M* HCl + 0·01*M* HF at a rate of 6 ml./hr.; 13·8 mg. pure ZrO_2 and 8·3 mg. pure HfO_2 were obtained. 9*M* HCl has also been used as eluant.[206]

The order of elution is Hf—Zr with HCl from a cationite[207] and Zr—Hf with H_2SO_4[208] or with 0·045*M* HCl + 0·09*M* citric acid.[209]

(*2*) Sepn. of Zr, Nb, Ta and Pa. For 1 mg. each of Zr and Ta, and tracer amts. of Nb and Pa, pass through Dowex 1 (200–230 mesh, 0·023 cm.² × 6 cm.) and elute with 9*M* HCl + 0·004*M* HF at a rate of 0·2 ml./cm.²/min.; Zr appears in the first 10 ml. and Pa in the 15–40 ml. fraction; Nb is eluted with 9*M* HCl + 0·18*M* HF, and Ta with 1*M* HF + 4*M* NH_4Cl. Pa and Fe are sepd. by eluting Pa with 9*M* HCl + 0·1*M* HF, and Fe with 0·5*M* HCl.[210] Zr and Nb are sepd. by eluting Zr with 6–7*M* HCl, and Nb with 1·5–4·0*M* HCl[206] or with 1*M* HCl + 0·01*M* $H_2C_2O_4$.[211]

(*3*) Sepn. of Nb and Ta. For 17 mg. mixed oxides in $H_2C_2O_4$ soln., adsorb on Dowex 2, transfer to a 0·5 cm. × 13 cm. column; if much Nb is present, elute it with 0·1*M* HCl + 0·5*M* $H_2C_2O_4$ at a rate of 3 ml./hr.; if the amt. is small, elute with $0{\cdot}01M$ $H_2C_2O_4$ + $2M$ HCl; elute Ta with $6M$ HCl.[212] With DeAcidite FF, elute Nb with $3M$ HCl + $0{\cdot}1M$ HF and Ta with $4M$ HCl + $1M$ NH_4F.[213]

(*4*) Sepn. of Ti, W, Mo and Nb. Fuse the mixed oxides with $KHSO_4$ and add HF + HCl + H_2O in the ratio 1:2:17. Pass through Dowex 1; elute Ti–W with 450 ml. 50% v/v HCl + 10% v/v HF, Mo with 350 ml. 25% HCl + 20% HF, and Nb with 350 ml. 14% NH_4Cl + 4% HF.[214]

(*5*) Al in Zr metal. To a 1 g. sample in a Pt dish, add 15–20 ml. H_2O, 3 ml. HF and 2 ml. HCl and dil. with H_2O to 100 ml.; pass through Dowex 1 (200–400 mesh, RCl, 30 g. dried resin, 1·6 cm. diam.) at a rate of 5 ml./min. Wash with 200 ml. $0{\cdot}06M$ HCl + $0{\cdot}8M$ HF; this seps. Al, Fe, a little V and Sn from Zr, Ti, Nb, Ta, Mo, SO_4^{2-}. Add $HClO_4$, evap., add cupferron, and ext. with $CHCl_3$; apply the aluminon method.[215] Zr is sepd. from Al by eluting Al with $1{\cdot}5M$ HCl and Zr with HCl (1:4) from a cationite.[216] Zr can be sepd. from Fe and Ni;[217] Zr can be purified by $H_2C_2O_4$ elution from Amberlite IR-120 (1 cm.^{2} × 30 cm.).[218]

(*6*) Sepn. of Pa and Ta. Elute with $6{\cdot}5N$ HF + NH_4OH at pH 3 at a rate of 2 ml./hr. from Amberlite IR-4B (200 mesh, 0·65 cm. × 85 cm.).[219] Pa and Zr are sepd. by eluting Zr with 6–$7M$ HCl and Pa with $3M$ HCl from Amberlite IRA-400.[220] Pa and Th are sepd. by eluting Pa with 1–$2M$ HNO_3 or 0·1–0·7% $H_2C_2O_4$ from Dowex 50-X12.[221]

(*7*) Sepn. of Zr, Ti and Th. This is possible with 1% citric acid at pH 1·75 using Dowex 50.[222] Ti is sepd. from Zr with $0{\cdot}75N$ H_2SO_4 on Amberlite IR-120. Th is sepd. from U by eluting Th with 0·01–$0{\cdot}001M$ $Fe(OAc)_3$ and U with $0{\cdot}2N$ HCl from Amberlite IRA-400 (REDTA, 0·8 × 20 cm.).[223]

4.4. Other ions

(a) Alkali metals. There are three typical methods.

(*i*) Difference of adsorbability. Pass the soln. contg. 15–28 mg. chlorides through Amberlite IR-100 (fine, RH, 1 cm.^{2} × 50 cm.); elute Na–K with $0{\cdot}1N$ HCl and Rb–Cs with $1N$ HCl.[224] Similar methods have been suggested.[225] Na and K have been detd. in silicates[226] or plant ash.[227]

(*ii*) Addn. of org. solvent. Use a soln. contg. less than 5 meq. of the metals in $0{\cdot}1N$ HCl contg. 20–30% MeOH; pass through Amberlite IR-120 (<100 mesh, 12 ml., 8 cm. long, treated with 20% MeOH); elute Li with $0{\cdot}2N$ HCl + 30% MeOH, Na with $0{\cdot}2N$ HCl + 10% MeOH, and K with $0{\cdot}5N$ HCl. This gives a better sepn. than the above.[228]

(*iii*) Use of complexing agent. Add uramildiacetic acid followed by dimethylamine or tetramethylammonium hydroxide to give pH 6·5–7·5 (for sepn. of Li and Na) or pH 9 (for sepn. of Li, Na and K); pass through Amberlite IR-120 (30–50 mesh, 1 × 6 cm., treated with $2N$ HCl, $0{\cdot}2N$ NaOH, $2N$ HCl).[229] In another method, $0{\cdot}12M$ LiOH, $0{\cdot}15M$ NaOH and trace Cs in $0{\cdot}13M$ EDTA at pH 10 is passed through 1-X4 (50–100 mesh, 0·41 cm.^{2} × 23 cm., treated with Dowex $0{\cdot}25M$ EDTA at pH 11 (with KOH)); $0{\cdot}25M$ EDTA at pH 10·9 elutes Cs, Na, and $0{\cdot}25M$ EDTA at pH 4·2 elutes Li.[230]

0·001% Na in K_2CO_3 or in LiCl, and 0·008% K and 0·02% Cs in RbCl can be analyzed after neutron activation.[193] Mg. amts. of Cs can be sepd. from 10^4-fold and 5-fold amts. of Na and Rb resp. using Amberlite IR-100 or Duolite C-3, which is fairly specific for Cs in alk. solns.[231]

(b) Alk. earths. Pass the soln. contg. 20 mg. each of Sr, Ba and 20 μg. Ra, through Dowex 50 (fine, 1 cm.^{2} × 15 cm.) and wash with $0{\cdot}5M$ citric acid at pH 7·8 and a rate of 0·3 ml./min.[232] Alternatively, use 0·04 meq. each of Sr and Ba, pass through Dowex 50 (RNH_4, 0·9 cm.^{2}, 5·5 ml.) and elute Mg with $0{\cdot}1M$ NH_4OAc, Ca with $1{\cdot}5M$ NH_4OAc, and Sr with $2{\cdot}0M$ NH_4OAc; elute Ba with a known amt. of EDTA and back-titrate. $0{\cdot}3N$ NH_4OH + $0{\cdot}6N$ NH_4Cl can be used to elute and sep. Mg from Ca, Sr, Ba, Ni, Co, Zn.[233] EDTA[234] or lactic acid[235] has also served for elution.

For 1 g. limestone or dolomite, add 10 ml. HCl (1:1) and 25 ml. H_2O, evap. to dryness for 1 hr. on steam a bath, and add 10 ml. HCl (1:1) + 25 ml. H_2O; filter, wash and dil. with H_2O to 500 ml. Dil. a 10 ml. aliquot to 75 ml. with H_2O, and pass through Dowex 50 (50–100 mesh, RH, 2·7 × 6·3 cm.) at a rate of 5 ml./min.; wash three times with 10 ml. H_2O, and then with 600 ml. $1{\cdot}05M$ HCl; discard the first 75 ml., titrate Mg in the next 475 ml. with EDTA; titrate Ca and Mg in a separate 10 ml. aliquot, and calc. the amt. of Ca.[236]

Pass 2 ml. of a soln. which is $0{\cdot}0114M$ in each of $BaCl_2$, $SrCl_2$ and $CaCl_2$ and $0{\cdot}03M$ in $MgCl_2$ through Dowex 1 (R-citrate, 0·27 cm.^{2} × 44 cm., treated with $0{\cdot}5M$ $(NH_4)_3$-citrate at pH 8); elute Ba–Sr–Ca with $0{\cdot}05M$ $(NH_4)_3$-citrate at pH 7·5 and Mg with $0{\cdot}5M$ $(NH_4)_3$-citrate. The sepn. of Be and Mg is unsuccessful.[237]

(c) Halogens. Pass the soln. contg. 0·7 meq. NH_4-salt (fluoride as NH_4HF_2) through Dowex 2 (100–200 mesh, RNO_3, 0·72 cm.^{2} × 91·5 cm.) and wash with $1M$ $NaNO_3$ at pH 10·4 (NaOH) and a rate of 1·3 ml./min. ((F + I)–Cl–Br–I).[238] Cl^- and I^- are detd. by eluting Cl^- with $0{\cdot}5M$ $NaNO_3$ and I^- with $2{\cdot}0M$ $NaNO_3$.[239]

For sepn. of ClO_3^-, BrO_3^-, IO_3^-, pass 200 ml. of soln. contg. 20 meq. halates/l. through the resin (ROH, 1 × 37 cm., treated with 10% NaOH) at a rate of 0·4 ml./min.; wash with H_2O until colorless to phenolphthalein; wash with $2N$ KOH at a rate of 0·2 ml./min. (IO_3^- appears in 180 ml. and BrO_3^- in 700 ml.), and then elute ClO_3^- with $0{\cdot}1N$ K_2SO_4.[240]

(d) Sepn. of Tc and Re. Tracer amts. of pertechnetate, and μg. amts. of perrhenate are sepd. on Dowex 2 (100–120 mesh, RSO_4, 0·7 cm.^{2} × 51 cm.), by washing with 0·1*M* $(NH_4)_2SO_4$ + 0·1*M* NH_4SCN at pH 8·3–8·5 (NaOH) at a rate of 1·7 ml./min.[238] A similar method has been described.[241] With Dowex 1, Mo is eluted with 1*M* HCl and sepd. from Tc which is eluted with 4*M* HNO_3; or W is eluted with 1·5*M* HCl and sepd. from Re which is eluted with 4·0*M* HNO_3.[242]

(e) Complex ions. Cr-complex,[243, 244] Co-complex[243, 245] and the partition of radioactive Fe between $Fe(CN)_6^{4-}$ and $Fe(CN)_6^{3-}$ have been studied.[246] For the sepn. of phosphate ions, see ref. 247.

5. OTHER USES

(a) Detn. of total salt concn. By the same principle as in Section 2.1 the salt conc. is easily detd.; this is applicable to waters and ind. analysis.[248] After detns. of the total ion concn., the alky., and the hardness (with EDTA) in natural waters, the concn. of Na can be calcd.[249]

(b) Purification. The prepn. of conductivity H_2O is particularly noteworthy; the effectiveness of deionization is indicated by the fact that the Cu concn. falls from 2 p.p.m. to 0·0035 p.p.m. by one treatment.[250]

Prepn. of NaOH or KOH free from CO_2. Pass 1 l. 0·1*N* NaOH through Amberlite IRA-400 (ROH, ca. 30 ml.); discard the part of the effluent in which Cl^- can be detected.[251]

The purification of KCl,[252] of gelatin (as protecting colloid in the nephelometry of SO_4^{2-}),[253] of NH_4SCN (removal of Fe using RSCN),[254] of HCl (RCl, removal of Fe) and of alcohol (RSO_3-form resin, removal of aldehyde) have been studied.

Colloidal solns. can be prepd. in a purer form by the ion exchange method than by dialysis.[255]

Pure heteropoly acids, silicic, vanadic, molybdic or tungstic acid can also be prepd.[48, 256]

(c) Mean at. wt. of rare earths. This can be calcd. from the values obtained by titration of the effluent and by weighing the oxide after ignition of the resin bed.[257]

(d) Recovery of expensive reagents. Ag solns. in Mohr's method can be recovered by cationic treatment and $Ca(NO_3)_2$ elution; Pt solns. by anionite (RCl) treatment, addn. of HCl and evapn.; U solns. by cationite treatment and AcOH elution. For tetraphenylborate recovery, see ref. 258.

6. CELLULOSE COLUMN

This technique has been largely developed in England.

(a) Sepn. of U from other elements. Evap. the soln. to dryness, add 2 ml. HNO_3, 8 ml. H_2O and dry cellulose pulp and transfer to a column (1–2 × 20–30 cm., treated with Et_2O + HNO_3); wash with 3·5 ml. HNO_3 in 100 ml. Et_2O (observe the greenish-yellow band).[259] Nitrated cellulose can also be used;[260] 20 ml. petr. ether + 190 ml. Et_2O + 10 ml. HNO_3 can serve as eluant.[261]

(b) Sepn. of Nb and Ta from Ti. To the mixed oxides add a few ml. HF, warm and evap. to dryness; add 6 ml. 10% HF and 1 g. NH_4F, warm to dissolve, add 4 g. coarse cellulose powder, stir, transfer to a 2 × 8–10 cm. column (treated with MeCOEt, MeCOEt + HF (85:15)), and wash with 400 ml. MeCOEt + HF; evap. to 10 ml., add 10 ml. H_2SO_4 (1:1), fume gently for 15 min., cool, and dil. with H_2O to 300 ml.; add 10 g. NH_4Cl, tannin, etc.; $(Nb, Ta)_2O_5$ is weighed and TiO_2 is found by difference. The ketone should be purified.

Sepn. of Nb from Ta. To the mixed oxides add HF, evap., and add 8 ml. 10% HF and 6 g. coarse cellulose powder (treated with MeCOEt equilibrated with H_2O); transfer to a 2 × 20–25 cm. column, wash with 250 ml. MeCOEt equilibrated with H_2O, etc., and det. Ta_2O_5. Nb, Ta, W can be sepd. from other elements by the first method.[262] Nb is sepd. from Ta, Ti by elution with MeCOEt + 10*M* HCl (3:1) but Ti is not sepd. from Ta.[263] For the behavior of Th, see ref. 264. Ba is sepd. from Sr by elution with MeOH + Et_2O + HCl;[265] and Al from Fe by MeCOEt + HCl (24:1).[266]

(c) Sepn. of Zn from Cu. Dissolve 0·1 g. Cu alloy (1–40% Zn) in aqua regia, add 1 ml. 5% $FeCl_3$, and evap. nearly to dryness. Add a little solvent (20% v/v HCl + BuOH (4:96)) and cellulose pulp, transfer to a 7 in. column, and wash with the solvent until the effluent has a yellow Fe color; do not allow all the Fe band to come through; evap. to 10–20 ml., add buffer, and titrate with EDTA (see Chapter 36, p. 278).

(d) Sepn. of Mo from Fe, Co, Cu, Cr, Mn, Ni and V. Acetylacetone elution is satisfactory and special steels, Al, etc. can be analyzed.[267] For example, dissolve 0·25 g. special steel in 2 ml. HCl (1:1), heat and evap., add 3 ml HCl (1:1) dropwise, then another 3 ml.; heat, add 6 drops HNO_3, evap. to dryness, and add 2 ml. HCl (1:1); dil. with HCl (1:1) to 5 ml. Transfer a 0·2 ml. aliquot to a column; elute Fe and Mo with 7 ml. acetylacetone, Co and Mn with 7 ml. MeCOPr + 5 ml. HCl, and V with another 13 ml. of the same solvent; elute Ni and Cr with 8 ml. H_2O + 2 ml. H_2SO_4 (1:20); apply colorimetric detns.

References

1. SAMUELSON, O., *Ion Exchangers in Analytical Chemistry*, Wiley, New York (1953); NACHOD, F. C. and SCHUBERT, J., editors, *Ion Exchange Technology*, Academic Press, New York (1956); OSBORN, G. H., *Synthetic Ion-Exchangers*, Chapman & Hall, London (1955); GRIESSBACH, R., *Austauschadsorption in Theorie und Praxis*, Akad. Verlagsges., Leipzig (1957); HONDA, M., *et al.*, *Ion-Exchange Resins*, Hirokawa, Tokyo (1955); KUNIN, R. and MCGARVEY, F., *Anal. Chem.*, **21**, 87 (1949); **22**, 64 (1950); **23**, 45 (1951); **24**, 64 (1952); **26**, 104 (1954); **27**, 1191 (1955); **28**, 729 (1956); *Ind. Eng. Chem.*, **40**, 41 (1948); **41**, 55 (1949); **42**, 65 (1950); **43**, 102 (1951); **44**, 79 (1952); **45**, 83 (1953); **46**, 118 (1954); **47**, 565 (1955); **48**, 540 (1956); BOYD, G. E., *Ann. Rev. Phys. Chem.*, **2**, 309 (1951); BAUMAN, W. C., *et al.*, *ibid.*, **3**, 109 (1953); JUDA, W., *et al.*, *ibid.*, **4**, 373 (1953); SCHUBERT, J., *ibid.*, **5**, 413 (1954); THOMAS, H. C. and FRYSINGER, G. R., *ibid.* **7**, 137 (1956); SCHUBERT, *Anal. Chem.*, **22**, 1359 (1950); TOMPKINS, E. R., *ibid.*, **22**, 1352 (1950); *Analyst*, **77**, 970 (1952); Diskussionstagung der

deutschen Bunsen-Gesellschaft, *Ionenaustauscher*, *Z. Elektrochem.*, **57**, 147 (1953); *Ion Exchange Symposium*, *J. Am. Chem. Soc.*, **69**, 2769 (1947).
2. Kimura, K., *et al.*, *Japan Analyst*, **3**, 335 (1954).
3. Stach, H., *Angew. Chem.*, **63**, 263 (1951).
4. Skogseid, A., Dissertation. Norges Tek. Högskole (1946); Ishibashi, M., *et al.*, *J. Chem. Soc. Japan*, **75**, 295 (1954).
5. Gregor, H. P., *et al.*, *Ind. Eng. Chem.*, **44**, 2834 (1952).
6. Blasius, E. and Olbrich, G., *Z. anal. Chem.*, **151**, 81 (1956).
7. Gregor, H. P., *et al.*, *J. Am. Chem. Soc.*, **77**, 3675 (1955).
8. Bregman, J. I., *et al.*, *J. Am. Chem. Soc.*, **74**, 1867 (1952); *Chem. Week*, **69**, Dec. 1, 22 (1951).
9. Kennedy, J., *et al.*, *Atomic Energy Research Estab. Gt. Brit.*, **C/A**-1896 (1956).
10. Cassidy, H. G., *et al.*, *J. Am. Chem. Soc.*, **71**, 402, 407 (1949); **75**, 1610, 1615 (1953); *Proc. Natl. Acad. Sci. U.S.*, **38**, 1341 (1952); Ezrin, M. and Cassidy, *Ann. N.Y. Acad. Sci.*, **57**, 79 (1954).
11. Manecke, G., *Z. Elektrochem.*, **57**, 180 (1953).
12. Fitch, F. T. and Russel, D. S., *Anal. Chem.*, **23**, 1469 (1951); also see Stark, J. B., *et al.*, *Anal. Chem.*, **29**, 861 (1957).
13. Boyd, G. E., *et al.*, *J. Am. Chem. Soc.*, **69**, 2849 (1947); Ketelle, B. H. and Boyd, *ibid.*, **69**, 2800 (1947).
14. Wickbold, R., *Z. anal. Chem.*, **142**, 401 (1951); Glueckauf, E., *J. Chem. Soc.*, 1302 (1948); Minami, E., *et al.*, *J. Chem. Soc. Japan*, **73**, 368 (1952).
15. Duncan, F. and Lister, B. A. T., *J. Chem. Soc.*, 3825 (1949); Jeffrey, R. N., *Anal. Chem.*, **23**, 936 (1951).
16. Wheaton, R. M. and Bauman, W. C., *Ann. N.Y. Acad. Sci.*, **57**, 159 (1953).
17. Mann, C. K., *Anal. Chem.*, **29**, 1385 (1957).
18. Yoshino, Y., *Bull. Chem. Soc. Japan*, **24**, 39 (1951); **26**, 401 (1953).
19. Honda, M., *J. Chem. Soc. Japan*, **74**, 371 (1953); *Japan Analyst*, **2**, 456 (1953).
20. Kimura, K. and Asano, Y., *Chem. & Chem. Ind. (Japan)*, **2**, 258 (1949).
21. Honda, M., *J. Chem. Soc. Japan*, **70**, 165 (1949); Weiss, D. E., *Nature*, **166**, 66 (1950); Idler, D. R., *J. Am. Chem. Soc.*, **71**, 3854 (1949).
22. Fitch, F. T. and Russel, D. S., *Can. J. Chem.*, **29**, 363 (1951).
23. Samuelson, O., *Ion Exchangers in Analytical Chemistry*, Wiley, New York, 117 (1953); Honda, M., *et al.*, *Ion-Exchange Resins*, p. 134, Hirokawa, Tokyo (1955); many other references.
24. Hirano, S. and Kurobe, M., *Japan Analyst*, **4**, 379 (1955).
25. Honda, M. and Tadano, H., *Japan Analyst*, **2**, 451 (1953); also see Chapter 7, Section 4.4.
26. Flaschka, H. and Amin, A. M., *Chemist Analyst*, **42**, 78 (1953); **43**, 6 (1954)
27. Whiteker, R. A. and Swift, E. H., *Anal. Chem.*, **26**, 1602 (1954).
28. Samuelson, O., *Ion Exchangers in Analytical Chemistry*, p. 142, Wiley, New York (1953).
29. Kodama, K., *Research Repts. Nagoya Municipal Ind. Research Inst.*, (12) 87 (1954).
30. Lur'e, Yu. Yu. and Filippova, N. A., *Zavodskaya Lab.*, **15**, 771 (1949).
31. Helrich, K. and Rieman, III, W., *Ind. Eng. Chem., Anal. Ed.*, **19**, 651 (1947); Goudie, A. J. and Rieman, *Anal. Chem.*, **24**, 1067 (1952); Samuelson, O., *Ion Exchangers in Analytical Chemistry*, p. 146, Wiley, New York (1953).
32. Cogbill, E. C., *et al.*, *Anal. Chem.*, **27**, 455 (1955); Carson, Jr., W. N. and Gile, H. S., *ibid.*, **27**, 122 (1955); Kindt, B. H., *et al.*, *ibid.*, **24**, 1501 (1952); Dijksman, J. C. W., *Rec. trav. chim.*, **68**, 57 (1949); Kubo, S. and Tsutsumi, C., *Bull. Chem. Soc. Japan*, **23**, 187 (1950).
33. Yoshino, Y., *Bull. Chem. Soc. Japan*, **26**, 401 (1953); *Japan Analyst*, **3**, 121 (1954); also see Salmon, J. E., *J. Chem. Soc.*, 2316 (1952).
34. McIsaac, L. D. and Voigt, A., *U.S. Atomic Energy Comm.*, **ISC-271** (1952).
35. Odencrantz, J. T. and Rieman, III, W., *Anal. Chem.*, **22**, 1006 (1950).
36. Yoshino, Y., *J. Chem. Soc. Japan*, **71**, 577 (1950); Samuelson, O., *Ion Exchangers in Analytical Chemistry*, p. 151, Wiley, New York (1953).
37. Shimizu, H., *High-polymer Chem. Japan*, **7**, 108 (1950); Honda, M., *J. Chem. Soc., Japan*, **71**, 59 (1950).
38. Honda, M., *J. Chem. Soc. Japan*, **70**, 103 (1949); Lagerström, O., *et al.*, *Svensk Papperstidn.*, **108**, 309 (1948).
39. Muto, S., *J. Chem. Soc. Japan.*, **72**, 976 (1951).
40. Kramer, H., *Anal. Chem.*, **27**, 144 (1955) (silicate); Martin, J. R. and Hayes, J. R., *ibid.*, **24**, 182 (1952) (steel); Shiokawa, T. and Sato, A., *Nippon-Kinzoku-Gakkai-Shi*, **15B**, 284 (1951) (steel); Brunisholz, G. and Bonnet, J., *Helv. Chim. Acta*, **34**, 2074 (1951); Norwitz, G. and Codell, M. (see Chapter 61).
41. Shaw, W. H. R. and Bordeaux, J. J., *Anal. Chem.*, **27**, 136 (1955).
41. Brooke, M., *Anal. Chem.*, **24**, 583 (1952).
43. Kodama, K. and Kanie, T., *Research Repts. Nagoya Municipal Ind. Research Inst.*, (12) 79 (1955).
44. Orlova, L. M., *Zavodskaya Lab.*, **21**, 9 (1955); Alimarin, I. P. and Medvedeva, A. M., *ibid.*, **21**, 1416 (1955).
45. Kakihana, H., *Bull. Chem. Soc. Japan*, **22**, 242 (1949).
46. Salmon, J. E. and Tietze, H. R., *J. Chem. Soc.*, 2324 (1952).
47. Hartmann, S., *Z. anal. Chem.*, **151**, 332 (1956).
48. Devlin, J. A., *et al.*, *J. Franklin Inst.*, **248**, 251 (1949).
49. Matsuo, T. and Iwase, A., *Japan Analyst*, **4**, 148 (1955); Iwase, A., *ibid.*, **4**, 176 (1955).
50. Samuelson, O., *Ion Exchangers in Analytical Chemistry*, p. 136, Wiley, New York (1953); Gehrke, C. W., *et al.*, *J. Agr. Food Chem.*, **3**, 48 (1955).
51. Lur'e, Yu. Yu. and Stefanovich, S. V., *Zavodskaya Lab.*, **13**, 660 (1947); Edelshteĭn, S. A. and Patatskiĭ, V. I., *ibid.*, **15**, 850 (1949); Mason, A. C., *Analyst*, **77**, 529 (1953); Brunisholz, G., *et al.*, *Helv. Chim. Acta*, **36**, 782 (1953); Brooke, M. and Holbrook, M., *Chemist Analyst*, **41**, 80 (1952); Shilz, W. E. and Krynauw, G. N., *Anal. Chem.*, **28**, 1759 (1956).
52. Day, Jr., H., *et al.*, *Anal. Chem.*, **26**, 611 (1954); Helger, B. and Rynninger, R., *Svensk. Kem. Tidskr.*, **61**, 189 (1949).
53. Kakihana, H., *J. Chem. Soc. Japan*, **71**, 480 (1950); Minami, E., *et al.*, *ibid.*, **74**, 746 (1953).

54. YOSHINO, Y. and KOJIMA, M., *Japan Analyst*, **4**, 311 (1955); also see WICKBOLD, R., *Z. anal. Chem.*, **132**, 401 (1951).
55. MACNEVIN, W. M. and LEE, I. L., *Anal. Chim. Acta*, **12**, 544 (1954).
56. KLEMENT, R. and SANDMANN, H. *Z. anal. Chem.*, **145**, 325 (1955).
57. KAKIHANA, H., *J. Chem. Soc. Japan*, **72**, 200 (1951); also see HONDA, M., *J. ibid.*, **72**, 361 (1951); **71**, 118 (1950).
58. AOKI, F., *Bull. Chem. Soc. Japan*, **26**, 480 (1953).
59. ISHIMORI, T. and OKUNO, H., *Bull. Chem. Soc. Japan*, **29**, 78 (1956).
60. KLEMENT, R., *Z. anal. Chem.*, **145**, 305 (1953).
61. KAKIHANA, H. and KOJIMA, S., *Japan Analyst*, **2**, 133, 421 (1953); **3**, 42 (1954).
62. SWEET, R. C., *et al.*, *Anal. Chem.*, **24**, 952 (1952).
63. YOSHINO, Y., *J. Chem. Soc. Japan*, **72**, 457 (1951).
64. LUR'E, YU. YU. and FILIPPOVA, N. A., *Zavodskaya Lab.*, **14**, 159 (1948); **13**, 539 (1947).
65. YOSHINO, Y. and KOJIMA, M., *Bull. Chem. Soc. Japan*, **23**, 47 (1950).
66. RYABCHIKOV, D. I. and OSIPOVA, V. F., *Doklady Akad. Nauk S.S.S.R.*, **96**, 761 (1954); *Zhur. Anal. Khim.*, **11**, 278 (1956).
67. KIMURA, K., *et al.*, *J. Chem. Soc. Japan*, **74**, 305 (1953).
68. SHIOKAWA and SATO[40]; also see SAMUELSON, O., *Ion Exchangers in Analytical Chemistry*, p. 177, Wiley, New York (1953); USATENKO, YU. I. and DATSENKO, O. V., *Zavodskaya Lab.*, **14**, 323 (1948).
69. BELYAVSKAYA, T. A. and SHKROBOT, E. B., *Trudy Komissii Anal. Khim., Akad Nauk S.S.S.R., Inst. Geokhim. i Anal. Khim.*, **6**, 343 (1955).
70. GINZBERG, L. B. and SHKROBOT, E. B., *Zavodskaya Lab.*, **21**, 1289 (1955).
71. SCHUBERT, J., *et al.*, *Chimia* (*Switz.*), **11**, 50 (1957).
72. GIERST, L. and DUBRU, L., *Bull. soc. chim. Belges*, **63**, 379 (1954).
73. PECSOK, R. L. and PARKHURST, R. M., *Anal. Chem.*, **27**, 1920 (1955); also see KLEMENT, R., *Z. anal. Chem.*, **136**, 17 (1952); ALIMARIN and MEDVEDEVA.[44]
74. USATENKO, YU. I. and DATSENKO, O. V., *Zavodskaya Lab.*, **15** 779 (1949); SHEMYAKIN, F. M., *et al.*, *ibid.*, **16**, 1124 (1950); SAMUELSON, O., *Ion Exchangers in Analytical Chemistry*, p. 153, Wiley, New York (1953).
75. TOMPKINS, E. R., *et al.*, *J. Am. Chem. Soc.*, **69**, 2769 (1947); *Nucleonics*, **3**, (5) 22 (1948); also see HONDA, M., *et al.*, *Japan Analyst*, **4**, 240 (1955).
76. DRAGANIC, I. G., *et al.*, *Bull. Inst. Nuclear Sci. 'Boris Kidrich'*, **4**, 37 (1954); DOLAR, D. and DRAGANIC, *Rec. trav. inst. recherches structure matiére*, **2**, 77 (1953); DIZDAR, Z., *ibid.*, **2**, 85 (1953).
77. DYRSSEN, D., *Svensk Kem. Tidskr.*, **62**, 153 (1950).
78. GORDON, L., *et. al.*, *Anal. Chem.*, **28**, 1476 (1956).
79. NADHARNI, M. N., *et al.*, *Anal. Chim. Acta*, **16**, 421 (1957).
80. RYABCHIKOV, D. I. and BUCKTIAROV, V. E., *Zhur. Anal. Khim.*, **9**, 196 (1954).
81. ALIMARIN, I. P. and TSINTSEVICH, E. P., *Zavodskaya Lab.*, **22**, 1276 (1956).
82. TAKETATSU, T., *J. Chem. Soc. Japan*, **78**, 157 (1957).
83. TAKETATSU, T., *J. Chem. Soc. Japan*, **76**, 756 (1955).
84. MINAMI, E. and ISHIMORI, T., *J. Chem. Soc. Japan*, **74**, 378 (1953).
85. HONDA, M., *Japan Analyst*, **4**, 384 (1955).
86. GOLOVALYĬ, R. N., *Naukovi Zapiski L'vis. Derzhav Univ. I. Franka*, **34**, *Ser. Khim.*, (4) 118 (1955); *Vinodelie i Vinogradarstvo, S.S.S.R.*, **13**, (4) 14 (1953).
87. VASIL'EV, A. M., *et al.*, *Uchenye Zapiski Kazan Univ.*, **113**, (8) 91 (1953).
88. BELYAVSKAYA, T. A. and FEDEEVA, V. I., *Vestnik Moskov Univ.*, **11** (6), *Ser. Fiz.-Mat. i Estestven. Nauk*, (4) 73 (1956).
89. STRYCHER, R. DE, *Industrie chim. belge*, **20**, *Spec. No.*, 482 (1955).
90. FUNASAKA, W., *et al.*, *Sulfuric acid* (*Japan*), **7**, 285 (1954).
91. KLEMENT, R. and DMYTRUK, R., *Z. anal. Chem.*, **128**, 106 (1948); SAMUELSON, O., *Ion Exchangers in Analytical Chemistry*, p. 155, Wiley, New York (1953).
92. HAHN, R. B., *et al.*, *Anal. Chim. Acta*, **9**, 223 (1953).
93. GROST, C., *et al.*, *Anal. Chem.*, **28**, 1571 (1956).
94. RYNASIEWICZ, J., *Anal. Chem.*, **26**, 355 (1954).
95. BROWN, E. G. and HAYS, T. J., *Mikrochim. Acta*, 522 (1954).
96. HELWIG, H. L., *et al.*, *U.S. Atomic Energy Comm.*, **UCRL**-2655 (1954)
97. FUNASAKA, W., *et al.*, *Japan Analyst*, **3**, 80 (1954); **4**, 514 (1955).
98. ZIPKIN, I., *et al.*, *Anal. Chem.*, **29**, 310 (1957).
99. COURSIER, J. and SAULNIER, J., *Anal. Chim. Acta*, **14**, 62 (1956).
100. SAMUELSON, O., *Ion Exchangers in Analytical Chemistry*, p. 204, Wiley, New York (1953).
101. NELSON, F. and KRAUS, K. A., *J. Am. Chem. Soc.*, **77**, 329 (1955).
102. KRAUS, K. A. and MOORE, G. E., *J. Am. Chem. Soc.*, **72**, 5792 (1950); **74**, 843 (1952); **75**, 1460 (1953); NELSON, F. and KRAUS, K. A., *ibid.*, **76**, 5916 (1954); KRAUS, K. A., *et al.*, *ibid.*, **76**, 989 (1954); **77**, 1371 (1955); **78**, 2692 (1956); *J. Phys. Chem.*, **58**, 11 (1954); KRAUS, K. A. and NELSON, F., *Proc. Intern. Conf. Peaceful Uses of Atomic Energy, Geneva, Aug. 1955, 7, Session 9B. 1, P/837*, pp. 113, 131, United Nations (1956).
103. JENTZSCH, D., *et al.*, *Z. anal. Chem.*, **144**, 8, 17 (1955); **146**, 88 (1955); **147**, 20 (1955); **148**, 321, 325 (1955); **150**, 241 (1956); **152** 134 (1956).
104. ISHIMORI, T., *Bull. Chem. Soc. Japan*, **28**, 432 (1955).
105. YOSHINO, Y., *Bull. Chem. Soc. Japan*, **28**, 382 (1955).
106. SASAKI, Y., *Bull. Chem. Soc. Japan*, **28**, 89 (1955).
107. HONDA, M., *et. al.*, *Ion-Exchange Resins*, p. 326, Hirokawa, Tokyo (1955).
108. BLASIUS, E. and NEGWER, M., *Naturwissenschaften*, **39**, 257 (1952).
109. AMIN, A. M. and FARAH, M. Y., *Chemist Analyst*, **44**, 62 (1955).
110. ATTEBERRY, R. W., *et al.*, *Abst. Am. Chem. Soc.*, *118th Meeting* (1950).
111. KALLMANN, S., *et al.*, *Anal. Chem.*, **28**, 230 (1956).
112. AOYAGI, I., *Repts. Govt. Ind. Research Inst. Nagoya*, **4**, 224 (1955); **5**, 28 (1956); KORKISCH, J. and HECHT, F., *Mikrochim. Acta*, 1230 (1955/56).
113. GILFRICH, J. V., *Anal. Chem.*, **29**, 978 (1957).
114. KOJIMA, M., *Japan Analyst*, **6**, 369 (1957); YOSHINO, Y. and KURIMURA, Y., *Bull. Chem. Soc. Japan*, **30**, 56 (1957).
115. OEHLMENN, F., *Chem. Tech.* (*Berlin*), **8**, 544 (1956).
116. THIERS, R. E., *et al.*, *Anal. Chem.*, **27**, 1725 (1955).

117. Hague, J. L., *et al.*, *J. Research Natl. Bur. Standards*, **53**, 353 (1954).
118. Liberman, A., *Analyst*, **80**, 595 (1955).
119. Herber, R. H. and Irvine, Jr., J. W., *J. Am. Chem. Soc.*, **76**, 987 (1954).
120. Baggott, E. R. and Willcocks, R. G. W., *Analyst*, **80** 53 (1955).
121. Teicher, H. and Gordon, L., *Anal. Chem.*, **23**, 930 (1951).
122. Venturello, G. and Gualandi, C., *Ann. chim. (Rome)*, **46**, 229 (1956).
123. Fisher, S. and Kunin, R., *Anal. Chem.*, **29**, 400 (1957); Seim, H. J., *et al.*, *ibid.*, **29**, 443 (1957); Arnfelt, A. L., *Acta Chem. Scand.*, **9**, 1484 (1955); Ishimori, T. and Okuno, H., *Bull. Chem. Soc. Japan*, **29**, 78 (1956); Šušić, M. V., *Bull. Inst. Nuclear. Sci. 'Boris Kidrich'*, **7**, 35 (1957).
124. Korkisch, J., *et al.*, *Mikrochim. Acta*, 485 (1957).
125. Ockenden, H. M. and Foreman, J. K., *Analyst*, **82**, 592 (1957).
126. Chen, Y. M., *et al.*, *J. Chinese Chem. Soc. (Taiwan)*, **2**, 111 (1955).
127. Murthy, T. K. S., *Anal. Chim. Acta*, **16**, 25 (1957).
128. Klement, R. and Kuhn, A., *Z. anal. Chem.*, **152**, 146 (1956).
129. Meloche, V. W. and Preuss, A. F., *Anal. Chem.*, **26**, 1911 (1954).
130. Fisher, S. A. and Meloche, *Anal. Chem.*, **24**, 1100 (1952); Okuno, H., *et al.*, *Japan Analyst*, **4**, 386 (1955).
131. Ryabchikov, D. I. and Lazarev, A. I., *Doklady Akad. Nauk S.S.S.R.*, **92**, 777 (1953); Alexander, T. R., Thesis, Univ. Wisconsin (1947).
132. Hecht, F., *et al.*, *Mikrochim. Acta*, 1283 (1955/56); Korkisch, J., *et al.*, *ibid.*, 1422 (1955/56).
133. Blasius, E. and Negwer, M., *Z. anal. Chem.*, **143**, 257 (1954).
134. Smith, G. W. and Reynolds, S. A., *Anal. Chim. Acta*, **12**, 151 (1955).
135. Samuelson, O., *et al.*, *Z. anal. Chem.*, **144**, 323 (1955); also see *Z. Elektrochem.*, **57**, 207 (1953); Samuelson, O., *Ion Exchangers in Analytical Chemistry*, p. 156, Wiley, New York (1953).
136. Samuelson, and Sjöström, E., *Anal. Chem.*, **26**, 1908 (1954); Hara, R. and Vallee, B. L., *ibid.*, **27**, 315 (1955).
137. Gabrielson, G., *Metal Finishing*, **53**, (2) 58 (1955).
138. Samuelson, O. and Sjöberg, B., *Anal. Chim. Acta*, **14**, 121 (1956).
139. MacNevin, W. M. and Crummett, W. B., *Anal. Chem.*, **25**, 1628 (1953); *Anal. Chim. Acta*, **10**, 323 (1954).
140. MacNevin, W. M. and McKay, E. S., *Anal. Chem.*, **29**, 1220 (1957).
141. Stevenson, P. C., *et al.*, *J. Am. Chem. Soc.*, **75**, 4876 (1953).
142. Senn, W. L. and Berg, E. W., *Anal. Chem.*, **27**, 1255 (1955).
143. Kraus, K. A., *et al.*, *J. Phys. Chem.*, **58**, 11 (1954).
144. Cluett, M. L., *et al.*, *Analyst*, **80**, 204 (1955).
145. Blasius, E. and Wachtel, U., *Z. anal. Chem.*, **142**, 321 (1954).
146. Coburn, H. G., *et al.*, *Anal. Chem.*, **28**, 1297 (1956).
147. Wolszon, J. D., *et al.*, *Anal. Chem.*, **29**, 829 (1957).
148. Yoshimura, J. and Waki, H., *Japan Analyst*, **6**, 362 (1957).
149. Ayres, J. A., *Ind. Eng. Chem.*, **43**, 1526 (1951).
150. Cranston, H. A. and Thompson, J. B., *Ind. Eng. Chem., Anal. Ed.*, **18**, 323 (1946).
151. Golovatyi, P. R. N., *Vinodeliei Vinogradarstvo, S.S.S.R.*, **10**, (5) 27 (1950).
152. Buchwald, H. and Wood, L., *Anal. Chem.*, **25**, 664 (1953).
153. Riches, J. P. R., *Nature*, **158**, 96 (1946); *Chem. & Ind. (London)*, 656 (1947).
154. Nydahl, F., *Proc. Intern. Assoc. Theor. & Applied Limnol.*, **11**, 276 (1951).
155. Egner, H., *et al.*, *Kgl. Lantbruks-Högskol. Ann.*, **16**, 593 (1949).
156. Zenin, A. A., *Gidrokhim. Materialy*, **24**, 68 (1955).
157. Mizutani, Y., *Japan Analyst*, **5**, 620 (1956).
158. Tompkins, P. C., *U.S. Atomic Energy Comm.*, **AECD**-2692 (1949).
159. Schubert, J., *et al.*, *Science*, **109**, 316 (1949).
160. Russel, E. R., *et al.*, *Nucleonics*, **7**, (1) 60 (1950).
161. Kojima, M., *J. Chem. Soc. Japan*, **73**, 767 (1952); **74**, 283 (1953).
162. Gaddis, S. J., *J. Chem. Educ.*, **11**, 327 (1943).
163. Kunin, R., *Anal. Chem.*, **21**, 87 (1949); Burstall, F. H., *et al.*, *Ind. Eng. Chem.*, **45**, 1648 (1953).
164. Davankov, A. B. and Laufer, V. M., *Zavodskaya Lab.*, **22**, 294 (1956); Ezerskaya, N. A. and Markova, N. V., *Zhur. Priklad. Khim.*, **30**, 1071 (1957).
165. Smales, A. A. and Salmon, L., *Analyst*, **80**, 37 (1955).
166. Hering, H., *Anal. Chim. Acta*, **6**, 340 (1952).
167. Kakihana, H., *et al.*, *J. Chem. Soc. Japan*, **75**, 907 (1957); **76**, 215 (1955); **77**, 936, 1233 (1956); **78**, 854 (1957).
168. Fujimoto, M., *Bull. Chem. Soc. Japan*, **27**, 48, 347 (1954); **29**, 776, 833 (1956); **30**, 83, 87, 93, 274, 278, 283 (1957).
169. Miller, W. E., *Anal. Chem.*, **29**, 1891 (1957); Abrahamczik, E., *Mikrochim. Acta*, 651 (1956).
170. Takiyama, K. and Suito, E., *Japan Analyst*, **4**, 8 (1955).
171. Grubb, W. T. and Zemany, P. D., *Nature*, **176**, 221 (1955).
172. Spedding, F. H., *Discussions Faraday Soc.*, **7**, 214 (1949); Cohn, W. E., *et al.*, *Nucleonics*, **3**, (5) 22 (1948); Steacie, E. W. R. and Cambron, A., *Research*, **2**, 225 (1949); Johnson, W. C., *et al.*, *Chem. Eng. News*, **25**, 2494 (1947).
173. Wilkinson, G. and Hicks, H. G., *Phys. Rev.*, **75**, 1370 (1949).
174. Ketelle, B. H. and Boyd, G. E., *J. Am. Chem. Soc.*, **73**, 1862 (1951).
175. Spedding, F. H. and Dy, J. L., *J. Am. Chem. Soc.*, **72**, 5350 (1950).
176. Spedding, F. H., *et al.*, *J. Am. Chem. Soc.*, **70**, 1671 (1948).
177. Spedding, F. H., *et al.*, *J. Am. Chem. Soc.*, **72**, 2349, 2354 (1950); **76**, 2545, 2550 (1954).
178. Vickery, R. C., *J. Chem. Soc.*, 4357 (1952).
179. Freiling, E. C. and Bunney, L. R., *J. Am. Chem. Soc.*, **76**, 1021 (1954); Mayer, S. W. and Freiling, *J. Am. Chem. Soc.*, **76**, 5647 (1954).
180. Spedding, F. H., *et al.*, *J. Am. Chem. Soc.*, **76**, 612, 2557 (1954); Wheelright, E. J. and Spedding, F. H., *U.S. Atomic Energy Comm.*, **ISC**-637 (1955).
181. Vickery, R. C., *Nature*, **170**, 665 (1952).

182. Archard, J. C., *Compt. rend.*, **241**, 800 (1955); Marsh, J. K., *J. Chem. Soc.*, 978 (1957); Brunisholz, G., *Chimia (Switz.)*, **11**, 97 (1957); Duyckaerts, G. and Fuger, J., *Anal. Chim. Acta*, **14**, 243 (1956); Fuger, *Bull. soc. chim. Belges*, **66**, 151 (1957); Meinhold, T. E. and Kremers, H. E., *Chem. Processing*, **20**, (3) 12, 18 (1957).
183. Loriers, J. and Carminati, D., *Compt. rend.*, **237**, 1328 (1953); Holleck, L. and Hartinger, L., *Angew. Chem.*, **68**, 411, 412 (1956).
184. James, R. A. and Bryan, W. B., *J. Am. Chem. Soc.*, **76**, 1982 (1954).
185. Cuninghame, J. G., *et al.*, *J. Inorg. & Nuclear Chem.*, **1**, 163 (1955).
186. Choppin, G. R. and Silva, R. J., *J. Inorg. & Nuclear Chem.*, **3**, 153 (1956).
187. Stewart, D. C., *Anal. Chem.*, **27**, 1279 (1955); Stewart, D. C., *et al.*, *Proc. Intern. Conf. Peaceful Uses of Atomic Energy, Geneva*, **7**, 321 (1955).
188. Higgins, G. H. and Street, Jr., K. *J. Am. Chem. Soc.*, **72**, 5321 (1950).
189. Marinsky, J. A., *et al.*, *J. Am. Chem. Soc.*, **69**, 2781 (1947).
190. Butement, F. D. S., *Nature*, **167**, 400 (1951).
191. Loriers, J., *Compt. rend.*, **242**, 261 (1956).
192. Tompkins, E. R., *et al.*, *J. Am. Chem. Soc.*, **69**, 2792 (1947); Spedding, *et al.*, *ibid.*, **69**, 2777, 2786, 2812 (1947); Yang, J. T., *Anal. Chim. Acta*, **4**, 59 (1950); Matheson, A. R., Thesis, Univ. Illinois (1948); Mazza, L. and Cotelli, N. E., *Ann. chim. (Rome)*, **45**, 781 (1955).
193. Brooksbank, W. R. and Leddicotte, G. W., *J. Phys. Chem.*, **57**, 819 (1953).
194. Hettel, H. J. and Fassel, V. A., *Anal. Chem.*, **27**, 1311 (1955).
195. Huffman, E. H. and Oswalt, R. L., *J. Am. Chem. Soc.*, **72**, 3323 (1950).
196. Thompson, S. G., *et al.*, *J. Am. Chem. Soc.*, **72**, 2798 (1950).
197. Street, Jr., K., *et al.*, *J. Am. Chem. Soc.*, **72**, 4832 (1950).
198. Street, Jr., K. and Seaborg, G. T., *J. Am. Chem. Soc.*, **72**, 2790 (1950).
199. Thompson, S. G., *et al.*, *J. Am. Chem. Soc.*, **76**, 6229 (1954); *Phys. Rev.*, **94**, 1080 (1954).
200. Glass, R. A., *U.S. Atomic Energy Comm.*, **UCRL**-2560 (1954); *J. Am. Chem. Soc.*, **77**, 807 (1955); Wish, L., *et al.*, *ibid.*, **76**, 3444 (1954).
201. Choppin, G. R., *et al.*, *J. Inorg. Nuclear Chem.*, **2**, 66 (1956).
202. Magnuson, L. B., *et al.*, *Phys. Rev.*, **78**, 363 (1950); Johanson, G., *Svensk Kem. Tidskr.*, **65**, 79 (1953).
203. Dizdar, Z. I. and Den Boer, D. H. W., *J. Inorg. Nuclear Chem.*, **3**, 327 (1956).
204. Coleman, J. S., *et al.*, *J. Inorg. Nuclear Chem.*, **3**, 327 (1956).
205. Surls, Jr., Z. P. and Choppin, G. R., *J. Inorg. Nuclear Chem.*, **4**, 62 (1957).
206. Huffman, E. H., *et al.*, *J. Am. Chem. Soc.*, **71**, 4147 (1949); **73**, 2902, 4474 (1951); also see Kraus, K. A. and Moore, G. E., *ibid.*, **71**, 3263 (1949); Forsling, W., *Ark. Kem.*, **5**, 503 (1953); Rajan, K. S. and Gupta, J., *J. Sci. Ind. Research*, **14B**, 453 (1955); **16B**, 459 (1957).
207. Street, Jr., K. and Seaborg, G. T., *J. Am. Chem. Soc.*, **70**, 4268 (1948); Newham, I. E., *ibid.*, **73**, 5899 (1951).
208. Lister, B. A. J., *J. Chem. Soc.*, 3123 (1951); Lister, B. A. J. and Hutcheon, J. M., *Research*, **5**, 291 (1952).
209. Benedict, J. T., *et al.*, *J. Am. Chem. Soc.*, **76**, 2036 (1954).
210. Kraus, K. A. and Moore, G. E., *J. Am. Chem. Soc.*, **73**, 9, 13, 2900 (1951); **71**, 3855 (1949); **72**, 4293 (1950); **77**, 1383 (1955).
211. Wacker, R. E. and Baldwin, W. H., *Nuclear Sci. Abst.*, **4**, 469 (1950).
212. Gillis, J., *et al.*, *Mededel. Vlaam. Chem. Ver.*, **15**, 63 (1953); Speecke, J. and Hoste, J., *ibid.*, **19**, 190 (1957).
213. Cabell, M. J. and Milner, I., *Anal. Chim. Acta*, **13**, 258 (1955).
214. Hague, J. L., *et al.*, *J. Research Natl. Bur. Standards*, **53**, 261 (1954).
215. Freund, H. and Miner, F. J., *Anal. Chem.*, **25**, 564 (1953).
216. Usatenko, Yu. I. and Gurceva, L. I., *Zavodskaya Lab.*, **22**, 781 (1956).
217. Alimarin, I. P., *et al.*, *Vestnik Moskov Univ.*, **11**, (3), *Ser. Fiz.-Mat. Estestven. Nauk*, (2) 67 (1956).
218. Aoyagi, I., *Repts. Govt. Ind. Research Inst. Nagoya*, **2**, 492 (1953).
219. Yang, J. T., *J. chim. phys.*, **47**, 806 (1950); *Compt. rend.*, **231**, 1059 (1950).
220. Maddock, A. G. and Pugh, W., *J. Inorg. Nuclear Chem.*, **2**, 114 (1956); Kahn, S. and Hawkinson, D. E., *ibid.*, **3**, 155 (1956).
221. Kimura, K., *et al.*, *Japan Analyst*, **6**, 637 (1957).
222. Brown, W. E. and Rieman, III, W., *J. Am. Chem. Soc.*, **74**, 1278 (1952).
223. Chen, Y. M., *J. Chinese Chem. Soc. (Taiwan)*, **1**, 46 (1954); **2**, 53 (1955).
224. Kayas, G., *J. chim. phys.*, **47**, 408 (1950); *Compt. rend.*, **229**, 1002 (1949).
225. Cohn, W. E. and Kohn, H. W., *J. Am. Chem. Soc.*, **70**, 1986 (1948); Wickbold, R., *Angew. Chem.*, **62**, 448 (1950); *Z. anal. Chem.*, **132**, 401 (1951); Jentzsch, D. and Frotscher, I., *ibid.*, **144**, 1 (1955).
226. Beukenkamp, J. and Rieman, III, W., *Anal. Chem.*, **22**, 582 (1950).
227. Watanabe, S. and Yamagata, N., *Japan Analyst*, **6**, 97 (1957).
228. Okuno, H., *et al.*, *Japan Analyst*, **2**, 428 (1953).
229. Buser, W., *Helv. Chim. Acta*, **34**, 1635 (1951).
230. Nelson, F., *J. Am. Chem. Soc.*, **77**, 813 (1955).
231. Ring, S. A., *Anal. Chem.*, **28**, 1200 (1956).
232. Tompkins, E. R., *J. Am. Chem. Soc.*, **70**, 3250 (1948); **69**, 2772 (1947).
233. Honda, M., *Japan. Analyst*, **3**, 132 (1954).
234. Bovy, R. and Duyckaerts, G., *Anal. Chim. Acta*, **11**, 134 (1954).
235. Lerner, M. and Rieman, III, W., *Anal. Chem.*, **26**, 610 (1954).
236. Campbell, D. N. and Kenner, C. T., *Anal. Chem.*, **26**, 560 (1954).
237. Nelson, F. and Kraus, K. A., *J. Am. Chem. Soc.*, **77**, 801 (1955).
238. Atteberry, R. W., *et al.*, *J. Am. Chem. Soc.*, **72**, 4805 (1950).
239. DeGeiso, R. C., *et al.*, *Anal. Chem.*, **26**, 1840 (1954); Rieman, III, W. and Lindenbaum, S., *Anal. Chem.*, **24**, 1199 (1952); also see Berne, F., *Acta Chem. Scand.*, **5**, 1260 (1951).

240. Kikindai, M., *Compt. rend.*, **240**, 1100 (1955).
241. Hall, N. F. and Johns, D. H., *J. Am. Chem. Soc.*, **75**, 5787 (1953).
242. Huffman, E. H., *et al.*, *J. Inorg. Nuclear Chem.*, **3**, 49 (1956).
243. King, E. L. and Dismukes, E. B., *J. Am. Chem. Soc.*, **74**, 1674 (1952); King, E. L. and Walters, R. R., *ibid.*, **74**, 4471 (1952).
244. Inoue, Y., *et al.*, *Japan Analyst*, **2**, 21, 121 (1953); **4**, 277, 281 (1955).
245. Mori, M., *et al.*, *J. Chem. Soc. Japan*, **76**, 1003 (1955); *Bull. Chem. Soc. Japan*, **29**, 947 (1956).
246. Cobble, J. W. and Adamson, A. W., *J. Am. Chem. Soc.*, **72**, 2276 (1950).
247. Lindenbaum, S., *et al.*, *Anal. Chim. Acta*, **11**, 530 (1954); Higgins, C. E. and Baldwin, W. H., *Anal. Chem.*, **27**, 1780 (1955); Grande, J. A. and Beukenkamp, J., *ibid.*, **28**, 1497 (1956).
248. Samuelson, O., *Ion Exchangers in Analytical Chemistry*, Chapter 5, §1, Wiley, New York (1953); Erler, K., *Z. anal. Chem.*, **129**, 209 (1949); **131**, 106 (1950); Wickbold, R., *ibid.*, **132**, 247 (1951); many other references.
249. Calmon, C., *J. Am. Water Works Assoc.*, **46**, 470 (1954); Samuelson, O., *Ion Exchangers in Analytical Chemistry*, p. 131, Wiley, New York (1953).
250. Liebig, G. E., *et al.*, *Soil Sci.*, **55**, 371 (1943).
251. Davies, C. W. and Nancolla, G. H., *Nature*, **165**, 237 (1950); Steinbach, J. and Freiser, H., *Anal. Chem.*, **24**, 1027 (1952); Grunbaum, B. W., *et al.*, *ibid.*, **24**, 1857 (1952); Stern, H., *Iowa State College, J. Sci.*, **25**, 358 (1951).
252. Kakihana, H., *J. Chem. Soc. Japan*, **72**, 255 (1951).
253. Honda, M., *J. Chem. Soc. Japan*, **70**, 55 (1949).
254. Fujimoto, M., *Japan Analyst*, **2**, 360 (1953).
255. Ryznar, J. W., *Ind. Eng. Chem.*, **36**, 821 (1944); Ayres, J. A., *J. Am. Chem. Soc.*, **69**, 2879 (1947).
256. Baker, L. C. W., *et al.*, *J. Am. Chem. Soc.*, **72**, 2374 (1950).
257. Kunin, R., *Anal. Chem.*, **21**, 87 (1949).
258. Reimers, H., *Chem.-Ztg.*, **81**, 357 (1957).
259. Schoeller and Powell, p. 304; Lewis, J. A. and Griffiths, J. M., *Analyst*, **76**, 388 (1951).
260. Maeck, W. J., *Anal. Chem.*, **26**, 1635 (1954).
261. Lebez, D. and Ostanek, M., *J. Stefan Inst.* (*Ljubljana*) *Repts.*, **2**, 9 (1955).
262. Schoeller and Powell, pp. 210, 211; Burstal, F. H. and Williams, A. F., *Analyst*, **77**, 983 (1952); Mercer, R. A. and Wells, R. A., *ibid.*, **79**, 339 (1954).
263. Bruninx, E., *et al.*, *Mikrochim. Acta*, 688 (1956).
264. Schoeller and Powell, p. 165; Williams, A. F., *Analyst*, **77**, 297 (1952).
265. Fouarge, J., *Anal. chim. Acta*, **12**, 342 (1955).
266. Bishop, J. I., *Analyst*, **81**, 291 (1956).
267. Ghe, A. M. and Fiorentini, A. R., *Ann. chim.* (*Rome*), **45**, 400 (1955); **47**, 759 (1957); Venturello, G. and Ghe, A. M., *Ann. chim.* (*Rome*), **47**, 912, 919 (1957); *Analyst*, **82**, 343 (1957).

14

COMPOUNDS FORMING PRECIPITATES WITH ANIONS

Organic bases which act as precipitants for metal halide or pseudohalide complexes are considered in Chapter 9. The compounds considered in this chapter are those which mainly precipitate NO_3^-, ReO_4^-, F^-, SO_4^{2-}, WO_4^{2-} and phospho- or silico-molybdic acids.

1. PRECIPITANTS FOR NO_3^-, ReO_4^-, F^-, ETC.[1]

(*1*) *Nitron* (I) [Yellow, m.p. 189°C, sol. in org. solvents and dil. AcOH, insol. in H_2O] is used gravimetrically for NO_3^-, ReO_4^- and BF_4^- (for B detn. only). It also ppts. ClO_4^-, Br^-, I^-, ClO_3^-, IO_3^-, SCN^-, CrO_4^{2-}, WO_4^{2-}, $Fe(CN)_6^{3-}$, $Fe(CN)_6^{4-}$, $C_2O_4^{2-}$, $PO_2F_2^-$, SO_3F^-, etc. The order of solubility of the complexes is picrate, ClO_4^-, NO_3^-, I^-, SCN^-, CrO_4^{2-}, ClO_3^-, NO_2^-, Br^-. *Fornitral* (nitron + HCOOH) also ppts. NO_3^-.

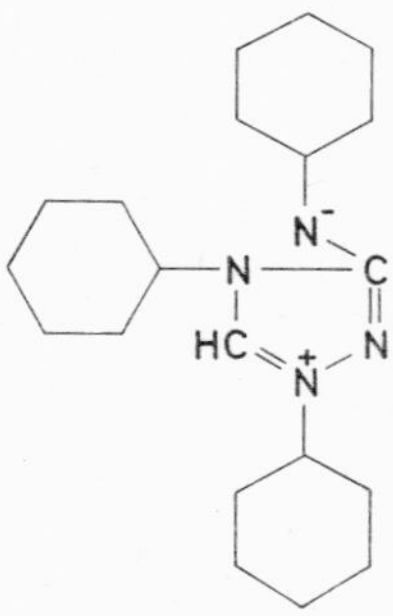

(I)

Di(1-naphthylmethyl)-amine (α-dinaphthomethylamine) ($(C_{10}H_7CH_2)_2NH$) ppts. NO_3^- and ClO_4^- and is more sensitive than nitron. The *2-naphthylmethyl analog* forms no ppt. N,N-*Diethylbenzohydrylamine* (diphenyldiethylaminomethane) ($(C_2H_5)_2N{\cdot}CH(C_6H_5)_2$) ppts. NO_3^-, while *diphenylbenzohydroxylamine* ppts. NO_3^-, ClO_4^- and I^-. *α-Phenyl-β-diethylaminoethyl-*p-*nitrobenzoate* ($O_2NC_6H_4COOCH(C_6H_5)CH_2N(C_2H_5)_2$) ppts. NO_3^- and ClO_4^-, the sensitivity being very similar to that of nitron.

Nitroquinetol (5-nitro-6-ethoxyquinoline) ppts. NO_3^-; *cinchonamine* ($C_{19}H_{24}ON_2$) ppts. NO_3^- and SCN^- but is inferior to nitron. p-*Tolyl-isothiourea* ($C_7H_7S(NH)(NH_2)$) is used gravimetrically for NO_3^- as is *dicyclohexylthallic sulfate* or *acetate*; the latter reagent also ppts. Cl^-, etc.

(*2*) *Aniline* ppts. ReO_4^- and I^- is pptd. as $6C_6H_5NH_2{\cdot}3H_2SO_4{\cdot}HI{\cdot}I_4$ if $K_2Cr_2O_7$ is added to the H_2SO_4 medium. The same ppt. is formed with phenylhydrazine in H_2SO_4 medium in presence of $K_2S_2O_8$.

ReO_4^- is also pptd. by *acridine*, *brucine*, *safranine T*, *trypaflavine* (acriflavine, 2,8-diamino-10-methochloride acridine) and *veratrine*. Veratrine is not sensitive. *Antipyrine* ppts. ReO_4^- and ClO_4^-, as does *strychnine* which is, however, less sensitive. *Tetron* (*N,N,N′,N′*-tetramethyl-*o*-tolidine) ppts. $ReCl_6^{2-}$ but not ReO_4^-.

(*3*) *Tetraphenylarsonium chloride* ppts. ReO_4^-; colorimetric detn. is possible after extn. with $CHCl_3$. $TlCl_4^-$ can be detd. gravimetrically. IO_4^-, ClO_4^-, MnO_4^-, I^-, SCN^-, Hg^{2+}, Sn^{4+}, Cd, Zn, BF_4^-, etc. are also pptd. Os forms characteristic crystals and can be detd. colorimetrically if Cl^- is added. Pt is detd. gravimetrically if Br^- is present. Co is detd. colorimetrically if SCN^- is added.

Triphenylmethylarsonium chloride ppts. Fe, Cu, Co and Mo in presence of SCN^-; Mo is detd. colorimetrically after $C_6H_4Cl_2$ extn. Sb is detd. colorimetrically and Cd gravimetrically if I^- is added. *Tetraphenylphosphonium* or *stibonium chloride* reacts similarly. With the former compd. Hg, Sn, Cd, Re, ClO_4^-, IO_4^-, MnO_4^- can be detd. gravimetrically or titrimetrically and Co colorimetrically (with SCN^- present); Ir is also detd. colorimetrically. MnO_4^- is detd. titrimetrically with the Sb-compd. F^- is extd. (97–98% recovery) by the Sb-compd. in CCl_4.[2]

Triphenylbenzylphosphonium chloride is used for the colorimetric detn. of Re after $CHCl_3$ extn. *Triphenylsulfonium* or *selenonium chloride* or *triethyltelluronium chloride* ppts. Bi in presence of I^-; the sensitivity is ca. 0·1 μg.[3] Other onium compds. have been described[4] and the reagents have been reviewed.[5]

(*4*) *Triphenyltin chloride* [m.p. 106°C, sparingly sol. in H_2O, EtOH, Et_2O] is used gravimetrically for F^-.

Methylene blue (II) forms a colored complex with BF_4^- which can be measured after extn. with $(CH_2Cl)_2$. The reagent also ppts. many ions.

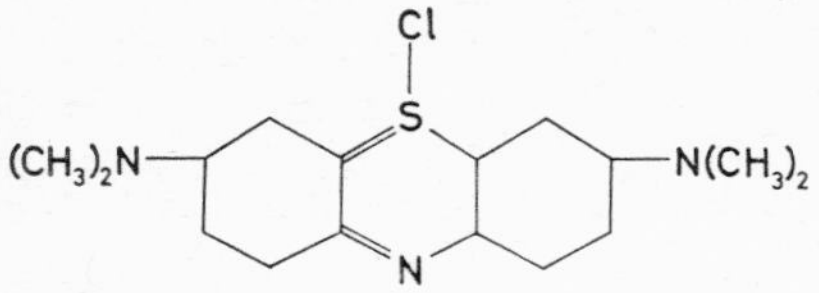

(II)

2. PRECIPITANTS FOR SO_4^{2-}, WO_4^{2-}, PHOSPHO- OR SILICO-MOLYBDIC ACID

(*1*) *Benzidine* serves for gravimetric detns. of SO_4^{2-}; colorimetry is possible if furfural is added. WO_4^{2-}, MoO_4^{2-}, PO_4^{3-}, phosphomolybdate, etc. are also pptd. SeO_4^{2-} is pptd. from dil. AcOH soln. but TeO_4^{2-} is not. F^- is pptd. as (III) from buffered soln. in presence of $Hg(OAc)_2$.

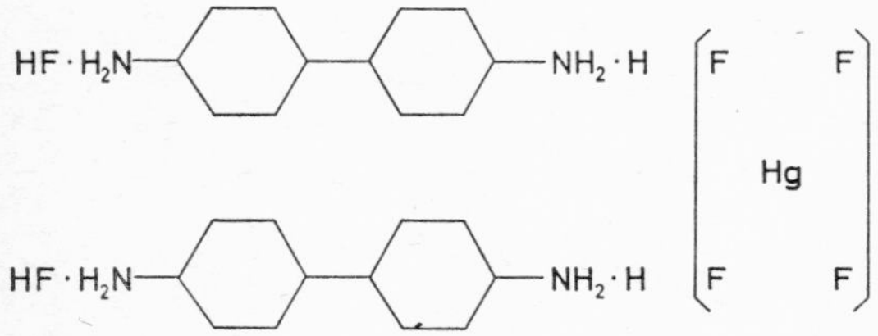

(III)

Among the substituted benzidines, *4-amino-4′-chlorodiphenyl*[6] is the best reagent for SO_4^{2-} and *1-amino-4(*p*-aminophenyl)-naphthalene*[7] is best for WO_4^{2-} since there is no copptn. of MoO_4^{2-}. *Naphthidine* or *4,4′-diaminotolane*[6] is better than benzidine for SO_4^{2-}.

1,8-Naphthylenediamine, *2,7-diaminofluorene*, p-*aminodiphenyl* + HCHO, p-*amino*-N,N-*dimethylaniline* are other reagents for SO_4^{2-}. o-*Tolidine* ppts. SO_4^{2-} and WO_4^{2-}.

(*2*) *Acridine* ppts. V, Mo, W and Cr in dil. AcOH soln. WO_4^{2-} is pptd. by *α-naphthylamine*, *phenylhydrazine*, *tetramethyl-4,4′-diaminobenzophenone*, *cumidine* (4-isopropylaniline), *4,4′-diaminotriphenylmethane*, *totaquine* (an alkaloid) and *veratrine*. WO_4^{2-} can be detd. gravimetrically with *6-* or *8-toluquinaldine*, *nemedine*, *rivanol*, *brucine* (VO_3^- also ppts.), *worcine* (>80% cinchonine-HCl and < 10% quinidine) and *anti-1,5-di-*(p-*methoxyphenyl*)-*5-hydroxamino-3-oximino-1-pentene* ($CH_3OC_6H_4CH(NHOH)CH_2C(NOH)CHCHC_6H_4$-$OCH_3$).

Diphenyline (2,4′-diaminodiphenyl) ppts. WO_4^{2-} (6 μg.); some Mo coppts. but SO_4^{2-} does not. *Bismarck brown* or *chrysoidine R* also ppts. WO_4^{2-}, and it has been shown that 2 NH_2-groups are necessary for pptn.[8] *β-Naphthoquinoline* ppts. WO_4^{2-} and is used gravimetrically for Ge in presence of $H_2C_2O_4$. o-*Dianisidine* reacts with both WO_4^{2-} and MoO_4^{2-}.

Tetrabase (Arnold's base, 4,4′-tetramethyldiaminodiphenylmethane) forms ppts. with MoO_4^{2-}, WO_4^{2-} (at pH 3·5) and VO_3^-.

Antipyrine ppts. WO_4^{2-} and *cinchonine* is used for its gravimetric or titrimetric detn.; both reagents are more satisfactory if tannin is added. Antipyrine also ppts. phosphomolybdate, while cinchonine is used gravimetrically for germanomolybdate (1 Ge: 2 or 4 cinchonine). *Diantipyrinylphenylmethane* ppts. V as $[(C_{11}H_{11}ON_2)_2CHC_6H_5]H_4V_6O_{17}$ and also ppts. CrO_4^{2-} and the cyano complexes of Fe and Co.[9]

Rhodamine B is used gravimetrically or colorimetrically for WO_4^{2-}; it also reacts with MoO_4^{2-}, Nb, Ta (0·2 μg.). *Phenarsazinic acid* (phenazarsinic acid) (IV) ppts. V, W and Mo and forms a red color with NO_3^-.[10]

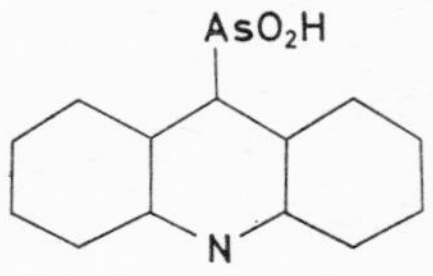

(IV)

Cinnamalanisalacetoneoxime or *dianisalacetoneoxime* is a specific reagent for WO_4^{2-}.

(*3*) *Pyridine* forms ppts. with germano- and silicomolybdate. *Quinoline* is the best reagent for phosphomolybdate and can be used titrimetrically or gravimetrically; silicomolybdate is detd. gravimetrically. *Dimethylquinoline* reacts with silicomolybdate, as do *5,6-benzoquinaldine* and *8-hydroxyquinaldine* which are used gravimetrically. For *oxine*, see Chapter 8, Section 1.1.

Hexamine and *urea* react with silicomolybdate. *Methyl violet* can be used colorimetrically for phosphomolybdate after dissoln. of the ppt. in Me_2CO, as well as for WO_4^{2-}. *Pyramidone* reacts with silicomolybdate and with WO_4^{2-}.

Several alkaloids have been used. *Strychnine* reacts with VO_3^-, arseno- and phosphomolybdate, *morphine* with silicomolybdate and ClO_4^-, and *coniine* with silicomolybdate; *cocaine* is used colorimetrically for arsenomolybdate. *Quinine* reacts with arseno- and phosphomolybdate and WO_4^{2-}; it ppts. Ge in presence of tannin, and fluoresces with SO_4^{2-} (hence SO_2, H_2S).

Quinidine reacts with $Fe(CN)_6^{3-}$ (0·1 μg.).

References

1. FEIGL, 305 (1949).
2. MOFFETT, K. D., *et al.*, *Anal. Chem.*, **28**, 1356 (1956).
3. SHINAGAWA, M., *et al.*, *Japan Analyst*, **3**, 199, 204 (1954); **5**, 23, 80 (1956).
4. ROSEN, J. M., *Anal. Chem.*, **21**, 1276 (1949).

5. SHINAGAWA, M., *Kagaku no Ryoiki*, **10**, 111 (1956).
6. BELCHER, R., *et al.*, *J. Chem. Soc.*, 544, 1516 (1951); 1334 (1953); *Anal. Chim. Acta*, **8**, 122, 146 (1953); *Mikrochim. Acta*, 51 (1953).
7. HOVORKA, V., *Collection Czechoslov. Chem. Communs.*, **10**, 518 (1938); **13**, 520 (1948); *Chem. listy*, **36**, 113 (1942).
8. LIANG, S. C. and CHANG, K. N., *J. Chinese Chem. Soc.*, **18**, 25 (1951).
9. GUSEV, S. I., *et al.*, *Zhur. Anal. Khim.*, **6**, 43 (1951); **7**, 219 (1952).
10. PIETSCH, R., *Mikrochim. Acta*, 1490, 1672 (1956); *Z. anal. Chem.*, **155**, 189 (1957).

15

REDOX REACTIONS

1. REACTIONS WITH OXIDANTS[1]

Benzene reacts with NO_3^- in H_2SO_4 medium to give the odor of nitrobenzene. *Nitrobenzene* reacts with NO_3^- on heating with H_2SO_4 to give a red color after addn. of Me_2CO and NaOH. *Anthracene* in CCl_4 forms white needle-like crystals with Br_2.

Citric acid gives a blue color with V. *Gallic acid* reacts with PbO_2 to give a red color, and with NO_3^-. *Salicylic acid* yields a yellow-red color with NO_3^- which turns yellow with NH_4OH, and a brown color with $S_2O_8^{2-}$ in presence of Ag^+.

Benzaldehyde forms benzoic acid with O_3 and can be detd. in this way. *Butyraldehyde* in hexane reacts sensitively with O_3 in presence of H_2O_2. *Vanillin* gives a dark brown color, then a violet ppt., with H_2O_2; if phloroglucinol is also added, vanillin also forms a red color with SO_2 or Cl_2.

Salicin (salicylaldehyde-glucoside) gives a red or violet color with NO_3^-. *Saponin* forms a blood-red color with NO_3^- in H_2SO_4 soln. *Arbutin* forms a yellow color with NO_3^- which becomes orange on addn. of KOH. *Aloin* (a yellow glucoside) gives a red color with Cu^{2+} and CN^-.

Hydroquinone forms a yellow color with NO_2^-; its sulfonic acid gives a greenish brown color with NO_3^- while NO_2^- does not react. *Quinitol* (hexahydroquinol) ppts. NO_3^- as nitroquinitol. *Anthrarufin* (1,5-dihydroxyanthraquinone) gives a yellow color with NO_3^- in H_2SO_4 and a violet color with NO_2^-. *Phenanthraquinone* behaves similarly with NO_3^-. *Juglone* (5-hydroxynaphthoquinone-1,4; ext. from walnut kernel) forms a red or blue color with NO_2^-; with large amts. of NO_2^- the color is yellow. *Adurol* (2-chlorohydroquinone) forms a brown color with O_2.

Phenol reacts with NO_3^- in H_2SO_4 to give a yellow-orange color. With NO_2^- in H_2SO_4, it forms a pink-red color (picric acid); the color is red with $Hg(NO_3)_2$ present, and yellow with sulfanilic acid present. Phenol can be used to remove excess of Br_2 in redox reactions. *1,2,4-Phenoldisulfonic acid* forms a yellow 6-nitro compd. with NO_3^- which can be utilized colorimetrically for < 1 mg. N. NO_2^- reacts when α-naphthylamine is also present, the color being violet if the amine is added first and yellow if it is added last; the former order is more sensitive. *Sulfosalicylic acid* behaves similarly. p-*Nitrophenol* gives a blue reaction with NO_3^- or NO_2^-. *Pentachlorophenol* forms an orangish color with NO_3^-, chloranil being formed. *Sozoiodol* (2,6-diiodophenol-4-sulfonic acid, Na salt) forms a blue color with NO_2^- on boiling.

Guaiacol (*o*-methoxyphenol) forms an orange-yellow color with NO_2^- or CrO_4^{2-}, and a pink color with Cu if CN^- is added. *Guaiaconic acid* reacts with H_2O_2, $Cu^{2+} + CN^-$, SCN^- or Cl^- and with CrO_4^{2-}.

o-*Cresol* reacts with NO_3^- in HCl medium, the color being dark green by reflected light and violet by transmitted light; NO_2^- does not react. It also forms a brown color with Sb^{5+} in $CHCl_3$; with As^{5+} in H_2SO_4, the initial pink-grey color becomes dark red and then brown on heating. *2,4-Xylenol* (2,4-dimethylphenol) reacts with NO_3^- to yield 5-nitro-2,4-xylenol, while *3,4-xylenol* gives the 6-nitro compd.; both are excellent for colorimetric detn. of NO_3^-. *Thymol* reacts with NO_3^- and NO_2^-, the latter also being possible in presence of chloramine T; thymol reacts with Sb^{5+} and As^{5+} similarly to *o*-cresol.

α-Naphthol gives a yellow reaction with NO_2^- and a yellow–dark red reaction with NO_3^-; with addn. of sulfanilic acid and NH_4OH, the color becomes pink or dark red and is more sensitive when sucrose is present. *β-Naphthol* is usually preferable to the α-compd. See also benzidine, p. 127. For the use of *1-naphthol-3,8-disulfonic acid* (ε acid), see fuchsine, p. 129. *C acid* (1-naphthol-5-sulfonic acid) is used colorimetrically for > 1 mg. N, forming a yellow color with NO_2^- (cf. benzidine, etc.). *G salt* (Na salt of 2-naphthol-6,8-disulfonic acid, β-acid) reacts with NO_2^- or NO_3^- in H_2SO_4 to give a red or yellow shade. *R salt* (Na salt of 2-naphthol-3,6-disulfonic acid, α-acid) can be used with fuchsine (p. 129).

Chromotropic acid gives a reddish reaction with CrO_4^{2-} or $Cr_2O_7^{2-}$, and a yellow reaction with NO_3^- in H_2SO_4, or with NO_2^-. *Resorcinol* reacts with NO_2^- in H_2SO_4 to give a yellow–red fluorescence due to resorufin; a red color is formed in HCl medium on boiling, which becomes purple with NH_4OH, dark green with

NaOH and blue to green on diln. Reaction with NO_3^- gives a pale yellow color which becomes red on heating and violet on addn. of NaOH. Cl_2 forms a green color with resorcinol. *Resorcinol sulfonic acid* gives a violet reaction with NO^- or NO_3^-. *Resorufin* forms blue tetrachloro- or tetrabromo-resorufin with Cl_2 or Br_2. *Orcinol* (5-methylresorcinol, 3,5-dihydroxytoluene) gives a yellow reaction with NO_2^- or NO_3^- in H_2SO_4, and a brown reaction with CrO_4^{2-}.

Pyrocatechol forms a red color with NO_2^- or NO_3^- and blue with Os. *Methylpyrocatechol* also reacts with NO_2^- in alk. medium to give a deep red color.

Veratrole gives a cherry color with Ce^{4+} which can be extd. with C_6H_6 and utilized colorimetrically. *Hydrocerulignone* (4,4′-dihydroxy-3,3′,5,5′-tetramethoxydiphenyl) gives a purple color with Cu^{2+} and CN^-. *Rubrophen* (trimethoxydihydroxyoxotriphenylmethane) gives a fading color with NO_3^- and NO_2^- in H_2SO_4.

Pyrogallol forms a blue color with 0·01 mg. Os/ml., a brown color with NO_2^-, and a yellow color with NO_3^-; the latter is violet in 1*N* H_2SO_4 soln. IO_3^- gives a red-brown reaction and O_2 a violet-brown reaction in alk. soln. The dimethyl ether reacts with CrO_4^{2-}, Fe^{3+} and NO_2^-. *pyrogallolsulfonic acid* reacts more sensitively with NO_3^- or NO_2^- to give a pink or brown color; CrO_4^{2-} and IO_3^- react to give yellowish products.

p-*Aminophenol* (rodinal) can be utilized colorimetrically for Tl^{3+} by means of a violet color. If halide is present, Cu (0·2 μg.), Fe (0·07 μg.), and NO_2^- (in AcOH) react to give reddish or brown colors. ClO_3^- oxidizes *p*-aminophenol in presence of V as catalyst. For the *o*-isomer, see benzidine, etc. *Amidol* (2,4-diaminophenol hydrochloride) reacts with NO_3^- (3 p.p.m.) NO_2^-, O_2, Cu and CrO_4^{2-}. *Picramic acid* (4,6-dinitro-2-aminophenol) gives a black reaction with Os.

H acid (1-amino-8-naphthol-3,6-disulfonic acid) forms a red color with NO_2^- in presence of phenol, etc. *K acid* (the 4,6-disulfonic acid) reacts very sensitively with NO_2^- (0·03 p.p.m.) giving a wine-red color if anthranilic acid is present; it also reacts with NO_3^- and Fe^{3+}. For other uses of these compds. as well as *1-amino-8-naphthol-3-sulfonic acid, J acid* (the 2,5,7-isomer) and *M acid* (the 1,5,7-isomer), see benzidine, pp. 127 and 129.

Urea is generally used for removal of NO_2^-. *s-Diethyldiphenylurea* forms a red color with 4 p.p.m. NO_3^-. *Diphenyleneglycine* gives a yellow-green color with NO_2^-.

Aniline reacts with BaO_2, H_2O_2, Na_2O_2, PbO_2, MnO_2, Cl_2, ClO_3^-, BrO_3^-, OBr^-, IO_3^-, MnO_4^{2-}, MnO_4^-, $Fe(CN)_6^{3-}$ UO_2^{2+}, CrO_4^{2-}. VO_3^- (3 μg.) forms a blue-green color; $S_2O_8^{2-}$ forms a brownish ppt., while NO_2 gives a red color. Br_2 forms characteristic crystals of tribromoaniline. NO_2^- forms yellow diazoaminobenzene; with phenol, resorcinol or salicylic acid added, the color is yellow; with α-naphthol or chromotropic acid, it is orange; with β-naphthol, H acid or K acid, it is red; and with α-naphthylamine, it is purple; the limits of sensitivity of these reactions are 10^{-6} to 10^{-7}. *Acetanilide* behaves similarly. *Aniline hydrobromide* is sensitive to Au.

N,N-*Dimethylaniline* forms yellow-brown *p*-nitrosodimethylaniline with NO_2^- (1 μg.); if sulfanilic acid is added, the methyl orange formed can be utilized colorimetrically. p-*Nitrosodimethylaniline* itself can be used colorimetrically for ClO_4^-. p-*Amino*-N,N-*dimethylaniline* reacts with Cl_2, Br_2, I_2, H_2O_2, MnO_2 and V to give blue or violet colors. CN^- reacts if Cu^{2+} is present. If $FeCl_3$ is added, S^{2-} (1 μg.) can be detd. colorimetrically by methylene blue formation. The *o*-amino compd. forms indophenol with α-naphthol which is used to test for Tl^{3+}. The *p*-diethyl compd. reacts with most of the above-mentioned oxidants to give pink to purple colors.

N,N-*Diethylaniline* reacts with 1 μg. Zn and $Fe(CN)_6^{4-}$, the color being yellow-brown in H_2SO_4-contg. solns. and yellow through red to brown in H_3PO_4-contg. solns. H_2O_2 gives a yellow reaction if $K_2Cr_2O_7$ and $H_2C_2O_4$ are present. Mn has a catalytic effect on the reaction of IO_3^- with the aniline.

p-*Anisidine* (*p*-methoxyaniline) gives a sensitive purple reaction with Au; it can be applied colorimetrically for Bi if $K_3Fe(CN)_6$ is added. The *o*-compd. gives a blue color with Pb or Cu. o-*Phenetidine* (*o*-ethoxyaniline, *o*-aminophenetol) reacts with CrO_4^{2-}, MnO_2 and Zn + $Fe(CN)_6^{4-}$ to give blue or violet colors. The *p*-isomer is used colorimetrically for Tl^{3+} and also reacts with CrO_4^{2-}; the catalytic effect of Mn or V on its reaction with an oxidant is more sensitive if pyrocatechol is present. With $K_3Fe(CN)_6$, the *p*-isomer allows colorimetric detn. of Ni. Fe, Cu, $Fe(CN)_6^{3-}$ and $Fe(CN)_6^{4-}$ can be detected by their catalytic effect on the reaction with H_2O_2.

Sulfanilic acid (*p*-aminobenzenesulfonic acid) gives a blood-red color with 2 μg. Ce^{4+}/ml. The reaction with NO_2^- is red in presence of α-naphthylamine, α-naphthol or β-naphthylamine, and yellow in presence of phenol or β-naphthol. Anthranilic acid and sulfanilamide are excellent coupling agents also. *Nitrition B* (*o*-aminoanilide of benzenesulfonic acid) can be used gravimetrically for NO_2^-, benzenesulfonyl-*o*-phenylenediazimide being formed.

m-*Toluidine* forms an orange-red ppt. with NO_2^-, which is sol. in Et_2O; a pale pink shade is obtained with H_2O_2. *o*-Toluidine reacts with Cr, V, Os, Ag, Pb; a violet color is formed with Cl_2 or I_2 in presence of aniline. Zn can be detd. colorimetrically if $K_3Fe(CN)_6$ is added. *p*-Toluidine can also be used for Zn; it also reacts with NO_3^- in H_2SO_4, the red double-layer reaction being more sensitive if aniline is also present. *Xylidine* gives red colors with H_2O_2 and NO_2^-.

m-*Phenylenediamine* reacts with CrO_4^{2-} or $Cr_2O_7^{2-}$ to give a red color which turns yellow on addn. of NH_4OH; it forms Bismarck brown with NO_2^- and also reacts with H_2O_2, Cl_2, OBr^-, BrO_3^-, O_3, Fe, Cu, V, and with H_2S in presence of $FeCl_3$. The *o*-isomer reacts with O_3 and

V; in alk. soln. H_2O_2 and NO_2^- do not react. The *p*-isomer behaves similarly to the *m*-isomer; its chloro deriv. can be used colorimetrically for NO_2^-. *1,2,4-Toluylenediamine* forms a red color with NO_2^- in acidic (AcOH) soln. The 1,2,5-compd. forms a lilac color with V, and the 1,3,4-compd. a red color with H_2O_2 in presence of $Cr_2O_7^{2-}$.

*Tetramethyl-*p*-phenylenediamine* forms blue colors with H_2O_2, O_3 and Os. *4,4′-Tetramethyldiaminotriphenylmethane* gives a very sensitive yellow color with MnO_4^- which allows colorimetric detn. of Mn. *Tetrabase* reacts with CrO_4^{2-}, PbO_2, MnO_2, MnO_4^- and Au to give blue or purple colors.

2,4-Diaminobenzoic acid reacts with NO_2^- and with CN^- in presence of Cu^{2+}.

α-Naphthylamine (α-aminonaphthalene) reacts with Fe^{3+}, Tl^{3+} and CrO_4^{2-} to give blue, purple or black products. The reaction with NO_2^- is yellow if phenol is present, red if H acid, α-naphthol, sulfanilic acid or amino G acid is present; with the last reagent, 0·01 μg. NO_2^- can be detected. *β-Naphthylamine* forms a blue color with Os and a violet ring with NO^- in H_2SO_4; the yellow reaction with NO_2^- becomes red in presence of metanilic acid, α- or β-naphthol or H acid. Also see fuchsine, p. 129.

For the use of *1-naphthylamine-5-sulfonic acid* (Laurent's acid), see benzidine, etc., and for use of the 2,5-acid (Dahl's acid) see fuchsine, etc. (below). *α-Naphthionic acid* (1-naphthylamine-4-sulfonic acid) gives a pink-red ring with NO_2^- in a double-layer reaction; the color with NO_2^- is red with α- or β-naphthol, α- or β-naphthylamine, ε acid, H acid, and yellow with phenol. *2-Naphthylamine-4,6-disulfonic acid* and the 2,4,7-isomer (Dahl's acids II and III) behave similarly to naphthionic acid with NO_2^- in presence of phenol etc. The use of *amino G acid* (the 2,6,8-isomer) is mentioned above.

N,N-*Dimethyl-α-naphthylamine* forms a red color with NO_2^-; if sulfanilic acid is added, the reaction is useful colorimetrically. *1,8-Naphthylenediamine* (1,8-diaminonaphthalene) forms an orange ppt. of 1,8-azimidonaphthalene with NO_2^- (0·1 μg.), a brown ppt. of di-*peri*-naphthoselenodiazole with SeO_3^{2-}, and an orange color with NO_3^-. N-*(1-Naphthyl)-ethylenediamine dihydrochloride* with sulfanilamide allows an excellent colorimetric detn. of NO_2^-.

The yellow color of *2-aminoanthraquinone* is bleached by NO_2^-; a red color is formed if phenol is present, and a blue color if α-naphthol, ε acid or H acid is present. The 1-amino compd. is also bleached by NO_2^-.

Benzidine reacts with 1·5 μg. Pb in presence of NH_4OH and H_2O_2, with 0·02 μg. Au in 1 μl., with 0·15 μg. Ce or Mn in NaOH soln. and with Bi, Os, Ir^{4+}, Tl^{3+}, Co^{3+}, Fe^{3+}, Br_2, I_2, H_2O_2, NO_2^-, MnO_4^-, CrO_4^{2-}, $S_2O_8^{2-}$, VO_3^- and $Fe(CN)_6^{3-}$; in all these cases the blue meriquinonoid form appears. Brownish colors are formed with O_3, Cl_2, BrCN, and $IO_3^- + H_2O_2$. Reaction with NO_2^- alone gives a yellow color; red, violet or purple colors appear if the reaction is done in presence of *m*-aminophenol, α-naphthol, α-naphthylamine, H acid, β-naphthol, G, J, M acids, 1-amino-8-naphthol-3-sulfonic acid, K acid or C acid. The sensitivity decreases roughly according to the order given above.

3,3′-Diaminobenzidine hydrochloride (3,3′,4,4′-tetraaminodiphenyl-HCl) gives yellow piazselenol with SeO_3^{2-} which can thus be detd. colorimetrically. *4-Dimethylamino-* or *4-methylthio-1,2-phenylenediamine* reacts similarly with 0·05 μg. SeO_3^{2-}.

o-*Tolidine* gives a bluish reaction with Ag_2O, PbO_2, Fe^{3+}, Os, NO_3^-, Cl_2 or I_2, and a yellowish reaction with Au, MnO_2 or NO_2^-.

Diphenylamine (*N*-phenylaniline, anilinobenzene) is pale yellow, m.p. 53°C, and sol. in EtOH, Et_2O and C_6H_6. It reacts with 0·5 μg. NO_3^- to give a blue color; Cl^- increases the sensitivity. Blue colors are also formed with ClO_3^-, BrO_3^-, IO_3^-, CrO_4^{2-}, Fe^{3+}, MoO_4^{2-}, NO_2^-, MnO_4^- and peroxides; Tl^{3+}, Cl_2 and 2·5 μg. V form violet colors, and Zn with $Fe(CN)_6^{4-}$ gives a violet-black color. With resorcinol added, NO_3^- gives a yellow-blue color which turns reddish on addn. of EtOH; the blue color with NO_2^- turns red on this addn. Substitution of NO_2 groups decreases the sensitivity of the reactions; substitution of OH or NH_2 groups changes the colors of the reactions, but does not affect their sensitivity.[2] See also Section 4.2. In general, diphenylbenzidine, diphenylamine-4-sulfonic acid, diphenylbenzidinesulfonic acid are more sensitive than diphenylamine itself. Diphenylamine-2,2′- or 2,3′- or 2,4′-dicarboxylic acid is also useful.

p-*Diaminodiphenylamine* forms a blue-green color with H_2O_2. The tetramethyl deriv. reacts with Cl_2. *Thiodiphenylamine* gives a yellow-brown reaction with NO_2^-. *Variamine blue* (variamine blue B base, 4-amino-4′-methoxydiphenylamine) allows colorimetric detns. of Fe^{3+} and Ce^{4+}, and forms a blue color with I_2 (see also Section 4.2).

1- or 2-Naphthylphenylamine forms a green color with NO_2^- or NO_3^- and a reddish color with ClO_3^-. *β-Dinaphthylamine* behaves similarly with these ions and forms a brown-violet color with CrO_4^{2-}. *3,3′-Dimethylnaphthidine* forms a purple color with 0·1 μg. V. *Phenylanthranilic acid* behaves similarly with V (see also Section 4.2). *Di(9,10-mono-hydroxyphenanthryl)-amine*, $(C_{14}H_8OH)_2NH$, gives a blue to red reaction with NO_3^- in H_2SO_4.

2,7-Diaminofluorene hydrochloride reacts with 0·001 μg. NO_3^-/ml. to form a green-yellow color, as well as with Br_2, Cl_2 and $S_2O_8^{2-}$; it is said to be better than benzidine. 2,7-Diaminodiphenylene oxide is sensitive to CrO_4^{2-} and $S_2O_8^{2-}$. o-*Dianisidine* forms reddish colors with Au, NO_2^-, NO_3^-, Cu^{2+} + SCN^-. V can be detected by its catalytic effect on the reaction with IO_3^-.

Phenylhydrazine reacts with 0·32 μg. MoO_4^{2-} in acidic (H_2SO_4) soln. to give a pink color; in neutral soln. a red ppt. forms which is sol. in $CHCl_3$. $S_2O_8^{2-}$ and VO_3^- form yellow and green colors resp. *as-Diphenylhydrazine* reacts with 0·05 μg. Se as SeO_3^{2-} to give purple $(C_6H_5)_2N{\cdot}N{:}C_6H_4{:}N{\cdot}C_6H_5$. o- or p-*Aminobenzalphenylhydrazone* reacts with NO_2^- to form a purple diazo compd. which turns yellow. *Luminol* (3-aminophthalohydrazide) can be used to detect H_2O_2, Fe, Cu, CN^-.

Brucine forms a yellow color with NO_2^- and with 0·06 μg. NO_3^-; in the latter case a red-brown color appears in a double layer test with H_2SO_4 soln. Ce^{4+} gives a pink color which turns brown with alkali. OCl^- gives a yellow color which turns red on boiling and does not change with HCl addn.; on the other hand ClO_3^- reacts to give yellow and then red colors only on boiling and the color fades on HCl addn. *Strychnine* forms blue to red colors with MnO_2, Co^{3+}, Cr^{6+}, Ce^{4+}, ClO_3^- and BrO_3^-. *Hydrostrychnine*, which is prepd. by reduction with Zn in HCl soln., forms red colors with NO_2^-, NO_3^-, Cl_2 and Br_2. *Strychnidine* is used colorimetrically for NO_3^-.

Apomorphine reacts with Cl_2, NaOCl, As^{5+}, Sb^{5+} and NO_2^- but not with NO_3^-. *Morphine* forms a brown-yellow color with IO_3^- and a pink color with Cu in presence of H_2O_2. *Heroin* (diacetylmorphine) and *veratrine* behave similarly. *Codeine* (methylmorphine) can be applied colorimetrically for SeO_3^{2-} in H_2SO_4 soln.; Cl_2 and OCl^- also react but ClO_3^-, NO_3^- and $S_2O_8^{2-}$ do not. *Colchicine* forms a yellow color with SeO_3^{2-}, while *aspidospermine* forms a violet color with this ion on heating in H_2SO_4 soln.

Berberine forms a dark red color with NO_3^-; *narcotine* can be utilized for colorimetry of NO_3^-. *Narceine* reacts with I_2 to give a blue color. *Novocaine* (procaine hydrochloride) and α-naphthylamine allow colorimetry of 0·2–35 μg. NO_2^-/ml.

p-*Aminoazobenzene* (spirit yellow, aniline yellow) forms an orange-red color with NO_2^- in presence of phenol, α-naphthol, α-naphthylamine, H- or ε- acid, etc. The color is red with α-naphthol in alkali soln. (most sensitive) and with resorcinol or ε acid. p-*Aminobenzeneazodimethylaniline* gives a blue color with NO_2^-. *Azo orseille R* (Colour Index 34) forms a purple shade with NO_2^-; the color is yellow in presence of phenol and alkali, red with resorcinol and violet with α-naphthol. *Azorubine S* (Colour Index 184) gives a ring test with NO_2^- in H_2SO_4, the color being red in the upper layer and violet in the lower.

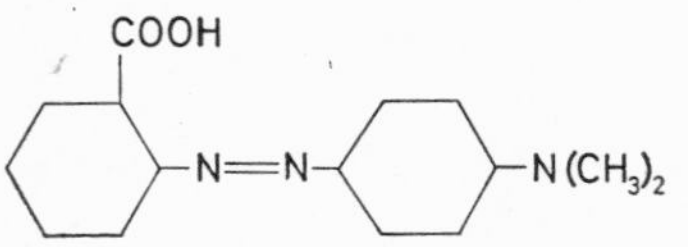

(I)

Phenylazodiaminopyridine forms yellowish colors with CrO_4^{2-} (2 μg.) and $Cr_2O_7^{2-}$. *Azocarmine B* (rosindulin 2B, bluish, Colour Index 829) gives a yellow color with Cl_2 (2 μg.) which turns blue with HCl. *Methyl red* (Colour Index 211) (I) fades on addn. of Cl_2 or NO_2^-. *Methyl orange* (Orange IV, helianthin, gold orange, tropaeolin D, Colour Index 142) (II) becomes colorless with Cl_2 (which can be used to test for MnO_2 or BrO_3^-), OCl^- and Br_2.

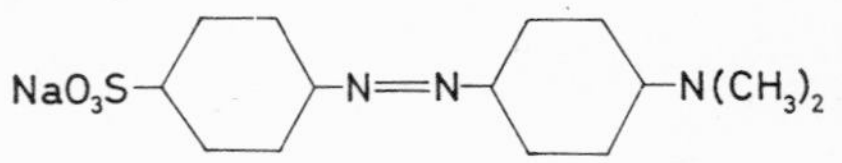

(II)

Pyrrole (azole, imidole) forms blue colors with Hg^{2+}, Au, V, CrO_4^{2-}, IO_3^-, SeO_3^{2-} in H_2SO_4, and silicomolybdate. *2,5-Bis(2,4-dimethyl-N-pyrrolyl)-3,6-dibromohydroquinone* reacts similarly with Cl_2, Br_2, Fe^{3+}, etc. *Pyramidone* forms violet colors with Cl_2, Br_2, NO_2, NO_2^- and IO_3^- and is used colorimetrically for Tl^{3+}. *Antipyrine* reacts with NO_2^- in H_2SO_4; if $HgHSO_4$ and an oxidant are added, the sensitivity is 0·1 μg. NO_2^-/ml. *Carbazole* (diphenylene-imine) (III) likewise reacts with NO_2^- or NO_3^- in H_2SO_4 to form a greenish color. *Indole* (benzopyrrole) (IV) gives a red color with NO_2^-. *Rivanol* (2-ethoxy-6,9-diaminoacridine lactate) allows colorimetry of NO_2^-, giving a yellow to red color. *Phenyldihydrodibenzoacridine* reacts with NO_2^-, NO_3^- and ClO_3^-.

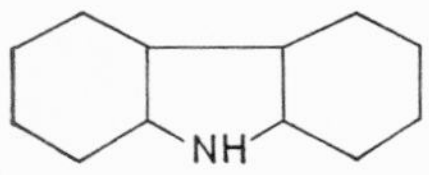

(III)

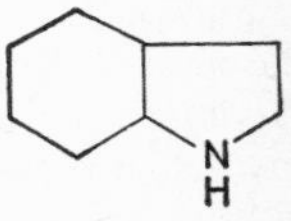

(IV)

Trypaflavine is decolorized by O_2; *dihydroacridine* fluoresces with O_3.

2,4-Diamino-6-hydroxypyrimidine (Merck's rosit) yields an orange ppt. of the 5-nitroso compd. with 12 μg. NO_2^-/ml.; NO_3^- does not react. *Chrysean* (aminothianamide of thiazole prepd. with HCN and H_2S) (V) yields a blue-brown ppt. with 0·25 μg. NO_2^-. *as-Phenylimino-γ-dinaphthoxazine* gives a violet color with

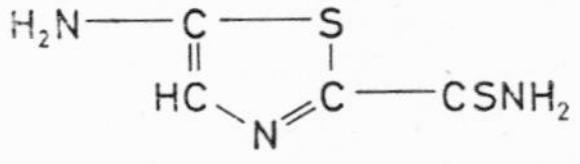

(V)

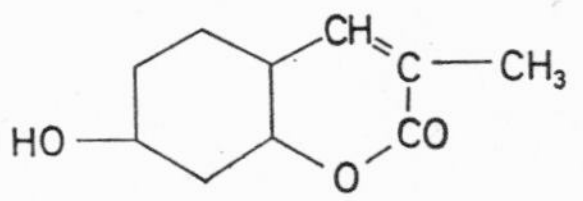

(VI)

NO_3^- in H_2SO_4; the β-naphthyl compd. behaves similarly. *β-Methylumbelliferone* (VI) gives a yellow-green color with NO_2^- or NO_3^- which turns brownish with NH_4OH and yellow on diln.; only NO_3^- reacts in H_2SO_4 soln.

TABLE 26. Reaction of Nitrite with Dyes, etc.

Name of dye	Colour Index	NO_2^- alone	With addn. of Phenol	With addn. of α-Naphthol	With addn. of α-Naphthylamine	With addn. of Other compds.
Benzocyanine B	476	red	purple	purple	—	—
Benzoflavine	791	colorless	—	red	red	H acid, red
Benzo red blue G	473	purple	purple	purple	purple	—
Chicago blue 6B (NOTE 1)	—	red	purple	orange	blue	Resorcinol, *m*-aminophenol, orange
Chrysaniline	793	—	yellow	red	red	H or K acid, chromotropic acid, red
Diamine catechu	—	yellow	—	—	—	—
Diamine red 3B (Deltapurpurine 5B)	452	purple	red	red	red	—
Diamine true blue	—	—	—	red	—	—
Dianiline red 5B	—	red	—	—	—	—
Direct black HB (NOTE 2)	401	blue	red	brown-yellow	blue	Metanilic acid, blue; *m*-aminophenol, orange
Eboli blue 2B	475	red	red	—	—	*m*-aminophenol, red
Fast yellow S (Acid yellow)	16	colorless	orange	blue	red	H or ε acid, blue; resorcinol or chromotropic acid, red-blue
Ice black DMO	265	—	red	red	—	ε acid, violet
Magdala red (Sudan red)	857	fluorescence disappears	—	—	—	—
New fuchsine O	678	yellow	yellow	red	red	—
Oxamine pure blue	613	—	purple	orange	—	—
Palatine chrome brown W	167	yellow	—	—	red	—
Phenosafranine	840	blue	purple	—	violet	—
Phosphine	793	—	—	red	red	Red with most phenolic compds.
Primuline	812	—	red	red	red	Red with most phenolic compds.
Rheonine A	795	yellowish	yellowish	yellowish	red	ε acid, red; resorcinol, orange
Rhodamine 3G extra	753	colorless	blue	green	blue	See NOTE (3)
Rhodulin violet	844	blue	—	—	blue	—
Rosolane O (methylene heliotrope OL)	845	blue	—	—	blue	—
Tannin heliotrope	852	blue	—	—	blue	—
True yellow S	—	—	orange	blue	red	—
Ursol D (Nako dye)	875	yellow-brown	—	orange	red	—
Victoria violet 4BS	53	—	purple	blue	—	H acid, violet; ε acid, blue

NOTES. (1) Chicago blue R (Colour Index 474) behaves similarly.
(2) Other names are oxamine black BHN, diamine black BH, diazo black BHN, naphthylamine black 10B.
(3) Resorcinol, amino R acid, *m*-aminophenol, β-naphthylamine or ε acid addn. leads to blue or violet colors.

Cardiazole (metrazol, pentamethylenetetrazole) (VII)

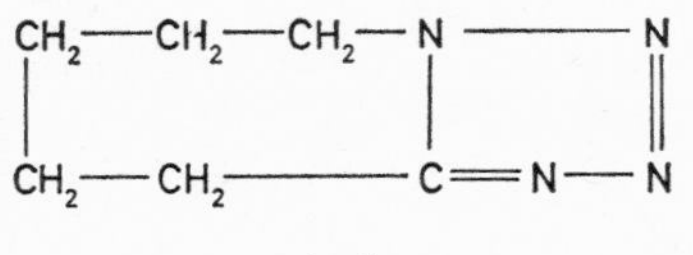

(VII)

ppts. CrO_4^{2-} and forms a blue color with $Cr_2O_7^{2-}$. *Thiosemicarbazide* reduces Cr^{6+} to Cr^{3+}.

Nicotinamide permits fluorimetric detn. of CN^- if chloramine T is added.

Many dyes react with NO_2^-, either alone or in presence of phenolic compds. etc., *Fuchsine* (magenta, a mixt. of rosaniline and pararosaniline, Colour Index 677) forms a yellow color with NO_2^- alone; the color formed is yellow in presence of phenol or *m*-aminophenol, red with α- or β-naphthol or H-, C- or ϵ- acid, or R salt, and violet with α- or β-naphthylamine. The reactions with phenol or α-naphthylamine are the most sensitive. This dye is also bleached by BO_3^-, CO_4^{2-} and $S_2O_8^{2-}$; in presence of AcOH, the first 2 ions give yellow colors, while the third is unchanged. If the dye is reduced with SO_2, it forms a blue color with Br_2 but not with Cl_2 or I_2. *Fuchsine S* (acid fuchsine, a mixt. of fuchsine and its sulfonate, Colour Index 692) is bleached by NO_2^-, but forms a yellow color in presence of phenol, and a red color with α-naphthol or α-naphthylamine present. Cl_2 gives a yellow color with the dye. *Neutral red* (Toluylene red, Colour Index 825) gives a violet shade with NO_2^- in H_3PO_4 (0·2 μg./ml.) and a blue color if α-naphthol is present. *Safranine T* (Colour Index 841) forms the blue monodiazosafranine with 4 μg. NO_2^-/ml.; NO_3^- reacts to give a purple color. *Trypan red* (Colour Index 438) forms an orange-violet color with NO_2^- (5 μg.) in acidic (H_2SO_4) soln. In presence of H_2O_2, 100 μg Cl^- and 30 μg. Br^- give yellow colors. Other dyes which give color reactions with NO_2^- are tabulated in Table 26.

The blue *chromotrope 2B* reacts generally with oxidants to form red-yellow colors. *Indigo carmine* (indigo sulfonate) is bleached by Cl_2, Br_2, ClO_3^-, BrO_3^-, IO_3^- NO_2^-, $Fe(CN)_6^{3-}$ (see also under Redox indicators); its leuco base can be applied colorimetrically for O_3, NO_2^-, NO_3^- and H_2O_2. *Indigosol 04B* (5,5′,7,7′-tetrabromo-indigo) gives a blue color with NO_2^-.

Crystal violet (Colour Index 681) has a leuco base (hexamethyltri-*p*-aminotriphenylmethane) that reacts with Cl_2, I_2 and NO_2^- and is useful for colorimetric detn. of Ir^{4+}. *Fast green FCF* is bleached by Cl_2 and Br_2. *Phenol red* forms the red or violet bromophenol red with Br_2 or with Br^- and OCl^-; *quinoline blue* (cyanine, Colour Index 806) gives a brown color with I_2. *Fluorescein* forms pink eosin with Br_2 (2 μg.); a 0·0001% soln. is bleached by O_3. The leuco base is useful for detection of Cu or CN^-. *Euchrysin 3R* (Colour Index 788) reacts with O_2, the fluorescence disappearing.

Chrome red acidol gives a red color with CrO_4^{2-}. *Plasmochin* forms a purple color with CrO_4^{2-} or $Cr_2O_7^{2-}$ at pH 6·5 in presence of $H_2C_2O_4$; W and Mo react in alk. soln. to give a true color. *Malachite green* (Colour Index 657) is bleached by Ti^{3+} in presence of MoO_4^{2-} or WO_4^{2-} which exert a catalytic action and can thus be detected; the leuco base of the dye is used in detection of free halogens, Ce^{4+}, Ir and Au.

Rhodamine B reacts with Co (2·5 μg.); its fluorescence disappears with 0·1 μg. Mn. *Methylene blue* is bleached by Ce^{4+}, Se in presence of Na_2S, and Co in presence of NaCN and Na_2CO_3; in the last case, the soln. eventually turns blue. The leuco base serves in detection of ClO_3^-. *Nitrobrilliant green* (nitrodiamond green) as its leuco base be can used for detection of Au or Tl^{3+}. *Phenolphthalin* (Kastle–Meyer's reagent, phthalophenone; the reduction product of phenolphthalein with Zn and NaOH) or o-*cresolphthalin* allows colorimetric detn. of Cu if CN^- is added.

The leuco base of *methyl green* (Colour Index 684) can be used to test for $Fe(CN)_6^{3-}$. *Metanil yellow* (tropeolin G, acid yellow R, Colour Index 138) is bleached by Zn if $Fe(CN)_6^{4-}$ is added.

Phenylarsine oxide may be used[3] in titrimetric detn. of I_2.

2. STRONG REDUCTANTS

In this section are collected those organic reductants which reduce metallic ions, e.g. Au, to the metal, and phosphomolybdate, etc., to molybdenum blue.

Acetylene and *ethylene* reduce Au and Pd salts resp. *Formic acid* reduces ions of Pt, Pd, Rh, Ir (+ SO_2), Ag, Hg and Cu, *oxalic acid* those of Au, Pt (*morpholine oxalate* is used for Au[4]), while *tartaric acid* reduces V salts and Ag salts in NH_4OH soln. l-*Ascorbic acid* (Vitamin C) reduces Ag, Au or Sb^{5+} salts and is also used colorimetrically for arseno- and phosphomolybdate; see also Chapter 5, Section 8.13.

Formaldehyde reduces Ag, Au, Hg, Bi to the metals in KOH soln. and can be used for the detection of NH_3 (0·003 μg.) after Ag^+ addn. *Methylal* (formaldehyde dimethyl acetal) reacts similarly. *Chloral* reduces Ag salts.

Au and Ag salts are reduced by o- or p-*aminophenol*, *hydroquinone*, or *citarin*; Au salts are reduced by *glycine*, *lactose*, m-*phenylenediamine*, *amidol*, *hydroxyhydroquinone* (also Ag, Cu, Hg), p-*phenylenediamine* (also Hg), *pyrocatechol* (also Pt), *pyrogallol* (also Pt, Pd) and *resorcinol*. Resorcinol reduces Pt in NH_4OH soln. *Sucrose* reduces Ag ions, whereas *glucose* in NaOH soln. reduces Ag, Au, Bi, Hg and Cu^{2+} (to Cu^+) salts. *Phenylhydrazine* reduces Au salts to give a brown color by reflected light and a blue color by transmitted light; it also reduces Hg to the metal in presence of Ag^+, and Se. Se also yields the metal with *thiosemicarbazide*. *Thiourea peroxide* (thiourea dioxide, formamidine-sulfonic acid)[5] reduces Pt and Pd to the metals and Sn^{4+} to Sn^{2+}. *Thioglycolic acid* also reduces Sn^{4+} to Sn^{2+}. *Phloroglucinol* (1,3,5-trihydroxybenzene) reduces Au salts; it forms a violet-black ppt. with Os, a yellow ppt. with Sb^{5+}, and a yellow ppt. with a violet supernate with Ru. *Glycerol* reduces Ag to the metal and Hg^{2+} to Hg^+ in NH_4OH soln.

Mono- or *di-ethanolamine* reduces Hg to the metal. *Triethanolamine* reduces Au and Ag salts; with Mo in HCl, it forms a double layer with a green ring and a blue ppt.; in presence of I_2, Hg forms a yellow ppt. which turns green and Hg ppts. on heating.

Many organic reductants have been suggested for the formation of molybdenum blue. *Metol* (monomethyl-*p*-aminophenol, *p*-*N*-methylaminophenol sulfate, photol, elon) is one of the more stable reductants and has been used colorimetically for silico- and phosphomolybdate; it also reduces Ag and Au to the metals.

Eiconogen (1-amino-2-naphthol-4-sulfonic acid, Na salt) has also been used colorimetrically for silico- and phosphomolybdate; the 1,2,6-, 2,3,6- and 1,8,4-(S-acid) isomers behave similarly. *Hydroquinone* (*p*-quinol, 1,4-dihydroxybenzene) reduces arseno-, silico-, and phosphomolybdate. p-*Hydroxyphenylglycine* has been used for silico- and phosphomolybdate as well as for Ag formation.

Phosphomolybdate can also be reduced to molybdenum blue with *pyramidone*, *gallic acid*, and *diphenylamine*. *Amidol* reduces silicomolybdate while *benzidine* is used colorimetrically for germano- and phosphomolybdate.

3. COMPOUNDS REACTING WITH REDUCTANTS

3-Acetamidophenoxazone-2 is used as a 0·1% soln. in EtOH; it forms a blue color with Sn^{2+} which becomes orange-red after 3–5 hr. *3-Aminophenoxazone-2* behaves somewhat similarly with fading initial colors.[6]

Filter paper impregnated with *2-benzylpyridine* after exposure to light changes from green to red with SO_2 or Sn^{2+}.

Cacotheline (nitro-deriv. of strychnine) gives violet colors with Sn^{2+} (0·2 μg.), Eu^{2+}, V^{3+} (0·2 μg.), Sb^{3+}, Mo^{3+}, W^{3+}, Ti^{3+}, Fe^{2+} (+ PO_4^{3-} or F^-), SO_3^{2-}, $S_2O_3^{2-}$, etc. *Cerulein* (Colour Index 783) forms a yellowish color with Sn^{2+} (0·02 μg.) or Mo^{3+} (0·025 μg.); it also reacts with V^{2+} (0·5 μg.), U, Ti and W.

Diazine green S(K) reacts with Sn^{2+} (2 μg.) and Ti^{3+}. *α-Dinitrodiphenylaminesulfonic acid* (sometimes erroneously called the sulfoxide) reacts with Sn^{2+} in presence of $FeCl_3$ to give thionine (violet). *2,4-Dinitro-1-naphthol* gives a pink color with $S_2O_4^{2-}$ in ammoniacal soln.

Fuchsine forms a fading color with SO_2, as do *indigo carmine* with Ti^{3+} or SO_2 (in presence of ClO_3^-), *malachite green* with SO_3^{2-} (1 μg.), *methylene blue* with Sn^{2+} and Ti^{3+} (see also Chapter 5, Section 6.7), and *methyl orange* with Sn^{2+}.

Naphthol yellow S reacts with Sn^{2+} in NaOH soln. and with $S_2O_4^{2-}$. *6-Nitro-2-naphthylamine-8-sulfonic acid* (NH_4-salt) reacts with Sn^{2+} (1 μg.) to form 2,6-diaminonaphthalenesulfonic acid which fluoresces blue under UV light; this permits a specific colorimetric detn.[7]

Orange II (Colour Index 151) forms a fading color with $S_2O_4^{2-}$.

p-*Phenylenediamine* gives a violet color with SO_2 in presence of HCHO.

Resazurin forms a brown-red fluorescence due to resorufin with $S_2O_4^{2-}$ and reacts with Sn^{2+}. *Resorufin* reacts with Sn^{2+}, Fe^{2+}, Cr^{2+} and Ti^{3+}. The *ethyl*, *acetyl*, and *tetrabromo derivs*. of both these compds. have been examined.[8]

Thionine (Lauth's violet, Colour Index 920) (VIII) gives a fading color with Sn^{2+} (see also Chapter 5, Section 6.7), as do *tropeolin O* (chrysoine, Colour Index 148) with $S_2O_4^{2-}$, and *true blue R* (fast blue R, Meldola's blue, Colour Index 909) with SO_2.

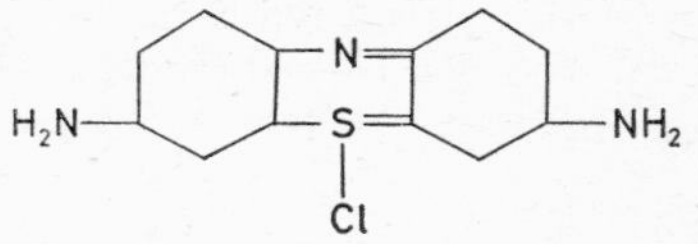

(VIII)

4. REDOX INDICATORS[9]

4.1. Ferroin and its analogs[10]

These compounds form the most important group of redox indicators and are especially useful in cerimetry. Their redox potentials are higher than those of most other indicators; the potentials are listed in Table 27.[11]

TABLE 27. Redox Potentials of Ferroin and Analogs

Concn. of H_2SO_4	0·5*M*	1*M*	6*M*	8*M*
Nitroferroin	1·26	1·25	1·12	1·01
Nitromethylferroin		1·23		
Bromoferroin	1·13	1·12		
Chloroferroin		1·11	0·97	
Ferroin		1·06	0·89	0·76
Methylferroin		1·02	0·86	0·70
5,6-Dimethylferroin		0·97	0·85	
Dipyridyl		0·97	0·85	
Dipyridyl-Ru	1·27	1·25		1·16

(*1*) *Ferroin* (ferriin is the oxidized form). Two prepns. can be used.

(*i*) 0·025*M*. Dissolve 6·95 g. $FeSO_4 \cdot 7H_2O$ and 14·85 g. *o*-phenanthroline monohydrate in 1 l. H_2O; use 1 drop/100 ml. soln.

(*ii*) Satd. ferroin perchlorate. Add dil. $HClO_4$ dropwise to the above soln. until the red color nearly disappears; filter or centrifuge and wash with a little water; prep. a satd. soln. (ca. 0·795 g./l.) in H_2O. Use 1 ml./100–150 ml. soln.

The oxidation potential of ferroin is 1·14 v. in *M* H_2SO_4; it decreases in stronger acid. Other workers state that the potential is 1·06 v. but that the color changes at 1·12 v.[12] The color change is from red (ferroin) to pale blue (ferriin) and is reversible. Ferroin is used in titrations with Ce^{4+} and MnO_4^- and for the titration of $Cr_2O_7^{2-}$ with Fe^{2+} (but not in the reverse titration).

Nitroferroin is prepd. from 5-nitrophenanthroline as described above. It has the highest oxidation potential (1·25 v.) in *M* H_2SO_4, the color changing from red to green-blue. It is mainly used for titrations with ceric perchlorate soln.

5,6-Dimethylferroin (0·05 ml. 0·025*M* soln./150 ml. soln.) is useful in $Cr_2O_7^{2-}$ titrations, the color changing from orange to green in HCl and to yellow-green in H_2SO_4 soln.

*Ru-*o*-phenanthroline* has a redox potential of 1·29 v. in *N* HNO_3, that of the *Os-analog* being 0·86 v.; the color changes from yellow-green to blue-green.[13]

(*2*) *2,2′-Dipyridyl.* The indicator soln. is prepd. by addn. of 50 ml. NH_4OH to 0·25 g. dipyridyl in 50 ml. soln., and is used in titrations of Fe^{2+} with oxidants, the color changing from pink to colorless.

2,2′-Dipyridyl-Ru[13, 14] is useful in titrations of Fe^{2+} or $C_2O_4^{2-}$ in *N* HNO_3 or $HClO_4$ soln. with Ce^{4+}, the color change being from orange or yellow to pale green or colorless; 2 drops of 0·02*M* soln./100 ml. is used. The *Os-analog* changes from green to red at an oxidation potential of ca. 1 v. but is not used.[13] All these indicators are reversible.

4.2. Diphenylamine and its derivatives and analogs

These indicators are most often used in titrations with $K_2Cr_2O_7$.

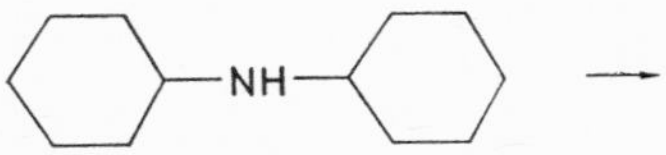

(IX)

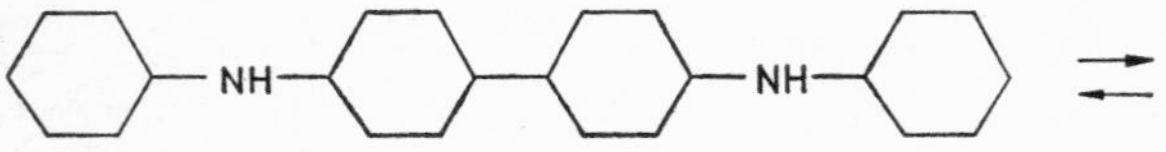

(X)

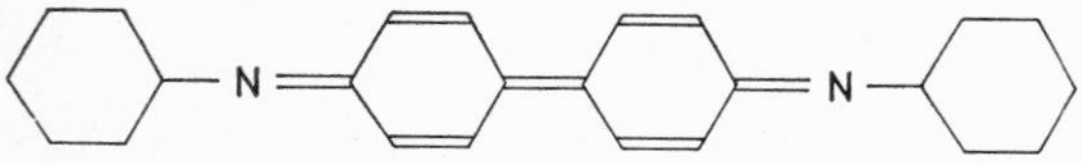

(XI)

(*1*) *Diphenylamine* (IX) and *diphenylbenzidine* (X). The 0·01*M* diphenylamine soln. is prepd. by dissolving 1·69 g. fused diphenylamine (m.p. 52·9°C) in 1 l. H_2SO_4; 5–6 drops are used for 0·1*N* solns. and 0·02–0·05 ml. for more dil. solns. An indicator correction is required.

Diphenylbenzidine soln. is prepd. by adding 5 ml. H_3PO_4 (d. 1·37) and 3–4 drops 0·1*N* $K_2Cr_2O_7$ to 10 ml. of a soln. of 0·1 g. diphenylamine in 10 ml. H_2SO_4 and 90 ml. AcOH; 0·01–0·02*N* $FeSO_4$ is then added to decolorize the soln. No correction is needed.

Diphenylamine has an oxidation potential of 0·76 ± 0·01 v. and the color changes from colorless to violet, or from green to blue-violet if Cr is present. It is difficultly sol. in H_2O so that not too much should be added. It forms an insol. ppt. when W is present (see below). Diphenylamine is oxidized to diphenylbenzidine violet (XI) and there is some danger of an irreversible color change to yellow-red occurring unless care is taken.

(*2*) *Diphenylamine-4-sulfonic acid* is normally used as the sodium or barium salt, both of which are water-sol.

A 0·005*M* Ba-salt soln. is prepd. by dissolving 3·17 g. in 1 l. H_2O; the addn. of some wetting agent (e.g. Aerosol) favors dissoln. A 0·2% soln. may also be used. For the Na-salt soln., add an equiv. amt. of Na_2SO_4 to the Ba soln.; use 0·3 ml./100 ml. soln.

The oxidized form is prepd. by adding 25 ml. H_2SO_4 and 900 ml. H_2O followed by 25 ml. 0·1*N* $K_2Cr_2O_7$ to 100 ml. of 0·005*M* Na-salt soln. and titrating with 0·1*N* $FeSO_4$ until a blue-green color appears.

The oxidation potential of diphenylamine sulfonic acid is 0·83 v. and the reversible color change is from green through grey to purple. It is the best indicator for Fe^{2+}—$Cr_2O_7^{2-}$ titrations; W does not interfere. It is also used in titrations with dil. MnO_4^- solns. and in titrations of As^{3+} with NaOBr and of $S_2O_3^{2-}$, SCN^- or Sn^{2+} with NaOCl in alk. solns.[15]

Diphenylamine polysulfonic acid appears to have no advantage.[16]

N-*Methyldiphenylamine-*p*-sulfonic acid* has an oxidation potential of 0·81 v. in 0·01–1*N* H_2SO_4, the color change being from colorless to purple; the color is stable in excess of oxidant and no ppt. is formed with WO_4^{2-}. The reagent is prepd. by heating $(C_6H_5)_2NCH_3$ and H_2SO_4 at 150°C.[17]

(*3*) *Phenylanthranilic acid* (phenanthranilic acid, *o*-diphenylaminecarboxylic acid, *o*-anilinobenzoic acid, ferrain) changes color from colorless to pale violet-pink reversibly and is stable in excess of oxidant. The oxidation potential is 0·89 v. This indicator is useful in titrations of Fe, Ti, V, etc. in 2*N* H_2SO_4 with Ce^{4+} or $KMnO_4$; 3–5 drops of 0·005*M* Na-salt soln. (1 g. acid in 20 ml. 5% Na_2CO_3 dild. to 1 l. with H_2O) is added for 100 ml. soln.

The *m*- and *p*-isomers have oxidation potentials of 1·12 v. and change color from green to blue-violet.[18] The o-*tolyl analog* turns purple at an oxidation potential of 1·01 v.[19] The *2,2′-*, *2,3′-* and *2,4′-diphenylamine-dicarboxylic acids* have been studied; they have high oxidation potentials (1·26 v. for the 2,2′-isomer) and should be used in 10–20*N* H_2SO_4 soln.

p-*Phenylaminobenzoic acid* is used in the detn. of V.[20]

(*4*) *Diphenylamine derivs.* p-*Nitrodiphenylamine* changes from colorless to violet at a potential of 1·06 v. in *N* H_2SO_4 and is used in the titration of Fe^{2+} with Ce^{4+} as a 0·01*M* soln. in AcOH. *Dinitrodiphenylamine* is not suitable as an indicator.

m- or p-*Tolylphenylamine* is similar to diphenylamine and is used as a 1% soln. in H_2SO_4. *2,4-Diaminodiphenylamine* changes from colorless to red at a potential of 0·70 v. in *N* H_2SO_4; it is used in titrations of Fe^{2+} with Ce^{4+} or $Cr_2O_7^{2-}$, or of Ti^{3+} with Ce^{4+}.

Variamine blue changes from colorless to yellowish blue;[21] it has an oxidation potential of 0·69 v. at pH 0 and of 0·375 v. at pH 6. It is used as a 1% soln. of the HCl salt, or as a 1:100 mixture of this salt with NaCl or Na_2SO_4, in iodimetry (at pH 2–7), in Fe^{3+}-EDTA titrations and in titrations with ascorbic acid.

2-Aminodiphenylamine-4-sulfonic acid can be used for titrations in alk. solns.[15] *Acetylaminodiphenylbenzidine* changes from colorless to green-blue at 0·69 v. p-*Aminodiphenylamine* and p-*acetylaminodiphenylamine* are of no value as indicators.

(5) *Diphenylamine analogs. Naphthidine* changes from colorless to deep blue reversibly and is better than diphenylamine in titrations of Fe^{2-} with $Cr_2O_7^{2-}$ and of Zn^{2+} with $Fe(CN)_6^{4-}$. *3,3′-Dimethylnaphthidine* or its *sulfonic acid* is the best indicator for the titration of Zn, Cd, Ca, In and Ga with $Fe(CN)_6^{4-}$.[22]

o-*Dianisidine* changes from colorless through brown-green to red-brown; it is used as a 1% soln. in AcOH (10 drops/100 ml.) for titrations of Fe^{2+} with $Cr_2O_7^{2-}$, Zn with $Fe(CN)_6^{4-}$ and Au^{3+} with hydroquinone but cannot be used for the titration of Tl^+ with I_2 or of Fe^{2+} with Ce^{4+}.[23] p-*Phenetidine* changes from colorless to purple and can be used in the same way as *o*-dianisidine; 1·3 g. hydrochloride is dissolved in 100 ml. H_2O, filtered and 1 drop HCl is added; 1 ml. of this soln. is used per 100 ml. soln.

Benzidine or *tolidine* is used as a 1% soln. in dil. HCl (0·5 ml./100 ml.); these indicators change from colorless to yellow and can be used in $KMnO_4$ and $K_2Cr_2O_7$ titrations. *Tetramethylbenzidine* has an oxidation potential of 0·86 v. in *M* H_2SO_4 and of 0·90 v. in *M* $HClO_4$; the color change from colorless to deep

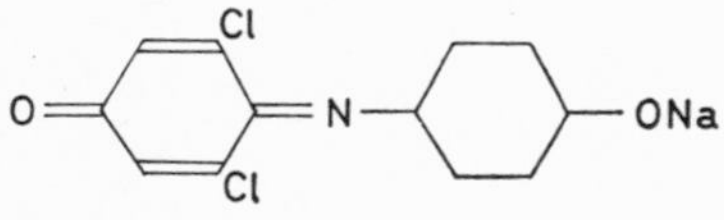

(XII)

yellow is only reversible after several drops of reductant have been added. *Tetramethylbenzidine-3-sulfonic acid* has redox potentials of 0·88 and 0·91 v. in *M* H_2SO_4 and *M* $HClO_4$ resp., the color change being reversible.[24] Both these indicators are used as 0·2% solns. in *N* HCl. The *ethyl analog* is of no value.

3-Methyl- or *3,3′-dimethylbenzidine* is satisfactory in titrations of Au^{3+} with hydroquinone.[25]

s-Diphenylcarbazide may be used for Fe^{2+}—$Cr_2O_7^{2-}$ titrations but is not satisfactory. *2,6-Dichlorophenolindophenol* (XII) is sol. in H_2O (blue), acid (blue) and EtOH; it liberates I_2 from KI and is bleached by ascorbic acid so that it can be used in titrations of Cu and $Fe(CN)_6^{3-}$ with ascorbic acid.

4.3. Dyes

(a) Azo dyes. These have their most important applications in titrations of As, Sb, anthranilates and oxinates with $KBrO_3$.

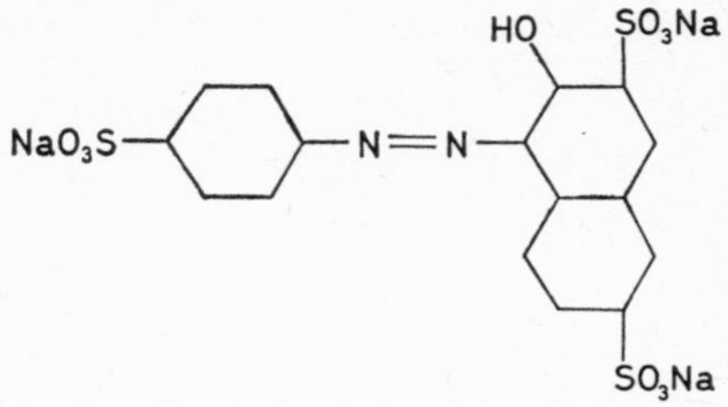

(XIII)

Amaranth (Bordeaux S, Colour Index 184) (XIII) is an excellent indicator; it is used as 1 drop of 0·1% soln. per 50 ml. 0·7–4*N* HCl soln. added near the end-point in titrations with $KBrO_3$ or KIO_3. *Brilliant ponceau 5R* (Colour Index 185) is used in *N* acid soln.; *naphthol blue black S* (Colour Index 246) is used similarly. *Bordeaux B* (Colour Index 88) may also be applied to hypochlorite titrations.

Methyl red is used as 1–2 drops of 0·2% soln. in 6*N* H_2SO_4/100 ml. 0·7–1*N* HCl soln. for titrations with $KBrO_3$. All these indicators are irreversible in $KBrO_3$ titrations but methyl red changes color reversibly from orange to violet in Fe^{2+}–Ce^{4+} titrations and is better than diphenylamine for this purpose. *Tropeolin OO* may be used similarly but methyl orange cannot.

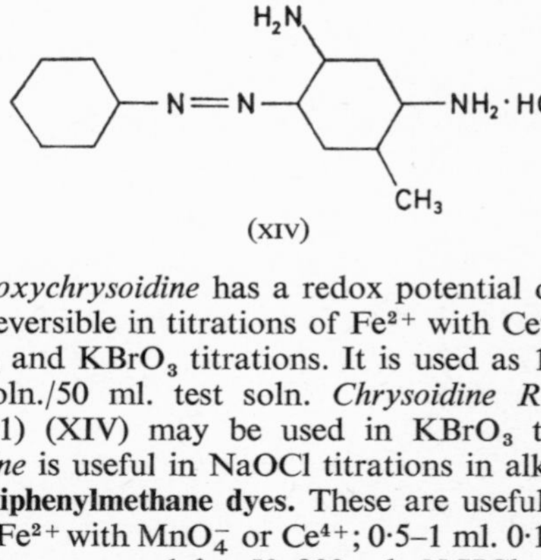

(XIV)

p-*Ethoxychrysoidine* has a redox potential of 0·76 v. and is reversible in titrations of Fe^{2+} with Ce^{4+} and in $KMnO_4$ and $KBrO_3$ titrations. It is used as 1 drop of 0·2% soln./50 ml. test soln. *Chrysoidine R* (Colour Index 21) (XIV) may be used in $KBrO_3$ titrations. *Tartrazine* is useful in NaOCl titrations in alk. soln.

(b) Triphenylmethane dyes. These are useful in titrations of Fe^{2+} with MnO_4^- or Ce^{4+}; 0·5–1 ml. 0·1% solns. of the dyes are used for 50–200 ml. *N* HCl or H_2SO_4 solns. The oxidation potentials are ca. 0·9 v.; some of the color changes are reversible. The dyes which have been tested are:

Erioglaucine A (Colour Index 671, green–pink, reversible), *patent blue A* (C.I. 714, green-yellow–pink), *patent blue V* (alphazurine G, C.I. 712), *Victoria blue BX* (C.I. 729, blue–pale pink), *xylene cyanol FF* (C.I. 715, yellow–yellow-red, reversible), *cyanine B* (C.I. 713, yellow–orange in H_2SO_4 soln., yellow–brown-yellow in HCl soln.), *eriogreen B* (C.I. 735, yellow–orange, reversible), *setocyanine* (setopalin, C.I. 663), *acronol brilliant blue* (C.I. 664), *xylene blue AS* (C.I. 673), *cyanol fast green 2G* (similar to eriogreen B), *xylene blue VS* (C.I. 672) and *crystal violet*.

Fuchsine (red-yellow–mauve) and *rubrophen* (red–colorless, reversible) are used in $KBrO_3$ titrations.

(c) Other dyes. *Indigo carmine* is used as 1 drop 0·5% soln. in H_2SO_4 per 100 ml. soln. in $KMnO_4$ and NaOCl titrations; it can also be used in titrations of Sb^{5+} with Ti^{3+} and of Fe^{3+} with Cr^{2+}.

Quinoline yellow (Colour Index 801) is an excellent indicator for titrations of As or Sb with $KBrO_3$ and of As with NaOCl.[26]

Fluorescein or *rhodamine B* changes to reddish brown in $KBrO_3$ titrations. *Brazilin* or *cochineal* may be used in NaOCl titrations. *Safranine T* has been used in Mo^{3+}–Cu^{2+} and Sb^{5+}–Fe^{2+} titrations. *Phenosafranine*, *neutral red* and *brilliant cresyl blue* are useful for the latter titration as well as for titrations of Fe^{3+} or Cu^{2+} with Cr^{2+}.

4.4. Miscellaneous indicators

α-Naphthoflavone changes color from green to red-brown reversibly in 15% H_2SO_4 solns. and is excellent in titrations of As or Sb with $KBrO_3$; it may also be used reversibly in iodimetry.

Apomorphine hydrochloride changes irreversibly from colorless to pink at 40–50°C in titrations of Sb with $KBrO_3$; 0·3 ml. of 0·1% soln./100 ml. is added. *Brucine* is said to be better than diphenylamine in $KMnO_4$ and $K_2Cr_2O_7$ titrations; 15–20 drops 1% soln. in 3*N* H_2SO_4 is added per 100 ml. of below 3*N* H_2SO_4 soln. *Cacotheline* is used as a satd. soln. in Fe^{3+}–Sn^{2+} titrations.

Dimethylglyoxime changes from red to yellow when Fe^{2+} is titrated with $Fe(CN)_6^{3-}$ in ammoniacal tartrate soln.; a correction of 2% is needed. *Phenoxazone* (XV) changes reversibly from red to blue in Fe^{3+}–Sn^{2+} titrations in dil. HCl soln.; the redox potential is 0·35 v.[27]

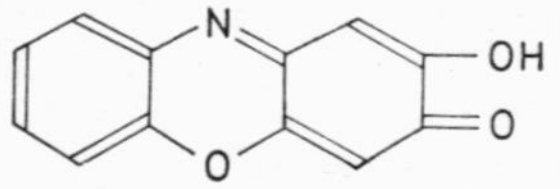

(xv)

Siloxene is used as a chemiluminescent indicator in titrations of Fe^{2+} with Ce^{4+}.[28] *Luminol* behaves similarly in hypochlorite titrations. *Lucigenin* (10,10′-dimethyl-9,9′-diacridinium nitrate) is used in titrations of Cr^{6+} with H_2O_2 stabilized by oxine.

Triphenylmethylarsonium chloride in $CHCl_3$, CCl_4 or $CH_2Cl{\cdot}CH_2Cl$ may be used in titrations with $KMnO_4$, $K_2Cr_2O_7$ or I_2.[29]

References

1. Welcher, **IV**, 472–598.
2. Yoe, J. H., *Va. J. Sci.*, **3**, 8 (1942).
3. Kramer, H. P., *et al.*, *Anal. Chem.*, **24**, 1892 (1952).
4. Malowan, L. S., *Mikrochemie ver. Mikrochim. Acta*, **35**, 104 (1950).
5. Nieuwenburg, C. J. van and Ligten, J. W. L. van, *Chim. anal.*, **36**, 41 (1954).
6. Ružička, E., *Chem. listy*, **48**, 45 (1954).
7. Anderson, J. R. A. and Garnett, J. L., *Anal. Chim. Acta*, **8**, 393 (1953); **15**, 246 (1956).
8. Ružička, E., *Chem. listy*, **49**, 1729 (1955); **51**, 173 (1957).
9. Brennecke, E., *Chem. Anal.*, **33**, 251 (1956); Whitehead, T. H. and Willis, Jr., C. C., *Chem. Revs.*, **29**, 69 (1941); Tomíček, O., *Chemical Indicators*, Butterworths, London (1951).
10. Smith, G. F. and Richter, F. P., *Phenanthroline and Substituted Phenanthroline Indicators. Their Preparation, Properties and Application for Analysis*, Smith Co., Columbus (1944); Moss, M. L., *et al.*, *Ind. Eng. Chem., Anal. Ed.*, **14**, 931 (1942); Brandt, W. W. and Smith, *Anal. Chem.*, **21**, 948, 1313 (1949); Case, F. H., *J. Org. Chem.*, **16**, 941 (1951).
11. Smith, G. F. and Richter, F. P., *Ind. Eng. Chem., Anal. Ed.*, **16**, 580 (1944).
12. Hume, D. N. and Kolthoff, I. M., *J. Am. Chem. Soc.*, **65**, 1895 (1943).
13. Burstall, F. H., *et al.*, *J. Chem. Soc.*, 953 (1950); Dwyer, F. P., *et al.*, *J. Proc. Roy. Soc., N.S.W.*, **80**, 212 (1946); **84**, 80, 83 (1950).
14. Steigman, J., *et al.*, *Ind. Eng. Chem., Anal. Ed.*, **14**, 30 (1942).
15. Willard, H. H. and Manolo, G. D., *Anal. Chem.*, **19**, 167 (1947).
16. Sarver, L. A. and Fischer, W. von, *Ind. Eng. Chem., Anal. Ed.*, **7**, 271 (1935).
17. Knop, J. and Kubelkova-Knopova, O., *Z. anal. Chem.*, **122**, 183 (1941).
18. Cherkasov, V. M., *Zhur. Obshcheĭ Khim.*, **23**, 121 (1953).
19. Lederer, M. and Ward, F. L., *Anal. Chim. Acta*, **6**, 1 (1952).
20. Stepin, V. V., *Zavodskaya Lab.*, **8**, 1039 (1939).
21. Erdey, L. and Bodor, E., *Z. anal. Chem.*, **137**, 410 (1953).
22. Belcher, R., *et al.*, *J. Chem. Soc.*, 1520, 3447 (1951); 1269, 2438 (1952).
23. Crawford, A. B. and Bishop, E., *J. R. Tech. Coll. Glasgow*, **5**, 52 (1950).
24. Adams, R. N. and Hammaker, E. M., *Anal. Chem.*, **23**, 744 (1951).
25. Belcher and Nutten, A. J., *J. Chem. Soc.*, 546 (1951).
26. Belcher, R., *Anal. Chim. Acta*, **5**, 27, 30 (1951).
27. Musha, S. and Kitagawa, T., *J. Chem. Soc. Japan*, **76**, 1289 (1955).
28. Kenny, F. and Kurtz, R. B., *Anal. Chem.*, **22**, 693 (1950).
29. Gibson, N. A. and White, R. A., *Anal. Chim. Acta*, **12**, 115, 413, 516 (1955).

16

SOLVENTS FOR EXTRACTION

Organic solvents have long been used in inorganic analysis, e.g. to decrease the solubility of certain salts (in Pb analyses, etc.) and in the separation of Group IV and V elements from each other by means of their differences in solubility. The introduction of organic reagents greatly increased the utility of extraction solvents, which are now very important in the field of separation and colorimetric determination of micro quantities.[1]

Chelate systems, e.g. the extraction of cupferrates, oxinates, diethyldithiocarbamates, dithizonates, acetylacetonates, etc., are the more important branch in this field and these are described in other parts of this book. Ion-association systems involving ethers, etc., for the extraction of metal ions are reviewed in the present chapter; these methods are old but their applications in the analysis of lanthanides, actinides, Zr, Th, Nb, Ta, etc., have been largely extended in recent years.

(*1*) *Ether* (ethyl or diethyl ether). The percentages of ions extd. from halogen acid solns. are listed in Table 28. The ether used should always be equilibrated previously with acid of the appropriate concn.

The removal of Fe^{3+} from HCl soln. is often applied in ferrous analysis, etc. For the effect of HCl concn. on extractability, see Sandell, p. 34. Max. data have been indicated for HBr solns.[2, 4] Extn. with 20 ml. Et_2O from 5 ml. soln. contg. 1–3 ml. 6·9*N* HI[3] gives different results from extn. from a soln. contg. 1·5*M* KI and 1·5*N* H_2SO_4.[4] In is sepd. from Zn by extg. the iodide.[5] In conclusion, Ag, Pb, Pd, Rh, Os, Ru, Fe^{2+}, Mn, U, Al, Be, Cr, rare earths, Th, Ti, Zr, Hf, W, Ca, etc. are not extd. from the above halogen acid solns.

For HF solns., extn. with 20 ml. Et_2O from 5 ml. soln. contg. 0·5–2 ml. 20% HF has been studied.[6] Extractability increases with increasing HF concns. when equal phase vols. are present over the range 1–20*M* HF.[7] In addn. to the data given in Table 28, the percentages indicated of the following ions are extd.: 0·05% Ag, 4% Be, 0·2% Al, < 0·1% Si, < 0·05% Ti, 2·9% Zr, 65·8% Nb, 79·3% Ta, < 0·1% Cr, 0·5% W, 1·1% U^{6+}, 1·3% Mn, < 0·1% Fe^{2+}.

When thiocyanate solns. are used,[8] the results are different from the above data if 1*M* metallic ion solns. are extd. with equal vols. of Et_2O; the appropriate data are given in Table 29. Au, V^{3+}, Nb^{3+}, Rh^{3+}, W, Re (Ag, Pb, Cu^{2+} and Tl^{+}) are also extd. but Sn^{2+}, Pt, Fe^{2+}, Mn, rare earths, Th, Zr, Hf, Ca, etc. are not. The method is applied in the detn. of Ca, Mg and Al in Ti after removal of Ti^{3+} by extn. (see Chapter 52, p. 391).

With nitrate solns.[9] the data given below refer to 8*M* HNO_3 unless otherwise stated. The amts. extd. are: 96·8% Ce^{4+} (> 90% with 4·5*M*), 97% Au, 65% U (see also below), 34·6% Th (56·5% with *M* HNO_3 + $LiNO_3$; 80·9% with *M* HNO_3 + $Zn(NO_3)_2$; 54·1% with *M* HNO_3 + $Al(NO_3)_3$), 0·1% Sc (83% with *M* HNO_3 + $LiNO_3$ at 35°C), Fe, 7·7% Tl, 6·8% Bi, 8% Zr, 14·4% As^{5+}, > 15% Cr^{6+}, 4·7% Hg, 20·4% PO_4^{3-}, 82% Nb, 100% Pu (+ NH_4NO_3), 100% Am (+ NH_4NO_3). Pr_2O, MeCOPr and EtOAc may be preferable.

The extn. of U is important. Multivalent metallic nitrates with pronounced hydration tendencies are most effective as salting-out agents;[10] $Al(NO_3)_3$ is widely used but Zn, Ca and Li nitrates are also useful owing to their greater soly.

(*2*) *Isopropyl ether* (diisopropyl ether) does not need previous equilibration with HCl and the com. reagent can be used. Extn. is more effective and the permissible range of acid concns. is wider than with ether. For example, 99·9% Fe^{3+} is extd. in 7·75–8·25*N* HCl, 99·5% Sb^{5+}, > 99·9% Ga, and 1·6% Sb^{3+}. The extn. of some elements is enhanced in presence of Fe^{3+}; the percentages of V^{5+}, V^{4+}, Mo, SO_4^{2-} and PO_4^{3-} extd. in absence and in presence of Fe^{3+} are resp. 22 and 43, 0·05 and 0·4, 21 and 45, 0 and 0·3, and 0·1 and 62. Tl^{3+} can be sepd. from Fe, Ga, etc., from > *N* HCl soln. In is sepd. from Zn by extg. the bromide from 0·5–6*N* HCl soln.[11] Au (p. 227.) can also be extd.

β,β′-Dichloroethyl ether permits extn. of 94·5% Fe^{3+} from 6·9*N* HCl soln. and 99·8% from 7·75*N* HCl. 90% Pa is extd. from 6*N* HCl soln. contg. 8*M* $MgCl_2$.[12]

(*3*) *Amyl ethyl ether* gives 99% extn. of Fe^{3+} from 7–9*N* HCl.[13] The optimum acidity for 5:1 mixtures of ether and amyl alcohol is 4·9*N* HCl, while that for ether and butyl ethyl ether is 5·7*N* HCl.[14] Fe^{3+} is almost completely extd. with amyl acetate from 10 ml. soln.

TABLE 28. Ether Extraction of Halides

Metal	HCl (5·5*N*)	HBr	HI	HF
Cu	0·05	6·2 (6*N*)	—	1·3
Au^{3+}	95	>99·9 (3*N*)	100	—
Zn	0·2	5 (2–4*N*)	11 (5*N*)	0·9
Cd	0	0·9 (6*N*)	100	1·4
Hg	0·2	94·0 (0*N*) 1·5 (6*N*)	100	2·7
Ga	97	96·7 (5*N*)	0	<0·05
In	trace	99·9 (4*N*)	8 (3*N*)	<0·05
Tl^{3+}	90–95	100 (0·1–4*N*)	100 (0·51*N*)	<0·05
Ge	40–60	—	—	6·7
Sn^{2+}	15–30	84 (4*N*)	100 (3*N*)	4·9 (100)
Sn^{4+}	17	85·4 (4*N*)	—	5·2 (100)
P	trace	0	0	14·8
As^{3+}	68	72·9 (6*N*)	62 (6·9*N*)	37·7 (63)
As^{5+}	2–4	—	—	13·6
Sb^{3+}	6	37·9 (2*N*)	100	6·3 (0·4)
Sb^{5+}	81	95·4 (5*N*)	—	0·1
Bi	0	0	34 (5–7*N*)	0
V^{3+}	—	0·001	—	12
V^{4+}	trace	0·001	—	8·5
Mo	80–90	54·1 (6*N*)	6·5 (3*N*)	9·3
Se	trace	31 (6*N*)	—	12·9 (3·1)
Te	34	2·2 (6*N*)	5·5 (3*N*)	23 (0·2)
Re	0·8	5	—	61·8
Fe^{3+}	99	97·1 (4–5*N*)	—	<0·1
Co	0	0·08 (6*N*)	—	1·7
Ni	0	0·03	—	0·7
Pt^{2+}	>95 (3*N* HCl + $SnCl_2$)	—	—	—
Ir	5	7	0	0

to which 50 ml. HCl and 40% H_2SO_4 have been added.[15]

Ethyl acetate is better than ethers for the extn. of Au (100% from 10% HCl) and Hg (80% from 0·125*N* HCl); for extn. of U from NO_3^- solns., see p. 298. Only 57·68% Mo is extd. with Et_2O from 6*N* HCl soln. but 81·11% is extd. by AmOH from 5·44*N* HCl, 82·48% with BuOAc, and 99% with 1:1 Et_2O + BuOAc, 1:1 Et_2O + AmOH., or Et_2O + butyl alc.[16] For extn. of Te with AmOH and Et_2O from *N* HCl and 0·6*N* I^- soln., see p. 221.

99·5% Ge is extd. with CCl_4 or C_6H_6 from 10·5*N* HCl soln.; 77% As^{3+} is extd. from 12–13*N* HCl while As^{5+} is not extd. In practice, Ge is extd. thrice from 8*N* HCl soln. contg. $KClO_3$ and Ge is stripped with H_2O.[17]

Mesityl oxide[18] is used in extn. of Th (p. 338) from Al^{3+} contg. HNO_3 soln.

Pentaether (dibutoxytetraethylene glycol)[19] is used with Et_2O (2:1) for the extn. of Th from 8*M* HNO_3 soln. in its sepn. from rare earths; the distribution coeffs. are 4·0 for Th and 0·01 for Eu. Pentaether is also used in U extn.

(*4*) *Hexone* (methyl isobutyl ketone, 4-methyl-2-pentanone) is used in the sepn. of Nb and Ta; with a soln. contg. 6*M* H_2SO_4, 10*M* HF, 2·2*M* NH_4F, 96% Nb, 99·5% Ta, 9·5% Mo and 26% W are extd., after which Nb is stripped with H_2O_2, H_2SO_4 is added, and the mixture is evapd. to fumes.[20] 98% Extn. of Ta is possible from 6*M* H_2SO_4 and 0·4*M* HF soln.; Ta is thus sepd. from U, Pu, Al, Cr^{3+}, Sr, V, Tl, Co, Fe, etc. but 2–3 mg. W, Nd, Ce, Zr, Ru, Au, 100 mg. Ti, 30 mg. Mo, and any amt. of F^- or PO_4^{3-} interfere.[21]

Ce^{4+} can be extd. from 50 ml. 8–10*M* HNO_3 soln. contg. 2 ml. 2*M* $NaBrO_3$ with 50 ml. hexone which has been equilibrated with 50 ml. 9*M* HNO_3 and 2 ml. 2*M* $NaBrO_3$; after shaking for 30 sec., the layers are sepd., washed twice with 10 ml. 9*M* HNO_3 and a few drops of $NaBrO_3$, stripped with 5 ml. H_2O contg. 2 drops 30% H_2O_2, etc.; the yield is 80%. 25% Zr–Nb, 55% Th, 86% U and 7% Np appear in the hexone ext. and 7% Zr–Nb, 1% Ru, 26% Th, 6% U and 7% Np in the back-ext.[22] The extn. of Th from 3*M* HNO_3 and 3*M* $Ca(NO_3)_2$ has been examined.[23]

Mo can be sepd. from Fe, Zr, U and Cr^{6+} by stirring 4 ml. soln. to which 5 ml. HCl and 1 ml. 4*M* HF have

TABLE 29. Ether Extraction of Thiocyanates

	0·5*M* HCl				pH 2–3		Remarks
NH_4SCN(*M*)	1	3	5	7	1	7	
HSCN	72·8	92·7	96·7	98·3			
Cu^+		2·9		0·4			
Be	3·8	49·9	84·1	92·2	4·1	87·8	0·2*M* Be
Zn	96·0	97·4	94·8	92·8			0·3*M* Zn, 1*M* NH_4SCN, neutral, 87·2; 0·5*M* NH_3, 42·0; 7*M*, 3 phases
Cd	0·1		0·2				0·5*M* Cd, Et_2O 10 : 1 and 6 : 1
Hg							0·2*M* Hg, 1*M* NH_4SCN, neutral, 0·15; 7*M* NH_4SCN, 0·2; Et_2O 10 : 1, 0·5*M* HSCN/l. Et_2O
Al		1·1	9·0	21·6 (6·2*M*)			Decrease when temp. raised
Sc	12·7	79·8		89·0			2*M* NH_4SCN, 55·4
Ga	65·4	90·5		99·3	61·5	97·5	0·5*M* NH_4SCN, 18·3
In	51·5	75·3	68·3	47·6			0·5*M* NH_4SCN, 26·0; 2*M*, 75·1
Ge	<0·3			<0·5			
Sn^{4+}	99·3	99·9	<99·9	<99·9			7*M* NH_4SCN, neutral, 97·2
Ti^{3+}	58·8	84·0	79·8	76·3			0·5*M* NH_4SCN, 14·7; 2*M*, 80·5
Ti^{4+}				~13			Max. at ca. 3*M* HCl
V^{4+}	15·0	8·7	2·2				1*M* NH_4SCN, 11·0; 7*M* and 0·005*M* HCl, 1·7
As^{3+}	0·4			0·4			0·8*M* HCl
As^{5+}	0·1						0·2*M* As^{5+}; 6*M* NH_4SCN, 0·03
Sb	hydrolyzes			2·3			
Bi	0·3			0·1			
Cr	0·06			3·4			Et_2O 10 : 1, 0·5*M* HSCN/l. Et_2O
Mo	99·3	97·2		97·3?			7*M* NH_4SCN, neutral, 97·2
Fe^{3+}	88·9	83·7	75·5	53·3	86·5		
Co	3·6	58·2	74·9	75·2			2*M* NH_4SCN, 37·7; 1*M* NH_4SCN, neutral, 0·1; 2*M*, 5·7; 7*M*, 3 phases
Ni							0·1*M* Ni, 1*M* NH_4SCN, neutral, 0·1; 0·2*M* Ni, 7*M* NH_4SCN, 0·003, Et_2O 10 : 1
Pd	1·7			<0·1			
U^{6+}	45·1	29·4	13·8	6·4			0·25*M* NH_4SCN, 7·6; 2*M*, 41·4; max. shifts to concd. NH_4SCN with increasing HCl concn.; greatest at 0·5*M* HCl

been added, with 10 ml. equilibrated hexone; after sepn. the aq. layer is thrice extd. with 5 ml. hexone and the combined exts. are washed thrice with 5 ml. H_2O.[24] Cr^{6+} and V can be sepd. from dil. HCl soln.[25] More than 99·9% Fe^{3+} can be extd. from 5·5–7*N* HCl soln.[26]

U is extd. from HNO_3 solns. contg. $Al(NO_3)_3$ at pH 0–3; tartrate is also added if Ti is present.[27]

Cu^{2+}, Cu^+, Zn, Co, Fe^{2+}, Fe^{3+}, Al, Mn, Sn^{2+} and Sn^{4+} are extd. from bromide solns. by hexone or MeCOEt.[28] With thiocyanate solns., hexone allows sepn. of Zn and Cd from Cu and Ni if thiourea is added and from Fe if NH_4F is added.[29] Hf is sepd. from Zr by extn. of thiocyanate solns. with 4:1 hexone–butanol.[30]

Diisopropyl ketone can be used to ext. Ta from a soln. contg. 10 mg each of Ta and Nb in 5 ml. 3*M* HCl and 0·4*M* HF; this is shaken for 1 min. with 5 ml. solvent and the layers are sepd. The aq. layer is re-extd. and is discarded, as is a washing with 3*M* HCl + 0·4*M* HF; the ext. is stripped twice with H_2O, H_3BO_3, NH_4OH, etc. 99·5% Ta and 0·5% Nb appear in the org. phase and 98% Nb and 2% Ta in the aq. phase. Fe^{3+}, Ga, Sb^{5+}, As^{3+}, Se^{6+} and Te^{6+} are extd. to a considerable extent, As^{5+} and Te^{4+} rather less, Sb^{3+} and Se^{4+} only slightly and Si, Sn^{4+}, Ti, Mn, Mo, Zr and Hf not at all. The concn. ratio of Ta to Nb extd. is 91 from 3·7*M* HCl, 880 from 3·9*M* HNO_3, 160 from 4·5*M* H_2SO_4, 290 from 4·6*M* $HClO_4$. Nb is extd. from 10*M* HCl and stripped with 6*M* HCl.[31]

100% Pa can be extd. from 8*M* HCl + 0·6*M* HF soln. which is satd. with $AlCl_3$.[32]

Methyl isopropyl ketone permits complete extn. of Pb from KI-contg. 5% HCl soln., and of Bi from slightly acidic soln.; Zn, Cd, Cu, As^{5+}, Sb^{3+}, Sn^{4+}, Ru, Rh, Pt are partially extd.[33]

Methyl ethyl ketone exts. Nb and Ta from HF soln.[34] *Diethyl ketone* is used similarly on the macro-scale.[35] *Methyl amyl ketone* and *bromoform* give complete extn.

of Fe^{3+} from $8M$ HCl; the mixture is heavier than H_2O.[36] *Cyclohexanone* is used to ext. Th (p. 338) from solns. contg. $Al(NO_3)_3$ and NH_4NO_3 at pH 0·65.

Tetrahydrofuran or *tetrahydrosylvan* exts. $UO_2(NO_3)_2$.[37] Tetrahydrofuran and Et_2O (3:5) serve to sep. Ga (20 mg.) from Al (100 mg.) with NH_4SCN-contg. 1·5–2·$5M$ H_2SO_4 soln.[38]

(*5*) *Diisobutylcarbinol* is better than methyldioctylamine for the sepn. of Nb from Pa; 98% Nb is extd. from solns. which are $6M$ in both HF and H_2SO_4.[39] *2-Octanol* is used for extn. of Co from 4·$5M$ HCl soln.; 9·1% is extd., the concn. ratio of Co to Ni being 70. With extn. from 0·$85M$ $CaCl_2$, the resp. figures are 9·1% and 10.[40]

(*6*) *Cyclohexane* is better than diisopropyl ketone for the sepn. of Ta from Ti; extn. is made from $(NH_4)_2SO_4$-contg. $2M$ H_2SO_4 soln. and stripping is done with 7 ml. of soln. contg. 4 g. $(NH_4)_2C_2O_4$ and 4 g. H_3PO_4/100 ml.[41]

(*7*) *Tributyl phosphate* (TBP, butyl phosphate) is used as a 22% soln. in *n*-hexane or isooctane (satd. with H_2O) for extn. of U; the extn. is favored by high concns. of TBP, by addn. of $NaNO_3$ and by increasing the HNO_3 concn. Stripping is done with 15 ml. 20% NaOH contg. 1% H_2O_2.[42] Mixtures of TBP with kerosene or iso-Pr_2O (3:7) can be used to ext. U from 1·$3M$ $Al(NO_3)_3$ soln.,[43] mixtures of TBP and Et_2O (1:1) from 4·$7M$ HNO_3 soln., and TBP and hexone (1:1) from $7M$ HCl soln.[44]

Zr is sepd. from Hf in $10M$ HNO_3 soln. by extn. with 20–50% TBP in xylene or CCl_4.[45] TBP and Bu_2O (6:4) is used for the same purpose with 5·$8M$ HNO_3 solns.;[46] Zr is extd. with 19% TBP in kerosene.[47]

Ce^{4+} (98–99%) is extd. with TBP from 8–$10M$ HNO_3 soln. and stripped with H_2O_2;[48] Ce can be sepd. from Th with 50% TBP in C_6H_6.[49] 98% Sc is extd. from $8M$ HCl soln.[50] and lanthanides and actinides can also be extd.[51] Extn. of Th with TBP and various other solvents has been studied.[52]

Po (80–90%) can be sepd. from Pb and Bi by extn. with 20% TBP in Bu_2O from $6M$ HCl soln.[53] The Fe^{3+}–SCN^- complex is extd. with TBP in CCl_4 (see p. 260). Cu, Ni and Co are sepd. from Cd in neutral soln. contg. thiourea and NH_4SCN with TBP and MeCOEt (1:1); this is used in the detn. of Cd with EDTA. The sepn. of Zn from Cd in NH_4SCN-contg. soln. with AmOH and Et_2O (1:4) is unsatisfactory.[54]

Butyl hydrogen phosphate in Bu_2O exts. many ions; a 70% (v/v) soln. contg. 4·5 parts of the dibutyl salt to 1 part of the monobutyl salt is prepd., washed with H_2O and suitably dild. With a 0·$06M$ soln. of the extractant and a sample soln. contg. M H_2SO_4, 2·$5M$ $(NH_4)_2SO_4$, 0·$04M$ $H_2C_2O_4$ and H_2O_2, it is possible to ext. > 95 % I_2 or Zr, 85% In, 15% Sn and < 5% Cs, Sr, Y, La, Ce^{3+}, Ag, Cd, Ge, Se^{4+}, Te^{4+}, Sb^{3+}, Sb^{5+}, As^{5+}, Pd, Ru, Rh, Mo, Nb. With a 0·$6M$ soln. of the extractant, > 95% Zr, Nb (not extd. if $4M$ HF is present), Y, Ho, In, I_2, 50% Sn^{4+}, 35% Ta, and < 5% Cs, Sr, La, Ce^{3+}, Ag, Cd, Ge, Se^{4+}, Te^{4+}, Sb^{3+} (not extd. if $4M$ HF is present), Sb^{5+}, As^{5+}, Pd, Ru, Rh, Mo are extd.[55]

(*8*) *Tribenzylamine* (8%) in $CHCl_3$ or CH_2Cl_2 can be used to ext. Nb from $8M$ HCl or 4·$5M$ H_2SO_4 and thus to sep. Nb from Ta.[56] Nb is also sepd. from Ta in $8M$ HCl soln. by extn. with *methyldioctylamine* in xylene.[57] Other extns. with methyldioctylamine in various solvents have been studied:[58] with an 8% (w/v) soln. in $CHCl_3$ from $4M$ HCl, in xylene from $3M$ HCl, and in $CHCl_2{\cdot}CH_2Cl$ from $2M$ HCl solns., Zn is almost completely extd., and most of the Fe, a little Cu and Cr, and traces of Co, Ni and Mn are extd. 5% Tribenzylamine in $CHCl_3$ with $3M$ HCl solns. behaves similarly. The amt. of extn. is greatest with $CHCl_2{\cdot}CH_2Cl$; it is slightly less with xylene and much less with $CHCl_3$. With higher HCl concns. the extn. of most of these metals is markedly increased; with $10M$ HCl, nearly all Zn, 93·4% Fe^{3+}, 85·4% Co, 72% Cu, 31·8% Mn, 7·6% Cr^{3+}, 0·9% Ni are extd.[58]

Extn. with 0·$1M$ solns. of long chain amines in kerosine below pH 1·5 has been studied with solns. contg. 1 g. U, 6 g. Fe^{3+}, 3 g. Al, 50 g. SO_4^{2-}, 2 g. PO_4^{3-} 1·7 g. F^-/l. U and Mo are extd. completely; V is only slightly extd. by itself but is co-extd. with Mo and its extractability increases sharply in the pH range 1·8–2·5. The extn. of Fe^{3+} is considerable with primary amines, small but significant with secondary amines and insignificant with tertiary amines. Small amts. of Ti are extd. but Al, Mg, Ca, Zn, Ni, Co, Cu, Mn and Cr are not extd.[59]

(*9*) *Trialkylphosphine oxides* (*n*-octyl, *n*-dodecyl, 3,5,5-trimethylhexyl, etc.) have also been used for extn. U is extd. from $6M$ HNO_3 soln. with 0·$1M$ oxide soln. in kerosine or CCl_4; Cr^{6+} and Fe^{3+} are also extd. while citrate and $C_2O_4^{2-}$ interfere. Extn. is also possible from solns. which are less than $12M$ in H_2SO_4, H_3PO_4 or HCl.[60, 61]

V^{5+} is extd. with 0·$6M$ trioctylphosphine oxide in kerosine from NO_3^- solns. at pH 1·5–2·0; SO_4^{2-} and CO_3^{2-} interfere and traces of Fe^{3+}, Al and Th are extd. but V^{4+} is not extd.[61] Cr^{6+} is extd. with 0·$1M$ trioctylphosphine oxide in cyclohexane from 1–$7M$ HCl or 1–$4M$ H_2SO_4 soln. With M HCl solns., Cr^{6+}, Au^+, Hf, Fe^{3+}, Mo, Sn^{4+}, U and Zr are extd. completely, and Sb^{3+}, Bi, Cd, In, Hg^{2+}, Pt^{2+}, Zn are partly extd. With $7M$ HCl solns., Sb^{3+}, Cr^{6+}, Ga, Au^+, Hf, Fe^{3+}, Mo, Sn^{4+}, Ti, U, V^{4+} and Zr are extd. completely.[62]

(*10*) *Caproic acid* in EtOAc can be used for the extn. of Cu, Fe, Ni, Pd, Co and Ru; Cu is extd. from solns. adjusted to pH 6·3–10·3 by NaOH or Na_2CO_3 addn.[63]

Butyric acid and $CHCl_3$ are used in the sepn. of Be from Fe, Al, Ti and Zr; the soln. is adjusted to pH 9·3–9·5, treated with 6 ml. 50% EDTA in 10% NH_4OH and 30–40 ml. acid to give a pH of 3·7–4·0 and extd. thrice. EtOAc, CCl_4 and C_6H_6 are less effective.[64]

Perfluorobutyric acid and Et_2O can be used to sep. Fe^{3+}, Al, Cr^{3+}, UO_2^{2+}, Mg and Be from mono-and bivalent cations. If *perfluorooctanoic* acid is used instead, Ca, Mg, Fe^{2+}, Pb and Zn can be sepd. from monovalent cations.[65]

Cinnamic acid, $CHCl_3$ or hexone has been used in the extn. of Pu, La, Th and U.[66]

References

1. West, T. S., *Liquid–liquid Extraction in Analytical Chemistry*, *Metallurgia*, **53**, 91, 102, 185, 234, 240, 292 (1956); **54**, 47, 103 (1956); Morrison, G. H. and Freiser, H., *Solvent Extraction in Analytical Chemistry*, Wiley, New York (1957); Alders, L., *Liquid–liquid Extraction, Theory and Laboratory Experiments*, Butterworths, London (1955).
2. Wada, I. and Ishii, R., *Sci. Papers Inst. Phys. Chem. Research* (*Tokyo*), **34**, 789 (1935); Kitahara, S., *Repts. Sci. Research Inst.* (*Tokyo*), **24**, 455 (1948).
3. Kitahara, S., *Repts. Sci. Research Inst.* (*Tokyo*), **24**, 455 (1948).
4. Bock, R., *et al.*, *Z. anal. Chem.*, **138**, 167 (1953).
5. Hoste, J. and Berghe, H. van der, *Mikrochim. Acta*, 797 (1956).
6. Kitahara, S., *Repts. Sci. Research Inst.* (*Tokyo*), **25**, 165 (1949) (in parentheses in the Table).
7. Bock, R. and Herrmann, M., *Z. anorg. allgem. Chem.*, **284**, 288 (1956).
8. Bock, R., *Z. anal. Chem.*, **133**, 110 (1951).
9. Bock, R. and Bock, E., *Naturwissenschaften*, **36**, 344 (1949); *Z. anorg. allgem. Chem.*, **263**, 146 (1950).
10. Furman, N. H., *et al.*, *U.S. Atomic Energy Comm.*, **AECD**-2938 (1946).
11. Kosta, L. and Hoste, J., *Mikrochim. Acta*, 790 (1956).
12. Maddock, A. G. and Miles, G. L., *J. Chem. Soc.*, 248, 253 (1949).
13. Taketatsu, T., *J. Chem. Soc. Japan*, **74**, 82 (1953).
14. Yamamoto, S., *J. Chem. Soc. Japan*, **74**, 292 (1953).
15. Wells, J. E. and Hunter, D. P., *Analyst*, **73**, 671 (1948).
16. Yamamoto, S., *J. Chem. Soc. Japan*, **76**, 417 (1955); **77**, 713 (1956).
17. Fischer, W., *et al.*, *Angew. Chem.*, **66**, 165 (1954).
18. Banks, C. V. and Byrd, C. H., *Anal. Chem.*, **25**, 416 (1953).
19. Lerner, M. W. and Petretic, G. J., *Anal. Chem.*, **28**, 227 (1956).
20. Milner, G. W. C., *et al.*, *Analyst*, **80**, 380 (1955); *Anal. Chim. Acta*, **13**, 230 (1955); also see Werning, J. R., *et al.*, *Ind. Eng. Chem.*, **46**, 644 (1954).
21. Waterbury, G. R. and Bricker, C. E., *Anal. Chem.*, **29**, 1474 (1957).
22. Glendenin, L. E., *et al.*, *Anal. Chem.*, **27**, 59 (1955).
23. Spedding, F. H., *et al.*, *U.S. Atomic Energy Comm.*, **TID**-5223, 486 (1952).
24. Waterbury and Bricker, *Anal. Chem.*, **29**, 129 (1957).
25. Weinhardt, A. E. and Hixon, A. N., *Ind. Eng. Chem.*, **43**, 1677 (1951).
26. Specker, H. and Dohl, W., *Z. anal. Chem.*, **152**, 178 (1956).
27. Nietzel, O. A. and DeSesa, M. A., *Anal. Chem.*, **29**, 756 (1957).
28. Denaro, R. and Occleshaw, V. J., *Anal. Chim. Acta*, **13**, 239 (1955).
29. Kinnunen, J. and Wennerstrand, B., *Chemist Analyst*, **42**, 80 (1953).
30. Grimes, W. R., *et al.*, *U.S. Atomic Energy Comm.*, **Y**-560 (1950).
31. Stevenson, P. C. and Hicks, H. G., *Anal. Chem.*, **25**, 1517 (1953); **26**, 1205 (1954).
32. Golden, A. J. and Maddock, A. G., *J. Inorg. Nuclear Chem.*, **2**, 46 (1956).
33. West, P. W. and Carlton, J. K., *Anal. Chim. Acta*, **6**, 466, 488 (1952).
34. Milner and Wood, A. J., *Atomic Energy Research Estab.*, *Gt. Brit.*, **AERE-C/R**-895 (1952).
35. Foos, R. A. and Wilhelm, H. A., *U.S. Atomic Energy Comm.*, **ISC**-694 (1954).
36. Kuznetsov, V. I., *J. Gen. Chem.*, *U.S.S.R.*, **17**, 175 (1947).
37. Branica, M., *et al.*, *Croat. Chem. Acta*, **28**, 9 (1956).
38. Specker, H. and Bankmann, E., *Z. anal. Chem.*, **149**, 97 (1956).
39. Moore, F. L., *Anal. Chem.*, **27**, 70 (1955).
40. Garwin, L. and Hixon, A. M., *Ind. Eng. Chem.*, **41**, 2303 (1949).
41. Chernikov, Yu. A., *et al.*, *Zavodskaya Lab.*, **22**, 639 (1956).
42. Bartlett, T. W., *U.S. Atomic Energy Comm.*, **K**-706 (1951); Wright, Jr., W. B. *ibid.*, **Y**-884 (1952); Guest, R. J. *Can. Dept. Mines Tech. Surveys*, *Mines Branch*, *Radioactivity Div.*, *Topical Rept.*, **TR**-128/55 (1955); Page, B. E., *et al.*, *Anal. Chem.*, **29**, 1027 (1957).
43. Fischer, D. J. and Thomason, P. F., *Anal. Chem.*, **28**, 1285 (1956).
44. Ebele, A. R., and Lerner, M. W., *Anal. Chem.*, **29**, 1134 (1957).
45. Hudswell, F., *et al.*, *Atomic Energy Research Estab. Gt. Brit.*, **C/R**-1520 (1956).
46. Foos, R. A., and Wilhelm, H. A., *U.S. Atomic Energy Comm.*, **ISC**-693 (1954).
47. Alcock, K., *et al.*, *J. Inorg. Nuclear Chem.*, **4**, 100 (1957).
48. Warf, J. C., *J. Am. Chem. Soc.*, **71**, 3257 (1949).
49. Kirby, H. W., *Anal. Chem.*, **29**, 1599 (1957).
50. Peppard, D. F., *et al.*, *J. Phys. Chem.*, **57**, 294 (1953).
51. Peppard, *et al.*, *J. Inorg. Nuclear Chem.*, **3**, 370 (1957); **4**, 326, 334, 344 (1957); McKay, H. A. C., *et al.*, *ibid.*, 304, 315, 321.
52. Katzin, L. I., *et al.*, *J. Am. Chem. Soc.*, **78**, 5139 (1956).
53. Meinke, W. W., *U.S. Atomic Energy Comm.*, **AECD**-2738.
54. Kinnunen, J. and Wennerstrand, B., *Chemist-Analyst*, **43**, 34 (1954).
55. Scadden, E. M. and Ballou, N. E., *Anal. Chem.*, **25**, 1602 (1953).
56. Ellenburg, J. Y., *et al.*, *Anal. Chem.*, **26**, 1045 (1954).
57. Leddicotte, G. W. and Moore, F. L., *J. Am. Chem. Soc.*, **74**, 1618 (1952).

58. MAHLMAN, H. A., *et al.*, *Anal. Chem.*, **26**, 1939 (1954).
59. BROWN, K. B., *et al.*, *U.S. Atomic Energy Comm.*, **ORNL**-1734, 1835, 1922, 1959 (1955).
60. WHITE, J. C., *U.S. Atomic Energy Comm.*, **ORNL**-2161 (1956).
61. BLAKE, C. A., *et al.*, *U.S. Atomic Energy Comm.*, **ORNL**-1964 (1955).
62. WHITE, J. C., *U.S. Atomic Energy Comm.*, **ORNL**-2326 (1957).
63. WEST, P. W., *et al.*, *Anal. Chim. Acta*, **6**, 400 (1952).
64. SUNDARAM, A. K. and BANERJEE, S., *Anal. Chim. Acta*, **8**, 526 (1953); BANERJEE, *et al.*, *Anal. Chim. Acta*, **10**, 256 (1954).
65. MILLS, G. F. and WHETSEL, H. B., *J. Am. Chem. Soc.*, **77**, 4690 (1955).
66. HARVEY, B. G., *et al.*, *J. Chem. Soc.*, 1016 (1947); HÖK-BERNSTRÖM, B., *Acta Chem. Scand.*, **10**, 163, 174 (1956).

17

MISCELLANEOUS REAGENTS

1. MISCELLANEOUS REACTIONS

1.1. Detection and colorimetric determination of NH_3

Amidol, p-*aminobenzenearsonic acid* (as test paper), *atoxyl* (+ $NaNO_2$), p-*nitroaniline* (+ $NaNO_2$ and NaOH) and *tannin* (+ $AgNO_3$) give yellow or yellow-red colors with NH_3. Amidol is said to be more sensitive than Nessler's reagent. *Hematoxylin* forms a reddish color, *resorcinol* gives a bluish green color if Na-nitroprusside is added, and *thymol* forms a blue-green color if NaOH and Br_2 or NaOCl are present; the thymol reaction may be used colorimetrically. The blue-green color with *phenol* in presence of NaOH and chloramine T, NaOCl or $Ca(OCl)_2$ can also be used quantitatively.

p-*Nitrodiazobenzene chloride* (*p*-nitrobenzene-diazonium chloride, Riegler's reagent) forms a red ppt. with NH_3 (0·07 μg.) in NaOH solns. *Phenylhydrazine diazonium chloride* is used for the detection of NH_3 in air. The pink color formed with p-*phenylenedia mine* (Ursol D) has also been used for NH_3 detection.

Formaldehyde may be used for the removal of NH_3; phenolphthalein becomes colorless owing to the formation of hexamine.

1.2. Detection of S and S compounds

Benzimidodi(4-methoxyphenyl)methane ((*N*-bis(*p*-methoxyphenyl)methylenebenzylamine, *N*-(4, 4′-dimethoxybenzhydrylidene)benzylamine) $((CH_3OOC_6H_4)_2CN\ CH_2C_6H_5)$ gives a blue color on heating with S for 10 min. at 210°C followed by C_6H_6 extn., owing to the formation of $(CH_3OC_6H_4)_2CS$.[1] When S is fused with *benzoin*, the H_2S formed can be detected with $Pb(OAc)_2$ paper.[2]

H_2S forms a yellow or red-brown color with p-*diazobenzenesulfonic acid*. S^{2-} gives a red color with *nitrobenzene* in KOH solns. and a blue fluorescence with *quinine* in feebly acidic solns.

Diethylaniline becomes yellow or yellow-brown with CS_2 in presence of $Cu(OAc)_2$; *triethylphosphine* forms red crystals with CS_2. *Phenylhydrazine* yields a ppt. with CS_2 in C_6H_6 soln. *Piperidine* gives a white ppt. with CS_2 in Et_2O, Me_2CO, decalin, etc.; the ppt. with H_2S dissolves on heating. For the reaction of acetylacetone with CS_2, see Chapter 10, Section 2.

1.3. Detection of As and Sb

Carvacrol $(1,2,4\text{-}CH_3C_6H_3OHCH(CH_3)_2)$ forms a reddish color with Sb^{5+} in $CHCl_3$ which becomes purple on further addn. of $CHCl_3$; As^{5+} in H_2SO_4 soln. gives a pale red color with the reagent, which becomes blood-red on heating. As^{5+} in H_2SO_4 gives a dark blue color with *ethylmorphine*.

Diazobenzene chloride (phenyldiazonium chloride) yields a raspberry color with As^{3+} at −5°C which turns yellow after 10 min. As_2O_3 gives the cacodyl odor on heating with *sodium acetate*.

Anthracene and *indene* form green and red colors resp. with Sb in CCl_4.

1.4. Detection and determination of other metals

Naphthenic acid (a mixt. of mono-, di-, and tricarboxylic acids of higher homologs of cyclopentane) forms green colors with Cu and Ni and a red color with Co.

Sozoiodol forms yellow crystals with Hg (5 μg.); Ag, Pb and Tl form ppts. *Allyl alcohol* is used in the titration of Hg. *Phenylboric acid* ppts. Hg as $Hg(C_6H_5)_2$.[3] *Ditolyl mercury* causes an increase in the sensitivity of the Hg detn. with dithizone (see p. 151). *Nitrosobenzene* and $K_4Fe(CN)_6$ form $[Fe(CN)_6NOPh]^{3-}$ in presence of Hg which can thus be detd. colorimetrically.

Acetylene forms a reddish ppt. of $CuC_2{\cdot}H_2O$ with Cu in NH_4OH and tartrate solns.; Ag and Pd also react. For *substituted acetylenes*, see ref. 4. *Borneolglucuronic acid* forms white ppts. with Zn and Cd in neutral or acidic solns.; the Zn ppt. is $Zn(C_{10}H_{25}O_7)_2{\cdot}2H_2O$.

Tetraline reacts with Mn in lithopone so that a pink color appears when the mixt. is heated.

Protein forms a ppt. with U.[5]

Trimethylphosphate and *dimethyl sulfate* are used in the detns. of Zr and Pb resp. (pp. 356 and 158).

1.5. Detection of halogens and pseudohalogens

Alloxan in the presence of butylamine, ethylamine, propylamine, pyridine, toluidine, *o*-anisidine, *p*-aminophenol, etc., forms a white ppt. with CN^- (catalysis of oxaluramide formation). *Bis*(3-*methyl*-1-*phenyl*-5-*pyrazolone*) in pyridine with 3-methyl-1-phenyl-5-pyrazolone can be used for the colorimetric detn. of CN^- (0·2 μg./ml.) or NH_3 when chloramine T is added; pyridine is converted to glutaconic aldehyde by CNCl and the aldehyde condenses with the pyrazolone derivs. to form Zolon red (p. 467). Nicotinamide permits fluorimetric detn. of CN^- if chloramine T is added. *Pyridine* and *sulfanilic acid* or *benzidine* and CN^- can be used colorimetrically for Cl_2 or Br_2 (König's reaction).

Congo red in presence of Ag may be used to detect CN^-. *Picric acid* forms red isopurpuric acid on heating in alk. soln. with CN^-.

Semicarbazide (aminourea) *hydrochloride* ppts. OCN^- quantitatively. *Methylxanthydrol* forms xanthylurea with OCN^- in AcOH solns.

When AgSCN is treated with *cyclohexene* and I_2 in EtOH, the characteristic odor of 2-cyclohexylisocyanate appears; when NH_3 is added, 2-iodocyclohexylurea crystals are formed.

I^- (0·05 μg.) forms HBr with o-*nitroaniline* and C_6H_5Br; the HBr is detected with Cl_2 in $CHCl_3$.

1.6. Reactions with H_2O

For details of *Karl Fischer's reagent* (pyridine, MeOH, SO_2 and I_2) see p. 461.

Acetylpyridinium chloride, *cinnamoyl chloride*, *α-naphthoxydichlorophosphine* and *acetyl chloride* react with H_2O to form HCl which can be titrated. *Acetic* and *benzoic anhydrides* react immediately with H_2O.

1.7. Others

p-*Nitrosothymol* forms red thymoquinonemonoxime with Na_2CO_3. p-*Nitrosodimethylaniline* changes from yellow to green with HCl gas. *Benzylpseudothiourea* forms characteristic crystals with HCl.

Quinonechloroimide (OC_6H_4NCl) forms a green color with $Fe(CN)_6^{4-}$ (5 μg.) and a brown ppt. with large amts.; $Fe(CN)_6^{3-}$ does not react.

2. PROTECTIVE COLLOIDS AND COAGULATING AGENTS

Starch, *dextrin*, *glycerol*, *gelatin*, *gum arabic*, *casein*, *agar-agar*, *albumin*, *colloidon* and *polyvinyl alcohol* have been used as protective colloids in colorimetry and nephelometry; in some cases, e.g. ZnS or SiO_2, they serve as coagulating agents.

Nitrobenzene prevents metathesis of AgSCN and AgCl in argentometric titrations of Cl^- so that filtration becomes unnecessary. When SeO_3^{2-} is titrated with KI, the end-point is sharper when the mixture is shaken with C_6H_6; Se collects at the boundary surface.

Shellac prevents adsorption of starch-I_2 indicator on the CuI ppt. when Cu is detd. iodometrically.

Sodium tauroglycocholate prevents Mg oxinate adhering to glass.

Acrolein (CH_2CHCHO) decreases the copptn. of Co with ZnS or Zn-anthranilate. *Crotonaldehyde* (CH_3-CHCHCHO) diminishes the copptn. of Zn with Cd or Cu sulfide. *Phenylsulfinic acid* (benzenesulfinic acid) allows easier filtration of ZnS.

3. OTHER REAGENTS

Organic acids and their salts are often used in buffer solns., as primary standards in alkalimetric titrations (see Chapter 5, Section 2.1) and as precipitants for Group III.[6] Organic bases also serve as primary standards and as precipitants for Group III.[6]

Ethanol, *ether*, *acetone*, etc., are often useful to wash ppts. in gravimetric analysis, since they can be readily removed by volatilization.

α-Furoic acid or *formaldehyde* may be added to stabilize $Na_2S_2O_3$ or starch solns. *Phthalic anhydride* stabilizes solns. of diphenylcarbazide in EtOH while *phenacetin* (*p*-acetophenetidine) stabilizes cupferron solns.

Acetone, *2-propanol*, *methyl ethyl ketone*, *butyl cellosolve* (ethyleneglycol monobutyl ether) and *methyl cellosolve* cause a deepening of the color formed by Fe^{3+} or Co^{2+} with SCN^-. For the acetone complex with phosphomolybdate, see p. 429.

References

1. ORY, H. A., *et al.*, *Analyst*, **82**, 189 (1957).
2. FEIGL, F. and STARK, C., *Anal. Chem.*, **27**, 1838 (1955).
3. HOLZBECHER, Z., *Chem. listy*, **46**, 20 (1952).
4. ZIEGLER, M. and GLEMSER, O., *Z. anal. Chem.*, **153**, 246 (1956).
5. GLOVER, N., *Nuclear Sci. Abst.*, **4**, 305 (1950).
6. YOE and SARVER, *Organic Analytical Reagents*, 38 (1948).

PART III

DETERMINATION OF THE ELEMENTS

18

SILVER

The principal sources for this chapter are Hillebrand and Lundell, Scott and Furman, and Kimura.[1]

In neutral solns. traces of Ag^+ are adsorbed on glass surfaces; this does not happen in acidic solns. or with Pyrex or quartz vessels.

Attack

Treat sulfides, arsenides or tellurides with HNO_3; fuse the residue with Na_2CO_3 and leach with HNO_3. Fuse halides with Na_2CO_3, ext. with H_2O and treat the residue with HNO_3. Dissolve metals or alloys in hot 33% HNO_3 (d. 1·20).

Fire assay[2]

In a preliminary test, mix 5 g. sample with fusion mixture (50 g. PbO, 18 g. $NaHCO_3$, 5 g. fused borax) in a crucible, cover with NaCl, fuse and weigh the button obtained (W g.).

Procedure. Mix 30 g. sample with the above fusion mixture and add as follows: for $W = 3$, nothing; for $W > 3$, 1 g. $KNO_3/(W - 3)$ g.; for $W < 3$, $(3 - W)/10$ g. KH-tartrate; for $W = 0$, 2 g. KH-tartrate. Cover with NaCl and fuse. Heat the resulting button (ca. 20 g.) on bone ash at 800°C for 30 min., treat with dil. HCl, wash with hot H_2O, dry and weigh the Ag + Au. Boil with HNO_3 (d. 1·16), decant, boil with 3 ml. HNO_3, decant, wash, ignite and weigh the Au.

NOTES. (1) If the Ag + Au bead does not react with HNO_3, fuse with Pb and an amt. of Ag depending on the color (equal amt. if white, double amt. if green-yellow, double to triple amt. if yellow to brown); then repeat as above. Alternatively, a better method is to heat in H_2 at 400°C with 4–5 times the bead weight of Zn–Cd alloy (87% Cd), treat with HNO_3 and MeOH (2 : 1), dry and weigh.[3]

(2) If the sample contains Te, some Au, Ag may be lost. Losses in cupellation have been studied with radioactive Ag.[4]

Separation

Sep. from SiO_2 by evapn. to fumes with H_2SO_4 or $HClO_4$. Addn. of HCl to the dil. HNO_3 soln. allows sepn. from many elements (see under Determination). Conc. with Hg^+ or with Tl^+ or Pb and HBr.

Internal electrolysis allows sepn. of Ag, Bi, Cu from Pb.[5] To 10 g. Pb in a 400 ml. beaker, add 1 g. tartaric acid, 100 ml. 1:3 HNO_3, and boil out NO_2. Dil. to 350 ml. with H_2O, heat to 40°C, add $KMnO_4$ till pink, heat to 60–70°C and add 0·05 g. urea. Use a Pt gauze cathode and 2 Pb wires (diam. 2·5 mm., length 70 cm.) wound round 5 mm. diam. glass tubing as anode. Stir rapidly (800–1000 r.p.m.). Use 3:97 HNO_3 as anolyte in alundum shells (19 × 90 mm.). During electrolysis, flush the anode chambers twice, wash down the beaker wall and anode shells, and add ca. 0·05 g. urea. When deposition is complete, remove the electrolyte by siphoning while slowly adding 1 l. H_2O; replace the beaker quickly with another contg. H_2O, remove this beaker, detach electrode and rinse with H_2O.

Sep. from Pb with $(NH_4)_2HPO_4$ from weakly ammoniacal tartrate-contg. soln., or with KI.

$K_3Co(CN)_6$ in HCl, HNO_3 or H_2SO_4 solns. permits sepn. of Ag, Cu, Bi, Cd, Fe^{2+}, Co, Ni, Zn, Mn, V^{4+} from Pb, As, Sb, Sn, Mo, Se, Te, Fe^{3+}, V^{5+}, U, Al, Be, Cr, Ce, Zr, Ti, Ca, etc.[6]

H_2S in acidic or alk. solns. allows sepn. from many elements. $K_2S_2O_7$ fusion gives sepn. from Cl^-. Dithizone in acidic soln. gives sepn. from Cu (see under Determination); Au, Pd, Hg, Cl^-, SCN^- interfere.

Copptn. with Te is convenient before colorimetry.[7] To 0·5–25 μg. Ag in 50 ml. 2*N* HCl soln., add 1 ml. $TeCl_4$ soln. (100 mg. Te evapd. to dryness with 1–2 ml. HNO_3, then evapd. to dryness with 1 ml. HCl, and dild. with 10 ml. HCl and 90 ml. H_2O) followed by $SnCl_2$ soln. (15 g./100 ml. 2*N* HCl) until colorless; add 10 ml. in excess and heat for 30 min. near the b.p. Filter through glass, wash with 50 ml. *N* H_2SO_4 and 50 ml. H_2O. Dissolve by adding 1 ml. portions of hot HNO_3, wash with H_2O, evap. to dryness, and dissolve in 0·4 ml. 1·25*N* HNO_3 + 1 ml. H_2O (for Ag < 3 μg.) or 1 ml. 0·25*N* HNO_3 + 1 ml. H_2O (for Ag > 3 μg.). Pb can be washed out with the min. amt. of 1*N* HCl. If > 0·2 g. Cu is present, recover Ag from filtrate as described above and add to the main ppt. If > 150 μg. Pd is present in a final vol. of 25 ml., sep. with 0·1 ml. 1% dimethylglyoxime before colorimetry with *p*-diethylaminobenzylidenerhodanine.

Determination

For macro analysis, gravimetric detn. with HCl is most accurate and can be used for at. wt. detn. However, Volhard's method is almost as good and is much quicker. The thionalide method is best for 1 mg. amts. although benzotriazole and its derivs. are also satisfactory. Smaller amts. can be detd. accurately with *p*-diethylaminobenzylidenerhodanine or with dithizone.

(a) Precipitation as halide or pseudohalide is the most widely used technique.

For gravimetry,[1, 8] to 0·1–0·2 g. Ag in 200–400 ml. 1:99 HNO_3 at 70°C add 0·2*N* HCl in excess and leave (preferably overnight) at 25–30°C in the dark. Filter on a Gooch crucible, decant and wash with 0·01*N* HCl. Dry at 130–150°C (70–600°C).

NOTES. (1) Pb interference is avoided by pptg. from more dil. soln. or by sepg. as sulfate. Hg^+, Cu^+, CN^-, $S_2O_3^{2-}$, org. compds. (boil with HNO_3), Tl^+ (boil with aqua regia) interfere. Pd, Bi, Sb interference is avoided by treating the ppt. with NH_4OH, filtration, acidification with HNO_3 and repptn.
(2) The ppt. must be protected from light. AgBr and AgI are too light-sensitive.
(3) If necessary, Ag can be detd. in the filtrate by nephelometry or colorimetry. For nephelometry, to 20 ml. soln. contg. <2 mg. Ag/l., add 10 ml. 1 : 160 HNO_3 and 10 ml. 0·005*N* HCl; maintain at 40°C for 30 min.; cool at once.[9]

For titrimetry, various adsorption indicators can be used for the detn. of quite small amts. of Ag (see Table 10 and Chapter 59, p. 442). In Volhard's method,[1] less than 0·3 g. Ag in 200 ml. 5:95 HNO_3 soln. below 25°C is titrated with 0·1*N* NH_4SCN in presence of satd. ferric alum soln. as indicator (bleached with HNO_3) to the color change to brown-red.

NOTES. (1) NO_2^-, Cl^-, SO_4^{2-}, Hg^{2+}, Pd^{2+}, Cu^+ interfere as do large amts. of Cu^{2+}, Ni and Co. Cu^{2+} (<7/10 Ag), As, Sb, Sn, Pb, Bi, Cd, Fe, Mn, Zn, Ni, Co do not interfere.
(2) Vigorous stirring is needed. If the end-point is indistinct, add a known amt. of 0·1*N* $AgNO_3$ and back-titrate. The filtrate can be titrated with Ce^{4+}.[10]
(3) Ag can be titrated with 0·1*N* KI in 0·2–0·3*N* H_2SO_4 soln. in presence of 3 ml. 0·5% starch and 0·1 ml. 0·1*N* Ce^{4+} as indicator.[11] NO_2,[12] 1 drop 0·1*N* $KMnO_4$, or 3 drops of 0·1*N* KIO_3, $KBrO_3$ or $K_2Cr_2O_7$[13] can serve as the oxidant; Pd^{2+} can be used as indicator. The end-point is sharper than in Volhard's method.
Bromophenol blue may serve as adsorption indicator: for 10^{-4} g. Ag in 1 g. Pb, add 2 ml. H_2O, 6 ml. HNO_3, evap. to dryness, add a little H_2O, 2–5 ml. 30% NH_4OAc, some 0·1% indicator soln. and titrate with <0·02*N* KI.[14] Potentiometric titration is suitable for 10^{-2}–10^{-4}*N* Ag soln.;[15] if EDTA is added, Pb, Bi, Cu, Cd, Zn, As, Sb, Fe do not interfere.[16]
(4) Ag can also be titrated with 0·1*N* KCN in 0·25*N* NH_4OH media; add 1–2 drops of *N* KI as indicator, titrate until clear, add 1 ml. *N* KI and continue titration to give a faint turbidity as the end-point.[17]
(5) For Mohr's method,[1] add excess 0·1*N* NaCl to the neutral soln. followed by K_2CrO_4 indicator and back-titrate with 0·1*N* $AgNO_3$ (see Chapter 59, p. 442). For Gay-Lussac's method in which titration is stopped when the ppt. suddenly coagulates, see Scott and Furman.[1] *p*-Dimethylaminobenzylidenerhodanine serves as indicator in the titration with KCl or KBr in less than 6*N* HNO_3 or 10*N* H_2SO_4 media.[18]
(6) $K_2Ni(CN)_4$ can be used colorimetrically or titrimetrically for Ag detn. Prep. the reagent by suspending 15 g. $Ni(CN)_2$ in 500 ml. H_2O, adding KCN until the soln. is nearly clear, stirring 1 hr. and filtering. For colorimetric detn. of 0·002–7 mg. Ag, add 4 parts 1 : 3 NH_4OH, 4 parts pyridine, 0·6 parts of satd. dimethylglyoxime in 1 : 3 NH_4OH and 1 part of $K_2Ni(CN)_4$ reagent; the final vol. varies from 100 ml. for 2·5–7 mg. Ag to 2 ml. for 0·002–0·02 mg. Ag. Measure at 400 mμ. The error is 3%; Cu, Co, Cr, Fe, Mn, Au interfere.[19]
For titrimetric detn. of Ag in 0·01–0·1*M* NH_4OH, add murexide indicator and 4 mg. $K_2Ni(CN)_4$ and titrate with 0·01*M* EDTA to a purple-red color.[20]

(b) Thionalide (1%) in EtOH is used gravimetrically or titrimetrically for Ag detn.[21] To 150–200 ml. of less than 0·5*N* HNO_3 or H_2SO_4 soln. at 80°C, add a 10-fold excess of reagent (at least 20 ml./150 ml. soln.), filter through a glass sinter, wash with H_2O and dry at 105°C. The yellow ppt. is $Ag(C_{12}H_6ONS)$. Alternatively, treat the ppt. with 5 ml. AcOH, 4–5 ml. 5*N* H_2SO_4, 0·1 g. KI and excess 0·02*N* I_2 and back-titrate after diln., with 0·02*N* $Na_2S_2O_3$. Pb, Tl, Cd, Fe^{2+}, Co, Ni, Zn, Al, Be, Cr do not interfere.

NOTES. (1) Sepn. for Pb is better than with the HCl method.
(2) 1% *p*-Mercaptoacetamidoacetanilide in AcOH yields $Ag(C_{10}H_{11}O_2N_2S)\cdot H_2O$ which can be weighed or detd. iodometrically.[22] *o*-(Mercaptoacetamido)-*p*-nitrophenol (in AcOH soln.) ppts. $Ag(C_8H_7O_4N_2S)\cdot H_2O$ from solns. of pH 1–1·5.[23] Other thioglycolanilides have been tested.[24]

(c) *p*-Diethylaminobenzylidenerhodanine (0·05% in anhyd. EtOH)[7] is one of the best reagents for Ag colorimetry. For 0·5–25 μg. Ag, add 0·4 or 1·0 ml. 1·25*N* HNO_3 per 9 ml. soln., and 0·4 or 1·0 ml. of reagent, and dil. with H_2O to 10 ml. (for < 3 μg. Ag) or 25 ml. (for > 3 μg. Ag). Measure the purple color at 495 mμ within 30 min. (see p. 228). Pd, Au, Hg and Cu^+ interfere; < 20 mg. Pb or < 19 mg. Cu^{2+} do not.

NOTES. (1) The acidity is important. Visual comparison is possible for <0·5 μg. Ag in <5 ml. final vol. with less reagent.
(2) The methyl analog is used for 2–20 μg. Ag and is 25 times more sensitive than the nephelometric chloride method.[25] The Ag complex can be pptd. from neutral soln. in presence of EDTA to mask heavy metals, washed with EtOH, dissolved in KCN soln., and the yellow color measured.[26]
(3) Rhodanine is used gravimetrically:[27] to 0·1–0·2 mg. Ag in 3–4 ml. soln., add 1–3 drops 1 : 10 HNO_3 and excess reagent (a soln. satd. by heating, cooled and filtered); after 5 min., filter through porcelain, wash with 1 : 99

HNO_3, EtOH and finally Et_2O, and dry at 110°C. Weigh as $Ag(C_3H_2ONS_2)$. Cu does not interfere. The reagent is also used colorimetrically for <1 p.p.m. Ag with <0·002% reagent soln.[28] Isonitrosorhodanine[29] is used similarly for gravimetric detns.

(d) Dithizone is important colorimetrically.[30] There are 2 methods.

(*1*) *Mixed color method.* (a) With 0·001% (w/v) dithizone in CCl_4. For 1–5 μg. Ag in 5–20 ml. 0·5*N* H_2SO_4 soln., add 2·0 ml. reagent, shake for 15 sec., sep., and measure visually or photometrically with a yellow-green filter. Alternatively, add standard Ag soln. to 0·5*N* H_2SO_4 + reagent, as a back-titration comparison soln. For < 25 μg. Ag, use 10 ml. reagent, shake for 30 sec., and measure with a yellow or orange filter.

(b) With Cu-dithizonate (shake Cu^{2+} in 0·05*N* H_2SO_4 with the above reagent for 1–2 min., and wash the org. layer with 0·01*N* H_2SO_4). For 0·5–5 μg. Ag in 5–20 ml. 0·5*N* H_2SO_4 soln., add 2·0 ml. reagent, shake for 2 min. and measure visually, or photometrically (yellow filter, 460 mμ) or use a comparison back-titration.

NOTES. (1) Au, Pd, Hg interfere; Cu does not.
(2) EDTA masks Pb, Bi, Cd, Pd, Pt, Au, Zn, Ni, Co, Tl^{3+} and a little Cu but not Ag or Hg.[31] Friedeberg's method[31] is as follows. Ext. the pH 2 soln. (if much Cl^- is present, adjust to pH 5) with 13 p.p.m. dithizone in CCl_4, combine and wash the org. phase twice with 3 ml. 20% NaCl soln. contg. 0·03*N* HCl. Dil. the aq. phase to 60 ml., ext. with dithizone and det. Ag. Shake the above CCl_4 phase twice with 3 ml. 6*N* HCl, combine, adjust to pH 1·5–2 with NH_4OH, add 1 ml. 0·01*N* EDTA (or more if >50 μg. Cu is present) and ext. with dithizone. Det. Hg in the CCl_4 phase. Treat the aq. phase with 1 ml. 0·1*N* $CaCl_2$ and 3 ml. 25% $(NH_4)_3$-citrate, adjust to pH 9 with NH_4OH, ext. with dithizone, combine, shake twice with 3 ml. 6*N* HCl, adjust to pH 2–3 with 6*N* NH_4OH, and ext. twice with dithizone for Cu.

(*2*) *Mono-color method.* For 10–100 μg. Ag in 10 ml. soln., add 1 ml. 4*N* HNO_3 or H_2SO_4 and 5 ml. reagent (5 mg. in 100 ml. CCl_4), shake for 1–2 min., sep. and repeat several times. Wash the aq. layer with 1–2 ml. CCl_4, combine, shake 1–2 times with 5–10 ml. 0·1*N* H_2SO_4 and twice with 5 ml. 1:1000 NH_4OH. Dil. with CCl_4 to a definite vol. and measure the yellow color at 460 mμ.

(e) 1,2,3-Benzotriazole is used gravimetrically or titrimetrically.[32] For 10–100 mg. Ag, add 1–10 g. EDTA (400 g./500 ml., cleared with NH_4OH and dild. to 1 l. with H_2O), neutralize with HNO_3 or NH_4OH, make slightly acid and heat to 60–90°C. Add 10 ml. reagent (2·5 g. and 30 ml. NH_4OH/100 ml.), digest for 15 min. at 60°C, allow to cool, filter on a G3 crucible, wash with 5–6 10 ml. portions of H_2O, dry at 110°C for 1–2 hr. and weigh as $AgC_6H_4N_3$. Alternatively, dissolve the ppt. in 10 ml. HNO_3 (1:1), dil. to 50 ml. with H_2O, make alk. with NH_4OH, add excess 0·05*N* KCN and back-titrate with $AgNO_3$ using 1 ml. 2% KI indicator.

NOTES. (1) I^-, CN^-, SO_3^{2-} interfere; Cl^-, Br^-, F^- and other metals do not.
(2) For homogeneous pptn., add a slight excess of 1–2% *o*-phenylenediamine and solid $NaNO_2$ (3 moles/mole amine) to the neutral soln., acidify with AcOH, heat to 70–80°C for 15–20 min., cool, filter and wash with 1% AcOH; Cu interferes.[33]
(3) 5-Bromobenzotriazole (1–2%)[34] and benzimidazole (1%)[35] have been used gravimetrically.

(f) 2-Mercaptobenzothiazole or bismuthiol II[36] can be used gravimetrically or titrimetrically. For 5–20 mg. Ag, add 1–2 ml. *N* NH_4OAc and EDTA soln. and make alk. to phenolphthalein with NH_4OH; dil. to 200 ml. with H_2O, heat and add excess reagent; filter through a G4 crucible, wash with hot H_2O, dry below 280°C and weigh as $AgC_8H_6N_2S_3$ (for bismuthiol II).

NOTE. Cu, Pb, Cd, Bi, Tl, Fe, Al, Cr, Ni, Co, Mn, Zn, do not interfere; Sb, Sn, Ti, Be interfere unless tartaric or citric acid is added. Os, Ir, Ru, Rh can be tolerated at pH 5–9 in presence of $Na_2S_2O_3$ or EDTA, Au at pH 8–9 in presence of $Na_2S_2O_3$, and Pd at pH 6 in presence of CN^-.

(g) Electrodeposition is often satisfactory.

(i)[37] For 0·05–0·6 mg. Ag in 0·5 ml. soln. add 2 drops H_2SO_4, some tartaric acid or EtOH and heat to 90°C; electrolyze at 1·3 v., cool, repeat at 1·7 v., dry and weigh. Cu, Pb, As, Co, Ni, Zn, Cd, Sb do not interfere; Sn is tolerated at 1·2 v.

(ii)[38] Add 10 ml. NH_4OH/150–200 ml. soln.; stir and electrolyze at 1·3 v. and 0·4 amp.; after Ag is deposited, add 10 ml. 0·25% H_2O_2 and pass 0·2 amp. for 2 min. Cu does not interfere. The method can be modified for micro work.[37]

(iii)[39] Add 3 g. KCN and 1 g. KOH/100–120 ml. and electrolyze at 6–8 v. (0·1–0·15 amp.); after several min., increase the current to 0·3–0·5 amp. Results are 1–2 mg. low.

NOTE. See Lingane's *Electroanalytical Chemistry* (1953) for methods involving internal electrolysis and controlled potentials (also Chapter 4, for sepn. of Ag from Pb, Cu, Bi, Cd, Ni, Zn, etc.).

(h) $[Cu(pn)_2]SO_4$ is used gravimetrically in conjunction with KI.[40] For 1·7 mg. in 50 ml. neutral or faintly ammoniacal soln., add KI until the soln. becomes clear, then add the hot Cu complex soln. (1*M* $CuSO_4$ mixed with 2*M* propylenediamine hydrate, freshly prepared). Allow to cool, filter on a glass crucible, wash with a mixture of 1% KI and 0·5% Cu complex soln. and then with EtOH and Et_2O. Dry at 155°C and weigh as $[Cu(pn)_2][AgI_2]_2$.

NOTES. (1) In a similar method,[41] KSCN is added to a neutral or slightly acidic soln. contg. 0·05 g. Ag in 50 ml. until the soln. clears; after boiling, 3–5 ml. Co complex soln. (29·1 g. $Co(NO_3)_2$, 20 g. KSCN and 23·4 g. ethylenediamine/l.) is added and the soln. is cooled, filtered, washed with a soln. contg. 1 g. KSCN and 1 ml. Co complex soln./100 ml., and then with EtOH and Et_2O. The ppt. is dried at below 144°C and weighed as $[Co(en)_2(SCN)_2][Ag(SCN)_2]$.

(2) To 0·25–5 mg. Ag in 30 ml. neutral soln., add 2% KCN until the ppt. just dissolves; add 1–2 drops neutral 5% HCHO, wait for 5 min., add 5 ml. 20% H_3PO_4 and satd. Br_2 soln. to give a yellow color. After 10 min., add 2 ml. 5% phenol; after 2 min., 0·5 g. KI; and after 10 min. in the dark, titrate with 0·01*N* $Na_2S_2O_3$. Cl^- and Br^- do not interfere.[42]

(i) Reducing agents have been used in Ag detns. Ascorbic acid[43] can be used gravimetrically: heat less than 0·1 g. Ag in 20 ml. slightly acidic (HNO_3) soln. with 10 ml. 4% ascorbic acid on a steam bath for 15 min., filter through paper, ignite and weigh. Au interferes but Pb, Cu, Bi, Cd, Ni, Zn do not. Direct titration with 0·001–0·1*N* ascorbic acid to variamine blue indicator is also possible.

Chloral, glycerol, HCHO, citarin may be used gravimetrically (see Welcher). Ag can be titrated with Fe^{2+} in presence of EDTA to a potentiometric endpoint.[44] Colorimetrically, reactions with $Na_2S_2O_4$[45] and tannin (see Welcher) with gelatin may be utilized. Hydroquinone, pyrogallol and gallic acid have been used in spot reactions.

(j) $NaIO_3$ serves in gravimetric or titrimetric detns.[46] To 0·1–0·15 g. Ag in 40–70 ml. neutral soln., add HNO_3 to give pH 2 followed by a small excess of 5% $NaIO_3$; after 2 hr., filter through glass, wash with 50–100 ml. H_2O, EtOH and Et_2O, dry at 115–120°C and weigh as $AgIO_3$.

(k) Other methods. Miscellaneous gravimetric methods, some of which may also be completed titrimetrically, require the following precipitants: Reinecke's salt,[47] K-xanthate,[48] H_2SeO_3 (pH 4–10),[49] α-nitroso-β-naphthol (pH 8·5)[50] and 5-nitro-8-quinolinecarboxylic acid (pH 2·13–5·3).[51]

Various rarely used titrimetric finishes are possible. Ag can be pptd. with $K_3Fe(CN)_6$ at 80–90°C in KNO_3-contg. soln., the ppt. filtered and washed with 2% KNO_3, and the excess $Fe(CN)_6^{3-}$ titrated iodometrically after addn. of $ZnSO_4$.[52] Alternatively, Ag (11–500 mg. in 50 ml.) is titrated with $K_4Fe(CN)_6$ soln. at pH 6–6·6 in presence of starch and I_2 as indicator.[53] For a method involving excess $C_2O_4^{2-}$ and back-titration with $KMnO_4$,[54] see p. 267 AgCl(2·5 mg.) may be dissolved in 1 ml. 0·2*N* $Na_2S_2O_3$ and 4 ml. AcOH; the Ag complex pptd. is filtered, washed and treated with excess 0·01*N* I_2, which is back-titrated with 0·005*N* $Na_2S_2O_3$.[55]

Numerous colorimetric procedures have been suggested. 2-Thio-5-keto-4-carbethoxy-1,3-dihydropyrimidine (0·01% in Me_2CO) is suitable for over 0·2 p.p.m. Ag at pH 2; Hg and large amts. of Cu, Co, Fe, Ni interfere.[56] H_2S water may be used for $<$ 0·1 mg. Ag/ml. in ammoniacal soln. followed by acidification;[57] gravimetric detn. is also possible.[58] *o*-Tolidine (1% in EtOH) yields a measurable blue color with 0·04 mg. Ag in 3 ml. of acetate-buffered soln.[59] Guanidylthiourea is used for 1–12 p.p.m. Ag in 0·1*N* NH_4OH soln.; Cu, Hg, Pb, Cd, Bi interfere.[60] The similar reagent, diallyldithiocarbamidohydrazine, is used gravimetrically in citrate-contg. soln. at pH 4·7–5·1.[61]

K_2CrO_4 gives a measurable red color with 25 μg. Ag.[62] 1–100 μg. Ag can be detd. with $Ce(SO_4)_2$ or $MnSO_4 + KMnO_4$ in dil. HCl by measuring the speed of fading.[63] The color obtained by suitable treatment of Ag (0·01–65 μg./ml.) with $K_2S_2O_8$ and $MnSO_4$ may be measured at 525 mμ.[64]

Na-diethyldithiocarbamate (0·1%) reacts with 10–200 μg. Ag at pH 2·6–5·0; the complex is extd. with CCl_4 and measured at 340 mμ.[65] Rubeanic acid has been used colorimetrically (390 mμ) and volumetrically (see p. 180) at pH 4·0–4·6.[66] The color of tetraethylthiuram disulfide (Cu salt) fades on addn. of Ag; this can be measured after C_6H_6 extn. and diln. with EtOH (420 mμ).[67]

Flame photometry at 338·3 mμ has been used for 0–500 μg. Ag/100 ml. after Me_2CO addn.[68]

References

1. Hillebrand and Lundell, p. 161 (204); Scott and Furman, p. 818; Kimura, p. 885; Wogrinz: see p. 231.
2. Mellor and Thompson, 336, 468 (1938); Kimura, 383; A.S.T.M. 465 (in Pb) 498 (in Ag solders after pptn. as AgCl); also see Smith, E. A., *The Sampling and Assay of the Precious Metals*, Charles Griffin, London (1947); Lewis, C. L., *Can. Mining Met. Bull.*, (539) 163 (1957).
3. Donau, J., *Z. anal. Chem.*, **104**, 257 (1936).
4. Nakamura, Y. and Fukami, K., *Japan Analyst*, **6**, 687 (1957).
5. Clarke, B. L., *et al.*, *Ind. Eng. Chem.*, *Anal. Ed.*, **8**, 411 (1936); A.S.T.M. 460.
6. Evans, B. S. and Higgs, D. G., *Analyst*, **70**, 158 (1945).
7. Sandell, E. B. and Neumayer, J. J., *Anal. Chem.*, **23**, 1863 (1951); Sandell, 540.
8. See also A.S.T.M. 498 (Ag solders), 464 (as AgI, in Pb).
9. Scott, A. F. and Hurley, F. H., *J. Am. Chem. Soc.*, **56**, 333 (1934); Sandell 549; A.S.T.M. 457, 460 (in Sb, Pb); also see Cl.
10. Joshi, M. K., *Z. anal. Chem.*, **152**, 355 (1956).
11. Bloom, A. and McNabb, W. M., *Ind. Eng. Chem.*, *Anal. Ed.*, **8**, 167 (1936).
12. Scott and Furman, 381.
13. Quinn, J. H. and McNabb, W. M., *J. Franklin Inst.*, **240**, 47 (1945).
14. Mannelli, G., *Anal. Chim. Acta*, **9**, 232 (1953).
15. Zürcker, M. and Hoepe, G., *Helv. Chim. Acta*, **21**, 1272 (1938); also Robinson, H. and Hugg, H., *Ind. Eng. Chem.*, *Anal. Ed.*, **9**, 565 (1937).
16. Doležal, J., *et al.*, *Chem. listy*, **48**, 267, 272 (1952).
17. Pierce, J. S. and Coursey, J. L., *Ind. Eng. Chem.*, *Anal. Ed.*, **4**, 64 (1932); also see Ni (Doležal). For gravimetry, see Scott and Furman, 823.
18. Goto, H. and Sato, S., *J. Chem. Soc. Japan*, **67**, 5 (1946).
19. Siggia, S., *Anal. Chem.*, **19**, 923 (1947).

20. AMIN, A. M., *Chemist Analyst*, **44**, 17, 19 (1955); also see GEDANSKY, S. J. and GORDON, L., *Anal. Chem.*, **29**, 566 (1957) (photometric, 0·1–10 mg. Ag).
21. WELCHER, **IV**, 170.
22. BUSCARÓNS UBEDA, F. and CAPITÁN, F., *Anales real soc. españ. fís. y quím.*, **46B**, 453, 569 (1950).
23. BUSCARÓNS UBEDA, F. and ARTIGAS, J., *Anales real soc. españ. fís. y quím.*, **49B**, 375 (1953).
24. SWAIN, R. C., *et al.*, *J. Indian Chem. Soc.*, **33**, 329 (1956).
25. CAVE, G. C. B. and HUME, D. N., *Anal. Chem.*, **24**, 1503 (1952).
26. RINGBOM, A. and LINKO, E., *Anal. Chim. Acta*, **9**, 80 (1953).
27. HECHT and DONAU, 146; WELCHER, **III**, 429.
28. ISHIBASHI, M., *et al.*, *Japan Analyst*, **3**, 74 (1954).
29. WELCHER, **III**, 428.
30. SANDELL, 544; WELCHER, **III**, 516.
31. FRIEDEBERG, H., *Anal. Chem.*, **27**, 305 (1955); ERDEY, L., *et al.*, *Magyar Kém. Folyóirat*, **60**, 193 (1954); GORYUSHINA, V. G. and GAĬLIS, E. YA., *Zavodskaya Lab.*, **22**, 905 (1956).
32. CHENG, K. L., *Anal. Chem.*, **26**, 1038 (1954).
33. TARASEVICH, N. I., *Vestnik Moskow. Univ.*, **10** (10), *Ser. Fiz. Mat. i Estestven. Nauk*, No. 7, 111 (1955).
34. TARASEVICH, N. I., *Vestnik Moskow. Univ.*, **3**, No. 10, 161 (1948).
35. DUTTA, R. L., *J. Indian Chem. Soc.*, **33**, 389 (1956).
36. MALÍNEK, M. and ŘEHÁK, B., *Chem. listy*, **49**, 1400 (1955); **50**, 157 (1956); *Z. anal. Chem.*, **150**, 329 (1956); also see UBALDINI, I. and NEBBIA, L., *Ann. chim. (Rome)*, **41**, 181 (1951); MAJUMDAR, A. K. and SINGH, B. R., *Z. anal. Chem.*, **155**, 81, 166, 265 (1957) (with bismuthiol II in acid soln.); ČÍHALÍK, J., *et al.*, *Chem. listy*, **50**, 1780 (1956); **51**, 76 (1957) (amperometric).
37. HECHT and DONAU, 148.
38. MILLER, W. L., *Ind. Eng. Chem., Anal. Ed.*, **8**, 436 (1936).
39. TCHAWDOW, D., *Z. anal. Chem.*, **112**, 258 (1938); NORWITZ, G., *Anal. Chim. Acta*, **5**, 197 (1951); SCOTT and FURMAN, 824.
40. HECHT and DONAU, 147; WELCHER, **II**, 451.
41. WELCHER, **II**, 383.
42. SCHULEK, E., *Mikrochemie, Emich Festschrift*, 260 (1930).
43. STATHIS, E. C., *Anal. Chem.*, **20**, 271 (1948); see ERDEY, L. and BUZÁS, L., *Acta Chim. Acad. Sci. Hung.*, **4**, 195 (1954).
44. PŘIBIL, R., *et al.*, *Chem. listy*, **47**, 1017 (1953).
45. MILLER, C. F., *Chemist Analyst*, **25**, (1) 8 (1936).
46. LITEANU, C. and EGER, I., *Acad. rep. populare Romîne, Filiala Cluj, Studii cercetări ştiinţ.*, **4**, 43 (1953); RADHAKRISHNA, M. N., *Z. anal. Chem.*, **148**, 40 (1956).
47. BAGBANLY, I. L. and MAMEDKULIEVA, M. M., *Doklady Akad. Nauk Azerbaidzan. S.S.R.*, **12**, No. 3, 173 (1956).
48. SPACU, P. and HLEVCA, M., *Comun. Acad. Rep. Romîne*, **3**, 211 (1953).
49. DESHMUKH, G. S. and SANKARANARAYANAN, K. M., *J. Sci. Research, Banaras Hindu Univ.*, **2**, 43 (1951/52).
50. WENGER, P. E., *et al.*, *Anal. Chim. Acta*, **3**, 660 (1949).
51. BELTRAN, F. G., *Rev. acad. cienc. exact. fís.-quím. y nat. Zaragoza*, **9**, 9 (1954).
52. PER'E, M. I. and LOBUNETZ, M. M., *Univ. état Kiev, Bull. sci., Rec. chim.*, **1** (4) 141 (1935).
53. FUJITA, Y. and KAYAMORI, H., *J. Chem. Soc. Japan*, **75**, 653 (1954).
54. KAWAGAKI, K., *J. Chem. Soc. Japan*, **73**, 640 (1952).
55. HASLEWOOD, G. A. D., *J. Chem. Soc.*, 1049 (1936).
56. WELCHER, **III**, 576.
57. JUST, J. and SZNIOLIS, A., *Z. anal. Chem.*, **109**, 367 (1937); also see Cl.
58. TAIMNI, I. K. and SALARIA, B. S., *Anal. Chim. Acta*, **12**, 519 (1955).
59. WELCHER, **II**, 471.
60. WELCHER, **III**, 565.
61. DUTT, N. K. and SEN SARMA, K. P., *Sci. and Culture (Calcutta)*, **22**, 344 (1956).
62. KRAINICK, H. G., *Mikrochemie*, **26**, 158 (1939).
63. GOTO, H. and SHIOKAWA, T., *J. Chem. Soc. Japan*, **63**, 840 (1943); GOTO and KAKITA, Y., *ibid.*, **66**, 39 (1945).
64. UNDERWOOD, A. L., *et al.*, *Anal. Chem.*, **24**, 1597 (1952); also see SAINI, G., *Ann. chim. (Rome)*, **40**, 55 (1950).
65. SUDO, E., *J. Chem. Soc. Japan*, **73**, 626 (1952).
66. XAVIER, J. and RÂY, P., *Sci. and Culture (Calcutta)*, **20**, 455 (1955).
67. MICHAL, J. and ZÝKA, J., *Chem. listy*, **51**, 56 (1957).
68. RATHJE, A. O., *Anal. Chem.*, **27**, 1583 (1955).

19

MERCURY

The principal sources for this chapter are Hillebrand and Lundell, Scott and Furman, Kimura, and Fresenius and Jander.[1] Mercury analysis has been reviewed by Beaumont and by Ferrey.[2]

Volatilization is a principal source of error in the determination of Hg. $HgCl_2$ should never be fused or its solns. evapd. Traces of Hg are found in commercial HCl, filter paper, gum and glassware (by adsorption on the surface), etc. For trace analysis, Pyrex glass washed with HNO_3 and then with H_2O is recommended.

Attack

(a) Volatilization. Heat at 700°C, as in org. elemental analysis, in a combustion tube of diam. 1·5 cm. and length 60 cm. packed as described below, while passing CO_2 at a rate of 3 bubbles/sec.; collect in H_2O and 1:1 HNO_3 or, for traces, in a U-tube cooled with liquid air.

The tube is packed as follows: 20 cm. empty, 1 cm. Cu gauze, 1 cm. asbestos, 5 cm. CaO, 5 cm. CaO (previously used as desiccant), 0·5 cm. layer contg. powd. sample mixed with 1 g. CuO and 0·5 g. CaO, 15 cm. freshly prepd. and powd. CaO, 2 cm. asbestos, 2 cm. Cu gauze, 2 cm. asbestos, 5 cm. empty tube. The end of the tube is drawn out and bent at 90°; the tip is dipped into H_2O in a flask which is connected to another flask contg. 1:1 HNO_3.

(b) Cinnabar and HgS precipitates. Place in a small Kjeldahl flask or Erlenmeyer fitted with a short-stemmed funnel. Add 5 ml. H_2SO_4, 0·5–1 g. $KMnO_4$ in small portions, and rinse the walls with 5 ml. H_2SO_4. Heat slowly to b.p. during 30 min., cool, add $H_2C_2O_4$ (to dissolve MnO_2), heat to white fumes and dil. to 100 ml. with H_2O; apply Volhard's method. Alternatively, dissolve in aqua regia.

(c) Chloride and oxychlorides. Heat in a glass tube; absorb Cl in Na_2CO_3 and Hg on Au wire for detn. of both.

(d) Hg and amalgams. Dissolve in HNO_3.

(e) Ores. Heat with a 2–4-fold amt. of HIO_3 previously heated at 95°C while passing air; add $Na_2S_2O_3$ and H_2S.

(f) Organic compounds. Treat as for ores. For the Carius method, heat with HNO_3 ($<$ 5 g./50 ml. of tube) at 270°C in a sealed tube. For the Kjeldahl method, heat with H_2SO_4 and $KMnO_4$ or HNO_3, or with fuming H_2SO_4 and H_2O_2 (30%). For compds. of the type RHgX, place the sample in a flask fitted with a condenser, add 2–3 ml. dioxane and 3–5 ml. ethanolamine followed by Na metal over 30 min.; cool, rinse the condenser with H_2O, heat and centrifuge.[3] Alternatively, place 0·2–0·3 g. sample in a 300 ml. Erlenmeyer, add 40 ml. AcOH and 2 ml. Br_2, and after 20 min. 3 ml. HCl. Keep below 50°C, add excess Zn powder, leave for 12 hr. and add 0·5 g. SiO_2 gel. Filter on a Gooch crucible (cover the asbestos with SiO_2 gel), wash with 1:1 HNO_3; dissolve in 10 ml. HNO_3 by warming, add concd. $KMnO_4$ until pink, leave for 5 min., remove excess MnO_4^- with $FeSO_4$ and apply Volhard's method.

Separation

Volatilization as described above allows sepn. from many elements. Other methods of sepn. are not very important.

Distn. from H_2SO_4 soln. by passing HCl gas seps. Hg from Pb, Cu, Bi, As^{5+}, etc.[4]

Sepn. from Fe, etc., is obtained with H_2S in acidic solns. Zn and Tl coppt. Hg can be collected and concd. with Cu^{2+}, Cd, As sulfides, or by passing the soln. of pH 5–7 through a CdS-contg. asbestos layer. Extn. of the sulfide ppts. with hot $(NH_4)_2S_x$ allows sepn. from As, Sb; Cu, Sn interfere by causing dissoln. of some Hg. Extn. with a 1:1 mixt. of 15% K_2S and 15% KOH (10 ml./0·1 g. Hg) gives sepn. from Ag, Pb; Cd, Zn, Sn interfere. The filtrate from this reaction can be treated with 20% NH_4NO_3 (pretreated with $(NH_4)_2S$ and filtered after 12 hr.) on a steam bath, which yields a sepn. from As, Sb, Te; if Sn is present, copptn. occurs and some Hg passes into the filtrate. Alternatively, the above filtrate is treated with a satd. soln. of 5 g. tartaric acid and 30% H_2O_2 until complete pptn. occurs and a 1 ml. excess is present; boiling, cooling, addn. of 1 g. $Na_2C_2O_4$, boiling and filtering give a sepn. from As, Sb, Sn.

Hg is sepd. from Bi, etc., by boiling the sulfide ppt. with 50 ml. HNO_3 (d. 1·2–1·3) for 30 min.; Cu, Cd,

2 ml. 10% reagent, heat on a steam bath for 5 min., cool for 30 min., filter on a glass crucible, wash with ammoniacal 2% NH_4NO_3, 50% EtOH and then EtOH, dry at 150°C and weigh as $Pb_3(PO_4)_2$.[49]

Na_2HAsO_4 ppts. $PbHAsO_4$, which can be weighed or titrated iodometrically, from solns. of pH 6.[50]

$NaIO_4$ is suitable for $< 0{\cdot}7$ g. Pb in 200 ml. $0{\cdot}025N$ HNO_3 (or in $0{\cdot}006N$ soln. for small amts.). Add 4% $NaIO_4$ soln. to the boiling soln., cool to 0°C for 30 min., filter on a glass crucible and wash with H_2O at 0°C. Dry at 110°C and weigh as $Pb_3H_4(IO_6)_2$, or at 140–280°C and weigh as $Pb_3(IO_5)_2$. Alternatively, dissolve the ppt. in excess As^{3+} in HCl soln. and back-titrate with $0{\cdot}1N$ KIO_3. Ni, Al, Zn, Ca, Mn do not interfere; nor do Cu or Cd if repptn. is carried out.[51]

HIO_3 ppts. Pb as $Pb(IO_3)_2$ from $1N$ HNO_3 soln.; the ppt. can be weighed or titrated iodometrically.[52] Ag, Hg, Bi, Ti, Zr, Th interfere.

HNO_3 can also be used: add 2·5 ml. H_2O, 5 ml. 70% HNO_3 and 13 ml. 100% HNO_3 to the dried nitrate; after 30 min., filter on a Gooch crucible, wash with 84% HNO_3, dry at 130°C for 2 hr. and weigh as $Pb(NO_3)_2$. Cl^- interferes but As, Cd, Bi, Cu, Hg and Ca do not.[53]

HCl (2%) in butanol can be used to ppt. $PbCl_2$; Bi does not interfere.[54] For < 3 g. Pb in dil. HNO_3 soln., evap. to dryness, cover, add 10 ml. HCl, rinse the vessel wall, evap. and repeat twice. Digest at 120–150°C for 10–15 min., add 15 ml. reagent, boil for 5 min., cool, filter, wash with reagent 5–6 times and dry at 110°C for 1 hr. and 250°C for 10 min.

$PbCO_3$ may be weighed after the neutral soln. has been treated with 1–2 drops of pyridine and gaseous CO_2 for 30–45 min.; Hg, Cu, Co, Ni, Cd, Tl do not interfere, nor does Ag if 3–5 ml. pyridine is added.[55] Pb(OH)(SCN) is pptd. on addn. of 2 g. NH_4SCN and 1 ml. pyridine in some H_2O to $< 0{\cdot}1$ g. Pb in 500 ml. soln.; the ppt. can be weighed[56] or the detn. may be done titrimetrically with NaOH in presence of SCN^- and cresolphthalein.[57]

Oxine allows the detn. of 5–10 mg. Pb in 20 ml. neutral soln.; it is unsuitable for smaller amts.[58] Acidify the soln. with AcOH, heat, add a 1·5-fold excess of satd. oxine soln. (boil oxine with H_2O, cool and filter), adjust to pH 8·5–9·5 with $0{\cdot}2N$ NH_4OH, filter on a G4 crucible after 12 hr., wash with cold H_2O, dry at 105°C and weigh as $Pb(C_9H_6OH)_2$ or titrate the ppt. with $KBrO_3$.

Bromoxine, 7-nitro-8-hydroxyquinoline-5-sulfonic acid[58] and 8-hydroxyquinaldine[59] are used similarly to oxine but appear to have no advantage.

Salicylaldoxime is applied gravimetrically.[60] To 0·05–0·1 g. Pb in 25 ml. soln., add 10 ml. salicylaldoxime soln. (1 g. in 5 ml. EtOH added to 95 ml. H_2O at 80°C), adjust to pH 9·5 with NH_4OH and dil. to 65 ml. with H_2O; filter on a G4 crucible after 1 hr., wash with H_2O, dry at 105°C (45–180°C) and weigh as $Pb(C_7H_6O_2N)$. Cu, Ni, Co, Bi, Fe, Mn, Hg, Mg interfere; Ag, Cd, Zn do not.

α-Isatoxime ppts. 0·005–0·5 g. Pb as $Pb(C_8H_4O_2N_2)$ from ammoniacal soln.[61] Dimethylglyoxime ppts. Pb at pH 8·5–9 as $Pb_2(C_4H_6N_2O_2)\cdot H_2O$ or as $Pb(OH)_2\cdot Pb(C_4H_6N_2O_2)$ depending on the drying temp.[62]

Diallyldithiocarbamidohydrazine ppts. Pb at pH 5·5 and can be used to sep. Pb and Cu at lower pH values (see Chapter 22, p. 180).[63]

2-Mercaptobenzothiazole ppts. Pb as $(C_7H_4NS_2)$-PbOH: add a 3-fold excess of hot 1% reagent to the hot neutral soln., filter on a glass crucible, wash with 2·5% NH_4OH and dry at 110°C.[64, 65] If the ppt. is yellow, add NH_4OH and boil until it turns white. 2-Mercaptobenzimidazole may be used similarly.[64] The ppt. formed with bismuthiol is eventually weighed as $PbSO_4$ [64] but that with bismuthiol II formed at pH 3–6·5 in citrate-contg. solns. is weighed as $Pb(C_8H_5N_2S_3)_2$.[66] In the latter case, Ag, Au, Hg, Tl, Cd, Pt interfere.

Gallic acid ppts. Pb as $Pb_2C_6H_2O_3CO_2$ from NaOAc-buffered solns.[67] Salicylic acid has also been examined.[68] Gallein forms $(C_{20}H_{11}O_8)Pb_2$ with Pb in AcOH–NaOAc-buffered solns.[69]

(j) EDTA titration.[70] Add 2 ml. 20% NaK-tartrate to the test soln. and neutralize with NH_4OH. Add 10 ml. buffer (54 g. NH_4Cl and 350 ml. NH_4OH/l.), dil. with H_2O to 125 ml., add 3 ml. 20% KCN and eriochrome black T indicator and titrate with $0{\cdot}01M$ EDTA at 40°C.

NOTES. (1) The interference of Cu, Ni, Co, Zn, Cd is prevented by KCN addn.; Fe interference by addn. of ascorbic acid and KCN. Ca, etc. interfere.
(2) CyDTA is used similarly and is said to give better results.[71]

(k) $H_2C_2O_4$ can be used titrimetrically or gravimetrically. For the former,[72] add 5 ml. AcOH/100 ml. soln. followed by 10 ml. satd. $H_2C_2O_4$; boil, cool, filter on a glass crucible and wash with cold H_2O. Dissolve in 130 ml. 1:25 H_2SO_4, warm and titrate with $0{\cdot}1N$ $KMnO_4$. For the latter,[73] ppt. PbC_2O_4 from $> 0{\cdot}05M$ Pb soln. at pH 3–7 and dry at 150–290°C.

(l) $NaHSO_3$ may be applied titrimetrically, nephelometrically or gravimetrically. For titrimetry,[74] add 5 ml. 10% $NaHSO_3$ to 50 μg. Pb as a nitrate soln., centrifuge after 10 min., add 3–5 ml. H_2O and centrifuge; repeat the washing and centrifuging twice. Add 0·5–2·0 ml. $2N$ NaOH and 4 ml. 0·001–$0{\cdot}01N$ I_2, acidify with 1:4 HCl, and back-titrate with $Na_2S_2O_3$ after 5 min. The error is $\pm 1\%$.

NOTES. (1) Ba, Sn interfere but Cu, Ag, Fe, Al, Ni, Ca, Mg do not.
(2) For nephelometry of 5–50 μg. Pb, acidify to methyl orange and add an equal vol. of 2% $NaHSO_3$.[75]
(3) For gravimetry, dry the ppt. at <60°C and weigh as $PbSO_3$ or ignite at >900°C and weigh as $PbSO_4$.[76]
(4) H_2SeO_3 may replace $NaHSO_3$.[77] Buffer the Pb soln. with AcOH and NaOAc, heat to 80–90°C, add reagent, dissolve the ppt. in 1 : 1 HCl and titrate iodometrically. Alternatively, remove the I_2 with H_3PO_2 and compare the color.

(m) Miscellaneous titrimetric methods. Pb can be detd. by addn. of NaCl and NaF (8·4 g. NaF and 11·692 g. NaCl/l.) to form PbClF; an aliquot of the filtrate is titrated with $AgNO_3$ soln. in presence of fluorescein or dichlorofluorescein indicator and starch.[78]

Titration is also possible after oxidation to PbO_2. To < 0·45 g. Pb in 50 ml. neutral soln., add 20–25 ml. 2·5*N* NaOH, 20 ml. 13·5% $Ni(NO_3)_2$ (catalyst) and 2 g. $K_2S_2O_8$ and stir for 1–2 min. Add 60–80 ml. 1:1 HNO_3 (slowly at first), wait for 2 min., add excess 0·1*N* As^{3+}, 10 ml. 1:1 HCl and 1 drop 0·005*M* KIO_3, and titrate with 0·1*N* $KMnO_4$.[79]

NOTES. (1) Co, Bi, Mn, Sb, Sn, halides, PO_4^{3-} and AsO_4^{3-} interfere; Cu, Zn, Fe, SO_4^{2-} and AcO^- do not.
(2) In an alternative method, oxidize with NaOCl, dissolve the PbO_2 in HCl and KI and titrate with $Na_2S_2O_3$.[80]
(3) Pb may be oxidized with $KMnO_4$ in 1*N* NaOH soln.; excess MnO_4^- is titrated potentiometrically with Tl^+ after acidification with HCOOH.[81]

$K_4Fe(CN)_6$ (1%) may be used to titrate Pb in solns. contg. 5 ml. AcOH/100 ml. at 60°C; satd. $UO_2(OAc)_2$ serves as external indicator (Scott and Furman[72]). Sb, Bi, Ba, Sr, Ca do not interfere. Diphenylcarbazone acts as an adsorption indicator for the titration;[82] starch-I_2 may also be used.[83]

$K_3Fe(CN)_6$ can also be applied. Add 10 ml. 10% $(NH_4)_2SO_4$, 1-2 ml. 2*N* H_2SO_4, 0·2–0·5 ml. 1% variamine blue indicator and 2 ml. 0·1*M* $K_3Fe(CN)_6$ to the soln., heat to 60°C and back-titrate with 0·1*N* ascorbic acid adding more indicator near the end-point.[84]

(n) Tetrabase is used colorimetrically.[85] To 5–50 μg. Pb in < 40 ml. soln. add 12 mg. Cu^{2+}, 4–6 g. NH_4NO_3 and NH_4OH until a blue color appears. Add 0·5 ml. 1*N* HNO_3, transfer to an electrolytic cell and dil. to 100 ml. Use Pt gauze as cathode and a rotating anode (500–700 r.p.m.) and electrolyze at 20–30°C with 0·5 amp. and 2·3 v. for 20 min. Wash with cold and then hot H_2O, dry in air, dip in 25 ml. tetrabase reagent (50 mg./100 ml. AcOH) and measure the blue color at 570 mμ (or at 600 mμ if Pb is < 20 μg.).

NOTES. (1) The error is ±10%; 1–2 μg. Pb remains in the electrolyte. Fe, Zn, Bi, Tl do not interfere but Cl^- and PO_4^{3-} do.
(2) Aniline[86] and diphenylcarbazide with pyridine[87] are also usable for colorimetric Pb detn.

(o) Na-diethyldithiocarbamate allows colorimetric detn.[88] Add 0·1% reagent to 25–300 μg. Pb at pH 3–9·5, ext. with CCl_4 and measure at 340 mμ. Alternatively, shake with $CuSO_4$ soln. and measure at 535 mμ[89] (see also Chapter 36, p. 281).

NOTES. (1) For gravimetric detn., ppt. with Na pentamethylenedithiocarbamate from dil. NaOH soln. contg. tartrate and CN^- and dry at 110–130°C; Tl, Hg, Mg interfere but Cd, Ag, Bi can be tolerated if repptn. is carried out.[90]
(2) A titrimetric finish is available:[91] to 3–400 mg. Pb in soln., add 10 ml. 10% tartaric acid, dil. with H_2O to 100 ml., neutralize with NH_4OH and just acidify with HCl to litmus. Add 10 ml. buffer (136 g. NaOAc and 26 g. AcOH/l.) and 5 ml. 0·005% dithizone in CCl_4, shake, and titrate with 0·001–0·1*N* Na diethyldithiocarbamate to the color change from red through violet to green. Ag, Hg, Cu, Ni, Co, Bi, Cd, Tl, Zn interfere.

(p) Miscellaneous colorimetric methods. HCl (50% v/v) forms a complex with 4–10 p.p.m. Pb which can be measured at 271 mμ.[92] KBr may be used similarly at 304 mμ (see Chapter 21, p. 167). KI and cocaine–HCl allow nephelometric detn.: treat 1–20 μg. Pb in 2 ml. 0·5–1% HCl or HNO_3 with 0·2 ml. 40% KI and 0·2 ml. 4% cocaine–HCl and measure after 5 min.[93]

H_2S gives a brown color with Pb in 2 ml. 3% AcOH soln. contg. 0·02 mg. gelatin; Cu, Ni, As, Zn, Sb, etc. interfere but Fe interference is prevented by $Na_2S_2O_4$ addn.[94] The reagent has also been used in alk. soln.[95] Pb may also be detd. by titration with H_2S soln. to a conductometric[96] or photometric[97] end-point.

Hematoxylin is suitable for ca. 50 μg. Pb: the acetate-buffered soln. at pH 6·5–6·8 is treated with gelatin and reagent (1 g./120 ml. EtOH). Heavy metals interfere and the error is ±1·5 μg.[98] Quinalizarin also forms a measurable color with Pb.[99]

(q) Flame photometry. The sensitivity is not good but the method can be used for detns. of Pb in gasoline.[100]

References

1. HILLEBRAND and LUNDELL, 178 (223); SCOTT and FURMAN, 500; KIMURA, 101; PIGGOTT, 232.
2. BILTZ, H. and HOEHNE, K., Über Bestimmung von As, Sb, Sn, Bi, in Bleiglanzen und ähnlichen Mineralien, *Z. anal. Chem.*, **99**, 1 (1934).
3. EVANS, B. S., Methods used in the Analysis of Certain Lead Alloys, *Analyst*, **58**, 450 (1933).
4. SATO, G., *Japan Analyst*, **5**, 304 (1956).
5. SMYTHE, J. A., *Analyst*, **75**, 21 (1950).
6. HEVESY, G. v. and HOBBIE, R., *Z. anal. Chem.*, **88**, 1 (1932).
7. PŘIBIL, R. and MARIČOVÁ, D., *Chem., listy*, **46**, 542 (1952).
8. KATO, T., *J. Chem. Soc. Japan*, **58**, 972 (1937).
9. WELCHER, **IV**, 179.
10. WEST, P. W. and CARLTON, J. K., *Anal. Chim. Acta*, **6** 406 (1952).
11. HECHT and DONAU, 152; A.S.T.M. 288 ff. (for brasses and many alloys); SCHRENK, W. T. and DELANO, P. H., *Ind. Eng. Chem., Anal. Ed.*, **3**, 27 (1931); NICHOLS, M. L., *ibid.*, 385.
12. NORWITZ, G., *Analyst*, **76**, 113, 314 (1951); SILVERMAN, L., *Anal. Chem.*, **20**, 906 (1948).
13. GOLDBERG, C., *Anal. Chem.*, **25**, 1405 (1953).
14. LINGANE, *Electroanalytical Chemistry*, 313 (1953); see also Chapter 4.
15. IPPOLITI, P. and SCARANO, E., *Ann. chim. (Rome)*, **45**, 492 (1955).
16. HECHT and DONAU, 150.
17. A.S.T.M. 290 ff.

18. ELVING, P. J. and ZOOK, W. C., *Anal. Chem.*, **25**, 502 (1953).
19. FRITZ, J. S. and FREELAND, M. Q., *Anal. Chem.*, **26**, 1593 (1954).
20. A.S.T.M. 124 (in steels).
21. DUBROSKAYA, T. F. and FILIPPOVA, N. A., *Zavodskaya Lab.*, **21**, 523 (1955).
22. IIJIMA, S., *Bull. Inst. Phys. Chem. Research* (*Tokyo*), **23**, 367 (1944); FEINBERG, S., *Z. anal. Chem.*, **96**, 415 (1934).
23. DUPUIS, T., *Anal. Chim. Acta*, **3**, 663 (1949).
24. IMAI, H., *J. Chem. Soc. Japan*, **76**, 770 (1955); KIBA, T., *ibid.*, **60**, 912 (1939).
25. SANT, B. R., *Z. anal. Chem.*, **148**, 176 (1955).
26. BROWN, D. J., *et al.*, *Ind. Eng. Chem.*, *Anal. Ed.*, **3**, 134 (1931).
27. SCOTT and FURMAN, 513.
28. GRUPP, A. *Z. anal. Chem.*, **119**, 333 (1940).
29. RAY, H. N., *J. Indian Chem. Soc.*, *Ind. & News Ed.*, **4**, 11 (1941).
30. KENNY, F. and KURTZ, R. B., *Anal. Chem.*, **25**, 1550 (1953); **28**, 1206 (1956) (in Pb–Sn alloy).
31. HOFFMAN, W. A. and BRANDT, W. W., *Anal. Chem.*, **28**, 1487 (1956).
32. GUZELJ, L., *Z. anal. Chem.*, **104**, 107 (1936); KARAOGLANOV, Z. and MICHOV, M., *ibid.*, **103**, 113 (1935); SARUDI, I., *ibid.*, **125**, 108, 370 (1943); GROTE, F., *ibid.*, **126**, 129 (1943); MILLER, C. C. and CURRIE, L. R., *Analyst*, **75**, 467, 471 (1950) (0·2–5 mg.); A.S.T.M. 451 (in Sb).
33. LETONOFF, T. V., *Ind. Eng. Chem.*, *Anal. Ed.*, **13**, 631 (1941); LETONOFF and REINHOLD, J. G., *ibid.* **12**, 280 (1940); (YOE, 255).
34. MAYNES, A. D. and MCBRYDE, W. A. E., *Anal. Chem.*, **29**, 1259 (1957).
35. SANDELL, 392.
36. SNYDER, L. J., *Anal. Chem.*, **19**, 684 (1947); CHOLAK, J. C., *et al.*, *ibid.*, **20**, 671 (1948).
37. MCCORD, WM. M. and ZEMP, J. W., *Anal. Chem.*, **27**, 1171 (1955).
38. WELCHER, **III**, 497.
39. SANDELL, 406.
40. CLIFFORD, P. A., *J. Assoc. Offic. Agr. Chemists*, **26**, 26 (1943).
41. YOUNG, R. S. and LEIBOWITZ, A., *Analyst*, **71**, 477 (1946).
42. SILVERMAN, L., *Anal. Chem.*, **20**, 906 (1948); **19**, 698 (1947); YOSHIMORI, T. and HIRANO, S., *Japan Analyst*, **3**, 470 (1954) (in steel); (SANDELL, 399; WELCHER, **III**, 499), A.S.T.M., 432 (Mg and its alloys), 517 (slab Zn, Zn-base die-casting alloys).
43. WAKAMATSU, S., *Japan Analyst*, **5**, 509 (1956) (in steel); OTA, K. and MORI, S., *ibid.*, 442 (in Sn.)
44. CHOLAK, J. C., *et al.*, *Ind. Eng. Chem.*, *Anal. Ed.*, **9**, 488 (1937).
45. SANDELL, E. B., *Ind. Eng. Chem.*, *Anal. Ed.*, **9**, 464 (1937).
46. VESTERBERG, R. and SJÖHOLM, O., *Mikrochemie ver. Mikrochim. Acta*, **36/37**, 967 (1951).
47. WELCHER, **II**, 200.
48. WELCHER, **IV**, 171; CIMERMAN, C. and ARIEL M., *Anal. Chim. Acta*, **12**, 13 (1955); **14**, 48 (1956) ($\pm$0·4%/2–5 mg. Pb).
49. HECHT and DONAU, 152; see also LIANG, S. C. and LU, K. I., *Anal. Chim. Acta*, **7**, 451 (1952) (optimum pH = 6·5–10·0, homogeneous pptn.).
50. DUNN, C. L. and TARTAR, H. V., *Ind. Eng. Chem.*, *Anal. Ed.*, **6**, 64 (1934); also see SHAKHTAKHTINSKIĬ, G. B. and MELIKOVA, R. A., *Trudy Azerbaidzan. Ind. Inst. im M. Azibekova*, No. 8, 80, 88 (1954) (iodometry).
51. WILLARD, H. H. and THOMPSON, J. J., *Ind. Eng. Chem.*, *Anal. Ed.*, **6**, 425 (1934).
52. GENTRY, C. H. R. and SHERRINGTON, L. G., *Analyst*, **71**, 31 (1946).
53. WILLARD, H. H. and GOODSPEED, E. W., *Ind. Eng. Chem.*, *Anal. Ed.*, **8**, 414 (1936).
54. KALLMANN, S., *Anal. Chem.*, **23**, 1291 (1951).
55. JÍLEK, A. and KOTÀ, J., *Collection Czechoslov. Chem. Communs.*, **5**, 396 (1933); **6**, 101 (1934).
56. TANII, K. and HASHIMOTO, J., *J. Chem. Soc. Japan*, **60**, 1121 (1939); SPACU, G. and DICK, J., *Z. anal. Chem.*, **72**, 289 (1927).
57. DENK, G. and ALT, J., *Z. anal. Chem.*, **142**, 357 (1954).
58. WELCHER, **I**, 296 ff.
59. PHILLIPS, J., *et al.*, *Anal. Chem.*, **24**, 1033 (1952).
60. WELCHER, **III**, 268.
61. HOVORKA, V. and DIVIŠ, L., *Collection Czechoslov. Chem. Communs.*, **14**, 473 (1949).
62. ISHIBASHI, M. and FUNAHASHI, H., *J. Chem. Soc. Japan*, **59**, 503 (1938).
63. DUTT, N. K. and SARMA, K. P. S., *Anal. Chim. Acta*, **15**, 21 (1956).
64. WELCHER, **IV**, 113 ff.
65. CIMERMAN, C. and BOGIN, D., *Anal. Chim. Acta*, **12**, 218 (1955) (2–8 mg.).
66. MAJUMDAR, A. K. and SINGH, B. R., *Z. anal. Chem.*, **154**, 413 (1957); **156**, 265 (1957); also see ČÍHALÍK, ref. 36, p. 149.
67. MAYR, C., *Monatsh.*, **77**, 65 (1947).
68. MURGULESCU, I. G. and DOBRESCU, F., *Z. anal. Chem.*, **128**, 303 (1948).
69. NAITO, T. and KINOSHITA, Y., *Reagent* (*Japan*), **1** 102 (1945).
70. KINNUNEN, J. and WENNERSTRAND, B., *Chemist Analyst*, **43**, 65 (1954) (in bronze, after extg. diethyldithiocarbamate complex with $CHCl_3$ from ammoniacal soln. contg. NaK-tartrate and KCN); KINNUNEN and MERIKANTO, B., *ibid.*, **44**, 75 (1955); PINKSTON, J. L. and KENNER, C. T., *Anal. Chem.*, **27**, 446 (1955); also WILHITE, R. N. and UNDERWOOD, A. L., *ibid.*, 1334 (photometric at 240 mμ); MINAMI, E. and SATO, K., *Japan Analyst*, **4**, 579 (1955); SUK, V., *et al.*, *Collection Czechoslov. Chem. Communs.*, **19**, 679 (1954) (dithizone as indicator); PŘIBIL, R., *ibid*, **18**, 783 (1953) (Mg-EDTA), SUK, V. and MALAT, M., *Chemist Analyst*, **45**, 1511 (1945) (pyrocatechol violet).
71. GOETZ, C. A. and DEBBRECHT, F. J., *Anal. Chem.*, **27**, 1972 (1955).
72. SCOTT and FURMAN, 509; FRORE, L., *Ann. chim. applicata*, **39**, 523 (1949) (better than iodometry of $PbCrO_4$); KAWAGAKI, K., *J. Chem. Soc. Japan*, **73**, 640, 705 (1952) (filtration method is better); STOLYAROV, K. P., *Zhur. Anal. Khim.*, **9**, 141 (1954) (photometric at 365 mμ with Ce^{4+}).

73. YAMAMURA, K., *J. Chem. Soc. Japan*, **51**, 788 (1930); ISHIBASHI, M. and MATSUMOTO, T., *Japan Analyst*, **5**, 343 (1956).
74. GAPCHENKO, M. W., *Zavodskaya Lab.*, **4**, 1014 (1935); *Z. anal. Chem.*, **109**, 206 (1937); see also SHEĬNTSIS, O. G., *Zavodskaya Lab.*, **10**, 377 (1941).
75. BADHAM, C. and TAYLOR, H. B., *Arch. Pharm.*, **27**, 81 (1933).
76. GASPAR Y ARNAL, T., *et al.*, *Anales fís. y quím.* (*Madrid*), **43**, 571 (1947).
77. NARUI, H., *J. Chem. Soc. Japan*, **62**, 764, 935 (1941); **63**, 71, 500, 605 (1942).
78. TANANAEFF, I., *Z. anal. Chem.*, **99**, 18, 21 (1934).
79. LANG, R. and ZWEŘINA, J., *Z. anal. Chem.*, **93**, 248 (1933).
80. TRAVERS, A., *Compt. rend.*, **196**, 548 (1933).
81. ISSA, I. M., *et al.*, *Anal. Chim. Acta*, **12**, 474 (1954); **13**, 108, 323 (1955).
82. RIPAN, R., *Z. anal. Chem.*, **123**, 244 (1942).
83. FUJITA, Y. and KAYAMORI, H., *J. Chem. Soc. Japan*, **74** 71 (1953).
84. ERDEY, L. and POLOS, L., *Z. anal. Chem.*, **153**, 401 (1956).
85. SANDELL, 402, WELCHER, **IV**, 562; GEUER, G., *Angew. Chem.*, **61**, 99 (1949).
86. WELCHER, **II**, 268.
87. WELCHER, **III**, 439.
88. SUDO, E., *J. Chem. Soc. Japan*, **73**, 626 (1952).
89. BODE, H., *Z. anal. Chem.*, **144**, 165 (1955).
90. BREMANIS, E., *et al.*, *Z. anal. Chem.*, **145**, 18 (1955).
91. WICKBOLD, R., *Z. anal. Chem.*, **152**, 266 (1956); **153**, 21 (1956); BOBTELSKY, M. and RAFAILOFF, R., *Anal. Chim. Acta*, **16**, 321 (1957) (photometric).
92. MERRITT, JR., C., *et al.*, *Anal. Chem.*, **25**, 572 (1953); SHERWOOD, R. M. and CHAPMAN, JR., F. W., *ibid.*, **27**, 88 (1955) (after dithizone sepn. only Sn^{2+} interferes); KRESS, K. E., *ibid.*, **29**, 803 (1957) (correction for Fe, Zn, Cu).
93. GALEA, V. and GHELBERG, N., *Acad. rep. populare Romîne, Filiala Cluj, Studii cercetări ştiinţ.*, **3**, No. 3/4 289 (1952).
94. JACKSON, P. G., *J. Soc. Chem. Ind.*, **5**, T211 (1937).
95. REITH, J. F. and BEUS, J. DE, *Z. anal. Chem.*, **103**, 13 (1935); RANDALL, M. and SARQUIS, M. N., *Ind. Eng. Chem.*, *Anal. Ed.*, **7**, 2 (1935); BUSH, G. H., *Analyst*, **79**, 697 (1954) (420–430 mμ with Na_2S or $Na_2S_2O_4$; in steel).
96. SCHNEIDER, A. and BEISKIN, H., *Z. anal. Chem.*, **141**, 326 (1954).
97. HIRANO, S., *J. Soc. Chem. Ind. Japan*, *Suppl.*, **38**, 648B (1935).
98. IIJIMA, S., *Bull. Inst. Phys. Chem. Research* (*Tokyo*), **23**, Chem. 1 (1944).
99. MOROZOV, V. A., *Gigiena i Sanit.*, No. 9, 46 (1954).
100. GILBERT, P. T., A.S.T.M. Symposium of Flame Photometry, 77 (1951).

21

BISMUTH

The principal sources for this chapter are Hillebrand and Lundell, Scott and Furman, Kimura and Fresenius–Jander.[1] Bismuth analysis has been discussed in a monograph[2] and has been reviewed.[3]

For general analytical purposes it should be noted that during electrolysis Bi deposits mainly on the cathode but also on the anode. Bi may coppt. with $PbSO_4$, and with SiO_2 as BiOCl or $BiONO_3$.

Attack

Minerals are decomposed in several ways.

(a) Add HNO_3, a little HCl, H_2SO_4, evap. to fumes and proceed in the usual way. Burn the paper and the residue separately, fuse with Na_2CO_3 and ext. with H_2O. Treat the residue with HNO_3 and ppt. as BiOCl.

(b) Treat 1 g. sulfide mineral with 5 ml. of a mixture of 50 g. Br_2 and 75 g. KBr in 500 ml.; after some time, add 15 ml. HNO_3, evap. to dryness, add 10 ml. HCl and 20 ml. H_2SO_4, evap. to fumes, add 50 ml. H_2O and warm the soln. Filter through paper and wash with 1:10 H_2SO_4.

(c) Fuse with Na_2CO_3 and leach with H_2O.

(d) For simultaneous SiO_2 and Pb detn., treat the mineral with HNO_3, HCl and H_2SO_4 as above. Ext. the residue with AcOH and NH_4OAc, ppt. with H_2S, ext. with $(NH_4)_2S$, add HNO_3, sep. as BiOCl, add H_2SO_4 and continue in the usual way.

Alloys are treated as follows. Treat with 20 ml. HCl and 5 ml. HNO_3 if the amt. of Pb present is small; if it is large, treat with 1:5 HNO_3. Dissolve Sn or Sb alloys in Br_2–HBr mixture (see Chapter 20, p. 157).

Separation

Bi is sepd. from Group III, etc. by treating 100 ml. soln. contg. 5–7 ml. HCl with H_2S. Concn. with Cu or Cd sulfides from 0·1–0·3N HCl solns. is useful before the detn. of Bi by the dithizone or KI methods resp.; the ppt. is filtered after 12 hr. Treatment with $(NH_4)_2S$ seps. Bi from the As group. Bi_2S_3 is appreciably sol. in Na or K sulfide or polysulfide and in Na or K sulfide and hydroxide mixtures.

Hydrolysis in dil. HCl soln. seps. BiOCl from Pb, Cu, Cd, Hg^{2+} (see under Determination). Bi is sepd. from Cu, Cd, Hg with $(NH_4)_2CO_3$ (p. 166), from large amts. of Pb and Mn with ZnO or HgO, and from Pb with $HCOONH_4$ (p. 166).

Sepn. from SiO_2 is obtained by evapn. with H_2SO_4 or $HClO_4$.

Internal electrolysis permits the sepn. of Bi from large amts. of Pb (see p. 145) and treatment with Sn^{2+} in NaOH soln. gives a sepn. from large amts. of Sn.

Bi is sepd. from Ag, Hg, Pb, Cd, As, Sb^{5+}, Al, Cr, Ni, Co, Zn, Mn, etc., by means of cupferron in 1N HCl or H_2SO_4 soln.; extn. with $CHCl_3$ is possible.

Dithizone in $CHCl_3$ allows sepns. of Bi from Fe in $(NH_4)_3$-citrate solns., from Cu, Ag, Cd, Zn in CN^--contg. solns. at pH 8·5–9·0, and from Pb (in the aq. layer) at pH 3·4. CCl_4 extn. requires a pH of 2·0.

Several concn. methods are available. MnO_2 obtained by heating the slightly acidic Mn^{2+}-contg. soln. with $KMnO_4$, concs. and seps. Bi, Sn, Sb, Mo from Cu, etc. $Fe(OH)_3$ seps. Bi from large amts. of Cu. Bi, As^{3+}, Cu, Hg are sepd. from Pb and Fe^{2+} by extn. of the diethyldithiocarbamates with Et_2O or $CHCl_3$ from slightly acidic solns., or by extn. with diethylammonium diethyldithiocarbamate in $CHCl_3$ from 2N HCl solns. (see also pp. 61, 158 and 204). The Bi–iodide complex can be extd. with EtOAc and AmOH (see under Determination). Methyl violet and KI may also be used for concn. purposes.[4]

Determination

A number of reactions can be utilized for specific detns. of Bi in presence of Group II elements. For example, the phosphate method is convenient for amts. greater than 1 mg. and the hydrolysis method as BiOCl is suitable for milligram amts. of Bi. The oxine method is reported to be satisfactory (Farini[5]).

The KI and dithizone methods are probably the best available for colorimetric detns. although the thiourea and diethyldithiocarbamate methods seem to be quite satisfactory.

(a) $(NH_4)_2HPO_4$ is normally applied gravimetrically; colorimetric and titrimetric finishes are also available. For gravimetry,[5,6] add 2 ml. HNO_3/100 ml. soln., boil, add 50 ml. hot 2·5% reagent and digest for 1 hr. on a steam bath; filter on a porcelain crucible, wash with 2% NH_4NO_3 contg. a few drops of HNO_3/l., ignite at 480–800°C (379–950°C) and weigh as $BiPO_4$.

NOTES. (1) No interference is caused by Ag, Hg, Cu, Cd, Zn, Mg, K, Na; Ti, Zr, Th, Sn, Nb, Ta and large amts. of Cd interfere. Pb, Cl^- and SO_4^{2-} interfere but can be sepd. as follows. Treat the sulfide ppt. with hot HNO_3, filter through paper and wash with 5% HNO_3. Add Na_2CO_3 until a ppt. appears and then add 1 g. in excess followed by 0·5 g. KCN; boil, filter on a paper pulp pad and wash with H_2O. Dissolve the ppt. in the vessel, pass through the filter and wash with H_2O. Add NH_4OH until a turbidity forms, add 2 ml. HNO_3 and dil. to 100 ml. with H_2O.
(2) For a colorimetric finish, det. the excess reagent in the filtrate as molybdenum blue after reduction of phosphomolybdate with hydroquinone.[6] Titrimetry is also possible.[7]
(3) $BiAsO_4 \cdot \frac{1}{2}H_2O$ can be weighed after drying at 100–110°C and $BiAsO_4$ after drying at 450–800°C[8] (47–400°C, $BiAsO_4$). A titrimetric finish is again possible.[6]

(b) HCl hydrolysis is most useful gravimetrically[1, 9] but can also be used titrimetrically. For gravimetric detn. of < 5 mg. Bi in 100 ml. dil. HNO_3 soln., heat, add 1:2 NH_4OH to form a turbidity, followed by 5 ml. 1:9 HCl, dil. to 400 ml. with hot H_2O and place on a steam bath for 2–12 hr. Filter, wash 2–3 times with hot H_2O, dissolve in boiling 1:9 HCl and rinse the filter with hot H_2O, hot 1:9 HCl and hot H_2O. Reppt., filter on a Gooch crucible, wash with hot H_2O, dry at 100°C and weigh as BiOCl.

NOTES. (1) According to Duval, the ppt. is $Bi(OH)_2Cl$ below 258°C, BiOCl at 328–805°C and Bi_2O_3 above 950°C.
(2) No interference arises from Cu, Cd, Pb; Ag, Hg^+, Tl^+, Sb, Sn, Zr, Ti, SO_4^{2-}, CrO_4^{2-}, AsO_4^{3-} and PO_4^{3-} interfere.
(3) For a titrimetric finish, dissolve the ppt. in 20 ml. 2*N* HNO_3, add 60 ml. H_2O, excess 0·1*N* $AgNO_3$, warm the soln. and back-titrate by Volhard's method.[6]
(4) A variety of other hydrolysis methods has been described; that involving $KBrO_3$ seems to be the best of these. For this, add 2–3 g. $KBrO_3$ to 200–300 ml. of slightly acidic (HNO_3) soln. and boil; if the soln. becomes turbid, clear it with HNO_3; add 10% KBr soln. when a turbidity and the Br_2 color appear. Boil to remove Br_2 and add more KBr. Continue in this way until pptn. is complete. Large amts. of Cl^- and NH_4^+ interfere.
Satd. $(NH_4)_2CO_3$ is suitable for >5 mg. Bi;[1] an excess of reagent is added to the dil. HNO_3 soln. after it has been almost neutralized with NH_4OH; eventually the ppt. is ignited at 550–800°C and weighed as Bi_2O_3. Cu and Cd do not interfere but SO_4^{2-}, Fe, etc. do; Cl^- and Br^- can be removed by repeated evapn. to dryness with HNO_3. The ppt. dissolves slightly in excess reagent and NH_4OH. In an alternative approach, $(BiO)_2CO_3$ is weighed after being heated at 68–308°C.[10]
KI can be used for <0·1 g. Bi in 20 ml. of slightly acidic soln.[6] Add KI to give a yellow or black ppt., and then 200–300 ml. H_2O; place on a steam bath until the supernate clears (if it is yellow owing to excess acidity, neutralize with 2% NaOAc to methyl orange). Filter on a glass crucible, wash with hot H_2O, dry at 110°C (<307°C) and weigh as BiOI. Alternatively titrate the filtrate with $AgNO_3$.[11]
With 0·25% NH_4NO_3, evap. the nitrate-contg. Bi soln. to a syrup after H_2O addn.; repeat 4 times, evap. to dryness, ext. with the NH_4NO_3 soln. and finally weigh as Bi_2O_3 after ignition[6] (see also Scott and Furman[1]).
$HCOONH_4$ is used to det. 0·5–300 mg. Bi in dil. HNO_3 soln.[6, 12] Add NH_4OH and $(NH_4)_2CO_3$ until the ppt. just dissolves, add reagent and boil. Add 8*N* HNO_3, reppt. and finally ignite to Bi_2O_3.
Other variations require as reagents H_2SO_4,[6] NH_4OH and 4% H_2O_2 (Scott and Furman[1]), pyridine[13] and ammoniacal EDTA soln. with Ca^{2+} addn.;[14] in the last case Pb does not interfere but Al and Fe do.

(c) Oxine acetate is applied in gravimetric, titrimetric and colorimetric detns. For gravimetry,[15] treat 0·1–2 mg. Bi_2O_3 in 2·5 ml. soln. with 0·3–0·5 ml. 50% tartaric acid for each mg. Bi; add 1 drop phenolphthalein and 1 drop methyl red followed by NH_4OH until the soln. is basic and then by 10% AcOH until acidic and the soln. contains an excess of 0·5 ml./3 ml. Heat to 70°C, add 0·5 ml. 4% reagent/mg. Bi, leave to cool, filter on a glass crucible and wash with hot H_2O. Dry at 115–125°C and weigh as $Bi(C_9H_6ON)_3 \cdot H_2O$ (the drying temp. is questionable). Alternatively, dissolve the ppt. in < 15% HCl, add 0·1*N* $KBrO_3$ and KBr and complete the detn. iodometrically. PO_4^{3-} does not interfere.

NOTES. (1) For colorimetry, treat the ppt. obtained from 0·005–0·05 mg. Bi with Folin–Denis reagent (see p. 397, and Welcher), or ext. with $CHCl_3$ at pH 4·0–5·2 and measure the absorbance at 395 mμ.[16]
(2) An amperometric titration has been suggested.[17]
(3) Oxine can be used in conjunction with KI (see below).

(d) Iodide provides one of the best colorimetric methods,[6, 18] and is used in conjunction with H_3PO_2 or ascorbic acid and Na_2SO_3 to prevent interference of oxidizing agents. For > 5 μg. Bi in 10–15 ml. 2*N* H_2SO_4 soln., add 1 ml. 30% H_3PO_2, or 5 ml. 1% ascorbic acid and 1 ml. 1% Na_2SO_3, followed by 1 ml. 10% KI and dil. to 25 ml. with H_2O; measure at 460 mμ. Alternatively, 10 min. after the KI addn., ext. with 2–3 ml. portions of AmOH and EtOAc (3:1) until the aq. layer is colorless, dil. to a known vol., filter and measure immediately at 460 mμ; the standard curve must be obtained in the same way.

NOTES. (1) Cu, Ag, Pt, Pd, Sb, Sn, Cl^-, and large amts. of F^-, Cd, As^{3+}, Fe^{3+} interfere. Pb and Tl (<0·5 mg.) can be tolerated. Larger amts. of Pb can be sepd. with 9-methyl-2,3,7-trihydroxyfluorone.[19]
(2) The sensitivity is greater at 337 mμ.[20] For 30–300 μg. Bi in 10 ml. 1–2*N* H_2SO_4, add 10 ml. 10*N* H_2SO_4, 20 ml. reagent (140 g. KI and 10 g. ascorbic acid/l.), dil. to 50 ml. with H_2O and measure at 337 mμ against a reference soln. contg. 2·5–3·5 g. KI and 1·5–2·5*N* in H_2SO_4. Cd,

Fe^{2+}, Mn, Zn, PO_4^{3-}, Cl^-, F^- and EDTA do not interfere; Sb, Pb, Hg^{2+}, 5 p.p.m. V or W, 10 p.p.m. Sn or Ag, 25 p.p.m. Co, 50 p.p.m. Cu or As^{3+}, 150 p.p.m. Ni and 500 p.p.m. Fe^{3+} interfere.

(3) If SO_2-water and H_3PO_2 are used, colloidal S may be formed. With SO_2-water alone[21] yellow $I(HSO)_2$ is produced. KI may be used by itself (Scott and Furman[1]). Ag, Hg, Au, Cu, As, Sb, Fe do not interfere if the soln. is extd. previously with dithizone.

(4) Halogen-complex formation is utilized in several other methods. Trimethylphenylammonium iodide permits gravimetric detn. Treat the 0·001–0·1*M* Bi soln. in 4*N* HCl with a 2·5% reagent soln. contg. 30 g. KI/l., filter on a glass crucible after 2 hr., wash with 1 : 3 reagent, 1 : 15 H_2SO_4 and 95% EtOH, dry at 110–120°C and weigh as $[(CH_3)_3C_6H_5N]BiI_4 \cdot 4H_2O$.[22] Similar procedures are possible with α-naphthoquinoline,[6, 23] hexamine and antipyrine,[24] and hexamine alone.[25]

$[Co(en)_2(SCN)_2](SCN)$ is used in conjunction with KI.[6, 26, 27] Heat 0·05–0·1 g. Bi in 30 ml. dil. HNO_3 soln., add 0·5 g. KI and 10 ml. hot reagent (25 g. $Co(SCN)_2$, 76 g. NH_4SCN and 6·0 g. ethylenediamine in 100 ml.) and allow to cool; filter on a glass crucible, wash with a soln. contg. 0·3 g. KI and 5 ml. reagent/100 ml., dry below 220°C and weigh as $[Co(en)_2(SCN)_2][BiI_4]$. Ag, Hg, Cu, Pb, etc. interfere.

$[Co(en)_3][BiI_4]_2I$ may be utilized similarly.[26] The ppt. formed with KBr and $[Cr(NH_3)_6](NO_3)_3$ can be detd. by distn. and titration of the NH_3 that it contains.[6] $[Cr_4(OH)_6(en)_6]I_4(BiI_4)_2$[28] and *trans*-$[Co(en)_2Cl_2][BiCl_6]$[29] have also been suggested.

KI and oxine serve in titrimetric or colorimetric detns. For 0·5–100 mg. Bi in very dil. HNO_3 or H_2SO_4 solns. add 5% oxine in 0·2*N* H_2SO_4 and 0·1*N* KI until the ppt. coagulates; filter on a glass crucible and wash with a soln. contg. 50 ml. 2*N* H_2SO_4, 25 ml. 0·1*N* KI, 1·8 g. oxine and some NH_2OH or $N_2H_4 \cdot H_2SO_4$/l. Dissolve the ppt. in 10% HCl, add 0·5 g. KCN and starch and titrate with 0·1*N* KIO_3. Cl^-, Br^-, Ag, Hg, Pb, Tl interfere but Cd, As^{3+}, Fe^{2+}, Ni, Co, Zn, Mn, Al, Be, Cr, U, Ba, Ca do not; the interferences of Fe^{3+}, Cu, and Sn or Sb are prevented by treatment with SO_2, pyridine, and $(NH_4)_2$-tartrate resp.[6, 30] Titration of I^- in the filtrate with KIO_3 in presence of $CHCl_3$ indicator may be preferable.[31]

The process can be used for direct colorimetry or the ppt. can be extd. with cyclohexanol or with 1 : 2 AmOAc–Me_2CO.[30]

Quinaldine, *o*-nitroquinoline[32] and caffeine[33] provide other possibilities for titrimetric detns.

KBr forms a color with 5–150 μg. Bi in 25 ml. 1*M* KBr soln. which can be measured at 365 mμ; moderate amts. of Pb, Fe^{2+}, Zn, Cd, HNO_3 can be tolerated but milligram amts. of Cu, Hg, Fe^{3+}, Sb interfere.[34] HCl (50% v/v) serves colorimetrically for 3–12 p.p.m. Bi at 327 mμ.[35]

NH_4SCN (2 ml. 50%) gives a measurable color (450 mμ) with 0·025–0·15 mg. Bi in 4·5 ml. 12*N* H_2SO_4 in presence of 4 drops 20% $SnCl_2$ in 18*N* H_2SO_4.[36] The color formed by 1*M* NaSCN with < 7 μg. Bi/ml. in 0·05–0·25*N* $HClO_4$ can be measured at 333 mμ (ϵ = 25 700).[37]

Other colorimetric methods involve KI in conjunction with tetraphenylarsonium chloride,[38] tetraacetylammonium hydroxide,[39] or quinine;[6, 40] in the last case the complex formed with 1–25 μg. Bi is extd. with cyclohexanol. The complex between KI, antipyrine and 1–50 μg. Bi can be extd. with $CHCl_3$ from 0·5–1·5*N* H_2SO_4 solns.[41] That of antipyrine and NH_4SCN with 1–100 μg. Bi is extd. with AmOH and Et_2O at pH 1·8–2·4 (see p. 153). Brucine and KI react with 10–400 μg. Bi and the $CHCl_3$ ext. can be measured at 425 mμ.[42] KI and cinchonine can be used nephelometrically.[6, 43]

Bi may be titrated amperometrically with diantipyrinylmethane in solns. which are 0·2–1·6*M* in H_2SO_4 and 0·03–0·12*M* in KBr.[44]

(e) Dithizone is particularly useful for colorimetric detns. in biological materials.[6, 45] For < 50 μg. Bi in 10 g. material, ash at 500°C in a muffle, add 2 ml. HNO_3, 10 ml. AcOH and dil. to 50 ml. with H_2O. Ext. with 10 ml portions of dithizone in CCl_4 (100 mg/l.) until there is no change in the green color; combine, wash with 50 ml. 0·2% HNO_3, sep. and add 50 ml. 0·2% HNO_3 and 5 ml. 40% w/v KBr. Shake, wash the aq. layer with 5 ml. CCl_4, add 5 ml. of a soln. contg. 25 g. KCN and 40 ml. 14*N* NH_4OH/l. (the pH becomes 9·5), and add 10 ml. dithizone in $CHCl_3$ (7 mg./l.). Shake, filter through a cotton plug and measure at 490 mμ.

NOTES. (1) Pb, Cu, Zn, Cl^- and PO_4^{3-} can be tolerated.
(2) Di-β-naphthylthiocarbazone forms a color which can be measured at 540 mμ (ϵ = 170 000).[46]

(f) Thionalide is used gravimetrically or titrimetrically.[6, 47] To a soln. contg. 10 ml. 2*N* HNO_3 or H_2SO_4/100 ml., add a 5-fold excess of 1% thionalide in EtOH; the final soln. should be at least 10% in EtOH. Place on a steam-bath for 30 min., filter on a G4 crucible, wash with hot H_2O, dry at 140–160°C (45–134°C) and weigh as $Bi(C_{12}H_{10}ONS)_3$. Alternatively, dissolve the ppt. in 50 ml. AcOH and 4–5 ml. 5*N* H_2SO_4, sat. with NH_4Cl, add 0·1 g. KI, excess 0·02*N* I_2 and titrate with 0·02*N* $Na_2S_2O_3$.

NOTE. If Fe is present, ignite to Bi_2O_3. If Pb is present, dil. the soln. to 200–400 ml. and add 5–6 ml. 2*N* HNO_3/100 ml. before the above reagent addn. Co, Zn, Cd, Tl, Mn, Al, Cr, Ca, Ba, Mg do not interfere.

(g) Pyrogallol allows gravimetric or colorimetric detns.[6, 48] For gravimetry, add 0·5*N* NH_4OH to 0·5–2 mg. Bi in acid soln. until a ppt. appears, then add 0·1*N* HNO_3 until it dissolves. Dil. to 3 ml. with H_2O, add excess reagent, place on a steam bath for 10–15 min., allow to cool, filter on a glass crucible, wash with 0·1*N* HNO_3 and H_2O, dry at 105°C and weigh as $Bi(C_6H_3O_3)$.

NOTES. (1) Heating to 191–409°C gives a compound of const. wt. but unknown compn. (Duval).
(2) Sb interferes; Pb, Cu, Cd, Zn do not.

(3) The colorimetric finish is based on reduction of Folin–Denis reagent by the ppt.
(4) Gallic acid is not a satisfactory reagent for Bi[6,49] (Duval). Picric acid has been suggested.[50]

(h) H_2S is applied gravimetrically or nephelometrically.[6,51] For the former, treat the $< 1{\cdot}2N$ HCl or H_2SO_4 soln. with H_2S, filter on a Gooch crucible, wash with H_2S water, EtOH, CS_2 and Et_2O, dry at 100–160°C (?) and weigh as Bi_2S_3.

(i) Electrodeposition can be done in dil. NaOH solns. contg. 2–3 g. NaK-tartrate and 2–3 g. KCN at 75°C with −0·76 up to −0·90 v. *vs.* S.C.E.[6,52] Cu does not interfere.

NOTES. (1) For the analysis of Bi metal,[53] warm 0·1–0·3 g. with 15 ml. HNO_3, add 15 ml. H_2O, boil for 10 min., add 10 ml. 3% H_2O_2, boil for 10 min. and dil. to 190 ml. with H_2O. Add 7 ml. HCl soln. (5 drops HCl/500 ml.), insert the Pt gauze and Pt coil electrodes, and electrolyze at 2 amp./dm.² for 10 min. and at 1 amp. for 50 min. Pb, Cu, Sb, Hg interfere.
(2) For Bi–Sn or Bi–Sn–Cd alloys[54] (Bi <0·3 g.), add 8 ml. 7·5*N* HNO_3 and 50 ml. HF, heat, add 25 ml. 50% tartaric acid and dil. to 150 ml. with hot H_2O. Insert a Cu-plated cathode, heat, stir and electrolyze for 20 min. Wash with H_2O and EtOH, and dry at 110°C.
(3) If less than 100 mg. Bi and 250 mg. Sb or Sn are present, proceed as follows.[55] Add 0·5 g. $N_2H_4{\cdot}H_2SO_4$ and 10 ml. H_2SO_4 to the alloy, warm to dissolve, cool and add 10–20 ml. H_2O, 30 ml. 1*M* Na-citrate, 3 g. NH_2OH or $N_2H_4{\cdot}H_2SO_4$. Adjust to pH 3 with 10*M* NaOH using a glass electrode, dil. to 120–140 ml. with H_2O and readjust to pH 3. Heat to 70–80°C and electrolyze (Pt electrode) at −0·2 v. *vs.* S.C.E. increasing the voltage slowly to −0·3 v. When the current density falls (ca. 25 min.), remove the electrode, wash with H_2O and Me_2CO, dry in air and weigh. The error for Bi is −1·3 mg.
To det. Sb subsequently, add 1 g. $NH_2OH{\cdot}HCl$ and 15 ml. HCl, heat to 50–70°C and electrolyze for 30–45 min. at 0·5 amp. and −0·3 v. For Sn detn. electrolyze at −0·6 to −0·65 v.; the error for Sn is +1·2 mg. Cu interferes with the Bi detn. and Pb with that of Sn.

(j) Miscellaneous gravimetric methods. With H_2SeO_3,[6] add a small excess of 5% reagent soln. to the boiling 0·35–0·38*N* HNO_3 soln. of Bi, cool, filter on paper, wash with H_2O and ignite above 948°C to Bi_2O_3. Ag, Hg, Pb, Sb, Sn^{2+}, Fe^{3+}, Ti, Th, Cr^{3+}, Ba, Sr, Mg interfere; Cu, Cd, Fe^{2+}, Al, Ni, Co, Zn, Mn, Ca can be tolerated.

For a titrimetric finish,[6] treat the ppt. with 1 g. tartaric acid and 20 ml. HCl, dil. to 150 ml., add 30 ml. CS_2 and a 1·5-fold excess of 0·5*N* KI and titrate with $Na_2S_2O_3$ until the CS_2 is colorless.

Na_2SO_3 ppts. Bi from 67·2% EtOH solns. contg. HNO_3;[56] the ppt. is dried at 340–380°C and weighed as $Bi_2(SO_4)_3$, or at 475–946°C and weighed as $(BiO)_2SO_4$ (Duval).

Phenylarsonic acid ppts. Bi as $C_6H_5AsO_3BiOH$ from acetate-buffered soln. at pH 5·1–5·3.[57] Many metals, F^-, Cl^-, $C_2O_4^{2-}$ and citrate interfere; Pb, Ag, Cu, Cd, Co, Ni, Hg^{2+} can be masked with KCN. Bi may be sepd from Zn, Mn, Ni, Co, Ca at pH 2–3 in HNO_3 solns.

Arsanilic acid ppts. Bi as $Bi(C_6H_7O_3NAs)(OH)_2$ at pH 2·0–3·0; the ppt. can be washed with hot H_2O and dried at 105°C. Cl^-, PO_4^{3-}, tartrate and SO_4^{2-} interfere.[58]

Salicylaldoxime is suitable for the detn. of < 0·1 g. Bi in 100 ml. soln. at pH 9–10; the ppt. must be ignited to Bi_2O_3 but Ag, Zn do not interfere.[59]

The ppt. formed by mercaptobenzothiazole with ca. 0·05 g. Bi also requires eventual ignition[6,60] (see ref. 36, p. 149 for a possible titrimetric finish). Bismuthiol and bismuthiol II may be used for colorimetric detn. of Bi. For 3 μg. Bi in acidic soln. add 5 ml. 1*N* HNO_3, 5 ml. 0·5% gum acacia, a little H_2O, several drops of 0·5% bismuthiol and dil. to 20 ml. with H_2O.[60] Bismuthiol II (0·5%) is used similarly with measurement at 460 mμ.[60] It can also be employed gravimetrically, $Bi(C_8H_5N_2S_3)_3{\cdot}1\frac{1}{2}H_2O$ being weighed after drying at 105°C (40–150°C);[61] Ag, Hg, Pb, Cu, Cd, Pd, Tl are pptd. from citrate-contg. soln. at pH 6–8 and Bi is detd. in the filtrate after acidification. Alternatively,[62] the ppt. is dissolved in EDTA which is back-titrated with Mg^{2+}.

Cupferron has already been mentioned under Separation; the ppt. can be ignited to Bi_2O_3 at 758–948°C and weighed.[6,63]

Fusion of Bi_2O_3 with KCN followed by H_2O extn. yields Bi which can be weighed.[64] In a similar process, K_2SnO_2 and agar–agar are used nephelometrically.[65] HCHO[66] and glucose[67] allow reduction to Bi in NaOH solns. before a gravimetric finish.

(k) EDTA titration.[68] Thiourea serves as indicator. To 30–80 mg. Bi in soln. add 0·5–0·8 g. thiourea, dil. to 10–15 ml. with H_2O, warm and add NH_4OH until the ppt. just dissolves. Dil. to 40–50 ml. with H_2O, adjust to pH 1·5–2·0 with $HClO_4$ and titrate with 0·05*M* EDTA.

NOTES. (1) Ni, Sn, V, Zr, $C_2O_4^{2-}$ and PO_4^{3-} interfere. Ag, Al, Ba, Ca, Cd, Ce, Co, Cr^{3+}, Cu, Hg, La, Mg, Mn, Pb, Sr, UO_2^{2+}, Zn, F^-, Cl^-, NO_3^-, SO_4^{2-} do not interfere. Fe interference is prevented by addn. of 0·3–0·4 g. ascorbic acid, Sb interference by tartrate, Th interference by SO_4^{2-} and Be, Nb, Ta interference by F^-.
(2) For colorimetry based on EDTA complex formation,[69] adjust the soln. contg. 2–25 p.p.m. Bi to pH 0·8–1·2, add 0·001*M* EDTA and measure at 263·5 mμ; Pb, Fe, Cu, Hg^{2+}, Sn^{2+}, Sb^{3+}, NO_3^- interfere.

(l) K_2CrO_4 is generally used titrimetrically but gravimetric and colorimetric finishes are also possible. Pour the 0·005*N* Bi soln. into a mixture of 5 ml. 0·1*M* NaOAc and 5 ml. 0·03*N* K_2CrO_4 and dil. to 50 ml. with H_2O after 5 min. Filter and titrate a 25 ml. aliquot of the filtrate with 0·005*N* $Na_2S_2O_3$ 10 min. after addn. of 0·1–0·2 g. KI, 5 ml. 6*N* H_2SO_4.[6,70]

NOTE. For gravimetry, heat at 250°C and weigh as $BiOCrO_4{\cdot}\frac{1}{2}H_2O$ or at 350–450°C (?) and weigh as $BiOCrO_4$.[71] A colorimetric method has been suggested.[72]

(m) Miscellaneous titrimetric methods. KIO_3 may be used similarly to K_2CrO_4 as described above; the $Bi(IO_3)_3$ formed can be weighed if required (Shchigol[70]).

$K_4Fe(CN)_6$ permits direct titration. For 5–70 mg. Bi in dil. H_2SO_4 (pH 1·6), add 1–5 ml. 0·1*M* KI as indicator, 2–10 ml. glycerol, dil. to 50 ml. with H_2O and titrate with 0·05*M* reagent.[73]

$K_3Cr(SCN)_6$ is applied in conjunction with oxidimetric titration. For 1–5 mg. Bi in 2–25 ml. 0·3–1*N* HNO_3 or H_2SO_4 soln., add excess reagent (recrystallized from EtOH; 1 g./25 ml. treated with 4–5 g. active carbon and filtered) and filter after 10 min. on a G4 crucible. Wash with cold H_2O, add 10 ml. 0·5–1% NaOH, suck into the original vessel and wash with H_2O and 10 ml. 0·5–1% H_2SO_4 alternately. Make alk. to litmus, boil for 10 min., filter on a G4 crucible and wash, receiving the filtrate in 20 ml. 0·1*N* $KMnO_4$ and 10 ml. 30% NaOH. After 30 min. dil. to 150–200 ml. wit h H_2O, add 10 ml. 50% w/w H_2SO_4 and excess $H_2C_2O_4$ and back-titrate with the $KMnO_4$ soln. in the usual way after $MnSO_4$ addn. NO_2 and Cl^- interfere but Cr, Mo, Al, Fe^{2+}, Zn, Mn, Ni, Co, SO_4^{2-} do not.[6, 74]

In the above method 48 equivs. of $KMnO_4$ are consumed. If $KBrO_3$ or KIO_3 is used, 36 equivs. are consumed.[75] If the Cr in the ppt. is oxidized to CrO_4^{2-} and titrated iodometrically, only 3 equivs. are required.[76] $BiCr(SCN)_6$ may be dried at 120–130°C and weighed.[6, 77]

Bi can be pptd. with $H_2C_2O_4$ from dil. HNO_3 soln. and the ppt. titrated with 0·1*N* $KMnO_4$; Pb, Ag, Cu, Fe, Zn, Te do not interfere.[77, 78] The ppt. can also be weighed; K, Na and NH_4^+ interfere.[79]

$Na_2S_2O_3$ has been applied in conjunction with a neutralization titration.[80] Dissolve the sample in the min. amt. of HNO_3 and neutralize with KOH to methyl red; add 10 g. $Na_2S_2O_3$ followed by dil. HNO_3 (dropwise) until the ppt. dissolves and a pink color persists, and then titrate with KOH to phenolphthalein indicator. The reaction is:

$$2\ Bi(S_2O_3)_3^{3-} + 5\ OH^- + NO_3^- = BiONO_3BiOOH + 6\ S_2O_3^{2-} + 2\ H_2O.$$

(n) Thiourea serves for colorimetric detn.[6, 81] For 0·3–8 mg. Bi in 15 ml. soln. contg. 10 ml. HNO_3, add 10 ml. 75% tartaric acid (if yellow, add 3–5 drops H_2O_2, warm and cool) and then add 25 ml. tartaric acid soln. Dil. to 100 ml. with 8% thiourea and measure at 420 mμ.

NOTES. (1) Cr, Co, Ni, Se, Te, Cl^-, Br^-, I^- interfere. Fe^{3+} interference is avoided by $N_2H_4{\cdot}H_2SO_4$ addn. and heating, and Sb interference by HF addn. Pb and small amts. of Ag, Hg, Cu, Cd, Tl^+, Sn do not interfere.

(2) For 30–300 μg. Bi in 10 ml. 1–2*N* $HClO_4$, add 10 ml. 1 : 1 $HClO_4$ and 25 ml. thiourea soln. (60 g. in 500 ml., warmed and filtered): dil. to 50 ml. with H_2O and measure at 322 mμ. Cu, Pb interfere. Cd, Co, Mn, Ag, Zn, EDTA, PO_4^{3-} do not (Lisicki and Boltz[20]).

(3) Diallyldithiocarbamidohydrazine may be used for 0·2–1 mg. Bi. Adjust the soln. to pH 2·4–2·7 with HNO_3, add 10 mg. reagent in Me_2CO and dil. to 100 ml. with H_2O; ext. with 10 ml. $CHCl_3$ and then with two 5 ml. portions, dil. to 25 ml. with $CHCl_3$ and measure the reddish color. Cu does not interfere if KCN is added.[82] Dithiocarbamidohydrazine is also suitable.[83]

(o) Miscellaneous colorimetric methods. Na-diethyldithiocarbamate permits detn. of 0–300 μg. Bi.[84] Add 10 ml. or more of a soln. contg. 50 g. EDTA and 50 g. NaCN in 1 l. of 1·5*M* NH_4OH, to 10–20 ml. sample soln.; add 1 ml. 0·2% reagent and 10 ml. CCl_4, shake for 30 sec., filter thıough Whatman No. 1 paper and measure at 370 or 400 mμ within 30 min. Large amts. of Hg or Cu interfere at 370 mμ; $(NH_4)_2$-tartrate is added if much Sb or Be is present. Other interferences are avoided by the addn. of the complexing soln.

p-Anisidine may be utilized in conjunction with $K_3Fe(CN)_6$; Ni, Pb, Mn, Fe, Cu, Cd, Zn interfere but Hg, Cr, Al do not.[85]

Pyrocatechol violet is suitable for 0·1–0·6 mg. Bi.[86] Add 1 ml. buffer pH 3·8 (0·2 ml. AcOH and 1 ml. 0·2*N* NaOAc), 1 drop 0·1% reagent, dil. to 25 ml. with H_2O and measure at 610 mμ. Pb, Cu, Cd, Ag, Co, Ni, Mn, Zn, Al, Be, Mg, Ca, etc., do not interfere, but Fe, Th and large amts. of Cl^-, F^-, PO_4^{3-}, $C_2O_4^{2-}$, tartrate and citrate do.

With Fast grey RA, 0·1–1 p.p.m. Bi can be detd. at 570 mμ at pH 2–3; Cu, Ni, Cd, V, Zr interfere.[87]

References

1. HILLEBRAND and LUNDELL, 186 (232); SCOTT and FURMAN, 149; KIMURA, 133; FRESENIUS–JANDER, **Va** γ, 519 (1951).
2. BUSEV, A. I., *Analytical Chemistry of Bismuth*, Moscow, (1953).
3. EINECKE, E. and REESE, J., *Z. anal. Chem.*, **102**, 41 (1935).
4. KUZNETSOV, V. I. and PAPUSHINA, L. I., *Zhur. Anal. Khim.*, **11**, 686 (1956).
5. BLASDALE, W. C. and PARLE, W. C., *Ind. Eng. Chem., Anal. Ed.*, **8**, 352 (1936); SCHOELLER, W. R., *Analyst*, **62**, 533 (1937); FARINI, P., *Bull. chim. farm.*, **73**, 284 (1934).
6. FRESENIUS–JANDER, **Va** γ, 519 ff (1951).
7. KRAUSE, H., *Z. anal. Chem.*, **129**, 43 (1949).
8. LI, K. W., *J. Chem. Soc. Japan*, **52**, 229 (1931).
9. A.S.T.M., 383 (Al and its alloys).
10. HECHT, F. and REISSNER, R., *Z. anal. Chem.*, **103**, 186 (1935).
11. SHCHIGOL, M. and HAL'DAS, M., *Farm. Zhur.*, **141**, (1) 13 (1941).
12. KALLMANN, S., *Ind. Eng. Chem., Anal. Ed.*, **13**, 897 (1941); WELCHER, **II**, 33.
13. WELCHER, **III**, 29.
14. PŘIBIL, R. and ČŮTA, J., *Collection Czechoslov. Chem. Communs.*, **16**, 391 (1951).
15. HECHT and DONAU, 163; WELCHER, **I**, 303; ISHIMARU, S., *J. Chem. Soc. Japan*, **56**, 70 (1935); FARINI, P., *Bull. chim. farm.*, **73**, 284 (1934).

16. MOELLER, T., *Ind. Eng. Chem., Anal. Ed.*, **15**, 346 (1943).
17. GILLIS, J., *et al., Mededeel. Koninkl. Vlaam. Acad. Wetenschap.*, (7) (1940).
18. SANDELL, 213 (see also McChesney, p. 202); BALLARD, E. J., *Analyst*, **74**, 53 (1949); ENGLIS, D. T. and BURNETT, B. B., *Anal. Chim. Acta*, **13**, 574 (1955) (in Pb, Cu); BACH, J. M., *Rev. obras. sanit. nacion.*, **13**, 118 (1949) (thioglycolic acid + SO_2 water).
19. FIANDER, S. J., *Analyst*, **80**, 476 (1955).
20. LISICKI, N. M. and BOLTZ, D. F., *Anal. Chem.*, **27**, 1722 (1955); GOTO, H. and SUZUKI, S., *J. Chem. Soc. Japan*, **74**, 142 (1953) (not extd. with CCl_4, C_6H_6).
21. HILLEBRAND and LUNDELL, 191 (239); YOE, 131.
22. BURKHALTER, T. and SOLAREK, J. F., *Anal. Chem.*, **25**, 1125 (1953).
23. WELCHER, **II**, 55.
24. TAKAGI, S. and NAGASE, Y., *J. Pharm. Soc. Japan*, **56**, 405 (1936).
25. WELCHER, **III**, 127.
26. WELCHER, **II**, 383.
27. TANII, K. and HASHIMOTO, J., *J. Chem. Soc. Japan*, **60**, 1121 (1939).
28. SPACU, G. and LUPAN, S., *Acad. rep. populare Romîne, Bul. ştiinţ., Sect. ştiinţ. teh. şi. chim.*, **4**, 425 (1952).
29. SPACU and POPEA, F., *Acad. rep. populare Romîne, Studii cercetări chim.*, **3**, 175 (1955).
30. WELCHER, **I**, 303.
31. KOLTHOFF, I. M. and GRIFFITH, F. S., *Mikrochim. Acta*, **3**, 47 (1938).
32. WELCHER, **III**, 62, 63.
33. WELCHER, **IV**, 222.
34. STOLYAROBA, I. A., *Zhur. Anal. Khim.*, **8**, 270 (1953); NIELSCH, W. and BÖLTZ, G., *Anal. Chim. Acta*, **11**, 438 (1954) (0–14 μg. Bi/ml., 20–48% HBr, 370–380 mμ); FLETCHER, W. and WARDLE, R., *Analyst*, **82**, 747 (1957) (HBr + ascorbic acid; in Pb and its alloys).
35. MERRITT, C., *et al., Anal. Chem.*, **25**, 572 (1953).
36. KOKORIN, A. I. and DERMANOVA, I. G., *Zavodskaya Lab.*, **12**, 59 (1946).
37. KODAMA, K., *Japan Analyst*, **4**, 447 (1955).
38. TEMPLETON, D. H. and BASSETT, L. G., *Natl. Nuclear Energy Ser., Div.* **8**, I 336 (1950).
39. WELCHER, **II**, 506.
40. WELCHER, **IV**, 252.
41. SUDO, E., *J. Chem. Soc. Japan*, **75**, 1291 (1954).
42. OOSTING, M., *Mikrochim. Acta*, 528 (1956).
43. WELCHER, **IV**, 228.
44. POPEL, A. A., *Uchenye Zapiski Kazan Univ.*, **115**, (3) 69 (1953).
45. LAUG, E. P., *Anal. Chem.*, **21**, 188 (1949); see also Chapter 20 p. 159, and SANDELL, 213; HUBBARD, D. M., *ibid.*, **20**, 363 (1948).
46. GRZHEGORZHEVSKIĬ, A. S., *Zhur. Anal. Khim.*, **11**, 689 (1956).
47. WELCHER, **IV**, 171, 175; UMEMURA, T., *J. Chem. Soc. Japan*, **61**, 28 (1940).
48. HECHT and DONAU, 164; WELCHER, **I**, 162.
49. WELCHER, **I**, 201; DICK, I. and MIHAI, F., *Acad. rep. populare Romîne, Baza cercetări ştiinţ. Timisoara, Studii cercetări ştiinţ., Ser. ştiinţe chim.*, **3**, 73 (112) (1956).
50. WELCHER, **IV**, 34.
51. SCOTT and FURMAN, 155.
52. KNY-JONES, F. G., *Analyst*, **66**, 101 (1941); see also p. 173; LINGANE, *Electroanalytical Chemistry* (1953), p. 313 for controlled potential electrolysis, p. 341 for internal electrolysis.
53. NORWITZ, G., *Anal. Chim. Acta*, **5**, 195 (1951).
54. GOLDBERG, C., *Metallurgia*, **42**, 108 (1950).
55. DEAN, J. A. and REYNOLDS, S. A., *Anal. Chim. Acta*, **11**, 390 (1954).
56. GASPAR Y ARNAL, T., *et al., Anales fís. y quím.* (*Madrid*), **43**, 571 (1947).
57. MAJUMDAR, A. K., *J. Indian Chem. Soc.*, **22**, 313 (1945); **21**, 119, 187, 188 (1944); MAJUMDAR and SARMA, R. N. S., *ibid.*, **26**, 477 (1949); WELCHER, **IV**, 57.
58. MUSIL, A. and PIETSCH, R., *Z. anal. Chem.*, **144**, 347 (1955); **150**, 190 (1956).
59. WELCHER, **III**, 270.
60. WELCHER, **IV**, 113; SANDELL, 217.
61. MAJUMDAR, A. K. and CHAKRABARTTY, M. M., *Z. anal. Chem.*, **154**, 262 (1957); IGLESIAS, A. R., *Anales. fac. farm. y bioquím., Univ. nacl. mayor San Marcos*, **2**, 709 (1951).
62. MAJUMDAR and CHAKRABARTTY, *Z. anal. Chem.*, **156**, 103 (1957).
63. WELCHER, **III**, 394.
64. SCOTT and FURMAN, 156.
65. MALOSSI, L., *Rend. acad. Sci. fis.-mat. Napoli*, [4] 2, 83 (1932).
66. WELCHER, **I**, 379.
67. WELCHER, **IV**, 281.
68. FRITZ, J. S., *Anal. Chem.*, **26**, 1978 (1954); also see UNDERWOOD, A. L., *ibid.*, 1323 (photometric at 745 mμ using Cu^{2+} or at 400 mμ using thiourea); WILHITE, R. N. and UNDERWOOD, *ibid.*, **27**, 1334 (1955) (pH 2·5, 265 mμ; only Fe, Th, Sn interfere); CHENG, K. L., *ibid.*, **26**, 1977 (1954) (KI as indicator); MÁLAT, M., *et al., Chem. listy*, **48**, 203 (1954); **49**, 1792, 1798 (1955) (HNO_3 acidic soln., pyrocatechol violet or pyrogallol red, and addn. of NH_4OH until blue or red, before titration); HAAR, K. TER and BAZEN, J., *Anal. Chim. Acta*, **10**, 108 (1954) (Th^{4+} and alizarin S); PŘIBIL, R. and MATYSKA, B., *Collection Czechoslov. Chem. Communs.*, **16**, 139 (1951) (amperometric); RÁDY, G. and ERDEY, L., *Z. anal. Chem.*, **152**, 253 (1956) (pH 2, thoron).
69. WEST, P. W. and COLL, H., *Anal. Chem.*, **27**, 1221 (1955).
70. SHCHIGOL, M. B., *Zavodskaya Lab.*, **14**. 276 (1948); also see UTSUMI, S., *J. Chem. Soc. Japan*, **73**, 342 (1952).
71. LI, K. W., *J. Chem. Soc. Japan*, **52**, 229 (1931).
72. BARRERA, P. A. and ORTEGUI, S. J. Y B., *Afinidad*, **32**, 90 (1955).
73. FUJITA, Y., *J. Chem. Soc. Japan*, **77**, 615 (1956).
74. STAMM, H. and GOEHRING, M., *Z. anal. Chem.*, **115**, 1 (1938/39).
75. MONTEQUI, R. and CARRERÓ, J. G., *Ann. real Soc, españ. fís. y quím.* (*Madrid*), **31**, 242 (1933); CARRERÓ, *ibid.*, **36**, 33 (1940).
76. MAHR, C., *Z. anorg. Chem.*, **208**, 313 (1932).
77. SCOTT and FURMAN, 156 ff.
78. Also see KAWAGAKI, K., *J. Chem. Soc. Japan*, **77**, 1464 (1956).
79. ISHIBASHI, M. and MATSUMOTO, T., *Japan Analyst*, **5**, 343 (1956).

80. MALAPRADE, L., *Ann. chim. anal. applic.*, **22**, 5 (1940).
81. HILLEBRAND and LUNDELL, (240); BENDIGO, B. B., *et al.*, *J. Research Natl. Bur. Standards*, **47**, 282 (1951); NIELSCH, W. and BÖLTZ, G., *Z. anal. Chem.*, **142**, 321 (1954); **143**, 13, 168 (1954); SANDELL, 217, WELCHER, **IV**, 179; A.S.T.M. 387 (Al and its alloys) 461, 463, (Pb) 473 (Pb, Sb-solder, 440 mμ) 482 (white metal-bearing alloys).
82. GUPTA, J. and SARMA, K. P. S., *J. Indian Chem. Soc.*, **28**, 89 (1951).
83. GUPTA, J. and CHAKRABARTTY, B., *J. Sci. Ind. Research (India)*, **8B**, 133 (1949).
84. CHENG, K. L., *et al.*, *Anal. Chem.*, **27**, 24 (1955); KINNUNEN, J. and WENNERSTRAND, B., *Chemist Analyst*, **45**, 109 (1956) ($CHCl_3$, CCl_4, AmOAc, EtOAc unstable; *n*-pentanol, BuOH stable); WARD, F. N. and CROWE, H. E., *U.S. Geol. survey Bull.*, 1036-I, 173 (1956) (in rock); SUDO, E., *J. Chem. Soc. Japan*, **73**, 753 (1952); BOBTELSKY, M. and RAFAILOFF, R., *Anal. Chim. Acta*, **16**, 488 (1957) (photometric titration).
85. IIJIMA, S. and HASHIMOTO, J., *Japan Analyst*, **2**, 537 (1953).
86. SVACH, M., *Z. anal. Chem.*, **149**, 325 (1956).
87. KHALIFA, H., *Anal. Chim. Acta*, **17**, 318 (1957).

22

COPPER

The principal sources for this chapter are given in ref. 1. Copper has been discussed in a monograph,[2] and the analysis of copper refinery slimes has been considered.[3]

For general analytical work for copper, care must be taken to avoid contamination from sieves, reagents and apparatus. Porcelain vessels and filter paper should be avoided when traces of copper are involved.

Attack

(a) Sulfides. Treat with HCl and HNO_3 or boil for 30 min. with 40 ml. HNO_3 and 3 ml. HCl, add H_2SO_4 and evap. to fumes. HNO_3 and $KClO_3$ are also used. See also Chapter 58, p. 434.

With $HClO_4$, add 15 ml. to the sample in a 500 ml. flask fitted with a special reflux and boil for 5 min. after adding glass beads (vapor condenses on the wall but does not distil); cool for 2 min., add 50 ml. H_2O, boil for 5 min., add 1:1 NH_4OH (also add H_2SO_4 if the soln. is blue rather than greenish brown), cool, add 2 g. NH_4F and det. Cu iodometrically.[4]

(b) Silicates. Treat with HF and H_2SO_4 or fuse with Na_2CO_3 or $K_2S_2O_7$.

(c) Metals and alloys. Treat with HNO_3 or with aqua regia and H_2SO_4, etc. For Sb or Sn alloys, use Br_2 and HBr (see Chapter 20). For steels, treat 5–10 g. sample with H_2SO_4, dil., add H_2S or $Na_2S_2O_3$ and eventually ignite; treat with HNO_3 or fuse with $K_2S_2O_7$, add dil. HCl and apply NaOH and NH_4OH sepns. before electrodeposition or gravimetry.

Dissolve Fe alloys in 1:1 HNO_3. With Fe–Cr, treat with HCl and $HClO_4$ and volatilize Cr as CrO_2Cl_2 (see p. 331). For Fe–W, treat with HCl and a min. amt. of HNO_3, boil, add H_2O, filter, add H_2SO_4, evap., add H_2S, etc.; recover Cu from the ppt. with NH_4OH, tartaric acid, H_2SO_4, H_2S, etc.

Separation

H_2S in dil. HCl or hot 1:4 H_2SO_4 soln. allows sepn. of Cu from Cd and group III elements. For concn. purposes, to 40–50 ml. 4% $(NH_4)_3$-citrate soln. of pH 2 add 5 mg. Pb as nitrate, pass H_2S for some min., shake for 1 hr. or leave overnight, filter on a glass crucible and wash with 0·1*N* HCl contg. 3% Na_2SO_4 and H_2S.

H_2S in NaCN soln. gives sepn. from Cd, Bi, etc., and in HF or $H_2C_2O_4$ soln. from Sn, Ge (see also p. 203).

Cu is sepd. from Zn, Ni and Cd with 10% $Na_2S_2O_3$ or $Na_2S_2O_4$; if much Cd is present, repptn. is needed. Neutralize the H_2SO_4 soln. with NH_4OH until turbid, and clear with H_2SO_4; add 50 ml. reagent and 20 ml. 1:5 H_2SO_4, boil for 15 min., filter on Whatman No. 42 paper and wash with hot H_2O. Concn. with $HgCl_2$ is useful. Sepn. with $Na_2S_2O_4$ can be used in steel analysis.[5]

Sepns. are obtained from Ag with HCl, from Hg by extn. of sulfide ppts. with hot 1:3 HNO_3, and from Pb with H_2SO_4.

Cu is sepd. from As, Sb, Sn, Se, Te with Na_2S in NaOH soln. and from As, Se, Te with NaOH at pH 10 in boiling soln. A final concn. of $< 1\%$ NaOH in hot solns. gives sepn. of Cu from Mo, V, W, As; org. compds. interfere. $(NH_4)_2CO_3$ or NH_4OH and KCN sep. Cu and Bi. Large amts. of Cu are sepd. from traces of Bi, As, Sb, Se, Te by treatment with Fe^{3+} or Al^{3+} and NH_4OH.

Distn. as chloride or bromide seps. Cu from Sn and Ge (see pp. 204 and 209).

SO_2 in HCl soln. allow sepn. of Cu from Se and Te; $AgNO_3$ (an amt. double the Se) is added for traces. SO_2 and NH_4SCN sep. Cu from Bi, Cd, As, Sb, Sn, Fe, Co, Ni, Mn (see under Determination).

Internal electrolysis is suitable for sepn. from much Pb (see p. 145). Electrolysis from dil. HNO_3 soln. gives sepn. from Ni, Co, Zn, Fe, Cd, and in nitrohydrofluoric acid soln. from Mo, W, Sn^{4+}, Sb^{5+}.

Pb in dil. HCl soln. allows sepn. from much Pb, Al, etc.; the ppt. is dried, dissolved in Br_2 and HBr and Cu is detd. colorimetrically. Cu, Cd, Sb and Sn are sepd. from Fe and Mo in presence of Al or Zn: treat 75 ml. of the 10% H_2SO_4 soln. with Al. Addn. of satd. H_2S increases contamination. If the Al is passive, add some drops of HCl.

Cu is sepd. from Fe, Mo, Pb, Cd, Zn, Co, Ni and F^- with 2% cupron in EtOH. For < 50 mg. Cu in 150–200 ml. of acidic soln., add 15 g. tartaric acid, make alk. to congo red with dil. NaOH (the soln. should still be acid to litmus), make alk. to litmus with NH_4OH and add 5 ml. in excess. Add a 4-fold excess of reagent, filter on a glass crucible after 15 min., and wash with 1:99 NH_4OH. Fume with 15 ml. HNO_3 and 10 ml. $HClO_4$, cool, add H_2O and det. Cu by titration or electrodeposition. V interferes.

Benzotriazole allows sepn. of Cu from Fe^{3+}, As, Sb, Sn, Mo, Se, Te, Al, Cr; Ag, Ni, Fe^{2+}, Cd, Zn, Co interfere.[6] For 0·2–15 mg. Cu in neutral soln. add 10 ml. AcOH, 7 g. tartaric acid and NH_4OH until the soln. is neutral to litmus. Dil. to 200–300 ml. with H_2O, add 50 ml. 2% reagent and digest on a steam-bath, after paper pulp addn. and stirring. Filter on Whatman No. 40 paper, wash with H_2O, ignite, add HNO_3, evap. to dryness, add H_2O and det. Cu iodometrically.

For extn. with 5% caproic acid in EtOAc from solns. of pH 6·3–10·3, see Chapter 16, p. 138.

Extn. with dithizone in CCl_4 from 0·1–0·2*N* HCl soln. seps. Cu, Ag, Pd, Au, Bi, Hg from Pb, Cd, As, Sb, Ge, Mo, Se, Fe, Ni, Co, Zn, Mn, Ga, V, W, P. Sepn. from Ag is obtained by HCl and KI addn., from Hg by shaking with 5 ml. 40% KBr and 50 ml. 0·25*N* HCl, and from Bi by shaking with an equal vol of 2% KI in 0·01*N* HCl contg. some sulfite, washing the H_2O layer with 5–10 ml. reagent and combining. To return the Cu to aq. soln., evap. the CCl_4 layer and heat with $HClO_4$ and H_2SO_4; alternatively, shake with acidic $KMnO_4$ soln. and then treat with a reductant or shake with 0·5 ml. Br_2 water and 10 ml. 5% H_2SO_4.

Cu, Bi, Hg and As^{3+} are sepd. from small amts. of Pb, Zn, Fe^{2+} by extn. with diethylammonium diethyldithiocarbamate in $CHCl_3$ from 2*N* HCl soln. (see also Chapter 8, Section 2.7, and pp. 158 and 204).

Determination

There are probably more methods available for the determination of Cu than for any other single element. Electrodeposition is the most satisfactory procedure and can be applied to amounts varying from 0·5 mg. to 5 g. According to Foote and Vance, the iodometric method and the titrimetric method based on NH_4SCN are as accurate as electrodeposition for macro or semimicro quantities. Of the methods suitable for milligram amounts based on organic reagents, those involving salicylaldoxime or analogs of oxine seem to be the most satisfactory. *o*-Phenanthroline analogs are excellent for colorimetric determinations. The dithizone and carbamate methods are convenient while the NH_4OH procedure is very simple. Zincon, rubeanic acid and HBr also provide useful procedures.

(a) Electrodeposition.[7,8] For 0·5 mg.–5 g. Cu, add 3 ml. HNO_3 and 5 ml. H_2SO_4/200 ml. soln. followed by 1 drop 1:99 HCl and 5 ml 10% sulfamic acid if Pb is present. Electrolyze at 0·5 amp./dm.^{2} and 2 v. for 12 hr., wash with H_2O and EtOH, dry at 100°C for 1 min. and weigh as Cu.

NOTES. (1) As interferes less in HNO_3 soln. and Mo in H_2SO_4 soln.; these interferences are avoided by replating. Sn, Sb, Au, Pt metals, Ag, Hg, Bi, Se^{4+}, Te^{4+}, HSCN, HCl and NO_2^- interfere as do large amts. of Pb, Fe^{3+} and HNO_3. Zn, Cd, Mn, Ni, Co, Fe^{2+}, $H_2C_2O_4$, AcOH, H_3PO_4, tartaric acid do not interfere. Pb does not interfere in HNO_3 solns. nor do Se^{6+} and Te^{6+}. Sn does not interfere in tartaric acid-contg. HNO_3 solns.

(2) Electrodeposition has been applied to many brasses, alloys and other metals.[8] For 1 mg. amts. of Cu, see ref. 9.

(3) In macro analysis, traces of Cu may remain in the electrolyte; these can be detd. colorimetrically if required. Incomplete deposition in bronze or brass analysis can be prevented by addn. of a drop of 0·1*N* HCl.[10] Good results are obtained when more than 10 ml. H_3PO_4 is added to mask Sb or Sn if HCl and HNO_3 are evapd. off after H_3PO_4 addn. and the soln. is dild., boiled and cooled before electrolysis.[11] Urea[12] or, better, sulfamic acid[13] should be added if Pb is present.

For internal electrolysis, see ref. 14. Rapid deposition causes high results.

(4) Various other conditions can be used.[9, 15] Electrolysis from solns. contg. NH_4OH and $(NH_4)_2CO_3$ permits sepn. from As^{5+} and from Sb^{5+} and Sn^{4+} if tartaric acid is added. Cu is sepd. from W and Mo by electrolyzing solns. contg. $H_2C_2O_4$ and $(NH_4)_2C_2O_4$. Solns. contg. KCN and $(NH_4)_2SO_4$ may also be used.

(5) It is possible to det. Cu, Bi, Pb and Sn successively.[16] Treat the sample with 10 ml. 1 : 2 HNO_3 or HCl and a min. amt. of HNO_3 when Sb and Sn are present. Add 1 g. urea, 50 ml. 1*M* Na_2-tartrate, 2 g. $N_2H_4{\cdot}2HCl$ and 1 g. succinic acid/0·1 g. Cu. Dil. with H_2O to 190 ml., adjust to pH 5·9 ± 0·1 with NaOH and electrolyze below 25°C for 45 min. at −0·30 v. *vs.* S.C.E. Wash with H_2O and Me_2CO, dry at 110°C for 2 min. and weigh as Cu. Using this Cu-covered electrode, electrolyze at −0·4 v. for Bi and −0·6 v. for Pb. Then add 20 ml. HCl and 2 g. $N_2H_4{\cdot}2HCl$ and deposit Sn at −0·6 to −0·65 v. The whole process takes 4 hr.

(6) A method involving short-circuit limited potential coulometry has been described.[17]

(b) Iodometric method.[18] For < 0·15 g. Cu in 20–40 ml. soln. contg. some H_2SO_4, add 25 ml. 6*N* AcOH and 12 ml. 6*N* NH_4OH to give pH 3·7. Add 3–5 g. KI, titrate with 0·1*N* $Na_2S_2O_3$ until the soln. is pale yellow, add 1–2 g. KSCN and starch indicator and titrate until the blue color disappears. The error is ±0·05% with a max. of −0·11%.

NOTES. (1) Interference by NO_2 is avoided by urea addn. and Fe^{3+} interference by NaF addn. As^{3+}, Sb^{3+}, Mo, Se, large amts. of Ag, Pb, Bi, NH_4OAc, and 3% v/v mineral acids interfere, as do As^{5+} and Sb^{5+} above pH 4.

(2) This procedure has also been applied to many metals and alloys.[8]

(3) Many modifications have been suggested. Better results may be obtained by adding 0·5–0·6 g. KI, titrating to yellow, adding starch, titrating until the blue color fades, adding 1–2 g. KSCN and titrating rapidly to the final end-point.[4, 19] Titration is inaccurate if KSCN is added immediately after KI.[20] For a titration on a similar principle, treat the neutral soln. with 10 ml. 20% NaK-tartrate and 5 ml. 20% KSCN followed by excess 0·1*N* $Na_2S_2O_3$ (stir vigorously). After 5 min., dil. to 100 ml.

with H_2O, add 2–3 ml. starch and 2 ml. 2% succinic acid and titrate with 0·1N I_2 until the blue color remains for 5 min.[21]
(4) If KSCN is not added, the end-point is obscure;[1] this can be avoided by addn. of a trace of $AgNO_3$,[22] of 0·5–1 ml. 4% shellac in EtOH,[23] or of Fe^{2+}.[24]
(5) When Fe^{3+} is present, add 1 g. NaF/0·1 g. Fe or add 1·5–2 g. $Na_4P_2O_7$; in this case the end-point is again less clear. If much Pb is present, add 10 ml. 1% $(NH_4)_2MoO_4$.[25]
(6) Several buffers have been proposed, *viz.* <0·7N HCOOH, <0·2N AcOH, <1·7N HF[26] and phthalic acid;[27] HCOOH is said to be best.
(7) If urea is added, proceed as follows:[22] treat 0·2 g. alloy with 10 ml. HNO_3, boil out NO_2 and add 10 ml. of soln. contg. 1·5 g. $Pb(NO_3)_2$, 100 g. urea and a little HNO_3/l.; stir, cool, add 10 ml. 10% KSCN and 10 ml. 10% KI, stir and titrate with 0·1N $Na_2S_2O_3$ in the usual way.
(8) Good results can be obtained without an indicator if Cu and Pb are kept in soln. by adding a large excess of KI.[28] For <150 mg. Cu in dil. HNO_3 soln., evap. nearly to dryness, add 3 ml. H_2SO_4, re-evap. and repeat if necessary (if much Fe and Cr are present, use $HClO_4$ and sep. Cr with $BaCl_2$). Add 25 ml. H_2O, 1 g. NaOAc (and 4 g. NaF if Fe or Sn is present), and 25 g. KI; swirl for 10–15 sec. and titrate with 0·05–0·1N $Na_2S_2O_3$. Mo, V, U, Sb and >10 mg. Bi/100 ml. interfere; Fe, As, Pb, Sn, Ag, Hg, ClO_4^-, PO_4^{3-}, $P_2O_7^{4-}$ and SO_4^{2-} do not.
(9) NaBr can be used instead of KI if a trace of KI is added with starch for indicator purposes.[29]

(c) NH_4SCN can be used gravimetrically or titrimetrically after reduction with SO_2.[1, 30] The titrimetric method based on an Andrews–Jamieson titration is usually preferred. For < 0·1 g. Cu in 150–300 ml. soln. contg. HCl or H_2SO_4, add satd. SO_2 soln. in 20 ml. increments until the soln. still smells of SO_2 and is pale yellow after 1·5 hr. on a steam-bath. Cool, add NaOH to give a turbidity followed by 8–10 drops HCl and 10 ml. 2% NH_4SCN in satd. SO_2 soln. for each 50 mg. Cu. After 12 hr., filter on Whatman No. 42 paper contg. some filter pulp and wash with 1% $(NH_4)_2SO_4$. Treat the ppt. with 30 ml. HCl, 20 ml. H_2O and 5 ml. $CHCl_3$ and titrate with 0·2N KIO_3 (standardized against Cu) shaking vigorously between addns. Alternatively, filter on a glass crucible, wash with 1% $(NH_4)_2SO_4$ and 20% EtOH, dry at 105–120°C and weigh as CuSCN.

NOTES. (1) Oxidizing agents, large amts. of strong acids, NH_4^+ and SCN^- (>0·05N) interfere, as do Pb, Hg, noble metals and moderate amts. of Se and Te. Interference of Bi, Sb, Sn is prevented by addn. of 2–3 g. tartaric acid. As, Fe, Ni, Co, Zn, Cd do not interfere.
(2) Numerous modifications have been proposed (Scott and Furman[1]).
(*i*) Treat the ppt. with 20 ml. 1 : 1 HCl, add 4 ml. 0·2753N KIO_3 for each 5 mg. Cu, dil. to 600 ml. with H_2O, add 0·5 ml. 10% KI for each 1 ml. KIO_3 added and titrate with $Na_2S_2O_3$.
(*ii*) Treat the ppt. with hot 10% NaOH, maintain at 50°C and add $KMnO_4$ using $FeCl_3$ as external indicator; add 30 ml. 1 : 1 H_2SO_4, stir and titrate with 0·1N $KMnO_4$ until the soln. is pink.
(*iii*) Use a known amt. of NH_4SCN for pptn. and apply Volhard's method to the filtrate.
(*iv*) Treat the ppt. with excess 0·1N NaOH, heat, filter and titrate with 0·1N acid.
(*v*) Treat the ppt. with a known vol. of boiled 0·1N $AgNO_3$, boil for 1 hr. and apply Volhard's method to the filtrate.[31]
(*vi*) Ppt. as described above but pass CO_2 through the soln. until the issuing gas no longer decolorizes $KMnO_4$ in dil. acid. Add 25 ml. 1 : 4 H_2SO_4 and 0·5M $Fe_2(SO_4)_3$ dropwise until no ppt. forms. Add 0·2M $Hg_2(NO_3)_2$ in an amt. equal to the KSCN used as precipitant, followed by 10 ml. H_3PO_4 and titrate with 0·1N $K_2Cr_2O_7$ to diphenylamine indicator.[32]
(*vii*) Treat the soln. with Fe^{2+}, NH_4SCN and adjust to 0·5N in HNO_3; titrate with 0·1N $Hg_2(NO_3)_2$.[33]

(d) Salicylaldoxime can be used gravimetrically, titrimetrically or colorimetrically.[34] The reagent soln. is prepd. by dissolving 1 g. in 5 ml. EtOH and dilg. to 100 ml. with H_2O; it should not be heated above 80°C. For < 0·1 g. Cu, add 10 ml. AcOH and 1 g. NaOAc/100 ml. soln. at pH 2·8; add 5 ml. reagent, filter on a G4 crucible, wash with H_2O, dry at 110–105°C and weigh as $Cu(C_7H_6O_2N)_2$. Alternatively titrate the ppt. bromometrically.

NOTES. (1) Pd and Au interfere but Ag, Hg^{2+}, Pb, Cd, As^{3+}, Co, Ni, Zn, U do not; $(NH_4)_2$-tartrate prevents interference by Sb^{3+} and Fe^{3+}.
(2) For colorimetric methods, see Table 30.
(3) Similar reagents have been studied including *p*-homosalicylaldoxime,[35] resacetophenoneoxime,[36] *β*-naphtholaldoxime,[37] resorcylaldoxime (at pH 1·8–2·4)[38] and *o*-hydroxyacetophenoneoxime.[39]

(e) 2-(*o*-Hydroxyphenyl)-benzoxazole is used gravimetrically.[40] For < 50 mg. Cu, add a 2–5-fold excess of EDTA and 5% NaOH to give pH 11·5; filter, add excess satd. reagent in EtOH (the excess is indicated by blue fluorescence) and place on a steam-bath for 15–30 min. Filter on a medium frit, wash with EtOH and Et_2O (1:1), and dry at 130–140°C. Weigh as $Cu(C_{13}H_8O_2N)_2$. Much Fe interferes unless 5 g. Na_2-tartrate is added. Al interference is avoided by pptn. at pH 3·0–4·0, dissoln. in HCl, addn. of 1 g. EDTA, etc. Other metals do not interfere.

Oxine and its derivatives and homologs have been widely studied but none of the methods is as satisfactory as the above.

Bromoxine is used gravimetrically for 1–2 mg. Cu in 100 ml. neutral soln.[41] Add 30 ml. Me_2CO, 10 ml. 1N HCl, heat to 50°C; add 5 ml. of warm satd. bromoxine in Me_2CO and boil; filter on a glass crucible, wash with a soln. of 15 ml. Me_2CO, 85 ml. H_2O and 0·15 ml. HCl, dry at 130–150°C (170–200°C) and weigh as $Cu(C_9H_4Br_2ON)_2$. Hg, Pb, Bi, Cd, As, Sb, Sn, Co, Ni, Mn, Zn, Al, Cr, U, Mg do not interfere; 20 ml. satd. $(NH_4)_2C_2O_4$ prevents Fe, Ti interference.

Chloroxine (Welcher[41]) and iodoxine[42] can be used similarly.

Oxine itself is used colorimetrically (see Table 30), gravimetrically or titrimetrically.[43] Three procedures are described, the last being least satisfactory.

(*1*) For < 0·12 g. Cu, add 10 ml. AcOH and 3 g. NaOAc/100 ml., heat to 60°C, add 2–3% oxine in EtOH and heat to 80–90°C; filter on a G4 crucible, wash with warm H_2O, dry at 105–110°C (60–269°C) and weigh as $Cu(C_9H_6ON)_2$. Alternatively, dissolve in HCl and titrate bromometrically. Be, Mg, Ca, Cd, Pb, As, Mn, PO_4^{3-} do not interfere.

(*2*) Add 3 g. tartaric acid to 100 ml. soln., neutralize with NH_4OH, add 15 ml. 1:9 HNO_3, dil. to 150 ml. with H_2O, heat to 60°C, add reagent and continue as above. Ag, Pb, Bi, Cd, Mo, Fe, Ni, Co, Zn, Mn, Al, Ti, V, Mg do not interfere.

(*3*) Add 3–5 g. tartaric acid to 50 ml. soln., neutralize with NaOH, add 20 ml. 2*N* NaOH or 5 ml. NH_4OH, dil. to 100 ml., add reagent, etc.; the titrimetric finish must be used. Ni, Co interfere but Al, Pb, Sn^{4+}, As^{5+}, Sb^{5+}, Bi, Cr^{3+}, Fe^{3+} do not.

8-Hydroxyquinaldine is used colorimetrically:[44] adjust the soln. to pH 6, ext. with $CHCl_3$, evap., add an equal vol. of C_6H_6 and pass through a column of activated alumina; develop with the reagent in 1:1 $CHCl_3$–C_6H_6, elute and measure at 400 mμ. Only Cr, Fe, Mo, V interfere.

Dimethyl-8-quinolinol allows gravimetric, titrimetric or colorimetric detns.[45] Colorimetry with methyloxine is said to be better than with oxine. Indoxine is used titrimetrically for 0·2–1 mg. Cu.[46] 8-Hydroxyquinoline-5-sulfonic acid is not recommended.[46]

4-Hydroxybenzothiazole[47] permits gravimetric detn. as $Cu(C_7H_4ONS)_2$ (see Chapter 36, p. 279).

Alizarin blue is used gravimetrically for < 2 mg. Cu in 20 ml., soln.[48] Add 20 ml. 6*N* H_2SO_4, heat, add reagent in pyridine dropwise and filter on a glass crucible after 30–60 min.; wash with 3*N* H_2SO_4, heat the ppt. for 30 min. with anhyd. AcOH, then wash several times with pyridine and EtOH. Dry at 100°C for 30 min.; the factor is 0·0991. Other elements do not interfere; CN^- is removed by H_2SO_4 addn. followed by some drops of HCHO and boiling.

(f) Neocuproine serves for colorimetry of 15–500 μg. Cu in acidic soln.[49] Add $NH_2OH{\cdot}H_2SO_4$ (if Fe is present, add enough to reduce it) followed by a 2-fold excess of 0·1% reagent in 50% EtOH, 1 g. NaOAc (if Fe is present, add 6 g. Na_3-citrate/g. Fe). Ext. twice with 10 ml. isoamyl alc., dil. with the alc. to 50 ml. and measure at 455 mμ.

NOTES. (1) Very few elements interfere; oxidizing agents, SCN^-, NO_2^- and $Fe(CN)_6^{3-}$ interfere.
(2) The complex is best extd. with *n*-hexanol and the sensitivity is almost as good as that of dithizone.
(3) Similar reagents have been suggested. For cuproine, bilepidine, biquinoline, *o*-phenanthroline, etc., see Table 30 and Chapter 9, Section 1.
Batho-cuproine is used for 4–150 μg. Cu.[50] Add HCl to the sample, evap. to a few ml., add 1·5 g. citric acid in H_2O, adjust to pH 5 (green) with 1 : 3 NH_4OH and transfer to a separatory funnel. Dil. to 25 ml. with H_2O, add 1 ml. 0·01*M* reagent in *n*-hexanol and 5 ml. 5% $NH_2OH{\cdot}HCl$; shake for 2 min., sep., wash with 5 ml. 10% NH_4OAc and 1 ml. $NH_2OH{\cdot}HCl$, dil. with *n*-hexanol to 25 ml. and measure at 479 mμ (ϵ = 14 200 is a max. for this type of reagent).

(g) Dithizone can be used colorimetrically for < 5 μg. Cu in 2 ml. slightly acidic soln.[51] Neutralize with NH_4OH to cresol red, add 2 ml. buffer pH 2·3 (8·3 g. Na_2HPO_4 and 38 g. citric acid in 250 ml. H_2O) and 20 ml. reagent (7·5 mg. dithizone in 1 l. CCl_4). Shake for 10 min., sep., shake the org. layer for 2 min. with 10 ml. of a soln. contg. 10 g. KI, 5 ml. 1*N* HCl and 450 ml. H_2O, and then, if necessary, shake it with 0·1*N* $Na_2S_2O_3$. Measure at 520 mμ; the error is ±0·2 μg.

NOTES. (1) No interference is caused by Pb, Bi, Cd, Sn^{4+}, Fe^{3+}, Ni, Co, Zn, Mn or traces of Ag or Hg.
(2) Cu, Pb, Zn may be detd. successively in rocks.[52]
(3) The *o*- or *p*-ditolyl analog is used at pH 3 with a citrate–hydrochloric acid buffer; the absorbance is measured at 538 or 554 mμ. Hg interferes (see p. 151).

(h) Zn-dibenzyldithiocarbamate serves for colorimetric detn. of 0·5–40 μg. Cu.[53] Place the soln. contg. 5 ml. H_2SO_4/100 ml. in a separatory funnel, add 10 ml. 0·01% reagent in CCl_4, shake for at least 30 sec., sep., and measure at 435 mμ. Other elements can be detd. in the aq. layer.

NOTES. (1) No interference arises from Al, As, Cd, Cr, Fe, Pb, Mn, Sn, U, Zn. Interference by Bi (0·1 mg.) is avoided as follows: add 5 ml. HCl to 30–40 ml. of the dil. H_2SO_4 soln., ext. with the reagent, wash with CCl_4 and combine the exts. Add 5 ml. 8*N* H_2SO_4 and 2 ml. 0·5*N* $KMnO_4$, shake, add 3 ml. 10% $NH_2OH{\cdot}HCl$ and shake. After 5 min., add 25 ml. HCl, shake, sep., add reagent, shake for 3 min. and measure.
Co and Ni interferences are prevented similarly except that 30 ml. H_2O is added to the combined layers and no HCl is added. Interferences from 1 mg. Ag, 0·2 g. Hg or 0·1 g. Sb are prevented by adding more reagent; if only Hg is present, add KBr.
(2) Several similar reagents have been proposed.
Na-diethyldithiocarbamate is used for <40 μg. Cu in 10–20 ml. soln.[54] Add 5 ml. 20% $(NH_4)_3$-citrate and adjust to pH 9–9·2 with NH_4OH (use thymol blue and a comparison soln.); add 1 ml. 0·1% reagent and 5 ml. CCl_4, shake for 2 min., sep. and measure at 440 mμ. CN^-, NO_2^- (add urea) and Bi (add KCN and deduct the residual absorbance) interfere. No interference arises from Pb, Sn, Al, Fe^{2+}, Cr^{3+}, small amts. Ag and Hg, <5 mg. Fe, <2 mg. Zn; 0·5 mg. Mn is tolerable if the soln. is stood for 20 min. after extn. If Co and Ni are present, add 1 ml. 0·5% dimethylglyoxime in EtOH, centrifuge and wash.
Cuprethol is suitable for <0·2 mg. Cu in 50 ml. 0·002–0·01*N* mineral acid soln.[55] Add 3% $Na_4P_2O_7$ (1 ml./2 mg. Fe^{3+}) and 20% NaOAc (pH 5–6); discard if a turbidity appears. Add 1 ml. reagent (just before required, mix equal vols. of solns. contg. 4·0 g. diethanolamine in

TABLE 30. Colorimetric Methods for Copper

Reagent	Conditions	Color, λ_{max}, mμ	Range (μg/ml.), Sensitivity, Error	Interf.	Ref.
0·1% Neo-cuproine/50% EtOH	pH 2·3–9·5, NH_2OH reduction, iso-AmOH extn.	Cu^+, orange, 455	0·3–10	SCN^-, $Fe(CN)_6^{3-}$, IO_4^-, NO_2^-, oxidant	(1)
0·01*M* Batho-cuproine/*n*-hexanol	pH 4–10 + citrate, extn.	Cu^+, red, 479	0·16–6·0, ϵ = 14 200	Same as above	(2)
0·1% *o*-Phenanthroline	1 ml. reagent, 2 ml. 6*N* NH_4OH, 20 ml. EtOH/50 ml., octanol extn. possible	Cu^+, orange, 425	0·1–2·0	Cd, Co, Ni, Zn; CN^-, $S_2O_3^{2-}$	(3)
0·02% Cuproine/*n*-AmOH	pH 4·4–7·5 + tartrate, extn.	Cu^+, purple, 545 (358)	>0·02, ±1%, ϵ = 6220 (ϵ = 52 000)		(4)
2,2′-Bilepidine	iso-AmOH extn.	Cu^+, 550	ϵ = 7020		(5)
1% 2,2′-Bipyridyl	10 ml., 2 ml. 6*M* NH_4OH, 20 ml. Me-carbitol/50 ml.	Cu^+, orange-brown, 430	between NH_4OH and *o*-phenanthroline	Fe, Cd, Cr, Ce, Ni, Zn; CN^-, $S_2O_3^{2-}$	(6)
Dithizone/CCl_4[a]	feebly acidic	purple, 520	>0·2, ±0·2/5		(7)
0·01% Zn-dibenzyldithiocarbamate/CCl_4	5 ml. H_2SO_4/100 ml., 10 ml. reagent, extn.	yellow, 435	0·5–40	nearly none	(8)
0·1% Na-diethyldithiocarbamate[a]	pH 9·0–9·2 + citrate, CCl_4 extn.	yellow-brown, 440	<40, ±1%/0·2	Bi, CN^-, NO_2^-	(9)
Cuprethol	pH 5–6	brown, 432	<2	many	(10)
Zincon (0·13 g./2 ml. 1*M* NaOH, H_2O to 100 ml.)	pH 5·2, 3 ml./50 ml.	blue, 600	0·5–2	none	(11)
NH_4OH	3*N*	blue, 620	200, ±1%	Co, Ni, Cr, Sn, org. compds.	(12)
Triethanolamine			a little better than NH_4OH		(13)
Tetraethylenepentamine			3·5-fold of NH_4OH		(14)
2% 3-Dimethylaminopropylamine	10 ml. reagent, 10 g. NH_4NO_3/50 ml.	595	<50		(15)
N,N-Diphenyl-*p*-phenylenediamine		685	<10		(16)
0·1% Rubeanic acid/EtOH	pH 2·5 ± 0·1, + gum arabic	yellow-green, 620 (420, 700)	<15, ±0·03	Ni, Fe^{2+} (correction)	(17)
0·1% Diphenylrubeanic acid/EtOH + 1*N* NaOH in 1 : 1		420		Au, Pt, Pd, Hg; Ni, Co, Pb (+EDTA)	(18)
0·1% Piperidine pentamethylenedithio-carbamate/EtOH	neutral	yellow-brown	1–80, 0·2	Fe	(19)
Mercaptobenzothiazole, AmOH extn., Bu_2NH + CS_2	pH 2·6–6·2	yellow-brown	2–20, ±5%		(20)
K-xanthate	neutral	yellow	5–20, 0·1, ±10%	Ni, adjust pH strictly	(21)
0·05% Phenylthiosemicarbazide/2*N* AcOH	2*N* AcOH	650	0·5–15	Ag, Hg, Pt, Fe	(22)
Thiosemicarbazide	acidic	blue, 530			(23)
1% Thiobenzamide/60% EtOH	50 ml. 1*N* HCl soln.: 100 ml. EtOH, 5 ml. reagent	400		Ag, Hg, Au, Pt, Ir only	(24)
0·01*M* Tetraethylthiuram disulfide/EtOH	acidic, +20% EtOH, or $CHCl_3$ extn.	yellow-brown, 445	0·1–1·8	Hg; Se (+EDTA)	(25)
Reinecke's salt, thiourea (or HNO_3)		530			(26)
Tetrabase	neutral	purple		decolorize	(27)
o-Dianisidine	AcOH acidic or $CHCl_3$ extn.	green			(28)
0·07% Cryogenin	buffer	red	0·5–30	Ag, Co, Ni, Cr	(29)
0·1% Phenylsemicarbazide	faintly ammoniacal	yellow	0·05–1		(30)
Oxine[a]	pH 4·0, $CHCl_3$ extn.	yellow, 410			(31)
Dimethyl-8-quinolinol	pH 4·4–6·2, $CHCl_3$ extn.	415			(32)
0·5% Cupron/EtOH	pH 11·3–12·3 + tartrate, 2 ml./100 ml., $CHCl_3$ extn.	green, 440	5–10	Ni (1 mg.), Co (0·15)	(33)
0·02*M* Salicylaldoxime/*n*-AmOAc	10 ml. soln.: 10 ml. pH 4 phthalate buffer, 10 ml. reagent	344	1·6–5·5		(34)
Formaldoxime	KOH alk.	violet		Ni	(35)
8-Hydroxy-5-methoxytetraloneoxime	acidic- neutral, $CHCl_3$ extn.	pale yellow	50		(36)
2-Nitrosochromotropic acid	neutral	purple	0·6–3		(37)
0·05% 2-Isatoxime methyl ether	pH 5–7 + NaK-tartrate, $CHCl_3$ extn.	539	1–20	Hg (+KI) only	(38)
Satd. cuprizone/50% EtOH	pH 7–10, 0·2 ml./3·5 ml.	blue, 595	<1, ϵ = 16 000	Pb, Zn, Ni, EDTA (0·5 p.p.m.), CN^-, (0·1), Fe, Al, etc. (1, + citrate)	(39)
Satd. oxalyldihydrazide/EtOH	NH_4OH alk. + CH_3CHO	542	ϵ = 29 500		(40)
EDTA	acidic- alk.	700–750			(41)
NTA	pH 3·2–6·0	690–710	40–7000		(42)
1,2-Diaminoanthraquinone-3-sulfonic acid	KOH alk.	blue	40–200		(43)

Benzidine/EtOH, KSCN		blue	1		(44)
Benzidine/20% EtOH, Na-salicylate, KCN	alk.	red	0·1–500	Ag	(45)
Guaiacum resin/EtOH, KCN		blue	0·5		(46)
1% *o*-Toluidine/EtOH, 30% NH_4SCN	pH 4	blue	0·2–8		(47)
Tolidine, KSCN					(48)
Kastle Meyer's reagent, KCN		pink, 546	1–10	Fe, Bi, Pb	(49)
Molybdate, KCN		blue	0·2		(50)
0·01*M* Na-salicylate, KNO_2 (59 mg./ml.)	pH 4·2, 2 ml. + 1 ml./20 ml., 80°C 1 hr.	red, 520	2–9	Fe, Bi, Al	(51)
25 g. Salicylic acid + 35 ml. pyridine/ 100 ml.	pH 4·5–7·0, 1 ml./50 ml., 5 ml. $CHCl_3$ extn.	blue	20–1000	Fe, Ni, Co (+NH_4HF_2), CN^-, S^{2-}, tartrate	(52)
0·02% β-Naphthol	NH_4OH	yellow-green			(53)
Naphthenic acid					(54)
Hydroquinone	NaOH	blue	4–95		(55)
0·1% Hydroquinone/0·01*N* HCl, pyridine, 0·1% H_2O_2	1 ml. each of reagent, 1 min., 1 ml. 5% AcOH/15 ml.	brown	15–300		(56)
0·1% Direct green B	pH 6–9	purple	0·1		(57)
0·005% Fast grey RA	3 ml. + 5 ml. 0·02*N* HNO_3/10 ml.	550	0·001–0·1	Fe^{3+} (+ascorbic acid)	(58)
Hematoxylin					(59)
Urobilin	weakly ammoniacal	yellow–red–purple	5	Hg (+KI or $Na_2S_2O_3$)	(60)
Na-tetrabromophenolphthalein		yellow	0–100	Fe, Al	(61)
Pyrocatechol violet	pH 6·5	blue		many	(62)
Ascorbic acid, Folin's reagent		blue	0·1–15	Fe	(63)
$FeCl_3$, NH_4SCN, $Na_2S_2O_3$, catalytic		decolorization	2, ±7%		(64)
Fe^{3+}, $S_2O_3^{2-}$, catalytic		decolorization	1–5		(65)
p-Phenylenediamine, H_2O_2, catalytic		violet	3–8		(66)
5% Resorcinol/iso-PrOH,catalytic	faintly acidic	green	±0·05/0–1/50 ml.	Ag (2μg), Fe (50)	(67)
$(NH_4)_2S_2O_8$, dimethylglyoxime, $AgNO_3$,	faintly alk.	purple, decolorize	0·1–2		(68)
Pyridine, NH_4SCN	pH 2–10 + citrate, $CHCl_3$ extn.	green, 415	25–250		(69)
Pyridine, KNCO	pH 8, $CHCl_3$ extn.			Co, Cd, Pb, Fe^{3+}, Al	(70)
Triphenylmethylarsonium thiocyanate			10–100, ±2%		(71)
50% NH_4SCN	HCl acidic, 50% Me_2CO	orange-brown, 380	1–10		(72)
HCl	6*N*	yellow, 940 or 270	8	Fe, Sn	(73)
HBr	+ a little Br_2 + 10 ml. H_3PO_4/50 ml.	purple, 600 or 510	10–250	Mo, V, Cr, Co, noble metals, some rare earths; Fe, Ni (>Cu)	(74)
HNO_3	0·07–0·7*N*	970	600	Fe (+NaF)	(75)
KI	5 g. + 1·5 ml. AcOH/20 ml.	420, filter	25	Fe (+NH_4F)	(76)
Satd. KI, 1% ascorbic acid	2 ml. + 2 ml. + 25 ml. NH_4OH/50 ml.	365–380			(77)
Na_3AsO_3		green	8		(78)
H_2S	acidic, +gelatin	brown	4	Ag, Hg, Pb, etc.	(79)
0·2% $K_4Fe(CN)_6$/0·02*N* NaOH	acetate buffer, +gelatin	red-brown	0·8	Fe, Zn	(80)
Na_2CO_3	2*M*	270	<20	Cr^{3+}, Co, Fe^{3+}	(81)

[a] For other analogs see under Determination.

References to Table 30

(1), (2) Separate entry.
(3) Williams, L. H., *Analyst*, **75**, 425 (1950); Wilkins, D. H. and Smith, G. F., see ref. 46, p. 261; (Welcher, **III**, 91).
(4) Guest, R. J., *Anal. Chem.*, **25**, 1484 (1953); Cheng, K. L. and Bray, R. H., *ibid.*, **655**; Elwell, W. T., *Analyst*, **80**, 509 (1955) (in steel); Hoste, J., *et al.*, *Anal. Chim. Acta*, **9**, 263 (1953); Gillis, J., see below; (Welcher, **III**, 68).
(5) Gillis, J., *Mededeel. Koninkl. Vlaam. Acad. Wetensch.*, **15**, (7) 3 (1953).
(6) Mehlig, J. P. and Koehmstedt, P. L., *Anal. Chem.*, **25**, 1920 (1953).
(7)–(10) Separate entry.
(11) Rush, R. M. and Yoe, J. H., *Anal. Chem.*, **26**, 1345 (1954).
(12) Separate entry.
(13) Yoe, J. H., *et al.*, *Ind. Eng. Chem.*, *Anal. Ed.*, **12**, 456 (1940).
(14) Crumpler, T. B., *Anal. Chem.*, **19**, 325 (1947); Williams, L. H., *Analyst*, **75**, 425 (1950).
(15) Meibohm, A. W., *Proc. Indiana Acad. Sci.*, **62**, 156 (1952).
(16) Wise, R. W. and Roark, J. N., *Anal. Chem.*, **27**, 309 (1955).
(17) West, P. W. and Compère, M., *Anal. Chem.*, **21**, 628 (1949); Willard, H. H., *ibid.*, 598; Miller, W. L., *et al.*, *ibid.*, **22**, 1572 (1950); (Welcher, **IV**, 151).
(18) Xavier, J. and Rây, P., *Sci. and Culture* (*Calcutta*), **21**, 170 (1955).
(19) Welcher, **IV**, 81.
(20) Separate entry.
(21) Yoe, 184; Welcher, **IV**, 98.
(22) Komatsu, S. and Uchiyama, H., *J. Chem. Soc. Japan*, **75**, 1280 (1954).
(23) Kinnunen, J. and Merikanto, B., *Chemist Analyst*, **45**, 103 (1956).
(24) Gagliardi, E. and Haas, W., *Mikrochim. Acta*, 593 (1954).
(25) Michal, J. and Zýka, J., *Chem. listy*, **48**, 915 (1954); Guseĭn-Zade, S. M., *Doklady Akad. Nauk Azerbaidzhan. S.S.R.*, **9**, 321 (1953).
(26) Separate entry.
(27) Welcher, **IV**, 568.
(28) Loriente, E. and Casas, J., *Nature*, **159**, 470 (1947).
(29) Sarada, U., *Jap. J. Med. Sci.*, [II] **2**, 247 (1933).
(30) Skibina, E. M., *Zhur. Anal. Khim.*, **7**, 244 (1952).
(31) Moeller, T., *Ind. Eng. Chem.*, *Anal. Ed.*, **15**, 346 (1943).
(32) Separate entry.
(33) Dunleavy, R. A., *et al.*, *Anal. Chem.*, **22**, 176 (1950); Nance, K. W., *ibid.*, 170; Madera, J., *ibid.*, **27**, 2003 (1955).
(34) Simonsen, S. H. and Burnett, H. M., *Anal. Chem.*, **27**, 1336 (1955) (in Al alloy).
(35) Welcher, **III**, 348.
(36) Momose, T., *Japan Analyst*, **5**, 332 (1956).
(37) Welcher, **III**, 291.
(38) Diviš, L. and Škoda, J., *Chem. listy*, **46**, 662 (1952); **48**, 539 (1954).
(39) Peterson, R. E. and Bollier, M. E., *Anal. Chem.*, **27**, 1195 (1955); Somers, E. and Garraway, J. L., *Chem. & Ind.* (*London*) 395 (1957); Wetlesen, C. U., *Anal. Chim. Acta*, **16**, 268 (1957) (in steel).

References to Table 30—(*contd.*)

(40) Gran, G., *Anal. Chim. Acta*, **14**, 150 (1956).
(41) Nielsch, W. and Böltz, G., *Z. anal. Chem.*, **143**, 1 (1954).
(42) Idem, *Z. anal. Chem.*, **142**, 406 (1954).
(43) Welcher, **IV**, 352.
(44) Welcher, **IV**, 311.
(45) Fleming, R., *Analyst*, **49**, 275 (1924).
(46) Mair, W., *Z. anal. Chem.*, **116**, 410 (1939).
(47) Fleming, R., *Analyst*, **49**, 275 (1924).
(48) Blum, H., *Arch. Eisenhüttenw.*, **24**, 207 (1953).
(49) Goto, H. and Musha, S., *J. Chem. Soc. Japan*, **66**, 37 (1945); (Welcher, IV, 543).
(50) Golse, J., *Bull. soc. pharm. Bordeaux*, **69**, 247, 270 (1931).
(51) Underwood, A. L., *Anal. Chem.*, **28**, 41 (1956); (Yoe, 183, Welcher, II, 124).
(52) Gordieyeff, V. A., *Anal. Chem.*, **22**, 1166 (1950).
(53) Welcher, I, 144.
(54) Welcher, II, 45.
(55) Welcher, I, 136.
(56) Raĭnes, M. M. and Larionov, Yu. A., *Trudy Komissii Anal. Khim., Akad. Nauk S.S.S.R.*, 7, 295 (1956).
(57) Welcher, **IV**, 353.
(58) Khalifa, H. and Zaki, M. R., *Z. anal. Chem.*, **158**, 1 (1957).
(59) Welcher, **IV**, 366.
(60) Thomas, B., *Biochem. Z.*, **293**, 396 (1937).
(61) Horvai, R., *Anal. Chim. Acta*, **4**, 91 (1950).
(62) See Chapter 21, p. 169.
(63) Goto, H. and Ikeda, S., *J. Chem. Soc. Japan*, **74**, 148 (1953).
(64) Suzuki, S., *J. Chem. Soc. Japan*, **71**, 353 (1950); Gothals, C. A., *Z. anal. Chem.*, **104**, 170 (1936).
(65) Goto and Sudo, E., *J. Chem. Soc. Japan*, **64**, 509 (1943); Yatsimirskii, K. B., *Zhur. Anal. Khim.*, **10**, 339 (1955).
(66) Goto and Suzuki, *J. Chem. Soc. Japan*, **71**, 94 (1950).
(67) Lambert, R. H., *Anal. Chem.*, **24**, 868 (1952).
(68) Welcher, **III**, 211.
(69) Titze, H. and Hecht, F., *Mikrochim. Acta*, 453 (1954) (in meteorite); Moeller, T. and Zogg, R. E., *Anal. Chem.*, **22**, 612 (1950); Welcher, III, 5.
(70) Spacu, G. and Scherzer, J., *Acad. rep. populare Romîne, Studii cercetări chim.*, **4**, 219 (1957).
(71) Ellis, K. W. and Gibson, N. A., *Anal. Chim. Acta*, **9**, 368 (1953).
(72) Kitson, R. E., *Anal. Chem.* **22**, 664 (1950), (see p. 259); Melnick, L. M. and Freiser, H., *ibid.*, **27**, 462 (1954) (Bu_3PO_4 extn.).
(73) Davis, Jr., O. G. and Hershenson, H. M., *Anal. Chim. Acta*, **13**, 150 (1955) (in steel); Nozaki, T., see below; (Yoe, 179).
(74) A.S.T.M. 241 (in electronic Ni) 386 (Al and its alloys) 419 (Mg and its alloys) 490 (Pb, Sn, Sb and its alloys) 528 (Zn-base die-casting alloys, Cu < 1%); Nielsch, W. and Böltz, G., *Z. anal. Chem.*, **142**, 94, 427 (1954); (Yoe, 181).
(75) Ikeda, S., *Japan Analyst*, **4**, 286 (1955).
(76) Idem, *Japan Analyst*, **4**, 431 (1955).
(77) Stolyarov, K. P. and Agrest, F. B., *Zhur. Anal. Khim.*, **11**, 286 (1956).
(78) Curie, A. N., *Biochem. J.* **18**, 1224 (1924).
(79) Yoe, 178; Scott and Furman, 381.
(80) Hahn, H., *Z. anal. Chem.*, **110**, 270 (1937); Yoe, 182; Scott and Furman, 377; Kimura, 488; Pigott, 192.
(81) Nozaki, T., *J. Chem. Soc. Japan*, **78**, 1247 (1957).

200 ml. MeOH and 1·00 g. CS_2 in 200 ml. MeOH), dil. to 100 ml. with H_2O and measure at 432 mμ. Co, Hg, Ni, Ag, and large amts. of CN^-, Cr^{6+} and NO_2^- interfere; Bi, U and Cr interferences may be compensated for by adding KCN and deducting the residual absorbance.

Diethylammonium diethyldithiocarbamate is not liable to interference from Fe, Co, Ni, etc.[56] To the acidic soln. add 20 ml. 1% EDTA, neutralize to litmus with NH_4OH, add 10 ml. reagent (10 g./l. $CHCl_3$), shake for 1 min., repeat and measure at 600 or 400 mμ.

For the dibutyl analog, see mercaptobenzothiazole, p. 179.

Dimine has been used gravimetrically and titrimetrically.[57]

(i) NH_4OH allows a simple colorimetric detn.[1, 58] For 0·1–10 mg. Cu as sulfate in 100 ml. soln., add NH_4OH to give a 3*N* soln. and measure the blue color at 620 mμ. The color varies with temp. and the sensitivity is increased by adding 1–2 drops phenol to the NH_4OH.[59] No interference arises from citrate, Pd, Ag, or from Pt and Au if $NaHSO_3$ is added. Sn interference is prevented by evapn. with H_3PO_4. Org. compds., filter paper exts., Co, Ni and CrO_4^{2-} interfere.

Various methods have been suggested which utilize the formation of ammine complexes. For gravimetry, the method involving isoquinoline and NH_4SCN seems the most accurate. See Table 30 for colorimetric methods.

(*1*) Pyridine and NH_4SCN can be used gravimetrically, titrimetrically or colorimetrically.[60] For < 0·1 g. Cu in 100 ml. 1% AcOH soln., add 1 ml. pyridine and 0·5 g. NH_4SCN; filter on a glass crucible and wash successively with solns. contg. 3 g. NH_4SCN and 3 ml. pyridine/l., 0·5 g. NH_4SCN and 8 ml. pyridine in 800 ml. EtOH and 192 ml. H_2O, abs. EtOH, and finally 2 drops pyridine in 20 ml. Et_2O. Dry below 40°C in a vacuum desiccator and weigh as $Cupy_2(SCN)_2$. Alternatively, dissolve the ppt. in NH_4OH, add excess $AgNO_3$, acidify with HNO_3 and apply Volhard's method or the filtration method.

(*2*) Isoquinoline and KSCN are used gravimetrically.[61] To 50 mg. Cu in 150 ml. soln. at pH 3·0 (thymol blue), add 8 ml. 0·5*M* KSCN and 16 ml. base soln. (26 g. dissolved in 50 ml. H_2O contg. 0·3 ml. HCl dild. to 1 l. with H_2O). Heat to 70°C, allow to cool for 1 hr., filter on a medium frit, wash with H_2O, dry at 105–110°C (< 103°C) and weigh as $Cu(C_9H_7N)_2(SCN)_2$. Br^-, SO_3^{2-}, NO_2^-, AsO_4^{3-}, CrO_4^{2-} and large amts. of Cl^- interfere; Pb, Cd, Sn, As^{3+}, Fe^{3+}, Co, Ni, Zn, Al, Cr^{3+} do not interfere.

Benzidine, tolidine,[62] and aniline[63] may also be used.

(*3*) Ethylenediamine and K_2HgI_4 permit gravimetric detn. of 0·01–0·1 g. Cu in 100 ml. of neutral or slightly acidic soln.[64] Add excess base, 1–2 g. NH_4SCN and 2 g. KI, heat and add hot K_2HgI_4 soln. (22·7 g. HgI_2 in 100 ml. 16·6% KI). Allow to cool, filter on a glass crucible and wash with a soln. contg. 1 g. $HgCl_2$, 20 g. KI, 10 g. NH_4SCN and 1·5 ml. base in 200 ml. H_2O; then wash with EtOH and Et_2O. Dry in a vacuum desiccator (< 99°C) and weigh as $[Cu(en)_2]HgI_4$. Alternatively, for < 2·5 mg. Cu, oxidize the I^- in the ppt. to IO_3^- and titrate iodometrically.[65]

Propylenediamine,[66] *o*-phenanthroline, *o*-phenylenediamine[67] and NH_4OH[68] may be utilized in similar procedures.

(*4*) Biguanide sulfate forms $[Cu(C_2H_7N_5)_2]SO_4{\cdot}3H_2O$ and is used gravimetrically (94–146°C) or titrimetrically.[69] *o*-Phenylenediamine can replace biguanide.[70]

(*5*) Pyridine and $K_2Cr_2O_7$ form $[Cupy_2]Cr_2O_7$, which can be dried below 64°C and weighed.[71] Na-benzoate or hexamine may replace $K_2Cr_2O_7$ or pyridine resp., but in both cases, the ppt. must be ignited to CuO.[72]

The ppt. formed with morpholine must also be ignited.[73] 8-Aminoquinoline ppts. Cu as $[Cu(C_9H_8N_2)_2]Br_2 \cdot H_2O$ from HBr-contg. solns. at pH 1–7; Pd, Ag, Tl and Pb interfere.[74]

(*6*) Reinecke's salt ppts. 2–10 mg. Cu from NH_4OH solns. as $[Cu(NH_3)_4][Cr(SCN)_4(NH_3)_2]_2 \cdot 5H_2O$, which must be washed with 0·1% reagent soln. contg. NH_4OH and then with EtOH and Et_2O, and dried *in vacuo*.[75]

(*7*) Triethylenetetramine serves for photometric titration of Cu at pH 10 in citrate or tartrate-contg. solns.; the color is measured at 565 or 600 mμ.[76]

(j) Miscellaneous gravimetric methods. Na-quinaldate is used for < 0·1 g. Cu:[77] add 2–10 ml. 2*N* H_2SO_4/150 ml. soln. of pH 1·5–6·96, then add 2·5% reagent, warm, filter on a glass crucible, wash with hot H_2O and weigh as $Cu(C_{10}H_6O_2N)_2 \cdot H_2O$ after drying at 110–140°C (< 105°C) or as the anhydrous salt after drying at 130–273°C. Cd is said to interfere[78] but this is not so;[79] according to Majumdar,[79] the Cu ppt. contains 0·05–0·07% Cd and the Cd ppt. 0·3% Cu. An amperometric method is possible.[80]

Analogous reagents have been proposed. Quinoline-8-carboxylic acid is used gravimetrically in NH_4OAc–AcOH solns. (Welcher[77]) or amperometrically.[80] For 5-nitro-8-quinolinecarboxylic acid, see Chapter 18, p. 148. 5, 6-Benzoquinaldic acid ppts. Cu as $Cu(C_{14}H_{18}O_2N)_2 \cdot 1\frac{1}{2}H_2O$ from solns. of pH 0·82–9·4; the ppt. can be dried at 110°C and weighed. No interference arises from Zn Co, Ni, Mn, Ag, Pb, Be, Th, U, Fe, Al, Cr, V, Mo, W or Bi.[81]

Na-anthranilate is suitable for < 0·05 g. Cu in 200 ml. neutral or slightly acidic soln.;[82] the ppt. is weighed as $Cu(C_7H_6O_2N)_2$ or titrated bromometrically. 5-Bromo-2-aminobenzoic acid is as good as the anthranilate but 3-aminonaphthoic acid is less satisfactory.

3-Hydroxy-1,3-diphenyltriazine has been used for 10–25 mg. Cu in 25 ml. soln.[83] Add 5 ml. 10% NaOAc or Na_2-tartrate, 5 ml. 1*N* HCl, 5 ml. EtOH and a 20–25% excess of 1% reagent in EtOH. Add 120–130 ml. hot H_2O (the pH should be 2·3–3·0), digest for 45 min. on a steam-bath, filter on a G3 crucible, wash twice with 0·5% HCl and 5–6 times with hot H_2O, dry at 120–125°C for 30–45 min. and weigh as $Cu(C_{12}H_{10}N_3O)_2$. Ag, Au, Os and Pd interfere but a wide variety of other metals does not interfere; PO_4^{3-} and F^- can be tolerated.

Benzotriazole may be used (see p. 147).

Thionalide is suitable for 3–100 mg. Cu, the detn. being completed gravimetrically or titrimetrically.[84] Heat the soln. (150–250 ml. of < 0·5*N* H_2SO_4 or HNO_3 soln.) on a steam-bath, add 25–40 ml. 1% reagent in EtOH to give a 10-fold excess and a 10% EtOH soln., filter on a preheated G3 crucible and wash with hot H_2O. Dry at 81–121°C and weigh as $Cu(C_{12}H_{10}ONS)_2 \cdot H_2O$ or at 140–200°C and weigh as the anhydrous salt. Alternatively, filter through paper, return to the original beaker, add 50 ml. AcOH, 4–5 ml. 5*N* H_2SO_4, 1 g. KI, 10 ml. ca. 1*N* NH_4SCN, a known vol. of 0·02*N* I_2 and water, and titrate with $Na_2S_2O_3$. A filtration method in which excess 1% thionalide in AcOH (standardized against Cu) is added is also possible.

p-Mercaptoacetamidoacetanilide allows gravimetric or titrimetric detns. (see Chapter 18, p. 146).

Thioglycolic acid may be used for < 0·03 g. Cu in 25 ml. soln. at pH 3·6–6·0;[85] the ppt. must be ignited to CuO. Ag and Cl^- interfere but Pb, Hg, Fe, Zn, Ni, Co, Mn, Cd, Bi, As, Sb, etc., AcOH and SO_4^{2-} do not.

H_2S is suitable for < 10 mg. Cu in 5% v/v HCl or H_2SO_4 solns.; pptn. is made from the boiling soln. and the ppt. is filtered on paper, washed with satd. H_2S in 1% HCl and ignited to CuO.[86] Alternatively, the ppt. is mixed with S, ignited in H_2 or in CO_2 bubbled through MeOH and weighed as Cu_2S.[87]

Cupron permits gravimetric, titrimetric or colorimetric detns. (see also under Separation and Table 30). For > 0·1 mg. Cu,[88] add 3 drops 1:10 HNO_3 for each 2 ml. soln. followed by 10% NH_4OH to give a blue color. Add 1 ml. 1% cupron in EtOH for each 0·5 mg. Cu and place on a steam-bath for 10 min., adding EtOH occasionally. Filter on a glass crucible, wash twice with 1 ml. 1% NH_4OH, twice with hot H_2O and once with warm EtOH; dry at 105–110°C, cool, heat with 1–2 ml. EtOH, redry at 105–110°C (60–143°C) and weigh as $Cu(C_{14}H_{11}O_2N)$. Alternatively, titrate the ppt. bromometrically.

Salicylamidoxime can be used at pH 4·0–4·5;[89] no interference arises from Hg, Pb, Cd, Zn, Mn, Co, Ni, nor from Fe^{3+}, Sb^{3+} or Bi if tartaric acid is added. Salicylimine (1 g. salicylaldehyde in 100 ml. NH_4OH) ppts. Cu from NH_4OH solns. contg. tartrate; Ni, Pd, Fe, Co, Hg, Zn, Cd, Re interfere.[90] Methods with disalicylidene–ethylenediamine[91] and disalicylidene–propylenediamine and its analogs[92] have been suggested.

Benzoylacetone serves for detn. of < 0·1 g. Cu in slightly acidic soln.;[93] add NaOAc until the soln. is neutral to Congo red, add 0·56 g. reagent in 15 ml. EtOH, heat, cool, filter on a glass crucible, wash with H_2O, dry at 110–115°C and weigh as $Cu(C_{10}H_9O_2)_2$. Fe^{3+}, Al, Co, Ni interfere but Ag, Hg, Pb, Cd, Zn, Ba, Mg do not.

Acetonedicarboxylic acid ethyl ester ppts. Cu as $Cu(C_{11}H_{12}O_7)$ which must be dried below 84°C (Welcher[90]).

Resacetophenone ppts. Cu at pH 5·6–6·2; the ppt. is dried at 130°C and weighed or dissolved in AcOH and HCl and titrated bromometrically in presence of methyl orange as indicator.[94]

2-Hydroxy-1-naphthaldehyde ppts. Cu from hot solns. contg. EtOH and NH_4OH; if tartrate is added, Fe, Mn, Al, Zn do not interfere.[95]

Mercaptobenzothiazole forms $Cu(C_7H_4NS_2)_2$ with Cu at pH 2·6–4·2, the ppt. being filtered on paper and ignited to the oxide; Ni, Co, Cd, Zn, Mn, Ca, etc. do not interfere.[96] This reagent can also be used colorimetrically by extn. with AmOH, adding butylamine and CS_2 and dilg. with EtOH.[97]

Bismuthiol and Cu form a ppt. which must be evaluated iodometrically after ignition.[96] Mercaptobenzimidazole gives a ppt. which must be ignited to CuO.[96]

2-Chloro-7-methoxy-8-thiolacridine has been used for the detn. of 5–10 mg. Cu in 10 ml. neutral soln. but is not very satisfactory[98] (see p. 154).

Diphenylthiovioluric acid ppts. Cu at pH 7·2–8·0.[99] *S*-Methylthiourea sulfate ppts. $CuSCH_3$ from ammoniacal soln.; Ni and Zn interferences are prevented by resp. $C_2O_4^{2-}$ and NH_4Cl addn.[100] Diallyldithiocarbamidohydrazine ppts. Cu from citric acid-contg. solns. at pH 2·5–3·5; the ppt. is ignited to the oxide and titrated iodometrically and Ni does not interfere.[101] Dithiocarbamidohydrazine is used for solns. contg. HCl and Na_2SO_3, the ppt. being ignited and titrated iodometrically; Fe, Zn, Cd can be tolerated.[102]

2-(*p*-Tolylimino)-4-thiazolidinone (2% in EtOH) is employed at pH 5·2; again the ppt. has to be ignited.[103]

Diphenylhydantoin ppts. Cu as $Cu(C_5H_{11}N_2O_2)_2$ from neutral or ammoniacal media.[104] Dicyanodiamidine sulfate (10%) has been used for 0·05 g. Cu by pptn. as $Cu(C_2H_5N_4O)_2$ from alk. media; Ni interferes but Pb, As, Sb, Al, Zn and CrO_4^{2-} do not.[105]

Isonitroso-3-phenylpyrazolone is applied as follows: to the soln. contg. AcOH and NaOAc, add 50 ml. 0·5*N* H_2SO_4, 2·5–5·0 g. $(NH_4)_2$-tartrate, and dil. to 100–150 ml. with H_2O. Add 90 ml. 1% reagent in MeOH or hot 50% EtOH all at one time; after 3 hr. filter on paper, wash with 1% $(NH_4)_2$-tartrate, mix with $H_2C_2O_4$ and ignite to CuO. No interference is caused by Pb, Cd, Fe, Ni, Co, Al.[106]

α-Nitroso-β-naphthylamine and the β-α- analog have been proposed for detns. of 10–50 mg. Cu as $Cu(C_{10}H_7ON_2)_2$ from tartrate-contg. solns. Neither is very satisfactory owing to doubtful drying temps.[107]

Cupferron ppts. Cu from dil. AcOH solns., the ppt. being ignited to CuO or weighed as $Cu(C_6H_5O_2N_2)_2$ after drying below 107°C; Cd, Fe^{2+}, Zn, As, Sb do not interfere.[108] An amperometric method has been described.[109] Neocupferron ppts. $Cu(C_{10}H_9O_2N_2)_2$ which can be dried below 89°C.[110]

N-Benzoylphenylhydroxylamine is suitable for ca. 25 mg. Cu in 400 ml. soln. contg. 5 ml. 1*N* H_2SO_4; boil, add 1·75 equivs. of reagent in EtOH, digest for 1–2 hr., filter on a glass crucible, wash with hot H_2O, dry at 110°C and weigh.[111] For tetralin analogs, see under Fe colorimetry (Chapter 33, p. 257).

Acetylene ppts. Cu from dil. NH_4OH solns. contg. citric or tartaric acid, $Na_4P_2O_7$ and $N_2H_4{\cdot}H_2SO_4$; town gas is passed through the soln. The CuC_2 can be weighed or titrated with KCN.[112]

α-Nitroso-β-naphthol ppts. $Cu(C_{10}H_6O_2N)_2$ from solns. contg. AcOH and NaOAc at pH 5·6;[113] an amperometric finish is possible.[114]

Benzohydroxamic acid ppts. Cu[PhC(OH):NO]$_2$ from NaOAc-buffered solns. Ag, Hg^{2+}, Fe^{3+}, Cr, Zn, Co, Ni interfere but Pb, Cd, As, Mn, Ca, etc., do not.[115]

Arsanilic acid can be used at pH 2; the ppt. is dried at 150°C and weighed or titrated with EDTA in presence of murexide indicator.[116]

$(NH_4)_2[Hg(SCN)_4]$ permits gravimetric, iodometric or colorimetric methods for Cu.[117] See p. 271 for a procedure involving copptn. with 30–40 mg. Zn and reflectance spectrophotometry.

NaOH ppts. Cu from dil. HNO_3 solns. on boiling; the ppt. is filtered on paper, washed with hot H_2O and 2% NH_4NO_3 and ignited to CuO at 600°C (Pigott[1]).

(k) EDTA may be utilized titrimetrically or colorimetrically. For < 20 mg. Cu in 100 ml. acidic soln., add 0·5 g. NH_4NO_3, 4–5 drops 0·1% pyrocatechol violet indicator and 0·5*N* NH_4OH to give a blue color; add 1–2 g. NH_4OAc and titrate with 0·02–0·1*M* EDTA to a yellow color.[118]

NOTES. (1) Ag, Mg, Ba, etc. can be tolerated; Al interference is prevented by F^- addn.

(2) Various other indicators have been recommended, *viz.* chrome azurol S at pH 6–6·5,[119] variamine blue at pH 5·5,[120] murexide in 0·01–0·1*M* NH_4OH.[121] If the end-point is detd. photometrically at 745 mμ in solns. of pH 2·4–2·8, Pb, Bi, Co, Ni and Fe^{3+} interfere.[122] Fe and Cu can be detd. simultaneously.[122] See also Chapter 19 and Chapter 5, Section 4.

(3) For colorimetric methods, see Table 30.

(4) Cu can also be titrated with NTA in presence of chrome azurol S indicator.[123]

(l) Miscellaneous titrimetric methods. For titration with 0·1*N* KCN, add 1 ml. NH_4OH/100 ml. soln. and titrate to colorless; Ag, Ni, Co, Cd, Zn interfere. Murexide can be used as indicator.[124]

Rubeanic acid is used with a photometric end-point; add 1 ml. 1% gum arabic followed by NH_4OH until a turbidity appears, and 3 ml. 80% AcOH before titration.[125]

Reinecke's salt and $K_2SnCl_4{\cdot}2H_2O$ can be employed in an iodometric procedure.[126] Boil < 50 mg. Cu in 100 ml. 1–3*N* HCl, add solid reductant (0·2–0·5 g. in excess) and Reinecke's salt (0·1 g. in 10 ml. warm 1–2*N* HCl for each 10 mg. Cu). After 5 min., filter on a glass crucible, wash with 2*N* HCl and hot H_2O. Add to the ppt. 1 ml. HNO_3, hot H_2O, 3 ml. H_2SO_4, 1 ml. 2*N* HCl and 0·5 g. $KBrO_3$/15 mg. Cu. Boil for 15 min., cool, add 2–5 g. $(NH_4)_2SO_4$ and 3 ml. 2*N* HCl and dil. to 100–150 ml. with H_2O. Boil for 10 min., cool, add 3–5 g. KI and titrate with 0·1*N* $Na_2S_2O_3$ in the usual way. Alternatively, dry the ppt. at 110°C (< 157°C) and weigh as $Cu[Cr(NH_3)_2(SCN)_4]$, but this is less satisfactory. Ag, Hg and Tl interfere.

For a colorimetric finish, treat the wet ppt. with solid thiourea and 2% thiourea soln. in MeCOEt and measure at 530 mμ.[127]

Cu can be reduced with Bi–Hg in solns. contg. 5–10*N* HCl and then titrated with 0·1*N* $K_2Cr_2O_7$ in presence of diphenylamine indicator.[128] Bi–Hg has been replaced by an Ag-reductor; the final detn. involves addn. of excess $Cr_2O_7^{2-}$, excess Fe^{2+} and back-titration with $Cr_2O_7^{2-}$ soln. to a diphenylaminesulfonate indicator, or reception of the effluent in excess Fe^{3+} and titration with Ce^{4+} soln. to ferroin indicator.[129]

Ascorbic acid is useful in conjunction with 2,6-dichlorophenolindophenol indicator.[130] For 30–320 mg. Cu in solns. which are just acidic in HCl, add 30 g. NH_4Cl, 2·5–5 g. NaOAc, and pass CO_2 for 15 min. Then add ascorbic acid until the Cu color fades, add 2 ml. 0·1% indicator and titrate to colorless; det. a blank. Bi, As, Sn, Cr^{6+}, PO_4^{3-}, SCN^-, $C_2O_4^{2-}$, etc. interfere; Fe^{3+} is masked by addn. of 0·5–3 g. NH_4F after the NaOAc addn.

Diamond black F (0·092 g./l. contg. 1 ml. 2*N* Na_2CO_3) permits titration of 0·01 mg. Cu/ml. in ammoniacal soln., the color change being from blue to red.[131]

$K_4Fe(CN)_6$ forms a ppt. with Cu which can be centrifuged, suspended in H_2O and titrated by Volhard's method.[132] Colorimetry is also possible (see Table 30). $Cu_3(AsO_4)_2$ can be detd. iodometrically[133] (see also p. 161). $H_2C_2O_4$ forms a ppt. with Cu which may be dissolved and titrated with $KMnO_4$ (see p. 267); this ppt. can also be weighed (see p. 161).

Ni-diethyldithiophosphate may be used for potentiometric titration of Cu; Sn^{2+} interferes, as does Fe^{3+} unless H_3PO_4 is added.[134]

(m) Peroxidase in conjunction with reductone allows the estimation of 0·0006 p.p.m. of Cu.[135]

(n) Colorimetric methods[136] are listed in Table 30.

(o) Nephelometry is possible in presence of EDTA and Fe^{2+}. Dil. the soln. contg. 10 p.p.m. Cu to 5 ml. with H_2O, add 1 ml. of a soln. contg. 10 g. EDTA, 10 g. tartaric acid and 10 g. NaOH/100 ml., followed by 5 drops of $FeSO_4 \cdot 7H_2O$ soln. (5 g./100 ml. 0·1*N* H_2SO_4). Mix after 2 min., dil. to 12·5 ml. with H_2O and measure the yellow CuOH. Ag, Au, Ir, Pd, NH_4^+ interfere.[137]

(p) Flame photometry may be used at 324·7 or 327·4 mμ.[138]

References

1. Hillebrand and Lundell, 193 (242); Scott and Furman, 349; Kimura, 155; Pigott, 181.
2. Butts, A., *Copper. The Science and Technology of the Metal, its Alloys and Compounds*, Reinhold, New York (1954).
3. Young, R. S., *Anal. Chim. Acta*, **4**, 366 (1950).
4. Goetz, C. A., *et al.*, *Anal. Chem.*, **21**, 1520 (1949).
5. Kitagawa, H. and Shibata, N., *Japan Analyst*, **4**, 358 (1955).
6. Curtis, J. A., *Ind. Eng. Chem.*, *Anal. Ed.*, **13**, 349 (1941); Welcher, **III**, 556.
7. Hillebrand and Lundell, 197 (247); Scott and Furman, 359; Kimura, 118.
8. A.S.T.M., 96 ff; Skowronski, S.; A.S.T.M., Bull., No. 174, 60 (1951).
9. Hecht and Donau, 159; MacNevin, W. M. and Bournique, R. A., *Ind. Eng. Chem.*, *Anal. Ed.*, **12**, 431 (1940).
10. Scherrer, J. A., *et al.*, *J. Research Natl. Bur. Standards*, **22**, 697 (1937).
11. Norwitz, G., *Anal. Chem.*, **21**, 523 (1949).
12. Biltz, H., *Z. anal. Chem.*, **90**, 277 (1932).
13. Silverman, L., *Ind. Eng. Chem.*, *Anal. Ed.*, **17**, 270 (1945).
14. Suzuki, S., *Kinzoku-Gakkai-Shi*, **B14**, (6) 44, (9) 32 (1950); **B15**, 133 (1951).
15. Treadwell, W. D., *Tabellen*, 107 (1938).
16. Lingane, J. J. and Jones, S. L., *Anal. Chem.*, **23**, 1798 (1951); also Hayakawa, H., *Japan Analyst*, **4**, 610 (1955) (sepn. from Bi); Lingane, *Electroanalytical Chemistry* (1953), p. 313 for controlled potential methods and p. 341 for internal electrolysis.
17. Musha, S. and Niwa, K., *J. Chem. Soc. Japan*, **78**, 1672 (1957).
18. Foote, H. W. and Vance, J. E., *Ind. Eng. Chem.*, *Anal. Ed.*, **9**, 205 (1937); Foote, *J. Am. Chem. Soc.*, **60**, 1349 (1938).
19. Oglethorpe, C. C. and Smith, C. G., *Analyst*, **68**, 325 (1943).
20. Krüger, D. and Tschirch, E., *Z. anal. Chem.*, **97**, 61 (1934).
21. Bitskei, J., *Z. anal. Chem.*, **102**, 35 (1935); *Magyar Kém. Folyóirat*, **61**, 23 (1955).
22. Hagen, S. K., *Z. anal. Chem.*, **117**, 26 (1939).
23. Welcher, **IV**, 307.
24. Hammock, E. W. and Swift, E. H., *Anal. Chem.*, **25**, 1113 (1953).
25. Jackson, W. H., *Chem. Eng. Mining Rev.*, **30**, 142 (1938).
26. Crowell, W. R., *Ind. Eng. Chem.*, *Anal Ed.*, **11**, 159 (1939).
27. Park, B., *Ind. Eng. Chem.*, *Anal. Ed.*, **3**, 77 (1931).
28. Meites, L., *Anal. Chem.*, **24**, 1618 (1952).
29. Erler, K., *Z. anal. Chem.*, **129**, 93 (1949).
30. Clardy, F. B., *et al.*, *Ind. Eng. Chem.*, *Anal. Ed.*, **17**, 791 (1945); Tantranon, K. and Cunningham, B. B., *Anal. Chem.*, **25**, 194 (1953) (±2% for 50 μg., ±0·2% for 1 mg., ±0·12% for 5 mg.); Bodnár, J. and Tolnay, V., *Z. anal. Chem.*, **120**, 336 (1940) (gravimetry using 19 ml. 0·1*N* NH_4SCN (recrystd.) for 0·1 g. Cu): Sarudi, I., *ibid.*, **130**, 301 (1950); Stathis, E. C., *Anal. Chim. Acta*, **16**, 21 (1957) (ascorbic acid reduction; Pb, Bi, Cd, Sb, Fe, Mn, Ni, Cr, Zn, PO_4^{3-} do not interfere).
31. Occleshaw, V. J., *J. Chem. Soc.*, 1438 (1937).
32. Burriel, F. and Lucena, F., *Anal. Chim. Acta*, **2**, 230 (1948).
33. Belcher, R. and West, T. S., *Anal. Chim. Acta*, **5**, 364 (1951); **6**, 337 (1952).
34. Welcher, **III**, 261; Hecht and Donau, 157 (0·07–1·3 mg. Cu); Ducret, L., *Bull. soc. chim.*, **12**, 880 (1945); Platonova, O. P. and Zaĭtseva, G. M., *Zavodskaya Lab.*, **22**, 165 (1956) (potentiometric, in steel); Fill, M. A. and Stock, J. T., *Analyst*, **69**, 178 (1944) (amperometric).
35. Welcher, **III**, 256.
36. Raju, N. and Neelakantam, K., *Current Sci.* (*India*), **19**, 383 (1950); Bhatki, K. S. and Kabadi, M. B., *J. Univ. Bombay*, **24A**, (3) 51 (1955).
37. Endo, J. and Mashima, M., *J. Chem. Soc. Japan*, **74**, 564, 622 (1953).
38. Mukherjee, A. K., *Anal. Chim. Acta*, **13**, 334 (1955).

39. Poddar, S. N., *Z. anal. Chem.*, **155**, 329 (1957).
40. Byrn, E. E. and Robertson, J. H., *Anal. Chem.*, **26**, 1604 (1954); Horiuchi, Y. and Saito, M., *J. Chem. Soc. Japan*, **78**, 607 (1957) (acetate buffer, yellow to methyl orange; in steel).
41. Berg, R., *Oxin*, 87 (1935); Hecht and Donau, 156 (0·1–0·6 mg.); Welcher, **I**, 324.
42. Mukherjee, A. K. and Banerjee, B., *Naturwissenschaften*, **42**, 416 (1955).
43. Welcher, **I**, 305; Ishimaru, S., *J. Chem. Soc. Japan*, **56**, 62 (1935); Ishibashi, M. and Fujinaga, T., *ibid.*, **71**, 27, 229 (1950) (amperometric).
44. Blair, A. J. and Pantony, D. A., *Anal. Chim. Acta*, **16**, 121 (1957).
45. Berges, L. S., *Anales real soc. españ. fis. y quím. (Madrid)*, 529, 535 (1953); Nievas, J. B. and Berges, L. S., *ibid.*, **50B**, 459 (1954).
46. Welcher, **I**, 323 ff.
47. Welcher, **I**, 210.
48. Feigl, F. and Caldas, A., *Anal. Chim. Acta*, **8**, 339 (1953).
49. Smith, G. F. and McCurdy, W. H., *Anal. Chem.*, **24**, 371 (1952); Brown, J. K. and Connel, J. C., *ibid.*, **25**, 519 (1953) (CH_3CHCl_2 extn.); Gahler, A. R., *ibid.*, **26**, 577 (1954) (in steel, $CHCl_3$ extn.); Sherwood, R. M. and Chapman, Jr., F. W., *ibid.*, **27**, 88 (1955) (iso-butanol extn.); Fulton, J. W. and Hastings, J., *ibid.*, **28**, 174 (1956) (in Pb–Sn, Al, etc.); Zak, B. and Ressler, N., *ibid.*, 1158; Frank, A. J., *et al.*, *ibid.*, **29**, 750 (1957) (in Ti; sepn. of Cr by $HClO_4$ and HCl, $CHCl_3$ extn., EtOH diln.); Crawley, R. H. A., *Anal. Chim. Acta*, **13**, 373 (1955) (in W); Ishihara, Y. and Taguchi, Y., *Japan Analyst*, **6**, 588 (1957) (in Zn, Cd, Pb, Bi, Sn); A.S.T.M. 223 (Ni–Cr, Ni–Cr–Fe; $CHCl_3$ extn.).
50. Smith, G. F. and Wilkins, D. H., *Anal. Chem.*, **25**, 510 (1953); Borchardt, L. G. and Butler, J. P., *ibid.*, **29**, 414 (1957).
51. Sandell, 300; Morrison, S. L. and Paige, H. L., *Ind. Eng. Chem., Anal. Ed.*, **18**, 211 (1946); (Welcher, **III**, 519). See also Chapter 18, p. 147.
52. Sandell, E. B., *Ind. Eng. Chem., Anal. Ed.*, **9**, 464 (1937); Sandell, 312.
53. Martens, R. I. and Githens, Sr., R. E., *Anal. Chem.*, **24**, 991 (1952); see also Stone, I., *et al.*, *ibid.*, **25**, 893 (1953); Andrus, S., *Analyst*, **80**, 514 (1955); Borchardt, L. G. and Butler, J. P., *Anal. Chem.*, **29**, 414 (1957).
54. Sandell, 304; Welcher, **IV**, 84; Murakami, Y., *Bull. Chem. Soc. Japan*, **23**, 3, 99 (1950) (+$NH_2OH{\cdot}HCl$, extn. better); Hague, J. L., *et al.*, *J. Research Natl. Bur. Standards*, **47**, 380 (1951); Sudo, E., *J. Chem. Soc. Japan*, **73**, 753 (1952) (for extn. AmOH + EtOAc best); Cheng, K. L. and Bray, R. H., *Anal. Chem.*, **25**, 655 (1953) (+EDTA, only Ag, Bi interfere; Beer's law is obeyed at 500 mμ); Chilton, J. M., *ibid.*, 1274 (simultaneous detn. of Cu, Co, Ni by absorbance at 436, 367, 328 mμ); Šedivec, V. and Vašák, V., *Chem. listy*, **45**, 435 (1951); Kovařik, M. and Vinš, V., *Z. anal. Chem.*, **147**, 401 (1955); Claassen, A. and Bastings, L., *ibid.*, **153**, 30 (1956) (the last 3 refs. use Pb-salt, and no interference occurs with Pb, Ni, Co, Fe, Mn, Zn); Tanaka, Y. and Ito, K., *Japan Analyst*, **6**, 728 (1957) (Zn-salt, after dithizone extn. and stripping with cuprethol); also see Wickbold, R., *Z. anal. Chem.*, **152**, 338 (1956) (titrimetric method, see p. 155), Bobtelsky, M. and Rafailoff, R., *Anal. Chim. Acta*, **14**, 558 (1956) (direct photometric).
55. Sandell, 309; Woelfel, W. C., *Anal. Chem.*, **20**, 722 (1948); Berkhout, H. W. and Goossens, N., *Chem. Weekblad*, **46**, 166 (1950).
56. Cluley, H. J., *Analyst*, **79**, 561 (1954) (in steel, Al, white metal); Borchardt and Butler, *Anal. Chem.*, **29**, 414 (1957); Lounamaa, K., *Z. anal. Chem.*, **150**, 7 (1956).
57. Welcher, **IV**, 179.
58. Yoe, 177; Mehlig, J. P., *Ind. Eng. Chem., Anal. Ed.*, **13**, 533 (1941); **14**, 903 (1942).
59. Mellor and Thompson, 372 (1938).
60. Welcher, **III**, 2; Spacu, G. and Rădulescu, E., *Acad. rep. populare Romîne, Studii cercetări chim.*, **3**, 7 (1955) (+$HSC_6H_4CO_2Na$; sepn. of Cu from Fe, Al); Joshi (see ref. 10, p. 148; Ce^{4+} titration).
61. Spakowski, A. E. and Freiser, H., *Anal. Chem.*, **21**, 986 (1949).
62. Welcher, **II**, 284.
63. Spacu, G. and Antonescu, El., *Acad. rep. populare Romîne, Studii cercetări chim.*, **3**, 167 (1955).
64. Welcher, **II**, 382.
65. Jean, M., *Bull. soc. chim.*, **12**, 672 (1945).
66. Welcher, **II**, 452.
67. Tarasevich, N. I., *Zhur. Anal. Khim.*, **4**, 108 (1949).
68. Taurinš, A., *Z. anal. Chem.*, **97**, 28 (1934).
69. Welcher, **II**, 331.
70. Tarasevich, N. I., *Zhur. Anal. Khim.*, **3**, 253 (1948).
71. Spacu, P. and Niculescu, M., *Z. anal. Chem.*, **116**, 119 (1939); also see Pirtea, P., *et al.*, *Acad. rep. populare Romîne, Studii cercetări chim.*, **3**, 233 (1955) (as [Cu py_4] $(ClO_4)_2$).
72. Welcher, **II**, 28; **III**, 127.
73. Welcher, **II**, 399.
74. Bankovskis, J., *Latvijs PSR Zinātņu Akad. Vestis*, No. 9, 119 (1955).
75. Spacu, P. and Hlevca, G., *Acad. rep. populare Romîne, Bul. Ştiinţ., Sect. ştiinţ. teh. şi. chim.*, **5**, 93 (1953).
76. Flaschka, H. and Soliman, A., *Z. anal. Chem.*, **158**, 254 (1957); **159**, 30 (1957).
77. Welcher, **II**, 212; Hecht and Donau, 158 (0·1–1 mg.); Kiba, T. and Sato, S., *J. Chem. Soc. Japan*, **61**, 636 (1940).
78. Lindsay, A. K. and Shennan, R. J., *Analyst*, **65**, 636 (1940).
79. Majumdar, A. K., *Analyst*, **68**, 242 (1943); Pritchard, L. E. and Chirnside, R. C., *ibid.*, 244; Majumdar, *J. Indian Chem. Soc.*, **21**, 24 (1944).
80. Stock, J. T., *J. Chem. Soc.*, 1793, 2470 (1949).
81. Majumdar, A. K. and Mallick, A. K., *J. Indian Chem. Soc.*, **29**, 255 (1952); Majumdar and De, A. K., *ibid.*, **30**, 401 (1953).
82. Welcher, **II**, 199 ff.
83. Sogani, N. C. and Bhattacharya, S. C., *Anal. Chem.*, **28**, 1616 (1956).
84. Welcher, **IV**, 169, 175; Umemura, T., *J. Chem. Soc. Japan*, **61**, 26 (1940).
85. Kuroda, R., *et al.*, *Japan Analyst*, **5**, 33 (1956).
86. Hillebrand and Lundell, 202 (252); Kimura, 117; A.S.T.M. 97 (in steels).
87. Hahn, F. L., *Ber.*, **63**, 116 (1930).

88. HECHT and DONAU, 155, WELCHER, **III**, 242.
89. BANDYOPADHAYAY, D. and RÂY, P., *J. Indian Chem. Soc.*, **33**, 21 (1956).
90. WELCHER, **I**, 223, 380, 404; DUKE, F. R., *Ind. Eng. Chem., Anal. Ed.*, **16**, 750 (1944).
91. HIRATA, T., *J. Chem. Soc. Japan*, **71**, 383 (1950).
92. TERENT'EV, A. P., *et al., Zhur. Anal. Khim.*, **7**, 120 (1952).
93. MUSANTE, C., *Gazz. chim. ital.*, **76**, 123 (1946).
94. RAMANUJAN, V. V., *Current Sci.* (*India*), **22**, 374 (1953); *J. Sci. Ind. Research* (*India*), **15B**, 212 (1956).
95. GUSEV, S. I. and KUMOV, V. I., *Zhur. Anal. Khim.*, **11**, 303 (1956).
96. WELCHER, **IV**, 112, 124, 128.
97. SERFASS, E. J. and LEVINE, W. S., *Monthly Rev. Am. Electroplater's Soc.*, **34**, 320 (1947).
98. WELCHER, **IV**, 118.
99. SINGH, R. P. and SHANKAR, V., *J. Indian Chem. Soc.*, **32**, 557 (1955).
100. SIDDHANTA, S. K. and KUNDU, PH. CH., *J. Indian Chem. Soc.*, **32**, 655 (1955).
101. DUTT, N. K. and SARMA, K. P. S., *Anal. Chim. Acta*, **15**, 21, 102 (1956).
102. GUPTA, J. and CHAKRABARTTY, B., *J. Sci. Ind. Research* (*India*), **8B**, 133 (1949); **10B**, 98 (1951).
103. PATNAIK, B. K., *J. Indian Chem. Soc.*, **34**, 75 (1957).
104. TAMAYO, M. L. and GARRIDO, J., *Anales real soc. fís. y quím.* (*Madrid*), **43**, 54 (1947).
105. WELCHER, **I**, 421.
106. HOVORKA, V. and VOŘIŠEK, J., *Chem. listy*, **37**, 5 (1943); WELCHER, **III**, 281.
107. WELCHER, **III**, 410, 411.
108. WELCHER, **III**, 361.
109. KOLTHOFF, I. M. and LIBERTI, A., *Analyst*, **74**, 635 (1949).
110. WELCHER, **III**, 401.
111. SHOME, S. C., *Analyst*, **75**, 27 (1950).
112. WELCHER, **I**, 50.
113. WENGER, P. E., *et al., Anal. Chim. Acta*, **3**, 660 (1949); *Helv. Chim. Acta*, **33**, 1438 (1950); (WELCHER, **III**, 317).
114. KOLTHOFF, I. M. and LANGER, A., *J. Am. Chem. Soc.*, **62**, 3172 (1940).
115. MUSANTE, C., *Gazz. chim. ital.*, **78**, 536 (1948).
116. MUSIL, A. and PIETSCH, R., *Z. anal. Chem.*, **140**, 421 (1953).
117. SIERRA, F. and ABRISQUETA, C., *Anales real soc. españ. fís. y quím.* (*Madrid*), **50B**, 421 (1954).
118. SUK, V., *et al., Chem. listy*, **48**, 1151 (1954); ŠIR, Z. and PŘIBIL, R., *ibid.*, **50**, 221, 539 (1956).
119. THEIS, M., *Z. anal. Chem.*, **144**, 275 (1955).
120. WEHBER, P., *Mikrochim. Acta*, 927 (1955).
121. AMIN, A. M., *Chemist Analyst*, **44**, 17 (1955).
122. SWEETSER, P. B. and BRICKER, C. E., *Anal. Chem.*, **25**, 253 (1953); UNDERWOOD, A. L., *ibid.*, 1910.
123. WEHBER, P., *Z. anal. Chem.*, **149**, 419 (1956).
124. SCOTT and FURMAN, 373; DOLEŽAL, J., *et al., Chem. listy*, **51**, 880 (1957).
125. TANANAEV, I. V. and LEVITMAN, KH. YA, *Trudy Komissii Anal. Khim., Akad. Nauk S.S.S.R.*, **7**, 21 (1956) (in Al alloy); BOBTELSKY, M. and BLUM, J., *Anal. Chim. Acta*, **15**, 62 (1956); also see Chapter 18, p. 148.
126. MAHR, C., *Z. anorg. Chem.*, **225**, 386 (1935).
127. MAHR, C., *Angew. Chem.*, **53**, 257 (1940); also see SAJÓ, I., *Magyar Kém. Folyóirat*, **57**, 8 (1951) (yellow color when ppt. dissolved in dil. HNO_3).
128. SOMEYA, K., *Sci. Repts. Tohoku Univ.*, (I) **16**, 515 (1927).
129. WILSON, W. J., *Anal. Chim. Acta*, **15**, 12 (1956); also see BIRNBAUM, N. and EDMONDS, S. M., *Ind. Eng. Chem., Anal. Ed.*, **12**, 156 (1940).
130. ERDEY, L. and SIPOSS, G., *Z. anal. Chem.*, **157**, 166 (1957).
131. WELCHER, **IV**, 484.
132. DELGA, J., *Ann. chim. anal.*, **27**, 70 (1945).
133. SHAKHTAKHTINSKIĬ, G. B. and EFENDIEV, T. D., *Zhur. Anal. Khim.*, **3**, 245 (1948).
134. BUSEV, A. I. and IVANYUTIN, M. I., *Zhur. Anal. Khim.*, **11**, 523 (1956).
135. YAMAZAKI, I. and FUJINAGA, K., *J. Chem. Soc. Japan*, **77**, 1213 (1956).
136. MILLER, R. H. and BURTSELL, A. T., *Mikrochemie ver. Mikrochim. Acta*, **28**, 209 (1940); CONN, L. W., *et al., Ind. Eng. Chem., Anal. Ed.*, **7**, 15 (1935); SAKURAI, K., *Analysis & Reagent* (*Japan*), **2**, 26 (1946).
137. CHENG, K. L., *Anal. Chem.*, **27**, 1165 (1955).
138. DEAN, J. A., *Anal. Chem.*, **27**, 1224 (1955) (0·0–5·0% Cu in non-ferrous alloys); DEAN and LADY, J. H., *ibid.*, **28**, 1887 (1956) (salicylaldoxime complex/$CHCl_3$, 10–150 μg); MANNA, L. and SMITH, D. H., *ibid.*, 1070 (1–8 μg/ml. 80% MeOH); DEAN, J. A. and CAIN, JR., C., *ibid.*, **29**, 530 (1957) (25–500 μg., diethyldithiocarbamate/$CHCl_3$ extn., O_2–C_2H_2 flame, in Al alloys); MASSEY, H. F., *ibid.*, 365 (dithizone/$CHCl_3$ + kerosine ext., in plants).

23

CADMIUM

The principal sources for this chapter are given in ref. 1.

Attack

The sample is usually treated with HCl or with HCl and HNO_3, followed by H_2SO_4 addn. and evapn. to fumes. The residue is fused with Na_2CO_3 which is leached with H_2SO_4. See also Chapter 36.

Separation

H_2S allows sepn. of Cd from group III metals, etc., in 4–5*N* H_2SO_4; H_2S is passed into the boiling soln. until it becomes cold, NH_4OH being added dropwise if necessary. Sepn. from Zn is complete in this way.[2] In general better sepns. are obtained if $(NH_4)_2SO_4$ is added (Hillebrand and Lundell[1]). When much Zn is present, fractional pptn. is required. HCl should not be used and large amts. of alkali chlorides must be absent. Cd can be concd. with Cu^{2+} at pH 3 in solns. contg. 2% Na_3-citrate.

Sepn. of Cd from Cu, Bi, As, Sb, Sn is obtained by passing H_2S for 30 min. through the 9*N* H_2SO_4 soln. at 95–100°C; the ppt. is washed with a satd. soln. of H_2S in the 9*N* acid. H_2S also allows sepn. of Cd from Cu in KCN-contg. media. Extn. of sulfide ppts. with cold 1:2 HCl seps. Cd from Cu, Hg, As and most of the Sb. Extn. with hot HNO_3 seps. Cd and Hg.

Na_2S seps. Cd from the As group. $(NH_4)_2S$ is also useful but NH_4HS is never employed.

Electrolysis seps. Cd from Zn in hot solns. contg. $H_2C_2O_4$ and $Na_2C_2O_4$ or in slightly acidic (H_2SO_4) solns. Cd is sepd. from Cu by electrolysis of fairly concd. HNO_3 solns. Electrolysis or treatment with H_2SO_4 seps. Cd and Pb.

Treatment with SO_2 and NH_4SCN or with $Na_2S_2O_3$ seps. Cd and Cu (p. 172).

Hydrolysis seps. Cd from BiOCl.

β-Naphthoquinoline and KI permit the sepn. of a little Cd from Zn.

Treatment with Fe in 2*N* H_2SO_4 media contg. some drops of SO_2 water seps. Cd from Cu, Pb, Ag, Sn, Hg, Bi.

Cd is sepd. from Cu, Zn, etc. by treatment with Al as follows. Boil the soln. contg. 1 ml. H_2SO_4/200 ml. with 0·3–1 g. of < 400 mesh Al for 5 min. Filter through cotton wool and wash with H_2O. Boil the filtrate with 0·1 g. Al for 5 min. and filter in the same way. Add 5 ml. 50% NaOH to the combined ppts. and filter on a hard paper, washing with H_2O. Treat the residue with 7 ml. HCl and 50 ml. Br_2 water, boil out the Br_2, cool, add 15 ml. NH_4OH and heat. Filter and wash with 2% NH_4Cl contg. some NH_4OH.[3]

Cd is sepd. from Bi, Sn, Fe, Al by repeated pptn. with NH_4OH.

Extn. with dithizone in $CHCl_3$ or CCl_4 from 1*N* NaOH solns. seps. Cd, Cu, Ag, Hg, Co, Ni from Pb, Zn, Bi. CCl_4 is better. Sepn. from Cu, Ag, Hg, Co, Ni is obtained by shaking the ext. with 0·01*N* HCl. Cd and Ni can be sepd. by extg. the 2-mercaptobenzothiazole complex with $CHCl_3$ from tartrate-contg. ammoniacal soln.; Cd is stripped with 6*N* HCl. $CHCl_3$ extn. of the pyridine–thiocyanate complex allows sepn. from Ag, Hg, Cu^+.

Cd and Zn are sepd. from Cu, Ni, Co by extn. of the thiocyanate complexes with 1:1 *n*-butyl phosphate–MeCOEt from neutral soln. contg. thiourea (see also Chapter 16, p. 137).

Extn. of the cupferrate complexes from acidic soln. with $CHCl_3$ gives a sepn. from Cu, Fe, etc. while extn. of the dimethylglyoxime complex with $CHCl_3$ gives sepn. from Ni.

Ion exchange resins allow sepn. of Cd from many elements (see Chapter 13, Section 2.1).

Determination

Oxine itself is not very satisfactory for the detn. of Cd but its analog, 2-(*o*-hydroxyphenyl)-benzoxazole, appears to be the best available reagent. However, Cd is usually detd. by weighing as the sulfate after pptn. as the sulfide. Org. bases such as β-naphthoquinoline used in conjunction with KI provide the best semimicro procedures. Dithizone is the most satisfactory reagent for colorimetric purposes.

(a) 2-(*o*-Hydroxyphenyl)-benzoxazole can be used in gravimetric, titrimetric and colorimetric methods.[4] For 1–80 mg. Cd, add 3 g. $(NH_4)_2$-tartrate and heat to 60°C.

(If Ca is present, filter off the tartrate ppt., add 1 g. $(NH_4)_2$-tartrate and reheat.) Adjust the pH to 3·5 with 3*N* AcOH, add a small excess of 1% reagent in EtOH, adjust to pH 4·0 with 3*N* NaOAc, digest to 60°C for 15 min. and allow to cool. Filter on a glass crucible, wash with H_2O and discard. Adjust the filtrate to pH 9 with 1*N* NaOH, heat to 60°C and add a small excess of reagent; adjust to pH 11 with NaOH, digest at 60°C for 15 min. and allow to cool. Filter on a glass crucible, wash with 1:1 NH_4OH–EtOH, dry at 130–140°C for 2 hr. and weigh as $Cd(C_{13}H_8O_2N)_2$. Alternatively, dissolve the ppt. in hot AcOH, add $KBrO_3$ and KBr and titrate the excess potentiometrically.

NOTES. (1) No interference arises from Fe, Bi, Cr, Mn, Zn or 0·1 g. Cu; if >20 mg. Co or Ni is present, prior sepn. is needed.
(2) $KMnO_4$ can be used in another titrimetric finish.[5] Dissolve the ppt. from 20 mg. Cd in 28% H_2SO_4 and dil. to 100 ml. with this acid; treat a 10 ml. aliquot with a 39–42% excess of 0·1*N* $KMnO_4$ for 60 min. at 22–24°C. Add H_2O, 10 ml. 5% KI and titrate with 0·1*N* $Na_2S_2O_3$.
(3) For colorimetry of 0·1–2 mg. Cd in 20–50 ml. soln.,[6] add an equal vol. of EtOH, heat to 60°C and add a small excess of reagent. Adjust to pH 11 with NH_4OH or NaOH and heat to 60°C for 15 min. Filter on a medium frit, wash with 50% EtOH contg. some NH_4OH and then with EtOH contg. some NH_4OH. Dry at 130°C, dissolve in AcOH and measure the fluorescence under UV light.
(4) Oxine is used gravimetrically or titrimetrically.[7, 8, 9] Heat the soln. contg. <0·5% AcOH (if necessary adjust to pH 6–7 with NaOAc) to 60°C and add 2–3% oxine in EtOH; boil, filter on a glass crucible, wash with warm then cold H_2O, dry at 100–105°C and weigh as $Cd(C_9H_6ON)_2 \cdot 1\frac{1}{2}H_2O$, or at 280–384°C and weigh as the anhydrous salt. Alternatively, finish the detn. bromometrically. Many metals interfere.

(b) H_2S is normally used gravimetrically but colorimetric and titrimetric methods are also possible. For < 0·02 g. Cd in 100 ml. soln. contg. 3 ml. H_2SO_4, start passing H_2S through the boiling soln. and continue to pass it for 45 min. while the soln. cools; add cold H_2O (a vol. half that of the initial soln.) and pass H_2S for 20 min. Filter on a glass crucible and wash with H_2S water contg. some H_2SO_4. Treat the ppt. with 1:3 HCl and dil. H_2SO_4, evap. to dryness, heat at 200–800°C (218–420°C) and weigh as $CdSO_4$. Alternatively, dry at 69–120°C and weigh as the monohydrate.[1, 8, 10]

NOTES. (1) The sulfate must be heated repeatedly after addn. of a drop of H_2O to const. wt.; if a yellow-brown color appears, the ppt. is heated after addn. of some H_2SO_4. For weighing as CdS after drying at 100°C, see Sarudi,[10] A.S.T.M.[11]
(2) For colorimetry of 0·2 mg. Cd in 20 ml. neutral soln.[8,12] add 1 ml. 1% NH_4OH followed by 10% KCN until the soln. is colorless with 4 ml. in excess. Add 1 ml. 10% $(NH_4)_2SO_4$ and 1 ml. 1% gelatin, dil. to 30 ml. with H_2O, add 5 ml. satd. H_2S soln., dil. to 50 ml. with H_2O, and measure the yellow color after 5 min. at 430 mμ. No interference arises from 1000-, 100- or 10-fold amts. of resp. Zn, Ni or Cu and Co. The method is 10 times more sensitive if the final measurement is made in the UV region.
(3) For titrimetry, treat the ppt. from 0·01–0·2 g. Cd with I_2 and back-titrate in the usual way; negative errors are obtained.[8] Other oxidimetric finishes have been applied.

(c) β-Naphthoquinoline and KI are best used titrimetrically.[8, 13] For < 0·05 g. Cd in 50 ml. 2*N* H_2SO_4, add 5 g. NaK-tartrate, a few drops of satd. SO_2 water, 15 ml. 10% KI, 30 ml. 2·5% base in 0·5*N* H_2SO_4 and dil. to 150 ml. with H_2O. After 1 hr. filter on a G4 crucible and wash with a soln. contg. 4 ml. 10% KI and 10 ml. base/100 ml. Dissolve the ppt. in 20 ml. 2*N* NH_4OH, neutralize with 2*N* HCl and add enough HCl to give a 0·6*N* soln. Add 5 ml. 10% KCN and starch indicator and titrate with 0·025*M* KIO_3 to colorless. Alternatively, dry the ppt. at 110–130°C and weigh as $(C_{13}H_9N)_2 \cdot H_2CdI_4$.

NOTES. (1) Pb, Cu, Bi, Hg, Ag interfere but can be sepd. by means of Fe or Al. No interference is caused by Zn (<1 g.), Sn, Sb, Fe^{2+}, Co, Ni, Mn, Al, Cr, Mg or tartrate.
(2) Several procedures based on similar principles have been suggested. Those with phenyltrimethylammonium iodide or with hexamine allyl iodide are similar in accuracy to the above; the method involving brucine is less accurate.
(*i*) With phenyltrimethylammonium iodide,[14] proceed as above but add 3 g. KI and 25 ml. 2·5% base; stand for 6 hr. before filtration and wash the ppt. with a soln. contg. 1 g. KI and 1 g. base/100 ml.
(*ii*) Hexamine allyl iodide is normally used gravimetrically.[15] For 20 mg. Cd in 20 ml. soln. at pH 2·6–5·6 and at 50–60°C, add KI and 15 ml. 5% base and leave for 2 hr. Filter on a G3 crucible and wash with a satd. soln. of the ppt. in EtOH. Dry at 105–110°C for 3 min. and weigh as $[C_2H_{17}N_4I]_2CdI_2$. Alternatively, titrate the ppt. as above.
(*iii*) With brucine,[16] treat the soln. contg. 20–50 mg. Cd/50 ml. with 1·5 ml. 1% brucine sulfate and 1·5 ml. 10% KI/1 mg. Cd. Filter on a glass crucible after 10 min. and wash three times with a 1 : 1 mixture of the base and KI solns. and then with 1 : 4 EtOH-toluene. Dissolve the ppt. in warm H_2O, add 5 ml. 0·5% eosin and titrate with 0·03*N* $AgNO_3$.
Brucine has also been used nephelometrically[17] and gravimetrically in conjunction with KBr.[18]
(*iv*) Antipyrine and KBr permit a gravimetric detn. of Cd.[19]
(*v*) $[Cu(en)_2](NO_3)_2$ is used gravimetrically with KI.[8, 20] Prep. the reagent by dissolving equiv. wts. of $Cu(NO_3)_2$ and ethylenediamine in water, heating until crystals appear, cooling, filtering and washing with EtOH and Et_2O. For the detn. add excess KI to the soln. (100–300 ml.), boil and add the hot concd. complex; cool, filter on a glass crucible, wash 4–6 times with a soln. contg. 1% KI and 0·3% complex then with 2 ml. EtOH 4–6 times and Et_2O 3–4 times. Dry in a vacuum desiccator and weigh as $[Cu(en)_2][CdI_4]$.
(*vi*) Fe^{2+}-2,2′-dipyridyl and KI are used gravimetrically.[21] Tetraphenylarsonium chloride is applied titrimetrically.[22] For tetraphenylphosphonium chloride, see Chapter 19, p. 153,

(d) Dithizone provides an excellent colorimetric method.[23] Neutralize the soln. with NaOH to thymol blue indicator and dil. with H_2O to 25 ml. Add 1 ml. 25% NaK-tartrate, 5 ml. 40% NaOH contg. 1% KCN, 1 ml. 20% $NH_2OH{\cdot}HCl$ and 15 ml. reagent (80 mg./l. $CHCl_3$). Shake, sep., add 10 ml. $CHCl_3$ and sep. Run the org. layers into 25 ml. 2% tartaric acid at 0°C, shake for 2 min. and sep. (If > 10 μg. Cd is present, take an aliquot and dil. to 25 ml. with 2% tartaric acid.) Add 5 ml. $CHCl_3$, shake for 1 min., sep., add 0·25 ml. $NH_2OH{\cdot}HCl$ soln., 15 ml. reagent (8 mg./l. $CHCl_3$) and 5 ml. of the NaOH–KCN soln. Shake for 1 min., sep., filter through cotton wool and measure at 518 mμ.

NOTES. (1) Tl interferes; this is avoided by shaking the first $CHCl_3$ layer with 25 ml. of a soln. contg. 0·1 g. $CoSO_4$, 5 g. NaK-tartrate and 40 g. $NaHCO_3$ in 1 l. H_2O, sepg., shaking with tartaric acid and then proceeding as above. 5–10 mg. of other ions can be tolerated.
(2) Errors may occur if the $CHCl_3$ layer is left in contact with the strongly alk. soln. for a long time.
(3) Di-β-naphthylcarbazone has been examined.[24]

(e) Electrodeposition.[1] Neutralize the Cd-contg. soln. (dil. H_2SO_4) with NaOH to phenolphthalein indicator and add 10% KCN until the soln. becomes clear (avoid any excess). Dil. with H_2O to 100–150 ml. and electrolyze first for 5–6 hr. at 0·5–0·7 amp. and 4·8–5·0 v. and then for 1 hr. at 1–2 amp. or for 12 hr. at 0·5 amp. Wash with EtOH, dry at 100°C and weigh Cd.

NOTES (1) Ag, Zn, Cl^-, etc. interfere. The method has been applied for several alloys, etc. (see A.S.T.M.[10]).
(2) Several alternative procedures are available. For 1–3 mg. Cd in 5 ml. soln. contg. 1·5 ml. NH_4OH, electrolyze at 0·1–0·15 amp./dm.^{2} (3 v.) for 10 min. while passing CO_2 through the soln.[25] Alternatively, heat the soln. contg. 20 ml. NH_4OH and 5 g. $(NH_4)_2SO_4$/100 ml. to 40–50°C and electrolyze at 0·7–1·5 amp. and 2·4–2·7 v. with a rotating electrode (600–800 r.p.m.). Neither As nor W interferes.[26]
If the soln. contains 5 g. $KHSO_4$/100 ml. soln., electrolyze at 0·1–0·2 amp. and 2·4–2·8 v. for 3 hr. No interference is caused by Ni, Co, Al, Zn or by Fe, Mn, Cr in presence of $N_2H_4{\cdot}H_2SO_4$. Alternatively, heat the soln. contg. 3 g. $KHSO_4$ and 3 g. NaOAc/100 ml. to 70°C and electrolyze at 0·5–1·5 amp. and 2·4–2·6 v. with a rotating electrode (800–1000 r.p.m.).[26]
With solns. contg. 12 g. $K_2C_2O_4$, 3 g. NaOAc and 3 ml. 20% AcOH/100 ml., heat to 70–80°C and pass 0·1–0·2 amp. at 2·9 v. using a rotating electrode (300–400 r.p.m.). If Zn is present, add 0·2 g. phenol and electrolyze for double or treble the time.[27]
(3) Internal electrolysis is possible with Pt gauze and a Zn plate in solns. contg. 1·65 ml. 85% AcOH and 5·9 g. NaOAc/250 ml. soln. at 70–80°C; Zn does not interfere.[28]
(4) Controlled potential electrolysis permits sepn. from Zn.[29]

(f) Na-quinaldate is used gravimetrically.[8, 30] For 0·1–0·2 g. Cd in 150 ml. of slightly acidic soln. add excess 2·5% reagent and adjust to pH 3·9–7·2 with NaOH. Digest on a steam-bath, cool, filter on a glass crucible and wash with cold H_2O. Dry at 120–125°C (66–197°C) and weigh as $Cd(C_{10}H_6NO_2)_2$.

NOTES. (1) Cu and Zn interfere; Sb or Bi interference is avoided by addn. of 2·4 g. NaK-tartrate. The interference of Zn has been studied[31] (see also Chapter 22, p. 179).
(2) Very similar procedures have been suggested with quinoline-8-carboxylic acid[32] (see also p. 179), and with 5,6-benzoquinaldic acid.[33] The latter reagent permits sepn. of Cd from Ag, Hg, Pb, Be, Th, Zr, U, rare earths, Fe, Al, Cr, Ti, Bi, Sb, Sn, V, W, P, As, Mo and tartrate.

(g) Miscellaneous gravimetric methods. Na-anthranilate is suitable for < 0·15 g. Cd in neutral soln. Add 20–25 ml. 3% reagent, filter on a glass crucible, wash with 1:20 reagent and with EtOH, dry at 105–110°C and weigh as $Cd(C_7H_6O_2N)_2$. Alternatively, titrate the ppt. bromometrically.[8, 34]

Salicylhydroxamic acid ppts. Cd at pH 4·4–5·4 but is not satisfactory.[35]

$(NH_4)_2HPO_4$ may be used gravimetrically or titrimetrically. The ppt. is weighed as $Cd_2P_2O_7$ or as $CdNH_4PO_4{\cdot}H_2O$ after heating at 600°C or at 90–122°C resp.[8, 36] For titrimetry, the ppt. is dissolved in $HClO_4$ and titrated with $BiOClO_4$ in presence of diallyldithiocarbamidohydrazine indicator in $CHCl_3$.[37]

Thiourea and Reinecke's salt allow gravimetric, titrimetric or colorimetric detns.[8, 38] For gravimetric detn. of > 1 mg. Cd in 0·1–1N acid soln., add 5% thiourea to give a 1% soln. and then add a satd. soln. of Reinecke's salt in 1% thiourea. Cool to 0°C for 0·5–1 hr. Filter on a glass crucible and wash with 1% thiourea and with EtOH, both at 0°C. Dry at 110–120°C (< 167°C) and weigh as $[Cd(NH_2CSNH_2)_2][Cr(NH_3)_2(SCN)_4]_2$. For the other finishes, see Chapter 22, p. 180.

Cu, Hg, Bi, Sn interfere in the above method but Zn (< 1 g.), As, Co, Ni, Mn do not; no interference is caused by Al, Cr, Fe, Pb in HNO_3 solns. or by Sb in tartrate-contg. H_2SO_4 solns.

$Cd[Cr(NH_3)_2(SCN)_4]_2$ can be pptd. and weighed or titrated with KIO_3 soln. using an extn. end-point.[39]

Pyridine and NH_4SCN can be used for gravimetric (or titrimetric) detns. of < 0·3 g. Cd in 100 ml. neutral soln.[8, 40] Add 1 g. NH_4SCN, boil, add 10–15 ml. pyridine, reboil and cool, filter on a glass crucible and wash with portions of the following solns.: (1) 5 ml. pyridine and 3 g. NH_4SCN/l.; (2) 5 ml. pyridine and 0·3 g. NH_4SCN/l. 25% EtOH; (3) 0·1 ml. pyridine/100 ml. EtOH; (4) 0·1 ml. pyridine/100 ml. Et_2O. Dry in a vacuum desiccator for 20 min. (77–101°C) and weigh as $Cdpy_4(SCN)_2$. Alternatively, dissolve the ppt. in NH_4OH, add excess $AgNO_3$, acidify with HNO_3 and apply Volhard's method or the filtration method. NH_4Cl and NH_4OAc interfere.

Several other procedures have been suggested involving the formation of ammine complexes. The soly. of $Cdpy_2(SCN)_2$ [8] is greater than that of the above complex.[40] $Cdpy_2Cl_2$,[8] $Cd(N_2H_4)_2(SCN)_2$,[41] $Cd(N_2H_4)_2I_2$,[42]

$Cd(dipyridyl)_2(SCN)_2$ [43] and $[Cdpy_4]Cr_2O_7$ [44] have all been utilized.

K_2HgI_4 and NH_4OH have been proposed for the gravimetric detn. of 10 mg. Cd in 5 ml. of neutral or slightly acidic soln.,[8] $[Cd(NH_3)_4][HgI_3]_2$ being pptd.

o-Phenanthroline is useful colorimetrically.[45] For solns. contg. 0–4·5 × $10^{-5}M$ $CdCl_2$ add sufficient reagent to give a concn. of 1 × $10^{-2}M$ in a final vol. of 50 ml. after adding 25 ml. 0·100*M* KH_2PO_4 and 1 ml. 0·193*M* NaOH; measure at 241 mμ. Fe, Zn, Sn, Hg, VO_3^-, SO_4^{2-}, CrO_4^{2-}, IO_3^-, I^-, NO_3^-, ClO_4^-, IO_4^- interfere.

Thionalide ppts. $Cd(C_{12}H_{10}ONS)_2$ from tartrate-contg. basic solns.[46] (see p. 179). Mercaptobenzothiazole ppts. $Cd(C_7H_4NS_2)_2$ from dil. NH_4OH solns.[47] whereas 2-mercaptobenzimidazole ppts. $Cd(OHNH_3)$-$C_7H_5N_2S$.[47] These 3 ppts. should be dried at resp. < 210°C, 115°C (< 45°C) and < 45°C.

$(NH_4)_2MoO_4$ ppts. Cd from neutral soln.; 2–12 hr. standing is required before the ppt. is filtered, washed with H_2O and dried at 120°C (82–250°C).[8] The reagent is prepd. by dissoln. of 120 g. in 400 ml. H_2O, addn. of NH_4OH to give a pink color with phenolphthalein, neutralization with AcOH, filtration and diln. to 1 l. with H_2O. Titrimetric finishes are possible by means of satd. pyrogallol in $CHCl_3$ as external indicator,[8] or by reducing the filtrate with Zn–Hg and titration with 0·05*N* $KMnO_4$.[48]

$(NH_4)_2C_2O_4$ ppts. $CdC_2O_4 \cdot 3H_2O$ from solns. contg. 33% EtOH; the ppt. can be weighed after drying *in vacuo*, or in the anhyd. form after drying at 105–110°C, or after ignition to CdO above 771°C.[8, 49]

Salicylaldehyde–thiosemicarbazone has been used for 4–140 mg. Cd in 25–75 ml. soln.[50] Add 40–50 ml. 0·5% reagent in EtOH/0·05 g. Cd followed by 10% NaOAc and boil until the ppt. coagulates; add more NaOAc (20–30 ml. altogether) and place on a steam-bath for 30 min. Cool, filter on a glass crucible, wash with 50–150 ml. H_2O at 0°C and with 5–10 ml. EtOH, dry at 110°C and weigh as $Cd(C_8H_8OH_3S)_2$. Cl^-, F^- and tartrate interfere.

Dithiocarbamidohydrazine ppts. Cd from ammoniacal soln.; the ppt. is treated with H_2SO_4 and HNO_3 and weighed as $CdSO_4$.

Nitromalonylurea (3% in 50% EtOH) ppts. Cd $C_8H_4O_6N_4(NO_2)_2 \cdot 8H_2O$ from 50% EtOH solns., the ppt. being washed with EtOH.[51]

Anthracenesuccinic acid ppts. $CdC_{18}H_{12}O_4 \cdot 2H_2O$ at pH 7; Cu does not interfere.[52]

$Li_4Fe(CN)_6$ allows gravimetric or titrimetric detns.[8, 53] Add the reagent to the hot neutral soln., filter, wash with hot H_2O, dry at 140°C and weigh as $Cd_2Fe(CN)_6$. Alternatively, titrate the ppt. with $KMnO_4$. Direct titration in presence of dimethylnaphthidine or its sulfonic acid, alizarin S, bromocresol purple or bromothymol blue indicator is also possible. See also Chapter 36, p. 281.

(h) EDTA is useful for differential titration of Zn and Cd.[54] Add 2 ml. buffer pH 10 to 100 ml. of the soln. followed by eriochrome black T indicator and titrate with 0·01*M* EDTA (Zn + Cd). Add Na-diethyldithiocarbamate and back-titrate with 0·01*M* $MgSO_4$ to give Cd. For other possibilities, see Chapter 36, p. 278.

(i) $K_3Fe(CN)_6$ in conjunction with KI permits an iodometric detn.[55] To 0·3–0·4 g. $CdCl_2$ in 50 ml. neutral soln. add 2·5 ml. 1*N* HCl, 10 ml. 10% KCl, and 10 ml. 1*N* KI; heat to 30–32°C and add 20 ml. 0·1*M* $K_3Fe(CN)_6$ dropwise. After 7 min. add 100 ml. cold H_2O and titrate with 0·1*N* $Na_2S_2O_3$ in the usual way.

NOTE. Cr, SO_4^{2-}, $C_2O_4^{2-}$, tartrate, Ni and Mn interfere; KF prevents Fe interference. Pb, Hg, Mg and Ca may be present.

(j) Na-diethyldithiocarbamate provides colorimetric or titrimetric methods. For the former, add reagent to the soln. contg. 50–300 μg. Cd which is below pH 9·5 or up to 2*N* in acid; ext. with CCl_4 and measure at 440 mμ. For the latter, ext. the complex with $CHCl_3$ from alk. soln. contg. tartrate and CN^-, add Cu^{2+} and titrate with Hg^{2+} soln. (see p. 155).[57]

(k) Diphenylcarbazide[58] and diphenylsemicarbazide[59] have been used colorimetrically.

(l) 4-Hydroxy-3-nitrophenylarsonic acid is suitable for the colorimetric detn. of 3 mg. Cd in 10 ml. soln. at pH 3·6–6·0.[60] Add 20 ml. 0·35% reagent, dil. to 35 ml. with H_2O and boil for 2 min. Filter, wash with 100 ml. H_2O, dissolve the ppt. in 100–150 ml. 0·05% EDTA in dil. NH_4OH, dil. to 250 ml. with H_2O and measure at 410 mμ.

References

1. HILLEBRAND and LUNDELL, 204 (254); SCOTT and FURMAN, 197; KIMURA, 168; FRESENIUS–JANDER, IIB, 221 (1945).
2. ZÖLLNER, C., *Z. anal. Chem.*, **114**, 8 (1938).
3. TOWNSEND, F. E. and CADE, JR., G. N., *Ind. Eng. Chem., Anal. Ed.*, **12**, 163 (1940).
4. WALTER, J. L. and FREISER, H., *Anal. Chem.*, **24**, 984, 1985 (1952); also see NORDLING, W. D., *Chemist Analyst*, **45**, 44 (1956).
5. HORIUCHI, Y. and SAITO, M., *J. Chem. Soc. Japan*, **77**, 1340 (1956).
6. EVCIM, N. and REBER, L. A., *Anal. Chem.*, **26**, 936 (1954).
7. HECHT and DONAU, 54; WELCHER, **I**, 285.
8. FRESENIUS–JANDER, IIb, 221 ff.
9. ISHIMARU, S., *J. Chem. Soc. Japan*, **56**, 62 (1935); **53**, 567 (1932); GOTO, H. and KAKITA, Y., *ibid.*, **62**, 925 (1941) (detn. from NaOH-tartrate soln. is inaccurate); STOCK, J. T., *Metallurgia*, **40**, 179, 229 (1949) (amperometric).
10. A.S.T.M., 499, 511 (Ag solders and slab Zn); SARUDI, I., *Z. anal. Chem.*, **121**, 348 (1941); YOSHIDA, I., *J. Chem. Soc. Japan*, **48**, 29 (1927).
11. A.S.T.M., 532 (Zn-base die-casting alloys).
12. SABON, F. and GRIGNON, H., *Bull. soc. pharm. Bordeaux*, **94**, 47 (1955) (with allylthiourea); (SANDELL, 236, WELCHER, **I**, 104).

13. WELCHER, **III**, 57; KIBA, T. and SATO, S., *J. Chem. Soc. Japan*, **61**, 136 (1940); SANDBERG, B., *Svensk Kem. Tidskr.*, **58**, 197 (1946) (amperometric).
14. WELCHER, **II**, 505; also see DWYER, F. P. and GIBSON, N. A., *Analyst*, **75**, 201 (1950 (gravimetric with triphenylmethylarsonium chloride).
15. ISHIBASHI, S. and NAKAJIMA, S., *J. Chem. Soc. Japan*, **62**, 13 (1941); (WELCHER, **III**, 121).
16. WELCHER, **IV**, 211.
17. FABRE, R., *et al.*, *Ann. pharm. franç.*, **9**, 30 (1951).
18. NIKITINA, E. I., *Zavodskaya Lab.*, **7**, 409 (1938).
19. GUSEV, S. I., *Zhur. Anal. Khim.* **4**, 175 (1949); KUMOV, V. I., *ibid.*, **7**, 301 (1952) (with diantipyrinyl-*o*-hydroxyphenylmethane); ZHIVOPITSEV, V. P., *Zavodskaya Lab.*, **16**, 1186 (1950) (with diantipyrinylmethylmethane); KUMOV, V. I., *Zhur. Anal. Khim.*, **9**, 229 (1954) (iodometry or alkalimetry with bromopyrine and KBr).
20. WELCHER, **II**, 381.
21. WELCHER, **III**, 81.
22. WELCHER, **IV**, 329.
23. SALTZMAN, B. S., *Anal. Chem.*, **25**, 493 (1953); SANDELL, 228; see also SILVERMAN, L. and TREGO, K., *Analyst*, **77**, 143 (1952); SHIRLEY, R. L., *et al.*, *Anal. Chem.*, **21**, 300 (1949); PETZOLD, A. and LANGE, I., *Z. anal. Chem.*, **146**, 1 (1955) (5–6% NaOH soln. + dimethylglyoxime, sepn. from Ni, Co); (WELCHER, **III**, 536).
24. SANDELL, 234.
25. HECHT and DONAU, 155.
26. TREADWELL, W. D., *Tabellen*, 119 (1938).
27. ŠEBOR, J., *Chem. listy*, **28**, 290, 297 (1934).
28. LURJE, J. J. and TROITZKAJA, M. I., *Z. anal. Chem.*, **107**, 34 (1936).
29. See Chapter 4 and LINGANE, *Electroanalytical Chemistry*, p. 313 (1953).
30. WELCHER, **II**, 213.
31. SHENNAN, R. J., *Analyst*, **64**, 14 (1939).
32. MAJUMDAR, A. K., *J. Indian Chem. Soc.*, **22**, 309 (1945).
33. MAJUMDAR, A. K. and DE, A. K., *J. Indian Chem. Soc.*, **29**, 499 (1952); **32**, 85 (1955).
34. WELCHER, **II**, 197.
35. BHADURI, A. S., *Z. anal. Chem.*, **151**, 109 (1956).
36. WIJS, J. C. DE, *Rec. trav. chim.*, **62**, 188 (1943).
37. SUBBARAMAN, P. R., *J. Sci. Ind. Research* (*India*), **13B**, 553 (1954).
38. RULFS, C. L., *et al.*, *Anal. Chem.*, **26**, 408 (1954); WELCHER, **IV**, 180.
39. BAGBANLY, I. L., *Izvest. Akad. Nauk Azerbaidzhan. S.S.R.*, (5) 29 (1956).
40. VORNWEG, G., *Z. anal. Chem.*, **120**, 243 (1940); WELCHER, **III**, 25, 81.
41. SARKER, P. B. and DATTA-RAY, B. K., *J. Indian Chem. Soc.*, **7**, 251 (1930).
42. JÍLEK, A. and KOHNT, B., *Chem. listy*, **33**, 252 (1939).
43. WELCHER, **III**, 81.
44. PIRTEA, D., *et al.*, *Acad. rep. populare Romîne*, *Studii cercetări chim.*, **3**, 237 (1955).
45. WADELIN, C. and MELLON, M. G., *Anal. Chem.*, **24**, 894 (1952).
46. UMEMURA, T., *J. Chem. Soc. Japan*, **61**, 28 (1940).
47. WELCHER, **IV**, 112, 128.
48. TAKAGI, K., *J. Chem. Soc. Japan*, **74**, 291 (1953).
49. MATSUMOTO, T., *Japan Analyst*, **3**, 221 (1953); KAWAGAKI, K., *J. Chem. Soc. Japan*, **78**, 1562 (1957) (60% AcOH soln.).
50. HOVORKA, V. and HOLZBECHER, Z., *Collection Czechoslov. Chem. Communs.*, **15**, 275 (1950).
51. DICK, I. and MIHAI, F., *Acad. rep. populare Romîne, Baza cercetări ştiinţ. Timisoara, Studii cercetări ştiinţ., Ser. ştiinţe chim.*, **3** (1/2) 67 (1956).
52. UBALDINI, I. and GUERRIERI, F., *Ann. chim.* (*Rome*), **41**, 247 (1951).
53. BASIŃSKI, A. and JAKUBOWSKI, ST., *Przemysl Chem.*, **9**, 190 (1953); BASIŃSKI and LAMÁNSKA, H., *ibid.*, 241; BASIŃSKA, H. and ORYLSKA, K., *Roczniki Chem.*, **30**, 281 (1956); also see FUJITA, Y., *J. Chem. Soc., Japan*, **77**, 12 (1956) (I_2 + starch as indicator with 0·05 *M* $K_4Fe(CN)_6$ in pH 6·0–6·6 soln.); DESHMUKH, G. S. and VENUGOPALAN, M., *J. Indian Chem. Soc.*, **33**, 222 (1956) (filtrate: Ce^{4+}, ferroin).
54. PŘIBIL, R., *Collection Czechoslov. Chem. Communs.*, **18**, 783 (1953); SWEETSER, P. B. and BRICKER, C. E., *Anal. Chem.*, **26**, 195 (1954) (photometric at 222 mμ in 0·6*N* NaOH + a little KCN soln.); TANAKA, N., *et al.*, *ibid.*, **28**, 1555 (1956) (amperometric and potentiometric).
55. AMIEL, J. and NORTZ, M., *Bull. soc. chim. France*, 226 (1950).
56. SUDO, E., *J. Chem. Soc. Japan*, **73**, 693 (1952); ORLIAC, M., *Compt. rend.*, **228**, 930 (1949).
57. WICKBOLD, R., *Z. anal. Chem.*, **152**, 342 (1956); also see BOBTELSKY, M. and RAFAILOFF, R., *Anal. Chim. Acta*, **17**, 267 (1957) (photometric).
58. GEUER, G., *Angew. Chem.*, **61**, 99 (1949).
59. MILLER, F., *Chemist Analyst*, **25**, 10 (1936).
60. NIELSCH, W. and BÖLTZ, G., *Chem.-Ztg.*, **79**, 364 (1955) (in Cu).

24

RHENIUM

The principal sources for this chapter are given in ref. 1. The chemistry of rhenium has been discussed in a monograph.[2] Geilmann and his collaborators[3] have made many contributions to the analytical chemistry of rhenium; the subject has been reviewed by Einecke *et al.*[4]

Quite generally, it is not advisable to boil solutions containing rhenium and HCl; H_2SO_4 and $HClO_4$ solutions can be heated safely below 200°C.

Attack

(a) The general method is to warm the sample with 5% NaOH and 30% H_2O_2. ReS_2 is not attacked by this process.

(b) Mo-contg. samples. Fuse 1·25 g. sample contg. > 5% Mo and 0·03% Re with 5 g. NaOH in a Fe crucible. Cool, fuse with 5 g. Na_2O_2, pour on to a Fe plate, cool, transfer to a 400 ml. beaker, rinse the crucible with H_2O and cover; the total vol. should be < 150 ml. Boil, add some filter paper pulp, filter on a Büchner funnel and wash 5 times with hot H_2O. Cool in ice, filter and wash again. Transfer to a 250 ml. measuring flask and dil. to the mark. Neutralize a 25 ml. aliquot with HCl and add 3 drops in excess. Add 10 drops Br_2 and boil out the Br_2.

For distn. heat the H_2SO_4 soln. at 260–270°C while passing a mixt. of steam and air or CO_2 (2:1). Collect 250 ml. distillate over a period of 2·5 hr. in an ice-cold receiver. Redistil if > 1 g. Mo is present.

Molybdenite is treated as follows: add HNO_3, fuming HNO_3, evap., evap. with HCl, add H_2SO_4 and distil Re.

(c) Pyrolusite. Dissolve 100 g. in HCl, filter and dil. to 300 ml. with H_2O. Add 20% $SnCl_2$ until the soln. is pink. Then add KSCN (0·6 g./100 ml. soln.) and $SnCl_2$ (0·5 g./100 ml. soln.). After 5 min. ext. twice with 60 ml. Et_2O, combine, evap. to 5–10 ml. below 70°C, add 15 ml. 1:1 HCl, and blow air over to evap. all the Et_2O. Add 30% H_2O_2 to decolorize the brown or red soln. and leave for 15 min. adding more H_2O_2 as required. Sep. Re and Mo as given below.

Heat 10–100 g. sample (< 5% Mo and 0·02–0·15 mg. Re) slowly with HNO_3, add HCl and heat further. Filter, evap., add HCl, evap. and repeat the HCl addn. and evapn. 6 times. Add 200 ml. H_2O and make alk. with NaOH. Filter, wash, transfer to a separatory funnel, add xanthate and proceed as below (Separation).

Separation

Re is sepd. from Mo and many other elements by distn. as described above.

Sepn. from group III elements, etc. is obtained by passing H_2S for 1 hr. at 70°C through the soln. contg. 4*N* HCl or 6*N* H_2SO_4. Filtration on a glass crucible is advisable and a pressure bottle should be used. As^{3+} is useful for concn. of Re.[5] Re is sepd. from Mo, As, etc. by H_2S treatment of NH_4OH solns. but the ppt. is difficult to filter.

Treatment with SO_2 allows sepn. from Se.

Sepn. from Mo is provided by extn. of thiocyanate with Et_2O. Evap. the soln. to dryness, add 10 mg. Fe^{3+} as $FeCl_3$, 1–2 drops satd. $KMnO_4$ soln. and excess NH_4OH and place on a steam-bath for 2–3 min. Cool, add 25 ml. 1:4 HCl and 2 ml. 20% KSCN and transfer to a separatory funnel. Add 25 g. Hg and 20 ml. Et_2O, shake for 1 min., sep., add 1 g. KSCN and 15 ml. Et_2O and ext. again. Repeat the extn. at least twice. 1–5% Re is extd. with the Mo; Re is completely extd. if reduced with $SnCl_2$.

Sepn. from Mo is also obtained by means of oxine. Treat < 150 ml. of neutral soln. with 5 ml. 1*N* H_2SO_4 and 5 ml. 2*N* NaOAc and add 5% oxine in EtOH. Oxine can be removed from the filtrate by shaking with $CHCl_3$. $CHCl_3$ extn. of Mo-oxinate is also feasible.

Cupron permits the sepn. of Re from 1 mg. Mo, which may be useful in colorimetry.

Re is sepd. from Mo, W, Sn by pptn. with cupferron in 2*N* H_2SO_4 soln. or by extn. of the cupferrates with $CHCl_3$.

Tetraphenylarsonium chloride is useful for the sepn. of Re from Mo.[6] To the soln. contg. 0·01–0·1 mg. Re which is 0·3*M* in Cl^- and 0·1*M* in SO_4^{2-} and at pH 8–9, add 1 ml. 0·05*M* tetraphenylarsonium chloride and 8 ml. $CHCl_3$. Shake for 2 min., sep. and ext. twice by shaking with 4 ml. $CHCl_3$ for 40 sec. Shake each $CHCl_3$ ext. with 0·5 g. anhyd. $CaCl_2$ and pass through glass wool covered with $CaCl_2$, adding more $CaCl_2$ if necessary and blowing air on to the wool to remove $CHCl_3$. Combine the filtrates, shake for 20 sec. with 20 ml. 6N HCl, add 1 ml. 20% NaSCN and shake for 5 sec. Add 1 ml. 35% $SnCl_2$, shake for 5 sec. and leave for 3 min. Shake for 20 sec. with 8 ml. iso-AmOH., sep., wash the aq. layer with $CHCl_3$ and iso-AmOH. Dil. to 25 ml. with the alc. and measure the absorbance of the soln. at 432 mμ.

Extn. with 1:1 CCl_4 and C_6H_6 after addn. of Na-xanthate from basic soln. seps. Re and Mo.[7] Opinions differ about the completeness of sepn. (Beeston and White,[6] Meloche *et al.*[8]).

Ion exchange is also suitable for the sepn. of Re and Mo (see Chapter 13, Section 4.4).

Determination

The gravimetric method with nitron and the colorimetric methods with KSCN and $SnCl_2$ are excellent. Tetraphenylarsonium chloride or electrodeposition is suitable for macroanalysis while the colorimetric method based on catalytic reduction of tellurate with $SnCl_2$ is satisfactory for microanalysis.

(a) Nitron is used as follows.[1,9] For < 0·1 g. Re as ReO_4^- in 50 ml. neutral soln., add 1 ml. 2N H_2SO_4, heat to 80°C and add 10 ml. 5% nitron in 3% AcOH. Allow to cool and then cool at 0°C for 2 hr. Filter on a glass crucible, wash 3–5 times with 2 ml. portions of 0·3–0·5% nitron acetate soln. satd. with the ppt. at 0°C and then wash with a satd. soln. of the ppt. in H_2O at 0°C. Dry at 110°C for 2–3 hr. and weigh as $(C_{20}H_{17}N_4)ReO_4$.

NOTES. (1) Br^-, I^-, NO_3^-, NO_2^-, CrO_4^{2-}, ClO_3^-, ClO_4^-, W, Pd, Pt, Au, Ge interfere, but Mo (<Re) does not.
(2) Re_2S_7 is detd. by treating with H_2O_2 and NaOH, neutralizing with H_2SO_4 and proceeding as above. H_2O_2 may contain NO_3^-.[10]
(3) The ppt. may increase slightly in weight during drying (Duval).

(b) $SnCl_2$ and KSCN are used for colorimetry of 10–500 μg. Re in 10 ml. 2N HCl soln.[1, 6, 7, 8, 11, 12] Add 2% $SnCl_2$ soln. until 0·2% is present followed by 2% KSCN to give a 0·4% soln. Ext. thrice with 25 ml. Et_2O pre-equilibrated with $SnCl_2$ and KSCN, combine the exts. and shake with 10 ml. 1:2 HCl. Sep. and measure the absorbance at 432 mμ.

NOTES. (1) Mo (see under Separation), Pt, Rh, W, V, Cu, Au, Se, Te, Fe interfere. No interference arises from Ce, Co, Cr, Ga, Ge, In, Ir, Pb, Ni, Os, Ru, Pd, Tl, U (2 mg. of each).
(2) If distillates are used, add some As^{3+} and pass H_2S. Add NH_4OH and H_2O_2 to the filtered ppt., evap. to dryness, add HCl and continue as above.

(c) Tetraphenylarsonium chloride is used gravimetrically or colorimetrically.[1, 13] Add NaCl to the hot neutral soln. to give a concn. of 0·5N followed by 1% reagent soln.; the final vol. should be 25–60 ml. Cool at 0°C for 12 hr. Filter on a Gooch crucible, wash with H_2O at 0°C, dry at 110°C (126–183°C) and weigh as $(C_6H_5)_4AsReO_4$.

NOTES. (1) V^{4+}, Te, Bi, Hg^{2+}, Sn^{4+}, Ag, Pb and large amts. of NO_3^-, MnO_4^-, ClO_4^-, IO_4^-, SCN^-, I^-, Br^- and F^- interfere. Zn and Cd do not if $Na_2S_2O_4$ is used instead of NaCl, nor does Mo if tartrate is added.
(2) For colorimetry,[14] 25–300 μg. Re is extd. with 10 ml. $CHCl_3$ from solns. contg. citrate at pH 8–9, the final measurement being made at 255 mμ.
(3) Triphenylbenzylphosphonium chloride can be used colorimetrically[15] whereas tetraphenylphosphonium chloride provides gravimetric or titrimetric detns. (see Chapter 19, p. 153).

(d) Electrodeposition[16] (Hillebrand and Lundell[1]). To the soln. contg. 6–9 mg. Re, add 5–25 g. NH_4Cl (or NH_4NO_3 or $(NH_4)_2SO_4$) in 25% NH_3 soln. Pass 6·5–9 amp. at 7–9 v. for 3 hr.; increase in temp. is unimportant.

Electrolysis can also be done[1] in 5% v/v H_2SO_4 soln. with 0·25 amp. at 2·34 v. for 12 hr.; wet O_2 is used to oxidize the deposit to $HReO_4$ which is titrated with standard NaOH.

(e) Miscellaneous gravimetric methods. TlOAc ppts. Re as $TlReO_4$.[17] Pptn. of $AgReO_4$, $KReO_4$ and NH_4ReO_4 is incomplete.

H_2S ppts. Re_2S_7 which can be converted to Re by heating at 1000°C in H_2 (Hillebrand and Lundell[1]).[18] Treatment with Zn in acidic soln. ppts. $ReO_2{\cdot}2H_2O$ which can be dried *in vacuo* or converted to ReO_2 at 250°C.[19] Neither of these methods is very satisfactory.

Tetron permits the detn. of H_2ReCl_6 in presence of ReO_4^- but the compn. of the ppt. is uncertain.[20]

(f) Reduction followed by oxidimetric titration has been used. For < 30 mg. Re^{7+} in 2·5% H_2SO_4 soln., boil, cool to 5°C, pass through a Jones reductor, receive in Fe^{3+} soln. under a CO_2 atmosphere and titrate with 0·1N $KMnO_4$ (Hillebrand and Lundell[1]). For 0·1–10 mg. Re in 20 ml. 18N H_2SO_4, add 2 ml. Bi–Hg, shake for 2 min., sep., add Fe^{3+} and titrate with 0·01N Ce^{4+} in presence of ferroin indicator.[21]

(g) Na_2TeO_4 and $SnCl_2$ are used colorimetrically.[12] For 0·001–0·1 μg. Re in 1·5 ml. soln. add 1 ml. reagent (5 ml. 5% Na_2TeO_4, 2 ml. 45% w/v tartaric acid, 1·5 ml. 0·5% gelatin and 1·5 ml. 40% $SnCl_2$ in HCl mixed); leave for 1–2 hr. (for 0·01–0·1 μg. Re) or for 24 hr. (for 0·001–0·01 μg. Re). Measure the absorbance at 430–470 mμ. Calculate as follows: x μg. Re $= aE_x/(E_{a+x} - E_x)$, where E_x = absorbance of the sample and E_{a+x} = absorbance of the sample + a μg. Re.

(h) α-Benzildioxime and $SnCl_2$ are used colorimetrically for 0·2–0·5 μg. Re in 0·5–1 ml. 12N H_2SO_4 soln.[22] Add 1–2 mg. reagent, 0·5 ml. isoamyl alc. and 4 drops 15% $SnCl_2$ in 9N H_2SO_4. Heat for 3 min. just below the b.p., add 1 ml. H_2O and compare the yellow–pink–red color in the alc. layer.

NOTES. (1) When more than 10-fold amts. of Mo are present, reduce in $9N$ H_2SO_4 soln., add reagent and then add H_2SO_4 to give a $16N$ soln.
(2) α-Furildioxime is suitable for <100 μg. Re.[8, 23] Add HCl to give a final concn. of 0·035N, dil. with H_2O to 30 ml., add 13 ml. 0·35% reagent in Me_2CO and 5 ml. $SnCl_2$ (100 g. $SnCl_2$ and 100 ml. HCl/l.) and dil. to 50 ml. with H_2O. Measure after 45 min. at 532 mμ ($\epsilon = 41\,300$). Mo, Cu, Pd interfere.
Dimethylglyoxime has also been suggested (Schoeller and Powell[1]).

(i) $N_2H_4 \cdot 2HCl$ is used for colorimetric detns. of Re as $ReCl_6^{4-}$. To 25 ml. $2N$ H_2SO_4 soln. which is $1\text{–}5 \times 10^{-5}M$ in Re (as perrhenate), add 50 ml. cupferron in $CHCl_3$ (0·5 g. recrystd. cupferron in H_2O extd. with 50 ml. $CHCl_3$ after H_2SO_4 addn.). Shake for 3 min., sep., and repeat until the aq. layer is colorless; add $CHCl_3$, shake, sep., add dil. NaOH, evap. to 5 ml., add 25 ml. HCl and 1 g. $N_2H_4 \cdot 2HCl$ and boil for 45–60 min. Dil. with H_2O to 50 ml. and measure at 281·5 mμ for Re and at 265 mμ for Mo against reference solns. treated similarly ($\epsilon = 11\,800$).[24]

NOTE. An alternative reduction method is possible for 0·07–1·4 mg. Re in 6–7 ml. soln. Add 25 ml. HCl, bubble N_2 through the soln. and add 1·00 ml. 0·045M Cr^{2+}; stopper for 1–2 min., pass air for a few min., dil. to 50 ml. with H_2O and measure at 281·5 mμ.[25]

(j) 2,4-Diphenylthiosemicarbazide may be used colorimetrically.[26] For < 50 μg. ReO_4^- in 10 ml. $6N$ HCl soln., add 2 ml. satd. reagent in MeOH heat at 80°C for 30 min., cool, add 25 ml. $CHCl_3$, ext. and measure at 510 mμ.

NOTES. (1) Mo (100 μg.) and many other metals interfere.
(2) Thiourea has been suggested for 10–15 μg. Re/ml.: add $SnCl_2$ or $TiCl_3$ to the 3–5N HCl soln., heat at 65–75°C for 5–7 min. and measure at 390 mμ. Hg, Cd, Bi, W, Mo, Te, Se, As and oxidants interfere.[27]

References

1. HILLEBRAND and LUNDELL, (317); SCOTT and FURMAN, 768; SCHOELLER and POWELL, 318.
2. DRUCE, J. G. F., *Rhenium*, Cambridge Univ. Press (1948).
3. GEILMANN, W., *et al.*, Beiträge zur analytischen Chemie des Rheniums, *Z. anal. Chem.*, **126**, 418 (1944); **128**, 489, 496 (1948); **130**, 222, 320, 323 (1950); **132**, 250 (1951); **133**, 177 (1951) (22nd rept.).
4. EINECKE, E., *Z. anal. Chem.*, **90**, 127, 214 (1932); EINECKE and HARMS, J., *ibid.*, **105**, 364 (1936).
5. GEILMANN, W. and LANGE, G., *Z. anal. Chem.*, **126**, 321 (1944).
6. BEESTON, J. M. and LEWIS, J. R., *Anal. Chem.*, **25**, 651 (1953); also see TRIBALAT, S., *Anal. Chim. Acta*, **6**, 142 (1952); **3**, 113 (1949); SANDELL, 520.
7. MALOUF, E. E. and WHITE, M. G., *Anal. Chem.*, **23**, 497 (1951).
8. MELOCHE, V. W., *et al.*, *Anal. Chem.*, **29**, 527 (1957).
9. HECHT and DONAU, 170; WELCHER, **III**, 142.
10. YOUNG, R. C. and BERNAYS, P. M., *Ind. Eng. Chem., Anal. Ed.*, **12**, 90 (1940).
11. PATROVSKÝ, V., *Chem. listy*, **51**, 1295 (1957).
12. SANDELL, 513 ff.
13. WELCHER, **IV**, 329.
14. ANDREW, T. R. and GENTRY, C. H. R., *Analyst*, **82**, 372 (1957).
15. TRIBALAT, S., *Anal. Chim. Acta*, **5**, 115 (1951).
16. VOIGT, A., *Z. anorg. u. allgem. Chem.*, **249**, 225 (1942).
17. KRAUSS, F. and STEINFELD, H., *Z. anorg. u. allgem. Chem.*, **197**, 54 (1931).
18. Also see TAIMNI, I. K. and SALARIA, B. S., *Anal. Chim. Acta*, **12**, 519 (1955) (dry *in vacuo* as Re_2S_7).
19. GEILMANN, W. and HURD, L. C., *Z. anorg. u. allgem. Chem.*, **214**, 260 (1933).
20. WELCHER, **II**, 462.
21. SPITZY, H., *et al.*, *Mikrochim. Acta*, 354 (1957).
22. TRIBALAT, S., *Compt. rend.*, **224**, 469 (1947).
23. FISHER, S. A. and MELOCHE, V. W., *Anal. Chem.*, **24**, 1100 (1952).
24. MEYER, R. J. and RULFS, CH. L., *Anal. Chem.*, **27**, 1387 (1955).
25. MELOCHE, V. W. and MARTIN, R. L., *Anal. Chem.*, **28**, 1671 (1956).
26. GEILMANN, W. and NEEB, R., *Z. anal. Chem.*, **151**, 401 (1956).
27. RYABCHIKOV, D. I. and LAZAREV, A. I., *Zhur. Anal. Khim.*, **10**, 228 (1955).

25

ARSENIC

The principal sources for this chapter are given in ref. 1. The analytical chemistry of arsenic has been reviewed by Wilson.[2]

It should be noted that $AsCl_3$ (b.p. 130°C) and AsF_3 (b.p. 63°C) are volatile but $AsCl_5$ is not; hence evaporation should always be carried out in the presence of oxidizing agents. As^{5+} can be formed by treating As_2S_3 with NH_4OH and H_2O_2 and then acidifying with HNO_3. As^{5+} is reduced to As^{3+} by treatment with Fe^{2+}, HI, SO_2, etc. in acidic solutions.

Attack

(a) Pyrites or arsenopyrites. Treat 1–20 g. sample with 10–15 ml. of a soln. contg. 75 g. KBr and 50 ml. Br_2/450 ml.; after 15 min. add 20–50 ml. HNO_3 dropwise and evap. to dryness. Add 10–25 ml. HCl, evap. to dryness and repeat the HCl addn. Add 100 ml. 1:3 HCl, filter and ppt. with H_2S or distil.

(b) Sulfides, arsenides. Dissolve in HNO_3 with Br_2 or HCl addn., or in HCl with $KClO_3$ addn. Alternatively, fuse with Na_2CO_3 and KNO_3, or suspend in KOH and pass Cl_2.

(c) Arsenates. Fuse with a min. amt. of Na_2CO_3 (with KNO_3 addn.), or with K_2CO_3 if Sb is present, or with $Na_2S_2O_3$.

(d) Oxides. Treat with NaOH and then with HCl. Alternatively, fuse with a min. amt. of K_2CO_3 and KNO_3 (1:1), leach with hot H_2O, add 200 ml. satd. SO_2 soln., boil out SO_2 and add dil. H_2SO_4.

(e) Metals and alloys. For steel, add 0·5 g. Cu to a 5 g. sample and dissolve in HNO_3 and H_2SO_4 (add HCl also if much W or Cr is present). Add $KMnO_4$ followed by SO_2 (and H_3PO_4 if much W is present), evap. to fumes, add HCl and NaH_2PO_2 and boil under reflux. Det. As iodometrically.

For Fe–W, fuse a 5 g. sample with 15 g. Na_2O_2–Na_2CO_3 (2:1); leach with H_2O, add H_3PO_4, acidify with HCl, boil, add more HCl, Fe^{2+} and HBr and distil.

For non-ferrous metals and alloys, dissolve a 5 g. sample in H_2SO_4 and HNO_3, conc. with Fe^{3+} and NH_4OH and distil. Alternatively, heat with 15 g. $KHSO_4$ and 20 ml. H_2SO_4, add HCl and distil.

(f) Organic compds. Digest with H_2SO_4, $HClO_4$ and HNO_3 in a ratio of 7:2:1. Many alternative digestion mixtures are possible.

For samples contg. 2–4 mg. As, it is also possible to decompose by Mg fusion.[3] Cover the sample with 35–45 mm. of Mg, fuse for 4–5 min. (Mg_3As_2), add dil. H_2SO_4 and sweep with N_2 or CO_2, receiving in Br_2 water; det. As iodometrically.

Separation

Distn. permits sepn. of As from many elements. Distil from 150–300 ml. soln. satd. with HCl gas, at a temp. below 108°C; absorb in 100–200 ml. H_2O at 0°C. If > 0·01 g. As is present, redistil after adding 50 ml. HCl and some reducing agent. Mo, Re, Se, Te, HNO_3 and NO_2^- interfere, as do Sb^{3+} and Hg^{2+} if the temp. is too high. Ge interference is circumvented by oxidation to As^{5+}, distn. of Ge, reduction and subsequent distn. of As. Interference of large amts. of Sn^{4+} is avoided by H_3PO_4 addn.; distn. of Sn can follow after addn. of 3:1 HCl–HBr.

As^{5+} is reduced by Cu_2Cl_2 (10–30 g.), $FeSO_4$, H_3PO_2, HI, HBr, $N_2H_4{\cdot}H_2SO_4$, the last-mentioned being the best reagent.

HCl sometimes contains As. An all-glass apparatus is advisable since $AsCl_3$ is absorbed by rubber.

If much As is present, HCl gas should be passed during the distn. Easier and more complete distn. is obtained if HBr is added, but Ge and Se are then also distilled. The following method is very suitable for small amts. of As. Add 2 ml. HBr and 0·3 g. $N_2H_4{\cdot}H_2SO_4$ to 10–15 ml. of the HCl soln. followed by 10 ml. HCl. Pass CO_2 or N_2 at 2–3 bubbles/sec. and heat, raising the temp. to 110°C after 15 min.

It is also possible to distil As as $AsBr_5$.[4]

As, Sb and Sn may be fractionally distilled.[5] The method of Heuss[5] is as follows. Evap. the H_2SO_4 soln. to fumes and add 5 ml. H_2O, 1·5 g. $N_2H_4{\cdot}H_2SO_4$, 80 ml. HCl and 1 g. borax in 5 ml. Distil for 30–60 min. while sweeping with HCl gas. The first distillate, contg. $AsCl_3$, is received in H_2O at 0°C and the As is titrated with $KBrO_3$ soln. To the residual soln. add 7 ml. 85% H_3PO_4 and distil at 155–165°C, while adding 100–200 ml. HCl dropwise. Receive this distillate, contg. $SbCl_3$, in 50 ml. H_2O and titrate with $KBrO_3$ soln. To this residual soln. add 1:3 40% HBr–HCl dropwise while distilling at 140–145°C. Receive the distillate in 10 ml. H_2O, add Al, and titrate Sn iodometrically.

As can be sepd. from W by distn. as above after addn. of H_3PO_4; 70% N_2 and 30% H_2 is used for sweeping.[6] Sepn. from Mo is difficult.

As^{5+} is sepd. from Sn, Sb, Bi, group III elements, etc. by passing H_2S rapidly through the soln. contg. 10*N* HCl at 0°C; Ge, Mo, Hg and Cu interfere. As^{3+} is sepd. from Sn, etc. by passing H_2S into the 9*N* HCl soln. at room temp. Sepn. from the Cu group is obtained by H_2S treatment of the alk. soln. or by extg. the sulfide ppt. with concd. NaOH. H_2S treatment of solns. contg. HCl and HF seps. As from Sn^{4+} and Ge (see Chapter 27, p. 204).

Magnesia mixture allows sepn. of As^{5+} from Sb, Sn^{4+}, Mo and Ge; P, etc. and large amts. of NH_4^+ interfere. Add 3 g. $(NH_4)_2$-tartrate/100 ml. followed by 50 ml. reagent and excess NH_4OH; filter through paper and wash with 5:95 NH_4OH. As can be concd. by copptn. with NH_4MgPO_4; this is suitable for > 0.075 mg. As in 50 ml. soln. and Fe, Sn, Al, Zn do not interfere while only repptn. is necessary with Sb.[7]

As^{5+} is sepd. from Sb, etc. by treatment of the alk. soln. with NH_4F and $AgNO_3$

Electrolysis of NH_4OH solns. gives a sepn. from Ag, Cu, Cd and Ni.

The following concn. and sepn. methods are also available. Those involving diethyldithiocarbamate and zinc are the most useful.

(*1*) Diethylammonium diethyldithiocarbamate seps. As ($> 25\ \mu$g.), Sb, Sn (and partly Cu, Hg, Bi) from Zn, Cd, Ni, Fe, Pb.[8] Heat 20 ml. 5–6*N* HCl soln. to 50°C, add 2 ml. 20% KI and 0·5 g. $Na_2S_2O_5$ and heat at 50°C for 15 min. Cool, transfer to a separatory funnel, dil. to 35 ml. with H_2O and add 15 ml. 0·1% reagent in $CHCl_3$. Shake for 4 sec., sep., add 0·5 ml. $CHCl_3$ and sep. without shaking. Add 2 ml. reagent, ext. and wash the combined exts. with 10 ml. 1*N* H_2SO_4. Evap., add Br_2 water, etc.

Sepn. from Cu and Bi is obtained by H_2O_2 addn. followed by extn., addn. of thioglycolic acid, ascorbic acid and KI, and repeated extn.

(*2*) As, Sb, Sn, Te, Se, P, W, V are sepd. from Mo, etc. by treatment with $FeCl_3$ and NH_4OH.

(*3*) Treatment with Zn in HCl or H_2SO_4-contg. solns. evolves AsH_3 which is passed through a quartz tube heated at 800°C for deposition, or absorbed in $HgCl_2$ and $KMnO_4$ or in I_2 and $NaHCO_3$ soln. As^{5+} must be reduced previously with KI and $SnCl_2$. Cu, Hg, Ni, Co interfere; no interference is caused by 10 mg. Ag, 50 mg. Pb, Fe, Cr. Mo or Se (see p. 194).

(*4*) Xanthate allows sepn. of As^{3+} from Sb, Al, Mn, Zn, Pb, Cd, Hg, Bi in acidic solns.; CCl_4 extn. is followed by washing with HCl and $SnCl_2$ mixture.[9]

(*5*) $SnCl_2$ with a little $HgCl_2$ seps. As from Fe, Cr, Ni, Co, V, Mo, Ti, Zr, Cu, Al, Mn, B; the soln. contg. $>$ 80% v/v HCl is heated with the reagent for 2 hr. at 60–80°C.

(*6*) H_3PO_2 gives a sepn. from Bi, Sn, Pb; the 50% v/v HCl soln. is treated with a little Cu^{2+} and then with the reagent for 2 hr. at 60–80°C. Unless only traces of As are present, sepn. from Se and Te is incomplete, and the ppt. must be dissolved so that Se can be sepd. with KI and Te with SO_2.

(*7*) Copptn. with MnO_2 may be useful (A.S.T.M.).

Determination

Both the gravimetric detn. as As_2S_3 and the titrimetric detn. with I_2, KIO_3 or $KBrO_3$ are accurate for 1–100 mg. amts. of As, but the titrimetric methods are more convenient. Milligram amts. of As can be titrated with Ce^{4+} after being reduced with $H_2PO_2^-$. Traces of As are usually detd. by the molybdenum blue method or by Gutzeit's method; opinions on the latter method are so varied that it is virtually impossible to decide how satisfactory it is for general purposes. The colorimetric detn. based on absorption of AsH_3 in Ag-diethyldithiocarbamate soln. appears to be useful.

(a) H_2S is normally used gravimetrically[1] but may also serve colorimetrically. Adjust the As^{3+} soln. to 9*N* in HCl and pass H_2S rapidly at 15–20°C; after 1 hr. filter on a Gooch crucible and wash with a soln. of H_2S in 8*N* HCl and then with EtOH, CS_2 and EtOH. Dry at 105°C (200–275°C) and weigh as As_2S_3. The method has been applied to Fe–W.[10]

NOTES. (1) To correct for impurities such as Hg, Mo, Ge, etc., treat the ppt. with half-satd. $(NH_4)_2CO_3$, 1:2 NH_4OH, H_2O and EtOH and reweigh; deduct this weight from the original ppt.

(2) Weighing as As_2S_5 seems to be inaccurate owing to contamination by As_2S_3 and S. In this case, pptn. is done from 10*N* HCl soln. at 0°C by passing H_2S for 1 hr.; the ppt. is washed with 4*N* HCl, H_2O and EtOH and dried at 105–110°C (78–245°C).

(3) Colorimetric detn. is possible for 0·1–1 mg. As.[11]

(b) Iodometric detn.[1] Cool the $AsCl_3$ distillate, make alk. with NaOH and acidify slightly with HCl. Add 15–25 ml. cold satd. $NaHCO_3$, 1 g. KI and starch indicator and titrate with 0·01–0·1*N* I_2 to the blue color.

NOTES. (1) Sb^{3+}, S^{2-}, SO_3^{2-}, $S_2O_3^{2-}$, Fe^{3+} and large amts. of NH_4^+ interfere. The method has been applied to brasses, etc.,[10] and to many other materials. Coulometric titration is possible[12] with I_2, Br_2 or Cl_2.

(2) After sepn. as $NH_4Mg(As + P)O_4$ (see under Separation), dissolve the ppt. in 20 ml. 3*N* HCl, add 0·5 g. KI and place for 2–3 min. on a steam-bath. Titrate with $Na_2S_2O_3$ until the soln. is colorless to starch, neutralize with $NaHCO_3$ and add excess; titrate with 0·01*N* I_2.[7]

(3) CCl_4 can also be used as indicator (Scott and Furman[1]). Add 50 ml. satd. $HgCl_2$ in 1*N* HCl to the As^{3+} soln. followed by HCl to give a 1·2–1·7*N* acid soln. and 5–20 ml.

CCl_4; titrate with 0·1N I_2 shaking between addns. until the org. layer becomes pink.
For microdetn. of As^{5+} in 5N HCl or 8N H_2SO_4 soln.,[13] add KI, dil. with H_2O to 3–4N in acid, add C_6H_6 or $CHCl_3$, shake and titrate with 0·01N $Na_2S_2O_3$. Triphenylmethylarsonium chloride in $CHCl_3$ or CCl_4 has been used as indicator for the titration with I_2.[14] NaOH should not be used in trace detns.[15]

(c) Other oxidimetric methods. KIO_3 titration of As^{3+} is normally used with $CHCl_3$ indicator in 11–20% HCl (30–50 ml. HCl/100 ml.) soln. (Scott and Furman[1]).[11] Various other indicators are suitable, e.g. OsO_4,[16] ferroin,[17] rubrophen[18] (see also Chapter 5, Section 7.2 and Chapter 15, Section 4.3).

$KBrO_3$ titration is useful on all scales,[11] the optimum HCl concn. being 15–35%. For 70–700 μg. As in 50 ml. 3N HCl soln. add 1 drop 0·1% amaranth indicator and titrate slowly to colorless, adding another drop of amaranth near the end-point.[15] The error is ±1% for 300 μg. As and ±5% for < 200 μg. This method has been applied to brasses, leads, etc., normally with methyl orange as indicator.[10] Naphthol blue black and brilliant ponceau 5R are good irreversible indicators[19] while ethoxychrysoidine and naphthoflavone are the best reversible indicators (see Chapter 5, Section 5.5 and Chapter 15, Section 4.3).

With Ce^{4+} titrant, use 0·5–2N H_2SO_4 soln. or 1–4N HCl soln. and add OsO_4 or ICl resp. as catalyst.[11] For 58–933 μg. As, titrate coulometrically with a photometric end-point at 320, 360 or 375 mμ.[20]

With $KMnO_4$ titrant, add 30–40 ml. 15% Na_2SO_3 to 100–200 ml. of slightly alk. soln. followed by 40–50 ml. 5% $(NH_4)_2MoO_4$ and 60–70 ml. 1:4 H_2SO_4. Boil out SO_2 and titrate with 0·1N $KMnO_4$ to a pink color.[11] Te^{6+} can be used as catalyst in direct titrations of > 2 μg. As in < 0·1N NaOH soln.[21] Coulometric titration is possible.[22]

For methods involving chloramine T and other oxidants, see ref. 11 and Chapter 5, Section 7.

(d) Molybdate is mainly used in colorimetric methods but may also be applied nephelometrically, gravimetrically or titrimetrically.

For colorimetry of < 40 μg. As^{5+} in 25 ml. neutral soln.,[11, 23] add 20 ml. reagent (25 ml. 2·5% Na_2MoO_4 in 10N H_2SO_4 and 10 ml. 0·15% $N_2H_4 \cdot H_2SO_4 \cdot H_2O$ dild. to 100 ml.; prepd. just before use); dil. with H_2O to 49 ml., heat for 10 min. in boiling H_2O, cool, dil. to 50 ml. and measure the blue color at 840 mμ (ϵ = 25 400; see also Chapter 57, p. 430).

NOTES. (1) P, Si and Ge interfere but can be sepd. by distn.; sepn. from P is also possible by extn. with AmOH from 0·1–0·4N H_2SO_4 soln.
(2) For 1–5 μg. As, add 0·2 ml. $HClO_4$, dil. to 5 ml. with H_2O, add 1 drop methyl red and adjust to a yellow color with NH_4OH; adjust to red with 2 : 3 HCl, and add 0·5 ml. in excess. Add 0·2 ml. 0·03% $KBrO_3$ and proceed as above (Luke and Campbell[8]).
With As^{3+} distillates, add HNO_3, evap. to dryness and heat for 0·5–1 hr. at 130°C before applying the molybdenum blue method. Alternatively, sep. as AsH_3, absorbing in 1 ml. 1·5% $HgCl_2$, 0·2 ml. 6N H_2SO_4 and 0·15 ml. 1% $KMnO_4$, filter off the Hg_2Cl_2 ppt. rapidly and proceed as above.
(3) Various other reductants have been suggested, e.g. $SnCl_2$,[11, 24] ascorbic acid (heat at 70°C for 15 min.)[11, 25] and hydroquinone.[11] For the 'reduced molybdate' reagent, which is suitable for <230 μg. As with measurement at 850 mμ, see p. 430. If no reductant is added, it is possible to det. P, As and Si by successive extn. with an org. solvent (see p. 430).

The vanadomolybdate method is suitable[26] for < 30 p.p.m. As^{5+}. Add 5 ml. reagent (25 g. Na_2MoO_4 in 70–80 ml. H_2O and 3·75 g. $NaVO_3$ in dil. NaOH neutralized with HCl mixed, and 50 ml. HCl added before diln. to 250 ml.) to the approx. neutral soln.; dil. to 50 ml. with H_2O and measure at 380–460 mμ (ϵ = 2500 at 400 mμ).

NOTES. (1) Interferences are Bi, Pb, Th, Zr, Fe, Ni, $Cr_2O_7^{2-}$, MnO_4^-, $S_2O_3^{2-}$, SCN^-, PO_4^{3-}, SiO_3^{2-}, GeO_3^{2-}, WO_4^{2-}, VO_3^-, I^-, $C_2O_4^{2-}$ and citrate.
(2) The method can be applied to As in Cu; if P is present, det. As and P in 0·2N HNO_3 soln. and det. P in 1·6N soln. (Baghurst and Norman[26]).
(3) Solns. of quinine molybdate are used nephelometrically.[11, 27] Prep. the reagent soln. as follows: dissolve 1·3203 g. As_2O_5 in dil. HNO_3; evap. and dil. to 1 l. with H_2O, then dil. 5 ml. to 1 l. To 5 ml. of this soln. add 0·5 g. quinine–HCl in 10 ml. soln. followed by 10 ml. 1 : 3 HNO_3 and 1 ml. Na_2MoO_4 soln. (3·5 g. Na_2CO_3 in 50 ml. mixed with 9·5 g. MoO_3, digested, cooled and dild. to 100 ml. with H_2O); stir, dil. to 100 ml. with H_2O and filter through paper washed with dil. HNO_3 and H_2O. For the detn. of 8–25 μg. As, add HNO_3 and Br_2, evap. to dryness, add 20 ml. reagent and measure the yellow color. Cocaine and strychnine can also be used[11] (Welcher[27]).
(4) The arsenomolybdate ppt. may be detd. by a neutralization titration on the macro scale.[11] $(NH_4)_7AsO(Mo_2O_7)_5 \cdot 4H_2O$ can be weighed directly.[28]

(e) Gutzeit's method.[1, 29] For 5–10 μg. As, add 5 ml. HCl to 30 ml. of the As soln. followed by 5 ml. 15% KI and 4 drops 40% $SnCl_2$. Heat at 25°C for 30 min., add a Zn stick (see Note (1)) and leave at 25°C for 1·5 hr. Pass the AsH_3 generated (swept with H_2) through a tube supporting $Pb(OAc)_2$ paper and $HgBr_2$ paper (see Note (1)) and compare the length of the pink colored zone with standard papers. The error is ±10%. The references cited should be consulted for details of apparatus.

NOTES. (1) Prep. the $HgBr_2$ paper as follows. Dissolve 4 g. $HgBr_2$ in EtOH, filter and dil. to 100 ml. with EtOH; soak 9 cm. long strips of filter paper in this soln., remove just before use, press between filter paper, dry in air and cut as required.
Prep. the Zn stick as follows. Prep. a cylinder of Zn (125 mm. long and 15 mm. diam.) in a Pyrex glass tube; cut the cylinder so that it is a little shorter than the diam. of the generator, coat both sides with gum arabic and

some $MgCO_3$, dry, and dip one side of the stick twice in 3 : 1 paraffin wax–Acrowax C so that just over half the length is covered. Treat the other side in the same way and rub down both sides. Dip in H_2O, activate by dipping in 1 : 7 $SnCl_2$–HCl and store under H_2O contg. 1 drop HCl. A 3·75 cm. stick lasts for 15 detns.
(2) Interferences are HNO_3, SO_2, S^{2-}, >0·1 mg. Sb, P, F, Hg, Ag, Pt, Ni, Co and pyridine and its analogs.

Many modifications of the above procedure have been suggested; the accuracy depends on the completeness of the AsH_3 generation and its absorption by the $HgBr_2$ paper ($HgCl_2$, $AgNO_3$ and $AuCl_3$ have also been used), hence the error must be detd. on standard solns. for whichever conditions are chosen. The procedures published up to 1936 have been tested:[30] for < 5 μg. As, it was recommended that AsH_3 be generated from 4–5*N* H_2SO_4 soln. with 8 Zn sticks (8 mm. diam., 5–10 mm. long) activated with 0·5% $CuSO_4$, the yellow color obtained on paper moistened with 66% $AgNO_3$ being compared.[31] For > 5 μg. As, generation is done from 1:4 H_2SO_4 with 5 g. Zn and Pt wire, the paper for absorption being moistened with 5% $HgBr_2$ in EtOH and dried.[32]

Accurate detn. of 0·05–1 μg. As (or up to 20 μg.) is possible[33] by generating AsH_3 with 10 g. Zn from 25 ml. 10% HCl or H_2SO_4 soln. contg. 3–4 drops 10% $CuSO_4$ and 4–5 drops 20% $SnCl_2$, and comparing the violet color obtained on paper moistened with 1% $AuCl_3$.[34] Even 0·01 μg. As can be estimated by comparing the spot on $HgBr_2$ paper when the AsH_3 is passed at a pressure of 0·25–0·5 atm.[35] 0·1–0·5 μg. As has been estimated by a reflectometric method.[36]

As can be removed from Zn by fusing, adding Na, stirring with a glass rod, removing the scum and repeating this operation 5–6 times; finally the Zn is poured into H_2O.

Al, Fe, Sn, etc. can replace Zn as the reductant; if Fe or Sn is used, P and Sb do not interfere, but these metals may contain As. Al in dil. NaOH soln. is a specific reductant for As^{3+} and As^{5+} must be reduced previously with $TiCl_3$.[37] Electrolytic reduction has been suggested[38] and internal electrolysis with Hg–Zn is said to be excellent.[39]

Any color caused by Sb disappears on exposure to HCl gas.

A variety of alternative methods of completion is available after the generation of AsH_3.[11]

(*i*) *Colorimetric methods.* For 0–40 μg. As/100 ml., absorb in 3·0 ml. 0·5% Ag–diethyldithiocarbamate in pyridine and measure the red-purple color.[40] Colorimetry is also possible after absorption in Ag^+–Ce^{4+} soln.[41] or $AuCl_3$ soln.[42] See above for the molybdenum blue method. If AsH_3 is passed through a heated capillary tube, the length of the Marsh mirror can be measured (Scott and Furman[1]).

(*ii*) *Titrimetric methods.* The Marsh mirror obtained as above from 5–100 μg. As can be dissolved in a known excess of ICl soln. which is then titrated with KIO_3; the error is ±5%.[43]

After absorption in $HgCl_2$ soln. the soln. may be neutralized to methyl orange indicator and the As detd. iodometrically;[44] for 0·5–10 mg. As, Hg_2Cl_2 must be filtered off before the titration with I_2 but direct titration is satisfactory for less As. Preoxidation with ICl and titration with KIO_3 may replace iodometry (Farag *et al.*[44]).

Other possibilities[11] involve absorption in excess $AgNO_3$ soln. and a Volhard titration of the filtrate[45] or iodometric titration of the ppt.,[46] or absorption in excess I_2 soln. and titration with 0·1*N* NaOH after removal of I_2 with $Na_2S_2O_3$.[47]

(f) Electrodeposition is suitable for 0·1–1 mg. As^{3+} in 5 ml. neutral soln. Add a known amt. of $CuSO_4$ (Cu ⩾ 5As), 1·5 ml. HCl, 6 drops $N_2H_4{\cdot}H_2O$, heat to 65–70°C and electrolyze at 0·9 v. for 20 min.[48]

(g) $Ca(H_2PO_2)_2$ is used as reductant in conjunction with a final cerimetric titration.[49] For 0·1–2 mg. As in 25 ml. soln., add 10 ml. 20% reductant in 6*N* HCl, and 35 ml. HCl; heat at 80–90°C for 10 min., boil for 5 min. and filter through a glass tube packed at one end with cotton wool and asbestos, washing 4 times with H_2O. Return to the original beaker, add a 25–50% excess of 0·005*N* $Ce(SO_4)_2$ in 1*N* H_2SO_4, heat at 40–50°C for 2–3 min., cool, add 0·1 ml. 0·25% OsO_4 in dil. H_2SO_4 and 2 ml. satd. ferroin perchlorate indicator and titrate with 0·005*N* As^{3+} soln. The error is ±0·57% for 0·15–0·27 mg. As_2O_3.

NOTES. (1) Interferences are Hg, Se, Te; Sb, Sn, Pb, Cu, Fe do not interfere.
(2) NaH_2PO_2 has been used in conjunction with $K_2Cr_2O_7$ or with iodometry. For the former,[50] reduce 0·75–5·6 mg. As in 50 ml. 1 : 1 HCl soln. in a way similar to the above; add excess 0·001*N* $K_2Cr_2O_7$ and 20 ml. 9*N* H_2SO_4, filter after 2–3 min., dil. to 175 ml. with H_2O, add 5 drops 0·1% diphenylamine blue and excess $FeSO_4$ soln. and back-titrate with $K_2Cr_2O_7$ soln. For the latter method,[11, 51] reduce 0·01 mg. As, centrifuge, add HCl and excess I_2 and back-titrate with $Na_2S_2O_3$ in the usual way.
(3) $SnCl_2$ or Cr^{2+} can also serve as the reductant.[11, 52]
(4) Nephelometric detn. of 20 μg. As/10 ml. soln. is possible with NaH_2PO_2,[53] $SnCl_2$ in acid soln.[54] or H_2PO_3 in alk. soln.[55] as reductant.

(h) Volhard's method.[1] To < 0·5 g. As^{5+} in 100–150 ml. neutral soln., add a 10 ml. excess of 0·1*N* $AgNO_3$ followed by 10% NaOH until the soln. is alk. to litmus, and 1:1 HNO_3 until the ppt. dissolves or the soln. is acid to litmus. Add 10 ml. satd. NaOAc soln., warm and cool. Filter on a Gooch crucible and wash with a satd. soln. of the ppt. Dissolve in 30 ml. warm 1:1 HNO_3, dil. to 100–150 ml., add 2 ml. satd. Fe-alum soln. and titrate with 0·01–0·1*N* KSCN.

NOTES. (1) PO_4^{3-}, MoO_4^{2-}, WO_4^{2-}, CrO_4^{2-} and large amts. of NH_4^+ or Na^+ interfere. Ge and small amts. of Sb or Sn can be tolerated.

(2) In an alternative finish, dissolve the ppt. in dil. HNO_3, add $6N$ H_2SO_4 to give a 1–2N soln., 3 ml. 0·5% starch soln. and 3 drops 0·1N $(NH_4)_2Ce(SO_4)_3$ and titrate with 0·1N KI to a blue end-point.[11]

(3) Gravimetric detn. is also possible. Filter on a G4 crucible, wash 2–4 times with 5 ml. H_2O, 2–3 times with 5 ml. EtOH and 2–3 times with 5 ml. Et_2O, ignite at 550–780°C and weigh as Ag_3AsO_4.[11] Alternatively, dissolve the ppt. in HNO_3, add HCl, etc. and finally weigh as AgCl; this procedure is said to be as accurate as the titrimetric method.[11]

(i) Miscellaneous methods involving arsenate pptn. Magnesia mixt. is suitable for the detn. of 0·01–0·4 g. As^{5+} in 50–60 ml. slightly acidic (HNO_3) soln.[11, 56] (Oxidize As^{3+} with Br_2, ignoring the excess.) Add 10 ml. reagent soln. (55 g. $MgCl_2$ and 105 g. NH_4Cl in 1 l. H_2O contg. a little HCl) for each 0·1 g. As, then add $1N$ NH_4OH until the soln. is faintly pink to phenolphthalein and more NH_4OH so that the soln. contains $\frac{1}{3}$ of its vol. of concd. NH_4OH. After 12 hr. filter on paper, dissolve the ppt. in 4–5 ml. $4N$ HNO_3, add several drops of reagent and reppt. Filter on a Gooch crucible, wash with 10% NH_4OH contg. 3% NH_4NO_3, dry in an electric furnace at 100°C, ignite at 400–450°C and then at 850–950°C (415–885°C) for 10 min. and weigh as $Mg_2As_2O_7$. For mg. amts. wash with 2·5% NH_4OH, EtOH and Et_2O, suck dry and weigh as $NH_4MgAsO_4·6H_2O$. A titrimetric finish is possible by dissolving the ppt. in HCl, adding EDTA and buffer and titrating with Mg^{2+} soln. in presence of eriochrome black T (see p. 428).[57]

Pptn. with TlOAc and $AgNO_3$ gives slightly high results.[11] For 0·05–0·1 g. $Na_2HAsO_4·7H_2O$ in 50 ml. soln. add 5–10 ml. 4% TlOAc and 5–10 ml. 0·1N $AgNO_3$ slowly; filter on a glass crucible, wash with H_2O, EtOH and Et_2O, dry *in vacuo* for 20 min. (20–846°C) and weigh as $TlAg_2AsO_4$.

With $UO_2(OAc)_2$, add 10 ml. $4N$ NH_4OH to 0·02 g. As^{5+} in 50 ml. neutral soln. followed by dil. AcOH until a faint odor is perceptible; boil, add 20 ml. 0·1N reagent and leave for 12 hr. Filter on paper, wash, ignite at 1000°C and weigh as U_3O_8, or dry at 200–310°C and weigh as $NH_4UO_2AsO_4·H_2O$. Alternatively, add H_2SO_4 to the filtrate, reduce with Zn–Hg and titrate with $KMnO_4$ (Chapter 39, p. 300).[11]

With a soln. of $Bi(NO_3)_3$ in dil. HNO_3, add a 5–6-fold excess of reagent, make alk. with NH_4OH, boil and add HNO_3 to give a 0·7N soln.; reboil, filter on a glass crucible, wash, dry below 180°C and weigh as $BiAsO_4·5H_2O$, or dry at 450–570°C (645–951°C) and weigh as $BiAsO_4$.[11]

$CoCl_2$, $CaCl_2$ and $BaCl_2$ have also been suggested.[11]

(j) Miscellaneous colorimetric methods. Na-diethyldithiocarbamate is suitable for 10–100 μg. As at pH 3–6, the complex being extd. with CCl_4 and measured at 340 mμ.[58]

$PdCl_2$ catalyzes the reaction of As^{3+} and $SnCl_2$. To 0·1–0·5 ml. 0·001M $PdCl_2$ add 6–8N HCl to give a final vol. of 15 ml., add 0·1–1 ml. sample soln. contg. < 2·5 μg. As^{3+}, and 0·8 ml. $5M$ $SnCl_2$; measure at 520 mμ after a definite time. Sb, Bi, As^{5+} do not interfere.[59] $HgCl_2$ behaves similarly to $PdCl_2$.

Hg_2Cl_2 is suitable for 0·005–100 μg. As in 5 ml. 30% HCl soln.; add 0·1 g. reagent, shake and compare the color. The error is ±5% for 100 μg. As. Au, Pt, Pd, Se, Te interfere (for separation, see Chapter 30, p. 221).[60]

Thionalide is used nephelometrically for 1–30 μg. As in 15 ml. soln.; add 5 drops $2N$ H_2SO_4, boil, add 3 drops 1% reagent and measure after 2–6 hr.[11]

References

1. Hillebrand and Lundell, 208 (259); Scott and Furman, 89; Kimura, 170; Pigott, 88; Fresenius–Jander, **Va** γ, 1 (1951).
2. Wilson, H. N., *Ann. Repts. Progress Chem.*, **41**, 278 (1944).
3. Jureček, M. and Jeník, J., *Chem. listy*, **50**, 84 (1956).
4. Magnuson, H. J. and Watson, E. B., *Ind. Eng. Chem., Anal. Ed.*, **16**, 339 (1944).
5. Heuss, W., *Chim. & ind. (Paris)*, **55**, 363 (1946); Scherrer, J. A., *J. Research Natl. Bur. Standards*, **21**, 95 (1938); Mogerman, W. D., *ibid.*, **33**, 307 (1944).
6. Millner, Th. and Kúnos, F., *Z. anal. Chem.*, **106**, 96 (1936).
7. Kolthoff, I. M. and Carr, C. W., *Anal. Chem.*, **20**, 728 (1948).
8. Luke, C. L. and Campbell, M. E., *Anal. Chem.*, **25**, 1588 (1953); Wyatt, P. F., *Analyst*, **80**, 368 (1955).
9. Also see Payne, S. T., *Analyst*, **77**, 278 (1952); Sugawara, K., *et al.*, *Bull. Chem. Soc. Japan*, **29**, 670 (1956).
10. A.S.T.M., 186 ff.
11. Fresenius–Jander, **Va** γ, 1 ff.
12. Also see Pitts, J. N., *et al.*, *Anal. Chem.*, **26**, 648 (1954).
13. Shakhtakhtinskiĭ, G. B., *Zhur. Anal. Khim.*, **9**, 233 (1954).
14. Gibson, N. A. and White, R. A., *Anal. Chim. Acta*, **13**, 546 (1955).
15. Tanaka, N., *J. Chem. Soc. Japan*, **64**, 443 (1943).
16. Szebellédy, L. and Madis, W., *Mikrochim. Acta*, **1**, 226 (1937).
17. Szebellédy and Madis, *Z. anal. Chem.*, **114**, 116 (1936).
18. Szebellédy, *Z. anal. Chem.*, **114**, 197 (1936).
19. Smith, G. F. and May, R. L., *Ind. Eng. Chem., Anal. Ed.*, **13**, 460 (1941).
20. Furman, N. H. and Fenton, Jr., A. J., *Anal. Chem.*, **25**, 515 (1956).
21. Issa, I. M. and El Sherif, I. M., *Rec. trav. chim.*, **75**, 447 (1956).
22. Tutundžic, P. S. and Mladenovic, S., *Anal. Chim. Acta*, **12**, 382, 390 (1955).
23. Sandell, 178; Boltz, D. F. and Mellon, M. G., *Anal. Chem.*, **19**, 873 (1947); Chase, O. P., *ibid.*, **20**, 902 (1948); Kingsley, G. R. and Schaffert, R. R., *ibid.*, **23**, 914 (1951); Bartlet, J. C., *et al.*, *ibid.*, **24**, 1821 (1952); Onishi, H. and Sandell, E. B., *Mikrochim. Acta*, 34 (1953) (in silicate); Wyatt, P. F., *Analyst*, **80**, 38 (1955); Berkhout, H. W. and Jongen, G. H., *Chemist Analyst*, **43**, 60 (1954); Goto, H. and Kakita, Y., *J. Chem. Soc. Japan*, **77**, 739 (1956) (in Ge); Tominaga, A. and Watanabe, S., *Japan Analyst*, **5**, 495 (1956) (in Fe ores); A.S.T.M., 487 (Pb, Sb, Sn and their alloys).

24. WOODS, J. T. and MELLON, M. G., *Ind. Eng. Chem., Anal. Ed.*, **13**, 760 (1941).
25. JEAN, M., *Anal. Chim. Acta*, **14**, 172 (1956); WELCHER, **I**, 81.
26. GULLSTROM, D. K. and MELLON, M. G., *Anal. Chem.*, **25**, 1809 (1953); BAGHURST, H. C. and NORMAN, V. J., *ibid.*, **29**, 778 (1957).
27. YOE, 128; WELCHER, **IV**, 238 ff.
28. DICK, I., *Acad. rep. populare Romîne, Baza cerceătri ştiinţ. Timisoara, Studii cercetări ştiinţ., Ser. ştiinţe chim.*, **3**, (1/2), 57 (1956).
29. GOLDSTONE, N. I., *Ind. Eng. Chem., Anal. Ed.*, **18**, 797 (1946); SANDELL, 185.
30. MÜHLSTEPH, W., *Z. anal. Chem.*, **104**, 333 (1936).
31. LOCKEMANN, G., *Z. anal. Chem.*, **100**, 20 (1935); **94**, 322 (1933).
32. DECKERT, W., *Z. anal. Chem.*, **88**, 7 (1932).
33. HINSBERG, K. and KIESE, M., *Biochem. Z.*, **290**, 39 (1937).
34. See also MOKRANJAC, M. ST. and RASAJSKI, B., *Acta Pharm. Jugoslav.*, **2**, 9 (1952).
35. SATTERLEE, H. S. and BLODGETT, G., *Ind. Eng. Chem., Anal. Ed.*, **16**, 400 (1944).
36. MARENOWSKI, N. C., *et al.*, *Anal. Chem.*, **29**, 353 (1957).
37. FISCHER, R. and LANGHAMMER, T., *Mikrochemie ver. Mikrochim. Acta*, **34**, 203 (1949).
38. OSLERBERG, A. E. and GREEN, W. S., *J. Biol. Chem.*, **155**, 513 (1944).
39. YOSHIMURA, C., *J. Chem. Soc. Japan*, **78**, 1586 (1957).
40. VAŠAK, V. and ŠEDIVEC, V., *Chem. listy*, **46**, 341 (1952); JUREČEK, M. and JENÍK, J., *ibid.*, **48**, 1771 (1954); **49**, 269 (1955) (treatment of sample with Mg metal); VEČEŘA, Z., *Slévárenstvi*, **12**, 366 (1956); VEČEŘA and BIEBER, B., *Giessereitechnik*, **3**, 61 (1957) (Fe).
41. MCCHESNEY, E. W., *Anal. Chem.*, **21**, 880 (1949).
42. CASSIL, C. C., *J. Assoc. Offic. Agr. Chemists*, **21**, 198 (1938).
43. BADNÁR, J., *et al.*, *Z. anal. Chem.*, **115**, 412 (1938/39).
44. STROCK, L. W., *Z. anal. Chem.*, **99**, 321 (1934); also see FARAG, A. and EL-MANGOURI, H. A., *Proc. Pharm. Soc. Egypt, Sci. Ed.*, **8**, 83 (1955).
45. VINOGRADOV, A. V. and JEFREMOVA, T. N., *J. Chem. Ind. (U.S.S.R.)*, **10**, 76 (1932).
46. ALLCRAFT, R. and GREEN, H. H., *Biochem. J.*, **29**, 824 (1935).
47. WILEY, R. C., *et al.*, *Ind. Eng. Chem., Anal. Ed.*, **4**, 396 (1932).
48. TORRENCE, S., *Analyst*, **64**, 263 (1939).
49. KOLTHOFF, I. M. and AMDUR, E., *Ind. Eng. Chem., Anal. Ed.*, **12**, 177 (1940); SMITH, G. F. and FRITZ, J. S., *Anal. Chem.*, **20**, 874 (1948).
50. AGNEW, W. J., *Analyst*, **68**, 171 (1943).
51. LESPAGNOL, A., *et al.*, *Bull. soc. chim.*, **10**, 378 (1943).
52. KAKITA, Y., *Kinzoku-Gakkai-Shi*, **9**, (4) 6, (5) 5 (1945).
53. TSYVINA, B. S. and DOBKIN, B. M., *Zavodskaya Lab.*, **7**, 1116 (1938); SILVERMAN, L., *Iron Age*, **164**, (24) 96 (1949).
54. KING, N. B. and BROWN, F. E., *Ind. Eng. Chem., Anal. Ed.*, **5**, 168 (1933).
55. VIGNOLI, L. and CRISTAU, B., *Bull. soc. pharm. Marseille*, **5**, 207 (1956).
56. HECHT and DONAU, 171.
57. Also see MALÍNEK, M. and ŘEHÁK, B., *Chem. listy.*, **49**, 765 (1955).
58. SUDO, E., *J. Chem. Soc. Japan*, **73**, 693 (1952).
59. SAKURABA, S., *J. Chem. Soc. Japan*, **73**, 501 (1952).
60. PIERSON, G. G., *Ind. Eng. Chem., Anal. Ed.*, **11**, 88 (1939).

26

ANTIMONY

The principal sources for this chapter are given in ref. 1. McNabb and Wagner[2] have made a detailed study of the evaluation of stibnite and the microanalysis of antimony has been reviewed.[3]

In all analytical work concerning antimony it should be remembered that Sb volatilizes from hot HCl solutions; $SbCl_5$ (b.p. 140°C) decomposes on heating to $SbCl_3$ (b.p. 221°C) and Cl_2. Solutions containing NaCl or KCl can be heated safely below 120°C. Sb salts are readily hydrolyzed but this is prevented by addition of tartaric acid.

Attack

(a) Sulfides. To 1 g. sulfide in a Kjeldahl flask, add 15 ml. H_2SO_4, 1 g. K_2SO_4, 5 g. $(NH_4)_2SO_4$ and 0·2 g. S powder or a small piece of filter paper. Heat slowly to fumes and until the soln. is clear. Cool and add 25 ml. H_2O and 2–3 g. tartaric acid. Filter through paper and wash with 1:9 H_2SO_4 and H_2O. Dry the residue, and ignite the ppt. and paper separately. Fuse with 1:1 Na_2CO_3–S and ext. with H_2O; acidify with H_2SO_4, filter. Treat the ppt. with 2–3 ml. hot 10% KOH contg. some H_2O_2, acidify with H_2SO_4 and add 2–3 ml. acid in excess. Evap. to fumes and dil. with H_2O to 10–15 ml. Combine this soln. with the filtrate from the first treatment and evap. to 20–30 ml. Add 50 ml. HCl, pass H_2S rapidly and filter through paper moistened with 2:1 HCl, washing with this acid. Dil. the filtrate with 3–4 vols. of warm H_2O, pass H_2S, filter on paper and wash with 1:99 HCl satd. with H_2S. To the ppt. add 8 ml. H_2SO_4 and 2 g. K_2SO_4, heat slowly until clear, cool, add 50 ml. H_2O, boil out SO_2 and treat with $KMnO_4$.

(b) Oxides. Fuse in a Fe crucible with NaOH and KNO_3, or in a porcelain crucible with $Na_2S_2O_3$ or with Na_2CO_3 and S.

(c) Metals, etc. Heat alloys with HCl contg. several drops of HNO_3, Br_2 or $KClO_3$; alternatively, use HNO_3 with Br_2, add Na_2SO_3 (or KI), evap. at below 108°C to volatilize As, add HCl and pass air through the gently boiling soln. to remove SO_2.

Dissolve the metal itself in H_2SO_4 by heating; alternatively, treat with HNO_3 and tartaric acid, with HCl and Br_2 or $KClO_3$, or with Br_2 and HBr (see Chapter 20, p. 157).

(d) Rocks. Fuse 0·2 g. of 80-mesh rock with 1·5 g. $K_2S_2O_7$, cool, add 6 ml. 6*N* HCl, filter into a 125 ml. separatory funnel, wash twice with 3 ml. hot 6*N* HCl and then with 2 ml. hot H_2O; add Ce^{4+} soln. and det. Sb colorimetrically.[4]

(e) Org. compds. Digest with 7–10 ml. fuming H_2SO_4, adding H_2O_2. Alternatively, fuse with Mg, add dil. H_2SO_4 and absorb the SbH_3 evolved in 6*N* HCl contg. $NaNO_2$.[5]

For blood or animal organs, treat 15 g. sample with 10 ml. H_2SO_4 and 5 ml. HNO_3; when carbonization starts, cool, add HNO_3 and heat further. Then cool, add 0·5 ml. $HClO_4$, heat, add 3 ml. H_2O and heat to fumes.

Separation

Heating the sample in a combustion tube while passing Cl_2 seps. Sb, Hg, Sn, As from Ag, Pb, Cu.

H_2S treatment of solns. contg. $<$ 15 ml. HCl/100 ml. seps. Sb from group III, etc. Concn. by copptn. with Cu or As is used in 0·15–1*N* HCl or H_2SO_4 solns; add tartaric acid if W or V is present, and $NH_2OH{\cdot}HCl$ if Fe is present. Sb is sepd. from As with H_2S in 6–9*N* HCl solns.; traces cannot be sepd. owing to copptn. Sepn. from Sn and Ge is obtained with H_2S in HF solns.; Sn is pptd. in the filtrate by adding H_3BO_3 and passing more H_2S. Sepn. from Sn^{4+} is also obtained from $H_2C_2O_4$ or H_3PO_4 solns. with H_2S.[6] In alk. tartrate solns. H_2S allows sepn. from the Cu group.

Distn. of HCl solns. below 107°C seps. Sb from As and Ge (see p. 192). Sb is sepd. from Cu, Pb, Mo, etc. by distn. from solns. contg. H_2SO_4 and S, at 200°C with HCl as the sweeping gas.

Sepn. of Sb from As by magnesia mixture is incomplete.

Treatment with HNO_3 and evapn. seps. Sb and Sn from many elements, but sepn. is incomplete unless Sn:Sb $>$ 1·5. H_2SO_4 gives incomplete sepn. of Sb and Pb; if 1% tartaric acid is present, Sb appears in the filtrate completely but some Pb accompanies it. Sb is sepd. from SiO_2 by evapn. with H_2SO_4 or $HClO_4$.

Reduction with Pb in HCl soln. seps. large amts. of Sb from Mo. Fe in hot 12% HCl soln. seps. Sb from Sn and Cd but Cu, Bi and Pb interfere. Sb is sepd. from much Cu, Pb, etc. by plating on Cu from 20% HCl soln.; this is useful for concn. purposes.[7]

Treatment with $Na_2S_2O_4$ in alk. CN^--contg. soln. seps. Sb from Cu; Ag, Hg, Bi, Se, Pb, As and Cd interfere.

Extn. with dithizone in $CHCl_3$ from slightly ammoniacal solns. contg. tartrate or citrate seps. Sb from Ag, Hg, Cu, Bi, Ni, Cd, Zn. For the possibilities of diethylammonium diethyldithiocarbamate, see pp. 193, 196 and 204, and Chapter 8, Section 2.8. Iso-Pr_2O exts. Sb^{5+} from 6·5–8·5*N* HCl solns. but not Fe^{2+}, Ga, Tl, or Sb^{3+}; any Fe^{3+} coextd. can be removed by shaking the ext. with 1*M* HCl contg. $NH_2OH{\cdot}HCl$.

Internal electrolysis with a Cu cathode and a Pb or Fe anode in hot dil. HCl solns. contg. $N_2H_4{\cdot}HCl$ and 1 mg. As allows sepn of Sb from large amts. of Cu.

Treatment with ca. 100 mg. Fe^{3+} and NH_4OH seps. Sb (< 10 mg.), P, Se, Te, V, Sn and W from Mo and Cu; Al^{3+} is not effective. Concn. with BiOCl is also useful.[8]

Concn. of Sb, Sn and Bi is possible by treatment with Mn^{2+} and $KMnO_4$ in hot 1:19 HNO_3 solns.; the ppt. is treated with H_2SO_4, etc. as described above for sulfides. This procedure has been studied with radioactive tracers.[8, 9]

SbH_3 can be used for sepn. purposes, being absorbed in a soln. of $HgCl_2$ in dil. HCl.

Ion exchange resins allow sepn. of Sb from Pb (see Chapter 13, Section 2.2).

Determination

Titration with $KMnO_4$ or $KBrO_3$ soln. provides the most accurate method for more than 1 mg. Sb; the latter titration is also suitable for smaller amts. For colorimetric detns. rhodamine B or KI used in conjunction with strong reductants seem to be best.

(a) $KMnO_4$.[1, 10] Adjust the Sb^{3+} soln. to a suitable acidity (see Note (1)) and titrate at 5–10°C with 0·03–0·1*N* $KMnO_4$ until the pink color remains for at least 10–20 sec.

NOTES. (1) The acidity should be adjusted as follows; the figs. indicate the no. of ml. of acid/200 ml. soln.

H_2SO_4:	0	10	20	30
HCl:	30–50	30–35	15–20	10–15

Sb^{5+} is reduced and As removed by boiling with SO_2.

(2) Interferences are As^{3+}, V^{4+}, Fe^{2+}, Te, SO_2, organic compds. and large amts. of Pb. Sn does not interfere; if reduced by SO_2 it can be detd. in the same soln. by iodometry. Fe^{3+} does not interfere and can be detd. after H_3PO_4 addn. and SO_2 redn. If $PbSO_4$ seps., add 40 ml. 30% NH_4OAc and continue titration; alternatively, let the ppt. settle, decant the supernate, warm the ppt. with 20–30 ml. 1 : 1 HCl, mix with the decanted soln., dil. to 200 ml., warm to 40°C, add methyl orange, titrate and correct the initial fig.

(3) The end-point is said to be sharper if 60 ml. $MnSO_4$ mixture (110 g. $MnSO_4$, 138 ml. H_3PO_4 and 130 ml. H_2SO_4/l.) is added for each 200 ml. soln.[11]

(4) If much Cu is present (0·4–0·8 g.), decolorize with 10% $CoSO_4$ soln.[12]

(5) As little as 3 μg. Sb can be titrated in 0·1*N* alk. soln. with an error of ±5%.[13]

(b) $KBrO_3$.[14, 15] Heat the Sb^{3+} soln., which should be 1:4 in HCl, to 60–80°C and titrate with 0·005–0·1*N* $KBrO_3$ to 2–3 ml. before the end-point; add methyl orange indicator and titrate to colorless.

NOTES. (1) Interferences are As^{3+}, HNO_3, reductants, oxidants, large amts. of Fe, Cu and very large amts. of Mg, Ca, NH_4^+ and $PbSO_4$. Pb, Zn, Sn, Cr do not interfere, nor does H_2SO_4. As, Sn, Cd, Bi do not interfere if reduced by shaking with 20–25 ml. Hg in 1 : 6 v/v HCl soln. for 5 min. (or 1 hr. for pyroantimonate) (Scott and Furman[1]). If Cu^+ is present, pass air for 15 min.

(2) Many other indicators can be used (see p. 194 and Chapter 15, Section 4.3). α-Naphthoflavone (colorless to brown) is said to be best.[16] $NaAuBr_2$ can be used for 10 mg. Sb, the accuracy being ±1%.[17]

(3) A variety of alternative oxidimetric titrations is available. With KIO_3[15, 18] add 15–20 ml. HCl/100 ml. (i.e. 2·5–3·5*N* soln.) or add <30 ml. HCl if 2–5 ml. 0·5*M* ICl is added and titrate to the usual extn. end-point; amaranth may also be used as indicator.

With 0·1*N* Ce^{4+}, adjust the soln. to contain 30–50% v/v HCl, add 1 drop methyl orange indicator and ICl (catalyst) and titrate to colorless. A small amt. of As can be tolerated;[15, 19] only 20–25% v/v HCl should be present when the amt. of Sb is small.

With $K_2Cr_2O_7$, add 10 ml. H_2SO_4 and 20 ml. HCl/150 ml. soln. followed by a small excess of oxidant; add 2–3 drops 1% Ba-diphenylaminesulfonate indicator, 5 ml. H_3PO_4 and a 0·2–0·3 ml. excess of Fe^{2+} soln. and back-titrate with the $K_2Cr_2O_7$ soln.[15]

For iodometry, titrate in 0·03*N* AcOH + NaOAc soln. or $NaHCO_3$ soln. contg. tartrate with 0·1*N* I_2 to a starch end-point.[15, 20] This method has been applied for brasses, etc.[21] Coulometric titration with Br_2 is also possible.[22]

(4) Sb^{5+} can also be titrated iodometrically.[15] To the soln. contg. 12–15% HCl, add 20 ml. 20% KI and 1 ml. CS_2 or CCl_4 and titrate with 0·1*N* $Na_2S_2O_3$; this is inaccurate. Titration with $Ti_2(SO_4)_3$ soln. is suitable for <0·2 g. Sb in 175 ml. 4*N* HCl soln. Add 5 drops Br_2, boil, add reagent until the yellow color disappears, add 5 drops 0·1% indigo carmine indicator and titrate to colorless.[15, 23] Cr^{2+} soln. may also be used.[15]

(c) Rhodamine B provides an excellent colorimetric method.[24, 25] For 15–40 μg. Sb^{5+} in 5 ml. 6*N* HCl soln., add 8 ml. 3*N* H_3PO_4, cool, add 5 ml. 0·02% rhodamine B and 10 ml. C_6H_6 and shake well for 1 min.; sep. and measure the red color at 563 mμ. For 0–15 μg. Sb, add H_3PO_4 as above and dil. with H_2O to give a 1·5*N* HCl soln.; add 5 ml. iso-Pr_2O, shake 100 times, discard the aq. phase, add 5 ml. reagent, shake, sep. and measure at 545 mμ; the accuracy is ±1 μg. over the range 2–15 μg. Sb.

NOTES. (1) Au, Tl^{3+}, Ga interfere, as do more than 1 mg. As, Bi, In, Mo, Pd, Se, Te, V, W, Hg, Pb, Pt, Sn^{2+}, Th, U, Zn, Zr, or 10 mg. Cu, Al, Ti; interference of <0·2 mg. Fe is avoided by addn. of H_3PO_4.

(2) Oxidation of Sb^{3+} to Sb^{5+} is crucial. Add 2 ml. 0·1*N* Ce^{4+} in 0·1*N* H_2SO_4 so that a yellow color appears; leave for 1 min., blow air through to remove Cl_2, add 5 drops 1% $NH_2OH{\cdot}HCl$ and again blow air through the soln.

(3) Several similar reactions have been utilized. Methyl violet is used similarly to rhodamine B with AmOAc extn.;[26] C_6H_6 is said to be better since the reagent is not extd.[27]

Fuchsine or malachite green is suitable for <6 μg. Sb;[28] add 5 ml. 6*N* HC*l*, 0·3 ml. 0·2% $Ce(SO_4)_2$ in 2*N* H_2SO_4, 5 ml. 1% $N_2H_4{\cdot}H_2SO_4$, 1 ml. 0·1% reagent and 10·5 or 9 ml. 30% Na_3-citrate. Ext. with 5 ml. AmOAc and measure at 555 or 628 mμ (ϵ = 63 300 or 76 100).

Brilliant green has been used for 50 μg. Sb^{3+}. Add 3–5 ml. HCl, 2 drops 5% $NaNO_2$ and 0·2 ml. 0·5% reagent in 25% EtOH and shake with 1 ml. toluene.[29]

Crystal violet may be used for 15 μg. Sb in 0·5 ml. soln.[5] (Tsao *et al.*[28]). Add 2·5 ml. 10*N* HCl, 0·5 ml. 1*N* $NaNO_2$, wait for 2 min., add 0·7 ml. urea (8 g./15 ml.) and shake for 1 min.; dil. to 20 ml. with H_2O, add 20 ml. C_6H_6 and 0·5 ml. 0·2% reagent, shake for 5 min. and measure at 602 mμ.

(4) Sb can be detd. gravimetrically with *trans*-$[CoCl_2(en)_2]Cl$.[30] For 1–50 mg. Sb in 50 ml. dil. HCl soln., pass Cl_2 gas for 5 min. or add 3 ml. HNO_3, warm and cool. Add excess reagent (0·2 g. in 10 ml. 2*N* HCl), filter after 2 hr. on a G4 crucible, wash with H_2O, dry at 100–110°C and weigh as $[CoCl_2(en)_2]SbCl_6$. Only 0·5 mg. Pb can be tolerated but 10 mg. Bi, 100 mg. Cd, Fe, Hg, Sn or 200 mg. As, Cu, Zn provide no interference.

Nitroso-R salt has been used[31] colorimetrically for 0–80 μg. Sb, Co in the ppt. being detd. (see Chapter 35, p. 270).

(5) Methylene blue has been used in conjunction with titrimetry.[32] For 0·3–5 mg. Sb in 4*N* HCl soln. at 60°C, add $NaNO_2$ and 0·1% dye soln., filter on a Gooch crucible wash with 4*N* HCl; dissolve in EtOH at 50°C, dil. to 60% EtOH, add KF and titrate with Ti^{3+} soln. under CO_2.

(6) HBr forms a yellow color with 2–500 μg. Sb^{5+}/ml. which is measurable at 340–360 mμ.[33]

(d) KI and ascorbic acid provide a simpler though less sensitive colorimetric detn. than rhodamine B.[24, 34] For 0–500 μg. Sb in 2–3 ml. soln. add H_2SO_4 to give a final concn. of 3·0*N* followed by 5 ml. of reagent contg. 112 g. KI and 20 g. ascorbic acid/l. Dil. with H_2O to 10 ml. and measure the yellow color after 5 min. at 420 mμ.

NOTES. (1) No interference arises from As, Hg^{2+}, Fe^{2+}, Cu^{2+}, Sn, Pb, W, PO_4^{3-}. Tl, Cl^-, SO_3^{2-} and large amts. of NO_3^- interfere; Bi interference can be allowed for by subtracting the absorbance found with a reagent soln. contg. 16 g. KI and 20 g. ascorbic acid under the same conditions as above.

(2) Other reductants can be used instead of ascorbic acid. The procedure involving NaH_2PO_2 has an accuracy similar to that of the above method (±2%). For >2 μg. Sb^{3+} in 5 ml. 1*N* H_2SO_4 soln., add 5 ml. reagent soln. contg. 100 g. KI and 10 g. NaH_2PO_2/l. Add starch and, if a blue color appears, decolorize it with 5% $Na_2S_2O_3$, adding 1 drop in excess. Measure the yellow color after 5 min.[35]

(3) $N_2H_4{\cdot}H_2SO_4$ is used in conjunction with KI and thiourea.[36] To the acidic soln. add 0·5 g. reductant, boil for 2 min., cool, add 2–3 g. thiourea and 40 ml. 50% KI and dil. to 200 ml.; filter and measure the color. Bi interferes.

(4) Various org. bases form insol. iodoantimonites which can be used colorimetrically. Pyridine is used for <0·1 mg. Sb in 3–4 ml. 1 : 3 H_2SO_4 soln.[15, 24] Pour this soln. into a reagent soln. contg. 1 ml. 1% gum arabic, 0·5 ml. 20% KI, 0·1 ml. 10% pyridine, 0·1 ml. SO_2 water (1 : 9 satd. soln.) and 6 ml. 1 : 3 H_2SO_4; dil. to 10 ml. with H_2O and measure the yellow color, which can be extd. with AmOH if necessary. Heavy metals and Cl^- interfere but traces of As or Sn do not.

Antipyrine and KI are suitable for 1–100 μg. Sb.[37] Add 5 ml. 8*N* H_2SO_4, 3 ml. 5% antipyrine and 2 ml. 10% KI; after 15 min. ext. with $CHCl_3$ and measure at 430–460 mμ (absorption max. 365 mμ). The optimum acidity is 2–5*N* H_2SO_4, 1–2·5*N* HCl or 1·5–4·5*N* HNO_3.

Triphenylmethylarsonium iodide and *o*-$C_6H_4Cl_2$ can be used for 10–100 μg. Sb/ml.[38]

(e) H_2S can provide gravimetric, titrimetric and colorimetric detns. For gravimetry,[1, 39] heat the Sb^{3+} soln. in 1:4 HCl to 90–100°C and pass H_2S rapidly until the ppt. changes from red to black. Add an equal vol. of hot H_2O and pass more H_2S. Filter on a Gooch crucible, wash with H_2O and EtOH, dry at 100–130°C for 2 hr. under CO_2 and then at 280–300°C for another 2 hr., and weigh as Sb_2S_3.

NOTES. (1) If <5 mg. Sb is present, treat the Sb_2S_3 or Sb_2S_5 ppt. with $(NH_4)_2S$, evap. to dryness and treat with HNO_3 gas (place near a dish of fuming HNO_3 in a bell-jar for 12 hr.). Add HNO_3, evap. to dryness and repeat. Add NH_4OH, evap., dry at 700–950°C (>900°C) for 1·5 hr. and weigh as Sb_2O_4. This technique has been applied to Fe–W.[21] (See p. 205 for the method of correcting for impurities in the oxide by heating with NH_4I).

In an alternative method,[40] add a known amt. of Fe_2O_3 and $Fe(NO_3)_3$ (3 : 1) to the sulfide ppt., heat above 800°C and weigh Sb_2O_5.

It is also possible to weigh as Sb_2S_5.[15]

(2) For a titrimetric finish, dissolve the sulfide ppt. in HCl, absorb the H_2S generated in $CdCl_2$ soln. and titrate iodometrically; this is unreliable.

(3) For colorimetry of 2–20 μg. Sb^{3+} in 10 ml. 2*N* HCl soln., add 0·1 ml. 1% gum arabic and 2 ml. satd. H_2S soln. and measure the yellow color.[15, 41]

(f) Miscellaneous gravimetric methods. Pyrogallol ppts. Sb^{3+} from dil. HCl solns. contg. NaK-tartrate[15, 42] if a 5-fold excess is added; the ppt. is filtered after 2 hr., washed with H_2O, dried at 100°C and weighed as $Sb(O_3C_6H_3)$. As does not interfere. The ppt. with gallic acid should be dried at 115–160°C.[43]

Thionalide is suitable for 20–40 mg. Sb^{3+} in acidic soln.[15, 44] Add 1–4 g. Na_2-tartrate and neutralize with Na_2CO_3; add 1–4 g. KCN, dil. to 150–200 ml. with H_2O and add 2% thionalide in EtOH (20 ml./20 mg. Sb). Boil, cool, filter on a G4 crucible and wash with cold H_2O until no CN^- remains and then with 10% EtOH. Dry at 100–105°C and weigh as $Sb(C_{12}H_{10}ONS)_3$.

No interference arises from Ag, Cu, As, Fe^{2+}, Zn, Al, Co. For a titrimetric finish, see Chapter 18.

Oxine acetate ppts. Sb^{3+} from acidic solns. on heating after adjustment to pH 6–7 with NH_4OH; the ppt. is washed with hot H_2O and EtOH, dried at 140°C and weighed as $Sb(C_9H_6ON)_3$. Tartrate does not interfere.[45] The method is said to be unreliable.[46]

Chloroxine or bromoxine in HCl solns. ppts. Sb^{5+} from >10*N* HCl solns.; the ppt. is washed with the reagent in HCl and then with HCl, dried over NaOH in a desiccator and weighed as $Sb(C_9H_4ONCl_2\,(\text{or }Br_2))_2Cl_3$. Few other ions interfere (Kudo[45]).

$[Cr(en)_3]Cl_3 3{\cdot}5H_2O$ reacts with SbS_4^{3-}. For the reagent, heat 6 g. ethylenediamine hydrate with 8 g. powd. Cr alum (dried at 100°C) for 2–3 hr. on a steam-bath in a flask fitted with an air condenser; mix to a paste with H_2O, filter, add NH_4Cl to the filtrate and recrystallize 2–3 times from H_2O. For the detn. treat 1–2 mg. Sb^{3+} as sulfide with hot Na_2S (avoid an excess) and 1 drop Na_2S_X; boil for 5 min., adjust the vol. to <25 ml., heat to 70–80°C and add solid reagent. Allow to cool, filter on a glass crucible and wash 6–7 times with cold, weakly ammoniacal H_2O, 4–5 times with 2 ml. EtOH and 4–5 times with 2 ml. Et_2O. Dry *in vacuo* over $CaCl_2$ and weigh as $[Cr(en)_3][SbS_4]{\cdot}2H_2O$.[15, 39, 47]

(g) Electrodeposition[15] (see also Scott and Furman[1]). For < 0·2 g. Sb, add 8 ml. Na_2S soln. (d = 1·14) and 2–3 g. KCN for each 150 ml. soln. Heat to 60–70°C, electrolyze for 2 hr. at 1·3 amp. and 2–3 v., wash with H_2O, EtOH and Et_2O, dry at 80°C and weigh Sb; the error is ±2%. Electrodeposition is also possible[48] from 3·5% v/v HCl soln. contg. 0·5–1 g. $N_2H_4{\cdot}H_2SO_4$.

(h) NaH_2PO_2 has been used in conjunction with iodometry.[49] Heat the test soln. with twice its vol. of a soln. contg. 100 g. NaH_2PO_2 in 150 ml. H_2SO_4 and 200 ml. H_2O. Filter on a G3 crucible, wash with 1:4 H_2SO_4 and add excess 0·01–0·1*N* I_2 and 1 ml. 10% tartaric acid soln. Then add an equal vol. of equinormal As^{3+} soln. and 10 ml. satd. $NaHCO_3$ and back-titrate with I_2 soln.

(i) Miscellaneous colorimetric methods. Morin is useful for fluorimetric detns. of 10–100 μg. Sb in 5 ml. 0·4*N* HCl solns.[50] Add 1 ml. 0·02% morin in EtOH (0·5 ml. if Sb is < 50 μg.) and 3 ml. EtOH and dil. with H_2O to 10 ml.; measure the yellow-green fluorescence under UV light.

Phenylfluorone may be used for 0·05–6 μg. Sb/ml. in 0·2–0·5*N* acidic soln. with measurement at 530 mμ (ϵ = 34160).[51]

SO_2-water and phosphomolybdic acid are applicable for 50–500 μg. Sb.[24] Add enough H_2SO_4 to give a 0·4*N* soln. on diln. to 30 ml. followed by satd. SO_2-water. Boil, dil. to 30 ml. with H_2O, add 2 ml. 5% phosphomolybdic acid and place for 10 min. in boiling H_2O. Cool, add 8 ml. 1:4 H_2SO_4, shake for 5 min., dil. to 50 ml. and compare the blue color. Folin–Denis' reagent can also be applied.

Silicomolybdovanadic acid or the germanium analog has been suggested.[52] The former is prepd. by heating 5 g. $Na_2SiO_3{\cdot}9H_2O$ dissolved in 125 ml. H_2O, 2 g. $NaVO_3$ dissolved in 100 ml. H_2O and 31 g. $H_2MoO_4{\cdot}H_2O$ under reflux for 2 hr.; after cooling and addn. of 115 ml. 1:1 H_2SO_4, the mixture is shaken with 100 ml. Et_2O, sepd. and the aq. layer washed with Et_2O pre-equilibrated with 6*N* H_2SO_4. The org. layer is then evapd. after H_2O addn., cooled, and the crystals are sepd. The Ge analog is prepd. by refluxing 1 g. GeO_2 in Na_2CO_3 soln., 9·6 g. $NaVO_3$ dissolved in H_2O and 18 g. $H_2MoO_4{\cdot}H_2O$ dissolved in alkali, after addn. of 1:1 H_2SO_4 to give a 2*N* soln.; after 2 hr. the mixture is cooled, extd. with Et_2O, etc. as above. For a detn. of 0·1–0·7 mg. Sb^{3+} in 3 ml. 1*N* H_2SO_4 soln., add 0·2 ml. 5% reagent, dil. to 10 ml. with H_2O after 1 min. and compare the blue color.

The Gutzeit method may be used for 25–150 μg. Sb[15,24,53] (see p. 194).

Thiourea has been proposed for 1–2 μg. Sb/ml., measurement being made at 366 mμ.[54]

References

1. Hillebrand and Lundell, 221 (273); Scott and Furman, 63; Kimura, 176; Fresenius–Jander, **Va**γ 388 (1951).
2. McNabb, W. M. and Wagner, E. C., *Ind. Eng. Chem., Anal. Ed.*, **1**, 32 (1929); **2**, 251 (1930).
3. Beaumont, F. T., *Metallurgia*, **33**, 101 (1945).
4. Ward, F. N. and Lakin, H. W., *Anal. Chem.*, **26**, 1168 (1954).
5. Jurečerk, M. and Jeník, J., *Chem. listy*, **51**, 1316 (1957).
6. Hillebrand and Lundell, 225, (278).
7. Grant, J., *Analyst*, **54**, 227 (1929).
8. Matsuura, J. and Kojima, E., *Japan Analyst*, **6**, 155 (1957).
9. Babko, A. K. and Shtokalo, M. I., *Zavodskaya Lab.*, **21**, 767 (1955).
10. Gibbons, D., *Ind. Chemist*, **29**, 363 (1953) (review).
11. Leeman, W. G., *J. Soc. Chem. Ind.*, **51**, T284 (1932).
12. Jílek, A. and Vřešt'al, J., *Chem. listy*, **28**, 132 (1934).
13. Issa, I. M., *et al.*, *Chemist Analyst*, **45**, 62, 78 (1956).
14. See also Anderson, C. W., *Ind. Eng. Chem., Anal. Ed.*, **11**, 224 (1939); Wooton, L. A., and Luke, C. L., *ibid.*, **13**, 771 (1941); Luke, *ibid.*, **15**, 625 (1943); **16**, 448 (1944); A.S.T.M. 465 (Pb), 472 (Pb, Sn-base solder).
15. Fresenius–Jander, **Va** γ, 388 ff.
16. Tsuda, K., and Sakamoto, H., *J. Pharm. Soc. Japan*, **61**, 217 (1941).
17. Szebellédy, L. and Madis, W., *Z. anal. Chem.*, **118**, 138 (1940).
18. Mutschin, A., *Z. anal. Chem.*, **100**, 1 (1936); Hammock, E. W., *et al.*, *Anal. Chem.*, **20**, 1048 (1948).
19. Petzold, A., *Z. anal. Chem.*, **150**, 111 (1956).
20. Pani, S., *J. Indian Chem. Soc.*, **23**, 389 (1946).
21. A.S.T.M., 315 ff.
22. Lingane, J. J. and Bard, A. J., *Anal. Chim. Acta*, **16**, 271 (1957); Brown, R. A. and Swift, E. H., *J. Am. Chem. Soc.*, **71**, 2340 (1949).
23. Holness, H. and Cornish, G., *Analyst*, **67**, 221 (1942).
24. Sandell, 165 ff.

25. Maren, T. H., *Anal. Chem.*, **19**, 487 (1947); Freedman, L. D., *ibid.*, 502; Luke, C. L. and Campbell, M. E., *ibid.*, **25**, 1588 (1953) (in Ge); Ward, F. N. and Lakin, H. W., *ibid.*, **26**, 1168 (1954) (in rock); Onishi, H. and Sandell, E. B., *Anal. Chim. Acta*, **11**, 444 (1954) (0–2·5 μg.); Nielsch, W. and Böltz, G., *Z. anal. Chem.*, (**143**, 264 (1954); Matsuura, J. and Kojima, E., *Japan Analyst*, **6**, 155 (1957) (in Pb).
26. Goto, H. and Kakita, Y., *J. Chem. Soc. Japan*, **73**, 339 (1952).
27. Jean, M., *Chim. anal.*, **31**, 271 (1949); *Anal. Chim. Acta*, **7**, 462 (1952); **11**, 82 (1954).
28. Goto and Kakita, *J. Chem. Soc., Japan*, **78**, 1521 (1957); Tsao, K. H., *et al.*, *Yao Hsüeh Hsüeh Pao*, **4**, 107 (1956).
29. Lapin, L. N. and Geĭn, V. O., *Trudy Komissii Anal. Khim., Akad. Nauk S.S.S.R.*, **7**, 217 (1956).
30. Belcher, R. and Gibbons, D., *J. Chem. Soc.*, 4775 (1952); also see Ishimori, T. and Ueno, K., *Bull. Chem. Soc. Japan*, **28**, 200 (1955) (radiometric using radioactive Co).
31. Nozaki, T., *J. Chem. Soc. Japan*, **77**, 960 (1956).
32. Bloch, J. M. and Veillerette, C., *Bull. soc. pharm. Nancy*, **30**, 14 (1956).
33. Nielsch, W. and Böltz, G., *Mikrochim. Acta*, 313 (1954).
34. McChesney, E. W., *Ind. Eng. Chem., Anal. Ed.*, **18**, 146 (1946); Elkind, A. E., *et al.*, *Anal. Chem.*, **25**, 1744 (1953) (more sensitive at 330 mμ).
35. Holler, A. C., *Anal. Chem.*, **19**, 353 (1947); Rooney, R. C., *Analyst*, **82**, 619 (1957) (in cast iron; MnO_2 copptn.).
36. Bartmen, J. H. and Kent, P. J. C., *Metallurgia*, **35**, 91 (1946); Zaĭkovskiĭ, F. V., *Zhur. Anal. Khim.*, **9**, 155 (1954); Finkel'stein, D. N. and Kryscova, G. N., *ibid.*, 150.
37. Sudo, E., *J. Chem. Soc. Japan*, **75**, 1291 (1954).
38. Figgis, B. and Gibson, N. A., *Anal. Chim. Acta*, **7**, 313 (1952).
39. Hecht and Donau, 174.
40. Goto, H., *J. Chem. Soc. Japan*, **55**, 326 (1934).
41. Yoe, 123.
42. Welcher, **I**, 161.
43. Gomez, J. O. and Romeo, J. G., *Téc. met.* (*Barcelona*), **4**, 461 (1948).
44. Welcher, **IV**, 173.
45. Kudo, I., *Japan Analyst*, **5**, 556 (1956); Pirtea, T. I., *Z. anal. Chem.*, **118**, 26 (1939/40).
46. Morandat, J. and Duval, C., *Anal. Chim. Acta*, **4**, 498 (1950).
47. Welcher, **II**, 384.
48. Treadwell, W. D., *Tabellen*, 113, (1938); also see Norwitz, G., *Anal. Chem.*, **23**, 286 (1951); Lingane, *Electroanalytical Chemistry*, p. 313 (1953) and Chapter 4 (controlled potential).
49. Fauchon, L. and Vignoli, L., *J. pharm. chim.*, **25**, 541 (1937).
50. Goto, H., *J. Chem. Soc. Japan*, **60**, 938 (1939).
51. Nazarenko, V. A. and Lebedeva, N. V., *Zhur. Anal. Khim.*, **11**, 560 (1956).
52. Kokorin, A. I. and Polotebnova, N. A., *Trudy Komissii Anal. Khim., Akad. Nauk S.S.S.R.*, **7**, 205 (1956).
53. Davidson, J., *et al.*, *J. Assoc. Offic. Agr. Chemists*, **21**, 314 (1938).
54. Nielsch, W. and Böltz, G., *Z. anal. Chem.*, **143**, 81 (1954).

27

TIN

The principal sources of this chapter are given in ref. 1.

The following points should be noted for the analysis of tin. $SnCl_4$ (b.p. 114°C) volatilizes from HCl solns. when they are evapd. unless H_2SO_4 is present. If precipitates must be ignited, care must be taken to ensure that all chloride has been washed out.

Sn hydroxides adsorbed on filter paper cannot be removed completely even by washing with acids. It is necessary to digest the paper with HNO_3 and H_2SO_4, or with H_2SO_4, $HClO_4$ and HNO_3 (3:1:2 v/v), or to ignite the paper in a porcelain crucible, fuse with Na_2CO_3 in a Pt crucible and then dissolve in acid.

Attack

(a) Oxides. Fuse in a Fe crucible with NaOH, Na_2O_2, Na_2CO_3 + S, or $Na_2S_2O_3$. Alternatively, fuse in a porcelain crucible with KCN and Na_2CO_3.

If CaO is used, mix the sample with an equal wt. and heat at 750–800°C in H_2 or NH_3; treat the residue with HCl and repeat; finally fuse the residue with Na_2CO_3. For cassiterite, mix 0·3 g. with 0·78 g. CaO and 0·048 g. charcoal, cover with a 2 cm. layer of CaO and ignite at 900°C for 1 hr.

With KHF_2, fuse, add H_2SO_4 and evap.

For oxides contg. > 2% sulfides, evap. to dryness with HNO_3, fuse with NaOH and finally treat with HCl or H_2SO_4.

(b) Silicates. Fuse with Na_2CO_3. If W is present, fuse with 1:1 Na_2CO_3–KCN after adding $\frac{1}{3}$ of the sample weight of CuO.[2]

(c) Alloys, etc. Treat with HCl and $KClO_3$, H_2SO_4, Br_2 and HBr, or with HNO_3, etc.

For bronzes, dissolve 1 g. in 5 ml. 1:1 HNO_3 on a steam-bath, boil out NO_2, add 50 ml. hot H_2O and some paper pulp and boil for 30 min. with occasional addn. of H_2O; filter on Whatman No. 40 paper contg. a little pulp and wash with 1% HNO_3.

For steels, dissolve 5–10 g. in HCl or HNO_3, recover Sn from the residue, sep. Sn with H_2S (adding tartaric acid if W is present), coppt. with $Fe(OH)_3$ and det. Sn iodometrically. Alternatively, dissolve 2·5–5 g. steel in dil. HNO_3, coppt. Sn with MnO_2 (reppt. if V is present) and treat the ppt. with dil. HCl and some H_2O_2.[3]

Separation

If Sn is detd. iodometrically, complete sepn. is rarely necessary.

H_2S provides various sepns. under different conditions. Sepn. from group III, etc. is obtained from solns. contg. 2·4 ml. HCl/100 ml. Fe^{2+} coppts. with Sn^{4+} from HCl solns. $HgCl_2$ or Cu^{2+} can be used to conc. Sn from solns. contg. tartrate but Ta and PO_4^{3-} interfere. H_2S can also be used to achieve the following sepns.: Sn is sepd. from As in concd. HCl soln., from As^{3+} and Sb^{3+} in $H_2C_2O_4$ or HF soln., from small amts. of W, V, Ti in acidic tartrate-contg. solns., from Cu in acidic thiourea-contg. solns., from Cu, Pb, Fe, etc. in ammoniacal tartrate solns., and from the Cu group in alk. solns. (this method cannot be used before colorimetry).

Sepn. from < 1 mg. Fe and from many other elements is obtained by digestion with 1:5 HNO_3 at 80–100°C for at least 3 hr. followed by filtration on Whatman No. 42 paper and washing with hot H_2O and hot 1:20 HNO_3. If much Fe is present, some Sn appears in the filtrate but can be recovered by pptn. with NH_4OH. The ppt. may be contaminated with Si, Nb, Ta, W, Sb, As, P and traces of Fe, Co, Zn.[4]

Treatment with NH_4OH and NH_4Cl seps. Sn from Cu, Ni, Co, small amts. of Mo and large amts. of W (in this case H_2S sepn. should follow). Fe^{3+} serves to conc. Sn under these conditions.

Hydrolysis permits sepn. from many elements; add some dil. NaOH to the hot HCl-contg. soln. to give pH 1·5 or add 5 ml. H_2SO_4/100 ml. soln. and place for 1 hr. on a steam-bath. Repptn. is needed when Fe or In is present.

Copptn. with MnO_2 seps. Sn from Pb, Fe, etc.; treat the 1:10 HNO_3 soln. with $MnSO_4$ and excess $KMnO_4$, boil, add a little more $KMnO_4$ and boil again.

Sepn. from SiO_2 is obtained by evapn. with H_2SO_4 or $HClO_4$. Treatment with H_2SO_4 seps. Sn from Pb.

Reduction with Zn, Cd or Al in dil. HCl soln. seps. Sn from many elements. Reduction with Fe in dil.

HCl soln. gives sepn. from Cu, Bi, Sb, As, Ge, Pt, Au, etc. With red P, which allows sepn. of Sn from Cu, add 2 g. P to the dil. H_2SO_4 soln. and boil for 15 min. Sn is sepd. from As by NaH_2PO_2.

Electrolysis of solns. contg. 5 ml. HNO_3 and 5 ml. HF/100 ml. soln. gives sepn. from Ag, Pb, Cu, Sb^{3+}, As^{3+}, Hg.

Distn. seps. Sn from Cu, Mo, Sb^{5+}, PO_4^{3-} (see p. 192).

Cupferron allows sepn. from Sb^{5+}, As^{5+}, Ge, Al, Cr, Mn, Zn, Co, Ni; and from Pb in dil. HNO_3 solns. (see under Determination). Extn. with $CHCl_3$ is also valuable.

Extn. with $CHCl_3$ of the dithizone complex from acidic or alk. citrate-contg. solns. seps. Sn from Cu.

Diethylammonium diethyldithiocarbamate can be used to sep. Sn^{2+}, Cu, Bi, Hg, Sb^{3+}, As^{3+}, Ag, Cd, In, Se, Te, Pd, Cr and, partly, Mo, Fe from Sn^{4+}, As^{5+}, Sb^{5+}, Fe^{2+} and PO_4^{3-}. Treat the soln. contg. < 80 μg. Sn^{4+} in a 125 ml. separatory funnel with 5 ml. H_2SO_4 and dil. to 50 ml. with H_2O. Add 25 ml. 1% reagent in $CHCl_3$, shake for 30 sec., sep., repeat if necessary, wash twice with 5 ml. $CHCl_3$ and drain the aq. layer into a flask; heat to 50°C, return to the funnel and add 2 ml. 10% thioglycolic acid and 1 ml. of a soln. contg. 6 g. KI and 1 g. ascorbic acid/40 ml. Leave for 10 min., cool, add 10 ml. reagent, shake, sep., drain into a 125 ml. flask and shake the aq. layer with 5 ml. $CHCl_3$. Combine the org. layers, add 2 ml. H_2SO_4, 1 ml. HNO_3 and 0·5 ml. $HClO_4$, evap. slowly to fumes, cool slightly, add 0·25 ml. $HClO_4$, evap. nearly to dryness, add 5 ml. 1:4 H_2SO_4 and evap. until fumes just appear. Add 9 ml. H_2O and continue to the detn. with phenylfluorone.

Ion exchange resins may be used for sepn. of Sn from Pb (see Chapter 13, Section 2.2). Sn can be sepd. from W (p. 422) on a silica gel column.

Determination

The iodometric detn. is the best and most widely used method and is suitable for more than 0·5 mg. Sn. Cerimetric titration is also a useful method. Among the gravimetric methods, that with H_2S is most accurate, while that with cupferron is most convenient; precipitation with NH_4OH (with or without tannin) is suitable for small amounts of Sn. In the gravimetric methods, corrections can be applied after the precipitate has been heated with NH_4I. Trace amounts of Sn are best determined with dithiol but many elements interfere. The phosphomolybdate method is less prone to interference. Polyhydroxy compounds have been suggested recently but their merits await assessment.

(a) Iodometry.[1] Place the soln. contg. $< 0·2$ g. Sn in a stoppered flask; the soln. should contain 10–15 ml. H_2SO_4 and 100 ml. HCl/300 ml. Add 2–3 g. Pb (granular) and boil for 30–40 min. while passing CO_2. Cool to below 10°C, add starch and titrate with 0·01–0·1*N* I_2 to a blue color.

This procedure has been used for a wide variety of alloys after reduction with Pb, Fe, Ni or Al.[5]

NOTES. (1) Interferences are HNO_3, W, Mo, V and >5 mg. Cu; Ti causes slightly high results regardless of the amt. present. No interference is caused by <15 mg. Sb, by small amts. of As, or by Ge, Pb, Bi, Fe, Ni, Co, Zn, Mn, U, Al, Cr, SO_4^{2-}, PO_4^{3-}, I^-, Br^- or F^-.

(2) Careful protection from atmospheric oxidation is essential. When traces of Sn are detd., the I_2 soln. should be prepd. with H_2O which has been boiled while CO_2 passed through, and then cooled.[6]

(3) In general, reduction with Ni granules or Ni plate which has been boiled for 10 min. with 6*N* HCl is preferable; the reduction is done in 2·4*N* HCl soln. When Pb, Zn, Al or Fe is used for reduction, some Sn coppts. with Sb or Cu if these are present; any residual Fe, Zn or Al must be filtered off. If Sb is used for reduction, results are high or low depending on whether the Sb is fine or coarse.[7]

NaH_2PO_2 is a useful reductant;[8] use 0·5 g. and 1 ml. 10% $Hg(CN)_2$ in 1:1 HCl solns. after addn. of 10 ml. 6*N* HCl. After concn. with MnO_2, add 20 ml. 1:1 HCl and some H_2O_2 and heat; dil. to 100 ml. with H_2O, add 50 ml. HCl, 50 ml. 1:1 H_2SO_4, boil, cool, add 1 ml. satd. $HgCl_2$ and 5 g. NaH_2PO_2 and boil for 5 min. while passing CO_2. Filter if necessary (if As is present) and titrate iodometrically.[3]

(4) Many other redox titrations have been suggested. For cerimetric titration,[9] use a dil. HCl soln., add 5 ml. of a soln. contg. 1 g. starch and 10 g. KI/100 ml. as indicator, and titrate with 0·1*N* Ce^{4+} soln. to a blue color; this method has the advantage that the titrant requires less frequent standardization than I_2 solns. It is normally used in conjunction with Ni reduction and gives better results than iodometry when Sb is present but Fe interferes.

With KIO_3, boil 50 ml. Sn-contg. soln. for 10 min. with 1·5–2 g. Zn in a CO_2 atmosphere. Add 7–8 ml. HCl, 0·1 g. $NiCl_2$ or $CoCl_2$, boil, cool and add 100 ml. 0·2*N* $NaHCO_3$. Titrate with 0·1*N* KIO_3 until a yellow color appears, rinse the walls of the vessel, add starch and titrate with 0·02*N* $Na_2S_2O_3$ to colorless.[10] As and Sb interfere; the error is usually $-0·7$%.

$KBrO_3$ or KIO_3 is also used in dil. HCl soln. after addn. of 10 ml. 0·1*N* KI, the excess being titrated with $Na_2S_2O_3$ soln.[11] This technique has been applied to many steels, brasses and other alloys,[5] as well as to Zr[12] and Ti;[13] in the last case, reduction with NaH_2PO_2 and concn. by means of CdS were used.

Titration with $KClO_3$ has been suggested[14] (see also Chapter 5, Section 7.7).

Methylene blue or thionine (standardized against Ti^{3+}) can be used for 3–20 mg. Sn in 6–8*N* HCl soln.; add 2 g. Al for reduction and finally dil. with H_2O to give 4–6*N* HCl and titrate with the reagent. A blank detn. is needed; no interference is caused by small amts. of Fe, Ni, Cu, As, W.[15]

$KMnO_4$ can be used for the titration in 5–10*N* mineral acid solns. after reduction with Bi–Hg at 45°C for over 10 min.;[16] the amalgam is sepd. before the titration.

Other possible titrants are $FeCl_3$ with indigo carmine indicator (Scott and Furman[1]), H_2O_2 (potentiometric; As interferes),[17] cacotheline[18] and $Na_2S_2O_3$ (after addn. of KBr and Cu^{2+}, see p. 174).

(b) **H_2S** is mainly used gravimetrically but other finishes are also possible. For gravimetry,[1, 19] add some paper pulp to the Sn^{4+} soln. contg. 5–10 ml. H_2SO_4 and 20–50 ml. 20% NH_4Cl/200–400 ml., and pass H_2S. Filter on paper and wash with H_2S-contg. 1% v/v H_2SO_4 until no Cl^- is present. Place in a porcelain crucible, heat slowly to 600–700°C, cool, add some $(NH_4)_2CO_3$, heat to 900–1000°C and weigh as SnO_2.

NOTES. (1) The ppt. must be protected from the gas flame. To correct for impurities in SnO_2, mix the ignited ppt. with a 15-fold amt. of NH_4I, heat to 425–475°C, cool, add 2–3 ml. HNO_3 and reignite; deduct the wt. found. Sb and Zn interfere but Fe, Cu and Pb (<20 mg. PbO) do not.[20]
(2) In an alternative method,[21] add 10 ml. HCl and 0·1 g. Mg to the neutral soln. and heat when the Mg has almost dissolved; then add 350 ml. hot H_2O, place on a steam-bath and pass H_2S for for 10 min.; filter and complete as above.
(3) For a calorimetric procedure, see ref. 22.
(4) A titrimetric method[23, 24] is available in which the reactions are:

$$K_6Sn_2(C_2O_4)_7 + 2\,H_2S = 2\,K_2SnS(C_2O_4)_2 + 2\,H_2C_2O_4 + K_2C_2O_4,$$

$$2\,K_2SnS(C_2O_4)_2 + 2\,I_2 + 2\,H_2C_2O_4 + K_2C_2O_4 = K_6Sn_2(C_2O_4)_7 + 4\,HI + 2\,S$$

To the soln. contg. 0·15 g. Sn, add 2 ml. 18*N* H_2SO_4 and a few ml. HNO_3, heat to expel HNO_3, cool and add 2–3 g. $K_2C_2O_4$. Wash down the beaker wall with 20 ml. 0·5% $H_2C_2O_4$ adjusted to pH 3 with $K_2C_2O_4$, and add more $K_2C_2O_4$ to give pH 2·2–2·8 (until the red color of thymol blue disappears). Dil. to 60 ml. with H_2O, add 3·5 ml. KHS soln. (20 g. KOH in 100 ml., satd. with H_2S), heat to 60°C for 5 min., add a few drops of KHS soln. and heat again for 1 min. Cool, dil. to 100 ml. with H_2O, and pass CO_2 for ca. 30 min. until $Pb(OAc)_2$ paper gives no test for H_2S. Add 0·1*N* I_2 to give a pale yellow color and back-titrate with $Na_2S_2O_3$. No interference arises from Cu, Sb, etc. if the soln. is filtered after the first 5 min. heating time.

(c) **NH_4OH** provides a good gravimetric detn.[1] Add NH_4OH to the Sn^{4+} soln., filter on paper and wash with 2% NH_4NO_3. Transfer to a porcelain crucible, ignite at 700–1000°C and weigh as SnO_2. Sb contamination is indicated by a blue color. If EDTA is added, only Sb, Ti, Be and U interfere.[25] For solders,[26] treat 0·5 g. sample with 2 ml. aqua regia, add H_2O and $(NH_4)_2C_2O_4$ and make slightly acidic; filter, add NH_4OH and 25 ml. 3% H_2O_2, boil for several min., filter and ignite.

Better results can be obtained if tannin is added.[27] Dissolve the ppt. formed with NH_4OH in 50 ml. hot soln. contg. 3–5 g. $(NH_4)_2C_2O_4$ in 1*N* HCl and add 25 ml. satd. NH_4Cl soln. Dil. to 200 ml. with H_2O, boil and add 1 g. tannin dissolved in a little H_2O followed by 1*N* NH_4OH dropwise. Filter on paper contg. paper pulp, wash with 2% NH_4NO_3 soln. and ignite. No interference arises from Cu, Pb, Fe, Al, Be, etc.; Sb interference is avoided by boiling with Ni powder.

NOTE. Various modifications have been recommended. For 0·1 g. Sn in 100 ml. soln. add NH_4OH until a ppt. appears followed by 50 ml. satd. NH_4NO_3 soln.; dil. to 400 ml. with hot H_2O, boil for 2 sec. and place on a steam-bath until the ppt. coagulates; filter on paper, wash by decantation 6 times with hot 3% NH_4NO_3 and then wash with hot H_2O (Scott and Furman[1]).
Homogeneous pptn. with urea has been suggested.[28] Pyridine or triethanolamine may also be used.[29] For dil. HNO_3 digestion, see under Separation (Ag solders[5]).

(d) **Dithiol** is an excellent colorimetric reagent for Sn.[30] The optimum acidity is 0·4–0·8*N* H_2SO_4 or 0·4–0·6*N* HCl. (See also Chapter 8, Section 2.9.) To the soln. contg. 0·2 ml. H_2SO_4 in 7 ml., add 1 drop thioglycolic acid, 0·05 ml. Santomerse S (1:19) and 0·5 ml. reagent (0·1 g. dithiol in 50 ml. 1% NaOH contg. 0·3–0·5 ml. thioglycolic acid. Heat at 50 ± 5°C for 5 ± 1 min., add 0·5 ml. 1:3 Santomerse S, cool, dil. to 10 ml. with H_2O and measure at 530 mμ. This procedure is suitable for 0·28–6 p.p.m. Sn. Det. the reagent blank by taking 5 μg. Sn through the procedure.

NOTES. (1) Interferences are Bi, Mo, F^-, PO_4^{3-}, NO_2^-, more than 10 μg. Se, Te, Sb and more than 50 μg As, Ge, Hg.
(2) 4-Chloro-1,2-dimercaptobenzene has also been applied.[31]

(e) **Phosphomolybdic acid** is used colorimetrically in conjunction with Al.[32] The reagent is prepd. as follows: (1) dissolve 2·5 g. MoO_3 in 50 ml. 2*N* NaOH and dil. to 100 ml. with 2*N* H_2SO_4; (2) dissolve 0·44 g. $NaH_2PO_4 \cdot H_2O$ in 100 ml. H_2O; mix 10 ml. soln. (1) with 4 ml. soln. (2) and dil. to 200 ml. with H_2O.

Boil the soln. contg. 0·02–2·5 mg. Sn in 25 ml. 1:1 HCl with 0·1 g. granular Al in a CO_2 atm. Cool to 0°C, add 15 ml. reagent and, after 5 min., shake with 9 ml. AmOH. Sep., add 1 ml. EtOH to the org. phase and measure at 660 mμ.

NOTES. (1) Cu interference is avoided by treating 100 ml. soln. with thiourea, almost neutralizing with NH_4OH, passing H_2S for 30 min., heating on a steam-bath for 30 min. and filtering after another 30 min.; the ppt. is washed with H_2S–water and the ppt. and paper are heated with H_2SO_4 and HNO_3 until the soln. is clear; HCl is then added and the procedure continued as above.
Ti interference is prevented by addn. of 2 g. tartaric acid.
(2) Silicomolybdic acid can also be used.[32]
(3) Various other methods have been based on the reducing action of Sn^{2+}.
Cacotheline is suitable for 0·01–0·1 mg. Sn^{2+} in 100 ml. 1% HCl soln.;[33] add 0·1 ml. 0·25% reagent and compare the violet color after 15 min. Many elements interfere.
NH_4-6-nitro-2-naphthylamine-8-sulfonate allows a fluorimetric detn.[34] To 10 ml. 5*N* HCl soln. contg. < 0·2 μg. Sn/ml., add 1 g. tartaric acid and boil while passing CO_2. Cool, add 1 ml. satd. $HgCl_2$ and 1 ml. 30% H_3PO_2, boil gently for 10 min., add 30 ml. 5*N* NH_4OH and cool. Add 10 ml. 0·1% reagent, dil. to 1 l. with H_2O after 2 hr. and

measure the blue fluorescence (the soln. is orange). Interferences are U^{6+}, V^{4+}, Fe^{3+} and Ti; the method has been applied to Cu alloys.
α-Dinitrodiphenylaminesulfonic acid has been used for 0·25 mg. Sn^{2+} in 5 ml. dil. HCl soln.[35] (for alternative reagent names, see Chapter 15, Section 3). Add 2 ml. of a soln. contg. 0·2 g. reagent in 100 ml. 0·1*N* NaOH, heat at 60°C for 2 min., add 2 drops 5% $FeCl_3$ and compare the violet color.
Methyl orange has also been applied colorimetrically.[36]
Gravimetry of Hg_2Cl_2 is possible after treating the Sn soln. with Zn and $HgCl_2$.[37]

(f) Cupferron provides a useful gravimetric method [1, 38, 39] which is more convenient than iodometry when preceded by distn. For distillates contg. 10–100 mg. Sn, dil. with H_2O to give a 6% v/v HCl soln., add 1*N* $KMnO_4$ to faint pink and enough H_2SO_4 to give a final concn. of 4%, and cool in ice. Add 6% cupferron soln. at 5°C (10, 40 or 110 ml. for resp. 10, 50 or 200 mg. Sn), stir, filter on Whatman No. 42 paper and wash 12–20 times with a soln. contg. 25 ml. 6% reagent/l. Transfer to a porcelain crucible, dry at a low temp., heat slowly to 1000°C and weigh as SnO_2. The error is ±0·2 mg.

NOTES. (1) Mo interferes. As^{5+}, Cd, Cr, Mn, Zn, Co, Ni and <20 mg. Sb^{5+} do not interfere; if more Sb is present, add tartaric acid. F^- does not interfere if H_3BO_3 is present, nor does Pb in HNO_3-contg. solns.
(2) *N*-Benzoylphenylhydroxylamine can also be used.[40] To the soln. contg. 10 ml. HCl in 200 ml., add 5 ml. 1% reagent for each 10 mg. Sn and 8 ml. in excess; place in an ice-box for 4 hr., filter on a glass crucible, wash with H_2O at 0°C and dry at 110°C. Weigh as $(C_{13}H_{11}O_2N)_2SnCl_2$. Cu, Pb, Zn do not interfere.

(g) Electrodeposition. The soln. should contain 25 ml. HCl and 25 g. $(NH_4)_2C_2O_4$ in 250 ml. Use a Cu-plated Pt cathode and pass 1 amp. at 3–4 v. at 60°C.[41] A little Pb can be tolerated. (See also Chapters 21 and 22, pp. 168 and 173.)

Alternatively, heat the soln. contg. 6 g. Na_2S, 5 g. KOH and 5 g. $Na_2S_2O_3$/100 ml. to 60°C and pass 0·4–1 amp. at 2–3 v. Other procedures are also possible.[42] Internal electrolysis has been used (see p. 158). Controlled potential electrolysis permits sepn. from Cd, Zn, Mn, Fe and partly from Ni.[43]

(h) Phenylarsonic acid may be used gravimetrically[44] for < 0·1 g. Sn^{4+} in 150 ml. 5% v/v HCl soln. Heat to 70°C, add 3 ml. satd. reagent, filter after 4 hr. on paper (add some paper pulp), wash with 4% NH_4NO_3, ignite and weigh as SnO_2.

NOTES. (1) Zr and Th interfere but Pb, Cu, Bi, Cd, Fe, Ni, Co, Zn, Al do not. The method is not suitable for small amts. of Sn.[45]
(2) NH_4-1-anthraquinonearsonate in alk. soln. seps. Sn from W, Sb, Cu, Cr, Mo, V, Nb, etc.; the ppt. is treated with H_2SO_4 and HNO_3 before iodometric titration or colorimetry with anthraquinone-1-azo-4-dimethylaniline (see below).[46]
(3) 3-Nitro-4-phenolarsonic acid may be applied gravimetrically, titrimetrically by $KBrO_3$ detn. of the ppt. (1 Sn = 8 Br), or nephelometrically.[47] With *p*-hydroxyphenylarsonic acid and bromometric detn., 1 Sn = 12 Br (Portnov[47]).
(4) *n*-Propylarsonic acid is used gravimetrically. Pptn. is done as described for Zr (p. 357) and the ppt. is ignited, mixed with NH_4I and reignited. The loss in weight represents Sn (Pigott[1]).

(i) H_2SeO_3 ppts. Sn from 2% v/v H_2SO_4 or HCl soln.[48] Add paper pulp and not more than a 4-fold excess of reagent; filter and wash the ppt. with 0·5% reagent soln.

(j) EDTA titration. Adjust the soln. to pH 2, add excess EDTA and back-titrate with Th^{4+} soln. in presence of xylenol orange indicator;[49] Cu does not interfere if thiourea is added. Back-titration with Zn^{2+} soln. with 3,3′-dimethylnaphthidine and ferri-ferrocyanide[49] or with pyrocatechol violet[50] as indicator is also suitable.

(k) Hematein is used colorimetrically.[51] The reagent is prepd. as follows: add 2 ml. 5% H_2O_2 to 0·3 g. hematoxylin in 20 ml. EtOH, place on a steam-bath for 15 min., cool and dil. to 100 ml. with H_2O.

For detn. of < 40 μg. Sn^{4+} in HCl-contg. soln., add 2 drops 10% H_2SO_4, 5 drops 10% tartaric acid, evap. on a steam-bath, and add 3 ml. H_2O, 1 ml. 1% gum arabic and 1 ml. reagent; after 50 min. dil. to 10 ml. with 0·5% H_2SO_4 and measure at 550 mμ, using the reagent as reference soln.

NOTES. (1) No interference is caused by Fe^{3+}, Mn, Cu, Zn; if large amts. of Pb are present, apply MnO_2 copptn. and ion exchange sepn. Ge interference is avoided by evapn. with HCl; tartaric acid prevents interference of less than 400 μg. Sb^{3+} or 200 μg. Bi.
(2) Hematoxylin is suitable for 0·05–7 mg. Sn.[32, 52] Add 5 ml. H_2SO_4, evap. to fumes and dil. to 100 ml. with HCl; pipet 10 ml., add 5·0 ml. 0·1% reagent in EtOH contg. 0·005*N* HCl and dil. with H_2O to 50 ml. (final pH 0·8). Fe, Sb, Ti, Bi interfere but Th, Ce, Cr, Al, U^{6+}, Mn, Zn, Ni, Co, Cu, Pb, Mg, NH_4^+ can be tolerated.
(3) Several other polyhydroxy compds. have been proposed. Phenylfluorone is used for <80 μg. Sn in 1 ml. H_2SO_4 soln.[53] Add 9 ml. H_2O, cool, add 1 ml. 3% H_2O_2, 10 ml. buffer (900 g. NaOAc in 700 ml. hot H_2O, filtered on Whatman No. 40 paper, mixed with 480 ml. AcOH and dild. with H_2O to 2 l.), 1 ml. 1% gum arabic, and 10·0 ml. reagent (0·05 g. dissolved in 5 ml. MeOH and 1 ml. HCl and dild. to 500 ml. with MeOH); after 5 min. dil. to 50 ml. with 1 : 9 HCl and measure at 510 mμ. Many elements interfere (see under Separation).
Flavanol provides a fluorimetric detn.[54] Add the soln. contg. 0·02–0·2 μM Sn in 10 ml. to 7·5 ml. *N,N′*-dimethylformamide and enough H_2SO_4 to give altogether 1 ml. 3*N*; add 2 ml. 0·05% flavanol in EtOH, dil. to 25 ml. with H_2O and measure the blue fluorescence under UV light after 15 min. Zr, Mo, Cl^-, F^-, PO_4^{3-} interfere but Cu, Cr, Co, Ni, Fe, As, Sb, Hg, Pb, Bi, Cd, Zn, Mn, Nb, Ta, Ti, W, Al, Th can be present.

Morin may also be used.[55] To the soln. add 2 ml. HCl, 5 ml. H_2O, and 2 ml. reagent (0·2 g. in 50 ml. EtOH dild. to 100 ml. with H_2O); dil. to 50 ml. with H_2O and measure the yellow color at 430 mμ. Interferences are Sb, Ti, Mo, W, Nb, Ta, Zr, Th, F^-, $C_2O_4^{2-}$ and much tartrate; Cu, Pb, Fe^{2+}, Cd, Zn, As, Bi, PO_4^{3-}, Ca, etc., and small amts. of Fe^{3+} and Al may be present.

Quercetin is said to be better than morin.[56] Treat the sample (0·1–1 g. brass, bronze, Cu or Zn metal) with some HCl, NaCl and 30% H_2O_2. Treat an aliquot with dil. NH_4OH to give a turbidity, then add 5 ml. HCl (d. 1·04), a small excess of 10% thiourea, 5 ml. 0·2% reagent in EtOH, and 25 ml. EtOH; dil. to 50 ml. with H_2O and measure the yellow color with a violet filter.

Quinalizarin gives a pink color at pH 4·75.[32]

(l) Miscellaneous colorimetric methods. HBr forms a yellow color with 8–100 μg. Sn which can be measured at 200–330 mμ.[57] For the use of tetraphenylarsonium or phosphonium chloride, see p. 153 and ref. 58.

Na-diethyldithiocarbamate has been suggested[59] for 1–7 mg. Sn in 10 ml. soln., the complex being extd. with $CHCl_3$.

Oxine is suitable for 100 μg. Sn in 10 ml. soln.[60] Add NH_4OH to give a blue color with bromothymol blue, acidify with 5*N* HCl and add 2 ml. in excess; dil. to 25 ml. with H_2O, add 15 ml. 0·1% oxine in $CHCl_3$, shake, add 10 ml. 1*N* NaOAc (pH $\leqslant$ 2·5), shake for 2 min. and measure at 385 mμ in a 4 cm. cell. The method is said to be unsatisfactory.[52]

Thiourea forms a yellow color with 50–80 μg. Sn in 14–16% HBr soln. which can be measured at 366 mμ.[61]

Anthraquinone-1-azo-4-dimethylaniline-HCl may be used semiquantitatively.[62] Test paper is prepd. by moistening filter paper with a soln. contg. 0·2 g. reagent, 4 ml. HCl, 30 g. NH_4Cl, 135 ml. H_2O and 60 ml. EtOH, and then dried. A drop of HCl soln. contg. 1 μg. Sn causes a blue-violet coloration.

References

1. Hillebrand and Lundell, 233 (285); Scott and Furman, 954; Kimura, 183; Pigott, 479.
2. Höltje, R. and Schlegel, H., *Z. anorg. u. allgem, Chem.*, **231**, 97 (1937).
3. Ikegami, T., *et al.*, *Japan Analyst*, **5**, 379 (1956).
4. See Gates, O. and Silverman, L., *Ind. Eng. Chem., Anal. Ed.*, **11**, 370 (1939); Dunbar-Poole, A. G., *Analyst*, **64**, 870 (1939); LaRosa, C. N., *Anal. Chem.*, **28**, 1447 (1956) (study using radioactive tracer).
5. A.S.T.M., 189 ff.
6. Okell, F. L. and Lumsden, J., *Analyst*, **60**, 803 (1935).
7. Evans, B. S. and Higgs, D. G., *Analyst*, **69**, 291 (1944); Holness, H., *ibid.*, **74**, 457 (1949).
8. Evans and Higgs, *Analyst*, **69**, 201 (1944).
9. Bassett, L. G. and Stumpf, L. F., *Ind. Eng. Chem., Anal. Ed.*, **6**, 477 (1934).
10. Ramsay, J. B. and Blann, J. G., *J. Am. Chem. Soc.*, **56**, 815 (1934); see also Bagshawe, B. and Dyke, E., *Analyst*, **74**, 249 (1949).
11. Ferjančič, S., *Z. anal. Chem.*, **98**, 246 (1934).
12. Wood, D. F. and Clark, R. T., *Analyst*, **82**, 624 (1957).
13. Challis, H. J. G. and Jones, J. T., *Analyst*, **82**, 658 (1957).
14. Azzarello, E. and Abramo, F., *Ann. chim. appl.*, **23**, 438 (1933).
15. Welcher, **IV**, 510, 570.
16. Someya, K., *Sci. Repts. Tohoku Imp. Univ.*, **16**, 515 (1927).
17. Vulterin, J. and Zýka, J., *Chem. listy*, **50**, 311 (1956).
18. Paul, I. I., *et al.*, *Gigiena i Sanit.*, **22**, (3) 83 (1957).
19. Lambie, D. A. and Schoeller, W. R., *Analyst*, **65**, 281 (1940).
20. Scott and Furman, 960.
21. Linke, B. and Preissecker, H., *Z. anal. Chem.*, **94**, 238 (1933); also see van Nieuwenburg, C. J. and van Ligten, J. W. L., *Chim. anal.*, **36**, 41 (1954) (thiourea dioxide + thioacetamide).
22. Compeau, G. M. and Blank, E. W., *Oil & Soap*, **21**, 275 (1944).
23. Willard, H. H. and Toribara, T. Y., *Ind. Eng. Chem., Anal. Ed.*, **14**, 716 (1942); Wheeler, C. G., *Analyst*, **63**, 883 (1938).
24. Welcher, **II**, 62.
25. Bieber, B. and Večeřa, Z., *Slévárenstvi*, **4**, (2) 48 (1956).
26. Emi, K. and Hayami, T., *J. Chem. Soc. Japan, Ind. Chem. Sect.*, **58**, 960 (1955).
27. Schoeller, W. R. and Holness, H., *Analyst*, **71**, 70, 217 (1946).
28. Willard, H. H. and Gordon, L., *Anal. Chem.*, **25**, 171 (1953).
29. Welcher, **III**, 30; **II**, 489.
30. Onishi, H. and Sandell, E. B., *Anal. Chim. Acta*, **14**, 153 (1956); also see Sandell, 565 and Welcher, **IV**, 192; Cheftel, H., *et al.*, *Bull. soc. chim. France*, 441 (1949); Williams, F. R. and Whitehead, J., *J. Appl. Chem. (London)*, **2**, 213 (1952); Fransworth, M. and Pekola, J., *Anal. Chem.*, **26**, 735 (1954); Dickinson, D. and Holt, R., *Analyst*, **79**, 104 (1954); Ovenston, T. C. J. and Kenyon, D., *ibid.*, **80**, 566 (1955).
31. Welcher, **IV**, 116.
32. Sandell, 567 ff.
33. Welcher, **IV**, 219; Bourson, M., *Chim. anal.*, **33**, 134 (1951).
34. Anderson, J. R. A. and Lowy, S. L., *Anal. Chim. Acta*, **15**, 246 (1956).
35. Welcher, **IV**, 197.
36. Welcher, **IV**, 532.
37. Fairchild, J. G., *Ind. Eng. Chem., Anal. Ed.*, **15**, 625 (1943).
38. Mogerman, W. D., *J. Research Natl. Bur. Standards*, **33**, 307 (1944).
39. Hecht and Donau, 179; Welcher, **III**, 388.
40. Ryan, D. E. and Lutwick, G. D., *Can. J. Chem.*, **31**, 9 (1953).
41. Foschini, A., *Z. anal. Chem.*, **119**, 281 (1940).
42. Treadwell, W. D., *Tabellen*, 116 (1938).
43. Lingane, *Electroanalytical Chemistry*, p. 313 (1953); also see Chapter 4.
44. Welcher, **IV**, 55.
45. Mark, H. v. and Hecht, F., *Mikrochim. Acta*, **2**, 227 (1937).
46. Kuznetsov, V. I., *Zavodskaya Lab.*, **11**, 363 (1945).

47. Karsten, P., *et al.*, *Anal. Chim. Acta*, **7**, 355 (1952); Jean, M., *ibid.*, **8**, 432 (1953); Dozinel, C. M. and Gill, H., *Chemist Analyst*, **45**, 105, 109 (1956); Portnov, A. I., *Zhur. Anal. Khim.*, **9**, 175 (1954).
48. de Carvalho, R. G., *Rev. quím. pura e apl.*, [4] **1** (1) 24 (1950).
49. Kinnunen, J. and Wennerstrand, B., *Chemist Analyst*, **46**, 34, 36 (1957).
50. Jankovsky, J., *Chem. listy*, **51**, 373 (1957).
51. Kojima, M., *Japan Analyst*, **6**, 139, 142 (1957) (in Zn, Pb).
52. Teicher, H. and Gordon, L., *Anal. Chem.*, **25**, 1182 (1953).
53. Luke, C. L., *Anal. Chem.*, **28**, 1276 (1956).
54. Coyle, C. F. and White, C. E., *Anal. Chem.*, **29**, 1486 (1957).
55. Patrovský, V., *Chem. listy*, **48**, 1694 (1954).
56. Liška, K., *Chem. listy*, **49**, 1656 (1955).
57. Nielsch, W. and Böltz, G., *Z. anal. Chem.*, **142**, 109 (1954).
58. Welcher, **IV**, 327.
59. Davies, J. and Easton, A. J., *Metal Ind.*, **82**, 418 (1953).
60. Wyatt, P. F., *Analyst*, **80**, 368 (1955); Gentry, C. H. R. and Sherrington, L. G., *ibid.*, **75**, 11 (1950) (pH 3·5).
61. Nielsch, W. and Böltz, G., *Z. anal. Chem.*, **143**, 81 (1954).
62. Welcher, **IV**, 474.

GERMANIUM

The principal sources for this chapter are given in ref. 1. The chemistry of germanium has been discussed in a monograph,[2] and its analytical chemistry has been treated in a number of important papers[3] as well as being reviewed.[4]

In general analytical work, it should be remembered that $GeCl_4$ (b.p. 86°C) volatilizes readily from solutions containing more than 50% v/v HCl and that appreciable loss can occur even from dilute HCl solutions. No volatilization takes place from a mixture of HF, H_2SO_4 and $HClO_4$.

Attack

Treat a 1 g. sample in a Pt dish with 10 ml. HNO_3, 10 ml. HF and 2 ml. 1:1 H_2SO_4, evap. at a low temp. (do not boil or fume) and transfer to a beaker. Make alk. with 6*N* NaOH, add 0·5g. Na_2S, boil for 15 min., cool, just acidify with 1:1 H_2SO_4 and leave for 12 hr. Filter, wash once with H_2O. Treat the filtrate with 1·5 times its vol. of HCl, add 2–3 g. Cu (dissolve 100 g. $CuSO_4$ in 1 l. H_2O, add excess Zn, acidify with 1:1 H_2SO_4, boil, decant, wash and store under H_2O) and leave for 1 hr.; if the Cu darkens distinctly, filter through acid-washed paper and add more Cu. Finally transfer to a distn. flask with 1:1 HCl and distil.

(a) Ores. For germanite, treat 0·5 g. with 12 ml. 1:1 HNO_3 and 1 ml. H_2SO_4, evap. to ca. 6 ml., dil. to 25 ml. with H_2O and boil. Filter on paper, wash with H_2O, return the ppt. to the original beaker and add some $(NH_4)_2S$. Filter and wash with 3% H_2O_2. Boil, combine the filtrates and dil. to 300–400 ml. with H_2O. Add 10 ml. 1:1 H_2SO_4 and 1 g. $(NH_4)_2SO_4$, boil, add 15 ml. 10% tannin and 2 g. $(NH_4)_2SO_4$. Filter on paper after 1 hr. (see under Determination).

For confieldite or argyrodite, fuse the sample with 5–6 times its weight of 1:1 Na_2CO_3 and S; ext. with H_2O and repeat. Combine the filtrates, acidify to 6*N* with H_2SO_4, pass H_2S, stopper the flask and filter after 24–48 hr.

(b) Other materials. For sulfides, add HNO_3, evap., add H_2SO_4, evap., add HCl and distil.

With ZnO, dissolve 20–100 g. of sample in an amt. of 1:1 NaOH soln. contg. half the sample weight of NaOH, add HCl and distil.

Distn. after HCl addn. is also used[5] for flue dusts after ashing with some Na_2O_2, and for coals after fusion with Na_2CO_3 at 600°C until no org. matter remains and then at 1000°C.

Ge itself can be dissolved in dil. alkali and H_2O_2, in HNO_3 or in H_2SO_4.

Separation

Distn. seps. Ge from As, Sn, Sb, Se, Te, etc.; it is carried out from 1:1 HCl contg. Cu (see above) for 30 min. with occasional addn. of HCl and rinsing of the condenser and delivery tube. Sepn. from As is also obtained by distn. from 3–4*N* HCl if Cl_2 is passed through the soln. If F^- is present, it must be previously volatilized from the H_2SO_4 soln. When the amt. of Ge is very small,[5] the distillate is received in cold H_2O and CCl_4; it is then acidified with HCl to give a 10*N* soln., shaken, sepd., extd. 4 times altogether, and the combined exts. are stripped by shaking for 4 hr. with H_2O.

H_2S is used to sep. Ge from group III in 5·5*N* H_2SO_4 or 3*N* HCl solns.; a pressure bottle is preferable. Sepn. from As^{3+} and Sb^{3+} is obtained in HF or $H_2C_2O_4$ solns. Sepn. from As is also given by treating 60–70 ml. soln. contg. 3 ml. 0·1*N* H_2SO_4 and 1 g. $(NH_4)_2SO_4$ in a pressure bottle with H_2S; the ppt. is washed with 1% $(NH_4)_2SO_4$ contg. H_2S. The filtrate can be adjusted to 6*N* in H_2SO_4 and Ge pptd. with H_2S.

$(NH_4)_2S$ seps. Ge from the Cu group; exact neutralization of the filtrate with AcOH ppts. As, Sb, Sn, but not Ge.

Treatment with NaH_2PO_2 in 3*N* HCl soln. seps. Ge from As. Treatment with Zn yields a sepn. from many elements.

Tannin seps. Ge from As, Ga, Zn, Cu, Fe, Mn, V, Al, Zr, Th, Ti, Mo (see under Determination). Addn. of Fe^{3+} or Al^{3+} and NH_4OH is useful for concn. purposes.

Electrolytic reduction[6] seps. GeH_4 from As^{5+}.

Extn. with CCl_4 from 9 (8–13)*N* HCl solns., repeated 3 times, seps. Ge from As if $KClO_3$ is added, and from all other elements.[7] The ext. is stripped with H_2O or 0·5*N* NaOH. Extn. with Et_2O from 6*N* HBr solns. is also useful.[8]

Determination

Tannin is the best available reagent for Ge, since few elements interfere. After sepn. of Ge by distn. or pptn. as GeS_2, the gravimetric methods described in (b) and (c) below are rapid and reasonably accurate. The method involving cinchonine molybdate is most suitable for mg. amounts of Ge. Phenylfluorone provides the best colorimetric method.

(a) Tannin is used gravimetrically.[1, 9] For < 60 mg. Ge in 150–200 ml. neutral soln., add 5–15 ml. $2N$ H_2SO_4 and 8–10 g. $(NH_4)_2SO_4$, boil, add 10–30 ml. 5% tannin and place for 1 hr. on a steam-bath. Filter on paper, decant and wash with a soln. contg. 5 ml. $2N$ HNO_3 and some tannin in 100 ml. 5% NH_4NO_3. Dry in a Pt crucible, ignite below 600°C for 1 hr., cool, add several drops of H_2SO_4 and HNO_3, heat slowly, ignite at 900–1000°C and weigh as GeO_2.

Pptn. from $0{\cdot}07N$ mineral acid soln. contg. $C_2O_4^{2-}$ is said to be better.[10]

NOTES. (1) No interference is caused by As, Ga, Zn, Cu, Fe, Mn; W, Nb, Ta interfere. To avoid interference by V, Ti, Zr, add 4–10 ml. $18N$ H_2SO_4/250–300 ml. soln., boil, add reagent and 2 g. $(NH_4)_2SO_4$ and continue as above. To prevent Mo interference, add 30 ml. $2N$ HNO_3 and 20 ml. 25% NH_4NO_3/300 ml. soln., heat to 80°C, add 10–15 ml. 10% tannin and filter after 12 hr.; wash, dissolve in $HNO_3 + H_2SO_4$ by heating and reppt.

(2) For a titrimetric finish,[11] add the sample dropwise to 1–5 ml. 6% tannin dild. to 25 ml. with a 1 : 1 mixture of $0{\cdot}5N$ HCl and $2M$ $(NH_4)_2SO_4$, determining the end-point electrometrically.

(3) A nephelometric method is possible with tannin and quinine.[12]

(4) 3,4-Dihydroxyazobenzene can be used gravimetrically or colorimetrically.[13] For 20 mg. Ge in 5 ml. soln., add 30 ml. 1% reagent in EtOH and 6 ml. HCl, filter, wash with H_2O and HCl, and ignite to GeO_2 or measure at 525 mμ.

(b) $GeCl_4$ distillates are best treated as follows: evap. the distillate with an equal vol. of HF, 1 ml. H_2SO_4 and 1 ml. 60% $HClO_4$ in a Pt dish, first on a steam-bath and then on a hot-plate; ignite and weigh as GeO_2 (Aitkenhead *et al.*[3]).

(c) GeS_2 precipitates can be detd. as follows: add NH_4OH and H_2O_2 and evap.; add H_2SO_4, heat, ignite at 900°C and weigh as GeO_2 (Davis and Morgan[3]). GeS_2 hydrolyzes readily on boiling with H_2O_2.[14]

(d) Cinchonine molybdate is used gravimetrically.[15] For < 4 mg. Ge in 40 ml. neutral soln., add 20 ml. 25% NH_4NO_3, 16 ml. 2% $(NH_4)_2MoO_4$, 20 ml. $2N$ HNO_3 dropwise, and 9 ml. 2·5% cinchonine in $0{\cdot}25N$ HNO_3; filter on a glass crucible after 4–12 hr., wash with 5 ml. portions of a soln. contg. 25 g. NH_4NO_3 and 50 ml. $2N$ HNO_3/l., dry at 160°C for 2 hr. and weigh as $(C_{19}H_{22}ON_2)_2{\cdot}H_4(GeMo_{12}O_{40})$ (Frederick *et al.*[15]).

Other bases can replace cinchonine and tungstate has been substituted for molybdate. None of these methods is entirely satisfactory and empirical factors must always be detd.

Oxine has been applied gravimetrically and titrimetrically.[16] For 0·05–10 mg. Ge in 50 ml. neutral or slightly acidic soln., add 2 ml. 5% $(NH_4)_2MoO_4$, 3 ml. 10% H_2SO_4 and dil. to 100 ml. with H_2O. After 5 min. add 9 ml. HCl (d. 1·19) dropwise, 20 ml. reagent (20 g. oxine in 120 ml. AcOH dild. to 1 l. with H_2O) and leave for 3–12 hr. Filter on a glass crucible, wash with a soln. contg. 7 ml. HCl and 25 ml. oxine soln./l., dry at 100°C (50–110°C), and weigh as $(C_9H_7OH)_4{\cdot}H_4(GeMo_{12}O_{40})$, or ignite at 500–900°C and weigh as $GeO_2{\cdot}12MoO_3$. In the former case the factor is 0·0311. The accuracy is ±10% for 0·1 mg. Ge, ±3% for 2 mg. and ±1% for 10 mg. Alternatively, dissolve the ppt. in hot H_2O contg. 10 ml. HCl and 10 ml. EtOH, dil. with H_2O, boil for 2 min., add 1 g. $H_2C_2O_4$, cool, dil. to 100–150 ml. with H_2O, add a 0·5–1 ml. excess of $0{\cdot}1N$ $KBrO_3$–KBr soln. and 0·2 g. KI and titrate with $0{\cdot}01N$ $Na_2S_2O_3$.

Bromoxine has also been proposed.[17] Acridine is suitable for 1–10 mg. Ge; SO_4^{2-}, ClO_4^-, Cl^-, $C_2O_4^{2-}$, tartrate, P, Si, As, W, V interfere.[18] The method involving pyridine[19] is inaccurate (Davis and Morgan,[3] Hecht and Bartelmus[15]). These bases can also be applied in conjunction with tungstate.[17]

(e) Molybdenum blue formation is useful for colorimetric Ge detn.[20, 21] For < 0·4 mg. Ge in 20 ml. neutral (litmus) soln., add 0·75 ml. $4N$ H_2SO_4, 1 ml. 10% $(NH_4)_2MoO_4$ (stored in polythene or a paraffined bottle), 2·5 ml. Fe soln. (5 ml. 2% $(NH_4)_2Fe(SO_4)_2$ contg. 1·5 ml. $4N$ H_2SO_4/500 ml., mixed with 20 ml. $4N$ H_2SO_4) and dil. to 25 ml. with H_2O. Measure the blue color immediately at 830 mμ. The error is ±2%. The procedure has been applied to rocks.

NOTES. (1) Interferences are Ba, Bi, Fe^{3+}, Pb, SiO_3^{2-}, VO_3^- and PO_4^{3-}, F^- (>100 p.p.m.). No interference arises from Al, Cd, Ca, Cr, Cu, Fe^{2+}, Mg, Mn, Ni, Ag, Zn, NH_4^+, AcO^-, AsO_4^{3-}, Br^-, Cl^-, ClO_3^-, NO_3^-, $C_2O_4^{2-}$, WO_4^{2-} (500 p.p.m. of the last 3) or citrate.

(2) The color deepens with time, hence the conditions must be adhered to. Other reducing agents which may be applied are hydroquinone,[22] $SnCl_2$,[23] ascorbic acid[24] (see also p. 430) and diphenylcarbazone.[25] The reduced molybdate reagent (see p. 430) is also suitable for Ge (<200 μg).

(3) 0·25–3 mg. Ge can be detd. without a reductant.[21, 26] Add 30 ml. AcOH, dil. to 80 ml. with H_2O, add 10 ml. 2·5% $(NH_4)_2MoO_4$, dil. to 100 ml. with H_2O and measure at 440 mμ within 15 min. Extn. is also possible (see p. 430).

(4) Molybdovanadate is also applicable.[27]

(f) Phenylfluorone is used colorimetrically for < 40 μg. Ge in 10 ml. soln.[7, 8, 28] (see also Cluley[3]). Add 1·5 ml. 1:1 H_2SO_4, 10 ml. buffer (900 g. NaOAc in 700 ml. hot H_2O, filtered, mixed with 480 ml. AcOH and dild. to 1 l. with H_2O), 1 ml. 1% gum arabic, 10 ml. reagent (30 mg. heated with 80 ml. EtOH and 5 ml. 1:1 H_2SO_4, cooled and dild. to 100 ml. with EtOH).

After 5 min. dil. to 50 ml. with 1:9 HCl and measure the orange color at 510 mμ.

NOTES. (1) Oxidizing agents and heavy metals interfere; the latter are sepd. by distn.; As and <2·5 mg. F^- can be tolerated.
(2) Other polyhydroxy compds. have been recommended for colorimetry. Dimethylaminophenylfluorone (0·05% in EtOH) is suitable for 0·05–1·2 p.p.m. Ge in 0·5*N* HCl, the color being measured at 510–520 mμ[29]. Other homologs can also be used.
Hematein forms a purple color with 2–40 μg. Ge in 5 ml. soln. at pH 2–4.[5, 30] Add 1 ml. 1% gelatin, 1 ml. reagent (3 g. hematoxylin in 500 ml. H_2O and 200 ml. EtOH mixed with 20 ml. 5% H_2O_2, heated in boiling H_2O for 15 min., cooled and dild. to 1 l. with H_2O); after 45 ± 1 min., dil. to 25 ml. with buffer pH 3·2 (250 ml. 0·1*N* KH-phthalate and 73·5 ml. 0·1*N* HCl dild. to 500 ml. with H_2O), and measure at 550 mμ. Sb, Sn, Pb interfere but Si (<80 p.p.m.) and As do not.
Quercetin reacts with <0·54 μg. Ge/ml. at pH 6·4–7·1 (phosphate buffer) in 40% MeOH soln. if 48 μg. reagent/ml. is added; the color is measured at 410 mμ.[31]
Quinalizarin acetate forms a red color with Ge.[32] Treat the soln. with 1 ml. 0·5% gelatin, 5 ml. 5% $(NH_4)_2C_2O_4$, $H_2C_2O_4$ (to give pH 5) and 2 ml. 1% reagent in MeOH, dil. to 25 ml. with H_2O, and measure at 490 or 510 mμ.
Resacetophenone gives a green fluorescence with Ge under UV light.[33] To 3 ml. reagent (0·5–1 g. in 100 ml. AcOH) and 6 ml. H_3PO_4, add the sample contg. 100 μg. Ge in 0·1–1 ml.; dil. to 10 ml. with H_3PO_4 and measure. B, NO_2^-, NO_3^-, F^-, $Cr_2O_7^{2-}$, Br^-, I^-, ClO_3^- interfere.
3-Hydroxytropolone ($1·5 \times 10^{-4}M$) reacts with <2 μg. Ge/ml. at pH 7.[34]

(g) Miscellaneous gravimetric methods. $MgSO_4$ permits the evaluation of GeS_2 ppts.[1] Boil the ppt. with NH_4OH and H_2O_2, acidify with H_2SO_4, dil. to 100 ml. with H_2O, add 20–25 ml. 2*N* $(NH_4)_2SO_4$ and 15–25 ml. 1*N* $MgSO_4$, and make alk. with NH_4OH, adding 15–20 ml. in excess/100 ml. soln. Boil, cool for 12 hr., filter on a Gooch crucible, wash with 1:9 NH_4OH (< 50 ml. altogether), ignite at 300–800°C and weigh as Mg_2GeO_4. Davis and Morgan[3] found the method inaccurate.

β-Naphthoquinoline and oxalic acid form a ppt. which must be ignited to GeO_2.[35] To 400 ml. soln. contg. 50–75 mg. GeO_2, add 5 g. $H_2C_2O_4$, heat, add 25 ml. reagent (10 g. β-naphthoquinoline and 5 g. $H_2C_2O_4$ in 50 ml. H_2O, heated, filtered and dild. to 500 ml.), filter on paper after 12 hr., wash with dil. H_2SO_4 and ignite.

$BaCl_2$ and tartaric acid react with Ge to form $Ba_2GeC_8H_8O_{14}·2H_2O$ which can be weighed.[36] To the soln. contg. 1 mg. Ge/ml., add 5 ml. reagent (13 g. $BaCl_2$, 14 g. tartaric acid and 240 g. NH_4Cl/l.) and 3·5 ml. NH_4OH; after 10 min., add 0·5–0·6 ml. Me_2CO; after 10 min. filter on a G2 crucible, wash with a soln. contg. 100 ml. Me_2CO and 100 ml. NH_4OH/l. and dry at 100°C.

(h) Miscellaneous titrimetric methods. Mannitol is used in conjunction with NaOH and bromocresol purple indicator (Cluley,[3] Schoeller and Powell[1]).[38] For 1–20 mg. Ge in acidic soln., add 2 drops indicator, make alk. with NaOH, acidify just to yellow with 1*N* H_2SO_4, dil. to 80 ml. with H_2O, boil for 5 min., cool, add 5 drops indicator and adjust to pH 6·2; add 10 g. mannitol and readjust to pH 6·2 with 0·0135*N* NaOH, comparing the color with that of a mixture of 33·9 ml. 1*M* citric acid and 66·1 ml. 0·2*M* Na_2HPO_4 with indicator.

Other polyhydric alcs. have been suggested. With fructose,[37] ppt. Ge with H_2S from 6*N* H_2SO_4 or 3–4*N* HCl soln. and filter after 12 hr. Heat the ppt. on a steam-bath with 0·5*N* NaOH and 5 ml. 3% H_2O_2, cool, add 2 drops phenolphthalein and neutralize with 0·5*N* H_2SO_4, boiling to check the end-point. Cool, neutralize with 0·02*N* acid or alkali, add 0·5 g. fructose, heat on a steam-bath for 30–60 min., add excess 0·02*N* NaOH and back-titrate with 0·02*N* H_2SO_4.

Glycerol may also be used.[38]

Iodometric titration has been proposed.[35] To 25 ml. soln. contg. 10–50 mg. GeO_2, add 20 ml. K_2S soln. (8 g. KOH in 100 ml., satd. with H_2S at 0°C) and 15 ml. 2·5*M* AcOH; after 5 min. pass CO_2 through the soln. until no H_2S remains (ca. 20 min.), dil. with H_2O to 1 l., add excess 0·1*N* I_2 and back-titrate after 15 min. with 0·1*N* $Na_2S_2O_3$ in the usual way.

Iodometric titration as above after reduction with NaH_2PO_2 in 3*N* HCl soln. by boiling for 40–50 min. is also suitable.[39] Reduction with Zn in 25% H_2SO_4 and titration with $KMnO_4$ soln. has been suggested.[40]

(i) Marsh mirror (Aitkenhead and Middleton[3]). The apparatus is as follows: a test-tube contg. 5 g. Zn has a stopper through which is placed a dropping funnel with a 25 cm. stem and an outlet tube connected through a glass filter to a glass tube packed with glass wool; this tube is drawn out on both sides of the packing. The tube is further connected to a Pyrex tube (outer diam. 0·6 cm., length 12 cm.) which is drawn out at both ends, one end being drawn to a 5 cm. long capillary. For an estimation, add 5 ml. HCl at 1 drop/sec. from the funnel and when all air has been removed, apply heat at a point 1·8 cm. from the capillary. Add the distillate contg. 0·001–0·1 mg. Ge and, after 15 min., 5 ml. HCl and compare the length of the mirror with standards.

Electrolytic reduction in alk. soln. has also been used.[6]

References

1. HILLEBRAND and LUNDELL, 241 (297); SCOTT and FURMAN, 429; KIMURA, 435; SCHOELLER and POWELL, 168.
2. The Germanium Research Committee: *Germanium* (1956), Asakura, Tokyo. See also *idem.*, *Japan Analyst*, **5**, 578 (1956).
3. DAVIS, G. R. and MORGAN, G., The Gravimetric Determination of Germanium, *Analyst*, **63**, 388 (1938); AITKENHEAD, W. C. and MIDDLETON, A. R., Determination of Germanium in Minerals and Solutions, *Ind. Eng. Chem., Anal. Ed.*, **10**, 633 (1938); CLULEY, H. J., The

Determination of Germanium, *Analyst*, **76**, 517, 523, 530 (1951); KRAUSE, H. H. and JOHNSON, O. H., Analytical Methods for Germanium, *Anal. Chem.*, **25**, 134 (1953); LUKE, C. L. and CAMPBELL, M. E., Determination of Impurities in Germanium (As, P, Sb, Cu), *ibid.*, 1588.
4. OKA, Y., *Japan Analyst* **3**, 277 (1954).
5. NEWCOMBE, H., *et al.*, *Anal. Chem.*, **23**, 1023 (1951).
6. COASE, S. A., *Analyst*, **59**, 462 (1934).
7. FISCHER, W., *et al.*, *Angew. Chem.*, **66**, 165 (1954); LUKE, C. L. and CAMPBELL, M. E., *Anal. Chem.*, **28**, 1273 (1956).
8. LADENBAUER, I. M., *et al.*, *Mikrochim. Acta*, 118 (1955).
9. DAVIS and MORGAN, *Analyst*, **63**, 388 (1938); WEISSLER, A., *Ind. Eng. Chem.*, *Anal. Ed.*, **16**, 311 (1944); WELCHER, **II**, 160.
10. HOLNESS, H., *Anal. Chim. Acta*, **2**, 254 (1948).
11. NAIR, A. P. M. and IBRAHIM, S. H., *Current Sci.* (*India*), **25**, 10 (1956).
12. VANOSSI, R., *Anales soc. cient. Arg.*, **139**, 29 (1945).
13. BÉVILLARD, P., *Bull. soc. chim. France*, 307 (1954).
14. MUELLER, J. H. and EISNER, E., *Ind. Eng. Chem.*, *Anal. Ed.*, **4**, 134 (1932).
15. DAVIS and MORGAN, *Analyst*, **63**, 388 (1938); WELCHER, **IV**, 234; SCHOELLER and POWELL, 172; HECHT, F. and BARTELMUS, G., *Mikrochemie ver. Mikrochim. Acta*, **36/37**, 466 (1951); FREDERICK, W. J., *et al.*, *Anal. Chem.*, **26**, 1328 (1954) (in coal).
16. ALIMARIN, I. P. and ALEKSEEVA, O. A., *J. Applied Chem.* (*U.S.S.R.*), **12**, 1900 (1939); WELCHER, **I**, 313; HECHT and BARTLEMUS, ref. 15.
17. BARTLEMUS and HECHT, *Mikrochim. Acta*, 148 (1954).
18. SUBBARAMAN, P. R., *J. Sci. Ind. Research* (*India*), **14B**, 640 (1955).
19. WELCHER, **III**, 31.
20. BOLTZ, D. F. and MELLON, M. G., *Anal. Chem.*, **19**, 873 (1947).
21. SANDELL, 334 ff.
22. FISCHER, W. and KEIM, H., *Z. anal. Chem.*, **128**, 128 (1948).
23. ORLIAC, M., *Compt. rend.*, **221**, 500 (1945).
24. SENISE, P. and SANT'AGOSTINO, L., *Mikrochim. Acta*, 1445 (1956).
25. DESHMUKH, G. S., *Zhur. Anal. Khim.*, **10**, 61 (1955).
26. KITSON, R. E. and MELLON, M. G., *Ind. Eng. Chem.*, *Anal. Ed.*, **16**, 128 (1944).
27. SHAKHOVA, Z. F. and MOTORKINA, R. K., *Zhur. Anal. Khim.*, **11**, 698 (1956).
28. SCHNEIDER, JR., W. A. and SANDELL, E. B., *Mikrochim. Acta*, 263 (1954); OKA, Y., *et al.*, *Japan Analyst*, **3**, 389 (1954); *J. Chem. Soc. Japan*, **76**, 874 (1955) (5 ml. 0·25% polyvinyl alc. better).
29. KIMURA, K., *et al.*, *Bull. Chem. Soc. Japan*, **29**, 635, 640, 812 (1956).
30. Also see MATSUURA, J., *J. Chem. Soc. Japan*, **74**, 337 (1953).
31. OKA, Y. and MATSUO, S., *J. Chem. Soc. Japan*, **76**, 610 (1955).
32. NAIR, C. K. N. and GUPTA, J., *J. Sci. Ind. Research* (*India*), **11B**, 274 (1952); STRICKLAND, E. H., *Analyst*, **80**, 548 (1955).
33. RAJU, N. A. and RAO, G. G., *Nature*, **174**, 100 (1954).
34. OKA, Y. and MATSUO, S., *J. Chem. Soc. Japan*, **77**, 1663 (1956).
35. WILLARD, H. H. and ZUEHLKE, C. W., *Ind. Eng. Chem.*, *Anal. Ed.*, **16**, 322 (1944); WELCHER, **III**, 59.
36. SCHRAUZER, G. N., *Mikrochim. Acta*, 124 (1953).
37. SAITO, K., *J. Chem. Soc. Japan*, **73**, 457, 519, 526, 573 (1952).
38. WELCHER, **I**, 103, 114.
39. IVANOV-EMIN, B. N., *Zavodskaya Lab.*, **13**, 161 (1947).
40. BARDET, J. and TCHAKIRIAN, A., *Compt. rend.*, **186**, 637 (1928).

29

MOLYBDENUM

The principal sources for this chapter are mentioned in ref. 1. Review papers have been published on the analytical chemistry of molybdenum and tungsten,[2] on the determination of molybdenum[3] and on the analysis of molybdenum-base alloys.[4] The chemistry and technology of molybdenum have formed the subject of a monograph.[5]

In analyses concerning molybdenum it should be remembered that solutions containing molybdenum effervesce strongly when evaporated; this can be prevented by passing air through the solution. Oxalate ions interfere in many molybdenum reactions,

Attack

A general method of attack is outlined in Table 31.[1]

(a) Molybdenite. Add 25 ml. satd. $KClO_3$ in HNO_3 and heat slowly until clear; add 0·5 g. $KClO_3$, evap. nearly to dryness, add 15 ml. HCl, evap., and add H_2O. Alternatively, treat with HNO_3 or aqua regia; or fuse with Na_2CO_3 and KNO_3 or NaOH; or fuse with Na_2O_2 and ext. with H_2O and $(NH_4)_2CO_3$.

(b) Molybdates. Treat with HCl, HNO_3 or H_2SO_4 contg. 1–2 drops HF; or fuse with Na_2CO_3.

(c) Wulfenite. Treat with H_2SO_4. Dissolve Powelite in HNO_3 and molybdite in dil. HCl or H_2SO_4.

(d) Steel. Treat 1–5 g. steel with 1:3 $HNO_3 + HClO_4$, add HF and $K_2Cr_2O_7$, evap., add H_2O and filter. Alternatively, warm with 100 ml. 1:5 H_2SO_4, add 25 ml. 25% $(NH_4)_2S_2O_8$, boil for 8–10 min., add 5 g. tartaric acid, NH_4OH, H_2SO_4, and pass H_2S (see below); or treat with HCl and HNO_3, add $HClO_4$, evap. and filter.

(e) Fe–W. For 2–10 g. add 100 ml. 1:1 HCl and 20 ml. 1:1 HNO_3, evap. just to dryness, add 10 ml. HCl and 50 ml. H_2O and boil; filter and wash with 1:9 HCl. Fuse the residue with Na_2CO_3, leach with H_2O, filter and wash with hot H_2O and once or twice with a little dil. H_2SO_4. Combine the filtrates, add 5 g. tartaric acid, neutralize with H_2SO_4, add 5 ml. H_2SO_4, boil, pass H_2S, etc.

Separation

H_2S allows sepn. of Mo from group III metals, V, PO_4^{3-}. For < 30 mg. MoO_3 in 100 ml. 0·02–0·1N mineral acid soln., pass H_2S rapidly for 5–10 min. boil for 10 min., cool for 10 min., filter through paper and wash with 0·02N H_2SO_4 contg. H_2S. 0·5 mg. MoO_3 passes into the filtrate but can be recovered by passing H_2S, boiling and letting stand for 1 day. This method and general pptn. with H_2S have been critically studied.[6] If much Fe^{3+} is present, 2–3 g. NH_4HSO_3 is added, SO_2 boiled out and then H_2S is passed.

Mo is sepd. from W and V in tartrate soln. Add $(NH_4)_2$-tartrate to the ammoniacal soln., boil, pass H_2S for 10 min., add dil. H_2SO_4 to give a 2% v/v soln., pass H_2S for 10 min., place on a steam-bath for 2 hr., filter on paper and wash with dil. H_2SO_4 contg. 20 g./l. tartaric acid and H_2S.

In an alternative method,[2] treat 10–15 ml. neutral soln. with 10 ml. 50% $HCOONH_4$, 10 ml. 30% tartaric acid, 100 ml. H_2S soln. (satd. at 0°C) and 10 ml. 2N HCOOH at 60°C for 1 hr.; add filter paper pulp, and 10 ml. 24N HCOOH and place in boiling H_2O for 30 min. Filter and wash with 5% HCOOH.

Sb^{5+} is useful for concn. purposes with H_2S.[7]

$(NH_4)_2S$ permits sepn. from Pb, Cd, Ag and partially from Cu. Na_2S in NH_4OH soln. seps. Mo from U, Ti, etc. Na_2S in NaOH soln. seps. Mo from Cu, Pb, Bi, etc.

NaOH allows sepn. of Mo from Fe; if much Fe is present, the final concn. of NaOH must exceed 10%. Treatment with Fe^{3+} and NH_4OH seps. Mo from Fe^{2+}, P, As, Sb, Bi, Sn, Ge, rare earths and partly from Ti, V, W; Fe^{3+} is added in an amt. $\geqslant$ 10 times the As and the soln. is poured into 1:4 NH_4OH and boiled. By similar treatment with $(NH_4)_2S$, Mo is sepd. from most elements. Sepn. from Cu is achieved by copptn. with MnO_2.

Treatment with cupron in 20% v/v H_2SO_4 soln. or 5% v/v HCl, HNO_3 or H_3PO_4 soln. seps. Mo from Fe, Re, etc. (see under Determination); the complex can be extd. with $CHCl_3$ from < 2M HCl soln.

$CHCl_3$ extn. of xanthate gives sepn. from W, of dithizonate from Cu, etc., and of cupferrate (from solns. of pH < 1·6) from Al, etc.

Extn. with Et_2O from 1:1 HCl soln. contg. $FeCl_3$ seps. Mo from Cu, Mn, Ni, Co, Cr, Al, etc., and from

TABLE 31. Attack of Mo Minerals

Place a 0·5–1 g. sample (or up to 5 g.) of 100 mesh contg. 0·2–0·3 g. Mo in a 150 ml. beaker, cover, add 10–35 ml. HNO_3 and 7–10 ml. H_2SO_4, heat and evap. to fumes. Cool, add 40–50 ml. H_2O, boil, cool, filter on paper and wash 8–10 times with H_2O, 3–4 times with hot 1 : 3 NH_4OH and 4–5 times with hot H_2O (Note 1).

R_1: Ignite in a porcelain crucible below 450°C, cool, transfer to a Pt crucible, add 0·5 ml. H_2SO_4, 2 ml. HNO_3 and 5 ml. HF and evap. to dryness. Fuse with Na_2CO_3, ext. with H_2O and add to F_2

F_1: Add 0·3–0·4 g. $Fe_2(SO_4)_3$ (Fe >10 As) (Note 2). Almost neutralize with NH_4OH, heat to boiling, pour into 75 ml. of hot 1 : 6 NH_4OH, add paper pulp, filter on paper and wash with hot H_2O.

- P_2: Dissolve in a small excess of hot 1 : 1 H_2SO_4, heat and pour into hot 1 : 6 NH_4OH
  - P_3(As, W, V)
  - F_3
- F_2

F_3 + F_2: Add 3 g. powd. tartaric acid (Note 3), warm, pass H_2S, filter and wash with dil. $(NH_4)_2S$.

P_4: Discard

F_4: Neutralize with 1 : 1 H_2SO_4, add 1 ml. acid/100 ml. soln. and digest for 15 min. near the b.p. Filter and wash with 1 : 99 H_2SO_4 and H_2S soln. contg. tartaric acid.

P_5: Transfer to a 250 ml. beaker, add 10 ml. HNO_3, 10 ml. H_2SO_4, heat, evap. to fumes, cool, add 5 ml. HNO_3, evap. to fumes, repeat until colorless and cool. Add 5 ml. H_2O and a few drops 2·5% $KMnO_4$, evap. to fumes, cool, add 75 ml. H_2O, boil for 2–3 min., add 2 g. Zn and let cool until the Zn almost completely dissolves. Filter on a Gooch crucible and wash with 1 : 99 H_2SO_4.

F_5: Add 15 ml. HNO_3, evap. to fumes, cool, add 5 ml. HNO_3, evap. to fumes, repeat and cool. Add H_2O, 2 g. tartaric acid, a 5 ml. excess of NH_4OH and H_2S. Heat at 40–60°C for 1 hr., filter and ppt. MoS_3 as above. Add to P_5 or det. separately.

P_6 (Cu)

F_6: Jones reductor and $KMnO_4$ titration.

NOTES. (1) For wulfenite, wash R_1 with hot NH_4OAc (1 : 1 NH_4OH neutralized with AcOH), ignite, add HF and H_2SO_4, evap. to dryness, fuse with $K_2S_2O_7$ and treat with H_2O, tartaric acid and H_2S.
(2) This is hardly necessary for molybdenite. If much As is present, evap. the sample to fumes with HNO_3 and H_2SO_4, cover, add 20 ml. satd. SO_2 soln., evap. to 10 ml., add 10 ml. SO_2 soln. and 50 ml. HCl, evap. to 10–20 ml., add 10 ml. HNO_3, evap. to fumes and proceed as before.
(3) For molybdenite, 1 g. suffices.

V if citric acid is added. Evap. the Et_2O phase, add 10 ml. dil. H_2SO_4, evap. to fumes, cool, add 100 ml. H_2O and 2–3 g. NH_4HSO_3, boil, pass H_2S, etc. 99% Extn. is possible with 1:1 Et_2O + BuOAc, AmOH or BuOH (see Chapter 16, p. 136).

For extn. of acetylacetonate with $CHCl_3$, see Chapter 10, Section 2.

Treatment with hot $Pb(ClO_4)_2$ of hot 2% $HClO_4$ solns. seps. Mo from V and Cr^{3+}.

Mo is sepd. from V by treatment with Mn^{2+} (Pigott[8]): to the ammoniacal soln. add NH_4Cl and reagent (25 g. $MnCl_2 \cdot 4H_2O$ and 25 g. NH_4Cl/l.), boil for 2 min., cool rapidly, filter through Whatman No. 40 paper and wash with hot H_2O.

Distn. from HCl soln. gives only incomplete sepn. from As.

Magnesia mixture seps. Mo from As and P; if Sn, Sb, Ge, V are present, citric or tartaric acid must be added.

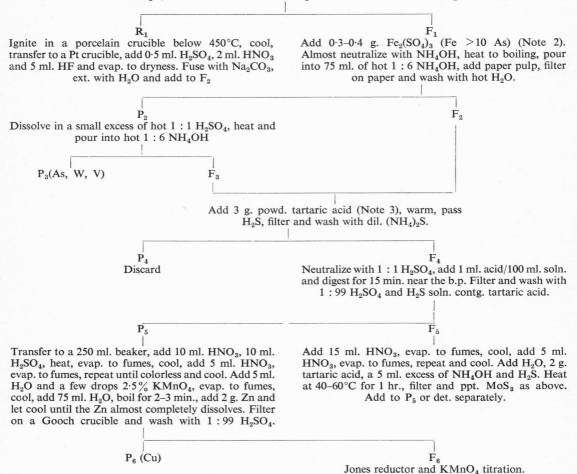

Pb allows sepn. from Sb; add 5 g. Pb to the soln. contg. 20–25 ml. HCl/100 ml. and boil for 30 min.; NO_3^- and SO_4^{2-} interfere. Mo is detd. in the filtrate after oxidation with HNO_3. Treatment with Fe in acidic solns. seps. Mo from Sb and As.

Fusion with Na_2CO_3 and extn. with H_2O seps. Mo from Fe, Zn, Ca, Ba. Fusion with Na_2CO_3 and Na_2O_2 and extn. with H_2O seps. Mo and W; add $CaCl_2$ to the extract, filter, add HCl and det. W; det. Mo in the filtrate as $CaMoO_4$.[9]

Treatment with H_2SO_4 allows sepn. from Pb, electrolysis gives sepn. from Cu, and treatment with $(NH_4)_2C_2O_4$ followed by repptn. seps. Mo from Ca.

Mo is sepd. from many elements by heating in a stream of HCl or $CCl_4 + CO_2$ at 600°C.[10]

Determination

The standard methods are titration with $KMnO_4$ or Ce^{4+} or gravimetric detn. as $PbMoO_4$. The H_2S method is convenient. The colorimetric methods involving thiocyanate or dithiol are satisfactory but the colors formed are said to be unstable. The phenylhydrazine method appears to be excellent. Oxine and cupron are the most suitable reagents for the determination of milligram amounts of Mo.

(a) Redox titration.[1] The usual procedure is to pass the soln. through a Jones reductor and titrate with 0·03–0·1*N* $KMnO_4$ which has been standardized against $Na_2C_2O_4$. Treat the Mo^{6+} soln. contg. 3–10% v/v H_2SO_4 with $KMnO_4$ until pink and pass the soln. through the reductor into an excess of Fe^{3+} (100 g. $Fe_2(SO_4)_3$, 150 ml. H_3PO_4 and 20 ml. 1:1 H_2SO_4/l.). Titrate.

NOTES. (1) Fe, Cr, Ti, As, Sb, V, W, U, Nb, HNO_3, org. compds. and polythionic acids interfere.

(2) The method has been applied to Fe–Mo and to Ti alloys.[11] Mo and V can be detd. simultaneously; SO_2 reduces V^{5+} to V^{4+} only, while Zn reduces the ions to Mo^{3+} and V^{2+} (Scott and Furman[1]). HCl solns. can be used provided that Zimmermann–Reinhardt soln. is added before the titration.

(3) Reduction with Zn/Hg[12] in 2*N* H_2SO_4 soln. is complete in 60 sec., and titration can be done immediately after sepn. or after passing air to oxidize Mo^{3+} to Mo^{5+}.

Titration with 0·01–0·1*N* Ce^{4+} in presence of ferroin or Ba-diphenylamine sulfonate or phenylanthranilic acid indicator is suitable for 0·3–100 mg. Mo in 3–10% H_2SO_4 soln. after passage through the Jones reductor.[13] The Ag reductor yields Mo^{5+} only from 2*N* HCl solns. contg. 3 ml. H_3PO_4 at 60–80°C.[14] Reduction with 25 ml. Hg in 3*N* HCl soln. [15] and with Zn–Hg in 2·4*N* H_2SO_4 soln. under CO_2 [16] have also been applied; in the latter case excess Ce^{4+} is titrated with Fe^{2+} to methyl red indicator.

Titration with 0·02–0·1*N* $K_2Cr_2O_7$ to Ba-diphenylamine sulfonate indicator can be used.[13]

Reduction with Cd–Hg in 6–7*N* HCl soln. yields Mo^{3+} which is titrated to Mo^{5+} with 0·1*N* Cu^{2+} in presence of 0·5% safranine indicator.[17] No interference arises from Fe, 50 mg. Ni, 30 mg. Co, 15 mg. Cu, 2 mg. W, 0·7 mg. As, 2 mg. Ti, 3 mg. V or 6 mg. Cr.

Reduction with Zn and titration with methylene blue soln. from pink through green to blue is applicable in presence of Fe, Cu, Al, Cr, P.[18]

An iodometric method is possible.[15] To the soln. contg. 20–25 ml. HCl in 60 ml. soln., add 0·2–0·6 g. KI, evap. to 25 ml., dil. to 125 ml. with H_2O, add 1 g. tartaric acid and neutralize with NaOH. Add $NaHCO_3$, excess 0·1*N* I_2, and back-titrate after 2 hr. with 0·1*N* As^{3+}. Alternatively, after the above dilution to 125 ml., add 0·5 g. $MnSO_4$ followed by 0·1*N* $KMnO_4$ (until pink) and the same vol. of 0·1*N* As^{3+}; then add 3 g. tartaric acid and excess $NaHCO_3$ and titrate with 0·1*N* I_2.

Titration with V^{5+} soln. is used in conjunction with Sn^{2+} reduction.[19] To 100 ml. neutral soln. add 10–20 ml. HCl and a small excess of 0·2*N* $SnCl_2$ in 2*N* HCl; then add the same vol. of 0·2*N* Br_2 in 0·1*N* KBr and the same vol. of As^{3+} soln. (0·5 g. As_2O_3 and 10 g. Na_2CO_3/l.); add 2 g. NaF and 3 drops of diphenylamine indicator and titrate with 0·1*N* NH_4VO_3.

Other titrations which have been applied involve $TiCl_3$ with a potentiometric end-point[20] and $K_3Fe(CN)_6$ with cacotheline indicator.[21]

(b) $Pb(OAc)_2$ can be used either gravimetrically or titrimetrically.[1] For < 0·1 g. Mo^{6+}/200 ml. soln. contg. 5 ml. AcOH and 25 ml. 50% NH_4OAc, boil the soln. and slowly add a 2–5 ml. excess of hot 4% $Pb(OAc)_2$ in 1% AcOH using 0·5% tannin as external indicator. Place on a steam-bath for 10–60 min., add filter pulp, filter on paper and wash with hot 2–3% NH_4NO_3 or NH_4OAc. Dry at 580–740°C (>505°C) and weigh as $PbMoO_4$.

NOTE. Cu, Co, Ni, Mn, Zn, Mg, Hg do not interfere. If SO_4^{2+} is absent, NH_4OAc is unnecessary.

The detn. can be done in HCl soln.: add a small excess of $Pb(OAc)_2$, heat, add NH_4OAc and proceed as before with filtration.

NOTE. No interference arises from Al, U, As, Cd, Cu, Co, Ca, etc. Interferences are much SO_4^{2-}, mineral acids, tartaric acid, Fe, Cr, W, V, SiO_2, Sn, Ti, Zr, Bi, etc. Small amts. of AsO_4^{3-} and PO_4^{3-} do not interfere if NH_4Cl is added:[8] neutralize the soln. (250 ml.) which is alk. in NaOH with AcOH, add 20 ml. AcOH and 30–35 g. NH_4Cl, boil, add filter pulp and 10 ml. 8% reagent, boil for 1 min., filter and wash with 2% NH_4OAc. If much P is present, dissolve the ppt. in 20 ml. 20% NaOH, dil. with H_2O to 150 ml., boil for 5 min., filter, wash with hot H_2O, add AcOH as above, boil, add 3 ml. reagent, etc.

Many indicators can be used for the titration of Mo^{6+} with Pb^{2+} soln. Diphenylcarbazone has been used with $Pb(NO_3)_2$ titrant in media contg. a few drops of HNO_3.[22] Tannin can be applied externally.[1] See Table 10, p. 25, for various adsorption indicators. Amperometric titration has been suggested.[23]

(c) Other inorganic reagents. $SrCl_2$ is used gravimetrically;[24] to 40 ml. soln. which is pink to phenolphthalein, add 0·5 ml. AcOH and 10 ml. NaOAc to give pH 6–8, boil, add 10% reagent, filter, wash with 25% EtOH and ignite to $SrMoO_4$.

$BaCl_2$ has been suggested for gravimetric detn., the ppt. being ignited above 320°C.[25] $CaCl_2$ is used gravimetrically with drying above 230°C, or titrimetrically after dissolving the ppt. in HCl, evapg. to dryness, heating and filtering, the final titration being with EDTA in presence of murexide indicator.[26] $Cd(NO_3)_2$ ppts. MoO_4^{2-} at pH 6–7, the drying temp. being 82–250°C.[27]

TlOAc is used gravimetrically for < 30 mg. MoO_3 in < 30 ml. soln.[2] Add 1 ml. NH_4OH, 60 ml. EtOH, heat to 70–80°C, add 10 ml. 3% TlOAc in EtOH and heat at 60–70°C for 1 hr. Filter on a Gooch crucible, wash with a mixt. of 60 ml. EtOH, 30 ml. H_2O and 1 ml. NH_4OH, dry at 110°C for 1 hr. and weigh as Tl_2MoO_4.

$AgNO_3$ can also be applied gravimetrically (Scott and Furman[1]). To 50 ml. soln. which is acid to methyl orange, add 1 g. NaOAc, boil, add reagent until the ppt. coagulates, filter on a Gooch crucible, wash 8 times with 5 ml. 0·5% $AgNO_3$ and thrice with 5 ml. EtOH, dry at 250–500°C (90–250°C) and weigh as Ag_2MoO_4.

$Hg_2(NO_3)_2$ ppts. MoO_4^{2-} in slightly alk. (Na_2CO_3) soln., the ppt. being finally ignited to MoO_3 at 600°C (780–880°C); Cr, V, W, P, As interfere.[1] Neither of the last 2 methods is very accurate.[3]

(d) Cupron provides a useful gravimetric procedure[1, 28] which has been applied to steels.[11] For <0·15 g. Mo^{6+} in 200 ml. soln. contg. 10 ml. H_2SO_4, cool to 5–10°C, and add 10 ml. 2% cupron in EtOH followed by 5 ml. for each 10 mg. Mo; add Br_2 water until the soln. is pale yellow (usually 10 ml. is enough), add 5 ml. reagent, leave for only 15 min., add filter pulp, filter on Whatman No. 42 paper and wash with a soln. contg. 25–50 ml. reagent and 10 ml. H_2SO_4/l. Ignite at 530–550°C (570–789°C) and weigh as MoO_3.

NOTES. (1) If VO_3^- or CrO_4^{2-} is present, add SO_2 water and boil before cooling and adding the reagent.
(2) Pd, Nb, Ta, SiO_2, F^- and tartrate interfere. The interference of W is corrected for by treating the ignited ppt. with NH_4OH, HCl and cinchonine, filtering after 12 hr., igniting to WO_3 at 580°C and subtracting the amt. found.
(3) Better results can be obtained by repptg. as the Pb salt. Return the ppt. to the original beaker, add 10 ml. NH_4OH, 10 ml. 30% H_2O_2, dil. to 75 ml. with H_2O and boil out the H_2O_2. Filter through the same paper, wash with hot 2:98 NH_4OH and pour into 100 ml. reagent soln. (4 g. $Pb(OAc)_2$ in 275 ml. H_2O, 500 ml. NH_4OH, 900 ml. 50% AcOH and 275 ml. HCl). Filter on a Gooch crucible and ignite as usual.
(4) A titrimetric (photometric end-point)[29] method is possible.

(e) Oxine is suitable for 1–50 mg. Mo in 50–100 ml. soln. which is < 5*N* in AcOH.[30, 31] Add excess 4% oxine in Me_2CO, boil off Me_2CO, cool, filter on a glass crucible, wash with warm H_2O, dry at 140–150°C (40–270°C) and weigh as $MoO_2(C_9H_6ON)_2$. Alternatively dissolve in H_2SO_4, dil. to 150–200 ml. with H_2O while cooling, and titrate with 0·1*N* $KBrO_3$–KBr. The optimum pH of pptn. is 3·3–7·6.

NOTES. (1) No interference is caused by Be, Mg, Zn, Cd, Hg, Bi, U, Mn, Re, PO_4^{3-}.
(2) The ppt. contains $\frac{1}{2}H_2O$ on drying below 138°C and is anhydrous between 138 and 326°C.[32]
(3) If EDTA is added, only W, U, V^{5+} and Ti interfere; some V^{5+} is reduced to V^{4+}, which does not interfere, on boiling with EDTA.[33] Pptn. in presence of EDTA and Na_2SO_3 allows sepn. from V.[34]

(f) H_2S provides gravimetric or colorimetric detns.[1, 3, 6, 11] Pptn. has been dealt with under Separation; the ppt. is ignited to MoO_3 at 500°C (485–780°C) in a porcelain crucible by elec. heating.

NOTES. (1) For the colorimetric detn. see ref. 35.
(2) Other reagents can be substituted for H_2S. Thioacetic acid[36] and thioacetamide[37] have been described. Thiosulfate is used[38] with NaH_2PO_2: for 50 mg. Mo in 50 ml. soln. add 8 ml. HCl, dil. to 150–175 ml. with H_2O, boil, add 20–25 ml. 10% $(NH_4)_2S_2O_3$ and 10–15 ml. 10% NaH_2PO_2 and stir for 5 min.; if the supernate is red-brown, add a little HCl, and boil gently for 10 min. Filter on Whatman No. 41 paper, wash with 1:99 HCl and hot H_2O and ignite to MoO_3 at 550–575°C.

(g) KSCN or NaSCN is applied colorimetrically with $SnCl_2$ for < 1 mg. Mo in 50 ml. soln. contg. ca. 2·5 ml. H_2SO_4 or $HClO_4$.[1, 39] Add 1 g. tartaric acid, 25 ml. 8% $Fe_2(SO_4)_3$ in 20% H_2SO_4 if Fe is absent from the sample, cool to 15°C, add 10 ml. 5% SCN^- and 5–10 ml. 35% $SnCl_2$ (350 g. in 200 ml. 1:1 HCl, dild. to 1 l. with H_2O, cooled and treated with Sn). Shake for 1 min. and compare the colors. Alternatively, ext. with 15, 10, 10 . . . ml. portions of Et_2O or cyclohexanol (pre-equilibrated with SCN^- and $SnCl_2$), combine, and measure the vermilion color at 475 mμ.

NOTES. (1) The procedure has been applied to steels with BuOAc or iso-Pr_2O extn. and to Ti and its alloys.[11] For details, see also ref. 40.
(2) No interference is caused by SiO_2, Fe, Al, Ti, Th, Nb, Ta, Mn, Cu, As, Cd, Ni, Co, Cr, V, U, PO_4^{3-}. Interferences are Hg, Re, Pt, Rh, much F^- (>100 Mo) and W (>50 Mo; add tartaric or citric acid and H_3PO_4); NO_3^- is removed by evapn. with $HClO_4$.
(3) The sensitivity decreases[41] if Cl^- is present before the addn. of SCN^- because the color depends on the formation of $[MoO(SCN)_5]^{2-}$. In HCl soln. the color deepens[42] in presence of NO_3^-. Fe^{3-} and $HClO_4$ stabilize the color. Extn. solvents which have been suggested are Et_2O, iso-Pr_2O, BuOAc, AmOAc, cyclohexanol and tributyl phosphate.[43] The color is stabilized by the addn. of 15 ml. butyl cellosolve/100 ml. soln.[44] The method is

useful for detn. of Mo in steels (Pigott[1])[39, 45] and in rocks.[39, 45]
(4) Various other reductants have been used. Cu_2Cl_2 and KI with Na_2SO_3 provide the most sensitive methods.
(*i*) With Cu_2Cl_2, treat <1 ml. H_2SO_4 or <2 ml. HCl soln. with 5 drops 0·1*M* Cu_2Cl_2 (add 10% $SnCl_2$ in HCl to $CuCl_2$ in HCl until the soln. is faintly green), a few drops of H_2O, and 15 ml. 1·0*M* NH_4SCN (anhyd., recrystd., in Me_2CO). Dil. to 24 ml. with H_2O, add 5 drops 10% $SnCl_2$ in HCl, dil. to 25 ml. with H_2O and measure at 460 mμ (ϵ = 18 700); the color is stable. Much Fe interferes but can be sepd. on Dowex 50; W does not interfere.
For 8*M* HCl soln., add 1 ml. 0·1*M* Cu_2Cl_2 and 3·0 ml. 3·0*M* NH_4SCN, ext. twice with 10 ml. Et_2O, dil. to 25 ml. with Et_2O and measure at 470 mμ (ϵ = 19 500); 100% Mo reacts as against 50% when $SnCl_2$ alone is used.[46]
(*ii*) Me_2CO can be used for 5–1000 μg. Mo in 20 ml. soln.:[47] add 7 ml. HCl, 3 ml. 10% KSCN, 15 ml. Me_2CO, heat at 60–70°C for over 20 min., cool, dil. with H_2O to 50 ml. and measure at 420 mμ. Below 100 p.p.m. Fe does not interfere if heating is continued for over 1 hr.
(*iii*) KI and Na_2SO_3 are suitable for 0·06–0·6 mg. Mo in 10 ml. acidic (H_2SO_4) soln. Add 35 ml. 3*N* HCl, 3 ml. 20% KSCN, 1 g. KI, 1 ml. 1% Na_2SO_3, dil. to 50 ml. with 3*N* HCl and measure at 520–560 mμ after 10 min.[48] The technique has been applied to scheelite;[49] <7 mg. W can be present, if 5 ml. 30% $(NH_4)_3$-citrate is added.
(*iv*) Thiourea has been proposed;[50] N_2H_4 is suitable for 1–6 p.p.m. Mo with iso-BuOH extn. and measurement at 320 mμ.[51] In the latter method, Ti, V, Cu and $Fe^{2+, 3+}$ interfere.
(5) KSCN is used gravimetrically in conjunction with cinchonine. For steels,[52] treat with 200 ml. 4·5*N* H_2SO_4 and 20 drops 30% H_2O_2, boil for 1 min. and add 100 ml. H_2O, 20 ml. 5% KSCN, 40 ml. $SnCl_2$ (500 g. in 400 ml. HCl dild. to 2 l. with H_2O), and 70 ml. cinchonine soln. (125 g./l. 6*N* HCl). Filter on paper, wash with a soln. contg. NH_4SCN and cinchonine and ignite the red ppt. ($H_{33}MoS_{13}C_{22}N_5O_7$?) to MoO_3. Cu interferes but Cr, Fe, Mn and V do not.

(h) Dithiol provides a good colorimetric detn.[53, 54] To the HCl soln. add an equal vol. H_2O, 5 ml. 20% w/v $SnCl_2$ in 1:1 HCl and 10 ml. 0·5% w/w dithiol in AmOAc and shake for 10–15 min. Sep., wash with 1:1 HCl, sep., dil. to 20 ml. with AmOAc, wash twice with 15 ml. 4:1 HCl, filter on Whatman No. 41 paper and wash with 1–2 ml. AmOAc. Dil. to 25 ml. with AmOAc and measure the green color at 690 mμ.

NOTES. (1) W does not interfere.
(2) For W ores,[55] use a reagent contg. 1 g. dithiol and 5 ml. thioglycolic acid in 300 ml. 1% NaOH; ext. with light petroleum from a soln. contg. H_3PO_4, citrate and Fe^{3+}. W is corrected for from the absorbancy at 630 mμ.

(i) Miscellaneous gravimetric methods. *o*-Dianisidine is used in neutral (to methyl orange) soln.[56] Add reagent (0·5 g. *o*-dianisidine and 8 ml. AcOH mixed with 8–10 ml. H_2O, cooled and dild. to 200 ml.) in 40–60% excess; after 3 hr. filter on a glass crucible, wash with H_2O, and dry at 80°C before weighing $(C_{14}H_{14}O_2N_2)_2$-$(Mo_2O_5)_2$. Alternatively ignite to MoO_3 at 600–780°C.

Vanillylidene–benzidine ppts. Mo but the ppt. must be ignited. β-Naphthoquinoline has also been suggested.[57]

$[Cr(NH_3)_5Cl]Cl_2$ is used with H_2S.[58] For 0·1 g. Mo in 20 ml. soln. add 1 ml. NH_4OH followed by H_2S to give a red color; pour into 50–80 ml. reagent (0·3% in slightly ammoniacal soln.), dil. with H_2O to 150–200 ml. and stir. Filter on a Gooch crucible, wash first with a soln. contg. 0·8 g. reagent, 0·5 ml. NH_4OH and some H_2S/l., and then with 95% EtOH, EtOH and Et_2O. Dry the brick-red ppt. *in vacuo* and weigh as $[Cr(NH_3)_5Cl][MoS_4]$.

(j) Electrodeposition.[59] Add 0·5 g. NH_4OAc to 150 ml. neutral Mo-contg. soln., insert a Cu-plated Pt gauze cathode, heat to 70°C and pass 0·2 amp. for 5 hr.; add 1 ml. AcOH after 2·5 hr. to adjust the pH to 5·4. Wash twice with H_2O and then with EtOH; heat on wire-gauze over the Bunsen burner and weigh as $Mo_2O_3 \cdot 4\frac{1}{2}H_2O$.

(k) Phenylhydrazine hydrochloride allows colorimetric detn.[60] of 20–100 μg. Mo^{6+}. Pour the test soln. into 50 ml. 50% AcOH, add 1·5 g. reagent, boil for 5 min., cool, add 25 ml. AcOH, dil. to 100 ml. with H_2O, and measure the red color at 505 mμ.

NOTE. Fe^{2+}, Mn, Ni and P do not interfere. Fe^{3+}, V, W, Cu and Co interfere if the amts. present are resp. 20, 1, 4, 20 and 20 times more than that of Mo; Fe^{3+} is avoided by passing the soln. through a Jones reductor.

(l) Thioglycolic acid is used colorimetrically[61] for 20–75 p.p.m. Mo in 5 ml. soln. of pH 3·5–4·5. Add 5 ml. buffer soln. (50 ml. 1*N* NaOAc and 35 ml. 1*N* HCl/250 ml., 7 ml. reagent (5% soln. neutralized with NH_4OH), 5 ml. 2% $KClO_3$, dil. to 25 ml. and measure the yellow color at 365 mμ.

NOTES. (1) Interferences are 0·5 p.p.m. Al, 1 p.p.m. W, Cu, Hg^{2+}, 2 p.p.m. Bi, Ce, Pb, Ti, U^{6+}, V^{4+}, 4 p.p.m. Co, Sb, 6 p.p.m. SiO_2, 8 p.p.m. Au, Be, Sn^{2+}, 10 p.p.m. As^{3+}, Mg, Sn^{4+}, 20 p.p.m. Ni, 50 p.p.m. Fe and any amt. of Cr or Hg^{+}.
(2) In 1:5 HCl soln. only Cu and large amts. of Cr interfere. The color intensity remains almost const. in 1–25% v/v HCl or in 5–30% $HClO_4$. For steels, evap. 0·2 g. to fumes with 5 ml. $HClO_4$, dil. with H_2O to 16 ml., add Al strip to remove Cu, boil, add 50% $SnCl_2$ in 1:1 HCl to give an excess of 1 drop, cool, dil. to 20 ml. with H_2O. Pipet 10 ml., add 0·5 ml. reagent, and measure with a blue filter using 0·5 ml. H_2O added to another aliquot as reference.[62]

(m) Miscellaneous colorimetric methods. Na-diethyldithiocabarmate is used for < 50 μg. Mo: add 5 ml. 1*N* HCl (or 0·3–2·5*N*), 2 ml. 0·1% reagent, 5 ml. $CHCl_3$, ext. and measure at 250 mμ (for 1–5 μg.; ϵ = 48 000) or at 340 mμ (for 5–50 μg.; ϵ = 6300). Pb, Ag, Hg, Cd, As, Cu, Bi, Ni, Mn, Cr, Zn, Sn, Fe interfere. For steels, NaOH sepn. is used and tartaric acid is added.[63]

K-xanthate is suitable for < 10 μg. Mo in slightly alk. (NaOH) soln.[64] Add 5 ml. reagent (100 ml. satd.

KOH and CS_2 shaken together), acidify with 30% AcOH, ext. with Et_2O and benzine and measure the unstable red color.

Thiocarbohydrazide allows colorimetric or gravimetric methods.[65] Ppt. at pH 2·0 and ignite to MoO_3, or ext. with 1:2 Me_2CO–BuOH and measure at 400 mμ; this is suitable for 15 μg. Mo/ml.

$Na_2S_2O_3$ can be used in presence of Fe.[66] Treat 10 ml. soln. with 2 ml. HCl, and 8 ml. 4:1 EtOAc–Et_2O, add 5 ml. 30% $Na_2S_2O_3$, ext., and measure the red color.

Tiron is used for 3–10 μg. Mo/ml.[67] Neutralize the soln. to pH 7·0 ± 0·4, add 5 ml. buffer (35 ml. 0·25*N* NaOH and 50 ml. 0·2*M* KH_2PO_4 dild. to 200 ml.) and 5 ml. 10% reagent; dil. to 25 ml. with H_2O and measure at 390 mμ. Interferences are Fe, Ti, Cr, V, W; W interference can be corrected for by measuring at 420 mμ.

Many similar reagents have been proposed. With chloranilic acid,[68] the Mo soln. contg. NaOH is evapd. to dryness, acidified with HCl after addn. of 3 ml. H_2O, re-evapd., dild. to 10 ml. with 2*M* $HClO_4$ and 3 ml. is transferred to a cell and measured at 350 mμ against 3*M* $HClO_4$ as reference; 3 ml. 0·09% chloranilic acid is then added to the flask and the absorbance is measured against reagent and $HClO_4$. This is suitable for < 8 μg. Mo/ml. Interferences are Bi, Sn, W, V (> 10 Mo); interferences of Fe, Zr, U, Cr^{6+} are avoided by extn. with hexone from solns. treated with HCl and HF, and by sepn. with NaOH.

Pyrocatechol is suitable for 50–600 μg. Mo^{6+} (see also p. 296). Add 10 ml. reagent (10 g. pyrocatechol, 500 ml. 0·4% NaOH, 15 g. $Na_2S_2O_5$ dild. to 1 l. with H_2O) and measure the orange-red color at 515 or 490 mμ. Co, Mn (40 mg.) can be tolerated but 50 μg. Fe interferes.

Pyrogallol (10 ml. 1% soln. in 2% AcOH) is satisfactory for 0·05–1 mg. Mo at pH 4·4 yielding a yellow to red color; Fe, W interfere.[70] Protocatechuic aldehyde forms a measurable color[71] with 0·2 μg. Mo/ml. at pH 6·6–7·0. The color formed by gallic acid with < 1 mg. Mo/ml. is measured at 305 mμ.[72]

Fluorimetry of 2–50 μg. Mo is possible with a satd. soln. of cochineal in EtOH.[73] Add 2 ml. 0·2*N* AcOH–NaOAc (1:4), dil. to 5 ml. with H_2O, add 1·5 ml. reagent, dil. to 10 ml. with H_2O and measure the red fluorescence under UV light; Al, W interfere.

Alizarin S forms a brown-red color with 10^{-3}–$10^{-4}M$ Mo at pH 2–5; $C_2O_4^{2-}$, AcO^- and citrate interfere but F^- does not, nor do Fe or Al if F^- is added.[74]

H_2O_2 permits detn. of < 5 mg. Mo in 25 ml. soln.[75] Add 10 ml. 1:1 $HClO_4$–H_2SO_4, dil. to 49 ml. with H_2O, add 1 ml. 3% reagent and measure at 330 mμ; Fe, W, V, Ti and F^- interfere. Alternatively, measure the color formed with 0·18*M* H_2O_2 in 1·5*M* H_2SO_4 at 360–380 mμ.[76] (see also Chapter 50, p. 362).

Salicylhydroxamic acid forms a complex with 10–20 p.p.m. Mo at pH 6·6–7·2 which is measured at 400 mμ (see Chapter 39, p. 301).

$SnCl_2$ is used for Fe–Mo:[77] treat 0·1 g. sample with 15 ml. 1:1 H_2SO_4 and 2 ml. HNO_3, evap. just to fumes, cool slightly, dil. to 50 ml. and filter. Add 0·2 ml. $CuSO_4$ (1 mg. Cu/ml.), dil. to 80 ml. with H_2O, add 10 ml. 10% $SnCl_2$ in 1:5 HCl, dil. to 100 ml. with H_2O and measure after at least 2 min. in a 4 cm. cell with a S57 filter. Up to 90 mg. Mo is detd. with an error of ±0·5 mg.; no interference arises from 2 mg. W, 0·7 mg. Cr, 10 mg. V, Ni, or from Cu or Fe; at least 0·2 mg. Cu and 5 mg. Fe must be present.

Mo catalyzes the reaction of Ti^{3+} with malachite green and can be detd. in the range 20–200 μg.;[78] interferences are W, Fe^{3+}, V, Ni, Pd, NO_3^-. The KI–H_2O_2 reaction is also catalyzed;[79] 0·17–0·87 μg. Mo/10 ml. is detd. with an error of ±10% by adding the sample to a KI–H_2SO_4–starch–H_2O_2 mixture and measuring at 553 mμ at 1 min. intervals.

$K_4Fe(CN)_6$ forms a color with Mo which can be measured at 450 mμ for 7–40 p.p.m. or 750 mμ for 20–200 p.p.m.[80] Conductometric titration of Mo with $K_4Fe(CN)_6$ at pH 1·7–2·2 is also possible.[81]

References

1. Hillebrand and Lundell, 245 (302); Scott and Furman, 585; Kimura, 438; Schoeller and Powell, 255; Pigott, 281.
2. Yagoda, H. and Fales, H. A., *J. Am. Chem. Soc.*, **58**, 1494 (1936); **60**, 640 (1938).
3. Lelubre, R., *Ingr. chimiste*, **25**, 101, 121 (1941).
4. Bush, G. H. and Higgs, D. G., *Analyst*, **80**, 536 (1955).
5. Killefer, D. H. and Linz, A., *Molybdenum Compounds: Their Chemistry and Technology*, Interscience, New York (1952).
6. Straumanis, M. and Ogrinš, B., *Z. anal. Chem.*, **117** 30 (1939).
7. Henrickson, R. B. and Sandell, E. B., *Anal. Chim. Acta*, **7**, 57 (1952).
8. Pigott, 275.
9. de Sousa, A., *Anal. Chim. Acta*, **10**, 29 (1954).
10. Hevesy, G. v. and Hobbie, R., *Z. anorg. u. allgem. Chem.*, **212**, 134 (1933).
11. A.S.T.M., 111 ff.
12. Ishimaru, S., *Kagaku-Zikken-Gaku*, **X**, 30 (1942).
13. Arrington, C. E. and Rice, A. C., *U.S. Bur. Mines, Repts. Invest.*, 3441 (1941).
14. Birnbaum, N. and Walden, G. H., *J. Am. Chem. Soc.*, **60**, 64 (1938).
15. Scott and Furman, 585 ff.
16. Takeno, R., *J. Chem. Soc. Japan*, **55**, 197 (1934).
17. Saito, K., *Japan Analyst*, **2**, 527 (1953); **5**, 153 (1956).
18. Welcher, **IV**, 520.
19. Lang, R. and Gottlieb, S., *Z. anal. Chem.*, **104**, 1 (1936).
20. Wirtz, H., *Z. anal. Chem.*, **116**, 240 (1939).
21. Kiboku, M., *Japan Analyst*, **6**, 356 (1957).
22. Deshmukh, G. S., *Bull. Chem. Soc. Japan*, **29**, 27 (1956).
23. Aylward, G. H., *Anal. Chim. Acta*, **14**, 386 (1956).
24. Carrière, E. and Dautheville, A., *Bull. soc. chim. France*, **10**, 264 (1943).
25. Liang, S. C. and Hsü, H. P., *J. Chinese Chem. Soc.*, **17**, 90 (1950).
26. de Sousa, A., *Anal. Chim. Acta*, **12**, 215 (1955).

27. JÍLEK, A. and BIEBER, B., *Acad. tchèque sci., Bull. intern., Classe sci., math., nat., med.*, **52**, 447 (1951).
28. WELCHER, **III**, 246.
29. BOBTELSKY, M. and YULIUS, I., *Anal. Chim. Acta*, **16**, 75 (1957).
30. WELCHER, **I**, 300.
31. SCHOELLER and POWELL, 255 ff.
32. BORRELL, M. and PÂRIS, R., *Anal. Chim. Acta*, **4**, 267 (1950).
33. PŘIBIL, R. and MALÁT, M., *Collection Czechoslav. Chem. Communs.*, **15**, 120 (1950).
34. MALÍNEK, M., *Chem. listy*, **48**, 38 (1954).
35. BERTRAND, D., *Bull. soc. chim. France*, **6**, 1676 (1939).
36. WELCHER, **IV**, 157.
37. MCNERNY, W. M. and WAGNER, W. F., *Anal. Chem.*, **29**, 1177 (1957).
38. RAY, H. N., *Analyst*, **78**, 217 (1953).
39. SANDELL, 455 ff.
40. Chemists of U.S. Steel Corporation, *Sampling and Analysis of Carbon and Alloy Steels*, 172 (1938).
41. UZUMASA, Y. and DOI, K., *Bull. Chem. Soc. Japan*, **14**, 337 (1939).
42. BARSHAD, I., *Anal. Chem.*, **21**, 1148 (1949).
43. MELNICK, L. M. and FREISER, H., *Anal. Chem.*, **26**, 425 (1954).
44. WRANGELL, L. J., *et al.*, *Anal. Chem.*, **27**, 1966 (1955).
45. WARD, F. N., *Anal. Chem.*, **23**, 788 (1951).
46. CROUTHAMEL, C. E. and JOHNSON, C. E., *Anal. Chem.*, **26**, 1284 (1954).
47. ELLIS, R., JR. and OLSON, R. V., *Anal. Chem.*, **22**, 328 (1950).
48. GINZBURG, L. B. and LUR'E, YU. YU., *Zavodskaya Lab.*, **14**, 538 (1948).
49. POPE, R. P., *Anal. Chem.*, **29**, 1053 (1957).
50. ZAĬCHIKIOVA, L. B., *Zavodskaya Lab.*, **15**, 1025 (1949).
51. MARKLE, G. E. and BOLTZ, D. F., *Anal. Chem.*, **25**, 1261 (1953); GOTO, H. and IKEDA, S., *J. Chem. Soc. Japan*, **77**, 82 (1956).
52. WELCHER, **IV**, 233.
53. SHORT, H. G., *Analyst*, **76**, 710 (1951).
54. Also see WELLS, J. E. and PEMBERTON, R., *Analyst*, **72**, 185 (1947); BICKFORD, C. F., *J. Am. Pharm. Assoc.*, **37**, 255 (1948); PIPER, C. A. and BECKWITH, R. S., *J. Soc. Chem. Ind. (London)*, **67**, 374 (1948); ALLEN, S. H. and HAMILTON, M. B., *Anal. Chim. Acta*, **7**, 483 (1952); CLARK, L. J. and AXLEY, J. H., *Anal. Chem.*, **27**, 2000 (1955) (0·02–10 μg Mo in soils and rocks, thioglycolic acid instead of $SnCl_2$); GREENBERG, P., *ibid.*, **29**, 896 (1957) (in Ti, Zr, Ta); ISHIBASHI, M., *et al.*, *Bull. Inst. Chem. Research, Kyoto Univ.*, **32**, 199 (1954) (in sea water); SANDELL, 459.
55. JEFFERY, P. G., *Analyst*, **82**, 558 (1957).
56. BUSCARÓNS, F. and GONZÁLES, E. L., *Anales fís. y quim. (Madrid)*, **40**, 1312 (1944).
57. GOLUBTSOVA, R. B. and SHEMYAKIN, F. M., *Zhur. Anal. Khim.*, **4**, 232 (1949).
58. SPACU, G. and GHEORGHIU, C., *Comun. acad. rep. populare Romîne*, **5**, 853 (1955); *Rev. chim. (Bucharest)*, **2**, 21 (1957).
59. NEMOTO, C. and TANABE, Y., *J. Electrochem. Soc. Japan*, **2**, (2), 53 (1934).
60. AYRES, G. H. and TUFFLY, B. L., *Anal. Chem.*, **23**, 304 (1951); PENNEC, L. *et al.*, *Chim. anal.*, **38**, 94 (1956) (in steel, SO_2 reduction); GOLDSTEIN, E. M., *Chemist Analyst*, **45**, 47 (1956) (in W); ZHAROVSKIĬ, F. G. and GAVRILOVA, E. F., *Zavodskaya Lab.*, **23**, 143 (1957) (BuOH extn., in steel).
61. WILL, F., III and YOE, J. H., *Anal. Chem.*, **25**, 1363 (1953); also see RICHTER, F., *Chem. Tech.*, **1**, 31 (1949).
62. PIGOTT, 278.
63. SUDO, E., *J. Chem. Soc. Japan*, **77**, 1446 (1956).
64. PAVELKA, F. and LAGHI, A., *Mikrochemie ver. Mikrochim. Acta*, **31**, 138 (1943); WELCHER, **IV**, 103.
65. DUVAL, C. and BALOE, T., *Compt. rend.*, **240**, 1097 (1955).
66. LOSANA, L. and JARACH, M., *Ind. chim. (Milan)*, **9**, 623 (1934).
67. WILL, F., III and YOE, J. H., *Anal. Chim. Acta*, **8**, 546 (1953).
68. WATERBURY, G. R. and BRICKER, C. E., *Anal. Chem.*, **29**, 129 (1957) (in Pu alloys).
69. SEIFTER, S. and NOVIC, B., *Anal. Chem.*, **23**, 188 (1951).
70. WELCHER, **I**, 164.
71. SHAPIRO, M. YA., *Zhur. Anal. Khim.*, **6**, 371 (1951).
72. VARDE, M. S. and ATHAVALE, V. T., *Proc. Indian Acad. Sci.*, **44A**, 228 (1956).
73. GOTO, H., *J. Chem. Soc. Japan*, **60**, 939 (1939).
74. NAZARCHUK, T. N., *Ukrain. Khim. Zhur.*, **20**, 417 (1954).
75. TELEP, G. and BOLTZ, D. F., *Anal. Chem.*, **22**, 1030 (1950).
76. BACON. A. and MILNER, G. W. C., *Anal. Chim. Acta*, **15**, 573 (1956).
77. MIZOGUCHI, S., *Japan Analyst*, **6**, 376 (1957).
78. SHIOKAWA, T., *J. Chem. Soc. Japan*, **71**, 1 (1950).
79. YATSIMIRSKIĬ, K. B. and AFANAS'EVA, L. P., *Zhur. Anal. Khim.*, **11**, 318 (1956).
80. RICCA, B. and D'AMORE, G., *Ann. chim. (Rome)*, **45**, 69 (1955).
81. FUJITA, Y., *J. Chem. Soc. Japan*, **78**, 1757 (1957).

30

SELENIUM AND TELLURIUM

The principal sources for this chapter are mentioned in ref. 1. A monograph on selenium has been published[2] and the analytical chemistry of selenium and tellurium has been reviewed.[3]

Both SeS_2, which is lemon-yellow when cold and orange-yellow when hot, and TeS_2, which is reddish brown, decompose spontaneously into their elements.

H_2SeO_4 dissolves in HCl to form H_2SeO_3 and Cl_2; when the mixture is heated on a steam-bath, $SeO_2{\cdot}2HCl$ volatilizes if the HCl concn. exceeds $6N$. The mixture is reduced to Se by H_2S, SO_2, filter paper, etc. via Se_2Cl_2 formation; Se_2Cl_2 is also readily volatile. Traces of Se are lost when HNO_3 or H_2SO_4 solns. are evapd. to dryness.

H_2TeO_3 is insol. in H_2O but dissolves as $TeO_2{\cdot}2HCl$ on boiling with HCl or on treatment with HCl and a reductant; $TeO_2{\cdot}2HCl$ is less volatile than the Se analog.

Selenides and tellurides attack Pt vessels when heated in them.

Attack

(a) Minerals. Fuse with Na_2O_2 or with 1:1 Na_2CO_3–KNO_3 in a Fe or Ni crucible, ext. with H_2O, filter, treat the filtrate with HCl to give a $< 6N$ soln. and heat below 100°C to expel Cl_2, etc.

Dissolve minerals contg. only small amts. of Se and Te in aqua regia or in HCl and $KClO_3$. On heating minerals to red heat in a stream of Cl_2, Se and Te volatilize along with As, Sb, V, Bi, Fe, S and can be collected in 1:1 HCl.

(b) Sulfides. To a 4 g. sample add 15 ml. H_2O and 50 ml. HNO_3 followed, after the reaction subsides, by 50 ml. H_2SO_4; heat to dissolve S, evap. at 190°C until grey, cool, add 1·0 ml. $HClO_4$ and 10 ml. H_2O and distil with HBr.[4] Alternatively,[5, 6] treat a 20 g. sample with 120 ml. HNO_3 added over 10 min. in a covered vessel, heat slowly below 110°C, remove and rinse the cover and boil out NO_2; filter on Whatman No. 42 paper (if S lumps remain, treat with HNO_3), make the filtrate alk. with NH_4OH, heat on a steam-bath, filter on paper, wash with hot H_2O, and treat with 1:1 HCl, $SnCl_2$, etc.

(c) Glass and frits. Evap. to fumes with H_2SO_4 and HF, add H_2O, filter, etc.

(d) Se and Te. Dissolve Se in 10% KCN; Se is pptd. on acidification. Alternatively, for Se, heat with 1:1 HNO_3, evap. to dryness on a covered steam-bath, add 10 ml. HCl, 20 ml. H_2O, filter, etc. Trace amts. of HNO_2 are best removed with urea. For Te, evap. to fumes with H_2SO_4, add H_2O, HCl, SO_2, etc. For Se + Te, treat with HCl and Br_2 followed by SO_2. For S, a combustion method is possible

(e) Cu. Treat a 5 g. sample with 30 ml. H_2O, 5 ml. H_2SO_4, 25 ml. HNO_3, boil, cool, add 100 ml. H_2SO_4, evap. and continue as for sulfides.[4] Alternatively,[5, 6] treat a 50 g. sample with 200 ml. HNO_3 in portions, boil and add H_2O; if a residue remains, collect it and treat with fuming HNO_3. Then add NH_4OH until $Cu(OH)_2$ just covers the bottom of the beaker, add $Fe(NO_3)_3$ and filter; add half the previous amt. of Fe^{3+} soln. and filter again. Treat the filtrates with NH_4OH and collect the whole ppt. on paper. Add 1:1 H_2SO_4, warm, filter, wash with hot 1:20 H_2SO_4, add NH_4OH to the filtrate and filter again. Treat the ppt. with 1:1 HCl, SO_2, etc.

(f) Steels. Heat a 2–5 g. sample with 30 ml. HNO_3 and 30 ml. HCl, add 35 ml. $HClO_4$, evap., fume for 5 min., add 50 ml. H_2O, warm, add 200 ml. HCl and 100 ml. satd. SO_2, etc.

(g) Org. compds. To a 10 g. sample[4] add 5 ml. H_2O and 10 ml. mixed acids (1·6 g. NH_4VO_3 in 300 ml. H_2O mixed with 1·5 l. HNO_3, 75 ml. HCl, 5 ml. 60% $HClO_4$ and 50 ml. H_2SO_4), heat slowly to 140–150°C until no more NO_2 appears and then to 210°C (if a green color appears, add 1 ml. $HClO_4$ and 10 ml. HNO_3, heat); finally cool and distil.

Alternatively,[7] to the org. compd. (after extn. of fats with $CHCl_3$) in a 100 ml. Kjeldahl flask, add 0·20 g. yellow HgO, 5–10 ml. H_2O, 30–40 ml. H_2SO_4, 2 glass beads, and heat for 6–10 hr. adding 5–10 drops 30% H_2O_2 occasionally; then dil. to 50 ml. with H_2SO_4, and centrifuge for 15–20 min.

Separation

Various reducing agents are of value in sepns. (see

also under Determination). Se and Te can be sepd. from Sb, Bi, Fe, etc. by treatment with 20% $SnCl_2$ or NaH_2PO_2 in warm 1:2 HCl soln. Sepn. from As may be incomplete. HNO_3 solns. can also be used; SO_2 must be absent. Se can be sepd. from Te, etc. by treatment with SO_2 in solns. contg. $> 3{\cdot}4N$ HCl, i.e. 28% v/v soln. ($>8N$ for sepn. from Te). NH_2OH also permits this sepn. (see p. 222). In $1{\cdot}2$–$5N$ HCl solns., i.e. 10–42% HCl, Te is sepd. from many elements by treatment with SO_2; HNO_3, Au, Pd, Sb, Bi, Cu interfere but the Cu interference is avoided by thiourea addn. and those of Sb and Bi by tartaric acid addn.

Hydroquinone seps. Se from Cu, Au, Pt metals, Hg and Ag.[8] Evap. the sample to dryness with HNO_3, add 50–75 ml. H_2O, 25–35 ml. reagent (15 g. hydroquinone and 80 g. Na_2SO_3 in 100 ml. H_2O and 100 g. NaOH in 100 g. H_2O mixed just before use), boil for 5 min., heat for 30 min. on a steam-bath, filter and wash with hot H_2O. Se is sepd. from Pb, Sb, etc. with Cu in 10% HNO_3 soln. contg. urea (see p. 222).

Se is sepd. from Te with KI soln.: to 100–150 ml. soln. contg. < 5% HCl, add 20 ml. 4% KI, filter after 1–1·5 hr. and wash with a mixt. of 5% KCl and 5% HCl. Thiourea permits sepn. of Se from Te.

H_2S in acidic soln. seps. Se^{4+} and Te^{4+} from group III elements, etc. Extn. with $(NH_4)_2S$ gives incomplete sepn. from the Cu group.

Te can be sepd. from Se and partly from Pb, Bi, Hg, Cu, Ag as follows: ext. the sulfide ppt. with $(NH_4)_2S_x$ and NH_4OH, add KCN until the soln. is colorless, boil and add 20–25 ml. satd. Na_2SO_3; boil for 10–20 min., dil. to 200–300 ml. with H_2O, add 2–3 ml. reagent, reboil and filter after some time.

Te is sepd. from Pb by H_2SO_4 treatment, from Bi by treatment with KBr and $KBrO_3$, from Hg with Na_2S and NH_4Cl, and from Cu, Au with $(NH_4)_2S_x$ and KCN. All these sepns. are complete when combined with the above Na_2SO_3 procedure.

Small amts. of Se^{4+} and Te^{4+} are sepd. from large amts. of Ag, Cu, Zn, Ni, etc. by treatment with Fe^{3+} and NH_4OH, Fe^{3+} being added in 30–50-fold amts. compared to Se. Se^{6+} and Te^{6+} do not coppt. Al^{3+} seems to give better results than Fe^{3+}.

Extn. with HNO_3 seps. Se and Te from Au in the elementary condition.

Distn. serves to sep. Se from Te. Place the H_2SO_4 or $HClO_4$ soln. contg. 0·02–4 mg. Se in an all-glass distn. app. (silicone grease for the joints) and pass air through at a rate of several bubbles/sec. Add 5 ml. 48% HBr, boil off Br_2, and add 10 ml. HBr dropwise at a rate of 1 ml./min. while heating at 125–130°C. Collect in 50 ml. 0·1% $N_2H_4{\cdot}H_2SO_4$, add 3 g. urea and 2·5 ml. 90% HCOOH, heat, neutralize with 45% NaOH to phenolphthalein, add 13 ml. 1:1 H_2SO_4, cool, and add 2 ml. 6% $K_3Co(CN)_6$ followed by 5 ml. soln. contg. 1·0 g. KI/100 ml. 0·1% starch. Titrate with 0·005–0·01N $Na_2S_2O_3$ until the color changes from violet to pink for at least 7 sec.[4] Distn. is also possible from solns. contg. 1 g. KBr and 20 ml. H_3PO_4/50 ml. in a stream of CO_2, from H_2SO_4 solns. at 300–330°C in a stream of HCl and from solns. contg. $HClO_4$ and HBr.[9]

Te can be sepd. from many elements[9] by extn. of the iodide complex with 1:2 AmOH–Et_2O. Add 6·6 g. NaI to 70 ml. soln. contg. 6 ml. HCl and ext. 3 times with 20 ml. solvent. Combine the solvent phases in a dry beaker, after washing each ext. with 15 ml. N HI and extg. the combined washings with 20 ml. solvent. Evap. to 15–20 ml., add 30–40 ml. H_2O and 5 ml. 30% H_2O_2, evap. all the solvent, add 10 ml. HNO_3 and 2 ml. $HClO_4$, evap. to fumes, rinse, evap. to dryness, add HCl, etc.

Hg_2Cl_2 permits sepns. as in the following scheme.[10]

Treat the 2% HCl soln. with $H_2C_2O_4$ to give a 1% soln. and boil

- Au
- cool, add Hg_2Cl_2
    - Pd + Hg_2Cl_2
    - Add $HgCl_2$ to give 0·01% soln., add Hg_2Cl_2 and boil
        - Pt
        - Add HCl to give 20% soln., cool, add 5% $NaHSO_3$, let stand and boil
            - Se
            - Cool, add Hg_2Cl_2
                - Te
                - Add HCl to give 28% soln., add Hg_2Cl_2
                    - As

Determination

SELENIUM

The methods involving SO_2 or NH_2OH are suitable for amounts of Se above 1 mg. and Te does not interfere. Many methods have been suggested for mg. amounts but the KIO_3 titration procedure of Evans appears to be the best. Diaminobenzidine seems to be the most satisfactory reagent for colorimetric detns.

(a) SO_2 allows a reliable detn. of < 0·25 g. Se^{4+} in 100 ml. HCl soln.[1, 11] Add 50 ml. satd. SO_2 in HCl and leave for 30 min. at 15–22°C. Filter on a Gooch crucible, wash with HCl, H_2O, EtOH and Et_2O, dry at 30–40°C for 3 hr. and at 120–130°C for 1 hr. (< 300°C) and weigh as Se.

NOTES. (1) Ag, Au, Cu, Bi, Sb, Hg interfere but Te does not. Interfering elements have been studied by Bode.[11]

(2) Sepn. of Se^{4+} from Se^{6+} is possible in 0·5–1N HCl soln. by treatment with SO_2 at 100°C under pressure. Se^{6+} is reduced in $4N$ HCl soln.[12]

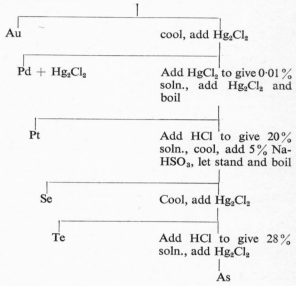

(3) Better results can be obtained[13] by washing with HCl and H_2O and drying in CO_2 at 140°C for 45 min. Alternatively, the ignition loss as Se can be weighed.[6]
(4) Apart from iodometric methods, which are discussed separately, several other detns. have been based on isolation of Se.
(*i*) *Gravimetric methods*. With satd. SO_2 in Me_2CO, add 5–20 ml. reagent soln. to 50 ml. Se soln. contg. from 5 ml. N HCl to 20 ml. concd. HCl.[14]
With $NH_2OH{\cdot}HCl$ (the sulfate is never used), treat 100 ml. soln. contg. <0·5 g. Se and 35–45 ml. HCl (or 25 ml. 25% tartaric acid or 100 ml. 5% citric acid) with 10 ml. 25% reagent, place on a steam-bath for 4 hr., filter on a Gooch crucible, wash with H_2O and EtOH and dry at 120–130°C; <0·2 Te can be tolerated.[5, 15] Other suitable reductants are phenylhydrazine,[16] $N_2H_4{\cdot}HCl$,[5] thiosemicarbazide[17] and tetraethylthiuram disulfide;[18] the last reagent is used in 50% EtOH soln. and only Hg^+, Cu, Co and much Bi interfere.
With KI as reductant, treat 400 ml. of <5% HCl soln. with 3–4 g. KI, boil out I_2, filter on a Gooch crucible, etc. (Scott and Furman[1]). NH_4SCN and $Na_2S_2O_3$ can be used similarly.
(*ii*) *Colorimetric methods*. KI is also applied colorimetrically.[5, 19, 20, 21] Dil. 0·5–20 ml. soln. contg. 50 μg. Se/ml. to 80 ml. with H_2O, add 8 ml. H_2SO_4, 10 ml. 10% reagent and 1 ml. 5% gum arabic (centrifuged) and heat at 55–60°C for 15 min. Cool, add 1 ml. 0·2% starch followed by dropwise addn. of half-satd. SO_2 until the blue color disappears. Then add 1 drop in excess and measure the red color. Te does not interfere.
$SnCl_2$ is suitable for 0·05–0·5 mg. Se in 20 ml. 1:1 HCl soln.[22] Add 1 ml. 10% reagent, 1 ml. 5% gum arabic, dil. to 50 ml. and measure the orange color; Te interferes.
SO_2 is used in conjunction with $NH_2OH{\cdot}HCl$ for 0·01–0·1 mg. Se;[23] add $SnCl_2$, filter, add 10% Br_2 in HBr, treat with SO_2 and $NH_2OH{\cdot}HCl$ and measure the red color.
Ascorbic acid is used nephelometrically for 1–5 μg. Se/ml., the brown color being measured at 530 mμ; a titrimetric finish is also possible.[24]
Thiourea is applicable in HCl solns. in presence of 1 ml. 1% phenol.[25]

(b) KIO_3 provides an excellent titrimetric procedure.[26] For 1–10 mg. Se in 10% HNO_3 soln. add 2 g. urea and Cu plate (1 × 1·5 in.), heat near the b.p. for 1·5 hr., boil for 10 min. and cool. Filter through paper, decant several times with H_2O without transferring the Cu and while protecting it from air, and discard the filtrate and washings. Add several drops of satd. KCN soln. to the beaker, pass through the filter and wash 5 times with the min. amt. of H_2O. To the filtrate add 2 ml. 1% gum arabic and 10 ml. HCl, pass air rapidly for 15 min. (yellow-red), add 1·5 vols. HCl (to give a 7·2N soln.) and titrate with M/60 KIO_3 using CCl_4 as indicator.

NOTES. (1) No interference arises from Te, Pb, Cu, Sb, etc.
(2) In a similar method,[27] treat the Se with >3 equivs. KCN, evap. to dryness, add 10 ml. H_2O, 2 ml. 1% gum arabic (this is unnecessary if <10 mg. Se is present), 10 ml. HCl, pass air for 15 min. and titrate with $KBrO_3$ until the red color disappears, or near the end-point add 0·5N ICl (to dissolve Se) and 4 ml. CCl_4 and titrate further.
(3) Various other iodometric or bromometric methods have been suggested. With $CHCl_3$ as indicator,[28, 29] evap. the soln. which is < 6N in HCl to 4 ml., cool, add 1 g. urea, dil. to 100 ml. with cold H_2O and, if Cu is present, add 2 ml. 10% $K_3Co(CN)_6$; after 1 min. add 10 ml. N KI and 5 ml. $CHCl_3$, shake and titrate after 5 min. with $Na_2S_2O_3$. This procedure has been applied to steels.[30] When starch is used as indicator in macro analysis the end-point is sharper if C_6H_6, toluene, Et_2O, etc. is added because the Se collects at the boundary.[31]
A potentiometric null-point method is suitable for 10–150 μg. Se in <15 ml. soln.[32] Pour the soln. into 3 ml. 1% v/v Br_2 in 30% HBr, add 15 ml. H_2O followed by 5% $Na_2S_2O_3$ until the soln. is nearly colorless, then add several drops 5% phenol, a 2–3 ml. excess of 0·001N $Na_2S_2O_3$, 1 ml. 10% KI and titrate with 0·001N KIO_3. The method is also applicable to sepd. Se.
Back-titration with I_2 soln. in presence of starch is satisfactory.[33] To the Se^{4+} soln. add starch, 5 ml. 6N HCl, dil. to 150 ml. with H_2O and add a <5 ml. excess of 0·001–0·1N $Na_2S_2O_3$ (no blue color should appear when 1–3 drops of 2·5% (for 0·1N $Na_2S_2O_3$) or 25% (for 0·01–0·001N $Na_2S_2O_3$) KI is added after each 5 ml. addn. of $Na_2S_2O_3$). Cool to 0–20°C, add KI to give a final concn. of 2% (this is unnecessary with 0·1N I_2) and titrate with 0·001–0·1N I_2 until a blue color appears. The accuracy of this method is ± 0·1%. Coulometric titration may be used for 14–140 μg. Se.[29] $HClO_4$, HBr or H_2SO_4 can replace HCl. The reaction in these procedures is:

$$H_2SeO_3 + 4\ Na_2S_2O_3 + 4\ HCl = Na_2SeS_4O_6 + Na_2S_4O_6 + 4\ NaCl + 3\ H_2O.$$

Another procedure involving formation of $CNSe^-$ is as follows:[34] to the soln. contg. 4–40 mg. Se, add 0·2 g. KCN, some drops EtOH and 10–15 drops H_2O, evap. to dryness, add some drops EtOH and H_2O and evap. again. Dil. to 100 ml. with H_2O, take a 5–10 ml. aliquot, add 70 ml. H_2O, 1 g. H_3BO_3 and some pumice, boil for 10 min., transfer to a 200 ml. flask, add 1 drop *p*-ethoxychrysoidine, neutralize with 0·1N HCl, add Br_2 until the mixt. is yellow, add 3–4 ml. 5% phenol after several min., leave for 5 min. add 2–3 ml. 20% HCl, 0·2 g. KI and titrate with $Na_2S_2O_3$ soln.
Reduction with $N_2H_4{\cdot}H_2SO_4$ soln. and back-titration with KIO_3 has been suggested.[35]
For 0·1–0·3 g. SeO_2, add 0·1N $KBrO_3$ (contg. 50 ml. HNO_3/l.), boil out Br_2, add excess As^{3+} soln. and 10 ml. HCl, cool, add 2 drops 0·5% fast red B and titrate with 0·1N $KBrO_3$.[36]
With Se^{6+} soln.,[37] treat with HBr, distil, collect in KI soln. and titrate with $Na_2S_2O_3$ soln.

(c) 3,3′-Diaminobenzidine-HCl provides an excellent colorimetric method for < 100 μg. Se.[38] Add 2 ml. 2·5M HCOOH, dil. to 50 ml. with H_2O, adjust to pH 2–3, add 3 ml. 0·5% reagent, leave for 30–50 min., adjust to pH 6–7 with 7M NH_4OH and add 10·0 ml. toluene. Shake for 30 sec., sep., centrifuge, and measure at (340 or) 420 mμ (ε = 19 900). The color is due to formation of piazselenol. Oxidants interfere; V interference is avoided by addn. of more reagent and those of Fe, Cu, Cr, Mo, Ni ,W, Co, Ti by EDTA addn.

(d) Miscellaneous gravimetric methods. Na_2S or $(NH_4)_2S$ yields SeS_2 from solns. acidified with HCl; the ppt. is washed with H_2O and dried at 110°C *in vacuo*.[39]

$Pb(NO_3)_2$ is used as follows:[40] boil the 0·01*M* Se^{6+} soln., add 0·5*M* reagent in 0·1–0·2 ml. excess, add EtOH to give a concn. of 30–35% and leave to cool for 4–5 hr. Filter on a glass crucible, wash with 30% EtOH, EtOH and Et_2O, dry below 280°C and weigh as $PbSeO_4$.

(e) $KMnO_4$ is useful titrimetrically for 40–120 mg. Se^{4+}. Pour the soln. into 50 ml. 0·1*M* $KMnO_4$ mixed with 25 ml. 25% NaOH; after 10–15 min. (discard if the mixt. has become green) add 500 ml. H_2O, 25 ml. 50% H_2SO_4, 50 ml. 0·25*M* $H_2C_2O_4$, 25 ml. 5% $MnSO_4$, heat to 50°C and titrate with $KMnO_4$.[41]

NOTES. (1) Te, etc. interfere.

(2) Alternatively to the above procedure,[42] titrate the 1–1·5*N* NaOH soln. contg. 1 g. H_2TeO_4 with $KMnO_4$ soln. and back-titrate with Tl^+ soln., or pour the mixt. into Fe^{2+} in H_3PO_4 and H_2SO_4 soln. and titrate with $KMnO_4$.

(3) Titration is also satisfactory in acidic soln.[43] Add 20 ml. 18*N* H_2SO_4 and dil. the soln. to 100 ml.; add 12 g. Na_2HPO_4 and excess 0·1*N* $KMnO_4$ and back-titrate after 30 min. with Fe^{2+} soln. using ferroin indicator.

(4) $K_2Cr_2O_7$ can replace $KMnO_4$.[44] To the soln. contg. <5 mg. H_2SeO_3, add 10 ml. 0·1*N* Fe^{2+}, 5 ml. $H_4P_4O_7$, 5 ml. ICl, 0·1–0·2 g. $KHCO_3$, and after 10 min., 15·0 ml. 0·1*N* $K_2Cr_2O_7$, 4 ml. 18*N* H_2SO_4 and 3–4 drops phenylanthranilic acid indicator and back-titrate with 0·1*N* Fe^{2+}.

(f) Benzidine may be used titrimetrically and Te does not interfere.[45] Prep. the reagent by heating 9 g. benzidine with 20 ml. AcOH, pour slowly into 1·5 l. hot H_2O contg. 75 ml. 0·1*N* HCl and filter after 24 hr. This soln. is stable for 3–4 days. For a detn. add the sample soln. slowly to 800 ml. reagent and 10 ml. AcOH dild. to 1 l. with H_2O; filter on paper, wash with 200 ml. H_2O, boil the ppt. with H_2O and titrate with 0·1*N* NaOH using phenolphthalein indicator.

(g) Argentometric methods. Adjust the 0·01*M* SeO_3^{2-} soln. to pH 9·6 with thymolphthalein indicator, add 0·2% phenolphthalein or diphenylcarbazone indicator and titrate with 0·01–0·1*N* $AgNO_3$ while shaking vigorously to the color change from yellow-pink to red or from violet to blue.[46] See also Table 10 (p. 25) for suitable adsorption indicators.

For Volhard's method, evap. the soln. to fumes with a few ml. of H_2SO_4, cool, dil. to 50–100 ml. with H_2O, add excess 0·01*N* $AgNO_3$, boil, add up to 100 mg. $N_2H_4 \cdot H_2SO_4$, heat for 1–2 hr. until Ag_2Se ppts. and cool; add 10 ml. 2*N* HNO_3 for each 50 ml. soln. and 1 ml. satd. Fe-alum soln. and titrate with 0·1*N* NH_4SCN. Te does not interfere.[47]

(h) Miscellaneous colorimetric methods. Codeine sulfate is suitable for 5–50 μg. Se in 10 ml. H_2SO_4 soln.[7] Add 3 drops satd. (3%) reagent and measure the blue color photometrically after 7 hr. in the dark. V interferes.

Pyrrole is used for 0–30 μg. Se in 2 ml. soln.[48] Add 1 ml. 5% $FeCl_3$, 7 ml. H_3PO_4, 0·5 ml. 1% pyrrole in EtOH and measure the blue color, which fades quite rapidly. SiO_2 interferes but 160 μg. As, 620 μg. Pb and 5 μg. Te can be present.

Methylene blue is useful in conjunction with Na_2S.[49] Add the sample soln. to 3·5 ml. 0·1550*N* Na_2S and enough H_2O to give a final vol. of 50 ml., then add 0·4 ml. methylene blue soln. (1% dild. 1:3 with H_2O just before use), and measure the time required for the soln. to become colorless. For 5–50 μg. Se, maintain the reaction temp. at 15°C and for 2–14 μg. Se at 20°C; 0·35–1·5 μg. Se can be detd. by a modified method.

The color formed with 50 ml. H_2SO_4 by 200 μg. Se on heating for 15 min. at 170°C can be measured at 350 mμ; Te does not interfere if its amt. is less than that of Se.[50]

TELLURIUM

The method involving reduction with N_2H_4 is probably the oldest and most widely used. The iodometric procedure of Evans is the best method for mg. amounts of Te; for smaller amounts, the colorimetric method with KI is to be recommended. Diethyldithiocarbamate or thiourea also appear to be satisfactory reagents for Te.

(a) N_2H_4 provides an excellent gravimetric detn.[1] Boil 50 ml. 3*N* HCl soln. contg. < 0·2 g. $Te^{4+,\,6+}$, add 15 ml. satd. SO_2 water and 10 ml. 15% $N_2H_4 \cdot HCl$, add 25 ml. satd. SO_2 water and boil for over 15 min. Filter on a Gooch crucible, wash with hot H_2O and EtOH, dry at 120–130°C and weigh as Te.

NOTES. (1) Some Te may be oxidized during the above procedure. To avoid this,[13] heat at 105°C for 45 min. in CO_2 after washing with hot H_2O. The procedure has been applied[51] to the detn. of Te in S after combustion and concn. with $Al(OH)_3$.

(2) For a titrimetric finish,[52] dissolve the ppt. in 25 ml. 10*N* HNO_3, dil. to 200 ml. with H_2O, add 2 g. urea, cool, add excess KI and titrate with $Na_2S_2O_3$.

(3) Several other methods are available in which Te is sepd. as the element. NaH_2PO_2 is used in conjunction with iodometry[53] or gravimetrically.[54] For the former, treat 40 ml. neutral soln. contg. 0·5–10 mg. Te with 5 ml. 1% gum arabic, 5 ml. H_3PO_4, dil. to 60 ml. with H_2O, and if Cu is present, add 2 ml. 2% $K_3Co(CN)_6$. Add 2–3 g. NaH_2PO_2, heat to b.p., cool, dil. with cold H_2O to 150 ml. and titrate with 0·01*N* I_2 using 4 ml. CCl_4 as indicator near the end-point.

For a colorimetric method,[9, 55] treat the dried salt from the sepn. process (p. 221) with 3 ml. HCl, 2 ml. H_2O, 1 ml. reagent (10% $SnCl_2$ in 20% HCl), dil. to 10 ml. with H_2O and measure at 440 mμ.

Alternatively,[54, 56] treat the soln. contg. 0·1–0·7 mg. Te^{4+} and 1–8 meq. HCl with 3 ml. 4% gum arabic, dil. to 35 ml. with H_2O, boil, add 5 ml. 3*M* H_3PO_2 rapidly from a pipet, heat for 15 min., cool, dil. to 50 ml. with H_2O and measure the red color at 240–290 or 420 mμ; discard if the color is blue-purple. Interferences are Se, Au, Pt, oxidants, Cu^{2+}, Fe^{3+}, Bi, V, Mo, Ti, Pb, Hg^{2+}, Tl, I^-, $S_2O_3^{2-}$.

(b) KI is used colorimetrically.[57] For 0·025–0·1 mg. Te in 30 ml. soln. add 5 ml. 2*N* HCl, 10 ml. 2*M* KI, dil. to 50 ml. with H_2O and measure the red-yellow color at 335 mμ within 20 min.

NOTES. (1) Bi interference is avoided by treating the 0·05*N* HCl soln. with 2 ml. KI and extg. several times with 3:1 AmOH–EtOAc. Se is removed similarly, or if Bi is absent by extn. with $CHCl_3$. If Fe or Cu is present, sep. with $SnCl_2$, dissolve in HNO_3, boil, neutralize with NH_4OH, etc. Other interferences are NO_2, CrO_4^{2-}, As^{5+}, Ag, Pb, Hg^+.
(2) HCl is used colorimetrically for 1–120 mg. TeO_2: dil. the soln. to 100 ml. with HCl, dil. a 10 ml. aliquot of this soln. to 100 ml. with HCl and measure at 376 mμ. Interferences are Fe^{2+}, Fe^{3+}, Cu^+, Cu^{2+}, Sn^{2+}, Ce^{4+}, 10 mg. V^{5+}, Cr^{6+}, I^-, 8 mg. SeO_2 and 300 mg. Bi/100 ml.; Co, Ni, P do not interfere.[58].
(3) HBr is suitable for <0·4 mg. Te in 3 ml. HBr soln.[59] Add 35 ml. HBr, 5 ml. 10% ascorbic acid, dil. to 50 ml. with H_2O, and measure at 442 mμ in a 4 cm. cell. Se does not interfere if the soln. is evapd.; interferences of Sb, Bi, Cu, Fe, Sn are avoided by pptg. with $SnBr_2$, dissolving in HBr + Br_2 and evapg.
(4) Tetraphenylarsonium chloride is applied gravimetrically or titrimetrically.[60] For 2·5–10 mg. Te in 20–25ml. HCl soln., heat to 60–80°C, add 0·02*M* reagent (1 ml. of excess/10 ml. sample soln.), cool for 45 min., filter on a glass crucible, wash with a little 4·5*N* HCl and then with 4·5*N* HCl satd. with ppt., dry at 110°C and weigh as $[(C_6H_5)_4As]_2TeCl_6$. Alternatively, titrate the ppt. with I_2 soln. using a potentiometric end-point. For the pptn. the final concn. of HCl should be 4–5*N*. Interferences are Hg, Sn, Cd, Bi, Fe, Zn, Tl, Pt, Au, Br^-, I^-, F^-, MoO_4^{2-}, WO_4^{2-}, NO_3^-.

(c) Pyridine can be used gravimetrically.[61] To 100 ml. dil. HCl soln. contg. 0·2 g. TeO_2, add NH_4OH until a ppt. appears, clear with HCl, boil and add 33% pyridine until the soln. is alk. to methyl orange. Filter on a glass crucible after 12 hr., wash with H_2O, dry at 120–130°C and weigh as TeO_2. Se does not interfere.

Various other methods are available for the detn. of tellurite. Scott and Furman[1] recommend making faintly alk. with NH_4OH, adjusting to pH 5 with AcOH and then proceeding as above. With hexamine,[61] add NH_4OH until a ppt. appears, add 10 ml. HCl, dil. to 100 ml. with H_2O, add 1 g. NH_4Cl, boil, add 10 ml. 20% hexamine and filter after 12 hr. Aniline, piperazine and dimethylaniline have also been investigated.[62]

$[Cr(NH_3)_6](NO_3)_3$ is suitable for 5–20 ml. 0·05*N* $Na_2H_4TeO_6$ in ammoniacal soln.;[63] heat to 80°C, add 40% reagent, filter on a glass crucible, wash with warm dil. NH_4OH, dry at 105°C and weigh as $[Cr(NH_3)_6]_2(H_2TeO_6)_3$.

For a colorimetric tellurate method,[64] treat the telluric acid soln. with 10 ml. 6·6*M* NH_4OH, dil. to 100 ml. with H_2O, and measure at 250, 260, 270 or 280 mμ for resp. < 75, 75–190, 190–340, 340–500 mg. Te. Small amts. of HNO_3, H_2SO_4, H_2SeO_4, HCl, $HClO_4$, H_3PO_4, AcOH, NaOH, SiO_2, Na_3AsO_3 and $Na_2HAsO_4 \cdot 12H_2O$ interfere.

(d) Miscellaneous gravimetric methods. For pptn. with Na_2S or $(NH_4)_2S$, see p. 223.

For electrodeposition,[65] treat the Te with HNO_3, evap. to dryness, add 10 ml. H_2SO_4, heat, add 30–40 ml. satd. NH_4H-tartrate and dil. to 250 ml. with H_2O. Heat to 60°C and electrolyze at 1·2–1·8 v. and 0·12–0·09 amp. with a rotating anode.

(e) Miscellaneous titrimetric methods. Titration with $K_2Cr_2O_7$ soln. is applicable in presence of Se.[66] To the neutral soln. contg. < 64 mg. Te^{4+}, add 20 ml. HCl, 10–15 ml. H_2SO_4 and 3 g. $MnSO_4$ and dil. to 100 ml. with H_2O; add excess 0·1*N* $K_2Cr_2O_7$ and back-titrate after 15 min. with 0·1*N* Fe^{2+} in presence of ferroin indicator to the color change from yellow-green to brown. Alternatively,[67] for 1–50 mg. Te in 150 ml. 1:9 HCl soln., add excess 0·025*N* $K_2Cr_2O_7$ and, after 30 min., excess 0·025*N* $FeSO_4$, diphenylamine and H_3PO_4, and titrate with the $K_2Cr_2O_7$ soln.

Addn. of excess $KMnO_4$ and back-titration with $H_2C_2O_4$ soln. has also been used.[68] With Ce^{4+} as titrant, add 10 ml. 1:1 H_2SO_4 and 10–20 mg. Cr^{3+}/200 ml. soln., boil for 5–10 min. with excess of Ce^{4+} and back-titrate with Fe^{2+} soln.[69]

In an iodometric method,[70] the reaction is:

$$TeI_6^{2-} + 5\ S_2O_3^{2-} = 6\ I^- + Te(S_2O_3)_3^{2-} + S_4O_6^{2-}$$

For 1–100 mg. Te^{4+} in 40–50 ml. 0·15–0·5*N* acid soln., add excess 0·1*N* $Na_2S_2O_3$, 10 ml. 0·1*N* KI and back-titrate potentiometrically with 0·1*N* I_2 after 3–5 min. Side reactions occur in the direct titration. Se interferes.

For an alkalimetric procedure,[71] which is accurate to ±0·5%, treat the H_2TeO_4 soln. with 20 ml. propylene glycol, dil. to 200 ml. with H_2O, add 3 drops phenolphthalein indicator and titrate with KOH soln.

(f) Na-diethyldithiocarbamate has been used colorimetrically.[72] Treat the soln. with 5 ml. 3*N* H_2SO_4, 3 ml. 0·1% reagent, dil. to 25 ml. with H_2O, shake for 30 sec. with 5 ml. C_6H_6 and measure the yellow color in a Pulfrich photometer using an Hg 436 filter. This is satisfactory for up to 200 μg./ml. The optimum pH range is wide (pH 3·32 up to 5*N* H_2SO_4). The complex can be extd. with $CHCl_3$, CCl_4, AmOH, AmOAc, toluene, etc.

NOTES. (1) Many elements interfere; interferences are avoided by sepg. with $SnCl_2$, dissoln. in HNO_3 (1:1), addn. of 2 ml. 1:1 H_2SO_4, evapn. to fumes, treatment with H_2O, etc.
(2) For 10–150 μg. Te in 25 ml. neutral soln.[73] add 5 ml. buffer soln. (5 g. H_3BO_3, 1 g. EDTA and 1 g. KH_2PO_4 in H_2O, adjusted to pH 8·5–8·7 with NaOH and dild. to 100 ml. with H_2O), 50 mg. KCN and 1 ml. 0·5% reagent; ext. with 10, 10 and 5 ml. $CHCl_3$, shaking for 2–3 min. for each extn., filter through paper, dil. to 25 ml. with $CHCl_3$ and measure at 428 mμ in a 5 cm. cell.
Interferences of Bi, Cu, Sb are removed by extg. the cupferrates at pH 1–2 with $CHCl_3$ and that of Tl by extn. of the HCl soln. with Et_2O. No interference is caused by 200 mg. Se (up to 10 g. Se can be tolerated if the soln. is re-extd. after evapn. to dryness), 100 mg. As, 20 mg. V or 4 mg. Ag, Au, Cd, Co, Fe, In, Mn, Ni, Os, Pd, Pb, Zn.

(g) Thiourea is suitable for 1·5–24 μg. Te/ml.[74] To 10 ml. acidic soln. add 6 g. reagent and 2·5–5 ml. HNO_3, dil. to 50 ml. with H_2O and measure the yellow color at 366 mμ. Cu does not interfere but Bi, Sb, Hg, Se, Os, Rh, Pt and Pd interfere.

(h) H_2SO_4 is suitable for the colorimetric detn. of 50 μg. Te/ml.; heat at 100°C for 10 min. and measure at 520 mμ (see p. 223).

References

1. Hillebrand and Lundell, 245 (329); Scott and Furman, 775; Kimura, 427; Schoeller and Powell, 228; Pigott, 410, 472.
2. Trelease, S. F. and Beath, O. A., *Selenium*, S. F. Trelease, New York (1949).
3. Frommes, M., *Z. anal. Chem.*, **97**, 447 (1934).
4. McNulty, J. S., *Anal. Chem.*, **19**, 809 (1947); **23**, 123 (1951).
5. Schoeller and Powell, 228 ff.
6. Schoeller, W. R., *Analyst*, **64**, 318 (1939).
7. Gortner, R. A. and Lewis, H. B., *Ind. Eng. Chem., Anal. Ed.* **11**, 198 (1939).
8. Welcher, **I**, 137.
9. Hanson, C. K., *Anal. Chem.*, **29**, 1204 (1957).
10. Pierson, G. G., *Ind. Eng. Chem., Anal. Ed.*, **11**, 86 (1939).
11. Hecht and Donau, 181; Bode, H., *Z. anal. Chem.*, **153**, 335 (1956).
12. Bode and Stemmer, H. D., *Z. anal. Chem.*, **155**, 96 (1957).
13. Seath, J. and Beamish, F. E., *Ind. Eng. Chem., Anal. Ed.*, **9**, 373 (1937).
14. Welcher, **I**, 400.
15. Hillebrand and Lundell, 265 (336).
16. Welcher, **II**, 448.
17. Mendoza, O. B., *Actas y trabajos congr. peruano quím., 3rd Congr.*, **2**, 433 (1949).
18. Michal, J. and Zýka, J., *Chem. listy*, **48**, 1338 (1954).
19. Hughes, W. C. and Wilson, H. H., *J. Soc. Chem. Ind.* (*London*), **55**, T359 (1936).
20. Yoe, 369.
21. Lambert, J. L., *et al.*, *Anal. Chem.*, **23**, 1101 (1951).
22. Shakov, A. S., *Zavodskaya Lab.*, **11**, 983 (1945); Boyer, W. J. and Fritzche, O. H., *Anal. Chem.*, **27**, 310 (1955) (in steel).
23. Robinson, W. O. *et al.*, *Ind. Eng. Chem., Anal. Ed.*, **6** 274 (1934).
24. Rudra, M. N. and Rudra, S., *Current Sci.* (*India*), **21**, 299 (1952); see also Simon, V. and Grimm, V., *Chem. listy*, **48**, 1774 (1954) (potentiometric); Yoshimura, C. *J. Chem. Soc. Japan*, **78**, 5 (1957) (photometric); Sušič, M. C. and Maksimovič, Z. B., *Bull. Inst. Nuclear Sci. "Boris Kidrich"* (*Belgrade*), **6**, 131 (1956).
25. Ishibashi, M., *Records Oceanogr. Works Japan*, **1**, 44 (1953).
26. Evans, B. S., *Analyst*, **64**, 87 (1939); Willis, U. F., *ibid.*, **67**, 219 (1942).
27. Coleman, W. C. and McCrosky, C. R., *J. Am. Chem. Soc.*, **59**, 1458 (1937).
28. Evans, *Analyst*, **67**, 346 (1942); Noakes, F. D. L., *ibid.*, **76**, 542 (1951).
29. See also McNulty, ref 4; Rowly, K. and Swift, E. H., *Anal. Chem.*, **27**, 818 (1955).
30. A.S.T.M., 93; Pigott, 417.
31. Welcher, **I**, 55.
32. Wernimont, G. and Hopkinson, F. J., *Ind. Eng. Chem., Anal. Ed.*, **12**, 308 (1940).
33. Coleman, W. C. and McCrosky, C. R., *Ind. Eng. Chem., Anal. Ed.*, **9**, 431 (1937).
34. Schulek, E. and Koros, E., *Z. anal. Chem.*, **139**, 209 (1953).
35. Suseela, B., *Z. anal. Chem.*, **147**, 13 (1955).
36. Adams, D. F. and Gilbertson, L. S., *Ind. Eng. Chem., Anal. Ed.*, **14**, 926 (1942).
37. Soth, G. C. and Ricci, J. E., *Ind. Eng. Chem., Anal. Ed.*, **12**, 328 (1940).
38. Cheng, K. L., *Anal. Chem.*, **28**, 1738 (1956); *Chemist Analyst*, **45**, 67 (1956) (in Fe and Cu); also see Hoste, J. and Gillis, J., *Anal. Chim. Acta*, **12**, 158 (1955); *Mededel. Koninkl. Vlaam. Acad. Wetenschap*, **16**, (12) (1954).
39. Taimni, I. K. and Agarwal, R. P., *Anal. Chim. Acta*, **9**, 121 (1953); Salaria, G. B. S., *ibid.*, **15**, 514 (1956).
40. Ripan-Tilici, R., *Z. anal. Chem.*, **102**, 343 (1935); Spacu, P., *Bull. soc. chim. France*, **3**, 159 (1936).
41. Stamm, H. and Goehring, M., *Z. anal. Chem.*, **120**, 230 (1940).
42. Issa, I. M. and Issa, R. M., *Anal. Chim. Acta*, **13**, 323 (1955); *Chemist Analyst*, **45**, 16 (1956).
43. Barabas, S. and Cooper, W. C., *Anal. Chem.*, **28**, 129 (1956).
44. Syrokomskiĭ, V. S. and Knyazeva, R. N., *Zavodskaya Lab.*, **15**, 1149 (1949).
45. Welcher, **II**, 314.
46. Ripan-Tilici, R., *Z. anal. Chem.*, **117**, 326 (1939).
47. Hahn, H. and Viohl, U., *Z. anal. Chem.*, **149**, 40 (1956).
48. Welcher, **III**, 573; Hirano, S., *J. Chem. Soc. Japan, Ind. Chem. Sect.*, **55**, 514 (1952) (in steel).
49. Goto, H. and Hirayama, M., *J. Chem. Soc. Japan*, **73**, 652 (1952).
50. Wiberley, S. E. *et al.*, *Anal. Chem.*, **25**, 1586 (1953).
51. Aaremae, A. and Assarsson, G. O., *Anal. Chem.*, **27**, 1155 (1955).
52. Schaefer, R. A., *Ind. Eng. Chem., Anal. Ed.*, **15**, 379 (1943).
53. Evans, B. S., *Analyst*, **63**, 874 (1938); **67**, 346, 387 (1942) (in Cu, Pb–Sb); Noakes, F. D. L., *ibid.*, **76**, 542 (1952).
54. Clauder, O. E., *Z. anal. Chem.*, **89**, 270 (1932).
55. Shakov, ref. 22; Geiersberger, K., *Z. anal. Chem.*, **135**, 15 (1952).
56. Johnson, R. A., *et al.*, *Anal. Chem.*, **25**, 1013 (1953); **27**, 120 (1955).
57. Johnson, R. A. and Kwan, F. P., *Anal. Chem.*, **23**, 651 (1951); Brown, E. G., *Analyst*, **79**, 50, 380 (1954) (in Pb); also see Geiersberger, K. and Durst, A., *Z. anal. Chem.*, **135**, 11 (1952).
58. Hanson, M. W. *et al.*, *Anal. Chem.*, **29**, 490 (1957).
59. Fletcher, N. W. and Wardle, R., *Analyst*, **82**, 743 (1957).
60. Bode, H., *Z. anal. Chem.*, **134**, 100 (1951).
61. Welcher, **III**, 35, 133.
62. Macarovici, C. Gh., *Bull. sect. sci. acad. roumaine*, **26**, 301 (1944).
63. Bersin, T., *Z. anal. Chem.*, **91**, 170 (1933).
64. Scott, C. W. and Leonard, G. W., Jr., *Anal. Chem.*, **26**, 445 (1954); Leonard and Henry, R. W., *ibid.*, **28**, 1079 (1956).

65. FISCHER, A., and SCHLEICHER, A., *Elektroanalytische Schnellmethoden, 2.* Aufl. 191, F. Enke, Stuttgart (1926).
66. LANG, R. and FAUDE, E., *Z. anal. Chem.*, **108**, 258 (1937); A.S.T.M., 354 (potentiometric; in Cu–Te).
67. WILLIS, U. F., *Analyst*, **66**, 414 (1941); KRUSE, F. H. *et al.*, *Anal. Chem.*, **25** 500 (1953); SCHOELLER and POWELL, 243.
68. LANG, R., *Z. anal. Chem.*, **128**, 484 (1948); AMIN, A. M. *et al.*, *Chemist Analyst*, **43**, 61 (1954) (3×10^{-5} *N*; potentiometric); ISSA, I. M. *et al.*, *Anal. Chim. Acta*, **11**, 512 (1954) (formate).
69. WILLARD, H. H. and YOUNG, P., *J. Am. Chem. Soc.*, **52**, 553 (1930).
70. JOHNSON, R. A. and FREDERICKSON, D. R., *Anal. Chem.*, **24**, 866 (1952).
71. EDWARDS, J. O. and LAFERRIERE, A. L., *Chemist Analyst*, **45**, 12 (1956).
72. GOTO, H. and KAKITA, Y., *Japan Analyst*, **3**, 299 (1954).
73. BODE, H., *Z. anal. Chem.*, **144**, 90 (1955).
74. NIELSCH, W. and BÖLTZ, G., *Z. Metallkunde*, **45**, 380 (1954) (in Cu); NIELSCH and GIEFER, L., *Z. anal. Chem.*, **145**, 147 (1955); **155**, 401 (1957) (2–6% H_2SO_4, 2–10% H_3PO_4 soln., 340 mμ); JÍLEK, A. and VŘEŠTÁL, J., *Chem. zvesti*, **6**, 497 (1952); **7**, 33 (1953) (0·2–2·0*N* $HClO_4$ soln.; in Se); VŘEŠTÁL, *Sborník celostátní pracovní konf. anal. chemiků. 1st Conf., Prague, 1952.* p. 173 (1953).

31

GOLD

The principal sources for this chapter are Hillebrand and Lundell, and Scott and Furman.[1] Some useful information is also to be found in Wogrinz's book.[2]

Attack

Aqua regia is always used, i.e. 4 parts HCl, 1 part HNO_3 and 5 parts H_2O. When the aqua regia soln. is evapd. rapidly, a little Au is lost both in the presence and absence of H_2SO_4; this does not happen if the aqua regia soln. contains $HClO_4$.

Fire assay

For details, see Chapter 18, p. 145. In cupellation processes, a little Au is absorbed by the bone ash and some also vaporizes.

Wet assay

If sulfides are present, roast the sample and ext. with HNO_3 before proceeding further. Treat the sample with 2:4 I_2–KI soln., shake and add more I_2 if decolorization occurs. Filter, shake with 5 g. Hg, decant, wash, add 10 ml. HNO_3, decant, wash, ignite and weigh. The yield is $> 50\%$.

Separation

Reducing agents are generally used (see also under Concentration, Determination); Mellor and Thompson[3] is worth consulting. SO_2 seps. Au from the Pt metals but traces of Pt and Pd accompany Au. $H_2C_2O_4$ seps. Au from the Pt metals but sepn. from Pd is incomplete; Cu, Pb, etc. interfere. $N_2H_4{\cdot}HCl$ allows sepn. from Pb, Hg, Cd, Co, Ni, U, Fe, Mn, Zn, Al, Cr, etc. but Cu again interferes. $FeSO_4$ seps. Au from Te and Pt metals if the soln. contg. 1·5% HCl is adjusted to pH 3 with NaK–tartrate.[4] Hydroquinone seps. Au from Cu, Ni, Zn, Te and Pt metals but Ag, W, Se interfere; see also under Determination, p. 228. Metol or *p*-phenylenediamine seps. Au from Pd, Pt, Se and Te. $NaNO_2$ in slightly acidic soln. gives the best sepn. from Pt metals (see also under Determination, p. 228). H_2, Zn, Al, Mg, etc. have also been applied as the reductant.

KSCN seps. Au from Cu and H_2SO_4 permits sepn. from Pb; in the latter sepn. some Au coppts. which is overcome by igniting the ppt. in H_2, dissolving in HNO_3 and repeating the sepn. NaOAc seps. Au from Bi and Sn.

Au can be sepd. from Pt, etc. by extn. with Et_2O from 5–10% HCl soln. repeated 5–6 times; Os interferes. Better sepns. can be achieved with EtOAc or by double extn. with equal vols. of iso-Pr_2O from 15–17 ml. soln. contg. 5 ml. HBr; the exts. are washed with 5 ml. 4*N* HBr in the latter case.[5]

Concentration

$TeCl_4$ is excellent for concn. of Au, especially in sea water, etc.[6] Sepn. from Fe, Cu, Pb, etc. is achieved; for details, see Chapter 18, p. 145 . For 0·01–2 mg. Au in 10 l. soln. add 1/20 of the vol. of HCl and 2 ml. $TeCl_4$ and pass SO_2 until the soln. is satd. Place on a steam-bath and then leave to cool for 12 hr. Filter on paper, wash with H_2O, ignite, add 6 drops HCl and 2 drops HNO_3, warm, etc.

For 0·1–10 μg. Au in 50 ml. soln. adjust to 2·5*N* with HCl, add 0·2 ml. $TeCl_4$, mix and add 5 ml. $SnCl_2$ soln. contg. 20 g. in 100 ml. 2*N* HCl (add more if Fe or Cu is present). Boil for 30 min., filter on a porcelain crucible, and wash 5 times with 5 ml. 1:4 HCl. Then add 1 ml. aqua regia to the original beaker, warm, pour on to the filter, suck dry and repeat twice before a final wash with a little H_2O. Evap. the soln. to dryness, add 0·01 ml. aqua regia, evap. at room temp. and proceed as under Determination, p. 228.

Treatment with $Pb(OAc)_2$ and $(NH_4)_2S$ also permits concn. of Au from sea water.[7]

Concn. with Hg_2Cl_2 can be used in 2% HCl soln.[8]; and concn. with $HgCl_2$ in conjunction with Mg.[9] For the latter, treat 2 l. soln. with 50 ml. satd. $HgCl_2$ soln. and 5 g. Mg; add 60 ml. HCl in small portions, filter after 2 hr., add 20 g. Pb and transfer to a layer of bone ash. Cover with Pb, place a piece of wood on the surface, heat to 1000°C and when the Pb surface is glowing hot, cool to 800°C. The recovery of Au is 95% and that of Ag 91% over the range 0·05–60 mg. Au and 8·8–262 mg. Ag. When cyanides are present, 10-fold amts. of $FeSO_4$ are added.

Determination

The reduction methods are excellent for any amount of Au; those in which SO_2 and $H_2C_2O_4$ or hydroquinone is used are particularly satisfactory for macro or semi-micro analysis. Among the colorimetric methods, that involving a rhodanine derivative is better than the $SnCl_2$ procedure; *o*-tolidine and HBr with rhodamine B are also good colorimetric reagents.

(a) SO_2 and $H_2C_2O_4$ are excellent for gravimetric analysis.[1] For 0·5–1 g. Au in 100 ml. soln. contg. < 5 ml. HCl, add 25 ml. satd. SO_2 soln., heat for 1 hr. on a steam-bath, add 5–10 ml. SO_2 soln. and leave to cool. Filter on a thick pulp pad, decanting and washing with 1:99 HCl. Dissolve in aqua regia (8 ml. HCl, 2 ml. HNO_3 and 10 ml. H_2O), filter through the same pad and wash with hot 1:99 HCl. Evap. to a syrup, add HCl, evap. again and repeat the process 2–3 times. Add 3 ml. HCl, 5 drops H_2SO_4, 75 ml. H_2O, 25 ml. satd. $H_2C_2O_4$, boil for 15 min., add 5–10 ml. $H_2C_2O_4$ soln. boil for 1–2 min. and place for at least 4 hr. on a steam-bath. Filter on paper, ignite and weigh as Au.

NOTES. (1) Interferences are Se, Te, Pb, Ca, etc.

(2) The color of the metal fades if it is contaminated by traces of Pt or Pd.

(3) Many other reducing agents have been suggested; hydroquinone is probably the best of these. For gravimetric detn. of 0·05–0·15 g. Au in 50 ml. 1·2*N* HCl soln.,[10] boil, add 5% hydroquinone soln. to give an excess of 3 ml. for each 25 mg. Au present, boil for 20 min., filter on a Gooch crucible, etc. Ag, W interfere and some Se coppts.; Cu, Pt metals, Ni, Zn, Te may be present. Pd can be detd. in the filtrate by means of dimethylglyoxime and Pt by means of HCOOH.

For titrimetric detn. of 0·1–2 mg. Au in 50 ml. of slightly acidic soln.[11] add 0·5 ml. 5% KHF_2, 1 ml. *o*-dianisidine indicator (0·5 g. in 500 ml. H_2O contg. 2 ml. HCl), leave for 10 min. to allow the red color to develop and titrate with hydroquinone soln. to the colorless end-point. Prepare the reagent by dissoln. of 0·4186 g. hydroquinone in 200 ml. H_2O, add 10 ml. HCl, dil to 500 ml. with H_2O, and dil. 20 ml. of this soln. to 500 ml. with H_2O. Pb interference is avoided by addn. of satd. Br_2 soln. and removing Br_2 by blowing air on to the surface of the soln.; NO and NO_2 are removed by blowing air in the same way. Colorimetric detn. is also possible.

$NaNO_2$ is used for 1 g. Au in 100 ml. soln. (Hillebrand and Lundell[1]). Adjust to pH 1·5 with NaOH using thymol blue indicator, heat, add 10 ml. 10% reagent, adjust to pH 8 using xylenol blue or cresol red and boil for 5 min.; filter on paper, wash with hot H_2O, hot 1:99 HNO_3 and hot H_2O, ignite at 900°C and weigh as Au.

Ascorbic acid has been used gravimetrically or titrimetrically;[12] heat the soln. contg. <0·3 g. Au and 3–5 ml. HCl/200 ml. to 80–90°C, add 10 ml. 4% reagent, heat for 5 min., cool, filter, etc. For a titrimetric finish the ascorbic acid in the filtrate is titrated iodometrically. Colorimetry is possible at pH 3–6 in presence of starch.[13]

Other reductants which have been applied gravimetrically are amidol,[14] glucose,[15] pyrogallol,[14] rodinal,[14] resorcinol,[14] phenol,[14] HCHO,[14] phenylenediamine, pyrocatechol, phloroglucinol, *o*-aminophenol,[14] citarin,[16] glycerol (see p. 229) and morpholine oxalate (17·5 g. morpholine and 9 g. $H_2C_2O_4$/50 ml.)[17]

Titrimetrically, Au can also be detd. by addn. of excess $FeSO_4$ and a little H_2SO_4 and back-titration with $KMnO_4$.[18] Eiconogen has been used as titrant with *o*-tolidine indicator.[14]

$SnCl_2$ is used colorimetrically for 10–100 μg. Au in 20 ml. 0·05*N* (< 1*N*) HCl soln.[19, 20] Add 2 ml. 10% $SnCl_2$ in 1*N* HCl, dil. to 25 ml. with H_2O, and measure the yellow color after 20 min. The color varies according to the exact conditions. Pt, Pd, Ru, Te, Se, Ag, Hg, W interfere.

Hg_2Cl_2 has been used colorimetrically for 0·1–10 μg. Au in 1–2 ml. of neutral or slightly acidic soln.[8, 19] Add 5 ml. 0·5*N* HCl (boiled with some reagent and filtered) and 0·10 g. reagent, shake for several min. and compare the pink-violet color. Interferences are Pd, Fe^{3+}, Cu^{2+}, oxidants and I^-.

Other reagents which have been applied colorimetrically are amidol,[14] glucose,[15] HCHO,[14] C_2H_2,[21] α-naphthylamine,[22] 5% K_2HgI_4 with 1% KI,[23] CO,[24] gallic acid.[25]

(b) *p*-Diethylaminobenzilidenerhodanine provides an excellent colorimetric detn. of 0·1–10 μg. Au after concn. with Te.[19, 26] Evap. the sample to dryness with aqua regia, add 0·01 ml. aqua regia and allow to evap. spontaneously. Add 0·3 ml. 2*N* HCl and 1 ml. H_2O, stir, transfer to a 5 ml. test-tube with H_2O (filter if turbid), add 0·25 ml. 1% NaF, dil. to 4 ml. with H_2O, add 0·30 ml. 0·05% reagent in EtOH, dil. to 5 ml. with H_2O, and measure the purple color after 10 min. by visual comparison or photometrically using a green filter.

NOTES. (1) Interference of Pd is removed by adding 0·05 ml. 1% dimethylglyoxime in EtOH before the addn. of reagent. Ag interference is prevented by pptn. with HCl and filtration. Other interfering elements are eliminated during the concn. with Te (see p. 227).

(2) The dimethyl analog is suitable for 0·1–0·2 μg. Au in dil. HNO_3 soln.;[27] add 1 ml. reagent soln. (1 ml. 0·03% in EtOH and 13 ml. C_6H_6 dild. to 50 ml. with $CHCl_3$) and measure the pinkish color.

(3) Rhodanine itself has been used for 0·5 p.p.m. Au in <0·2*N* HCl, a 0·001% reagent soln. being applied.[28]

(c) Miscellaneous gravimetric methods. Thionalide is used in the same way as for Ag (p. 146).[29] The ppt., $Au(C_{12}H_{10}ONS)_3$, is dried below 230°C.

Mercaptobenzothiazole forms a ppt. with $AuCl_3$ soln.;[30] EtOH from the reagent soln. is removed on a steam-bath and the ppt. is eventually ignited to Au.

Reinecke's salt may be applied for 5–10 mg. Au in 50 ml. 1–2*N* HNO_3 soln.[31] Add 2 ml. 0·5*N* As^{3+}, heat, add 1–1·5 ml. 1% reagent, cool rapidly, filter, wash with 0·01*N* HCl, dry and weigh as $Au[Cr(NH_3)_2(SCN)_4]$.

Thiophenol ppts. Au from < 0·6*N* HCl or HNO_3 soln. (see Chapter 32, p. 245).

Electrodeposition can be used in 120 ml. soln. which is alk. with KOH and contains 3 g. KCN; electrolysis is carried out at 60°C for 1·5 hr. with 0·38 amp. at 2·7–4 v.[18]

Dimethylglyoxime is suitable for 30 mg. Au in 100 ml. soln.[32] Add 0·5 ml. HCl, 10 ml. 1% reagent in EtOH, boil for 30 min., cool, filter on a Gooch crucible, wash, ignite and weigh as Au.

(d) Miscellaneous titrimetric methods. Na-diethyldithiocarbamate or EDTA may be applied titrimetrically (see Chapter 32, p. 245.

$NaClO_2$ reacts with Au^{3+} to form Au metal and ClO_2. This can be used[33] for the detn. of 1–7 mg. Au^{3+}: add excess 0·01*M* $NaClO_2$, leave for 15 min., bubble CO_2 through the soln. at a rate of 2 bubbles/sec. for over 1 hr. and collect ClO_2 in 1% NaI contg. a little HCl; det. the ClO_2 iodometrically. No interference arises from Ag, Cu, Zn, Ni, Fe, Pt, Cd.

(e) *o*-Tolidine is suitable[19, 34] for the colorimetric detn. of 0·5–10 μg. Au^{3+}. Evap. the soln. to dryness, add 25 ml. reagent (a satd. soln. in *N* H_2SO_4 mixed with 19 vols. of *N* H_2SO_4) and measure the yellow color at 437 mμ in a 5 cm. cell.

NOTES. (1) Fe^{3+}, Os, Ru, Pd, W, V, NO_2^- and Cl_2 interfere but Ag, Cu, Ni, Zn do not.

(2) Various other procedures have been based on the oxidizing action of Au^{3+}. *o*-Dianisidine is useful for 0–300 μg. Au in 50 ml. soln. contg. a few drops of mineral acid;[19, 35, 36] add 0·5 ml. 5% KHF_2, 0·1 ml. 0·1% reagent in 0·05*N* HCl and measure the red color after 10–15 min. Benzidine may be applied similarly.[36]

Leuco malachite green is used[19, 37] at pH 3·6, the soln. being boiled with the reagent (0·05 g. in 15 ml. EtOH and 35 ml. NaOAc–AcOH buffer pH 3·6) for 2 min., cooled and extd. with $CHCl_3$. Ir interferes; Fe interference is masked by F^-.

(3) Iodometric titration is carried out by adding KI to the very dil. Au^{3+} soln. until the ppt. dissolves, and titrating with 0·001*N* $Na_2S_2O_3$ in presence of starch.[18, 38]

(f) HBr is applied colorimetrically to the detn. of 0·5–1 mg. Au in 10–12 ml. soln.[5, 19, 39] Add 5 ml. reagent, ext. twice with iso-Pr_2O, wash with 4*N* HBr, strip 3 times with 10 ml. H_2O, add 1 ml. HBr and evap.; add 5–10 drops H_3PO_4 if Fe is present, dil. to a definite vol. with H_2O, and measure the orange-red color at 380 mμ. Os interferes.

Several other methods utilize the formation of halogen complexes. HCl is used colorimetrically at pH 1 or in acetate-buffered soln., the color being measured at 311·5 mμ.[39]

Tetraethylammonium chloride is applied gravimetrically.[40] Add 8 ml. 15% reagent to 20 ml. soln. contg. $< 0·2$ g. Au and 3 ml. HCl, filter after 15 min. on Whatman No. 42 paper and wash 5 times with the reagent soln. Return the ppt. to the original beaker, boil for 1 min. with 35 ml. 20% glycerol and 2 g. NaOH and add an equal vol. of H_2O. Filter on paper, decant, add 25 ml. HCl, boil, add an equal vol. of H_2O, filter, wash with hot H_2O, and ignite to Au. No interference arises from Pt or Pd.

Na-*N*-(*N*-bromo-*C*-tetradecylbetainyl)-*C*-tetradecylbetaine is used gravimetrically in HBr media.[41]

Rhodamine B has been used colorimetrically[42] for 0·30 μg. Au^{3+} in 0·5*N* HCl soln. contg. NH_4Cl; the complex is extd. with iso-Pr_2O and measured at 570 mμ.

Reaction with KCN and eventual titration with Ni^{2+} in presence of murexide indicator has been utilized (see Chapter 34, p. 267).

(g) Dithizone provides a colorimetric method for 0·5–20 μg. Au in 10 ml. 0·1*N* HCl soln.[43] Add 0·2 ml. dithizone in CCl_4 (equiv. to 5–20 μg. Au), ext., wash with 0·5 ml. CCl_4 and repeat until no yellow color remains. Dil. to 10 ml. with CCl_4, wash with H_2O contg. some drops of NH_4OH (1:1000) until the aq. phase remains colorless, and then wash once with 1:1000 HCl. Measure the color at 400–420 mμ in a 0·5 cm. cell.

NOTES. (1) Alternatively, a titrimetric method with Cu^{2+} as indicator can be applied; the amt. of Cu should be only about 3 times that of Au.

(2) Pd is removed with dimethylglyoxime and Ag by addn. of 0·1–0·5 ml. NaBr soln. before the detn. Pt does not interfere and can be detd. in the residual soln. after addn. of $SnCl_2$.

References

1. HILLEBRAND and LUNDELL, 269 (339); SCOTT and FURMAN, 431.
2. WOGRINZ, A., Analytische Chemie der Edelmetalle, *Chem. Anal.*, **36** (1936).
3. MELLOR and THOMPSON, 462 (1938).
4. LENHER, V. *et al.*, *Ind. Eng. Chem.*, *Anal. Ed.*, **6**, 43 (1934).
5. MCBRYDE, W. A. E. and YOE, J. H., *Anal. Chem.*, **20**, 1094 (1948).
6. POLLARD, W. B., *Analyst*, **62**, 597 (1937); SANDELL, 341.
7. HABER, F., *Z. angew. Chem.*, **40**, 303 (1927).
8. PIERSON, G. G., *Ind. Eng. Chem.*, *Anal. Ed.*, **6**, 437 (1934); **8**, 86 (1936).
9. CALDWELL, W. E. and SMITH, L. E., *Ind. Eng. Chem.*, *Anal. Ed.*, **10**, 318 (1938); CALDWELL and MCLEOD, K. N., *ibid.*, **9**, 530 (1937).
10. WELCHER, **I**, 135; BEAMISH, F. E. *et al.*, *Ind. Eng. Chem.*, *Anal. Ed.*, **9**, 174 (1937); SEATH, J. and BEAMISH, *ibid.*, 373.
11. JAMIESON, A. R. and WATSON, R. S., *Analyst*, **63**, 702 (1938); also see MILAZZO, G., *Anal. Chim. Acta*, **3**, 126 (1949); BELCHER, R. and NUTTEN, A. J., *J. Chem. Soc.*, 546 (1951) (3-methylbenzidine or 3,3′-dimethylbenzidine is best as indicator); SIMON, V., and ZÝKA, J., *Chem. listy*, **49**, 1646 (1955).
12. STATHIS, E. C. and GATOS, H. C., *Ind. Eng. Chem.*, *Anal. Ed.*, **18**, 801 (1946).
13. SHNAĬDERMAN, S. YA., *Ukrain. Khim. Zhur.*, **21**, 261 (1955).
14. WELCHER, **I**, 152 ff.
15. WELCHER, **IV**, 282.
16. WELCHER, **II**, 221.
17. MALOWAN, L. S., *Mikrochemie ver. Mikrochim. Acta*, **35**, 104 (1950).
18. SCOTT and FURMAN, 435 ff.
19. SANDELL, 343 ff.

20. Yoe, 192
21. Welcher, **I**, 52.
22. Welcher, **II**, 410.
23. Nider, D., *Kolloid. Z.*, **44**, 139 (1928).
24. Costeanu, R. N., *Z. anal. Chem.*, **102**, 336 (1935).
25. Heredia, P. A. and Cuezzo, J. C., *Monit. farm. y terep.* (*Madrid*), **57**, 361 (1951).
26. Sandell, E. B., *Anal. Chem.*, **20**, 253 (1948).
27. Welcher, **III**, 423; Natelson, S. and Zuckerman, J. C., *Anal. Chem.*, **23**, 653 (1951).
28. Ishibashi, M. *et al.*, *Japan Analyst*, **3**, 74 (1954).
29. Umemura, T., *J. Chem. Soc. Japan*, **61**, 26 (1940).
30. Welcher, **IV**, 114.
31. Mahr, C. and Denck, W., *Z. anal. Chem.*, **149**, 67 (1956).
32. Welcher, **III**, 208.
33. Riolo, C. B. and Garrini, E., *Ann. chim.* (*Rome*), **45**, 767 (1955).
34. Also see Schreiner, H. *et al.*, *Mikrochemie ver. Michrochim. Acta*, **36/37**, 1056 (1951).
35. Block, W. P. and Buchanan, O. H., *J. Biol. Chem.*, **13**, 379 (1940).
36. Welcher, **II**, 288, 343.
37. Welcher, **IV**, 514.
38. Also see Ebert, L. and Dirscherl, A., *Mikrochemie ver. Mikrochim. Acta*, **35**, 346 (1950); Herschlag, V. E., *Ind. Eng. Chem.*, *Anal. Ed.*, **13**, 561 (1941) (with As^{3+}).
39. Vydra, F. and Čelikovský, J., *Chem. listy*, **51**, 768 (1957).
40. Welcher, **II**, 508.
41. Harvey, A. E., Jr. and Yoe, J. H., *Anal. Chim. Acta*, **8**, 246 (1953).
42. McNulty, B. J. and Woollard, L. D., *Anal. Chim. Acta*, **13**, 154 (1955).
43. Shima, M., *Repts. Sci. Research Inst.* (*Tokyo*), **32**, 152 (1956); also see Chapter 32, p. 245.

32

THE PLATINUM METALS

The principal sources for this chapter are given in ref. 1. A large number of monographs, reviews and general papers have been published which deal with the analytical chemistry of the platinum metals. A detailed report of a symposium on platinum metals is available.[2]

The various colorimetric procedures for the determination of these metals have been critically evaluated[3] and solvent extraction methods have been discussed.[4] The most important paper on the separation and gravimetric determination of these metals is that of Gilchrist and Wichers.[5] Gilchrist has also reviewed the subject.[6] The chemistry of the platinum metals has also been discussed by Klaus,[7] while methods developed in the 25 years before 1948 have been reviewed.[8] Some useful information is given in Wogrinz's monograph on the analytical chemistry of the noble metals.[9]

Among the general contributions are papers on the determination of fine platinum alloys,[10] the detection and determination of small amounts of platinum metals,[11] the micro separation and determination of the platinum metals[12] and a series of papers by Geilmann and Neeb.[13] The determination of the platinum metals as their sulfides[14] has been described as unreliable.[15] Frommes[16] has reviewed the literature up to 1934.

In general work with the platinum metals Pyrex apparatus is to be recommended but it must be free from scratches. In the sections below the reactions described are normally those of the metal chlorides; if other anions are present the reactions may be different.

Attack*

(a) Pulverization. Mix the sample in a quartz crucible with a 10-fold amt. of Zn, cover with $ZnCl_2$ and heat at 500–600°C for 2–3 hr.; cool, add HCl, filter and dry. Explosions may occur on ignition of the residue. Alternative procedures are fusion with Sn and dissoln. in Li_2SO_4–H_2SO_4, or fusion with Pb and dissoln. in HNO_3.

(b) Aqua regia (4 parts HCl, 1 part HNO_3 and 1 part H_2O) can be used at 70°C if necessary, under reflux; the residue is fused with NaOH and Na_2O_2 as described below. Pd dissolves quickly and Pt and Pt contg. some Ir, Rh or Ru also dissolve; Os dissolves very slowly. Ir, Rh and Os–Ir are scarcely attacked, while Pt–Ir contg. over 30% Ir is not attacked.

(c) NaOH–Na_2O_2 fusion dissolves Os–Ir, Pd–Ir Pt–Ir, Ru, Rh and Os. In a Ni or Ag crucible, fuse an amt. of NaOH equal to the residue from the aqua regia treatment and add this residue mixed with Na_2O_2 in the ratio of 1:4 in small portions; fuse for 30 min. with occasional stirring (Ni spatula), cool, leach with H_2O, and add HCl or HBr (in a distn. flask if Os is present; HBr is preferable when Ir predominates). If any residue remains, repeat the fusion or treat with Cl_2 as described below. When the fused mass is extd. with H_2O, Na_2OsO_4 and Na_2RuO_4 dissolve but Ir and Rh do not dissolve.

Fusion with NaOH and $NaNO_3$ in a Au crucible and fusion with $Ba(NO_3)_2$ and BaO_2 in a Ni crucible have also been applied. K-salts should not be used.

(d) Dry chlorination attacks Rh, Rh–Ir, Ir and most other alloys.[17] Mix the sample with a 10-fold amt. of NaCl in a porcelain boat, place in a quartz U-tube of diam. 2·5 cm., and heat at 700°C for 8 hr. while passing Cl_2 which has been dried with H_2SO_4 or P_2O_5. Ru, Os, Pb, Ag and Au (also Fe) vaporize and are collected in 2 absorption tubes contg. 1:1 HCl satd. with SO_2. The residue in the boat and the sublimate in the tube are dissolved in 50 ml. 0·1*N* HCl.

In an alternative procedure, seal the sample in a tube contg. HCl and Cl_2, HNO_3, $NaClO_3$, $HClO_4$, etc.; place the tube in an iron bomb, add dry ice and $CaCO_3$ and heat for 24 hr. at 250–300°C.

(e) NaOCl soln. dissolves Os and Ru.

(f) $Na_2S_2O_7$ fusion attacks only Rh when repeated several times.

Fire assay[18]

The actual procedure is described in Table 32. Flux A consists of 100 g. PbO, 60 g. Na_2CO_3, 40 g. borax, 41 g. SiO_2, 200 mg. Ag and the amt. of flour required to give a 30 g. button. Flux B consists of 60 g. Na_2CO_3, 76 g. borax, 19 g. SiO_2, and 79 g. PbO.

A little Ru and Os is lost during the assay; in cupellation Ru is largely lost, whereas Os is completely lost. Recoveries of 99% are obtained when Os-contg.

* For details, see Schoeller and Powell.[1]

TABLE 32. Fire Assay of Pt Metals

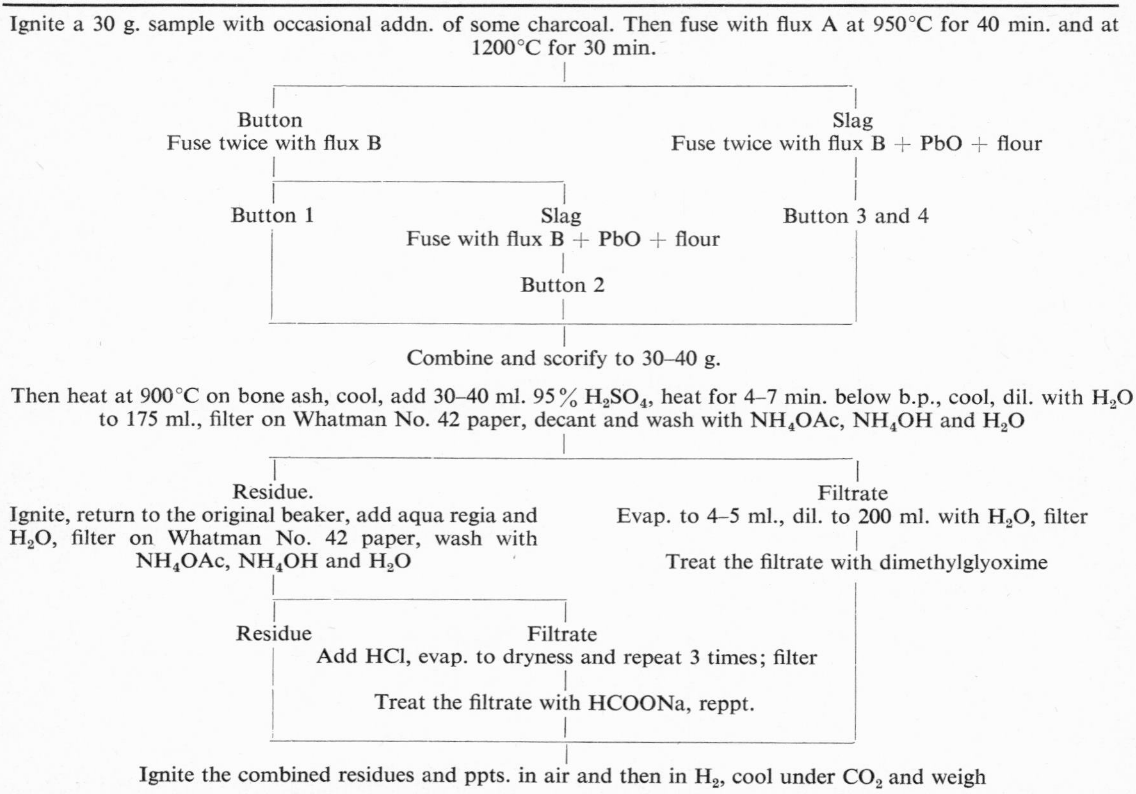

samples are fused rapidly with neutral or acid flux. Buttons contg. Os and Ru should be parted with acid as described below (see also ref. 19). For the treatment of buttons contg. Rh, see ref. 20. Ir, Rh, Os and Ru, as well as part of the Pt when much is present, do not dissolve in Ag and tend to be lost as a fine powder on cupellation. For the recoveries attainable, see Table 33. Valuable information is given in Schoeller and Powell.[21]

Separation

Reducing agents are regularly used for sepn. With H_2, Zn, Al, Mg, etc., Pt, Pd, Rh, and some Os and Ru, ppt.; pptn. of Ir is incomplete except with Zn–Mg mixtures. After being washed, the ppt. is treated with 10 ml. 20% $Fe_2(SO_4)_3$ in 10% H_2SO_4 to remove Cu and Zn.[21]

Hg in a soln. contg. a NH_4-salt allows sepn. of Pt from Ir; Cu powder in 0·1*N* HCl behaves similarly.[22] HCOOH with NaOAc ppts. Pt and Pd but Cu coppts.

$TiCl_3$ ppts. Pt, Pd, Rh and also Au, Cu, Bi, Hg, Te; this reagent is particularly useful for the sepn. of Rh from Ir. Ru ppts. partly when the soln. is heated. $Ti_2(SO_4)_3$ with $HgSO_4$ is said[21] to be better than $TiCl_3$. 5% VCl_2 or $CrCl_2$ in hot 10% HCl or H_2SO_4 soln. is also satisfactory. In these cases, copptd. Cu or Bi can be removed with $Fe_2(SO_4)_3$ soln. as described above.[21]

NaH_2PO_2 seps. Pt, Pd, Rh from Ir.[21] Evap. the chloride soln. nearly to dryness, add 2 ml. 1:1 HCl, 5 g. NaCl and 50 ml. hot H_2O, boil, add a mixt. of equal vols. of 5% $HgCl_2$ and 1% NaH_2PO_2 in 2% HCl, boil gently for some min., add more reagent, and place on a

TABLE 33. Recovery of Pt Metals in Fire Assay Buttons

	First	Second	Third
Ru	75–95%	ca. 100%	
Ir	90%	with acid flux, ca. 100% with alk. flux, ca. 95% (Second and Third)	
	when Cu or Ni is present 40–80% (all)		
Rh	97–98%	97–99%	
Os	96–99% (neutral flux)		
	99% + gas loss (acid flux) (all)		

hot plate for 30 min. Filter on Whatman No. 41 paper, wash with hot 2% HCl and return to the original beaker. Add 5 ml. satd. Br_2 in 1:1 HCl and reppt. Only Pd ppts. when $HgCl_2$ is absent. Ir is recovered from the filtrate by twice-repeated hydrolysis with BrO_3^-.

Hg_2Cl_2 allows sepn. of Pt and Pd from Cu, Ni, Fe, Ir, Rh,[21] being especially useful for the sepn. of Pd from Ir and Rh. It is also used for concn. purposes.

Satd. $H_2C_2O_4$ seps. Pt and Pd from Rh, Ir, Fe, etc.[21] Boil the chloride soln. in a flask with 10 ml. HNO_3 and 10 ml. H_2SO_4 until free from brown fumes; add 5 ml. 10% $HgSO_4$, heat to white fumes, cool, add 50 ml. H_2O, boil, cool and filter. Add 10 ml. satd. $H_2C_2O_4$ soln. to the filtrate and heat slowly until effervescence ceases; cool, add H_2O and boil. Filter, wash with hot H_2O and reppt.

Sb dust seps. Rh from Ir (see Table 36).[23] Te dust seps. Pd and Pt from Rh and Ir (see Table 36).[24]

H_2S ppts. Pt, etc. from hot solns. contg. 2–5% v/v HCl or H_2SO_4. Ir is pptd. from solns. contg. 20% v/v HCl or H_2SO_4 and some $AlCl_3$ by means of H_2S. The ppts. dissolve in aqua regia. The Ru soln. becomes blue and the vessel should then be stoppered and allowed to stand. Traces of Pd can be concd. with Pb.

Distn. processes can be applied in several ways.[25] Os is sepd. from Ru, Pt, etc. by distn. from solns. contg. 20 ml. HNO_3/140 ml.; Br^- does not interfere but Cl^- and EtOH do (see Table 34). Ru is sepd. from Pt, etc. from solns. contg. H_2SO_4 and $NaBrO_3$. Os can be distd. from H_2SO_4 solns. contg. Cl^- but not if Br^- is present. 99·5% Recovery of Ru is obtained[26] by distn. from 9*M* H_2SO_4 soln. contg. 0·5 g. $KMnO_4$. Os can be distd. from solns. contg. H_2SO_4 and H_2O_2 while Ru is distd. from H_2SO_4–$HBrO_3$ solns. (see Table 36). Distn. is also possible from 50% H_2SO_4 soln. contg. 5–10 ml. 20% CrO_3 soln. if air is passed through.[13]

Distn. from $HClO_4$ soln. is used for the parting of the Pb button; N_2 is passed and Os is distd. from the $HClO_4$–HBr soln. Ru is distd. from the residual soln. after addn. of NaOH by passing Cl_2. See the original papers[18] for details of apparatus and procedure. HNO_3 is also used for the parting of the Pb button.[21] Distn. from NaOH soln. with a stream of Cl_2 generally seps. Ru from Pt, etc. (see above).

Extn. with $CHCl_3$ or CCl_4 from 5–6*M* HNO_3 soln. seps. Os^{8+} and Ru^{8+} from other Pt metals (see p. 239). OsO_4 can also be extd. with CCl_4 from NaOH soln. Ru can be sepd.[13] from much Os by extn. of the diphenylthiourea complex with $CHCl_3$; to the soln. of $RuCl_6^{3-}$ and $OsCl_6^{2-}$ in 6*N* HCl, add 2–5 ml. satd. reagent in MeOH, heat to 80°C for 30–45 min. and ext. with $CHCl_3$. Os is sepd.[13] from much Ru by extn. of the tetraphenylarsonium chloride complex from 0·1–0·3*N* HCl with $CHCl_3$.

Hydrolysis with $NaBrO_3$ and $NaHCO_3$ or $BaCO_3$ seps. Pt from Pd, Ir and Rh. Pt^{2+}, Pd^{2+}, $Ir^{3+, 4+}$, Os^{4+}, Ru^{4+}, Rh ppt. almost completely but Pt^{4+} and Ru (as $RuNOCl_3$) do not ppt. Ir ppts. slowly when BrO_3^- is absent. The sepn. is 99·94% complete when the amt. of Pt exceeds 20 mg. but significant errors arise when < 10 mg. Pt is present, according to a spectrochem. study.[27] For the concn. of Pd and its sepn. from 20 mg. Pt proceed as follows. To the soln. contg. 2 μg. Pd add 0·2 mg. Fe^{3+} and 100 mg. NaCl and evap. to dryness (if HNO_3 is present, add HCl, evap. to dryness and repeat several times); then add a few drops of HCl and 25 ml. H_2O, boil, add 20 ml. 10% $NaBrO_3$, adjust with 10% $NaHCO_3$ until pink to cresol red, add 2 ml. $NaBrO_3$ soln. and boil for 15 min. Filter on a glass crucible and wash with hot 1% NaCl soln. at pH 6–7, before evapg. with HCl and detg. the metal colorimetrically (see p. 243). Pd, Ir, Rh, Ru and Os can be concd. with Al^{3+} or Fe^{3+} and NH_4OH.

Extn. of the phenylthiourea complex with AmOAc seps. 20 mg. Pd from other Pt metals.[28] Treat the soln. with 20 ml. 0·5% phenylthiourea, 25 ml. 20% NH_4Cl and dil. to 100 ml. with 0·2*M* HCl. Ext. with 25 ml. AmOAc, wash with 25 ml. 20% NH_4Cl, evap. to dryness, heat at 150°C and add 6*M* HNO_3 gradually; finally evap. to fumes with HCl and $HClO_4$ and dil. to a definite vol.

Extn. of the 4-phenylthiosemicarbazide complex with hexone seps. Pt from Pd.[24] Neutralize the soln. with NaOH to bromocresol purple, add 5 ml. 1*M* Na_2HPO_4–KH_2PO_4 buffer (pH 7), heat, add 5 ml. 0·5% reagent in 50% EtOH and place on a steam-bath for 1 hr. Ext. with 5, 5, 2·5 and 2·5 ml. portions of hexone, combine the exts., evap. to dryness, heat to 450–500°C, treat with aqua regia, NaCl, HCl, evap. and eventually treat with $SnCl_2$.

Dimethylglyoxime is suitable for the sepn. of < 0·1 g. Pd from Pt, Ir, Ru, etc. Dimethylglyoxime is most suitable for < 0·01 g. Pd while α-nitroso-β-naphthol is best for larger amts.[29] For an extn. method,[30] add 3–4 drops HNO_3 to 100 ml. 0·2–0·3*N* HCl or 1*N* H_2SO_4 soln., 0·5 g. EDTA if Fe is present, 3 ml. 1% Na-dimethylglyoxime and leave for 1 hr.; ext. with 50, 25, 15, 10 ml. portions of $CHCl_3$, combine the exts. in a beaker, evap., add 10 ml. 1:1 HNO_3–H_2SO_4, evap. to fumes, add H_2O, evap. to fumes and repeat the last 2 steps. Finally, add 25 ml. H_2O, cool, filter, add KI, etc. (see p. 246).

Extn. with $CHCl_3$ of the α-furildioxime complex is also useful for sepn. and concn.

Extn. of the nitrosoamine complex with purified $CHCl_3$ seps. Pd from Rh, Ir and Pt.[31] For < 500 μg. Pd in 10 ml. soln. at pH 2–5, add 0·5 ml. 0·5% *p*-nitrosodimethylaniline in EtOH and 5 ml. EtOH; after 5 min., ext. with 10 ml. $CHCl_3$, add 0·5 ml. reagent and ext. with 10 ml. $CHCl_3$. Evap. to dryness, heat on a hot plate, add 5 ml. fuming HNO_3, evap. nearly to dryness, add 5 ml. HNO_3, evap to 2 ml., add 30% H_2O_2, evap. nearly to dryness, add 5 ml. HCl, evap. to dryness and repeat the HCl treatment twice more. If Pt is present, add 5 drops 1% Na-bisulfite, evap. to dryness and finally add H_2O. The *p*-nitrosodiphenylamine complex which is extd. into EtOAc can also be utilized.[32]

Extn. with dithizone in $CHCl_3$ or CCl_4 from acidic soln. seps. Pd, Au, Cu, Hg, Ag from Pt, Ir, Rh, Os, Ru.

Extn. with $CHCl_3$ of the diethyldithiocarbamate complex seps. Pd and Pt from other Pt metals.[31] For 200 μg. Pt or 100 μg. Pd in 5 ml. soln., add 5 ml. HCl, 4 ml. 2% KI (if > 50 μg. Pd is present, use solid KI), and, after 5 min., 2 ml. 1% Na-diethyldithiocarbamate; ext. twice with 5 ml. $CHCl_3$, add 2 ml. 2% KI and carbamate and ext. again. Combine the exts., evap. to dryness, add HNO_3 and H_2O_2, etc.

NH_4Cl seps. Pt^{4+}, Ru^{4+} (and partly Ir^{4+}) from Ir^{3+}, Pd^{2+}, Au, Fe, Cu, etc. Ag, Sn, Pb and alkali metals interfere. This is useful for the sepn. of much Pt from other metals but the sepn. is not complete. Pt^{4+} and Ir^{4+} in soln. are converted to Pt^{4+} and Ir^{3+} by boiling with NaOH and EtOH and acidifying with HCl. For details, see ref. 21. Pt^{4+} and Ir^{4+} are sepd. from Rh by treatment with NH_4Cl and Cl_2 or HNO_3. NH_4Cl ppts. Os^{4+} from 3*N* HCl soln. $[Rh(NH_3)_5Cl]Cl_2$ is pptd. and sepd. from Pd, Ir and Pt by treating the chloride soln. with NH_4Cl, heating, adding NH_4OH and then making 10% in HCl before filtration.[33]

HNO_3 extn. seps. the bulk of the Pd (as $PdCl_2$) from Pt, Rh and Ir.[21] Evap. the chloride soln. to a few ml., add 25 ml. HNO_3 and heat on a hot plate until the brown fumes have been removed. Decant, wash 4 times with a few ml. of HNO_3, add 5 drops HCl, heat, cool rapidly, filter on a G3 crucible and wash with 3 ml. HNO_3. Evap. the filtrate, add HCl, evap. again and recover Pd by the dimethylglyoxime method. Heat the ppt. with 5% HNO_3, add an equal vol. of H_2O and 5 ml. 10% $Hg(NO_3)_2$ for each 0·1 g. Pd, boil, add 10 ml. 3% $NaBrO_3$ for each 1 g. Pd, etc.

KI ppts. Pd as PdI_2, thus sepg. it from Pt, etc., but the ppt. dissolves in excess reagent; Pd can be sepd. from Rh by means of AgI.[34] $Hg(CN)_2$ can be used similarly to KI.

KNO_2 seps. Ru and Rh from Ir: neutralize the acidic soln. with Na_2CO_3, add excess KNO_2 and then add Na_2S gradually until a chocolate color appears; boil, allow to cool, acidify slightly with dil. HCl, filter and wash with hot H_2O. Traces of Ir coppt. but this remains as a residue when the ppt. is extd. with anhyd. EtOH.

$NaNO_2$ seps. Pt, Rh, Ir from Pd and many other elements. Treat the chloride soln. with 1 g. NaCl, evap. to dryness, add 4 drops 1:1 HCl, 100 ml. warm H_2O and 5 g. $NaNO_2$ and boil gently until the red fumes disappear. Adjust to pH 7 with 2% NaOH, boil for several min., adjust to pH 8 (blue to xylenol blue) with 2% $NaHCO_3$ and boil for 2 min. Filter, wash with hot 1% NaCl, dissolve in the min. amt. of HCl and reppt. Det. Pd with dimethylglyoxime and then det. the other base metals in the ppt. Evap. the filtrate and det. Pt, etc. which are dissolved in the filtrate as $Na_3[M(NO_2)_6]$ where M = Rh or Ir, or as $Na_2[Pt(NO_2)_6]$. Pb can be sepd. from Ir by means of Na_2HPO_4.

Fusion with a 10-fold amt. of Pb or Ag at 900–1000°C and successive extn. with 1:4 HNO_3 and dil. aqua regia seps. Pt, Pd and Rh from Ir; Zn, Ru, Fe interfere and the method is particularly useful for the analysis of Pt–Ir.[35] Fusion with $Na_2S_2O_7$ and extn. with H_2O seps. Rh from Ru and Ir. Ru is sepd. from Rh and Ir by fusion with NaOH, extn. with H_2O and treatment of the residue with HNO_3.

Treatment with SO_2 followed by $H_2C_2O_4$ seps. the Pt metals from Au, Se and Te (see p. 227). Sepn. from Au can be obtained[36] also with SO_2, $N_2H_4{\cdot}HCl$ or $NaNO_2$.

Extn. with AmOAc from 6*N* HCl soln. seps. the Pt metals from Au and Mo; EtOAc and Et_2O can also be used. Sepn. of Pt^{2+} from Fe, Cu, etc. is attained in this way.

2-Mercaptobenzothiazole allows sepn. of Ir from Pb (see p. 249) and Rh from Ir (see p. 237). Pd can be sepd. from the other Pt metals with Bismuthiol II (see p. 244).

Treatment with dil. HCl seps. Pd from Ag; add NH_4OH to the nitrate soln. until the ppt. dissolves, acidify with AcOH, heat, add a small excess of dil. HCl and reppt. Pd can be recovered from the filtrate by means of H_3PO_2 and $HgCl_2$.

KSCN and SO_2 permit sepn. of the Pt metals from Cu; Pd coppts. H_2SO_4 seps. them from Pb, and NaOAc seps. them from Bi and Sn.

$TeCl_4$ and $SnCl_2$ (with or without Au, see p. 227) serve to sep. the Pt metals from Fe, Cu, etc. and are useful for concn. purposes. Heating in Cl_2 with or without NaCl seps. these metals from As, Sb, Se and Te, while volatilization from H_2SO_4 solns. contg. HBr or HCl seps. them from As, Sb, Se and Sn.

For the sepns. possible with ion exchange resins, see Chapter 13, Section 2.3.

Active charcoal can be used to conc. Pt metals other than Ir.

For the application of paper chromatography, see ref. 37.

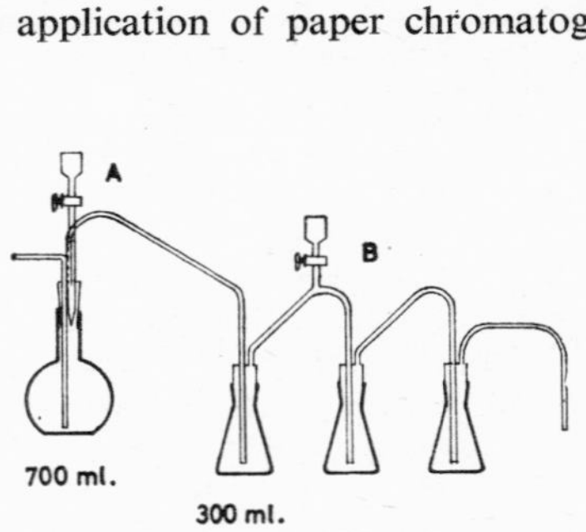

FIG. 4. Distillation flask with train for Os, Ru.

Schemes for the Separation and Determination of the Platinum Metals

Gilchrist and Wicher's method[5] is detailed in Table 34; the apparatus required for the sepn. of Os and Ru is shown in Fig. 4.

TABLE 34. Separation and Determination of Platinum Metals*

Pt metals sample contg. ca. 2 g. (<5 g.) in 100 ml. soln. in the distn. app. made of all Pyrex glass (Fig. 4). Add 40 ml. 1 : 1 HNO_3, boil 1 hr. passing air slowly and with occasional drops of H_2O from (A) and satd. SO_2 from (B) (Note 1).

- Distillate *Os*
- Residual soln.
  Transfer to beaker, evap. to dryness, add 5–10 ml. HCl, evap. to dryness, repeat until no NO_2, add 20–30 ml. H_2O, and 10 ml. H_2SO_4, evap. to fumes, return to distn. flask, add H_2O to 100 ml., add 100 ml. 10% $NaBrO_3$, distil 1·5 hr. passing air and dropping H_2O from (A), and satd. SO_2 soln. from (B), cool, add 25 ml. $NaBrO_3$, distil 1 hr. as above.
  - Distillate *Ru*
  - Residual soln.
    Transfer to 1 l. beaker, carefully add HCl, evap., repeat, wash distn. flask with 5–10 ml. aqua regia which is evapd. several times with HCl and is combined with main soln., evap. to as small a vol. as possible, dil. with H_2O to 200 ml., boil, add 20 ml. 10% $NaBrO_3$ and $NaHCO_3$ until dark green ppt. appears or until blue to bromocresol blue paper, add 10 ml. $NaBrO_3$, boil 5 min., add $NaHCO_3$ until faintly pink to cresol red, add 10 ml. $NaBrO_3$, boil 15 min., remove from heat, let settle; filter on porcelain filter, decant and wash with hot 1% NaCl at pH 8.
    - Ppt.
      Return with filter to the beaker, add 10–20 ml. HCl, remove ppt. on the lip of beaker with moist NaCl on finger and combine, heat on steam-bath, wash and remove filter, heat filter 2–3 times with 5 ml. HCl in 250 ml. beaker and add to main soln., add 2 g. NaCl, evap. to dryness, add 2 ml. HCl, dil. with H_2O to 300 ml., reppt. (Note 2).
      - Ppt.
        Treat with HCl, etc. as above; filter (Note 3), dil. with H_2O to 200 ml., add 1% dimethylglyoxime in EtOH in 10% excess, leave for 1 hr.; filter on glass crucible, wash with 1 : 99 HCl and hot H_2O.
        - Ppt. *Pd*
        - Filtrate (Note 4).
          Evap. and transfer to a 500 ml. Erlenmeyer, add 10 ml. H_2SO_4 + 2–3 ml. HNO_3, put short stem funnel in flask, heat, evap. to fumes, adding HNO_3 at times, cool, add 20 ml. H_2O, evap. to fumes, transfer to 500 ml. beaker, dil. with H_2O to 200 ml., add 20% $TiCl_3$ until supernate is pale violet or if much Ir is present, until no more ppt. appears and the liquid is orange, boil 2 min.; filter on paper, wash with 2·5 : 97·5 H_2SO_4.
      - Filtrate
        20 ml. HCl, evap.
    - Filtrate.
      Add 20 ml. HCl, evap.

    (Both filtrates combined:) Evap. to dryness, if bromate still remains, add HCl, evap., add H_2O; filter, wash with 1 : 99 HCl; dil. with H_2O to 400 ml., add HCl to 5 ml./100 ml., pass H_2S, etc.
    - Ppt. *Pt*

TABLE 34—*(contd.)*

Ppt.
Transfer to 500 ml. Erlenmeyer, add 10 ml. H_2SO_4, heat until carbonization begins, add 5 ml. HNO_3, heat, evap. to fumes, reppt.

Ppt.
Dissolve by treating as above, add 20 ml. H_2O, 10 ml. HCl, boil 15 min.; filter on paper, wash with HCl and 1 : 99 HCl; dil. with H_2O to 400–500 ml., pass H_2S, etc.

Ppt.
Rh

Filtrate

Filtrate

Dil. with H_2O to 800 ml., cool with ice, add a small excess of ice-cold fresh 6% cupferron, filter on paper, wash with cold 2·5 : 97·5 H_2SO_4 + a little cupferron; return to the beaker, add 20 ml. HNO_3, heat, add 20 ml. H_2SO_4, heat to fumes, add HNO_3, heat, dil. with H_2O to 800 ml., reppt.

Filtrate
Combine, evap. until ca. 10 ml. H_2SO_4 remains, dil. with H_2O; filter on paper, wash; dil. with H_2O to 200 ml., add NaOH to nearly neutral, heat, add $NaHCO_3$ until blue to bromocresol purple, add 20 ml. $NaBrO_3$, boil 25 min.; filter on paper, wash with 1% NH_4Cl; etc.

Ppt.
Ir

*The notes mentioned appear below.

NOTES. (1) A boiling time of 1 hr. is needed with osmate or bromoosmate but chloroosmate requires 7–8 hr.; in the latter case, H_2SO_4 should replace HNO_3.
(2) For completeness of sepn. see p. 233.
(3) It may be more convenient to proceed as follows: make the soln. slightly alk. with NH_4OH, pass through Amberlite IR-100, elute Pd with 0·1*M* HCl, and det. Rh and Ir in the effluent by electrodeposition.[38]
(4) Rh and Ir are sepd. from each other, the ultimate purity of the 2 metals being 99·7%; their detns. are only accurate owing to compensation of error.[39] If the soln. can be divided, det. Rh in one portion as above, and Rh + Ir in another portion as follows: ppt. as hydrated dioxides as in the sepn. from Pt, filter, wash with hot 1% NH_4Cl neutralized to bromothymol blue, transfer to a porcelain crucible, dry, moisten with NH_4Cl and ignite carefully. A better method is to destroy the org. material with H_2SO_4 and HNO_3, evap. to 10 ml., ppt. with $NaBrO_3$, filter, treat with HCl and aqua regia, evap. to dryness, add HCl, evap. to dryness, add 15 ml. H_2O and 5 ml. 1:10 HCl and electrolyze the soln. (see p. 246). Treatment with NaH_2PO_2 and $HgCl_2$ is better in most cases.[21]
(5) OsO_4 or RuO_4 is collected in 1:1 HCl satd. with SO_2, 150 ml. being placed in the first flask and 50 ml. in each of the other 2 flasks. RuO_4 is completely absorbed by 3% H_2O_2 at 0°C; the H_2O_2 must not contain acetanilide as stabilizer.[40]
(6) For further information, consult Schoeller and Powell[21] and Holzer and Zaussinger.[10]

The method described by Ubaldini and Nabbia[41] is shown in Table 35. Westland and Beamish[12] have described a sepn. and colorimetric detn. (see Table 36) while Wölbling[11] has also given a colorimetric method (see Table 37).

Determination

The methods available for the determination of the Pt metals are described below with separate sections for each metal.

OSMIUM

Macro amounts of Os can be determined accurately by hydrolysis, mg. amounts with thionalide, 2-phenylbenzothiazole or H_2S, and micro amounts with thiourea or with naphthylamine sulfonic acids. Tetraphenylarsonium chloride seems to provide a useful colorimetric method, while iodometric titration appears to be very convenient.

(a) $NaHCO_3$ permits a gravimetric detn. of Os.[5, 42, 43] Collect the OsO_4 distillate in 1:1 HCl satd. with SO_2 as described above. Evap. nearly to dryness, add 10 ml. HCl, heat for 15 min., evap. and repeat this treatment thrice more. Add 150 ml. H_2O, boil and add 10% $NaHCO_3$ until the ppt. coagulates suddenly; then add several drops of 0·04% bromophenol blue and add reagent until a blue color appears. Boil for 5–10 min., filter on a Munroe crucible and wash with hot 1% NH_4Cl. Cover the ppt. with NH_4Cl, add a few drops of hot 1% NH_4Cl soln. and suck until the bottom of the filter is covered with solid NH_4Cl. Wipe off this NH_4Cl, place a Pt cup under the filter, cover the filter with a quartz Rose lid and introduce through the hole in the lid

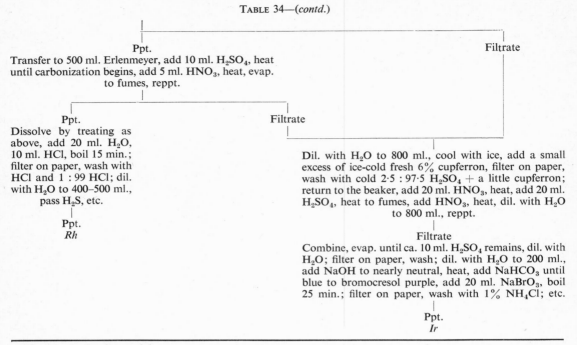

TABLE 35. Separation of Pt Metals[41]

Pt alloy
Treat with aqua regia, HCl, etc. and add $NaBrO_3$ and $NaHCO_3$

- Ppt. Treat with dimethylglyoxime
  - Ppt. *Pd*
  - Filtrate. Make alk. and treat with mercaptobenzothiazole
    - Ppt. *Rh*
    - Filtrate. Treat with AcOH and mercaptobenzothiazole
      - Ppt. *Ir*
- Filtrate. Make alk. and treat with mercaptobenzothiazole
  - Ppt. *Pt*

TABLE 36. Separation and Colorimetric Determination of Platinum Metals[12]

Place 30 ml. 9*M* H_2SO_4 sample soln. in a distg. app. (Note 1), heat, add 10% H_2O_2 dropwise, heat at 110°C for 15 min., cool, add 25 ml. H_2O and 5 ml. 30% H_2O_2 and boil for 15 min. passing distillate through 5 ml. boiling $HClO_4$ in a trap.

- Distillate (Os). Collect in 3 receivers contg. 15, 5, 5 ml. 40% HBr (gravimetry) or 5% thiourea in EtOH–HCl (1 : 1) (colorimetry)
- Residual soln. Cool, add 3 vols. H_2O, boil out H_2O_2, add 5 ml. 5% $HBrO_3$ (satd. $Ba(BrO_3)_2$ soln. and H_2SO_4), boil for 15 min., add 5 ml. $HBrO_3$ and boil for 15 min. Pass distillate through trap contg. 1 : 1 H_2SO_4; add 5 ml. $HBrO_3$ to the trap at 2nd. $HBrO_3$ addn. and boil.
  - Distillate (Ru). Collect in 15, 5, 5 ml. 1 : 1 HCl–EtOH and det. colorimetrically with thiourea
  - Residual soln. Transfer to beaker, evap. to 1 ml., add some H_2O and 5 ml. HCl, boil for 30 min. adding HCl, evap. to initial SO_3 fumes, dil. to 10 ml. with H_2O, cool, add 50 mg. Te powder, boil for 10 min., add 3 ml. HCl, a few crystals of $Na_2S_2O_5$ and 1 drop 1% KI, swirl for 15 min., add more $Na_2S_2O_5$, filter on Whatman No. 42 paper, wash with 0·2% $Na_2S_2O_5$ in 3*N* HCl.
    - Ppt. (Pd, Pt). Char in a silica crucible, ignite for 15 min. on a Meker in H_2, ignite in air, add aqua regia, heat on a steam-bath for 3 hr., rinse walls, add 40 mg. NaCl, evap. to dryness, add HCl, repeat thrice, add HCl. Det. Pt and Pd with *p*-nitrosodimethylaniline (Note 2).
    - Filtrate. Evap. below 200°C to 0·5 ml., cool, dil. to 8 ml. with H_2O, add 75 mg. Sb dust, boil for 1·5 hr. adding H_2O, filter on Whatman No. 42 paper and wash with 5 ml. H_2O.
      - Ppt. (Rh). Ignite at 400–450°C for 10 hr., cool, add 0·5 ml. H_2SO_4, 1 ml. 30% H_2O_2, 2 ml. HCl, evap. to 1 ml.; add 1 ml. HCl, dil. to 5 ml. with H_2O and add $SnCl_2$, or add 10 ml. HCl and use 2-mercapto-4,5-dimethylthiazole.
      - Filtrate (Ir). Add 10 ml. H_2SO_4, 0·5 g. $N_2H_4 \cdot H_2SO_4$, pass N_2, heat to fumes, then heat at 160–200°C; add 75 ml. HCl dropwise, evap. to 2 ml., dil. to 50 ml. with H_2O and det. with *p*-nitrosodimethylaniline.

NOTES. (1) See *Anal. Chem.*, **26**, 739 (1954).
(2) If Pd exceeds 20 μg., sepn. by extn. of the dimethylglyoximate or diethyldithiocarbamate may be preferable.

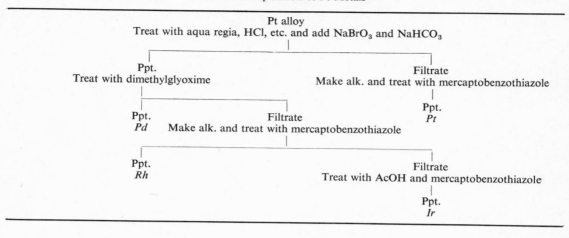

TABLE 37. Colorimetric Method for Separation of Pt Metals[11]

Sample soln.
Distil

- Os, Ru
  Add thiourea, HCl, $SnCl_2$, heat and ext. the red Os complex with EtOAc
  - EtOAc layer.
    Red. *Os*
  - Aq. layer.
    Treat with rubeanic acid. *Ru*
- Convert to chlorides, add NH_4OH, make 1*N* in HCl, add $SnCl_2$ till yellow-orange, shake with 2 vols. of EtOAc, sep., shake ext. with $SnCl_2$ in 1*N* HCl, sep.
  - EtOAc layer.
    Yellow-orange.
    Pt
  - Aq. layer.
    Leave for 1–2 hr., ext. with EtOAc
    - EtOAc layer.
      Rh
    - Neutralize with NH_4OH. If the green Pd color is pale, add KI and leave for 12 hr. Filter
      - Dissolve in Cl_2 water, add NH_4OH. Green. *Pd*
      - Add excess Cl_2 water.
        Ir

a H_2 inlet tube; the H_2 supply is adjusted so that the flame is small when ignited. After leaving the ignited H_2 supply flowing for 5 min., heat the filter slowly over a burner, ignite for 10 min., remove the burner and extinguish the H_2 flame by stopping the gas flow momentarily. Leave to cool with H_2 passing over the filter, leave for some time under a stream of CO_2 and finally weigh as Os.

NOTE. This method is inaccurate when small amts. are present.[44] The ppt. obtained by neutralizing the distillate which has been collected in dil. NaOH and EtOH,[21] is difficult to filter and is liable to deflagrate on heating.

(b) Thionalide provides a good gravimetric method.[44] For 5 mg. Os in 100 ml. dil. HCl soln., boil gently, add 3–4 drops of a soln. of 80 mg. thionalide in 15 ml. EtOH and then add the rest of this soln. gradually during 2 hr. Boil for 2 hr., place on a steam-bath for 2 hr., filter on a porcelain A2 crucible by decanting, add 25 ml. 0·2*N* HCl, heat for 15–30 min. on a steam-bath, decant and repeat the washing and decantation 4 times, transferring the ppt. Heat in H_2 for 2 hr., cool, weigh, ignite in air and then in H_2 and weigh. Os is detd. by difference.

(c) H_2S is also used gravimetrically.[21, 42] Pass H_2S through the OsO_4 distillate which has been collected in dil. NaOH and EtOH, heat, acidify with HCl, pass H_2S and leave for 12 hr. Filter on a Gooch crucible, wash with hot H_2O, ignite in H_2, cool in CO_2 and weigh as Os.

(d) Thiourea is used colorimetrically for 0·1–10 mg. Os in 50 ml. soln.[45, 46, 47] Add 10 ml. 6*M* H_2SO_4, 1 ml. 10% thiourea and dil. to 100 ml. with H_2O. Measure the pinkish color after 10 min. at 480 mμ. The error is ±2·9% for 0·8–4 mg. Os and ±12% for 0·1–0·3 mg. Os.

NOTES. (1) Interferences are > 5 p.p.m. Pd (yellow) and > 2 p.p.m. Ru (green-blue). Rh, Ir, Pt, SO_2 do not interfere.
(2) For analysis of chloroosmate or bromoosmate add 10% $SnCl_2$ in 1:4 HCl, heat for 10–15 min. in boiling H_2O, etc. When thiourea is added to a distillate which has been absorbed in SO_2–HCl, the initial color is deep but becomes quite pale after 7 hr. and has disappeared after 24 hr. It is better to absorb the distillate in a thiourea soln. in 2*N* H_2SO_4.
(3) For 5–1000 μg. Os in 25 ml. soln.,[48] add 5 ml. 6*N* H_2SO_4, 2·5 ml. H_3PO_4 followed by 5% $KMnO_4$ to give a pink color. Then add 25 mg. $Fe(NH_4)_2(SO_4)_2$, 15 ml. HNO_3 while cooling, and 10 ml. $CHCl_3$ or CCl_4. Shake for 2 min., sep., ext. 3–4 times, combine the exts., add 5 ml. 0·1*M* thiourea in 1*N* H_2SO_4, shake for 5 min. and measure the red color at 480 mμ. No interference arises from Ru, etc.
(4) *o,o'*-Ditolylthiourea is suitable for 15–175 μg. Os in 10–20 ml. 6*N* HCl soln.[49] Add 1 ml. 5% $SnCl_2$ in 6*N* HCl, 1 ml. satd. reagent soln. in MeOH, boil for 15 min., cool, add 10 ml. $CHCl_3$, ext. and measure in a 2 cm. cell at 490 mμ. Small amts. of Ir, Pt can be tolerated but Pd, Ru, Rh and oxidants interfere.
(5) 1,4-Diphenylthiosemicarbazide is useful for 100 μg. Os in very dil. HCl soln.[49] Add 1 ml. satd. $NaHCO_3$, 1 ml. satd. reagent soln. in MeOH, heat at 45°C for 30 min., cool, add 2–3 ml. HCl, 2 ml. $SnCl_2$ soln., ext. with 10 ml. $CHCl_3$ and measure in a 2 cm. cell at 520 mμ. Ir, Rh, Pt can be present, but Pd, Ru, NO_3^-, SO_4^{2-} and much Cl^- interfere.

(e) 1-Naphthylamine-3,5,7-trisulfonic acid is suitable for the colorimetric detn. of Os^{6+} (0–6 p.p.m.) at pH

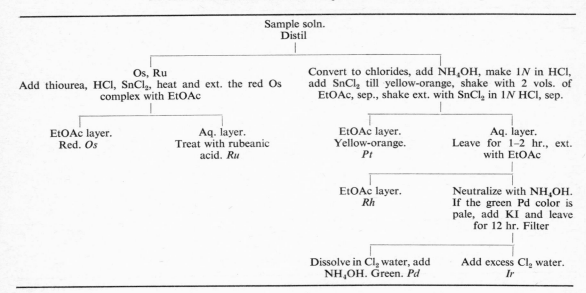

1·5 in solns. contg. 10 ml. buffer (97 ml. 0·2*N* HCl and 50 ml. 0·2*N* KCl/200 ml.). The reagent soln. contains 0·0505 g. of the acid/250 ml. H_2O and the violet color is measured at 560 mμ. Many elements interfere unless the Os^{6+} is distd. from 6*N* HNO_3 soln.[50]

(f) Miscellaneous gravimetric methods. Al can be used to reduce the OsO_4 distillate after collection in NaOH and EtOH; the ppt. is filtered, washed with H_2O and 5% H_2SO_4, heated in H_2 and weighed as Os.[42]

2-Phenylbenzothiazole is used for 3·5–27 mg. Os as $(NH_4)_2OsBr_6$ in 25 ml. 4*N* HCl soln. (Hoffman *et al.*[44]). The necessary amt. of reagent is added as a soln. in 25 ml. 4*N* HBr and the ppt. is filtered on a porcelain crucible, washed with 0·2*N* HCl, ignited in H_2 and weighed as Os. If the Os distillate is collected in 40% HBr, dil. the distillate, heat for 30 min. on a steam-bath with 200 mg. $NH_2OH{\cdot}HCl$, add excess (0·8 mg./ml.) of reagent and continue as above.[12]

Strychnine sulfate is suitable for 4–17 mg. Os as $(NH_4)_2OsBr_6$ in 50 ml. soln. Add satd. reagent soln., heat for a few min. on a steam-bath, cool, filter on a porcelain A2 crucible, wash with 0·02*N* HCl, ignite in H_2, etc. (Hoffman *et al.*[44]).[42, 47] The method is inaccurate when applied to distillates which have been collected in SO_2–HCl mixtures. Ru does not interfere.

Quinine may replace strychnine, but in both cases the compn. of the ppt. depends on the type of the Os salt.[51]

(g) Iodometric titration provides a rapid detn. of 25 mg. Os^{8+} in 25 ml. soln. (Ayres *et al.*[45]). Add 15 ml. 6*M* H_2SO_4 and 2 g. KI and titrate with 0·025*N* $Na_2S_2O_3$ using starch as external indicator.

NOTE. Colorimetric detns. based on the oxidizing action of Os have been suggested, tetramethyl-*p*-phenylenediamine,[52] *o*-toluidine or benzidine[53] being used as reagent.

(h) Miscellaneous colorimetric methods. Tetraphenylarsonium chloride is suitable for < 25 μg. Os as $OsCl_6^{2-}$ in 20 ml. 0·2*N* HCl soln. contg. < 0·5 g. NaCl; add 2 ml. 1% reagent and 10 ml. $CHCl_3$, shake for 3–5 min., filter and measure the absorbance at 346 or 375 mμ. Ru and Rh can be tolerated but SO_2, ClO_4^-, Pd, Pt and Ir interfere.[54]

KSCN forms a blue complex with Os in acidic soln. which can be extd. with Et_2O or AmOH;[55] if AcOH and EtOH are added, an orange or brown color due to $Os(SCN)_4$ or $[Os(SCN)_6]^{2-}$ appears.

The catalytic effect of Os on the reaction of Ce^{4+} with As^{3+} may be applied for the detn. of 0·025–0·5 μg. Os. Evap. the soln. with $FeSO_4$ and H_2SO_4, add 20 ml. H_2O, 2–3 ml. H_3PO_4, 5% $KMnO_4$ and then $FeSO_4$ to discharge the pink color. Transfer to a separatory funnel, add HNO_3 to give a 5–6*M* soln., adjust to 20–25°C and ext. 3 times with 10 ml. portions of $CHCl_3$ or CCl_4. Combine the exts., wash with a little 2*M* HNO_3, transfer to a bottle, and stopper. Then add 5 ml. As^{3+} soln. (500 ml. 0·1*N* As^{3+} and 500 ml. 3*M* H_2SO_4), shake for 10 min. and sep. Add 1 mg. Ag_2SO_4, transfer a 4 ml. aliquot to a 10 ml. beaker, add 1 ml. 0·1*N* $Ce(SO_4)_2$ and compare the time required for the transmittancy at 340 mμ to be decreased to 40% of the initial value. Alternatively, insert a Pt wire and connect up a calomel cell by means of a KNO_3 bridge, then add 1 ml. of the Ce^{4+} soln. and compare the time required for the voltage to become 0·75 v.[56] Interferences are Cl^-, Mo, Mn, > 100 μg of other Pt metals, > 10 mg. Fe, Cu, Hg, Ti and > 1 mg. Ni or Co.[57]

Several similar procedures have been suggested.[57] For 1·5–7 μg. Os, add enough H_2O to give a final vol. of 20 ml., 5 ml. 0·1*N* As^{3+} in 1*N* H_2SO_4, 10 ml. 4*N* H_2SO_4 and 3 ml. 0·1*N* $KMnO_4$ to a suitable vessel, then add the Os soln. and proceed as above. For 0·15–1·8 μg. Os, add the sample soln. to a mixture of H_2O (enough to give a final vol. of 8 ml.), 0·5 ml. 1% $KClO_3$, 2·0 ml. 2·5% H_2SO_4, 2 ml. 4% KI and 0·5 ml. 0·5% starch; measure the time for the transmittancy at 572 mμ to decrease from 60% to 10% of the initial value. Ni, Co, Cu and Fe interfere. For 0·3–1·5 μg. Os, add the sample soln. to a mixture of H_2O, 2 ml. 0·05% *p*-phenylenediamine, 3 ml. 0·5% H_2O_2, and measure the time for the transmittancy at 434 mμ to decrease from 30% to 10% of the original value; Fe, Cu, Co, Mn and Ni interfere.

The color of Os^{6+} itself can be utilized.[58] Fuse the sample with NaOH and Na_2O_2, leach with H_2O, heat with EtOH for 15 min. at 30–40°C and filter if Ru is present; the final soln. should contain 0·1*N* NaOH and 5% EtOH. Measure the purple color at 520 mμ.

Ephedrine hydrochloride gives an orange complex with Os in NaOH soln. which can be extd. with CCl_4.[59]

RUTHENIUM

Hydrolysis provides the most appropriate method for macro analysis. The best procedure for semimicro amounts involves colorimetric detn. of ruthenate. Phenylthiosemicarbazide and its analogs, as well as *o*-phenanthroline, are excellent reagents for micro quantities. Thionalide seems to permit a satisfactory detn. of semimicro amounts of Ru.

(a) $NaHCO_3$ is a good reagent for hydrolytic detn.[5, 21, 42, 43, 60] Evap. the RuO_4 distillate (see p. 233) to a moist state, add 10 ml. HCl, cover and place on a steam-bath for 1 hr.; add 50 ml. H_2O, boil, filter through paper and wash with 1:99 HCl. Dil. the filtrate to 200 ml., boil, add 10% $NaHCO_3$ until a ppt. appears, then add some 0·04% bromocresol purple and adjust to pH 6 (blue) with the reagent. Boil for 6 min., filter on paper, and wash first with hot 1% $(NH_4)_2SO_4$ until no Cl^- remains and then 3–4 times with cold 2·5% $(NH_4)_2SO_4$. Transfer to a porcelain crucible, dry below 100°C, heat slowly in air and then in H_2; cool under H_2, ext. with H_2O, filter on paper, ignite as before and finally weigh as Ru. Deflagration may occur.

(b) Ruthenate itself gives a measurable color.[61] Fuse the sample contg. 8 mg. Ru for 20–30 sec. at dull redness with 1 g. KNO_3 and 0·3 g. KOH, cool, dissolve in

H_2O and add KOH to give a final concn. of 2*M*; dil. to a definite vol. and measure the orange-red color at 465 mμ. Measurements can also be done at 350 or 490 mμ.[58]

NOTES. (1) No interference arises from the other Pt metals if their amt. is less than 1/5 that of Ru. Most other elements can be present.

(2) The green–yellow color of perruthenate can also be utilized.[62] To 0·1–12 mg. Ru in 1% HCl soln. in a 500 ml. distn. flask, add 10 ml. H_2O, 1 g. $NaBiO_3$, 1 ml. H_3PO_4, 10 ml. $HClO_4$ and boil gently for over 30 min. while passing air through the soln. at a rate of 2 bubbles/sec. Collect the distillate in 50 ml. 2·0*M* KOH, dil. to 100 ml. with H_2O and measure at 380 mμ after 30 min. Os interference can be prevented by distn. from HNO_3 soln.

(c) Phenylthiosemicarbazide is excellent for the colorimetric detn. of < 25 μg. Ru in 10 ml. 4*N* HCl soln.[46] Add 5 ml. 1% reagent in EtOH, place in boiling H_2O for 10 min., cool, dil. to 25 ml. with H_2O and measure the reddish color photometrically with a blue–green filter. The complex can be extd. with BuOH. Fe interferes.

Several similar reagents have been suggested. Thiourea is used for 0·2–1·5 mg. Ru.[46, 60, 63] Add 40 ml. 1:1 HCl–EtOH and 5 ml. 10% thiourea, heat at 85°C for 10 min., cool, dil. with 1:1 6*N* HCl–EtOH to 100 ml. and measure the blue color at 620 mμ. Interferences are 0·7 p.p.m. Pd (yellow), 0·2 p.p.m. Os (pink), Co (blue), Cr (green), NO_2^- and NO_3^-.

s-Diphenylthiourea is suitable for 6–18 p.p.m. Ru. Add 30 ml. 1:1 HCl–EtOH and 5 ml. 2% reagent in AcOH, dil. to 45 ml. with the HCl mixture, heat for 5 min. at 85°C, cool, dil. to 50 ml. with the HCl mixture and measure the blue color at 630 mμ 30 min. after removal from the heat. Moderate amts. of Os, Ir, Pd, Rh and Pt can be tolerated, and this is said to be the best reagent.[64] Alternatively, for 100 μg. Ru in 20 ml. 6*N* HCl soln.[49] add 1 ml. satd. reagent soln. in MeOH, heat for 30 min. at 80°C, ext. with 10 ml. $CHCl_3$ and measure at 650 mμ in a 2 cm. cell; in this case, Pt interferes.

2,4-Diphenylthiosemicarbazide (satd. soln. in MeOH) has been used for 30 μg. Ru in 15 ml. 6*N* HCl soln.[49] Add 1 ml. reagent soln., boil for 10–15 min., cool, ext. with 10 ml. $CHCl_3$ and measure at 565 mμ in a 2 cm. cell; 10-fold amts. of Os can be tolerated, as can 3–5-fold amts. of Ir, Pt, Pd and Rh.

(d) *o*-Phenanthroline is satisfactory for the colorimetric detn. of 10–150 μg. Ru.[65] Evap. the soln. to fumes in a distn. flask with 10 ml. H_2SO_4 (if HNO_3 is present, evap. several times with HCl and then evap. with H_2SO_4). Add 1 ml. $HClO_4$ and heat while bubbling dry air through the soln.; collect in 30 ml. 0·2*N* HCl and 4 ml. 5% $NH_2OH{\cdot}HCl$ soln., placing some ml. HCl and 1 ml. NH_2OH soln. in a bubbler. Combine the absorbents, evap. to 20–30 ml., add 10 ml. 0·01*M* reagent, 10 ml. 20% NaCl and 5 ml. NH_2OH soln., adjust to pH 6·0 with NaOH or HCl, place for 2 hr. in boiling H_2O, cool and dil. to 100 ml. with H_2O. Measure the yellow color at 448 mμ in a 2 cm. cell (ϵ = 18 500 ± 200). The results are slightly low if the Ru is not distd.

(e) Thionalide provides an alternative gravimetric procedure.[66] Dil. the distillate which has been collected in 3% H_2O_2 at 0°C and contains < 10 mg. Ru, to 150 ml. with H_2O, add 0·6 ml. HCl and boil off all the H_2O_2. Add reagent (an excess dissolved in 3 ml. EtOH), boil, filter on Whatman No. 42 paper and wash with hot H_2O. Carbonize in a porcelain crucible, ignite in air for 2 min. and then in H_2, cool under H_2 and weigh as Ru. HNO_3 interferes. The method has been reported as giving results which are 10% low[60] but it is also said to be accurate.[67]

(f) Miscellaneous gravimetric methods. H_2S ppts. Ru from solns. contg. 7–8 ml. HCl/100 ml. on boiling; the ppt. is ignited to Ru after filtering and washing with dil. HCl and hot H_2O.[21, 42] Pptn. is incomplete from H_2SO_4 solns. unless HCl is added. If > 0·2 g. Ru is present, most of the Ru is pptd. first with NH_4Cl; this ppt. is ignited and the remaining Ru is recovered from the filtrate by the H_2S method.[21] Ignition in air yields RuO_2.[68]

Ru can be pptd. as the metal by treatment with Mg or Zn in acidic soln.; the ppt. is washed with 5% H_2SO_4 and ignited.[42] Distillates which have been collected in 10–15% KOH and EtOH, can be evapd., boiled with anhydrous EtOH and filtered; the ppt. is washed with hot H_2O, dil. HCl and hot H_2O and ignited.[42] A reductimetric potentiometric titration with $TiCl_3$ has been proposed.[69]

(g) 5-Hydroxyquinoline-8-carboxylic acid provides a good colorimetric method.[46, 70] Boil the RuO_4 distillate from an HBr soln., which has been collected in H_2O_2, with 2·5 ml. 1:20 HBr for 10 min., cool, add 5·0 ml. 6*N* H_2SO_4 and 10 ml. reagent (0·5 g. suspended in 1 l. H_2O and heated with 0·5 g. Na_2CO_3 at 40°C), boil for 5 min., cool and dil. to 50 ml. with H_2O. Measure the dark blue color at 500–560 mμ with a Wratten 66 + 15 filter.

NOTES. (1) Other Pt metals can be present but HNO_3, HNO_2, Fe^{2+} and large amts. of HCl interfere.

(2) Oxine itself forms a green complex with Ru^{3+} in solns. contg. AcOH and NaOAc; the complex is extd. by $CHCl_3$. Ru^{4+} forms a green-brown complex.[46]

(h) Miscellaneous colorimetric methods. *p*-Nitrosodimethylaniline may be used to det. 6–60 μg. Ru (as chloride) in 5 ml. of almost neutral soln.[67] Add 1 ml. 4*M* AcOH–1*M* NaOAc and 2 ml. reagent soln. (150 mg./100 ml. heated for 25 min. in boiling H_2O and cooled), heat at 70 ± 4°C for 5 min., cool, dil. to 25 ml. with H_2O and measure the green color at 610 mμ. Os interferes. The color formed is weaker if *p*-nitrosodiethylaniline is used, whereas no color at all is formed with *p*-nitrosodiphenylamine.

Rubeanic acid is suitable for 0·03–0·8 mg. Ru.[71] Add 40 ml. 1:1 AcOH/EtOH and 15 ml. 0·2% reagent in AcOH and heat at 80°C for 30 min.; cool, dil. to 100 ml. with 1:1 6*N* HCl–EtOH and measure the blue color at 650 mμ. The error is ±1%; up to 5 μg. Os can be tolerated.

The catalytic action of Ru on the $KClO_3$ reaction with KI has been utilized.[72] To a mixture of H_2O (to give a final vol. of 15 ml.), 0·5 ml. 4% $KClO_3$, 2·5 ml. 5*N* H_2SO_4, 2·0 ml. 8% KI and 1·0 ml. 0·5% starch, add the sample soln. contg. 10–40 μg. Ru and measure the time required at 25 or 35°C for the color to match that of a soln. contg. 1 ml. 0·1% Congo red, 29 ml. KCl–HCl mixture of pH 1·6 which has been prepared 2 hr. previously.

HBr forms a colored complex with Ru on warming the sample soln. with 20% HBr; the color is measured at 400 mμ.[73] Ru^{3+} (0·6 μg.) forms a green color in 6*N* HCl soln.[46]

KSCN reacts with 0·5 μg. Ru in 0·2–1*N* HCl soln. to give a pink color which can be extd. with BuOH; F^- and PO_4^{3-} interfere.[46]

KI can be used to det. Ru in 7·5 × 10^{-4}–10^{-5}*N* concns.[74] For 5 ml. sample soln. which is 4*N* in H_2SO_4, pass Cl_2 for 10 min., boil for 10 min., dil. to 45 ml. with H_2O, add 1 g. KI, dil. to 50 ml. with H_2O and measure at 410 mμ.

PLATINUM

A peculiarity of Pt analysis is that no reagent is satisfactory for its detn. in a mixt. of Pt metals. Amts. exceeding 1 mg. are usually detd. by means of reducing agents; smaller amts. are better detd. with $SnCl_2$, KI, dithizone or *p*-nitrosodimethylaniline.

(a) HCOOH is applied gravimetrically.[5, 43, 75] Heat the 400 ml. soln. contg. 20 ml. HCl, pass H_2S rapidly, filter on paper and wash with 1:99 HCl. Ignite the ppt. in a porcelain crucible, ext. with HCl and re-ignite. Dissolve the S-contg. Pt in aqua regia, treat with HCl, evap., filter on paper and wash with 1:99 HCl. Dil. the filtrate to 100 ml. with H_2O, add 1 ml. HCOOH/0·25 g. Pt and make just alk. to bromophenol blue with NaOH. Place on a steam-bath for 5 hr., filter on paper, wash with 1% NH_4Cl, ignite, ext. with H_2O and re-ignite.

NOTES. (1) A Zn suspension is preferable for 1–10 mg. Pt.[76] Evap. the soln. contg. 10 mg. Pt to a syrup, add 0·5 ml. HCl and dil. to 85 ml. with H_2O. Add the Zn suspension (5·5 mg./ml.) in 0·5 ml. portions every 10–15 sec. until 100 mg. is present, then every 30 sec. until 200 mg. is present. Boil gently for 1 hr., filter on paper and wash with 5 ml. 1% HCl and 60–70 ml. 1% NH_4Cl. Ignite at 600°C for 1 hr., cool, heat over a Méker burner in a H_2 atmosphere for 1 hr., cool in N_2, then in air and weigh Pt. For 1–5 mg. Pt, add 50 mg. Zn in 20 ml. during 1 hr., boil for 15 min., add 0·5 ml. 3*N* HCl, boil for 45 min., etc.
(2) NH_2OH, Hg, Mg and Fe[42] can also be used as the reductant.
(3) 2% H_3PO_2 and satd. thiourea peroxide are suitable resp. for large and small amts. of Pt.[21] To the 10% v/v HCl soln. add $HgCl_2$ (Hg ⩾ 3 Pt), boil, add reagent, filter on Whatman No. 41 paper, wash with hot 10% HCl and H_2O and ignite.
(4) Satd. $H_2C_2O_4$ soln. is satisfactory (see p. 233).[21]
(5) Ascorbic acid is applied titrimetrically,[77] excess being added to the soln. at pH 1·7, or contg. up to 0·02*N* HCl, and back-titrated potentiometrically with $FeCl_3$.

(b) $SnCl_2$ allows a colorimetric detn.[21, 46, 78–80] For 30–250 μg. Pt in slightly acidic (HCl) soln., add 10 ml. HCl, 25 ml. 20% NH_4Cl, 20 ml. 1*M* reagent in 3·5*M* HCl (cover the stock soln. with xylene), and measure the yellow color at 403 mμ. Alternatively, ext. with an equal vol. of 1% resorcinol in iso-AmOAc and measure at 398 mμ. A differential method allows a wider range to be detd.

NOTES. (1) Fe, Cu and Co do not interfere. The amts. in p.p.m. of other metals which can be tolerated in the direct and extn. methods resp. are: Ir 4·8 and 11; Ru 1·4 and 40; Rh 0·8 and 0·1; Pd 0·4 and 2·3; Os 1·5 and 50; Au 0·5 and 0·7; Te 0·3 and 0·1; Cr 10 and 90; Ni 40 and 200.
(2) The optimum amt. of reductant is said to be 5 ml. 20% $SnCl_2$/100 ml. 2*N* HCl soln.[79] The color formed is probably caused by formation of $(Pt^{\circ}Sn_4Cl_4)^{4+}$ or its halide.[81] The extinction coeff. is 30 000–40 000. The acidity must be strictly regulated. The interference of Rh is at a minimum after 3 hr.[79]

(c) KI is used colorimetrically for 25–300 μg. Pt.[46] Add 1·0 ml. 1:10 HCl and 1·00 ml. 5% KI, dil. to 50 ml. with H_2O, place in the dark for 1 hr. and measure the pink color at 490 mμ. 0·4 mg. Cu can be added as a catalyst.[82] Pd, Au, Fe, Cu, Bi, oxidants and reductants interfere.

Several other procedures have been suggested to utilize the formation of halide complexes.

(*i*) HCl is used for 3–11 μg. Pt/ml. at pH 3·5–6 (acetate buffer), the color being measured at 262 mμ.[83] Interferences in μg./ml. are Rh (0·05), Ru (0·08), Pd (0·1), Ir (0·3) and Os (5).

(*ii*) 15% NH_4Cl is applied gravimetrically.[42, 76, 84] Evap. the HCl soln. to dryness, add 30 ml. Cl_2 water, evap. to 20 ml., add 30 ml. reagent, cool, filter on a Gooch crucible after 1 hr., wash with NH_4Cl soln. and EtOH, dry at 100°C and weigh as $(NH_4)_2PtCl_6$. Alternatively, ignite in H_2 and weigh as Pt. Other Pt metals interfere, particularly Rh and Ir. Similar methods have been suggested with pptn. of K_2PtCl_6, Tl_2PtCl_6 and Cs_2PtCl_6.

(*iii*) Quinine or cinchonine have been used in conjunction with KI;[85] the ppt. is formed from slightly acidic soln., dried at 105°C and weighed as $C_{20}H_{24}O_2N_2\cdot$ (or $C_{19}H_{22}ON_2\cdot$)H_2PtI_6. Hexamine can be utilized similarly.[85] α-Phenylpyridine has also been proposed for colorimetry.[86]

(*iv*) Tetraphenylarsonium bromide is used gravimetrically or titrimetrically along with HBr.[87] Add some Br_2 water to the soln. contg. 5–20 mg. Pt, evap. to dryness, add 10–30 ml. 0·2*N* HBr, boil and add a small excess of 0·02M reagent. Filter on a glass crucible, wash with a satd. soln. of the ppt. in 0·2N HBr, dry at 110°C and weigh as $[(C_6H_5)_4As]_2PtBr_6$. Alternatively, dissolve the ppt. and titrate with 0·02N I_2. Phenylbenzyldimethylammonium chloride has been used.[88]

(d) H_2S is applied gravimetrically.[42, 43] Boil the soln. contg. < 0·5 g. Pt, a few ml. HCl and a few ml. H_2SO_4/100 ml., pass H_2S for 30–40 min. and complete the detn. in the usual way. The Pt formed is impure. If nitrogen oxides are present, add NH_4Cl, evap. and proceed as above.[89] The ppt. coagulates readily on addn. of some $HgCl_2$.

(e) Miscellaneous gravimetric methods. Thionalide may be used under the same conditions as for Ag (p. 146), the ppt. being dried below 170°C and weighed as $Pt(C_{12}H_{10}ONS)_4$; see also under Rh, p. 246.[90]

Thiophenol ppts. 10–25 mg. Pt in 200 ml. soln.[91] Add 4 drops HCl to give a < 0·05N acid soln., followed by 1 ml. 10% v/v reagent in EtOH (discard the stock soln. if an orange ppt. appears); place on a steam-bath for 2 hr., cool, filter on Whatman No. 42 paper, wash with H_2O, ignite slowly in a porcelain crucible and weigh as Pt. Interferences are Pd, Rh, Ir, Au, Cu. Mercaptobenzothiazole can also be used.[41]

For electrodeposition,[42] dissolve the K_2PtCl_6 ppt. in 2% v/v H_2SO_4, heat to 60–65°C, and electrolyze with a Cu-plated Pt dish as cathode for 4–5 hr. at 1–2 v. and 0·05 amp./100 cm.^{2}.

α-Furildioxime (2% in EtOH) ppts. Pt from acidic soln. contg. 10% EtOH on boiling for 30 min.; the ppt. is washed with dil. EtOH and ignited to Pt.[92] Pptn. is incomplete with dimethylglyoxime.[92]

(f) Miscellaneous titrimetric methods. Na-diethyldithiocarbamate can be used in the same way as for Pd (p. 245).[93]

Cu_2Cl_2 reduces Pt to the divalent state, which is titrated with $KMnO_4$ after passing air for 4 hr. and adding H_2SO_4, $MnSO_4$.[43] Fe^{2+} can also serve as the reductant,[43] excess being titrated with NH_4VO_3 with phenylanthranilic acid indicator after addn. of PO_4^{3-} or F^-.

(g) *p*-Nitrosodimethylaniline is used colorimeically[12, 31] for 35–120 μg. Pt in 10 ml. soln. at pH 2–3. Add 10 ml. buffer (50 ml. 4M NaOAc and 53 ml. 4M HCl), 1·00 ml. reagent (5 mg./ml. abs. EtOH) and 5 ml. H_2O, and heat at 100°C for 20 min. (alternatively add 4 ml. abs. EtOH and heat at 85°C for 1 hr.), cool, dil. to 50 ml. with 95% EtOH and measure at 525 mμ.

NOTES. (1) The interference of Pd can be corrected for by deducting the absorbance of a similar soln. which has not been heated. Rh, Ir, Os, Ru interfere. Au up to 50-fold the amt. of Pt, Fe and Cu up to 100-fold, and Cr up to 300-fold can be tolerated.

(2) In an alternative method[12] at pH 2·2, add 3 ml. reagent (16·5 mg./100 ml. H_2O heated and stirred for 30 min.), heat at 85°C for 25 min., dil. to 50 ml. with H_2O and measure at 515 mμ in a 5-cm. cell.

(h) Miscellaneous colorimetric methods. Dithizone can be used (see pp. 229 and 245).

Satd. thiosemicarbazide soln. is used for 50–100 μg. Pt in solns. satd. with Na_2CO_3 or NaOAc; 2 ml. reagent is added, and the complex is extd. with AmOAc and measured at 585 mμ.[94] The method is reported as unreliable (Hoffman and Beamish[91]).

Phenylthiosemicarbazide has been applied colorimetrically;[96] add 2 ml. reagent (0·01% in 2N AcOH) to 10 ml. soln. which is 2N in AcOH, ext. with 10 ml. EtOAc for 2 min. after 24 hr. and measure at 810 mμ. 0·07–19 μg. Pt/ml. can be detd. Interferences of Hg and Ag are prevented by NH_4Cl, of Fe by PO_4^{3-}, of Au by $NaNO_2$ reduction, and of Cu and Pd by filtration before extn. For the gravimetric method, see ref. 97.

sym-Di-*o*-tolylthiourea has been used gravimetrically in < 0·6N HCl but the results are high (Currah *et al.*[91]).

Acetamide allows colorimetric detn. of 25–90 μg. Pt^{2+}/l.[95] The slightly acidic soln. is boiled for 15–20 min. with a 200-fold excess of reagent; measurement is done at 660 mμ. Many metals interfere.

PALLADIUM

Palladium is the only one of the Pt metals which behaves similarly to Ni and Co, hence there are many excellent reagents available for its detn. In general the oximes and nitrosamines are to be preferred, dimethylglyoxime, nioxime or salicyaldoxime being excellent for moderate amts. and methylbenzoylglyoxime for mg. amts.; *p*-nitrosodimethylaniline and *p*-nitrosodiphenylamine are the best colorimetric reagents. 2-Mercapto-4,5-dimethylthiazole or dithizone is also suitable for very small amts. of Pd.

(a) Dimethylglyoxime is excellent for gravimetric detns.[5, 21, 42, 43, 98, 99] For 4–200 mg. Pd in a soln. contg. 2–5% v/v HCl, add 1% reagent in EtOH (25 ml./100 mg. Pd), leave for 1 hr., filter on a glass crucible, wash with 1:99 HCl and 30% EtOH, dry at 110°C (45–171°C) and weigh as $Pd(C_4H_7O_2N_2)_2$. An aq. reagent soln. has also been recommended; if Pt is present, 0·5 ml. 30% H_2O_2 should be added.[10]

NOTES. (1) Au and Se interfere but other Pt metals, Ag, Sn Ni, etc. do not; if Fe is present, more reagent should be added. If Pt^{4+} is present, do not boil the soln.

(2) For a colorimetric method, ext. with $CHCl_3$ and measure at 366 mμ;[100] the range is 11–63 μg. Pd/ml.

(3) A photometric titration of 1–2 mg. Pd in 20 ml. soln. at pH 5 is feasible.[101]

(4) Various other oximes have been recommended, of which nioxime seems most satisfactory.

Methylbenzoylglyoxime is suitable for gravimetric detn. of 1–4 mg. Pd in slightly acidic (HCl) soln.;[98] add hot reagent soln. (a hot satd. soln. cooled and filtered), leave to cool for 30 min., filter on a glass crucible and wash with H_2O and 30% EtOH alternately; dry at 110°C (52–150°C) and weigh as $Pd(C_{10}H_9O_3N_2)_2$. NH_4^+ interferes but no interference arises from Pt, Rh, Ir, Ag, Hg, Bi, Cu, Cd, Sn, Sb, As, Co, Zn, Mn, Cr, V, Mo, U, W.

Nioxime is used for 5–20 mg. Pd in 200 ml. soln. at pH 1–5:[102] heat to 60°C, add 0·43 ml. 0·8% nioxime per mg. Pd, digest at 60°C for 30 min., filter on a glass crucible, wash 5 times with hot H_2O, dry at 110°C for 1 hr. and weigh as $Pd(C_6H_9O_2N_2)_2$. Au interferes but Pt, Ru, Cd, Zn, Al, Be, U, La, etc. do not. 4-Methyl-4-isopropylnioxime and other derivatives have been examined.[103]
α-Furildioxime has also been studied.[104] Colorimetrically, the color formed with < 5 μg. Pd/ml. in 0·1–1·4*N* HCl soln. contg. 10% EtOH and measured at 420 mμ is nnstable; the color is stable and measurable at 380 mμ after $CHCl_3$ extn.[105]
For diaminoglyoxime, see ref. 106.

(b) Salicylaldoxime can be applied gravimetrically.[98, 107] For 1–4 mg. Pd in solns. contg. < 1% w/w HCl or < 5% H_2SO_4, add hot reagent soln. (hot satd. soln., cooled and filtered), leave for 30 min., filter on a glass crucible, wash with H_2O and 30% EtOH alternately, dry at 110°C (93–197°C) and weigh as $Pd(C_7H_6O_2N)_2$.

NOTES. (1) Pt, Ir, Ru, Au, Ni, Fe^{3+} and Pb do not interfere.
(2) For titrimetric detn. of 5–40 mg. Pd, treat the above filtrate with $Fe_2(SO_4)_3$ and H_3PO_4 and back-titrate with 0·1*N* $KMnO_4$; only Cu interferes.[108]
(3) Salicylaldoxime can also be applied colorimetrically (Peshkova *et al.*[100]).
(4) Cupron (Pshenitsyn *et al.*[107]) and *o*-hydroxyacetophenoneoxime (see p. 174) have also been used gravimetrically for Pd.

(c) *p*-Nitrosodiphenylamine is suitable for the colorimetric detn. of < 5 μg. Pd in slightly acidic (HCl) soln.[46, 109] Add 10 ml. buffer (240 ml. 1*N* HCl and 200 ml. 1*M* NaOAc/l.) and 1 ml. reagent (5 mg. in 50 ml. EtOH dild. to 100 ml. with H_2O) and dil. to 50 ml. with H_2O. Measure the deep red color after 30 min. at 510–525 mμ.

NOTES. (1) Au forms a purple complex which can be avoided by prior extn. with ether; > 2 mg. Pt must be removed by treatment with $FeCl_3$, $NaBrO_3$ and $NaHCO_3$. Ag does not interfere in HNO_3 solns. Other interferences are Hg^+, oxidants, strong reductants, I^-, CN^-, large amts. of Co, Cu, Fe^{3+}, Ir, Ni, Rh and neutral salts (> 0·03*M* NaCl).
(2) The *p*-nitroso derivatives of dimethylaniline (see p. 242),[31, 46, 109] diethylaniline and aniline[109] have also been examined.

(d) $NaBrO_3$ is applied gravimetrically.[21] Evap. the chloride-contg. soln. with HNO_3, add 10% $Hg(NO_3)_2$ (5 ml./0·1 g. Pd), dil. with H_2O to give a 2·5% HNO_3 soln., boil, add 3% reagent (10 ml./0·1 g. Pd) and digest on a hot plate. Filter on Whatman No. 41 paper, wash with hot H_2O, ignite, heat under H_2, etc.

(e) α-Nitroso-β-naphthol is satisfactory for gravimetric, titrimetric and colorimetric detns. For gravimetry of 1–30 mg. Pd in 20 ml. soln.,[110] add 10 drops 30% H_2O_2, make alk. with NaOH, add 30 ml. AcOH and dil. to 150 ml. with hot H_2O. Boil, add 15 ml. 1% reagent in 50% AcOH, filter on a glass crucible, wash with 20% AcOH and H_2O, dry at 130°C (50–245°C) and weigh as $Pd(C_{10}H_6O_2N)_2$.

NOTES. (1) Co, Ni, Zn, Mn interfere; Fe, Cr, Cu, Mo, Si, Ti and W interfere but can be removed on a ZnO suspension.
(2) The β-α-analog is better than the α-β-compd. for colorimetry because Fe and Co do not interfere.[111] For 5–25 μg. Pd, add 2 drops 3*N* HCl, 1 ml. 3% EDTA, dil. to 10 ml. with H_2O, add 0·1 ml. 1% reagent in EtOH and, after 10 min., 5 ml. toluene and 1 ml. 1:1 NH_4OH. Shake and centrifuge and measure the violet complex at 370 mμ. CN^- interferes, but Pt, Ir, Rh, Ru, Os, Au, Zr, Fe, Co, Cu, Ni, Cr do not.
(3) Photometric titration of 0·2–0·5 mg. Pd in acidic alc. soln. is possible;[112] an amperometric titration is also applicable (see p. 180).
(4) 4-Nitrosoresorcinol has been applied colorimetrically[110] and 1-nitroso-2-hydroxy-3-naphthoic acid gravimetrically at pH 2·6–4·8 (see p. 301).

(f) Oxine acetate allows gravimetric detn. of 50 mg. Pd in 100 ml. soln.[113] Add 3 g. NH_4OAc, AcOH to give a 20% soln. and 3% reagent soln.; filter on paper, wash with hot H_2O, add $H_2C_2O_4$ and ignite to Pd above 890°C. Alternatively,[114] ppt. from slightly acidic (HCl) soln., filter on a glass crucible, wash with cold H_2O and 40% EtOH, dry at 120–140°C and weigh as $Pd(C_9H_6ON)_2$.

5-Methyl-8-hydroxyquinoline has also been used gravimetrically.[115]

(g) 3-Hydroxy-1,3-diphenyltriazine is suitable for gravimetric or colorimetric detns.[116] For 10–25 mg. Pd in 150 ml. soln. add 1·5–3 ml. 10% NaK-tartrate or NaOAc, adjust to pH 2–3 with 1*N* HCl, add a 20–25% excess of 1% reagent, heat for 25–40 min. on a steam-bath till the color changes from green to yellow-brown. Filter on a glass crucible (G3), wash with hot H_2O, dry at 120–125°C for 30–45 min. and weigh as $(C_{12}H_{10}N_3O)_2Pd$.

NOTES. (1) Au, Ag, Os^{4+}, Sn^{2+} interfere. Ir, Ru, Rh can be tolerated. If Pt ⩽ Pd, heat for 15–20 min.; if Pt > 2 Pd, ppt. in the cold, leave for 5 min., filter, wash with cold dil. HCl, return to the original beaker, add 2 ml. 2*N* HCl, dil. with H_2O to 50–70 ml., heat for 1 hr. on the steam-bath, etc. If Fe is present, heat for more than 45 min. Zr, Ce can be present if tartrate and acetate are absent. No interference arises from Ni, Co, Zn, Al, Cr, Cd, Mn, Sb, Bi, As, Be, UO_2^{2+}.
(2) For colorimetry, treat the soln. of pH 1·7–4·4 with 5 ml. 0·1% reagent, dil. with H_2O to 100 ml.; measure at 420 mμ against the reagent as reference for 0·2–5 p.p.m., or at 430 mμ against H_2O for 0·4–6 p.p.m.

(h) 6-Nitroquinoline is used gravimetrically for 0·2 g. $PdCl_2$ in 150 ml. neutral soln.[117] Add hot satd. reagent, boil for 5 min., filter on a Gooch crucible, wash with H_2O, dry at 50–198°C and weigh as $Pd(C_9H_6O_2N_2)_2$. The compn. of the ppt. is doubtful. Pt, etc. can be tolerated.

NOTE. *m*-Nitrobenzoic acid hydrazide in EtOH soln. forms with Pd, $Pd(O_2NC_6H_4CONHNH_2)_2$ which can be dried at 85–214°C.[118]

(i) α-Naphthylphthalanilic acid is used gravimetrically[119] for Pd at pH 3·1 (2·7–4·6). Boil the soln. and add a small excess of reagent (1% in 80% EtOH or 1% Na-salt in slightly acidic (AcOH) soln.). Heat on the steam-bath for 5 min., filter after 12 hr. on a glass crucible, wash with hot EtOH and hot H_2O, dry at 115–120°C and weigh as $Pd(C_{24}H_{12}O_3N)_2$.

NOTES. (1) Fe, Th, Zr interfere. Pt, Cu, Al, Zn, Ca, etc. do not. Repptn. is needed in presence of Ni, Co, U.
(2) Phthalanilic or *p*-tolylphthalanilic acid is inferior to the above.
(3) *p*-Aminosalicylic acid is used gravimetrically at pH 3·7–4·2 or titrimetrically (with $KBrO_3$–KBr).[120] No interference is caused by Pt, Au, U, V, Cu, Al, Zn, Co, Ni, Fe, Zr, Th; Ti can be present if sulfosalicylic acid is added.

(j) *o*-Phenanthroline can be used gravimetrically or colorimetrically[121] without interference from other Pt metals. For gravimetry, add 0·5% reagent (or 2,2′-dipyridyl) to the soln. contg. 1–20% HCl; eventually dry at 110°C (50–389°C). The results are slightly high. For colorimetry, add a known excess of reagent, filter after 1 hr. and treat the filtrate with Fe^{2+} soln.

Several other methods have been based on the same principle.

(*i*) *p*-Aminoacetophenone is applied gravimetrically for 6–24 mg. Pd in 0·1*N* HCl soln.[122] Add excess reagent (1% in 2% v/v HCl), filter on a G1 crucible after 5 min., wash with H_2O until there is no color reaction with 0·2% $Ce(SO_4)_2$ in 5% HCl, dry at 80°C and weigh as $(NH_2C_6H_4COCH_3)_2PdCl_2$. Interferences are Ce, and Pt, Rh, Ir, Ru, Au if the amt. is larger than that of Pd. The reagent can also be applied nephelometrically.[122, 123]

p-Aminobenzophenone has also been proposed for use with HBr.[124]

(*ii*) α-Furfuraldoxime is suitable for gravimetric detn. of 30 mg. Pd in 100 ml. 0·36*N* HCl soln. (Pshenitsyn *et al.*[107]);[125] add 2 ml. 10% reagent, filter, wash with 1% HCl and H_2O, dry for 2 hr. at 110°C (51–156°C) and weigh as $(C_4H_3OCHNOH)_2PdCl_2$. The ppt. can be titrated with NH_4VO_3 soln.[43] Au, Ag, Hg^+, Pb, Ce^{4+}, NO_3^- and SO_4^{2-} interfere but Pt, Ir, Ru, Ni, Co, Fe^{3+} do not.

For a colorimetric finish,[126] treat the ppt. with 2–15 ml. AcOH, pipet 1 ml. of soln., add 5 ml. 2% bromoaniline in AcOH (4:1), heat for 5 min. at 70°C, cool and measure the pink color after 55 min. at 520 mμ; this is suitable for 2·4–6·0 μg. Pd.

(*iii*) 1,2,3-Benzotriazole (2·5% in 56% AcOH) can be used[127] for gravimetric detn. of 2–50 mg. Pd; add 10 ml. 2*M* acetate buffer, 5–10 ml. 4% EDTA and a slight excess of reagent and heat for 10 min. at 60–90°C. Cool, filter on a glass crucible, wash with 1:100 HCl and then with H_2O, dry at 110°C for 1 hr. and weigh as $(C_6H_5N_3)_2PdCl_2$. Amperometric titration can also be applied. Other Pt metals (< 10 mg.), Fe, Al, Ni, Co, Zn can be tolerated.

(*iv*) Piazselenol has been suggested[128] for gravimetric detn. of 4–20 mg. Pd in 100 ml. of slightly acidic soln.; boil, add a 10 ml. excess of 1% reagent in MeOH, cool for 30–45 min., filter on a microporcelain crucible, wash 3 times with H_2O and twice with MeOH, dry at 110°C for 1 hr. and weigh as $(C_6H_4N_2Se)_2PdCl_2$.

(*v*) Ethylenediamine may be applied in conjunction with 0·09*M* K_2HgI_4 (0·3239 g. HgI_2, 1·0 g. KI/100 ml.).[129] Evap. the soln. to dryness with HBr repeatedly, add ethylenediamine soln., heat, adjust the pH to 6–8, add K_2HgI_4, filter on a glass crucible after 10 min., wash with H_2O, dry at 115°C and weigh as $[Pd(en)_2]HgI_4$. Interferences are Pt, Au, Cr, Cu, Ni.

(*vi*) *p*-Thiocyanoaniline forms $PdCl_2{\cdot}2NH_2C_6H_4SCN$ with Pd at pH > 0·25; the ppt. is dried at 130–140°C. Fe^{3+}, Cu, Pt, Ir^{4+} do not interfere.[130]

(*vii*) Pd^{4+} can be detd. by means of the green color formed with NH_4OH.[11]

(k) Miscellaneous gravimetric methods. 2-Furoyltrifluoroacetone is suitable for 0·1 g. Pd in 100 ml. soln.;[131] adjust to pH 7 with NaOH, add 3 g. NaOAc and 10% reagent in EtOH, filter on a glass crucible, wash with hot 3% NaOAc and then with H_2O, dry at 110°C for 1 hr. and weigh. Repptn. is needed in presence of Pt, Ir, Rh.

Violuric acid forms $Pd(C_4N_2O_3H_2NO)_2$ which can be dried at 110°C. Cu, Pb, Pt, Fe^{3+}, Ni, Co, Zn, Mn, alk. earths can be tolerated.[132]

p-Ethylsulfonylbenzalthiosemicarbazide (0·1% in 5*N* HCl) can be used to det. 0·6–11 mg. Pd in 300–400 ml. of 0·3–0·4*N* HCl soln.;[133] add a 2·5–4-fold excess of reagent, filter on a G4 crucible, wash with 1% HCl and H_2O, dry at 110–120°C for 1 hr. and weigh as $(C_{10}H_{12}O_2N_3S)_2Pd$. Interferences are Pt, Au, Ag, Cu, Hg.

Phenylthiourea can be used in 0·01*N* HCl media, phenylthiohydantoic acid in < 0·6*N* HCl, and thiobarbituric acid in < 0·3*N* HCl soln. (Currah *et al.*)[91]

Thiourea has been used for 0·2–1·2 mg. Pd;[134] add 16·5 ml. HCl, 5 g. thiourea, dil. to 50 ml. with H_2O and measure the color at 360–380 mμ.

Thionalide can be used gravimetrically[135] in the same way as for Ag (p. 146), or nephelometrically.[136]

Hydrorubeanic acid (in EtOH) may be used to det. 1 mg. Pd;[137] after 12 hr., the ppt. is filtered on a glass crucible, washed with HCl and dil. HCl, dried for 3 hr. at 110°C and weighed as $(C_2S_2N_2H_2)Pd{\cdot}C_2S_2N_2H_4$.

Rubeanic acid is applied colorimetrically.[138] Treat the soln. with 1–5 ml. 1% EDTA, 3 ml. pyridine, adjust to pH < 7, add 1 ml. 0·1% reagent, 5 ml. iso-AmOH, ext. 3–4 times, filter, dil. with iso-AmOH to 25 ml. and measure the yellow-orange color at 410 mμ; Co, Cu, Ni, Cd, Sn, Fe, W, Mo, V, Hg can be present.

Bismuthiol II forms $Pd(C_8H_5N_2S_3)_2$ from EDTA-contg. soln. at pH 8 up to 0·1*N* acid;[139] the ppt. can be weighed or dissolved in KCN and titrated with Ag soln. Sn^{2+} and CN^- interfere but Os, Ru, Rh, Ir and Pt do not. Thiophenol (10% v/v in EtOH) ppts. Pd from solns. less than 0·6*N* in HCl or HNO_3 but the ppt. must be ignited (Currah *et al.*[91]). A colorimetric method has also been proposed.[140]

KI can be applied gravimetrically or titrimetrically.[42, 84, 141] Add a small excess of 10% KI to the 1:4 HCl soln., boil, filter, wash with 1:4 HCl, dry at 200–350°C and weigh as PdI_2; Au interferes. For titration,[142] treat 10 ml. H_2PdCl_4 soln. with 5 ml. HCl, 15 ml. 20% $FeSO_4$ and 0·01*N* KI (0·5 ml. less than the equiv. amt.); shake for 5 min., remove 5 ml., centrifuge, add 1 drop reagent, observe cloudiness, return the soln. to the titrating vessel, add reagent, etc. No interference arises from Bi, Co, Cu, Cr, Ir, Fe, Mn, Mo, Ni, Pt, Rh, Ru, Sn, W.

$Hg(CN)_2$ can be used gravimetrically.[142] Neutralize the chloride soln. with Na_2CO_3, add reagent, heat, cool, filter on paper after 12 hr., wash with 1% $Hg(CN)_2$ and ignite to Pd above 900°C. For a titrimetric method, add KCN to the neutral soln. until it is colorless, followed by HgO, and titrate with 0·01*N* H_2SO_4 to a phenolphthalein end-point.[143] For titration of excess KCN with Ni^{2+} soln., see p. 267.

Several reducing agents have been applied. With HCOOH, add Na_2CO_3 until the soln. is neutral or slightly alk., then boil with the reagent, etc. [42,75] With satd. thiourea peroxide,[21] add reagent to the slightly acidic soln. at 30–40°C until the red color stops darkening, then add 5% $HgCl_2$ until pptn. ceases; filter on Whatman No. 1 paper, wash with slightly acidic (HCl) H_2O, ignite, etc. Pt, Au, Se, Te interfere but Rh, Ir, Ru do not.

Ethylene is used by passing the gas through the slightly acidic soln. at 80°C; Pt, etc. do not interfere.[144] Other reductants are acetylene,[144] NH_2OH, H_3PO_2 or CO in slightly acidic soln., and EtOH in alk. soln.

Electrodeposition can be done from 120 ml. of 30% w/w H_2SO_4 soln. below 65°C with a rotating anode at 0·75 v. and 0·2 amp. increasing to 1·15 v. at 0·05 amp. Alternatively, 150 ml. soln. contg. $Pd(NH_3)_2Cl_2$ and 20–30 ml. NH_4OH is treated with 0·07–0·1 amp. for 12–14 hr.[145]

Trypaflavine has been used along with NaOAc.[146] To 2–3 ml. soln. contg. 0·1–1 mg. Pd/ml. at b.p. add 4–5 ml. 10% NaOAc and 2 ml. 0·03% trypaflavine; filter, ignite under CO_2 at 850–900°C and weigh Pd. Au, Cu, Al, Pb, Sn, Bi interfere but a little Pt, Rh, Ir, V, Sb, Cd, Mn, Ni, Co, Cr, Fe^{3+} can be present. A brown ppt. of $Pd(OH)_2$ may form.

(l) EDTA can be used titrimetrically or colorimetrically for Pd. For 0·6–30 mg. Pd,[147] add a small excess of EDTA, adjust to pH 10 ± 1 with 0·1*N* KOH, add 5 drops eriochrome black T (0·1 g./50 ml. contg. 3 drops *N* KOH) and back-titrate with Zn soln. (1·8 g. metal dissolved in a min. of 1:1 HNO_3 and dild. to 1 l. with H_2O).

NOTES. (1) Os, Rh, NH_3 and much Ir or Ru interfere; Pt does not interfere.

(2) In an alternative titration[148] of < 30 mg. Pd in 50 ml. neutral soln., add 5 ml. 0·1*N* HCl, 10 ml. 2·5% $K_2Ni(CN)_4$, 5–10 ml. buffer (350 ml. NH_4OH and 54 g. NH_4Cl/l.), excess of 0·01*M* EDTA and, after 15 min., 0·1 g. ascorbic acid, some 0·4% eriochrome black T in EtOH; finally back-titrate with 0·01*M* $MnSO_4$. EDTA can also be used with murexide indicator.

(3) For colorimetry,[149] add excess of EDTA, adjust to pH 7 ± 1 or 1·8 ± 0·2 with HCl or KOH and measure at 337 mμ for 9–90 p.p.m. or 377 mμ for 18–180 p.p.m.

(m) Miscellaneous titrimetric methods. Na-diethyldithiocarbamate can be applied[150] for the detn. of 0·01–1·0 mg. Pd in 5 ml. soln.; add 5 ml. HCl, 1 ml. $SnCl_2$ (400 g./200 ml. HCl, add Sn, heat and filter), wait for a few min., add 5 ml. C_6H_6 and titrate with 0·5% reagent soln. (standardized against 0·1% Pd) until the soln. is almost colorless. Then add 5 drops 0·001% $HgCl_2$, shake and titrate further to colorless. For 1–10 μg. Pd, use 2 ml. 6*N* HCl, 2 drops $SnCl_2$ and 1 drop $HgCl_2$, otherwise proceed as above. A photometric titration is also possible.[151]

Pd^{4+} can be detd. by addn. of excess Fe^{2+} and back-titration with $K_2Cr_2O_7$, V^{5+} or Ce^{4+} in presence of phenylanthranilic acid indicator.[43] Titration with $Na_2S_2O_3$ in neutral soln. at 80°C, PdS being pptd., is also possible.[152]

(n) 2-Mercapto-4,5-dimethylthiazole is used colorimetrically for < 1·5 mg. Pd.[153] Add 2 ml. HCl, 20 ml. EtOH and dil. with H_2O to 75 ml.; add 1 ml. reagent (0·5 g./100 ml. 50% EtOH) for each 5 μg. Pd, dil. to 100 ml. with H_2O and measure at 430 mμ. CN^- and NO_3^- interfere. Pt can be sepd. by hydrolysis. No interference is caused by < 1 mg. Rh or Au, or 3·5 mg. Ir, or by Pb, Sn^{2+}, Sb, Ce, I^-, Br^-, $C_2O_4^{2-}$, PO_4^{3-}, AsO_4^{3-}. The method is specific for Pd if preceded by extn. of the *p*-nitrosodiphenylamine complex.

(o) Dithizone has been used colorimetrically for analysis of the button obtained from fire assay.[154] Heat the button to fumes with 5 ml. 1:1 H_2SO_4, cool, add H_2O, decant or filter and wash with H_2O. Collect the filtrate in a 100 ml. separatory funnel, add 2 ml. 1% Na-dimethylglyoxime and, after 10 min., ext. twice with 5 ml. $CHCl_3$. Combine the exts., evap., add 4 ml. HCl and 3 ml. HNO_3, evap. to dryness, add 5 ml. HCl, heat, cool and transfer to a 50 ml. separatory funnel, washing with 15 ml. H_2O. Adjust the HCl content to about 25%, add 0·2 ml. $SnCl_2$ (80 g. in 180 ml. warm HCl dild. to 300 ml. with H_2O and Sn added) and add reagent (see Note 1) from a buret, shaking vigorously and discarding the lower layer; when the dark olive green of $PdDz_2$ becomes pale green, add 1 drop $SnCl_2$ and add further reagent until the color does not change. Calc. the amt. of Pd from the vol. of the reagent added.

NOTES. (1) For the reagent soln. dissolve 45 mg. dithizone in 200 ml. CCl_4 and store in a 250 ml. separatory funnel

under 30–40 ml. satd. SO_2 soln. Dil. 10-fold before use and standardize so that 1 ml. corresponds to 10 μg. Au or Pt or 50 μg. Pd using the method described above.
(2) No interference arises from Os, Rh, Ir; if Au and Pt are present, ext. the dimethylglyoxime complex from the soln. contg. 0·2 ml. HCl and 0·1 ml. HNO_3/10 ml. To det. Au and Pt, evap. the residue from the H_2SO_4 treatment to dryness with aqua regia, add a min. amt. of H_2O and transfer to a 50 ml. separatory funnel (total vol. 10–15 ml.). Add 0·2 ml. HCl and 0·1 ml. 10% NaBr and titrate as above adding 0·2 ml. portions of reagent. Calc. the Au content from this vol. of reagent, discard the CCl_4 phases, add 0·2–0·3 ml. $SnCl_2$, shake, leave for some min. and then titrate the Pt.

(p) KI can be employed in conjunction with NH_4OH for colorimetric detn.[30, 155] For 0·1–1 mg. Pd in H_2SO_4 soln., add 1 ml. reagent (500 g. KI and 5 ml. NH_4OH/l.) for each 100 μg. Pd, add 5 ml. Na_2SO_3 (1·5 g./250 ml.), dil. with H_2O to 100 ml. and measure the dark brown color at 408 mμ. The final H_2SO_4 concn. should be 2*N*.

Several other methods have been suggested which also utilize the formation of a colored halide or pseudo-halide complex.

(*i*) KI and antipyrine are suitable for 1–20 μg. Pd (cf. Chapter 19, p. 153). Add 5 ml. 1*N* HCl (the limits are 0·3–1·5*N*), 3 ml. 5% antipyrine, 1 ml. 10% KI and 5 ml. $CHCl_3$, ext. and measure at 340 mμ (ϵ = 21 500). Interferences are Cu, Al, As, Bi, Sb, Fe, Hg.

(*ii*) HBr can be used for 4–20 mg. Pd in dil. $HClO_4$ solns.[156] Add 10 ml. 40% HBr, dil. to 100 ml. with H_2O and measure the red color at 505 mμ.

(*iii*) NH_4SCN is applicable for 0·1–1 mg. Pd.[157] Add a 6–8-fold excess of 0·01*M* reagent, dil. to 15 ml. with H_2O and measure the red color at 420 mμ. Alternatively, ext. with BuOH or iso-AmOH from soln. of pH below 5 and measure at 436 mμ. The error is ±2·5% for 0·2–0·9 mg. Fe can be present if 2 ml. satd. Na_2HPO_4 is added; Pt and Ir can be tolerated if more reagent is added.

(*iv*) KI and quinine have been applied gravimetrically,[158] $C_{20}H_{24}O_2N_2{\cdot}2HPdI_3$ being pptd. from weakly acidic (HCl) soln. Pt interferes.

(*v*) NH_4Cl has also been used gravimetrically,[42] the ppt. being ignited to Pd.

(q) Miscellaneous colorimetric methods. $SnCl_2$ can be applied for < 0·6 mg. Pd in 60 ml. dil. HCl soln. or neutral nitrate-contg. soln.[11, 159] Add 10 ml. HCl, 10 ml. H_2O, 1 ml. $CuCl_2$ (0·2 mg. Cu/ml.), 20–25 ml. 10% $SnCl_2$, 10–15 ml. Et_2O, and a little NaH_2PO_2; this soln. is pink. Prep. a comparison soln. contg. exactly the same reagents and an amt. of Pt equal to that present in the sample, and add standard Pd soln. until the colors of the 2 solns. match.

Hg_2Cl_2 forms a greyish color with Pd in the same way as with Au (see p. 228). *p*-Dimethylaminobenzilidene-rhodanine forms a red color with Pd in 0·08*N* HCl soln.[46]

$(NH_4)_2MoO_4$ and NaH_2PO_2 can be utilized for the detn. of Pd by its catalytic effect.[160] Mix 0·5 ml. 4% $(NH_4)_2MoO_4$, 2 ml. 4% NaH_2PO_2, 0·0–2·5 ml. 1*N* HCl and 1 ml. sample (4–11 μg. Pd), dil. to 10 ml. with H_2O, read at 600 mμ and measure the time required for the absorbance to attain a definite value. Interferences are Hg, > 10 μg. SCN^-, 20 μg. Ni or Fe^{3+}, 300 μg. Co and 100 μg. Pt; Zn or NH_4^+ can be present.

Silicotungstic or phosphotungstic acid can be used rather similarly but this reaction is more sensitive to interference.[160] Phosphomolybdic acid is suitable when used with CO;[161] for 0·1–0·5 mg. Pd in 2 ml. 0·01*N* HCl soln. add 0·5 ml. 1% gum arabic, 1 drop capryl alc. and pass coal gas washed with H_2O. Add 1 ml. phosphomolybdic acid and 0·5 ml. HCl, heat on a steam bath for 5 min., cool, add 10 ml. HCl and compare the green color formed.

RHODIUM

The most satisfactory methods for the gravimetric detn. of Rh involve electrodeposition, H_2S or thionalide, but separation must always precede the actual detn. The reduction methods with NaH_2PO_2 or Ti^{3+} are also satisfactory. 2-Mercapto-4,5-dimethylthiazole is the best colorimetric reagent, although $SnCl_2$ and NaOCl are also satisfactory.

(a) Electrodeposition is best carried out in a Lingane-type cell with an automatically controlled cathode potential.[162] Evap. the soln. contg. 0·006–0·03 g. Rh to 10 ml., add 2 ml. HNO_3, evap. to dryness, add 2 ml. HCl, evap. to dryness and repeat this process. Add 15 ml. H_2O, 5 ml. 1:10 HCl and pass Cl_2 for 5 min. Heat at 50°C for 5 min., cool to 25°C, add 18·7 g. NH_4Cl, dil. with H_2O to 50 ml., heat to 95°C, cool rapidly to 25°C and pass more Cl_2 for 5 min. Add 1 g. $NH_2OH{\cdot}HCl$ and 1 g. $(NH_4)_2SO_4$, dil. to 100 ml. with H_2O and insert the Pt cathode which has been treated as follows: pass N_2 through the reduction app. for 15 min., turn to H_2, heat for 30 min. at 450°C, let cool for 30 min., turn to N_2, cool and weigh to 0·01 mg. Electrolyze at −0·25 v. *vs*. S.C.E. for 20 min. and at −0·30 v. for 20 min. Add 1 g. $NH_2OH{\cdot}HCl$ and electrolyze at −0·35 v. for 25 min. and at −0·40 v. for 25 min. Then remove two 5 ml. portions of the soln. into 2 test tubes, add 5 μg. Rh to one tube and 5 ml. 20% $SnCl_2$ to both and place in boiling H_2O for 15 min.; if the colors of the 2 solns. differ distinctly, then less than 5 μg. Rh remains. When this is achieved, remove the cathode while washing it, stop the current, dip the electrode in H_2O and then EtOH, dry at 115°C for 5 min., heat as described above in H_2, etc. and finally weigh as Rh. Ir does not interfere if Ir < 10 Rh.

(b) H_2S is suitable[5, 42, 43] for detn. of < 0·5 g. Rh in 100 ml. soln. contg. 2–3 ml. HCl and 2–3 ml. H_2SO_4. Boil the soln., pass H_2S rapidly for 30–40 min., filter on paper, wash with 2·5:97·5 H_2SO_4 and 1:99 HCl, transfer to a porcelain crucible, ignite in air and then in H_2, cool in H_2 and weigh as Rh.

(c) Thionalide can be used titrimetrically or gravimetrically.[163] For 0·25–10 mg. Rh as sulfate in 30–50 ml. soln., add excess 1–2% reagent in AcOH, boil, filter on paper and wash with AcOH. Dissolve the ppt. in excess 0·01N I_2 and back-titrate with 0·01N $Na_2S_2O_3$ in the usual way. Alternatively, dry at 79–250°C and weigh as $Rh(C_{12}H_{10}OSN)_3$. Rh and Ir can be detd. in 1–2% AcOH soln. and Pt and Pd in neutral soln.[164]

(d) 2-Mercapto-4,5-dimethylthiazole is excellent for the colorimetric detn. of Rh.[23, 165] To 40 ml. soln. contg. 50–800 μg. Rh and 10 ml. HCl at b.p. add 0·5% reagent in 50% EtOH (1 ml./0·1 mg. Rh), boil for 1 hr. adding H_2O occasionally, cool, dil. to 100 ml. with H_2O and compare the color.

NOTES. (1) Pt and Au do not interfere; Pd must be sepd. with dimethylglyoxime and Ir requires a correction.
(2) If the soln. contains sulfate, add 50 ml. 20% NaCl, evap. until crystals appear, dil. to 50 ml. with H_2O, add 10 ml. HCl, boil, etc.
(3) 2-Mercaptobenzoxazole is suitable for colorimetric detn. of 0·01–1 mg. Rh in very dil. HCl soln.[166] Add 1–2 ml. AcOH and a few drops of 1% reagent in EtOH, dil. to 20 ml. with H_2O, boil for 15 min., cool and remove the supernate with a filter stick. Dissolve the residue in Me_2CO, dil. to 100 ml. and measure the yellow-red color with a blue filter (420 mμ). Pt, Pd, Ru interfere but Ir does not if Ir < 2 Rh.
(4) 2-Mercaptobenzoxazole or 2-mercaptobenzothiazole can also be used gravimetrically[167] as 1·5% reagents in AcOH. Add reagent to the soln. which is < 0·5N in HNO_3 and contains NH_4Cl, filter after 1 hr. and dry at 110°C (92–150°C). For sepn. from Ir, see ref. 41.

(e) $SnCl_2$ also allows a colorimetric detn.[21, 46, 168, 169] of 4–20 p.p.m. Rh. Add 10 ml. HCl and 10 ml. 1M reagent in 2·5M HCl to the soln., dil. with H_2O to 30 ml., boil gently for 10 min., cool, add 10 ml. reagent, dil. to 100 ml. with H_2O and measure the red color at 475 mμ.

NOTES. (1) Interferences in p.p.m. are Pt, Ru (1), Pd (2), Au, Cr^{6+} (5), Os (8), Fe^{3+}, Co, Cu (50) and I^- (75). Pt and Rh can be detd. simultaneously by measuring at 403 and 475 mμ. Ni and 450 p.p.m. Ir can be tolerated. With HCl soln., Au can be extd. with AmOAc, as can Pd and some of the Pt after addn. of phenylthiourea. Alternatively, dimethylglyoxime can be employed. The soln. is then treated with HNO_3 and $HClO_4$ before the detn.[168]
(2) The method can be combined with colorimetric detn. of Ir with Ce^{4+}. Evap. the combined solns. after detn. of Ir (p. 248) to 10 ml., add 0·1–0·2 g. Na_2SO_3, fume for 1–2 min., add 20 ml. 20% NH_4Cl, evap. and dry at 100–115°C. Add 5–7 ml. H_2O, 10 ml. 10% $SnCl_2$ in 2N HCl, place in boiling H_2O for 80 min., cool, dil. with 2N HCl to 50 ml. and measure at 470 mμ.[170]
(3) If the >2N HCl soln. is extd. with EtOAc, Ru, Os, Ir do not interfere, but Pt does; the Rh color fades on standing.

(f) NaOCl is suitable for colorimetric detn. of 0·5–2 mg. Rh.[171] Pour the sample soln. into a mixt. of 10 ml. buffer (50 ml. AcOH and 200 g. NaOAc/l.) to give a pH of 4·2–7·2, and 50 ml. 5% NaOCl, dil. to 100 ml. with H_2O and measure the blue color after 1 hr. at 665 mμ. The error is ±0·6%. The color of the soln.[172] is yellow-orange at pH 11–12, green at pH 8, blue at pH 6 owing to RhO_3^- or $RhCl_6^-$ and purple at pH 2 owing to RhO^{3+} or RhO_2^+.

NOTES. (1) I^- and IO_3^- interfere; no interference arises from 2 mg. Pd, 0·5 mg. Pt, 0·7 mg. Fe, 0·1–0·2 mg. Au, Cr, Ni, Ru, Os, 0·05 mg. Co, Mn, Cu or 0·03 mg. Ir.
(2) $(NH_4)_2S_2O_8$ and $AgNO_3$ can be used similarly.[46] For 10 ml. soln. which is below 0·2M in H_2SO_4, add 0·2 g. oxidant and 10 mg. $AgNO_3$ and measure the purple color at 360 or 525 mμ after 15 min.

(g) Miscellaneous gravimetric methods. $NaBrO_3$ and $NaHCO_3$ can be used in the same way as for Ir (see p. 248).

HCOOH is an old reducing agent for this detn.[42, 173] Make the soln. alk. with KOH, add HCOOH until the soln. is acid, boil, filter on paper and wash with H_2O; add dil. aqua regia, filter on a Gooch crucible, wash with H_2O and ignite to Rh below 500°C. According to Duval,[163] the temp. of ignition should be below 662°C.

Zn or Mg can be used similarly;[84] NH_2OH is applied in KOH solns. With $N_2H_4{\cdot}HCl$, add the reagent to the neutral soln., boil until the ppt. turns orange-yellow, add dil. Na_2CO_3, boil, make just acid with HCl, filter on Whatman No. 40 paper, wash with 5% HCl, and continue as above.[21]

NaH_2PO_2 is suitable for < 0·1 g. Rh in 50 ml. soln. contg. 2 ml. HCl.[21] Boil the soln. gently, add 5 g. NaCl and 20 ml. reagent (10 g. NaH_2PO_2 in 100 ml. 1:9 HCl, and 5% $HgCl_2$ mixed 1:1 just before use), boil and add more reagent if a pink color persists. Place on a steam-bath for 30 min., filter on Whatman No. 40 paper and wash with hot 2% HCl.

$Ti_2(SO_4)_3$ (10% in 30% v/v H_2SO_4) is applicable for similar concentrations of Rh in solns. contg. 10 ml. H_2SO_4/40–50 ml.[21] Add 2 ml. 5% $HgSO_4$, boil and add reagent dropwise; reboil, add an equal vol. of H_2O, filter on Whatman No. 41 paper and wash with hot 10% H_2SO_4 and with H_2O. Ir does not interfere in the latter two methods.

α-Nitroso-β-naphthol has been applied gravimetrically and colorimetrically.[174] For < 35 mg. Rh in 100 ml. soln., add 100 ml. reagent (1 g. in 50 ml. AcOH, dild. to 100 ml. with H_2O and filtered) to give at least a 5-fold excess, adjust to pH 4·8–5·6, boil for 15 min., leave to cool for at least 2 hr., filter and wash with H_2O. Dry at 110°C and weigh as $(C_{10}H_6NO_2)_3Rh$ or dissolve the ppt. in Me_2CO or C_6H_6 and measure at 420 mμ. Interferences are Pd, Ru, Fe, Co.

Thiobarbituric acid is suitable for 2·5 mg. Rh in 200 ml. soln.[175] Add 0·5–5 ml. HCl to give pH 0·9–1·1, boil, add 10 ml. 1·4% reagent in EtOH and boil for 2 hr. with a little paper pulp, adding H_2O occasionally; filter on Whatman No. 42 paper, wash with H_2O, dry, ignite at 800°C for 15 min. and in H_2 for 5 min., cool in N_2 and weigh as Rh. Cu interferes, but Ni and Zn do not; repptn. is needed if Pb is present.

(h) $NaBiO_3$ can be used in conjunction with a reductimetric titration.[176] Treat the chloride soln. with 50 ml. H_2O and 15 ml. H_2SO_4, fume for 20–30 min. until the pink color becomes yellow, cool to 15–20°C, dil. with H_2O to 100–200 ml., recool, add 1 g. oxidant, filter after 2–12 hr. and wash with $3{\cdot}5N$ H_2SO_4 4–5 times. Add 0·04% phenylanthranilic acid indicator and titrate with $0{\cdot}01N$ Fe^{2+} until the color starts to fade; wait for 1–2 min. and then titrate slowly to the purple-yellowish end-point. Other Pt metals cause no interference.

(i) NaBr provides a colorimetric detn.;[177] to 2 ml. soln., add 2 ml. 1:6 H_2SO_4 and 2 g. reagent, boil for 1 min., add H_2O and compare the deep pink color.

Satd. $KHSO_3$ and HCl also give a pink color with dil. HCl solns. of Rh.[178]

IRIDIUM

Hydrolysis provides the best gravimetric method. Reduction with Sn^{2+} in HBr solns., evapn. with mixed acids or addition of leuco crystal violet are the most suitable colorimetric procedures.

(a) $NaBrO_3$ and $NaHCO_3$ are utilized in the hydrolytic detn.[5, 42, 43, 179] Boil the acidic soln. with 10 ml. 10% $NaBrO_3$ for 10–20 min. until dark green, add 1–2 drops 10% $NaHCO_3$ to make the soln. alk. to bromocresol purple. Boil for 30 min., place on a steam-bath for 4 hr., filter on paper and wash with hot 1% NH_4Cl. Transfer to a porcelain crucible, dry slightly, add some drops of satd. NH_4Cl, heat carefully and ignite in air and then in H_2. Cool, ext. with dil. HCl, filter on paper and wash with H_2O. Ignite below 650°C in air and then in H_2, cool under H_2 and weigh as Ir.

NOTES. (1) Semimicro amts. of Ir can also be detd. by the above method. Some Ir is lost on heating above 800°C (Hill and Beamish[179]).

(2) In an alternative procedure,[21] evap. the soln. to slight fumes with 5 ml. $HClO_4$ and some HNO_3, cool, add 20 ml. warm H_2O, filter and wash with warm 5% $HClO_4$. Dil. to 100 ml. with H_2O, add 10 ml. 5% $Hg(NO_3)_2$ and 3–4 drops 10% $NaBrO_3$ and boil for 10 min. If the color of the soln. persists, add 10% Na_2CO_3 dropwise until the purple color disappears and then place on the steam-bath for 10 min. Filter on Whatman No. 41 paper, wash with hot H_2O, dry, add some drops of satd. NH_4Cl, heat slowly, maintain at 900°C for 10 min., heat in H_2, etc.

(b) $SnCl_2$ with HBr provides a satisfactory colorimetric detn.[180] To 5 ml. soln. contg. < 75 μg. Ir add 5 ml. HBr, place in boiling H_2O for 10 min., add 5 ml. 25% $SnCl_2$ in 40% HBr, heat for 2 min. and cool rapidly. Dil. to 25 ml. with H_2O and measure the yellow color at 402 mμ (ϵ = 49 600). This is suitable for 0·5–3 p.p.m.

NOTE. Pt absorbs at 455 mμ, Rh at 430 mμ and Pd at 385 mμ under these conditions; these metals can be sepd. with Sb dust and the Sb can be distilled off with HCl. Other interferences are oxidants, Au, 40 p.p.m. Cu, 80 p.p.m. Sb^{3+}, 20 p.p.m. Ni, 10 p.p.m. Co, 16 p.p.m. Fe^{2+}, 13 p.p.m. Cr^{3+} and 6 p.p.m. Ti. With fumed H_2SO_4 solns., add 5 ml. HBr and boil until only 1–2 ml. HBr remains.

(c) H_3PO_4, $HClO_4$ and HNO_3 (50:50:5) allow a useful colorimetric detn.[39, 181] For 3–5 mg. Ir, add 10 ml. reagent and heat at 110°C for 1 hr. and 150°C for 30 min. (or for 7 min. after the yellow color has turned blue); cool, dil. to 50 ml. with 1% HNO_3 and measure at 564 mμ (ϵ = 4570).

NOTES. (1) Over 1·25 mg. Pd interferes but the Ir can be calcd. from the absorbances at 415 and 564 mμ. No interference arises from the other Pt metals or from Fe, Co, Ni.

(2) Several similar procedures have been proposed. For 30–120 μg. Ir/ml., evap. the soln. to fumes with 4–5 ml. H_2SO_4 and 2 ml. HNO_3, and measure the violet color at 575 mμ.[182]

For 5–100 μg. Ir/ml., evap. the soln. to fumes with $HClO_4$, add H_2O, boil for 30 min. and measure the reddish color at 510 mμ.[183]

$Ce(SO_4)_2$ is applicable for 5 mg. Ir in 20 ml. soln.[170] Add 6 ml. H_2SO_4, fume for 15–20 min. until colorless, cool slightly, add 35 ml. H_2O, heat at 90–92°C for 5–10 min., add 1 ml. $0{\cdot}1N$ $Ce(SO_4)_2$ and maintain at 92 ± 2°C for at least 6 hr. Cool, dil. to 50 ml. with H_2O and measure the red color at 510 mμ (ϵ = 1790). The range is 20–75 μg./ml. Pd (35 μg./ml.) interferes.

Various colorimetric methods have been suggested in which the oxidative power of Ir^{4+} is utilized. With leuco crystal violet[183] which is suitable for 0·5–4 p.p.m. Ir, treat the soln. with 10 ml. 70% $HClO_4$, 10 ml. HNO_3 and H_3PO_4 to give a final concn. of $1M$; boil until no $HClO_4$ remains, cool, add H_2O, boil for 30 min., and dil. with H_2O to a known vol. Treat an aliquot with 1 ml. 0·1% dye in $1M$ H_3PO_4 and 10 ml. buffer (700 ml. AcOH and 300 ml. $6M$ NaOH) to give pH 3·5–4·7, dil. to 25 ml. with H_2O and measure at 590 mμ (ϵ = 48 000). Au interference is prevented by treating the 1–$2M$ HCl soln. with hydroquinone, adding some Hg, shaking for 1 min., filtering and washing. Os and Ru are removed by distn. Other interferences are Rh, Co, Pt, Pd, Ni (10, 30, 50, 100, 200 p.p.m. resp.).

o-Dianisidine is used for 2–20 p.p.m. Ir.[184] Add a few drops of HNO_3 to the soln., evap. to dryness with 1 ml. 0·2% NaCl, add a few drops of dil. HCl, evap. and repeat this process 3 times; dil. with H_2O to 25 ml. Treat a 5 ml. aliquot with 1 ml. 0·5% *o*-dianisidine in Me_2CO and 2 ml. $0{\cdot}1M$ acetate buffer of pH 4·7, dil. to 25 ml. with $12M$ HCl and measure the purple color at 530 mμ (ϵ = 12 500).

Benzidine (0·1 ml. of a soln. of 1 g. in 10 ml. AcOH dild. to 50 ml. with H_2O) forms a violet complex with 5 μg. Ir in 10 ml. neutral soln.[46, 185]

A few redox titrations are also available for Ir detn. For detn. of 2–20 mg. Ir with Ce^{4+} soln., evap. the sample to fumes with H_2SO_4, add H_2O and excess Ce^{4+} soln. and back-titrate potentiometrically with Fe^{2+} soln.[186]

Hydroquinone or $K_4Fe(CN)_6$ is used with *o*-dianisidine indicator.[187] Evap. the 0·5*N* HCl soln. to 0·2–0·3 ml., add 0·5 ml. aqua regia, dry *in vacuo* over NaOH and repeat twice. Add HCl to give a final concn. of 0·1–0·5*N*, dil. with H_2O to 50 ml., adjust to pH 0·5–1·0 with NaOAc, add 1 ml. 0·2% indicator in 0·5% HCl and titrate with 0·005*N* reagent to the color change from red to colorless or from orange to yellow. Titration with 0·01*N* Fe^{2+}, 0·02*N* $TiCl_3$ or hydroquinone in presence of diphenylamine indicator, or with Fe^{2+} in presence of ferroin has also been proposed.[188] KI, ascorbic acid[189] and other organic reductants[190] have been studied.

(d) Miscellaneous gravimetric methods. 2-Mercaptobenzothiazole is suitable for < 5 mg. Ir in 5 ml. dil. HCl soln.[41, 191] Add 10 ml. AcOH, 1 ml. 20% NH_4OAc and 25 ml. H_2O and heat nearly to boiling. Add 10 ml. 1% reagent in EtOH and some paper pulp, boil for 1 hr., rinse the vessel down with 2% AcOH and 2% NH_4OAc mixed, dil. to 50–70 ml. with this buffer and leave for 12 hr. Filter on Whatman No. 42 paper, wash with hot buffer soln. (as above), dry, heat at 350°C, then at 650–750°C for 45 min., cool, heat in H_2, cool under $H_2 + N_2$, then in a desiccator contg. $Ca(NO_3)_2$ and weigh as Ir. Pb does not interfere.

For the use of thionalide, see Rh (p. 246). H_2S is suitable for < 0·5 g. Ir in 100 ml. 3*N* HCl soln.;[43] add 0·5 g. $AlCl_3·6H_2O$, boil, pass H_2S for 3 hr., filter on paper, wash with 1:99 HCl, ignite, etc. Zn ppts. Ir from 5% HCl soln.[42] Mg, Al and HCOOH + NH_4Cl can also be used.

(e) Miscellaneous colorimetric methods. Satd. Cl_2 soln. forms a brown color on boiling with the 0·1–0·2*N* HCl sample soln.; small amts. of the other Pt metals can be tolerated.[11, 21, 46] Other methods utilize the formation of halide complexes. Tetraphenylphosphonium chloride is suitable for 15–150 μg. Ir^{4+} in 15–20 ml. 0·1*N* HCl soln.;[192] add 3 ml. 2% reagent, 10–25 ml. $CHCl_3$, shake, sep. and measure at 500 mμ; Pt, Pd, Os, Ru interfere but Rh does not.

NOTE. For a gravimetric detn. based on the same principle,[193] treat the slightly acidic sample soln. with 10% H_2O_2 and satd. KCl soln., add an equal vol. of EtOH, filter after 12 hr. on paper and wash with 0·1*N* KCl in 50% EtOH; ignite in air, etc. and weigh as Ir. NH_4Cl can be applied similarly.[42]

p-Nitrosodimethylaniline can be used[194] for 1·5–10 p.p.m. Ir. Evap. the 0·5*N* HCl soln. to dryness with 2 ml. 2% NaCl, then with 4 ml. aqua regia, and then 3 times with a little HCl; dissolve in the min. amt. of H_2O, transfer to a test tube contg. 2 ml. buffer (10 g. Na_2HPO_4 and 4·1 g. KH_2PO_4 in 100 ml.) and 2 ml. reagent (150 mg. in 100 ml. EtOH, filtered), dil. to 8 ml. with H_2O, heat for 40 min. at 70°C, cool, dil. with 6*N* HCl to 10 ml. and measure the cherry red complex at 530 mμ. (ϵ = 19 300). Other Pt metals, SO_4^{2-} and salts which are difficult to remove, interfere. The color formed with the diethyl analog or *p*-nitrosodiphenylamine is weaker.

EDTA forms a colored complex[195] with 5–60 p.p.m. Ir^{4+} at pH 11·4–11·6 on heating at 80–90°C for 10 min. if a 2–3-fold excess of EDTA is added; the complex can be measured at 313 mμ (ϵ = 3200). Interferences are 0·1 mg. Pd, 0·2 mg. Pt^{4+}, 0·7 mg. Pt^{2+}, 0·07 mg. Rh, 0·06 mg. Os, 0·02 mg. Ru and NO_3^-.

References

1. HILLEBRAND and LUNDELL, 268 (339); SCOTT and FURMAN, 710; KIMURA, 370; SCHOELLER and POWELL, 325; FRESENIUS–JANDER, **VIIIb** γ (1953).
2. *Anal. Chem.*, **25**, 1612 (1953).
3. BEAMISH, F. E., and MCBRYDE, W. A. E., *Anal. Chim. Acta*, **9**, 349 (1953).
4. MCBRYDE, *Analyst*, **80**, 503 (1955).
5. GILCHRIST, R., and WICHERS, E., *J. Am. Chem. Soc.*, **57**, 2565 (1935).
6. GILCHRIST, *Chem. Revs.*, **23**, 277 (1943); *Rev. mét.*, **52**, 287 (1955).
7. KLAUS, K. K., *Selected Works on Chemistry of Platinum Metals*, Moskow (1954).
8. PSHENITSYN, N. K., *Izvest. Sektora Platiny i Drug. Blagorod. Metal., Inst. Obshcheĭ i Neorg. Khim., Akad. Nauk S.S.S.R.* **22**, 7, 136 (1948).
9. WOGRINZ, A., *Chem. Anal.*, **36** (1936).
10. HOLZER, H., and ZAUSSINGER, E., *Z. anal. Chem.*, **111**, 321 (1937/38).
11. WÖLBLING, H., *Ber.*, **67**, 773 (1934).
12. WESTLAND, A. D. and BEAMISH, *Mikrochim. Acta*, 625 (1957).
13. GEILMANN, W., and NEEB, R., *Z. anal. Chem.*, **152**, 96, 158 (1956); **154**, 17, 23 (1957); **156**, 411, 420 (1957).
14. TAIMNI, I. K., and SALARIA, G. B., *Anal. Chim. Acta*, **11**, 329 (1954).
15. BEAMISH and WESTLAND, *Anal. Chem.*, **30**, 805 (1958).
16. FROMMES, M., *Z. anal. Chem.*, **99**, 305 (1934).
17. HILL, M. A., and BEAMISH, F. E., *Anal. Chem.*, **22**, 590 (1950); also see DELEPINE, M., *Bull. soc. chim. France*, 282 (1956) (CCl_4 at 550–600°C).
18. BEAMISH, F. E., and MCBRYDE, W. A. E., *Anal. Chem.*, **25**, 1613 (1953); BAREFOOT, R. R., and BEAMISH, *ibid.*, **24**, 840 (1952); THIERS, R., *et al.*, *ibid.*, **20**, 831 (1948); SEATH, J., and BEAMISH, *Ind. Eng. Chem., Anal. Ed.*, **12**, 169 (1940); THOMPSON, S. O., *et al.*, *ibid.*, **9**, 420 (1937); RUSSEL, J. J., *et al.*, *ibid.*, 475; BEAMISH and RUSSEL, *ibid.*, **8**, 141 (1936); BAREFOOT and BEAMISH, *Anal. Chim. Acta*, **9**, 49 (1953); FRASER, J. G. and BEAMISH, *Anal. Chem.*, **26**, 1474 (1954) (Pd); HOFFMAN, I., *et al.*, *ibid.*, **28**, 1174 (1956) (direct assay better than leaching process); HOFFMAN and BEAMISH, *ibid.*, 1188 (loss of Pt may occur because of migration of Pt to pot walls by creeping); COBURN, H. G., *et al.*, *ibid.*, 1297 (Ferronickel assay button).
19. ALLEN, W. F., and BEAMISH, *Anal. Chem.*, **24**, 1569 (1952).
20. ALLEN and BEAMISH, *Anal. Chem.*, **22**, 461 (1950).
21. SCHOELLER and POWELL, 325 ff.
22. AOYAMA, S., and WATANABE, K., *J. Chem. Soc. Japan*, **75**, 20 (1954).
23. WESTLAND, A. D., and BEAMISH, F. E., *Mikrochim. Acta*, 1474 (1956).

24. WESTLAND, A. D., and BEAMISH, F. E., *Mikrochim. Acta*, 625 (1957).
25. WESTLAND, A. D. and BEAMISH, F. E., *Anal. Chem.*, **26**, 739 (1954).
26. KAHN, B., *Anal. Chem.*, **28**, 216 (1956).
27. AYRES, G. H., and BELKNAP, H. J., *Anal. Chem.*, **29**, 1536 (1957).
28. AYRES, G. H., and TUFFLY, B. L., *Anal. Chem.*, **24**, 949 (1952).
29. POLLARD, W. B., *Analyst*, **67**, 184 (1942).
30. FRASER, J. G., *et al.*, *Anal. Chem.*, **26**, 495 (1954).
31. YOE, J. H., and KIRKLAND, J. J., *Anal. Chem.*, **26**, 1335, 1340 (1954).
32. RYAN, D. E., *Analyst*, **76**, 310 (1951).
33. LEBEDINSKIĬ, V. V., *Ann. inst. platine* (*U.S.S.R*), **13**, 73 (1936).
34. PSHENITSYN, N. K. and GLADYSHEVSKAYA, K. A., *Izvest. Sektora Platiny i Drug. Blagorod. Metal., Inst. Obshcheĭ i Neorg. Khim., Akad. Nauk S.S.S.R.*, **27**, 5 (1952).
35. HILLEBRAND and LUNDELL (368).
36. SCHOELLER and POWELL, 343.
37. KEMBER, N. F., and WELLS, R. A., *Analyst*, **80**, 735 (1955); MACNEVIN, W. M., and DUNTON, M. L., *Anal. Chem.*, **29**, 1806 (1957).
38. MACNEVIN, W. M., and CRUMMETT, W. B., *Anal. Chem.*, **25**, 1628 (1953); see Chapter 15, Section 2.3.
39. AYRES, G. H., and MADDIN, C. M., *Anal. Chem.*, **26**, 671 (1954).
40. BEAMISH, F. E., *et al.*, *Ind. Eng. Chem., Anal. Ed.*, **12**, 561 (1940).
41. UBALDINI, I, and NEBBIA, L., *Chim. e Ind.* (*Milan*), **33**, 360 (1951).
42. SCOTT and FURMAN, 710 ff.
43. HILLEBRAND and LUNDELL, 268 (339) ff.
44. ALLAN, W. J., and BEAMISH, F. E., *Anal. Chem.*, **24**, 1608 (1952); HOFFMAN, I., *et al.*, *ibid.*, **25**, 1091 (1953).
45. AYRES, G. H. and WELLS, W. N., *Anal. Chem.*, **22**, 317 (1950); also see DWYER, F. P., and GIBSON, N. A., *Analyst*, **76**, 104 (1951).
46. SANDELL, 481 ff.
47. WELCHER, **IV**, 183, 272.
48. SAUERBRUNN, R. D., and SANDELL, E. B., *Anal. Chim. Acta*, **9**, 86 (1953).
49. GEILMANN, W., and NEEB, R., *Z. anal. Chem.*, **152**, 96 (1956).
50. WINGFIELD, H. C., and YOE, J. H., *Anal. Chim. Acta*, **14**, 446 (1956); STEELE, E. L. and YOE, *Anal. Chem.*, **29**, 1622 (1957) (other analogs).
51. GILCHRIST, R., *Bur. Standards, J. Research*, **6**, 427 (1931).
52. KUL'BERG, L. M., *J. Gen. Chem., U.S.S.R.*, **8**, 1139 (1938).
53. TANANAEFF, N. A., *Z. anal. Chem.*, **108**, 30 (1937).
54. NEEB, R., *Z. anal. Chem.*, **154**, 23 (1957).
55. HIRSCH, M., *Chem. Ztg.*, **46**, 390 (1922); SINGLETON, W., *Ind. Chemist*, **3**, 121 (1927).
56. SAUERBRUNN, R. D., and SANDELL, E. B., *Mikrochim. Acta*, 22 (1953).
57. SHIOKAWA, T., *J. Chem. Soc. Japan*, **70**, 314 ff (1949).
58. WATANABE, K., *J. Chem. Soc. Japan*, **78**, 983 (1957).
59. THOMPSON, S. O., *et al.*, *Ind. Eng. Chem., Anal. Ed.*, **9**, 421 (1937).
60. AYRES, G. H., and YOUNG, F., *Anal. Chem.*, **22**, 1277 (1950).
61. MARSHALL, E. D., and RICKARD, R. R., *Anal. Chem.*, **22**, 795 (1950).
62. STONER, G. A., *Anal. Chem.*, **27**, 1186 (1955).
63. MUSIL, A., and PIETSCH, R., *Z. anal. Chem.*, **137**, 259 (1952).
64. KNIGHT, S. B., *et al.*, *Anal. Chem.*, **29**, 571 (1957).
65. BANKS, C. V., and O'LAUGHLIN, J. W., *Anal. Chem.*, **29**, 1412 (1957).
66. ROGERS, W. J., *et al.*, *Ind. Eng. Chem., Anal. Ed.*, **12**, 561 (1940).
67. CURRAH, J. E., *et al.*, *Anal. Chem.*, **24**, 1980 (1952).
68. GOTO, H., *J. Chem. Soc. Japan*, **55**, 330 (1934).
69. PSHENITSYN, N. K., and GINZBERG, S. I., *Izvest. Sektora Platiny i Drug. Blagorod. Metal., Inst. Obshcheĭ i Neorg. Khim., Akad. Nauk S.S.S.R.*, **32**, 20 (1955).
70. BRECKENRIDGE, J. G., and SINGER, S. A. G., *Can. J. Research*, **25B**, 49 (1947).
71. AYRES and YOUNG, *Anal. Chem.*, **22**, 1281 (1950).
72. SHIOKAWA, T., *J. Chem. Soc. Japan*, **71**, 87 (1950).
73. MCBRYDE, W. A. E., and YOE, J. H., *Anal. Chem.*, **20**, 1098 (1948).
74. EL GUEBELY, M. A., *Anal. Chim. Acta*, **15**, 580 (1956).
75. WELCHER, **I**, 37.
76. BLACKMORE, A. P., *et al.*, *Anal. Chem.*, **24**, 1815 (1952).
77. MAKSIMYUK, E. A., *Izvest. Sektora Platiny i Drug. Blagorod. Metal., Inst. Obshcheĭ i Neorg. Khim., Akad. Nauk S.S.S.R.*, **30**, 180 (1955).
78. AYRES, G. H., and MEYER, A. S., JR., *Anal. Chem.*, **23**, 299 (1951); see also SHERWOOD, R. M., and CHAPMAN, F. W., JR., *ibid.*, **27**, 88 (1955).
79. MILNER, O. I., and SHIPMAN, G. F., *Anal. Chem.*, **27** 1476 (1955).
80. AYRES *et al.*, *Anal. Chem.*, **27** 1742 (1955); (see Rh).
81. AYRES, *Anal. Chem.*, **25**, 1626 (1953).
82. BARTORI, M., *Boll. chim. farm.*, **95**, 3 (1956).
83. KIRKLAND, J. J., and YOE, J. H., *Anal. Chim. Acta*, **9**, 441 (1953).
84. KIMURA, 370.
85. TAKAGI, S., and NAGASE, Y., *J. Pharm. Soc. Japan*, **58**, 60, 66 (1938).
86. WELCHER, **III**, 45.
87. BODE, H., *Z. anal. Chem.*, **133**, 95 (1951).
88. RYAN, D. E., *Can. J. Chem.*, **34**, 1683 (1956).
89. JACKSON, D. S., and BEAMISH, F. E., *Anal. Chem.*, **22**, 813 (1950).
90. UMEMURA, T., *J. Chem. Soc. Japan*, **61**, 25 (1940).
91. CURRAH, J. E., *et al.*, *Ind. Eng. Chem., Anal. Ed.*, **18**, 121 (1946); HOFFMAN, I., and BEAMISH, F. E., *Anal. Chem.*, **28**, 1188 (1956).
92. WELCHER, **III**, 209, 232.
93. WELCHER, **IV**, 89.
94. RUBINI DE TRECCO, D., *Rev. asoc. bioquim. Arg.*, **15**, 355 (1951); BARKOVSKIĬ, V. F., and KUL'BERG, L. M., *Izvest. Sektora Platiny i Drug. Blagorod. Metal., Inst. Obshcheĭ i Neorg. Khim., Akad. Nauk S.S.S.R.*, **29**, 149 (1955).
95. BARKOVSKII and KUL'BERG, *Izvest. Sektora Platiny*, **28**, 235 (1954); **29**, 141 (1955).
96. KOMATSU, S., and ONISHI, K., *J. Chem. Soc. Japan*, **76**, 661 (1955).
97. NAITO, T., *et al.*, *J. Pharm. Soc. Japan*, **69**, 361 (1949).

98. HECHT and DONAU, 184; WELCHER, **III**, 204, 233.
99. AYRES, G. H., and BERG, E. W., *Anal. Chem.*, **25**, 980 (1953).
100. NIELSCH, W., *Z. anal. Chem.*, **142**, 30 (1950); also see PESHKOVA, V. M., *et al.*, *Vestnik Moskov Univ.*, **9**, *No.* 5, *Ser. Fis.-Mat. i Estestven. Nauk*, *No.* 3, 83 (1954) (C_6H_6 extn.).
101. BOBTELSKY, M., and MAYER, B., *Anal. Chim. Acta*, **15**, 373 (1956).
102. VOTER, R. C., *et al.*, *Anal. Chem.*, **20**, 652 (1948).
103. BANKS, C. V., and HOOKER, D. T., *Anal. Chem.*, **28**, 79 (1956).
104. REED, S. A., and BANKS, C. V., *Proc. Iowa Acad. Sci.*, **55**, 267 (1948).
105. MENIS, O., and RAINS, T. C., *Anal. Chem.*, **27**, 1932 (1955).
106. DAS GUPTA, P. R., *J. Indian Chem. Soc.*, **30**, 761 (1953).
107. FRASER, J. G., *et al.*, *Anal. Chem.*, **26**, 495 (1954); PSHENITSYN, N. K., and NEKRASOVA, G. A., *Izvest. Sektora Platiny i Drug. Blagorod. Metal.*, *Inst. Obshcheĭ i Neorg. Khim.*, *Akad. Nauk S.S.S.R.*, **30**, 126 (1955).
108. GAHIDE, W., *Bull. soc. chim. Belges.*, **45**, 10, 13 (1936).
109. WELCHER, **III**, 405 ff.
110. WELCHER, **III**, 313, 331.
111. CHENG, K. L., *Anal. Chem.*, **26**, 1894 (1954); also see ALVAREZ, E. R., *Anales direc. gen. ofic. quím. nacl.* (*Buenos Aires*), **2**, 88 (1949).
112. BOBTELSKY, M., and MAYER, B., *Anal. Chim. Acta*, **15**, 164 (1956).
113. BERG, R., *Oxin*, 75 (1935).
114. TREADWELL, W. D., *Tabellen*, 63 (1938); KIBA, T., and IKEDA, T., *J. Chem. Soc. Japan*, **60**, 913 (1939).
115. SA, A. M., *Rev. asoc. bioquím. Arg.*, **16**, No. 64, 11 (1949).
116. SOGANI, N. C., and BHATTACHARYA, S. C., *Anal. Chem.*, **28**, 81 (1956); **29**, 397 (1957).
117. WELCHER, **III**, 61.
118. VOŘIŠEK, J., and VEJDĚLEK, Z., *Chem. listy*, **37**, 50, 65, 91 (1943).
119. DATTA, S. K., *Z. anal. Chem.*, **148**, 239 (1955).
120. DATTA, *J. Indian Chem. Soc.*, **32**, 785 (1955).
121. RYAN, D. E., and FAINER, P., *Can. J. Research*, **27B** 67 (1949); RYAN, *ibid.*, 938; *Analyst*, **77**, 46 (1952).
122. SCHÖNTAL, R., *J. Chem. Soc.*, 1099 (1938); *Mikrochemie*, **24**, 20 (1938).
123. WELCHER, **II**, 249.
124. DE HOVRE, E., *Ing. chim.* (*Milan*), **35**, 83 (1953).
125. WELCHER, **III**, 349.
126. RICE, E. W., *Anal. Chem.*, **24**, 1995 (1952).
127. WILSON, R. F., and WILSON, L. E., *Anal. Chem.*, **28**, 93 (1956).
128. ZIEGLER, M., and GLEMSER, O., *Z. anal. Chem.*, **153**, 246 (1956).
129. WATT, G. W., *et al.*, *Anal. Chem.*, **28**, 556 (1956).
130. PRZHEVAL'SKIĬ, E. S., *et al.*, *Vestnik Moskov. Univ.* **9**, No. 10, *Ser. Fis.-Mat. i Estestven. Nauk.* No. 7, 59 (1954).
131. MCINTYRE, R. T., *et al.*, *Anal. Chem.*, **28**, 1316 (1956).
132. ZIEGLER, M., and GLEMSER, O., *Mikrochim. Acta*, 1152, 1515 (1956).
133. KOMATSU, S., *et al.*, *J. Chem. Soc. Japan*, **77**, 1439 (1956).
134. NIELSCH, W., *Mikrochim. Acta*, 232 (1954).
135. UMEMURA, T., *J. Chem. Soc. Japan*, **61**, 26 (1940).
136. BERG, R., *et al.*, *Mikrochemie Festschr. H. Molisch*, 42 (1936).
137. WÖLBLING, W., and STEIGER, B., *Mikrochemie*, **15**, 295 (1934).
138. XAVIER, J., and RÂY, P., *Sci. and Culture* (*Calcutta*), **20**, 609 (1955); **21**, 170 (1955) (diphenylrubeanic acid, 395 mμ).
139. MAJUMDAR, A. K., and CHAKRABARTTY, M. M., *Z. anal. Chem.*, **155**, 1, 7 (1957); MAJUMDAR and MOHAN, M., *ibid.*, **156**, 103 (1957).
140. MANN, F. G., and PURDIE, D., *J. Chem. Soc.*, 1555 (1935).
141. TASHIRO, M., *J. Chem. Soc. Japan*, **52**, 232 (1931); BEAMISH, F. E., and DALE, J., *Ind. Eng. Chem.*, *Anal. Ed.*, **10**, 697 (1938).
142. RHODA, R. N., and ATKINSON, R. H., *Anal. Chem.*, **28**, 535 (1956); *Analyst*, **80**, 838 (1955); also see PSHENITSYN, N. K., and GINZBERG, S. I., *Izvest. Sektora Platiny i Drug. Blagorod. Metal.*, *Inst. Obshcheĭ i Neorg. Khim.*, *Akad. Nauk S.S.S.R.*, **25**, 192 (1950); **32**, 31 (1955) (potentiometric).
143. BURRIEL, F., and PÉREZ, F. P., *Anales real soc. españ. fís. y quím.* (*Madrid*), **47B**, 261 (1951).
144. WELCHER, **I**, 52, 58.
145. BERL-LUNGE, *Chemisch-technische Untersuchungsmethoden*, Bd. II, 966, Springer, Berlin (1932).
146. SAINI, G., *Ann. chim.* (*Rome*), **40**, 59 (1940).
147. MACNEVIN, W. M., and KRIEGE, O. H., *Anal. Chem.*, **27**, 535 (1955).
148. KINNUNEN, J., and MERIKANTO, B., *Chemist. Analyst*, **44**, 11 (1955); FLASCHKA, H., *Mikrochim. Acta*, 226 (1953).
149. MACNEVIN, W. M., and KRIEGE, O. H., *Anal. Chem.*, **26**, 1768 (1954).
150. WELCHER, **IV**, 90.
151. BOBTELSKY, M., and EISENSTADTER, S., *Anal. Chim. Acta*, **16**, 479 (1957).
152. RYABCHIKOV, D. I., *Zhur. Anal. Khim.*, **1**, 47 (1946).
153. RYAN, D. E., *Analyst*, **76**, 310 (1951).
154. YOUNG, R. S., *Analyst*, **76**, 49 (1951).
155. ZVYAGINTSEV, O. E., *Ann. inst. platine* (*U.S.S.R.*), **1**, 364 (1926).
156. AYRES, G. H., and TUFFLY, B. L., *Anal. Chem.*, **24**, 949 (1952).
157. PRZHEVAL'SKIĬ, E. S., and SHLENSKAYA, V. I., *Vestnik Moskov Univ.*, **7** (5), *Ser. Fis.-Mat. i Estestven. Nauk*, (3), 61 (1952); PRZHEVAL'SKIĬ *et al.*, *ibid.*, **9** (6), *Ser. Fis.-Mat. i Estestven. Nauk* (4), 71 (1954).
158. TAKAGI, S., and NAGASE, Y., *J. Pharm. Soc. Japan*, **58**, 60 (1938).
159. KUZAZHEVA, G. V., *Izvest. Sektora Platiny i Drug. Blagorod. Metal.*, *Inst. Obshcheĭ i Neorg. Khim.*, *Akad. Nauk S.S.S.R.*, **22**, 129 (1948).
160. SHIOKAWA, T., *et al.*, *Japan Analyst*, **4**, 224 (1955).
161. MCALLISTER, R. A., *Analyst*, **78**, 65 (1953).
162. MACNEVIN, W. M., and TUTHILL, S. M., *Anal. Chem.*, **21**, 1052 (1949).
163. WELCHER, **IV**, 175; DUVAL, C., *et al.*, *Anal. Chim. Acta*, **12**, 138 (1955).
164. PSHENITSYN, N. K., and PROKOF'EVA, I. V., *Zhur. Neorg. Khim.*, **2**, 569 (1957).
165. RYAN, D. E., *Analyst*, **75**, 557 (1950); **76**, 731 (1951).
166. RYAN, *Anal. Chem.*, **22**, 599 (1950).

167. HAINES, R. L., and RYAN, *Can. J. Research*, **27B**, 72 (1949).
168. AYRES, G. H., *et al.*, *Anal. Chem.*, **27**, 1742 (1955); AYRES and TUFFLY, B. L., *ibid.*, **25**, 521 (1953).
169. BOUVET, P. *Ann. pharm. franç.*, **5**, 293 (1947).
170. MAYNES, A. D., and MCBRYDE, W. A. E., *Analyst*, **79**, 230 (1954).
171. AYRES, G. H. and YOUNG, F., *Anal. Chem.*, **24**, 165 (1952).
172. AYRES, *Anal. Chem.*, **25**, 1624 (1953).
173. GOTO, H., *J. Chem. Soc. Japan*, **55**, 330 (1934).
174. WATANABE, K., *J. Chem. Soc. Japan*, **77**, 547, 1008 (1956).
175. CURRAH, J. E., *et al.*, *Ind. Eng. Chem.*, *Anal. Ed.*, **18**, 120 (1946); ALLEN, W. F., and BEAMISH, F. E., *Anal. Chem.*, **22**, 461 (1950).
176. SYROKOMSKIĬ, V. S., and PROSHENKOVA, N. N., *Zhur. Anal. Khim.*, **2**, 247 (1947).
177. ZSCHIEGNER, H. E., *Chem. Abst.*, **31**, 5722 (1937).
178. RYABCHIKOV, D. I., *Izvest. Sektora Platiny i Drug. Blagorod. Metal., Inst. Obshcheĭ i Neorg. Khim., Akad. Nauk S.S.S.R.*, **22**, 28 (1948).
179. HILL, M. A., and BEAMISH, F. E., *Anal. Chem.*, **22**, 590 (1950); BAREFOOT, R. R. and BEAMISH, *ibid.*, **24**, 840 (1952).
180. BERMAN, S. S., and MCBRYDE, W. A. E., *Analyst*, **81**, 566 (1956).
181. AYRES, G. H., and QUICK, Q., *Anal. Chem.*, **22**, 1403 (1950).
182. MACNEVIN, W. M., and CRUMMETT, W. B., *Anal. Chem.*, **25**, 1628 (1953).
183. AYRES, G. H., and BOLLETER, W. T., *Anal. Chem.*, **29**, 72 (1957); **26**, 1851 (1954).
184. BERMAN, S. S., *et al.*, *Anal. Chim. Acta*, **15**, 363 (1956).
185. WELCHER, **II**, 289.
186. MCBRYDE, W. A. E., and CLUETT, M. L., *Can. J. Research*, **28B**, 788 (1950).
187. MILAZZO, G., and PAOLONI, L., *Monatsh.*, **81**, 155 (1950).
188. PSHENITZYN, N. K., and PROKOF'EVA, I. V., *Izvest. Sektora Platiny i Drug. Blagorod. Metal., Inst. Obshchei i Neorg. Khim., Akad. Nauk S.S.S.R.*, **28**, 239 (1954).
189. PSHENITSYN, *et al.*, *Izvest. Sektora Platiny i Drug. Blagorod. Metal., Inst. Obshchei i Neorg. Khim., Akad. Nauk S.S.S.R.*, **25**, 192 (1950); **30**, 176 (1955).
190. BERKA, A., and ZÝKA, J., *Chem. listy*, **50**, 829 (1956).
191. BAREFOOT, R. R., *et al.*, *Anal. Chem.*, **23**, 514 (1951).
192. NEEB, R., *Z. anal. Chem.*, **154**, 17 (1957).
193. TREADWELL, W. D., *Tabellen*, 96 (1938).
194. WESTLAND, A. D., and BEAMISH, F. E., *Anal. Chem.*, **27**, 1776 (1955).
195. MACNEVIN, W. M., and KRIEGE, O. H., *Anal. Chem.*, **28**, 16 (1956).

33

IRON

The principal references for this chapter are Hillebrand and Lundell, Scott and Furman, Kimura, and Pigott.[1] The analysis of iron has been reviewed by Fuchs[2] and by Jean.[3]

In determination of iron, it should be remembered that Pt ware is attacked when $FeCl_3$ and HCl is evaporated in it. In general, when micro or trace amounts of Fe are determined, Pt ware should be avoided.

Attack

(a) Oxides. Dissolve in HCl + $SnCl_2$ (a few drops of HF may be added) or in aqua regia. Alternatively, fuse with Na_2CO_3 + KNO_3, $Na_2S_2O_7$ or KHF_2.

(b) Sulfides or arsenides. Dissolve in aqua regia or fuse with Na_2CO_3 and KNO_3.

(c) Sulfate (jarosite). Digest with dil. NaOH.

(d) Carbonates. Dissolve in HCl; HNO_3 can also be added.

(e) Silicates. Fuse with Na_2CO_3 or treat with H_2SO_4 and HF. In the latter case, samples contg. only a little SiO_2 but much Mg may stick to the bottom of the vessel; the sample should be mixed with coarsely ground quartz. With quartz sand, evap. to fumes with HF and H_2SO_4, fuse the residue with Na_2CO_3 and treat with HCl; fuse this residue with $Na_2S_2O_7$.

(f) Iron ores.[4] Dissolve in $HClO_4$ and H_3PO_4.

(g) Metals and alloys. Dissolve metals in HCl and HNO_3, in 1:1 HNO_3, or in 1:3–10 H_2SO_4. Treat Sn or Sb alloys with Br_2 in HBr (see Chapter 20, p. 157). Evap. Al alloys with HF and H_2SO_4; colloidal SiO_2 may interfere with the detn. of Fe.[5]

With special steels, the method of attack depends on the element which is to be detd. Treatment with aqua regia, HF, or H_2SO_4, H_3PO_4 and $HClO_4$ can be applied; if graphite remains after treatment with the mixed acids, add $K_2Cr_2O_7$. Fusion methods, e.g. with Na_2O_2, are also useful.

Treat Fe–Ti with 5% H_2SO_4 and H_2O_2; Fe–V with HCl and H_2O_2; and Fe–W or Fe–Mn–Si with HF and H_2O_2.[6]

Separation

(See also Chapter 2, p. 9 et seq.). H_2S in acidic soln. seps. Fe from group II metals and Pt; Fe^{2+} coppts. with Sn^{4+} in HCl soln. $(NH_4)_2S$ in $(NH_4)_2$-tartrate soln. seps. Fe, Ni, Co, Zn and, partly, Mn from Al, Zr, Ti, Nb, Ta, U, V, P, etc. This can be applied as a concn. method: treat the neutral or slightly acidic soln. with NaK-tartrate, 1 ml. 0·1*M* $CdCl_2$ and $(NH_4)_2S$, stir occasionally during 30–60 min., filter, wash, boil with 1:1 HCl, add $KMnO_4$, etc. (see p. 259).

Electrolysis seps. Fe from large amts. of Cu. Electrolysis at the Hg cathode serves to remove Fe.

NH_4OH and NH_4Cl are used to sep. Fe, Al, etc. from Mn, Ni. The sepn. from Co, Zn, Cu is incomplete; with excess of NH_4Cl, sepn. from Cu and Zn is nearly complete, but sepn. from Mn, Ni, Co is incomplete and the pptn. of Al is incomplete. Trace amts. of Cu, etc. coppt. Sepn. from Cr is possible if $(NH_4)_2S_2O_8$ is added. Better results can be obtained with pyridine.

Fe is sepd. from Zn, Mn, Ni, Co by the basic acetate or succinate method or by treatment with $BaCO_3$, ZnO and similar suspensions. In the hydrolytic methods, interferences are caused by tartrate, citrate, $C_2O_4^{2-}$, F^-, PO_4^{3-}, $P_2O_7^{4-}$, AsO_3^{3-}, AsO_4^{3-}, BO_2^-, and org. compds.

Boiling with dil. NaOH seps. Fe from Al, V, W, Mo, As, P (see Chapter 43, p. 320).

Fusion with Na_2CO_3 and extn. with H_2O seps. Fe from V, W, Mo, As, P, Cr and partly from Al, U.

Ion exchange resins, and particularly anion resins, are useful for sepns. from Al, etc. (see Chapter 13, p. 107 et seq.).

Extn. with Et_2O from ca. 20% HCl soln. or with iso-Pr_2O from 7·75–8·25*N* HCl soln. serves to sep. Fe from Cu, Co, Mn, Ni, Al, Cr, Zn, V^{4+}, Ti, SO_4^{2-}; interferences are Mo, PO_4^{3-}, V^{5+}, EtOH and large amts. of alkali metal salts. The Et_2O used must be pre-equilibrated with HCl of the appropriate concn. (see also Chapter 16, p. 135 et seq.).

Cupferron seps. small amts. of Fe, Ti, Zr, V from large amts. of Al, Cr, Mn, U, etc. The complex formed can be extd. with Et_2O, $CHCl_3$, etc. and this is useful for concn. purposes (see Chapter 8, Section 1.10). If the ppt. is washed with NH_4OH, the Fe complex is converted to the hydroxide and Fe is sepd. from Cu, V, U and Ce.

Extn. with dithizone in CCl_4 seps. Fe from Cu. Extn. with α-nitroso-β-naphthol in $CHCl_3$ from soln. of pH 4 seps. Fe from Co, which is extd.; if the soln. is slightly acidic in HNO_3, Fe is sepd. from Al and Mg.[7]

Several concn. methods are mentioned above; other useful procedures are extn. of the oxine complex from AcOH and NaOAc soln. with $CHCl_3$, extn. of the isonitrosoacetophenone–Fe^{2+} complex from soln. of pH 8–9 with $CHCl_3$, and copptn. with MnO_2 (see p. 259).

Determination

For macro amts. of Fe, the most satisfactory methods are gravimetric detn. as Fe_2O_3 or with oxine and its derivs., or titrimetric detn. with $K_2Cr_2O_7$, $KMnO_4$ or Ce^{4+}. Of the titrimetric procedures, the $K_2Cr_2O_7$ method is less prone to interferences than the others. The vanadate method is said to be most suitable for the detn. of Fe^{2+} in silicates. $Hg_2(NO_3)_2$ is claimed to be the best reducing titrant for Fe^{3+}. As was indicated in Chapter 5, Section 5, the redox titration of Fe has been studied profoundly, because it is fundamental in redox work. About 100 colorimetric methods have been suggested for the detn. of Fe; *o*-phenanthroline and its derivs. and 5-phenylsalicylic acid provide by far the best procedures. The method involving *m*-methoxy-*o*-nitrosophenol is very sensitive; the thiocyanate method has been very widely studied.

(a) NH_4OH provides the classical gravimetric procedure.[1, 8] To the acidic sample soln. add NH_4Cl and filter pulp, boil, add NH_4OH, boil, filter on Whatman No. 40 paper and wash with 2% NH_4Cl or NH_4NO_3. Ignite at 1000–1100°C (> 470°C) and weigh as Fe_2O_3. Ignition must be carried out in an elec. furnace, otherwise the oxide may be reduced by gas vapors penetrating the Pt crucible. Heating above 500°C is satisfactory for Fe alone, but if Al is present, the higher temp. is essential (see also p. 320).

NOTES. (1) If NH_4Cl is used for washing, the ppt. must be washed finally once with H_2O to prevent a minute loss of Fe.
(2) Many elements interfere; see under Separation.
(3) If only traces of Fe are present, tannin may be added.
(4) Similar procedures involving pyridine or hexamine have been suggested;[9] see also Chapter 2, Section 3.3.

(b) Redox titrations (*i*) $K_2Cr_2O_7$ is generally used with diphenylamine sulfonate indicator.[1] To the Fe^{2+} soln. contg. 5 ml. HCl or 2·5 ml. H_2SO_4/100 ml. add 6–8 drops 0·2% indicator soln. and titrate with 0·1*N* $K_2Cr_2O_7$ until the color is dark green; add 5 ml. 25% H_3PO_4 for each 35 ml. soln. and titrate to the end-point. If the end-point is overshot, add a known amt. of Fe^{2+} soln. and retitrate.

NOTES. (1) Cu (> 1 mg.) and Pt interfere; V, BF_4^-, PO_4^{3-} and F^- do not interfere, but F^- is not desirable because it promotes atmospheric oxidation. The procedure has been applied to a wide variety of metals.[10]
(2) Fe^{3+} can be reduced by many different procedures. With the Jones reductor, or with Al, Cd, etc., interferences are Ti, V, Nb, Cr, Mo, W, U, As, NO_3^-; triphenylmethylarsonium chloride with an extn. end-point ($(CH_2Cl)_2$) has been recommended after this reduction.[11] With $SnCl_2$,SO_2 or H_2S, interferences are Au, Mo, W, U, Cu, As, Sb. With the Ag reductor, V, Mo, U, W, Cu interfere but Ti and Cr do not. Several metal amalgams have been examined for the reduction.[12] When reduction is done with $SnCl_2$, silicomolybdic acid may be added[13] to indicate the destruction of the excess $SnCl_2$ with $K_2Cr_2O_7$; phenylanthranilic acid then serves as indicator for the actual titration of Fe^{2+}.
(3) Alternative indicators have been discussed in Chapter 5, Section 5.5 and Chapter 15, Section 4. $K_3Fe(CN)_6$ may be used as an external indicator.

(*ii*) $KMnO_4$ serves as its own indicator:[1] titrate the Fe^{2+} in 1–5% v/v H_2SO_4 soln. until the pink color remains for at least 30 sec. Fe^{3+} is reduced in the Jones reductor or with Zn–Hg in 2*N* H_2SO_4 by shaking for 30 sec.[12] When much Fe is present, add H_3PO_4. If V^{4+} is present, titrate the hot soln.

HCl, Cu^{2+} and F^- interfere; in the last case, better results are obtained if H_3BO_3 or K_2SO_4 is added.

The Zimmermann–Reinhardt method is used for HCl soln. The reagent consists of 200 g. $MnSO_4$ in 1 l. H_2O mixed with 400 ml. H_2SO_4, 120 ml. H_2O and 400 ml. H_3PO_4 added while cooling. For titration of Fe^{2+} in 3–15% v/v HCl soln. add 25 ml. of this reagent, dil. to 400 ml. with H_2O and titrate slowly to the pink end-point. Results are slightly high, especially if $KMnO_4$ is added rapidly.

NOTES. (1) For reduction of Fe^{3+} in 25 ml. 1:1 HCl soln., add 5% $SnCl_2$ in 2*N* HCl to the hot soln. until colorless (do not add more than 0·2 ml. in excess), cool, add 10 ml. cold satd. $HgCl_2$ all at once (discard if a grey ppt. appears), leave for 5–10 min. and proceed as above. Zn–Hg is used in 5% v/v HCl soln., the above method being applied after sepn.[12]
(2) Various substitutes for the Zimmermann–Reinhardt soln. have been suggested.[14]
(3) Titration with $KMnO_4$ has been applied to detn. of Fe in many alloys and metals.[10]
(4) Sharper end-points, particularly on micro scale, are obtained if indicator is added. Diphenylamine can be used, after reduction with Zn or the Jones reductor and after addn. of 15 ml. H_2SO_4 and H_3PO_4.[15] Erioglaucine A gives a green to pink color change.[16]

(*iii*) $Ce(SO_4)_2$ is generally used[1] with ferroin indicator in *M* H_2SO_4, HCl or $HClO_4$ soln. after addn. of some H_3PO_4; the end-point is from pink to pale blue or colorless. Diphenylamine sulfonic acid indicator is also used (Pigott[1]). If 2–3 drops 0·01*M* diphenylamine sulfonic acid and 1 drop 0·01*M* ferroin are added per 100 ml. soln., the former color change indicates 99·1% oxidation of Fe^{2+} and the end-point is marked by a change from red-orange through wine-red to violet.[17]

Cacotheline can be used[18] to indicate complete oxidation of excess Sn^{2+} by Ce^{4+}, the color changing from violet to yellow; ferroin is then added and the titration completed for Fe^{2+}. Erioglaucine A and diphenylamine have also been applied for the direct titration of Fe^{2+}; with the latter indicator U^{4+} does not interfere if much H_3PO_4 is added.[19]

NOTES. (1) F^-, NO_3^-, AcO^-, citrate and oxalate interfere; F^- interference is prevented by H_3BO_3 addn. The method has been applied for analysis of Mg and its alloys.[10]
(2) The Ag reductor is normally used here for reduction of Fe^{3+}. With a potentiometric end-point, 0·27–0·5 mg. Fe can be detd. with an accuracy of 0·2%.[20] For a coulometric titration, see ref. 21.
(3) For detn. of FeO in chromite,[22] treat the sample with a known wt. of $Ce(SO_4)_2$ and 4:1 H_3PO_4 and H_2SO_4 for 90 min. at 290–300°C and then titrate with Fe^{2+}.

(*iv*) NH_4VO_3 is normally used with phenylanthranilic acid or diphenylamine indicator. For silicates,[23] add 50 ml. 0·01–0·1*N* VO_3^- to the sample in a Pt dish followed by 2·50 ml. H_2SO_4 and 5 ml. HF, heat, transfer to a beaker, dil. to 150 ml. with H_2O, add indicator and back-titrate with Fe^{2+} soln.

NOTE. For detn. of FeO in chromite,[24] place 0·25 g. sample in a 300 ml. Erlenmeyer flask, add some H_2O and 30 ml. V^{5+} soln. (1 g. V_2O_5/100 ml. H_3PO_4 and 200 ml. H_2SO_4, heat to white fumes, cool, pipet out 30 ml. and titrate with 0·1*N* $KMnO_4$ (A ml.); add 9 × A ml. of $KMnO_4$ to the remaining soln. and stir). Heat to white fumes at 250°C for 12–13 min. or at 300°C for 5 min. Cool, transfer to a 500 ml. flask, dil. to 250 ml. with H_2O, add Co soln. in an amt. greater than 3 times that of Cr (4·94 g. $Co(NO_3)_2$ in H_2O heated to fumes with 100 ml. H_2SO_4, cooled and dild. to 1 l. with H_2O) and finally titrate with 0·1*N* $KMnO_4$ until the pink color remains for 1 min.

(*v*) $K_3Fe(CN)_6$ is applied to dil. H_2SO_4 sample solns.[25] Reduce with Zn–Hg, sep. and titrate until the soln. is blue; then add 2–4 g. Na-triphosphate or pyrophosphate, adjust to above pH 4·3 with NaOH and titrate to a yellow end-point. Alternatively, use cacotheline as indicator.

(*vi*) $TiCl_3$ or $Ti_2(SO_4)_3$ is used with NH_4SCN indicator.[1] For < 0·28 g. Fe^{3+} in 10% v/v HCl or H_2SO_4, add 6–25 ml. 10% NH_4SCN, pass CO_2 through the soln. and titrate at 50–60°C in a CO_2 atmos. to a colorless end-point. Methylene blue can also serve as indicator. For potentiometric titration, see ref. 26 and for coulometric titration, see ref. 27. Interferences are HNO_3, oxidants, org. compds., Cu, Sb, Mo, Pt, W, V; HF interferes unless H_3BO_3 is added.

(*vii*) Ascorbic acid is used for Fe^{3+} detn. in 0·1–0·2*N* HCl media at 50°C in presence of NH_4SCN or variamine blue indicator.[28]

(*viii*) $SnCl_2$ is applied in 1:1 HCl media with NH_4SCN indicator:[1] MoO_4^{2-} with SCN^- may also be added as indicator.[29]

(*ix*) $Hg_2(NO_3)_2$ (5·96 g. in 1 l. 1:20 HNO_3) is suitable for titration of Fe^{3+} in 0·5*N* HNO_3 solns.; add 10 ml. 40% NH_4SCN and titrate slowly near the end-point.[30] HCl and H_2SO_4 cause slightly high results unless more indicator is added.

(*x*) $Na_2S_2O_3$ has been applied with a potentiometric end-point.[31]

(*xi*) Cr^{2+} is used for potentiometric titration of Fe^{3+} in solns. contg. 2*N* H_2SO_4 or HCl; add 7 g. $(NH_4)_2SO_4$ and titrate at 80°C in a CO_2 atmos.[32] It is possible to det. simultaneously Ti and Fe, V and Fe, Mo^{6+} ($\rightarrow Mo^{5+}$) and Fe, Cr^{6+} ($\rightarrow Cr^{3+}$) and Mo and Fe.

(*xii*) Iodometric titration is used in solns. contg. 2 ml. 4*N* HCl per 10 ml.;[15, 33] add 1–2 g. KI, wait for 3 min., add starch soln. and titrate.

(*xiii*) KIO_3 is used with CCl_4 as indicator.[34] Reduce 10 ml. Fe^{3+} soln. which is 0·8*N* in H_2SO_4 under CO_2 with Zn–Hg, sep., add 20 ml. HCl, 5 ml. ICl and 7 ml. CCl_4 and titrate to the colorless extraction end-point. $C_2O_4^{2-}$, tartrate, citrate and EtOH do not interfere.

(*xiv*) $KBrO_3$ has been applied with naphthol blue black indicator.[35] Add HCl to the Fe^{2+} soln. (25 ml.) to give a 1–1·5*N* acidity, add 10 ml. catalyst soln. (12·5 g. $(NH_4)_2HAsO_4$, 0·425 g. $CuCl_2$ and 250 ml. H_3PO_4 in 500 ml.) and 1 drop of indicator soln. and titrate slowly with strong shaking.

(*xv*) For reduction methods involving org. acids or ultraviolet light, see p. 261.

(c) Bromoxine has been applied gravimetrically and titrimetrically. For 0·4 mg. Fe^{3+} in 100 ml. neutral soln.,[36] add 2 g. tartaric acid, 30 ml. Me_2CO and 10 ml. 1*N* HCl, heat to 50°C, add 5 ml. warm satd. bromoxine in Me_2CO and boil. Filter on a G4 crucible, wash with a warm mixture of 15 ml. Me_2CO, 85 ml. H_2O and 1·5 ml. 1*N* HCl and then with warm H_2O; dry at 120–140°C (72–95°C) and weigh as $Fe(C_9H_4Br_2ON)_3$. Amperometric titration is possible.[37]

NOTES. (1) No interference is caused by Al, Co, Ni, Zn, Mn, Be, U, Pb, Hg, Cd, Bi, Ca, etc. Cu interferes; Ti interference is prevented by tartaric or malonic acid addn.
(2) A very similar method is available with chloroxine; here the ppt. is ignited above 550°C and weighed as Fe_2O_3.
(3) Oxine acetate can be applied gravimetrically, titrimetrically or colorimetrically. For 0·1–5 mg. Fe^{3+} in 1–5 ml. of slightly acidic soln.[38, 39] heat to 60–70°C, add a 2–2·5-fold excess of 4% reagent, reheat, add 0·7–1·0 ml. 50% NH_4OAc, place on a steam-bath for 10 min. and leave to cool. Filter on a glass crucible, wash with hot H_2O, dry at 120–125°C (< 284°C) and weigh as $Fe(C_9H_6ON)_3$. Alternatively, dissolve the ppt. (from < 50 mg. Fe) in 2*N* HCl, add 10–15 ml. H_3PO_4, dil. to 200 ml. with H_2O and titrate bromometrically. For the colorimetric method, see Table 38. Mn, Be, Ca, Mg and PO_4^{3-} do not interfere; Al interference is prevented by pptg. from soln. at pH 3·5–4·6 contg. 0·1–1 g. Na-malonate, or by 3–4 g. $(NH_4)_2$-tartrate and 3 g. NaOAc in 100 ml. soln. contg. 15–20% AcOH.

(d) *o*-Phenanthroline monohydrate provides an excellent colorimetric procedure.[40, 41] For 0·01–0·2 mg. Fe in acidic soln. add 1 ml. 1% hydroquinone, 2 ml.

TABLE 38. Colorimetric Methods for Iron

Reagent	Conditions	Color, $\lambda_{max.}$, mμ	Range (μg./ml.), Sensitivity, Error	Interferences	Ref.
o-Phenanthroline	pH 2–9, NH_2OH or hydroquinone reduction	Fe^{2+}, red, 515	0·05–6, 0·005, ϵ = 11 100		(1)
0·0025*M* Batho-phenanthroline/iso-AmOH	pH 4·0–5·0, extn.	Fe^{2+}, red, 530	ϵ = 22 400		(2)
0·0025*M* Terosite/1:1 $CHCl_3$ – EtOH	pH 5·0, extn.	Fe^{2+}, 583 or 383	ϵ = 30 200 or 20 740		(3)
3,5,6,8-Tetramethylphenanthroline	pH 4–5, +$NaClO_4$, $CHCl_3$ extn.		0·04–0·4		(4)
0·01*M* 4,7-Dihydroxyphenanthroline	10 ml. 10*M* NaOH, 2 ml. 20% $Na_2S_2O_4$, 2 ml. reagent/25 ml.	520	ϵ = 14 800		(5)
5-Nitro-1,10-phenanthroline		490 or 505	0·5–4, ϵ = 8650		(6)
0·2 g. α,α′-Dipyridyl/2 ml. HCl (1:9), 18 ml. H_2O	pH 3–4, 2 ml. + 1 ml. 10% Na_2SO_3/50 ml.	522	0·2–17, 0·007	Cu^+	(7)
0·1% 2,2′,2″-Tripyridyl/0·1*N* HCl + 1 ml. 10% $NH_2OH{\cdot}HCl$ + 5 ml. 60% ethylenediamine	pH 3–10, 5 ml./100 ml.	555	0·05–2		(8)
5-Phenylsalicylic acid	pH 2·8–3·2, 40% EtOH	Fe^{3+}, violet, 505	<10, 0·03	U	(9)
KSCN	1>*N* HCl or HNO_3	Fe^{3+}, red, 480	0·1–1, 0·008	many	(10)
SCN^- + Me_2CO	as above	as above	0·05–5, 0·004		(11)
SCN^- + triphenylmethylarsonium chloride	pH 1–2, o-$C_6H_4Cl_2$ extn.		1–10		(12)
SCN^- + antipyrine	feebly acidic, EtOAc extn.	470	0·2–10, ϵ = 28 000	Cu, Bi, Co	(13)
SCN^- + Bu_3NHOAc	feebly acidic, AmOAc extn.	480		Bi, Mo, W	(14)
1% Dimethylglyoxime/EtOH	feebly ammoniacal, 0·5 ml./50 ml., NH_2OH, dithionite, ascorbic acid, etc. reduction	Fe^{2+}, red, 529	0·04–0·6, ±2%	Al, etc.	(15)
Ditto + pyridine	pH 8, 1 ml. 10% Na_2-tartrate, 1 ml. reagent, 2 ml. pyridine, 5 ml. $CHCl_3$ extn.				(16)
1% Dimethylaminobutanedionedioxime/EtOH	as dimethylglyoxime	541	as dimethylglyoxime		(17)
0·2% Nioxime	as above except 2 ml. reagent	543	as above		(18)
0·1% Salicylaldoxime	pH 6·2–6·6, 10 ml./100 ml.	Fe^{3+}, red–orange, 480	0·1–2·2, 0·011	Cr, Co, Mo, U; PO_4^{3-}, tartrate, etc.	(19)
0·2% Resorcylaldoxime	as above, 1 ml./50 ml.	Fe^{3+}, red	0·3–5	Au, Pd, Mo, Ti, U	(20)
Resacetophenoneoxime		Fe^{3+}, red			(21)
Salicylamidoxime	pH 8·3–10·0	Fe^{3+}, orange-red, 400		many	(22)
m-Methoxy-*o*-nitrosophenol	pH 3·8	Fe^{2+}, green, 700	0·01–1·0		(23)
1% Nitroso-R salt	pH 5·0 (2*M* NH_4OAc), 10 ml. + 0·5 ml. 10% $NH_2OH{\cdot}HCl$/50 ml., 95°C 5–10 min.	Fe^{2+}, green, 720	<1·2, ±2%	W, Mo; F^-, citrate, CN^-. Time-consuming	(24)
o-Nitrosophenol	pH 5·2 NaOAc + AcOH buffer	as above	0·01	Cu, Ni, Hg	(25)
0·1% Isonitrosodimedone	pH 4–5, 10 ml./50 ml., NH_2OH reduction	$Fe^{2+, 3+}$, blue, 620	0·5–6	Cu, Ni, Co; good	(26)
0·75% Isonitrosoacetophenone/$CHCl_3$	pH 7–9, N_2H_4 reduction	Fe^{2+}, blue	0·01–0·5	Cu, Ni, Co	(27)
Ethyl Isonitrosoacetylacetate	pH 7·8, $CHCl_3$ extn.	as above			(28)
0·2% Isonitrosomalonylguanidine	pH 6, 5 ml./100 ml.	Fe^{2+}, blue, 630			(29)
1% Violuric acid	pH 8·75, NH_2OH reduction	Fe^{2+}, dark blue		Cu, Co, Cd, Zn, Ag, Hg, CN^-	(30)
Diphenylvioluric acid		Fe^{2+}, 660			(31)
Formohydroxamic acid	strong acid	Fe^{3+}, purple	1–100		(32)
Oxalohydroxamic acid	as above	as above			(33)
Salicylhydroxamic acid	pH 8–11	blue filter	<5	U, V, Mo, etc., sensitive to pH	(34)
Salicylaldehyde aminoacetohydroxamic acid	pH 2·35–3·34 or 5·06–10·26	Fe^{3+}, violet, 535–550 or 460–510	0·05–30	PO_4^{3-}, etc.	(35)
0·2% Ferron	pH 2·7–3·1, 5 drops/40 ml.	Fe^{3+}, green, 610	0·1–54, 0·015	Cr, Ni, Co, Cu, Sn, Ti, CN^-, PO_4^{3-}, ClO_4^-. See Al	(36)
0·1% Ferron, Bu_3NHOAc	acetate buffer, 4 ml. + 1·2 ml., iso-AmOH extn.	as above	<15	Bi, F^-, $P_2O_7^{4-}$, $C_2O_4^{2-}$	(37)
Oxine	pH 3, $CHCl_3$ extn.	as above, 475, 590	0·5–5	V	(38)
8-Hydroxyquinoline-5-sulfonic acid	pH 4·0 phthalate buffer	as above	<0·5	Cu, Zn, Cd, Mg, Al, Sn^{4+}, Pb, Co, Ni, H_2O_2, F^-, citrate, PO_4^{3-}, AsO_4^{3-}	(39)
8-Hydroxyquinoline-disulfonic acid	pH 2	Fe^{3+}, blue-green	0·1		(40)
8-Hydroxyquinaldine	pH 5·3	Fe^{3+}, 580			(41)
Iodoxine		380			(42)
1% Quinaldic acid	100 mg. NaCN, 50 mg. $NH_2OH{\cdot}HCl$, 10 mg. reagent/50 ml.	Fe^{2+}, pink, 515	0·17	Cu, $C_2O_4^{2-}$, etc.	(43)
5,6-Benzoquinaldic acid		as above, 515	2·4–14		(44)
Quinoline-8-carboxylic acid					(45)
1% 2-Picolinic acid	1 ml. 5% $NH_2OH{\cdot}HCl$, 1 ml. reagent, 1 ml. 10% KCN/50 ml.	Fe^{2+}, orange-yellow, 440	1·6–8		(46)
Benzothiazole-2-sulfonic acid	2·7 × 10^{-3}*M* reagent, 2*M* CN^- or 3 × 10^{-2}*M* reagent, 50% EtOH	Fe^{2+}, red, 482·5 or 465	<56 or <140		(47)
0·1*M* Sulfoanthranilic acid	pH 3·6–4·4	Red, 455	2–60	Cr (20 p.p.m.), Co (75)	(48)
p-Aminosalicylic acid	pH 1·4–3·05 or 3·36–5·05	480–500 or 450–470	0·05–15		(49)

Cupferron	strong acid, $CHCl_3$ extn.	Fe^{3+}, brown, 480	0·2–5, ±0·4		(50)
Tetralin analogs of cupferron	as above	Fe^{3+}, red, 385 (α), 398 (β)	0·3 (α), 0·1 (β)		(51)
1% Pyramidone	0·2 ml. H_2SO_4, 11–20 ml. reagent/50 ml.	Fe^{3+}, blue	0·4–2		(52)
1% Alloxantin/1*N* NaOH	5 ml./15 ml.	Fe^{3+}, blue	>1		(53)
10% v/v Thioglycolic acid, NH_4OH to neutral	pH 7–12, 2 ml./100 ml., shake with air, add citrate	$Fe^{2+, 3+}$, purple, 540	0·1–14, 0·014	Co, Ni, Pb, Bi, Hg, Ag, Au, U, W; NO_2^-, CN^-	(54)
2% Sulfosalicylic acid[a]	pH 3·0, 2 ml./100 ml.	$Fe^{2+, 3+}$, yellow, 436, 462	>0·1	Cu, Mn, Cr, Pb, CN^-, F^-, Tar^{2-}	(55)
Ditto	add 0·5 ml. 2*N* HCl to the above	Fe^{3+}, red, 493, 509	>0·2	detn. of Fe^{2+}, Fe^{3+}, see above	(56)
Ethylenediamine-bis-(sulfosalicylaldehyde)	pH 2·8–5·5	violet-red, 510–520	0·25–10	Mo, BO_2^-, F^-, PO_4^{3-}	(57)
4% Tiron[b]	pH 4·0 ± 0·1	Fe^{3+}, blue, 560		see Ti, sensitive to pH	(58)
1% Na-salicylate	pH 2·5–2·7, 5 ml./50 ml.	Fe^{3+}, pink, 520	0·2–45, 0·03	Ti, Al, F^-, Cl^-, PO_4^{3-}	(59)
0·7% 2-Fluorobenzoic acid	pH 3·0–3·5 formate buffer	Fe^{3+}, amethyst, 525	2–20, ε = 13 000	Ag, Al, As, Bi, Hg, Nb, Pb, Sn^{4+}, Ta, Th, Ti, V, U, F^-, PO_4^{3-}, SiO_2	(60)
5-Nitrosalicylic acid 3,5-dinitrosalicylate	pH<5·8	Fe^{3+}, red	0·5–50	Cu (+CN^-)	(61)
Na-naphtholtrisulfonic acid	pH 5·2 acetate buffer	Fe^{3+}, blue			(62)
Phenylpyruvate	pH 3·5	Fe^{3+}, purple	2·5		(63)
1% Protocatechuic acid/EtOH	pH > 8·5 + Cit^{3-}	$Fe^{2+, 3+}$, red	0·25–30	Cu (>Fe)	(64)
Protocatechualdehyde	faintly acidic or alk.	Fe^{3+}, green-pale violet or red–red-orange		Mo (neutral), V (neutral-acid), Ce^{3+} (ammoniacal)	(65)
2% Gallic acid	NaOAc	Fe^{3+}, blue-violet	100		(66)
β-Resorcylic acid	pH 2·5–3·0	Fe^{3+}, red, 425–450	20		(67)
1% Pyrocatechol	neutral, 10 ml./100 ml.	Fe^{3+}, violet	20, ±5%		(68)
5% Pyrogallol	pH 7·0–7·8, 10 ml. 4% $(NH_4)_2C_2O_4$, 10 ml. 20% Na_2SO_3, 5 ml. reagent/100 ml.	Fe^{2+}, violet, 550	1–10	Ni, Cr	(69)
2% Tannin	pH 4·5–6·0, BuOH removal of reagent	Fe^{3+}, purple, 550	comparable with SCN	Ti, Mo, Ta	(70)
0·1% Kojic acid	pH 6·3–6·5, 10 ml. 25% NH_4OAc, 10 ml. reagent/100 ml.	Fe^{3+}, blue, 440	<20	Al, Zn, Sn, V; F^-, CN^-, I^-, NO_2^-, PO_4^{3-}, SO_3^{2-}, org. compds.	(71)
0·01*N* Meconic acid	pH 1, 2 ml. 2*N* HCl, 5 ml. reagent/20 ml.	Fe^{3+}, red, 475	0–30		(72)
Citrinin/EtOH	neutral	Fe^{3+}, blue, 640–700	<50		(73)
10% Acetylacetone	3 ml. reagent, 20 ml. 10% $(NH_4)_2S_2O_8$, adjust pH to 6, 25 ml. $CHCl_3$ + BuOH extn.	Fe^{3+}, red, 460			(74)
0·06*M* Thenoyltrifluoroacetone/EtOH	pH 1·9, 1 ml. reagent, 10 ml. 2-propanol/25 ml.	Fe^{3+}, red, 502	2–14	Zr, F^-, PO_4^{3-}, $C_2O_4^{2-}$	(75)
Tartaric acid	pH 2·4–4·8 or 8·0–10·9	Fe^{3+}, yellow, 350 or 300	20 or 15	Cu, Ni, Mn, Co, Cr	(76)
Citric acid		Fe^{3+}, yellow	<17		(77)
EDTA	0·1*N* HCl, 0·001*M* reagent	260 or 366	8–28 or 4–500	Cu, Hg, Ti, etc.	(78)
EDTA + H_2O_2	ammoniacal, see Co	violet, 525	<100	Cu, Co, Ni (+KCN), Cr	(79)
NTA	pH 4·5–7·7	366	<50		(80)
AcOH	2 ml. + 0·2–0·5 ml. HCl/50 ml.	337·5	200–1000		(81)
0·5% $K_3Fe(CN)_6$	H_2SO_4 acidic	Fe^{2+}, blue	0·7		(82)
0·5% $K_4Fe(CN)_6$	neutral	Fe^{3+}, blue, 715	10–40		(83)
10% Na_2S	5 ml. tartaric acid, 5 ml. reagent/100 ml. neutral to litmus soln.	Fe^{2+}, blue-green	0·05–3		(84)
KI, starch	acidic	Fe^{3+}, blue	0·03–3		(85)
p-Phenylenediamine, H_2O_2, catalytic			0·5–5		(86)
HCl	const. boiling, or 5 ml. 28%/30 ml.	Fe^{3+}, yellow, 370 or 400	2–20 or <100	Cu, Ni, V	(87)
HBr		Fe^{3+}, yellow, 365–490, 280–310	<20		(88)
H_2SO_4	$HClO_4$ acidic, 8 ml./100 ml.	320	<16	Cu, Cr	(89)
$HClO_4$	10 ml. 70%/100 ml.	260	ε = 2880	Cr^{6+}, V, Mo, Ti, Cu, Bi, Mn^{7+}, F^-, Cl^-, NO_3^-	(90)
Hematoxylin		Fe^{3+}, blue-violet, 660			(91)
Alumocreson	pH 4·37	Fe^{3+}, violet-pink, 530			(92)
Calcodur yellow 4GL	pH 3·8	Fe^{3+}, dark olive green, 475			(93)
Chrome yellow O		Fe^{3+}, yellow–brown, 380–520	0·8–5		(94)
1% Variamine blue	pH 1–4, 1 ml./50 ml.	Fe^{3+}, blue, 570	<6	Bi, Sn^{2+}, $C_2O_4^{2-}$, F^-, etc.	(95)
Hydrazinophthalazine	pH 11·2–11·3, 50 mg./100 ml.	violet, 535	<1	Co, Ni, Cr, Mo, W, Mn, $C_2O_4^{2-}$, etc.	(96)

[a] 0·1–2·0 mg. Fe/100 ml. can be detd. at pH 1·5 (500 mμ), 5·0 (460 mμ), 8·2 (420 mμ, most sensitive); PO_4^{3-}, SO_4^{2-} interfere (correction). (Ref.) KENNARD, M. and JOHNSON, C. R. *Proc. and Trans. Texas Acad. Sci.*, 27, 45 (1944).

[b] Blue at pH <5, violet at pH 5·5–6·5, red at pH >7; more sensitive (0·009 μg/cm²) at 480 mμ.

I

References to Table 38

(1) Separate entry (see p. 255).
(2) PETERSON, R. E., *Anal. Chem.*, **25**, 1317 (1953); SHERWOOD, R. M. and CHAPMAN, JR., F. W., *ibid.*, **27**, 88 (1955); ZAK, B. and RESSLER, N., *ibid.*, **28**, 1158 (1956); CRAWLEY, R. H. A., *Anal. Chim. Acta*, **13**, 373 (1955); SMITH, G. F., *et al.*, *Analyst*, **77**, 418 (1952).
(3) SCHILT, A. A. and SMITH, G. F., *Anal. Chim. Acta*, **15**, 567 (1956).
(4) HOSTE, J. and GILLIS, J., *Mededel. Koninkl. Vlaam. Acad. Wetenschap. Belg., Kl. Wetenschap.*, **13**, (2) 3 (1951).
(5) SCHILT, A. A., *et al.*, *Anal. Chem.*, **28**, 809 (1956).
(6) WELCHER, **III**, 84.
(7) A.S.T.M., 426 (in Mg and its alloys); WELCHER, **III**, 74.
(8) MORRIS, R. L., *Anal. Chem.*, **24**, 1376 (1952); WELCHER, III, 100.
(9)–(14) Separate entries.
(15) GRIFFING, M. and MELLON, M. G., *Anal. Chem.*, **19**, 1017 (1947); IINUMA, H. and YOSHIMORI, T., *Japan Analyst*, **5**, 149 (1956) (V^{4+} as stabilizer); MURAKAMI, T., *ibid.*, **6**, 172 (1957) (in Cu, Cu increases sensitivity); (YOE, 248; WELCHER, III, 211).
(16) OI, N., *J. Chem. Soc. Japan*, **75**, 1067, 1069 (1954).
(17)–(18) GRIFFING and MELLON, ref. 15.
(19) HOWE, D. E. and MELLON, M. G., *Ind. Eng. Chem., Anal. Ed.*, **12**, 448 (1940); MEHLIG, J. P. and DURST, D., *Chemist Analyst*, **38**, 76 (1949); WELCHER, III, 266.
(20) CHIEN, S. L. and SHIH, F. M., *J. Chinese Chem. Soc.*, **5**, 154 (1937); (WELCHER, III, 259).
(21) NEELAKANTAM, K., *Current Sci.* (*India*), **14**, 320 (1945).
(22) See p. 302; BANDYOPADHAYAY, D., *J. Indian Chem. Soc.*, **33**, 276 (1956).
(23) Separate entry.
(24) DEAN, J. A. and LADY, J. H., *Anal. Chem.*, **25**, 947 (1953); OKA, Y. and MIYAMOTO, M., *Japan Analyst*, **1**, 23 (1952); *J. Chem. Soc. Japan*, **75**, 864 (1954); **76**, 672 (1955); (WELCHER, **III**, 335).
(25) WELCHER, **III**, 327.
(26) SHOME, S. C., *Anal. Chem.*, **20**, 1205 (1948).
(27) KRÖHNKE, F., *Z. anorg. Chem.*, **251**, 240 (1938).
(28) BOUCHERLE, A., *Ann. pharm. franç.*, **11**, 546 (1953).
(29) JEAN, M., *Anal. Chim. Acta*, **11**, 451 (1954) (in Zn, Al).
(30) ČERNÝ, P., *Chem. listy*, **51**, 735 (1957).
(31) MALÍK, L. C. and SINGH, R. P., *J. Indian Chem. Soc.*, **33**, 335 (1956).
(32) VONESCH, E. E., *et al.*, *Anales asoc. quím. Arg.*, **41**, 162 (1953).
(33)–(34) See p. 301.
(35) MUKHERJEE, A. K., *Naturwissenschaften*, **42**, 127 (1954).
(36) DAVENPORT, JR., W. H., *Anal. Chem.*, **21**, 710 (1949); (SCOTT and FURMAN, 487; WELCHER, I, 336).
(37) ZIEGLER, M., *et al.*, *Z. anal. Chem.*, **154**, 170 (1957); *Mikrochim. Acta*, 215 (1957).
(38) WELCHER, I, 308; see also p. 321.
(39) WELCHER, I, 334.
(40) KUDO, I., *Japan Analyst*, **3**, 76 (1954).
(41) MOTOJIMA, see p. 364.
(42) See p. 174.
(43) MAJUMDAR, A. K., *J. Indian Chem. Soc.*, **27**, 245 (1950); SHINRA, K., *et al.*, *J. Chem. Soc. Japan*, **75**, 44 (1954); WELCHER, **II**, 217.
(44) MAJUMDAR and SEN, B., *Anal. Chim. Acta*, **9**, 529 (1953).
(45) MAJUMDAR, *J. Indian Chem. Soc.*, **22**, 309 (1945).
(46) MAJUMDAR and SEN, B., *Anal. Chim. Acta*, **9**, 536 (1953); **8**, 369, 384 (1953).
(47) YOSHIKAWA, K. and SHINRA, K., *J. Chem. Soc. Japan*, **75**, 1220 (1954).
(48) ZEHNER, J. M. and SWEET, T. R., *Anal. Chem.*, **28**, 198 (1953).
(49) MUKHERJEE, A. K., *Anal. Chim. Acta*, **13**, 273 (1955).
(50) PAULAIS, R., *Compt. rend.*, **206**, 783 (1938); BUSCARÓNS and MALUMBRES, see ref. 52, p. 364.
(51) MOMOSE, T., *et al.*, *Japan Analyst*, **5**, 276 (1956).
(52) WELCHER, **III**, 114.
(53) WELCHER, **I**, 194.
(54) WILL, F., III, and YOE, J. H., *Anal. Chem.*, **25**, 1363 (1953); MAYER, A. and BRADSHAW, G., *Analyst*, **76**, 715 (1951); (SANDELL, 378, WELCHER, IV, 160).
(55) THIEL, A. and HENGEL, E. VAN, *Ber.*, **70**, 2491 (1937); WELCHER, II, 131.
(56) THIEL and PETER, O., *Z. anal. Chem.*, **103**, 161 (1935); WELCHER, II, 131.
(57) MUKHERJEE, *Anal. Chim. Acta*, **13**, 268 (1955).
(58) POTTER, G. V. and ARMSTRONG, C. E., *Anal. Chem.*, **20**, 1208 (1948); WELCHER, I, 249, 261.
(59) SCOTT, R. O., *Analyst*, **66**, 142 (1941); MEHLIG, J. P., *Ind. Eng. Chem., Anal. Ed.*, **10**, 136 (1938); WELCHER, II, 118; A.S.T.M., 300 (Cu–Ni–Zn).
(60) BUCHANAN, JR., E. B., and WAGNER, W., *Anal. Chem.*, **29**, 754 (1957).
(61) GÉCZY, G., *Magyar Kém. Folyóirat*, **56**, 434 (1950).
(62) WELCHER, I, 254.
(63) CASTAGNOU, R. and GAUCHER, G., *Bull. trav. soc. pharm. Bordeaux*, **88**, 104 (1950).
(64) PEREIRA, R. S., *J. Biol. Chem.*, **137**, 417 (1941).
(65) SHAPIRO, M. YA., *Zhur. Anal. Khim.*, **7**, 214 (1952).
(66) BERNOULLI, A. L., *Helv. Chim. Acta*, **9**, 835 (1926).
(67) VIVARELLI, S., *Chim. e ind.* (*Milan*), **38**, 461 (1956); ARMSTRONG, A. R., Dissertation, Univ. Virginia, (1945); WELCHER, **II**, 116.
(68) HANISET, P., *Ing. chim.*, **32**, 57 (1950); WELCHER, **I**, 158.
(69) YANA, M., *Japan Analyst*, **4**, 505 (1955); (WELCHER. **I**, 167).
(70) YOSHIMURA, C. and OGAMI, K., *J. Chem. Soc. Japan*, **78**, 320 (1957).
(71) MEHLIG, J. P. and SHEPHARD, JR., M. J., *Anal. Chem.*, **21**, 642 (1949); (WELCHER, **I**, 211).
(72) MANNELLI, G. and BIFFOLI, R., *Anal. Chim. Acta*, **11**, 168 (1954).
(73) LIANG, SH. C., *Sci. Record* (*China*), **2**, 72, 373 (1949).
(74) KINNUNEN, J. and WENNERSTRAND, B., *Chemist Analyst*, **42**, 30 (1953).
(75) KINGDON, F. W. and MELLON, M. G., *Anal. Chem.*, **28**, 860 (1956).
(76) YASUOKA, S., *et al.*, *Japan Analyst*, **4**, 434 (1955); NIELSCH, W. and BÖLTZ, G., *Metall*, **8**, 374, 866 (1954).
(77) UHER, E., *Hustnické listy*, **1**, 63 (1957).
(78) UZUMASA, Y. and NISHIMURA, M., *Bull. Chem. Soc. Japan*, **28**, 88 (1955); **30**, 433 (1957); NIELSCH and BÖLTZ, *Mikrochim. Acta*, 481 (1954); also see p. 261.
(79) SCHNEIDER, P. and JANKO, J., *Chem. listy*, **50**, 899 (1956); LOTT, P. F. and CHENG, K. L., *Anal. Chem.*, **29**, 1777 (1957) (in clay); also see p. 272.
(80) NIELSCH and BÖLTZ, *Z. anal. Chem.*, **144**, 402 (1955).
(81) REISS, W., *et al.*, *Anal. Chem.*, **24**, 1646 (1952).
(82) YOE, 242.
(83) LARUMBE, F. H., *Anales asoc, quim. Arg.* **45**, 52 (1957); BABA, S., *J. Agr. Chem. Soc. Japan*, **17**, 139 (1941); YOE, 241.
(84) ROELEN, L., *Z. anal. Chem.*, **117**, 385 (1939); (YOE, 239).
(85) SUGAWARA, K., *J. Chem. Soc. Japan*, **61**, 1014 (1940).
(86) GOTO, H. and SUZUKI, S., *J. Chem. Soc. Japan*, **71**, 7 (1950).
(87) ISHIBASHI, M., *et al.*, *Bull. Chem. Soc. Japan*, **30**, 433 (1957) (differential); DESESA, M. A. and ROGERS, L. B., *Anal. Chim. Acta*, **6**, 534 (1952); YOE, 238; A.S.T.M., 365 (in Cu and its alloys).
(88) NIELSCH and BÖLTZ, *Z. anal. Chem.*, **142**, 102 (1954); also see p. 177.
(89) BASTIAN, R., *et al.*, *Anal. Chem.*, **25**, 284 (1953); ISHIBASHI, M., *et al.*, *J. Chem. Soc. Japan*, **76**, 758 (1955); *Japan Analyst*, **5**, 279 (1956).
(90) BASTIAN, R., *et al.*, *Anal. Chem.*, **28**, 459 (1956); ISHIBASHI, M., *et al.*, *Bull. Chem. Soc. Japan*, **29**, 57 (1956).
(91) WELCHER, **IV**, 366; see p. 323.
(92) See p. 322.
(93) MAIR, R. H., *Chemist Analyst*, **42**, 61 (1950).
(94) OTT, C., *Chim. anal.*, **35**, 149 (1953).
(95) ERDEY, L. and SZABADVÁRY, F., *Magyar Kém. Folyóirat*, **60**, 311 (1954).
(96) RUGGIERI, R., *Anal. Chim. Acta*, **16**, 242 (1957).

0·5% reagent and 25% w/v Na-citrate to give a pH of 3·5 (the amt. required is detd. on a separate portion with bromophenol blue indicator). Store above 20°C for 1 hr., dil. to 25 ml. with H_2O and measure the red color after 15 min. at 508 mμ.

$NH_2OH{\cdot}HCl$ is said to be a better reductant but should not be applied in presence of citrate (Fortune and Mellon[41]). Add 1 ml. 10% reductant, adjust to pH 3–6 with NaOAc, add 2 ml. 0·5% reagent, dil. to a definite vol. with H_2O and measure the color after 5–10 min. (or after 1 hr. if PO_4^{3-} is present).

NOTES. (1) Interferences are CN^-, Hg^{2+}, Ni, about 10 p.p.m. of Hg^+, Zn, W, Cu, Co, Cd, and large amts. of CrO_4^{2-}, ClO_4^-, SiO_2, $C_2O_4^{2-}$, NO_2^-. Interference of Bi is avoided by citrate or EDTA addn. and that of large amts. of PO_4^{3-}, PO_3^- or $P_2O_7^{4-}$ by addn. of citrate after the reduction. The method has been applied to a variety of metals and alloys.[10, 42] If Ni or Zn is present, add an equiv. amt. of reagent for Ni and double the equiv. amt. for Zn.[43]

(2) The complex can be extd. with $PhNO_2$ from 1*M* $NaClO_4$ solns. at pH 4–5.[44] The Fe^{2+} complex absorbs at 512 mμ and the Fe^{2+} and Fe^{3+} complexes absorb at 396 mμ, hence the 2 oxidation states can be detd. simultaneously in solns. contg. 5 ml. of 0·2*M* KH-phthalate buffer. Interferences at 396 mμ are 1–2 p.p.m. Hg^{2+} and Ni, 10 p.p.m. Cu, Hg^+ and Co, 50 p.p.m. Zn or Cd, 100 p.p.m. Zr, and 500 p.p.m. of Mn, Ca, F^-, CO_3^{2-}, AcO^-, NO_2^-, $C_2O_4^{2-}$ or citrate.[45]

For simultaneous detn. of Fe and Cu,[46] treat the soln. contg. < 130 μg. of both metals in 5 ml. with 1 ml. 2 × 10^{-5}*M* reagent, 2 ml. 5% $NH_2OH{\cdot}HCl$, 5 ml. phosphate buffer pH 8·3 and 4 ml. octanol; shake for 2

min., leave for 5 min., sep. and dil. the aq. phase to 25 ml. with EtOH. Measure the Fe complex in this phase at 510 mμ; then dil. the org. phase to 10 ml. with EtOH and measure the Cu complex at 435 mμ. The error for each metal is $\pm$ 1 μg.
(3) For the various derivs. and analogs of *o*-phenanthroline which have been recommended, see Table 38 and Chapter 9, Section 1.

(e) 5-Phenylsalicylic acid also provides a satisfactory colorimetric method.[47] For 5–50 μg. Fe^{3+} in 50 ml. soln., add 25 ml. EtOH, dil. to 40–45 ml. with H_2O, add 1*N* NaOH until alk. to congo red paper and then 0·1*N* HCl until blue (pH 2·8–3·2). Add 1 ml. 1% reagent in EtOH, dil. to 50 ml. with H_2O and measure the violet color at 575 mμ.

NOTES. (1) Interferences are U^{6+}, PO_4^{3-}, F^-, $C_2O_4^{2-}$ and tartrate. Ti interference is compensated by addn. of 0·1*N* HCl until the color is violet and comparison with a standard contg. an equal amt. of HCl; if much is present the comparison should be made at pH 2·5.
(2) For silicates, fuse with Na_2CO_3, add HCl, filter, dil. to a definite vol., take an aliquot and proceed as above.

(f) *m*-Methoxy-*o*-nitrosophenol is suitable[48] for the colorimetric detn. of 2·5–12·5 μg. Fe^{2+}. Add 5 ml. buffer pH 3·8 (50 ml. of a soln. contg. 136·08 g. NaOAc/l. mixed with 42·5 ml. 1*N* HCl and extd. with dithizone in CCl_4), and 5 ml. reagent (40·2 mg./100 ml.). After 15 min., shake for 30 sec. with 5 ml. CCl_4 and repeat until the org. phase is colorless. Filter, dil. to 25 ml. with H_2O and measure the green complex at 700 mμ. The process is suitable for 0·01–1 μg. Fe/ml.; it is three times more sensitive than the *o*-phenanthroline method.

NOTES. (1) No interference is caused by V, Ag, Sn, Sb, Mo if less than 25 μg. is present, or by Ni, Zn, Hg, Mn, Bi, Cd, Cr, Pb, Ti if less than 1 mg. is present. Fe^{3+} can be detd. after reduction with $NH_2OH{\cdot}HCl$. Cu does not interfere if Cu $<$ Fe; if Cu $<$ 10 Fe, addn. of 5 ml. 5% $Na_2S_2O_3$ prevents interference.
(2) α-Nitroso-β-naphthol is suitable for $<$ 50 mg. Fe^{2+} in 50 ml. soln.[49] Neutralize with NH_4OH, add some drops of HCl and excess 1% reagent in 50% AcOH, filter on paper after 3 hr., wash with 50% AcOH and H_2O and ignite to Fe_2O_3; Cu and Co interfere. Titrimetry is also possible.[49]

(g) KSCN is frequently used for colorimetric detn.[1, 40, 50] Two procedures are available.

(*i*) Treat the acidic (HCl or HNO_3) soln. with excess 1·5*M* KSCN and dil. with H_2O until the soln. is 0·3*M* in SCN^- and 0·05–1*N* in acid. Measure the red complex immediately at 480 mμ for $<$ 10 p.p.m. Fe or in a Dubosq colorimeter for 20 p.p.m. Fe. Add Me_2CO to give a 50–60% soln. if desired.

(*ii*) For $<$ 50 μg. Fe in 25 ml. soln. in a 125 ml. separatory funnel, add 5·0 ml. HCl, 10·0 ml. 20% KSCN and 25·0 ml. iso-BuOH, shake for 2 min., sep., swirl gently, sep., add 0·1 g. anhyd. Na_2SO_4, shake and measure at 485 mμ.

In both cases, the color intensity depends on the conditions, such as reagent excess, concn. and type of acids and salts present, temp., time of standing, etc.; light also has an effect. The conditions, and especially the concn. of SCN^-, must be fixed. The absorption max. and extractability with Et_2O depend on the SCN^- concn.[51] When SCN^- is in excess of 0·183*M* (optimum concn. 0·9*M*), the absorption max. is at 480 mμ; the complex is almost completely extd. with Et_2O and can be measured at 503 mμ, which is suitable for detn. of Fe^{3+}. $Fe(SCN)_4^-$, etc. are present in the ionic form. When Fe^{3+} is in excess ($SCN^- < 4{\cdot}2 \times 10^{-2}M$) the orange complex has max. absorbance at 457 mμ and is not extd. This $FeSCN^{2+}$ ion is suitable for SCN^- detn. as well as for Cl and CN^- (see pp. 442 and 467). Between the 2 concns. mentioned, the predominant form is $Fe(SCN)_3$ and the extractability varies.

NOTES. (1) No interference in the above procedures arises from Al, Be, Ce, Mn, Mg, Na, K, Li, NH_4^+. Interferences are Ag, Hg, Cu, Bi, Cd, Sb, Mo, Pt, Ru, Os, Zn, Ti, U, Co (but see below), $C_2O_4^{2-}$, tartrate, AsO_4^{3-}, much PO_4^{3-}, much SO_4^{2-}, reductants. MnO_4^- interference is avoided by H_2O_2 addn., that of F^- by addn. of more reagent or by $Al(NO_3)_3$, and that of PO_3^- or $P_2O_7^{2-}$ by $Al(NO_3)_3$.
(2) The process has been applied to a variety of Cu alloys.[10]
(3) The method can be applied after a concn. procedure. For $>$ 1 μg. Fe in 100 ml. soln. contg. 1 ml. 1:1 HCl, add 0·5 ml. 0·5% $KMnO_4$ and NH_4OH until its odor is apparent; then add 1 ml. EtOH and heat almost at b.p. until the ppt. coagulates. Filter on paper, previously washed with 1:1 HCl and H_2O, wash with H_2O and Me_2CO, evap. off the Me_2CO, and pass the paper through 5 ml. portions of the reagent soln. (20 ml. 1·5*M* KSCN, 8 ml. 1:1 HCl and 50 ml. Me_2CO dild. to 100 ml. with H_2O) until colorless. Then compare the color.
(4) The color can be stabilized by addn. of 3 drops 30% H_2O_2 per 100 ml. of soln.[52] or with 10 ml. 0·5% $(NH_4)_2S_2O_8$.[10]
(5) When Me_2CO is added, the color deepens and its fading diminishes; moreover, interferences by F^- and by $C_2O_4^{2-}$ decrease. The deepening of the color is greater with methyl cellosolve (85% greater than with H_2O soln. and 27% greater than with Me_2CO),[53] but in this case, the color is yellow.
Cu or Co (50–500 μg.) and Fe (5–50 μg.) can be detd. simultaneously if Me_2CO is present.[54] Add 2 ml. HCl, 0·5 ml. satd. $(NH_4)_2S_2O_8$ (or if only Co is present, 5 ml. $SnCl_2$ soln. (20 g. in 40 ml. HCl dild. to 100 ml. with H_2O)), and 25 ml. Me_2CO mixed with 2·5 ml. 50% w/v NH_4SCN; dil. to 50 ml. with H_2O, and measure Fe at 480 mμ, Cu at 380 mμ and Co at 625 mμ. Interferences are Ba, Ca, Pb, Hg^+, Ag, Sr, CrO_4^{2-}, $Cr_2O_7^{2-}$, Ce^{4+}, $S_2O_3^{2-}$, WO_4^{2-}, BiO^+, MoO_4^{2-}, Ti (and Hg^{2+} for Cu). No interference arises from AcO^-, Al, NH_4^+, Sb, As, Be, Cd, CO_3^{2-}, Cl^-, $HCOO^-$, Li, Mg, Mn, Ni, NO_3^-, $C_2O_4^{2-}$, PO_4^{3-}, K, SiO_3^{2-}, Na, SO_4^{2-}, Tl, Zn or Zr.
An alternative method which gives a very stable color and a 90% increase in sensitivity is as follows.[55] To 30 ml. of soln., add 2 ml. 2*N* HCl, 20 ml. Me_2CO, 40 ml. MeCOEt, 3 ml. 4% KSCN and dil. to 100 ml. with H_2O; measure at 490 mμ. This is suitable for 0·1–2·0 p.p.m.

(6) Several org. solvents have been suggested for the extn., among which are AmOH, 2:1 AmOH–Et_2O, butyl cellosolve and Et_2O, EtOAc. Extn. with 25 ml. 1:1 tributyl phosphate–CCl_4 (shaken with 1:1 H_2SO_4, NH_4OH and H_2O) from soln. of pH 1·5 is convenient,[56] because the mixt. is heavier than H_2O and here SCN^-: Fe ≑ 4–5.
(7) $Hg(SCN)_2 \cdot 2HSCN$ has been suggested as reagent but has no advantage. For colorimetric detn. of < 60 μg. Fe after pptn. as the Hg–Zn double salt, see Chapter 35, p. 271.
(8) The color of the complex can be stabilized by addn. of an onium compd. or by org. bases.
Triphenylmethylarsonium chloride can be applied in the detn. of 10–100 μg. Fe in 10 ml. soln. at pH 1–2.[57] Add 5 ml. o-$C_6H_4Cl_2$, 1 ml. 2% reagent, 1 ml. 25% NH_4SCN, shake, sep., filter the solvent phase through a G2 crucible, ext. with 1 ml. solvent, add 1 ml. reagent, ext. with 1 ml. solvent and repeat the process again. Combine the extracts in a 25 ml. measuring flask., dil. to vol. and measure the red color at 478 mμ. Interferences are Cu, F^-, $C_2O_4^{2-}$, $P_2O_7^{4-}$, I^-, NO_2^-, $S_2O_3^{2-}$, $Cr_2O_7^{2-}$. No interference arises from 1*N* SO_4^{2-}, 0·1*N* NO_3^- or Cl^-, from Cr^{3+}, Ni, Sb, Cd, Hg^{2+}, Zn, from Ag or Hg^+ if the soln. is filtered, or from Co in amts. 20-fold that of Fe.
Antipyrine has been used[58] with KSCN for detn. of 0·2–10 μg. Fe. Add 5 ml. 0·1*N* HCl, 5 ml. 20% KSCN, 5 ml. 5% antipyrine, ext. with EtOAc and measure at 470 mμ (ϵ = 28 500). Cu, Bi, Co interfere but Hg, Pb, Cd, As, Sn, Zn, Al, Cr, Ni, Mn, Ca, etc. can be tolerated. The procedure has been applied to the analysis of Al, Mg, Zn and Pb metals.
Bu_3NHOAc[59] and 2-furyldiantipyrinylmethane[60] have also been used.

(h) Cupferron allows gravimetric, titrimetric and colorimetric detns.[1, 61] For gravimetry, add 6% reagent to the cooled soln. contg. < 10% v/v H_2SO_4 or < 20% v/v HCl until the momentary appearance of a white ppt. Filter on paper, wash with 2*N* HCl, H_2O, NH_4OH and H_2O, ignite above 610°C and weigh as Fe_2O_3. Below 98°C, the ppt. is $Fe(C_6H_3N_2O_4)_3$ (Duval).

NOTES. (1) For the colorimetric detn. see Table 38.
(2) Neocupferron forms $Fe(C_{10}H_7N_2O_4)_3$ below 101°C (Duval; Welcher[61]). *N*-Benzoylphenylhydroxylamine can be used with pptn. at 65°C and drying at 110°C (see Chapter 22, p. 180). Ammonium 2-fluorenylnitrosohydroxylamine has been suggested.[62] For analogs of tetralin, see Table 38.

(i) Benzenephosphinic acid has been suggested for gravimetric detn. of 10–250 mg. Fe in 50 ml. ca. 0·5*N* HCl or H_2SO_4 soln.[63] Boil the soln., add a 50–200% excess of 0·2*M* reagent (cover the reagent with Et_2O, shaking occasionally during 1 day, decant and repeat), digest for 0·5–1·5 hr., cool, filter on a G3 crucible, wash 3–4 times with H_2O, dry at 110°C for 2 hr. and weigh. A slight negative error is obtained.

NOTE. Al, Cr, V coppt.; Ti, Mo, Zr, Ce^{4+}, U^{6+}, W, Sn, Bi, Ag, Hg^{2+} and Cu also interfere. Ni, Co, Mn, Cd, Ca, etc., As, P, citrate, tartrate, $C_2O_4^{2-}$ and Cl^- do not interfere, nor does Zn if the soln. is digested for 3 hr.

(j) Miscellaneous gravimetric methods. Paraperiodic acid is suitable[64] for pptn. of 50–100 mg. Fe^{3+}. Add 8 ml. HNO_3, 3 g. reagent, dil. to 100 ml. with H_2O, add 9 g. acetamide, dil. to 150 ml. with H_2O and digest at 95°C for 1 hr. Filter on Whatman No. 40 paper and wash with H_2O slightly acidified with HNO_3. Digest the filtrate at 95°C for 2–2·5 hr., filter, combine the ppts. and ignite at 1000°C before weighing as Fe_2O_3. Al (100 mg.) can be tolerated.

Dimine has been suggested[65] for detn. of 0·1 g. Fe_2O_3; add 10 ml. 10% NH_4Cl, dil. to 100 ml. with H_2O, add 0·8% reagent soln. and dry below 95°C or ignite to Fe_2O_3 above 959°C before weighing.

p-*n*-Butylphenylarsonic acid has been used for 0·1 g. Fe^{3+} in 200 ml. 0·4*N* HCl or H_2SO_4 soln.;[65] boil the soln., add 0·75% reagent soln., leave for 30 min., filter on a Gooch crucible and wash with 0·2*N* HCl before ignition to Fe_2O_3 above 434°C. Interferences are Ce, Sn, Ti, Zr, F^-, PO_4^{3-}.

Electrodeposition is suitable for 0·1–0·2 g. Fe in 30 ml. of slightly acidic soln.[66] Add H_2O_2 or $K_2S_2O_8$, boil, cool, add 15 ml. 23% w/v $(NH_4)_2HPO_4$ and then 150 ml. buffer (1570 g. $(NH_4)_2CO_3$ and 700 ml. NH_4OH dild. to 1 l.), adding the first 10 ml. slowly for neutralization. Heat to 60–70°C, insert a Pt gauze electrode and electrolyze at 5·2 v. and 6–7 amp. for 90 min. or for 15 min. after there is no reaction with $(NH_4)_2S$. Then decrease the current to 1 amp., remove the electrode, wash with H_2O and EtOH, heat over a 30–35 cm. long flame and weigh as Fe. Ni, Co, Mo, W, NO_3^- interfere but Mg, SO_4^{2-}, Cl^- and moderate amts. of Al, Cr, Ti and Mn can be tolerated. Electrodeposition can also be used for 1–10 mg. Fe in soln. contg. 0·3–0·5 g. $(NH_4)_2C_2O_4$; 0·3–0·6 amp. is applied for 15–30 min.[67] For internal electrolysis, see ref. 68.

α- or β-Naphthylsulfinic acid and phenylsulfinic acid have been suggested.[69]

Na-penicillin G has been used for detn. of < 200 μg. Fe/ml. in AcOH–NaOAc buffered solns.;[70] the ppt. is washed with H_2O and dried at room temp., 13·45 mg. corresponding to 1 mg. Fe.

NH_4-*m*-nitrobenzoate ppts. Fe at pH 1–1·5 but ignition is needed;[71] Ni, Mn, Zn, Co, Mg and Ca can be present.

(k) EDTA titration has been recommended at pH 2–3 in presence of tiron, salicylic acid, or sulfosalicylic acid as indicator.[72] PO_4^{3-} interferes, but Al, Ca and Mg do not. PO_4^{3-} does not interfere if SCN^- is used as indicator.[73] For 3–30 mg. Fe, dil. the soln. to 25 ml. with dil. HCl, add 0·2 g. $(NH_4)_2S_2O_8$, add 3*M* NH_4OH until a turbidity appears, then add 1 ml. 20% NH_4SCN and 20 ml. AmOH and titrate with 0·1*M* EDTA in 0·5 ml. portions until colorless. Adjust to pH 2–3 with NH_4OH, add more AmOH and back-titrate with Fe^{3+} soln. to a rose color.

NOTES. (1) Other indicators which have been proposed are variamine blue,[74] pyrocatechol violet (in conjunction with

Bi^{3+} as back-titrant),[75] chrome azurol S.[76] For others, see Chapter 5, Section 4. Photometric end-points are also applicable.[77]

(2) For simultaneous detn. of Al, Fe and Ti,[78] add excess EDTA, make alk. to phenolphthalein with NH_4OH and then acid with HCl, add 20 ml. buffer (50 g. NH_4OAc and 2 ml. AcOH/100 ml.) and boil for 3 min. Add 1 ml. 1% benzidine in AcOH, 1 ml. 0·2% $K_3Fe(CN)_6$ and 1 ml. 0·1% $K_4Fe(CN)_6$ as indicator and titrate with standard Zn^{2+} soln. (this gives the sum of the 3 metals). Then add $(NH_4)_2HPO_4$ and titrate further after 3–4 min. (Ti). Add 30 ml. satd. NaF soln., boil, cool and titrate to find Al. Calc. Fe by difference.

(3) For colorimetric methods, see Table 38. EDTA is the most sensitive of the 6 analogs, but the wavelength of max. absorption is larger with the aromatic analog.[79]

(l) Miscellaneous titrimetric methods. Various org. acids (e.g. oxalic, citric, mandelic), ultraviolet light, or sunlight can be used to reduce Fe^{3+} and the resulting soln. can be titrated with 0·05N $NaVO_3$ in presence of diphenylbenzidine indicator.[80]

A mixt. of 0·45% $(NH_4)_2HAsO_4$, 5% NH_4Cl and 5% AcOH can be applied in conjunction with iodometry.[81] Add the slightly acidic (AcOH) soln. to the reagent soln., boil, filter, wash with 90% EtOH, dissolve in 2·5N HCl, add KI (1·5 g./25 ml. soln.) and titrate with 0·1N $Na_2S_2O_3$. Al interferes.

Indigo sulfate or methylene blue can be applied in conjunction with NH_4SCN.[82] To the soln. contg. 0·05 μg. Fe/ml., add 0·5 ml. HCl, 4 ml. 20% NH_4SCN, 0·5 ml. 20% v/v H_2O_2, and titrate with 0·05‰ indigo sulfate or 0·1‰ methylene blue, comparing the violet color against standards. α,α′-Dipyridyl, $NH_2OH{\cdot}HCl$, etc. can also be applied.

Aluminon is suitable for photometric titration of 0·2–0·5 mg. Fe in 100 ml. of slightly acidic (HNO_3) soln.[83]

(m) Miscellaneous colorimetric methods. A plethora of reagents has been recommended for colorimetric detn. of Fe. These are summarized in Table 38 and earlier reagents have been reviewed.[84]

(n) Flame photometry.[85] Measure at 386·0 mμ using Co as internal standard, or at 372 mμ. Mg interferes.

References

1. Hillebrand and Lundell, 294 (384); Scott and Furman, 462; Kimura, 207; Pigott, 215.
2. Fuchs, O., *Z. anal. Chem.*, **118**, 415 (1939–40).
3. Jean, M., *Chim. anal.*, **32**, 179 (1950).
4. Goetz, C. A. and Wadsworth, E. P., *Anal. Chem.*, **28**, 375 (1956).
5. Kitahara, S. *et al.*, *Repts. Sci. Research Inst.* (*Tokyo*), **31**, 325 (1955).
6. Kawamura, K., *Japan Analyst*, **3**, 347 (1953).
7. Babko, A. K. and Mikhal'chishin, G. T., *Ukrain. Khim. Zhur.*, **22**, 676 (1956).
8. Hecht and Donau, 189.
9. Welcher, **III**, 15, 124.
10. A.S.T.M., 207 ff.
11. Gibson, N. A. and White, R. A., *Anal. Chim. Acta*, **12** 413 (1955).
12. Ishimaru, S., *Kagaku-Zikken-Gaku*, X, 29 (1942).
13. Titus, A. C. and Still, C. W., *Ind. Eng. Chem.*, *Anal. Ed.*, **13**, 416 (1941).
14. Somasundaram, K. M. and Suryanarayana, C. V., *Proc. Indian Acad. Sci.*, **39A**, 41 (1954); Ishibashi *et al.*, *Japan Analyst*, **5**, 637 (1956).
15. Scott and Furman, 462
16. Knop, J. and Kubelková, O., *Z. anal. Chem.*, **110**, 161 (1935).
17. Heumann, W. R. and Belovic, B., *Anal. Chem.*, **29**, 1226 (1957).
18. Hume, D. N. and Kolthoff, I. M., *Anal. Chim. Acta*, **16**, 415 (1957).
19. Yoshimura, C., *J. Chem. Soc. Japan*, **76**, 883 (1955).
20. Wells, I. C., *Anal. Chem.*, **23**, 511 (1951).
21. Furman, N. H. *et al.*, *Anal. Chem.*, **23**, 945, 1662 (1951).
22. Groswami, N., *Sci. and Culture* (*Calcutta*), **22**, 398 (1957).
23. Ishibashi, M. and Kusada, Y., *J. Chem. Soc. Japan.*, **71**, 160 (1950); Wilson, A. D., *Bull. Geol. Survey Gt. Brit.*, No. 9, 56 (1955).
24. Nagaoka, T. and Yamazaki, S., *Japan Analyst*, **3**, 408 (1954).
25. Kiboku, M., *Japan Analyst*, **5**, 503 (1956).
26. Steuer, H., *Z. anal. Chem.*, **118**, 390 (1939–40).
27. Malmstadt, H. V. and Roberts, C. B., *Anal. Chem.*, **28**, 1412 (1956); Lingane, J. J. and Kennedy, J. H., *Anal. Chim. Acta*, **15**, 465 (1956).
28. Flaschka, H. and Zavagyl, H., *Z. anal. Chem.*, **132**, 170 (1950); Erdey, L. and Bodor, E., *ibid.*, **137**, 410 (1953).
29. Szabó, Z. and Sugár, E., *Anal. Chem.*, **22**, 361 (1950).
30. Belcher, R. and West, T. S., *Anal. Chim. Acta*, **5**, 260 (1951).
31. Kreĭmer, S. E., *Zavodskaya Lab.*, **21**, 778 (1955).
32. Brinzinger, H. and Rost, B., *Z. anal. Chem.*, **115**, 241 (1938–39); **117**, 1 (1939).
33. Deibner, L., *Mikrochemie ver. Mikrochim. Acta*, **35**, 488 (1950).
34. Tashiro, M., *J. Chem. Soc. Japan*, **53**, 16 (1932).
35. Smith, G. F. and Bliss, H. H., *J. Am. Chem. Soc.*, **53**, 4291 (1931).
36. Berg, R., *Oxin.*, 89 (1935); Welcher, **I**, 324.
37. Sandberg, B., *Svensk Kem. Tidskr.*, **58**, 197 (1946).
38. Hecht and Donau, 188.
39. Welcher, **I**, 308; also see Ishibashi, M and Fujinaga, T., *Bull. Chem. Soc. Japan*, **23**, 27 (1950) (amperometric).
40. Sandell, 375.
41. Welcher, **III**, 87; Fortune, W. B. and Mellon, M. G., *Ind. Eng. Chem.*, *Anal. Ed.*, **10**, 60 (1938); Mehlig, J. P. and Hulett, H. R., *ibid.*, **14**, 869 (1942).
42. Pepi, M. S., *Anal. Chem.*, **22**, 560 (1950); Ota, K., *Japan Analyst*, **5**, 3 (1956).
43. Ryan, J. A. and Botham, G. H., *Anal. Chem.*, **21**, 1521 (1949).
44. Margerum, D. W. and Banks, C. V., *Anal. Chem.*, **26**, 200 (1954).
45. Harvey, A. E., Jr. *et al.*, *Anal. Chem.*, **27**, 26 (1955).
46. Wilkins, D. H. and Smith, G. F., *Anal. Chim. Acta*, **9**, 538 (1953).

47. YOE, J. H. and HARVEY, A. E., JR., *J. Am. Chem. Soc.*, **70**, 648 (1948).
48. TORII, T., *J. Chem. Soc. Japan.*, **76**, 333 (1955); PEACH, S. M., *Analyst*, **81**, 371 (1956).
49. WELCHER, **III**, 314; also see WILSON, R. F., and LOVELADY, H. G., *Anal. Chem.*, **27**, 1231 (1955) (amperometric); BOBTELSKY, M. and JUNGREIS, E., *Anal. Chim. Acta*, **12**, 351 (1955) (photometric).
50. WOODS, J. T. and MELLON, M. G., *Ind. Eng. Chem., Anal. Ed.*, **13**, 551 (1941); PETERS, C. A. and FRENCH, C. L., *ibid.*, 604; HACKER, W. *et al.*, *Z. anal. Chem.*, **129**, 104 (1949).
51. IWASAKI, I. and SHIMOJIMA, H., *J. Chem. Soc. Japan*, **76**, 749 (1955).
52. HOULIHAN, J. E. and FARINA, P. E. L., *Analyst*, **78**, 559 (1953).
53. WINSOR, H. W., *Ind. Eng. Chem., Anal. Ed.*, **9**, 452 (1937).
54. KITSON, R. E., *Anal. Chem.*, **22**, 664 (1950).
55. BAILEY, P., *Anal. Chem.*, **29**, 1534 (1957).
56. MELNICK, L., *et al.*, *Anal. Chem.*, **25**, 856 (1953).
57. DWYER, F. P. and GIBSON, N. A., *Analyst*, **76**, 548 (1951).
58. SUDO, E., *J. Chem. Soc. Japan*, **75**, 968 (1954); **77**, 1446 (1956).
59. ZIEGLER, M., *et al.*, *Z. anal. Chem.*, **154**, 81 (1957).
60. ZHIVOPISTSEV, V. P. and MININA, V. S., *Uchenye Zapiski Molotov. Gosudarst. Univ. im. A.M. Gor'kogo*, **8**, *Mat. Fiz. i Khim.*, No. 3, 37 (1954).
61. WELCHER, **III**, 362, 401; also see KOLTHOFF, I. M. and LIBERTI, A., *Analyst*, **74**, 635 (1949) (amperometric).
62. OESPER, R. E. and FULMER, R. E., *Anal. Chem.*, **25**, 908 (1953).
63. BANKS, J. E., *et al.*, *Anal. Chem.*, **29**, 109, 113 (1957).
64. GORDON, L. and GINSBURG, L., *Anal. Chem.*, **29**, 38 (1957); GINSBURG *et al.*, *ibid.*, 46.
65. WELCHER, **IV**, 59, 79.
66. ARMISTEAD, W. H., *Ind. Eng. Chem., Anal. Ed.*, **14**, 207 (1942).
67. OKÁC, A., *Chem. listy*, **26**, 595 (1933).
68. SCARANO, E. and IPPOLITI, P., *Ann. chim.* (*Rome*), **45**, 502 (1955).
69. WELCHER, **IV**, 202.
70. MALISSA, H. and WEIGERT, E., *Mikrochim. Acta*, 413 (1954).
71. CREPAZ, E. and MARCHESINI, L., *Atti ist. veneto sci., lettere ed arti. classe sci. mat. nat.*, **110**, 33 (1952).
72. CHENG, K. L., *et al.*, *Anal. Chem.*, **25**, 347 (1953); **24**, 1640 (1952).
73. BUTT, L. T. and STRAFFORD, N., *Anal. Chim. Acta*, **12**, 124 (1955).
74. FLASCHKA, H., *Mikrochim. Acta*, 361 (1954).
75. FLASCHKA and SADEK, F., *Z. anal. Chem.*, **149**, 345 (1956).
76. MUSIL, A. and THEIS, M., *Z. anal. Chem.*, **144**, 351 (1955).
77. SWEETSER, P. B. and BRICKER, C. D., *Anal. Chem.*, **25**, 253 (1953); UNDERWOOD, A. L., *ibid.*, 1910.
78. SAJÓ, I., *Magyar Kém. Folyóirat*, **60**, 331 (1954).
79. HILL-COTTINGHAM, D. G., *Analyst*, **80**, 906 (1955); **82**, 524 (1957).
80. SASTRI, M. N. and KALIDAS, C., *Z. anal. Chem.*, **149**, 181 (1956); *Z. anorg. u. allgem. Chem.*, **281**, 221 (1955); RAO, G. G. and ARAVAMUDAN, G., *Anal. Chim. Acta*, **13**, 328 (1955).
81. DAUBNER, W., *Angew. Chem.*, **49**, 137 (1936).
82. GRAT-CABANAC, M., *Anal. Chim. Acta*, **12**, 50 (1955).
83. BOBTELSKY, M. and BEN-BOSSAT, A., *Anal. Chim. Acta*, **14**, 439 (1956).
84. WEST, T. S., *Metallurgia*, **43**, 204, 260, 263, 313, 315 (1951).
85. DEAN, J. A. and BURGER, J. C., JR., *Anal. Chem.*, **27**, 1052 (1955); also see DEAN and LADY, J. H., *ibid.*, 1533 (acetylacetone extn., 372·0 mμ).

34

NICKEL

The principal references for this chapter are Hillebrand and Lundell, Scott and Furman, Kimura, and Pigott.[1] A series of papers on the analysis of metallic nickel has been published.[2]

Attack

(a) Minerals. Dissolve 0·5–1 g. in 40 ml. HNO_3 by boiling, cool, add 3 g. $KClO_3$, heat, evap. to dryness, add 10 ml. HCl, evap. to dryness and repeat. Add HCl and H_2O, filter, fuse the residue with Na_2CO_3 or $Na_2S_2O_7$, dissolve in HCl and combine the solns.

(b) Basic rock. Treat 0·25 g. in a Pt dish with 0·5 ml. $HClO_4$ and 2·5 ml. HF, evap. nearly to dryness, add 1–2 ml. HF, evap. to dryness, add 0·5 ml. $HClO_4$ and some ml. of H_2O, evap. to dryness and heat with 0·5–1 ml. HCl and 5 ml. H_2O. Add 5 ml. 10% Na_3-citrate and make just alk. to litmus with NH_4OH. If the residue is large, ignite it, fuse with 0·1 g. Na_2CO_3, heat with dil. HCl, add 2–3 ml. Na_3-citrate, make slightly alk. with NH_4OH and ext. the dimethylglyoxime complex with $CHCl_3$. Similarly ext. the complex from the main soln. and combine.

(c) Alloys. In general, treat with aqua regia or HNO_3 and then evap. to fumes with H_2SO_4. In non-ferrous alloys, Ni is usually detd. after electrodeposition of Cu. With Al alloys, treat with NaOH, add the min. amt. of HCl and HNO_3 required for dissoln., and then add H_2O and H_2S; boil, add HNO_3, boil, add tartaric acid, etc.

For steel, if Cr is absent, warm with 1:1 HCl and then boil with 1:1 HNO_3, add tartaric acid and NH_4OH, filter, add HCl and dimethylglyoxime, etc. If Cr is present, treat with HCl and HNO_3 (and HF if the Si content is high) and then evap. to fumes with $HClO_4$, etc. If the Ni content is low, treat with HCl and HNO_3 (if much Si is present, evap. and sep.) and finally ext. Fe with Et_2O.

For Fe alloys, heat with 3:2 HCl or 1:3 H_2SO_4, boil with HNO_3, evap. nearly to dryness, add 30 ml. HCl, evap. to 15 ml., add 40 ml. H_2O, filter and ignite the residue; treat with HF and H_2SO_4, ignite again, fuse with $K_2S_2O_7$, etc. (if W is present, sep. it with NaOH).

Separation

Dimethylglyoxime allows the sepn. of Ni from most elements (see p. 264). Trace amts. can be sepd. by extn. of the complex with $CHCl_3$ from citrate soln. of pH 8·5–9·0; if Mn is present, NH_2OH is added and if Cu or Co is present, the ext. is shaken with NH_4OH. Ni is stripped from the org. layer with 0·5*N* HCl.

Ni can be sepd. from group II elements with H_2S in solns. contg. 3–5 ml. H_2SO_4 or 5–7 ml. HCl/100 ml. soln.; Ni coppts. with Sn^{4+}. H_2S treatment of HCOOH-buffered or neutral solns. contg. acrolein seps. Ni from Zn (see p. 278). Mn is sepd. from Ni with H_2S in soln. which is alk. with pyridine or contains 5 g. NaOAc/g. of Ni and Co in 200 ml. AcOH-contg. soln. (see Chapter 2, Section 3.2). In NH_4OH soln. H_2S seps. Ni from group IV elements; concn. with Fe^{2+} is possible.

$Na_2S_2O_3$ seps. Ni from Cu (p. 172).

Treatment with excess NH_4OH and NH_4Cl or with ZnO, NaOAc, etc. seps. Ni from Fe, Al, Ti, etc. KCN improves the sepn. but it is still not suitable for trace amts.

Electrolysis of solns. contg. NH_4OH, $(NH_4)_2SO_4$ and Na_2SO_3 seps. Ni from $< 0·01$ g. Mn. If the soln. contains HNO_3 and H_2SO_4, Ni is sepd. from large amts. of Cu. In acidic solns. with a Hg-cathode, Ni is sepd. from U, Al, etc.

$NaClO_3$ and HNO_3 allow sepn. of Ni from $> 0·1$ g. Mn; traces of Mn remain in soln. when $KClO_3$ is used.

Ni is sepd. from V, P, Zn, Cr and U when the sample soln. is poured into a hot NaOH soln. contg. an oxidant ($Na_2S_2O_8$, Na_2O_2, NaOCl, NaOBr, Cl_2, Br_2, etc.). Cr must be preoxidized in acidic soln. and Na_2CO_3 must be added if U is present. NH_4^+ interferes and sepn. from Al is incomplete if Fe^{3+} is absent.

Extn. with Et_2O from HCl soln. seps. Ni from large amts. of Fe. Cupferron allows sepn. from Fe, Ti, Zr, etc.

Ni can be sepd. from moderate to large amts. of Co by means of Na_3PO_4 or KNO_2 (see p. 269).

Sepn. from As is obtained by boiling with $Na_2S_2O_3$, HCl and H_2SO_4.

Ion exchange resins enable the sepn. of Ni from Fe, Cu, Co, Zn, etc. (see Chapter 13, Section 2.2.)

A column (0·2 cm.^{2} × 8 cm.) contg. $CaCO_3$ seps. Ni from Pb when the neutral citrate-contg. soln. is passed at a rate of 0·15 ml./min. under pressure.

Determination

The α-dioximes are certainly the best reagents for Ni; dimethylglyoxime is most frequently used. If Co must be detd. as well as Ni, dimethylglyoxime can be used for Ni and α-nitroso-β-naphthol for Co, aliquots of the soln. being taken; alternatively, Ni can be detd. after Co (see p. 270). In another procedure, both Ni and Co are detd. by electrodeposition and then whichever is present in the smaller amt. is detd. by one of the above methods after dissoln. in acid.

For very small amts. of Ni, diethyldithiocarbamate seems to be quite satisfactory.

(a) Dimethylglyoxime has been used for gravimetric, titrimetric and colorimetric detns. of Ni.[1, 3, 4] For gravimetric detn. of < 30 mg. Ni in 200 ml. of slightly acidic soln., add excess 1% reagent in EtOH (5 ml./10 mg. Ni, or more if other elements are present), place on a steam-bath, adjust to pH 7·5–8·1 with NH_4OH (neutral red indicator), leave on the bath for 1 hr. (or longer for small amts.) and allow to cool for 1–12 hr. Filter on a glass crucible, wash with cold H_2O, dry at 110–120°C (79–172°C) for 45 min. and weigh as $Ni(C_4H_7O_2N_2)_2$.

The error is −0·5% if the soln. is filtered hot and washed with hot H_2O.[5] If Cu or Co is present, dissolve the ppt. in aqua regia, evap. and reppt. Larger amts. of Ni can be detd. if the pH is regulated with urea and if a 1% reagent in 1-propanol is used.[6]

NOTES. (1) Interferences are caused by large amts. of NH_4OH, NH_4Cl, pyridine, Fe^{2+} or EtOH, and by CN^-, Pd, Pt and Au. Interference of Co is prevented by $(NH_4)_3$-citrate, that of Co + Fe^{3+} by pptn. from acetate-buffered soln. (see below), and that of Cu by NaK-tartrate or $Na_2S_2O_4$.

No interference is caused by Zn, Mn, Mg, Ca, etc. if NH_4Cl is present, or by Fe^{3+}, Cr, Al, Bi if 1–2 g. $(NH_4)_2$-tartrate is added.

The method has been applied to a wide variety of alloys.[4]

(2) When Co, Mn, Zn, Cu or Fe^{2+} is present, better results can be achieved by pptn. from soln. contg. AcOH and NaOAc but Fe^{3+}, Al and Cr interfere. Fe and Co can be masked with *N,N*-dihydroxyethylglycine (Fe does not ppt. at pH > 11), the excess reagent being masked by addn. of Zn^{2+}. EDTA addn. is not suitable for this detn.[7] Thioglycolic acid can be used[8] to mask Fe, Co, Cu, Ag, Pb, As, Bi. For sepn. of Ni from large amts. of Co, treat 200 ml. acidic soln. with 2–15 ml. 15% H_2O_2 and add NaCN until the ppt. disappears; evap. to 75 ml. by boiling, heat at 60°C while adding 0·5–0·75 g. solid dimethylglyoxime and 5–10 ml. 40% HCHO, cool, leave for 1–3 hr. and filter.[9] For a study of the copptn. of Co, see ref. 10.

For colorimetric detn. of 5–100 μg. Ni in 5–20 ml. of slightly acidic soln., add 5 ml. 10% Na_3-citrate (treated with dimethylglyoxime and extd. with $CHCl_3$ to remove Ni), make faintly alk. with NH_4OH and add 2 ml. 10% $NH_2OH·HCl$ (if Mn is present), 2 ml. 0·1% dimethylglyoxime (or more if Co or Cu is present), and ext. thrice with 2–3 ml. $CHCl_3$. Combine, shake with 5 ml. 1:50 NH_4OH, sep., shake the aq. layer with 1–2 ml. $CHCl_3$; shake the combined org. layer twice with 4 ml. 0·5*N* HCl, combine, add 5 drops satd. Br_2 water (if more than 1 μg. Ni/ ml. is present, add 1 ml. and leave for 15 min.), and then destroy the Br_2 color with NH_4OH. Add 3–4 drops more NH_4OH and 0·5 ml. reagent, dil. to 10 ml. with H_2O and measure the red or red-brown color at 445 mμ, which is more sensitive, or at 540 mμ, which is more stable.[11, 12, 13]

NOTES. (1) The method has been applied to Cu and Cu alloys after electrolysis, and to several other alloys.[4]

(2) Two forms of the complex exist, a high pH and a large excess of reagent favoring the more stable form.[14] For < 200 μg. Ni (< 4 μg. Ni/ml.) add 0·5 ml. indicator (0·5% starch, 3% KI and 20% KCl) followed by Br_2 to give a blue color. Then add 5 ml. 10% NH_4Cl in NH_4OH (filter on a glass crucible when the ppt. appears and wash with NH_4OH contg. NH_4Cl and H_2O). Add 2·5 ml. 20% Na_2-tartrate, 3 ml. 1% reagent in EtOH and, after 1 min., 3·5 ml. 10% NaOH, dil. to 50 ml. with H_2O and measure at 460 or 540 mμ.

(3) For 40–200 μg. Ni in 20 ml. soln. contg. < 0·5 ml. H_2SO_4, add 5 ml. $(NH_4)_3$-citrate (540 g./l.), 10 ml. 0·1% reagent and, immediately, 5 ml. 0·02*N* I_2 (8 g. KI in H_2O contg. 2·6 g. I_2 dild. to 1 l. with H_2O); dil. to 50 ml. with H_2O and measure at 540 mμ, 10 min. after the I_2 addn.[15, 16] Corrections can be applied for Cu, Mn and Co.[4]

(4) Better results are said to be obtained with $(NH_4)_2S_2O_8$; and the sensitivity is greater at 460 mμ with the violet 1:4 complex than at 520–530 mμ with the 1:2 complex.[17] Sep. the Ni by $CHCl_3$ extn. of the dimethylglyoxime complex as above, strip to the aq. phase, add 2 ml. 2·5% dimethylglyoxime in 1*N* NaOH, 1 ml. 10*N* NaOH, 0·3 ml. 10% $(NH_4)_2S_2O_8$ and dil. to 25 ml. with H_2O; measure at 460 mμ in a 5 cm. cell.

(5) If the complex is formed at pH 6·5 or 8·9 in soln. contg. NH_2OH and NH_4Cl, the complex can be extd. with $CHCl_3$ and measured at 366 mμ for < 5 μg Ni/ml. Cu does not interfere if $Na_2S_2O_3$ is added, nor does Fe if Na-tartrate is added.[18]

(6) Other methods which have been suggested are: pptn. from NH_4OH soln., extn. with 5 ml. Et_2O and washing with H_2O before pouring into a mixt. of 5 ml. EtOH and 5 ml. collodium;[19] and pptn. of 2–52 μg. Ni and dissoln. in pyridine.[20]

(7) For a titrimetric finish, several alternatives are available. Dissolve in $K_2Cr_2O_7$ in dil. H_2SO_4, add excess Fe^{2+} soln. and back-titrate with $KMnO_4$;[21] or dissolve in acid and titrate with EDTA in presence of murexide indicator.[22] Amperometric titration has been recommended.[23] For other methods, see ref. 24.

Apart from dimethylglyoxime, several other α-dioximes have been recommended; heptoxime and α-benzildioxime are the best of these.[25]

Heptoxime is suitable for gravimetric detn. of 6–35 mg. Ni in 200 ml. soln.[25] Adjust to pH > 3·8 with NH_4OH, heat to 50°C, add 0·48% reagent (15 ml./10 mg. Ni and 5 ml. extra), digest at 80°C for 10 min., allow to cool for 30 min., filter on a glass crucible, wash with cold H_2O and dry at 110–120°C for 1 hr.

NOTES. (1) Al, Cr, Sb, As, Fe^{3+}, Ti, Bi do not interfere if 20 ml. 33% citric acid soln. is added for each 1 g. metal present. Repptn. is needed if much Co is present. To remove Cu, add 10 ml. 10% Na_2SO_3, heat to 50°C, add 2 ml. or more of 50% v/v NH_4SCN, stir and filter. Addn. of 5 ml. 20% NH_4OAc prevents Pb interference. No interference arises from Mn, V, Mg, Zn, Cd, Be, Mo, AcO^-, tartrate, citrate, ClO_4^-, SO_4^{2-}, SCN^-.
(2) The method can be modified for trace amts. of Ni.[26]
(3) For colorimetric detn.[27] of < 154 μg. Ni in 10 ml. soln. add 5 ml. Br_2 water, 10 ml. NH_4OH, 3 ml. reagent, and dil. to 100 ml. with H_2O; measure at 443 or 536 mμ. For 1–10 μg. Ni, the complex formed without Br_2 addn. is extd. with $CHCl_3$ and measured at 377 mμ.[28]

α-Benzildioxime (0·2 g./l. EtOH contg. 50 ml. NH_4OH) is used in almost the same way as dimethylglyoxime,[1, 30] the complex formed being $Ni(C_{28}H_{22}O_4N_4)$. For < 1 p.p.m. Ni, the complex is extd. with $CHCl_3$ and measured at 275 mμ, and for < 4 p.p.m. at 358 or 406 mμ.[29]

α-Furildioxime can be applied gravimetrically, titrimetrically or colorimetrically.[30, 31] The composition of the complex formed depends on the pH of the soln.[32] Extn. with o-$C_6H_4Cl_2$ from soln. of pH 7·5–8·3 and measurement at 438 mμ is suitable for 0·2–3 p.p.m. Ni.[33] The reagent has been applied in the analysis of Mg alloys.[4] $CHCl_3$ extn. has been recommended.[34] Addn. of gelatin and measurement at 480 mμ are suitable for detn. of < 7 μg. Ni/ml.[35]

Diaminoglyoxime has been suggested but Fe and Co interfere.[30, 36] Dicarbamidoglyoxime is another possible reagent.[30]

Nioxime can be used for the colorimetric detn. of 10–150 μg. Ni in 50 ml. soln. at pH 4–6 contg. 1 ml. 20% $(NH_4)_3$-citrate;[37] add 1 ml. 10% gum arabic, 1 ml. 0·8% nioxime, dil. to 100 ml. with H_2O and measure at 550 mμ after 1 hr. Gravimetric detn. is unreliable.[38]

Nitroaminoguanidine has been applied.[30]

(b) Electrodeposition is suitable for the detn. of > 30 mg. Ni (as sulfate) in 150–200 ml. soln. contg. 35 ml. NH_4OH and 20 g. $(NH_4)_2SO_4$; pass 0·2–0·3 amp./dm.^{2} at 3–4 v. for 6–8 hr., wash with H_2O and EtOH, dry at 100°C for a few min., and weigh as Ni. Results tend to be slightly high.[1, 4] Ni can be sepd. from 150 mg. Zn by controlled potential electrolysis.[39]

NOTES. (1) Interferences are group II elements, Co, Fe^{2+}, Mo, Zn, CrO_4^{2-}, tartrate, NO_3^-, pyridine and large amts. of Fe^{3+}, V and W; Al, Mg, K and Cl^- do not interfere, nor do a little Mn or Cr^{3+} if Na_2SO_3 is added.
(2) If Co is present, add 0·2–1 g. $NH_2OH{\cdot}HCl$ or 2 g. $NaHSO_3$, electrolyze, weigh, dissolve in HNO_3 (1:4) and evap. to fumes with H_2SO_4; det. Ni with dimethylglyoxime and calc. the Co content by difference. 0·1–1 mg. of Ni and Co remains in the electrolyte unless 1 g. urea/100 ml. soln. is added. Alternatively, recover the Ni + Co by boiling with excess $(NH_4)_2S_2O_8$, treating with H_2S, filtering, igniting and weighing, and apply a correction.
When $NaHSO_3$ is added, ca. 1 mg. S contaminates the deposit; to correct for this, dissolve in HNO_3, evap. with HCl, det. the S as $BaSO_4$ and subtract the weight found.
(3) For 1 g. Ni in 125 ml. soln. contg. 24 g. $(NH_4)_2SO_4$ and 25 ml. NH_4OH, electrolyze at 2·0 v. and 0·1 amp./dm.^{2} for 20–24 hr. at 20–30°C to find the sum of Ni and Co. Det. Ni in the electrolyte and Cu and Zn in the deposit and apply suitable corrections. Det. Co in a separate sample by the $K_3Fe(CN)_6$ method and subtract. When the sum of Ni and Co is below 99·94% proceed as follows. Heat a 1 g. sample with 30 ml. 1:3 HNO_3, fume with 20 ml. 1:1 H_2SO_4, add 30 ml. H_2O, fume, cool and dil. to 100 ml. with H_2O. Warm the soln., add 400 ml. hot H_2O, pass H_2S, filter and wash; then reppt. Evap. the filtrates to 150 ml., add 10 ml. 5% $(NH_4)_2S_2O_8$, boil, add NH_4OH to give an excess of 50 ml., boil for 5 min. with 2 g. $(NH_4)_2S_2O_8$ and if Fe is absent, add 15 ml. Fe^{3+} soln. (0·2 mg./ml.), Digest for 15 min., cool, filter and reppt. thrice. Combine the filtrates, evap. to 100 ml. and, if the soln. is black, add H_2SO_4 and then neutralize. Add 30 ml. NH_4OH, dil. to 150 ml. with H_2O and then proceed as described above.[2] Alternatively, det. the Ni in the H_2S ppt. and the NH_4OH ppt. by a photometric method.[2]
(4) It is said[40] that better results are obtained in presence of SCN^-.

(c) Salicylaldoxime can be used to det. Ni gravimetrically in the filtrate from the Cu detn. (see p. 174).[41, 42] Adjust to pH 7–8 with NH_4OH, filter on a G3 crucible, wash and dry at 100–105°C. Various analogs have also been utilized: p-homosalicylaldoxime, resorcylaldoxime, resacetophenoneoxime,[43] salicylamidoxime, o-hydroxyacetophenoneoxime, 8-hydroxy-5-methoxytetraloneoxime (further details of these reagents are given in Chapter 22, p. 174 et seq.).

(d) Miscellaneous gravimetric reagents. Various reagents for copper also give reasonably satisfactory results for Ni. Salicylimine[44] and disalicylalpropylenediamine have been suggested. 3-Hydroxy-1,3-diphenyltriazine is used at pH 5–5·5 in acetate-buffered soln., the ppt. being washed with 20% hot EtOH; Zn, Mn, Cd, Be, As, Mg, F^-, PO_4^{3-} do not interfere. Further details of these methods are similar to those given in Chapter 22 (see p. 179).

Na-anthranilate is suitable for 0·1 g. Ni in 300 ml. of neutral or slightly acidic (AcOH) soln.[45] Add 3% reagent to the boiling soln., filter on a glass crucible, wash, dry at 105–110°C (< 307°C) and weigh as $Ni(C_7H_6O_2N)_2$; alternatively, titrate the ppt. bromometrically. 5-Bromo-2-aminobenzoic acid has also been applied.[45]

Oxine has been used for 10–100 mg. Ni in 100 ml. soln. contg. 5 ml. AcOH and 1–2 g. NaOAc.[46, 47] Add 4% reagent in EtOH to the soln. at 60°C, boil, filter on a glass crucible, wash, dry at 130°C (100–232°C) and weigh as $Ni(C_9H_6ON)_2$ or titrate the ppt. bromometrically. PO_4^{3-} and tartrate do not interfere. 4-Hydroxybenzothiazole has been applied titrimetrically in a similar way[47] (see Chapter 36, p. 279).

Diphenylhydantoin can be employed to det. 9–22 mg. Ni in 100 ml. soln. contg. 2 ml. NH_4OH.[48] Add 10 ml. reagent (2·5 g. in 5 ml. 2*N* NaOH dild. to 100 ml. with H_2O) to the soln. at 90°C, filter on a G3 crucible, wash, dry at 90°C and weigh as $(C_{15}H_{11}O_2N_2)_2$-$Ni \cdot 2NH_3 \cdot 4H_2O$; alternatively, filter on paper, dissolve in excess 0·05*N* H_2SO_4 and back-titrate with 0·05*N* NaOH.

Biguanide sulfate has been applied similarly.[49] Add tartaric acid to the acidic soln., add reagent in 1% NH_4OH and make alk. with 2*N* NaOH; filter, wash with cold H_2O, dissolve in 1*N* H_2SO_4 and back-titrate with NaOH. No interference arises from Al, Cr, Fe, Zn, Ti, U, Be.

Dicyanodiamidine sulfate is also used in a similar manner.[50] Treat the soln. with 1 g. NaK-tartrate for each 0·2 g. Fe + Ni, make alk. with NH_4OH and, if Co is present, add 10 ml. 10% cane sugar. Add 10–20 ml. 10% reagent followed by 10% KOH until pptn. is complete; after 12 hr., filter on a Gooch crucible, wash with dil. NH_4OH, dry at 120–130°C (123–240°C) and weigh as $Ni(C_2H_5N_4O)_2$. Alternatively, treat the dried ppt. with 40 ml. 0·2*N* HCl and titrate with 0·2*N* NaOH. No interference arises from Fe, Co, Cr or Zn.

Pyridine is used in conjunction with NH_4SCN[51] (cf. Chapter 22, p. 178). For 0·1 g. Ni in 100 ml. neutral soln., add 1 g. NH_4SCN as a satd. soln. and 2 ml. pyridine, filter on a glass crucible and wash with portions of the following solns.: (*i*) 4 g. NH_4SCN, 6 ml. pyridine in 993 ml. H_2O; (*ii*) 1 g. NH_4SCN and 15 ml. pyridine in 615 ml. H_2O and 370 ml. EtOH; (*iii*) 3·5 ml. pyridine in 95 ml. EtOH; (*iv*) 2 drops pyridine in 25 ml. Et_2O. Dry in a vacuum desiccator (< 63°C) and weigh as $Ni\,py_4(SCN)_2$ or dry at 110–130°C and weigh as $Ni\,py_3(SCN)_2$; alternatively, dissolve in HNO_3, add a known excess of $AgNO_3$ and complete by Volhard's method. Interferences are Cd, Co, Cu, Mn, Zn.

Various similar procedures have been suggested. KCN and pyridine (2 g. and 10 ml./l. resp.) ppt. Ni from neutral soln., the filtrate being titrated with standard Ni^{2+} soln.[51] $Ni(N_2H_4)_2(SCN)_2$ can be utilized in the same way as the analogous Co compd. (see p. 273). $[Ni\,py_4]Cr_2O_7$ is also used gravimetrically (see Chapter 23, p. 187). $[Ni(NH_3)_6][HgI_3]_2$ can be pptd. from neutral or slightly acidic soln. by addn. of NH_4OH and 10% K_2HgI_4 (cf. Chapter 23, p. 187) and weighed after drying in a vacuum desiccator; Co interferes unless a modification is introduced.[52]

Ammine complex formation has been utilized in two other methods. For colorimetric detn. of 50–100 mg. Ni, neutralize with NH_4OH, dil. with 1·5*M* NH_4OH to 100 ml. and measure the absorbance at 582 mμ; interferences are Cu, Co, CN^-, $Cr_2O_7^{2-}$, Fe, etc.[53] The violet complex formed with diethylenetriamine can be measured at 850 or 540 mμ (see Chapter 35, p. 273).

Oxanilic acid thioamide ppts. Ni from slightly ammoniacal soln.[54] but the ppt. must be ignited to NiO after filtration and washing with H_2O and EtOH.

H_2S can be used gravimetrically, the ppt. being ignited above 850°C to NiO; results tend to be high.[55] Colorimetric detn. is possible with Na_2S.[56]

α-Nitroso-β-naphthylamine, or the β-α analog, ppts. Ni analogously to Cu (see p. 180), the 2 ppts. being dried at 80–90°C or 80–220°C resp.

Diallyldithiocarbamidohydrazine ppts. Ni as $(C_8H_{12}$-$N_4S_2)Ni \cdot \frac{1}{2}H_2O$ at pH 8·1–8·7; the drying temp. is 105°C (see Chapter 22, p. 180).

(e) EDTA provides useful titrimetric or colorimetric detns. For < 30 mg. Ni in 100 ml. soln., add 0·1 vol. buffer (equal vols. of 1*N* NH_4OH and 1*N* NH_4Cl) and 3–5 drops 0·1% pyrocatechol violet indicator and titrate with 0·01*M* EDTA to the green-blue to violet end-point.[57] For simultaneous detn. of Ni and Co, add excess EDTA and back-titrate with Mg^{2+} soln. to give the sum; then add 2–3 ml. 30% H_2O_2, leave for a few min., add KCN and titrate further with Mg^{2+} to find Ni.[58]

In an alternative method,[59] add 0·5 g. NH_4NO_3 to the slightly acidic soln., adjust to pH 2 with 1:1 NH_4OH, add excess EDTA, readjust to pH 2, cool to 0°C, add pyrocatechol violet indicator and excess Bi^{3+} soln. and back-titrate with EDTA to the violet to yellow end-point. If Ni and Co are present, det. the sum with murexide as indicator, acidify the soln., destroy murexide with $(NH_4)_2S_2O_8$ and det. Ni as above. For the Ni detn. no interference arises from Cr, Pb, Hg, Zn, Cd, Cu, Co, As, Ag, Tl, Ca, etc., tartrate, citrate, $C_2O_4^{2-}$, F^- or much Cl^-; interferences are Fe, In, Ga, Bi, Th, Al, Sb.

NOTES. (1) Several other indicators have been proposed for the Ni titration, e.g. murexide in direct titration, or eriochrome black T in back-titration of excess EDTA with Mg^{2+} or Zn^{2+} soln.[60] Pyrogallol red is also suitable for the direct titration (see ref. 68, p. 170). Back-titration of excess EDTA at pH 2·7–3·9 with Th^{4+} soln. and alizarin S indicator can be applied in presence of 10 mg. Co.[61]
(2) Photometric titration at 1000 mμ in soln. of pH 4 (1:1 0·1*M* NaOAc–1·6*M* AcOH) has been suggested.[62]
(3) EDTA can be utilized colorimetrically for 0·4–50 mg. Ni/ml. at pH 4·6–6·8, absorbance being measured at 580 or 750 mμ.[63]

(f) KCN allows titrimetric detn. of Ni with diphenylcarbazone as indicator.[64] For 0·01–9·92 mg. Ni in neutral soln. add 20 ml. 20% NH_4NO_3, 1·5 ml. 0·2*N* Na_2CO_3, dil. to 150 ml. with H_2O, add 10 ml. Et_2O and 10 ml. Me_2CO and shake; after 15 min., add 20 ml. C_6H_6 and 0·3 ml. 1·5% diphenylcarbazone in EtOH, and titrate with KCN soln. (4·8 g. KCN and 2·3 g. KOH/l.) until the C_6H_6 layer is colorless (or the same color as a blank).

NOTES. (1) In the original method[1, 4] AgI is used as indicator but a correction is necessary; addn. of SO_4^{2-} sharpens the end-point so that the appearance of a white film in the surface of the soln. becomes unimportant. For this titration, add 1–5 ml. NH_4OH/250 ml. soln., 10 ml. KI

soln. (8 g./l.) and 10 ml. $AgNO_3$ soln. (0·5 g./l.), cool below 20°C and titrate to the disappearance of the turbidity. Interferences are Cu, Zn, Co, Ag, Au, Pt metals, W; $(NH_4)_3$-citrate prevents interference of Fe, Cr, Sb, As, and NH_4Cl that of Mn.
(2) NaCN can be used with murexide indicator in solns. contg. 1–2 ml. NH_4OH/50 ml.[65] α-Benzildioxime can serve as indicator.[1]
(3) Addn. of excess KCN and back-titration with Ni^{2+} soln. in presence of 2% resacetophenoneoxime in 40% EtOH as indicator is possible at pH 6·2–11.[66]

(g) Miscellaneous titrimetric methods. Ni can be detd. by pptn. of the arsenate and iodometric titration (see Chapter 35, p. 271). It is also possible to ppt. Ni with $Na_2C_2O_4$ from 30% HCOOH medium; the ppt. is washed with dil. HCOOH, dissolved in 10% H_2SO_4 and titrated at 70°C with $KMnO_4$ soln.[67] Titration with $K_4Fe(CN)_6$ in presence of starch-I_2 indicator has been suggested for 1·2–17 mg. Ni[68] (see Chapter 37, p. 287).

(h) Na-diethyldithiocarbamate provides a useful colorimetric detn. of 5–80 μg. Ni in 25 ml. 0·5*N* HCl soln.[69] First prep. a soln. of 200 g. $(NH_4)_3$-citrate in 600 ml. H_2O, adjust to pH 9–9·5, add 10 ml. reagent (1 g. in 100 ml. H_2O, filtered and dild. to 500 ml.), ext. with 20 ml. CCl_4, add 5 ml. reagent, ext. again and repeat until no yellow color remains; dil. with H_2O to 1 l. For a detn., add 5 ml. of this soln. to the sample soln., neutralize with NH_4OH to litmus and add 8–10 drops in excess; add 10 ml. iso-AmOH and 5 ml. reagent, shake for 2 min., sep., and measure the yellow-green color at 385 mμ. The error is ±5%. Cu, Bi, Co interfere but can be sepd. from Ni by extn. of the dimethylglyoxime complex with $CHCl_3$ (see also Chapter 22, p. 175). Pb is sepd. with a $CaCO_3$ column.

(i) Miscellaneous colorimetric methods. 3-Nitrososalicylic acid can be used for Ni as well as for Co (see p. 270).[70] 2-Nitroso-1-naphthol-4-sulfonate is also applicable.[71]

Dithizone allows the detn. of 20–120 μg. Ni in 25 ml. acidic soln.[72] Add NH_4OH to give a 0·3*N* soln., ext. with 0·06% dithizone in $CHCl_3$ until there is no further color change, combine the exts., wash with 0·5*N* NH_4OH, dil. to 100 ml. with $CHCl_3$ and measure at 665 or 480 mμ. Cu, Co, Pb, Zn interfere but Ni can be sepd. by $CHCl_3$ extn. of the dimethylglyoxime complex; evapn. and treatment with $HClO_4$ and HNO_3 is then necessary.

Di-β-naphthylthiocarbazone has been used at pH 8·0 with absorbance measurement at 540 mμ (ϵ = 90 000); see Chapter 21, p. 167.

K-dithio-oxalate (0·05% in H_2O, O_2 boiled out and stored in the dark) is suitable for 3–30 μg. Ni in 10 ml. neutral soln.[73] Add 3 ml. reagent and 0·04 ml. 6*N* HCl, dil. to 100 ml. and compare the pink color. Excess reagent causes decolorization. Fe, Co, Ag, Au, Pt, Pd, Tl, Bi, Cu, Cd, Sb, Sn, Ce, Mn, Ti, V, Zn interfere hence prior sepn. with dimethylglyoxime is essential.

Similar reagents are K-dithiocarbonate (0·5 ml. 4% reagent mixed with 18 ml. 0·5% NH_4OH and 0·5 g. NH_4NO_3) which is used in slightly acidic soln.[74] and K-xanthate (see Chapter 35, p. 272).

Rubeanic acid is used at pH 9·5–10·5 with measurement at 530 mμ (see Chapter 18, p. 148); the complex with diphenylrubeanic acid is measured at 510 mμ (see Chapter 22, p. 176).

β-Mercaptopropionic acid has been suggested for < 0·5 mg. Ni in 50 ml. soln.[75] Add 10 ml. 1% reagent, dil. to 90 ml. with H_2O, adjust to pH 9·1 ± 0·5, dil. to 100 ml. with H_2O and measure the reddish complex at 330 or 410 mμ. Interferences are Fe, Co, $C_2O_4^{2-}$ and tartrate. β-Isothioureidopropionic acid can be applied similarly.[76]

Formaldoxime (7 g. $NH_2OH{\cdot}HCl$ and 3 g. trioxymethylene heated with 15 ml. H_2O and cooled) has been applied[77] for 2 mg. Ni in 20 ml. neutral soln.; add 2 drops reagent and 4 drops 10*N* NH_4OH and compare the brown color (if the color is yellow, no Ni is present). Co does not interfere.

In 6*N* HCl soln. Ni can be detd. by measuring at 650 mμ; Cu interferes unless 4 g. NaH_2PO_2 is added.[78] $HClO_4$ may be employed to det. 98–100% Ni in 1·000 g. samples;[79] treat with HNO_3, evap. to white fumes with 8 ml. $HClO_4$, dil. to 100 ml. with H_2O and measure at 395 and 790 mμ. The error is ±0·05% if the differential method is applied. Corrections can be applied for Cu after measuring at 510 mμ, for Cr at 350 and 510 mμ, for Fe, etc.

p-Phenetidine (0·5 ml. in 20 ml. EtOH) is used[80] in conjunction with 2% $K_3Fe(CN)_6$ for 15 ml. soln. which is 0–30 × $10^{-4}M$ in Ni^{2+}; add 7 drops of the latter reagent and 5 drops of the former and measure at 425 or 515 mμ. Interferences are Co, Cu, Zn, Mn.

S-Methylthiourea sulfate can be applied colorimetrically or gravimetrically.[81] For colorimetry, adjust the soln. to pH 9·14–9·51 with dil. NH_4OH, add reagent and measure at 495–510 mμ after 1 hr. The gravimetric detn. is also done in ammoniacal medium (see Chapter 22, p. 180).

(j) Flame photometry Ext. Ni diethyldithiocarbamate with $CHCl_3$, burn in an O_2–C_2H_2 flame and measure at 352·5 mμ; 25–500 μg. Ni can be detd. (see Chapter 22, p. 181).

References

1. HILLEBRAND and LUNDELL, 312 (404); SCOTT and FURMAN, 614; KIMURA, 226; PIGOTT, 285.
2. YOKOSUKA, S., *Japan Analyst*, **4**, 99 (Pb), 103 (Cu), 141 (Mg), 509 (Fe) (1955); **5**, 71 (Al), 74 (Ca), 282 (Mn), 285 (Si) (1956); **6**, 431 (Zn), 690 (Co), 695, 753, 756 (Ni) (1957).
3. HECHT and DONAU, 190; WELCHER, **III**, 176.
4. A.S.T.M., 100 ff.
5. NUKA, P., *Z. anal. Chem.*, **91**, 29 (1932).
6. BICKERDIKE, E. L., and WILLARD, H. H., *Anal. Chem.*, **24**, 1026 (1952).

7. ROBERTSON, J. H., and BYRN, E. E., *Anal. Chem.*, **26**, 1854 (1954).
8. TREPKA-BLOCH, E., *Chemist Analyst*, **43**, 63 (1954).
9. EVANS, B. S., *Analyst*, **68**, 67 (1943).
10. SCHWEITZER, G. K., and MCDOWELL, B. L., *Anal. Chim. Acta*, **14**, 115 (1956).
11. SANDELL, 470.
12. WELCHER, **III**, 189.
13. MITCHELL, A. M., and MELLON, M. G., *Ind. Eng. Chem., Anal. Ed.*, **17**, 380 (1945).
14. YAMAZAKI, K., and MATSUMOTO, C., *J. Chem. Soc. Japan*, **78**, 833 (1957).
15. COOPER, M. D., *Anal. Chem.*, **23**, 874, 880 (1951).
16. HAIM, G., and TARRANT, B., *Ind. Eng. Chem., Anal. Ed.*, **18**, 51 (1946).
17. OELSCHLÄGER, W., *Z. anal. Chem.*, **146**, 339, 345 (1955); also see CLAASSEN, A., and BASTINGS, L., *Rec. trav. chim.*, **73**, 738 (1954).
18. NIELSCH, W., *Z. anal. Chem.*, **150**, 114 (1956).
19. OCHOTIN, V. P., and SYTSCHOFF, A. P., *Z. anal. Chem.*, **90**, 109 (1932).
20. PASSAMANECK, E., *Ind. Eng. Chem., Anal. Ed.*, **17**, 257 (1945).
21. ISHIMARU, S., *J. Chem. Soc. Japan*, **54**, 367 (1933).
22. HARRIS, W., and SWEET, T. R., *Anal. Chem.*, **24**, 1062 (1952).
23. FILL, M. A., and STOCK, J. T., *Analyst*, **69**, 178 (1944).
24. WELCHER, **III**, 194.
25. VOTER, R. C., and BANKS, C. V., *Anal. Chem.*, **21**, 1320 (1949).
26. FERGUSON, R. C., *et al.*, *Mikrochemie ver. Mikrochim. Acta*, **38**, 11 (1951).
27. FERGUSON and BANKS, *Anal. Chem.*, **23**, 1486 (1951).
28. GILLIS, J., *et al.*, *Chim. anal.*, **36**, 43 (1954).
29. UZUMASA, Y., and WASHIZUKA, S., *Bull. Chem. Soc. Japan*, **29**, 403 (1956).
30. WELCHER, **III**, 225ff.
31. PESHKOVA, V. M., *et al.*, *Zhur. Anal. Khim.*, **8**, 114 (1953).
32. REED, S. A., and BANKS, *Proc. Iowa Acad. Sci.*, **55**, 267 (1948).
33. GAHLER, A. R., *et al.*, *Anal. Chem.*, **23**, 502 (1951).
34. TAYLOR, C. G., *Analyst*, **81**, 369 (1956).
35. YAMAZAKI, K., *et al.*, *J. Chem. Soc. Japan*, **77**, 651 (1956).
36. KURÁS, M., *Mikrochemie*, **32**, 192 (1944); *Collection Czechoslov. Chem. Communs.*, **12**, 198 (1947).
37. FERGUSON and BANKS, *Anal. Chem.*, **23**, 448 (1951); also see JOHNSON, W. C., and SIMMONS, M., *Analyst*, **71**, 554 (1946).
38. FEINSTEIN, H. I., *Anal. Chem.*, **22**, 723 (1950).
39. LINGANE: *Electroanalytical Chemistry*, pp. 313 (controlled potential), 341 (internal) (1953); ISHIBASHI, M., *et al.*, *Japan Analyst*, **4**, 365 (1955).
40. CSOKÉN, P., *Z. anal. Chem.*, **119**, 498 (1940).
41. ASTIN, S., and RILEY, H. L., *J. Chem. Soc.*, 314 (1933); DUCRET, L., *Bull. soc. chim.*, **12**, 880 (1945).
42. WELCHER, **III**, 267.
43. BHATKI, K. S., and KABADI, M. B., *J. Sci. Ind. Research (India)*, **12B**, 226 (1953).
44. WELCHER, **I**, 388.
45. WELCHER, **II**, 199, 204.
46. ISHIMARU, S., *J. Chem. Soc. Japan*, **56**, 67 (1935).
47. WELCHER, **I**, 209, 307.
48. TAMAYO, M. L., and MARQUES, J. G., *Anales fis. y quím. (Madrid)*, **43**, 1011 (1947).
49. MAJUMDAR, A. K., *J. Indian Chem. Soc.*, **20**, 289 (1943); WELCHER, **II**, 332.
50. WELCHER, **I**, 418.
51. WELCHER, **III**, 8.
52. TAURINŠ, A., *Z. anal. Chem.*, **97**, 33 (1934).
53. MEHLIG, J. P., and KITSON, R. E., *Ind. Eng. Chem., Anal. Ed.*, **14**, 289 (1942); **15**, 606 (1943); *Chemist Analyst*, **34**, 4 (1945).
54. WELCHER, **IV**, 135.
55. HILLEBRAND and LUNDELL, 319 (415).
56. MICKWITZ, A., *Z. anorg. u. allgem. Chem.*, **196**, 613 (1931).
57. MALÁT, M., *et al.*, *Collection Czechoslov. Chem. Communs.*, **19**, 1156 (1954).
58. PŘIBIL, R., *Collection Czechoslov. Chem. Communs.*, **19**, 1171 (1954).
59. FLASCHKA, H., and PÜSCHEL, R., *Z. anal. Chem.*, **147**, 354 (1955).
60. SCHWARZENBACH, G., *Die komplexometrische Titration*, 66, 68 (1955).
61. TER HAAR, K., and BAZEN, J., *Anal. Chim. Acta*, **14**, 409 (1956).
62. SWEETSER, P. B., and BRICKER, C. E., *Anal. Chem.*, **25**, 253 (1953).
63. NIELSCH, W. and BÖLTZ, G., *Anal. Chim. Acta*, **11**, 367 (1954).
64. EVANS, B. S., *Analyst*, **71**, 455 (1946); **72**, 10 (1947).
65. BRAKO, F., *Metal Finishing*, **54**, No. 9, 61 (1956); DOLEŽAL, J., *et al.*, *Chem. listy*, **51**, 880 (1957).
66. BHATKI, K. S., *Analyst*, **82**, 26 (1957).
67. LEDRUT, J., and HAUSS, L., *Bull. soc. chim.*, [5] **4**, 1136 (1937); also see KAWAGAKI, K., *J. Chem. Soc. Japan*, **73**, 640 (1952).
68. FUJITA, Y., *J. Chem. Soc. Japan*, **75**, 658 (1954).
69. SANDELL, 475; ALEXANDER, O. R., *et al.*, *Ind. Eng. Chem., Anal. Ed.*, **18**, 206 (1946); ROBER, K. L., *Anal. Chem.*, **27**, 1200 (1955) (in W); CLUETT, M. L., and YOE, J. H., *ibid.*, **29**, 1265 (1957) (in human blood; 325 mμ, ϵ = 37 000).
70. VAN DERVOORT, G., *et al.*, *Z. anal. Chem.*, **128**, 517 (1948).
71. TOLMACHEV, V. N., and KOROBKA, L. A., *Zhur. Anal. Khim.*, **9**, 134 (1954).
72. SHERWOOD, R. M., and CHAPMAN, F. W., JR., *Anal. Chem.*, **27**, 88 (1955); also see YOUNG, R. S., *et al.*, *Analyst*, **71**, 474 (1946) (titration method).
73. MEHLIG, J. P., and NEWBY, B. J., *Chemist Analyst*, **41**, 28 (1952); YOE, 298; WELCHER, **IV**, 143.
74. YOE, 296; WELCHER, **IV**, 143.
75. LEAR, J. B., and MELLON, M. G., *Anal. Chem.*, **25**, 1411 (1953).
76. UHLIG, L. J., and FREISER, H., *Anal. Chem.*, **23**, 1014 (1951).
77. WELCHER, **III**, 348; RAĬNES, M. M., and LARINOV, YU. A., *Trudy Komissii Anal. Khim., Akad. Nauk SSSR., Inst. Geokhim. i Anal. Khim.*, **7**, 295 (1956).
78. GOLDBERG, C., *Chemist Analyst*, **39**, 56 (1950).
79. BASTIAN, R., *Anal. Chem.*, **23**, 580 (1951).
80. IIJIMA, S., and HASHIMOTO, J., *J. Chem. Soc. Japan*, **74**, 558 (1953).
81. SIDDHANTA, S. K., and BANERJEE, S. N., *Sci. and Culture (Calcutta)*, **19**, 573 (1954).

35

COBALT

The principal references for this chapter are given in ref. 1. The chemistry of cobalt has been dealt with in a monograph.[1]

Attack*

(a) Minerals. Dissolve in HCl and HNO_3 and fuse any residue with $K_2S_2O_7$ or Na_2CO_3. If Ag or As is present, use HNO_3 and H_2SO_4. Na_2O_2 fusion may also be useful.

(b) Rocks. Treat as described for Ni, apply dithizone extn., etc.

(c) Steels. Boil with HCl and HNO_3 and evap. until crystals appear; then add 100 ml. hot H_2O, almost neutralize with NH_4OH, treat with ZnO, etc.

(d) Stellite (Co–Cr–W). Treat with $HClO_4$ (see also Chapter 56, p. 420).

Separation*

H_2S allows sepn. of Co from Sn on treatment of 1*M* HCl soln. contg. 0·5 ml. acrolein at 60°C. In the usual method, Co coppts. with Sn^{4+} but not with Sn^{2+}.

Co is sepd. from Fe and Al only incompletely on treatment with NH_4OH and NH_4Cl; this method is even less satisfactory than that with Ni.

ZnO seps. Co from Cr, Al, Mo, Cu, V, U, Be, Zr, W and incompletely from Fe.[2] If much Co or Ni is present, repptn. is necessary; if much Cr is present, it must be removed as $CrOCl_2$. Results are best in cold, moderately dild. solns. A study with radioactive tracer has shown that a 1% loss occurs if Co is below 3% in steel; the loss is larger if Co exceeds 3% or if SO_4^{2-} or Cu is present.[3]

α-Nitroso-β-naphthol seps. Co from Ni, etc.; see under Determination, p. 270. The Co complex can be extd. with CCl_4 or $CHCl_3$ from soln. at pH 3–4. With the β-α compd. Co is sepd. from Cu and Fe by shaking the ext. with HCl.

KNO_2 allows sepn. of Co from much Ni, Fe, Cr, etc.[4] Make the soln. contg. 5 g. tartaric acid/75 ml. alk. to litmus with satd. KOH soln. and if a ppt. appears, add more KOH to dissolve it; just acidify with AcOH, add 4 ml. in excess, warm, add 200 ml. hot reagent (100 g. KNO_2 and a few drops of AcOH/200 ml.), heat almost at boiling for 10 min. or until no brown vapors appear, leave for 4–12 hr., filter on Whatman No. 40 paper, wash 8 times with 3% KNO_2 and once with H_2O. Sepn. of Co from W is possible if the ppt. is dissolved in H_2SO_4 and HNO_3 and then repptd. Interferences are Pb, Ba, Sr, Ca and As + Fe. If EtOH is added, the filtrate contains traces of Co and may explode on heating.[5]

Na_2O_2 treatment of hot solns. allows sepn. of Co from Cr.

Phenylthiohydantoic acid seps. Co from Al, Cr, V, U, W, Mo, As, Ti, Zn, Mn, Mg, Ca.[6] Treat 100 ml. neutral soln. contg. < 0·2 g. Co and citrate with 10 ml. 2*N* NH_4Cl, 80 ml. 1% reagent in 2*N* NH_4OH and 8 ml. 10% NH_4OH and boil for 10 min.; after 1 hr. filter and wash with hot H_2O. Add $H_2C_2O_4$ and ignite above 1050°C to CoO. Cu and Sb interfere; interference by Fe or Ni is small.

Extn. of the thiocyanate complex with 65:35 Et_2O–AmOH seps. Co from Ni, Fe, etc.[7] To ca. 20 ml. soln. contg. 5 ml. 1:1 HCl, add 20 ml. 60% NH_4SCN followed by $(NH_4)_3$-citrate (210 g. in 500 ml. neutralized with NH_4OH and dild. to 1 l. with H_2O) until the Fe color has been removed. Dil. to 50 ml. with H_2O, add 4 ml. Et_2O and ext. 3 times with 20 ml. portions of solvent. Combine the exts., shake twice with 20 ml. 2*M* NH_4OH, evap. the combined aq. layers to dryness, then evap. to dryness with 20 ml. 6*M* HNO_3 and finally with NH_4OH.

Ether extn. of a HCl soln. seps. Co from large amts. of Fe and Mo.

$(NH_4)_2HPO_4$ allows sepn. from Mn which is pptd. Add 1–2 g. reagent to 200 ml. of acidic soln. contg. 2 g. citric acid, boil, add NH_4OH, etc. (see Chapter 37, p. 287). Na_3PO_4 seps. Co from Fe, Al, Zr, Ti; U requires repptn.[8] To 350 ml. acidic soln. add 25 ml. reagent (34·05 g. $Na_3PO_4 \cdot 12H_2O$/l.) for each 0·1 g. Fe and then 5–10 ml. in excess; make alk. to litmus with NH_4OH, add 10 ml. AcOH to give pH 3–3·5, add 5–10 ml. 3% H_2O_2, boil, filter on Whatman No. 41 paper and wash with a soln. contg. 25 ml. AcOH/l. At pH 5·3, Na_3PO_4 seps. Co from Ni.

* Cf. Chapter 34, p. 263.

Extn. of the diethyldithiocarbamate complex from soln. of pH 6·5 contg. citrate with CCl_4 seps. Co from Fe, large amts. of Ca and PO_4^{3-}. Extn. with 0·01% dithizone in CCl_4 of the soln. contg. NH_4OH and $(NH_4)_3$-citrate above pH 8 seps. Co from Fe, Cr, V, etc.[9] Extn. with this dithizone soln. at pH 2 (dil. HCl) seps. Co from small amts. of Cu, Ag, Hg.[9] Extn. with $CHCl_3$ is slower. Co can be extd. from alk. soln. but the extd. complex is stable to acids, hence sepn. of Co from Ni and Zn is possible by shaking the ext. with 0·1*N* HCl.[10]

Oxine can be used at pH 5·1–5·2 along with Fe or Al for concn. of Co.

Ion exchange resin allows sepn. from Ni, Al, etc. (see Chapter 13, Section 2.2).

Determination

α-Nitroso-β-naphthol provides the best method for more than 1 mg. Co. For colorimetric detn., analogs of this reagent or NH_4SCN are to be preferred. Macro or semimicro amts. of Co can be weighed as the sulfate after pptn. as sulfide, or titrated potentiometrically with $K_3Fe(CN)_6$. Smaller amts. may be determined colorimetrically with diethyldithiocarbamate.

(a) α-Nitroso-β-naphthol is the best reagent for the gravimetric detn. and can also be used colorimetrically or titrimetrically.[1, 11] For < 0·1 g. Co in 200 ml. soln. contg. 10 ml. HCl, heat to 60°C, add a 1·5-fold excess (0·15 g./0·01 g. Co and at least 10 ml.) of reagent soln. (1 g./15 ml. AcOH), stir for 1 min. and allow to cool for 1 hr. Filter on Whatman No. 40 paper, wash with at least 100 ml. 1:19 HCl (warm) and transfer to a porcelain crucible. Ignite at 800–900°C to Co_3O_4 (for < 10 mg. Co); for > 10 mg. Co, ignite above 1050°C, cool in CO_2 and weigh as CoO, or heat in H_2 and weigh as Co, or treat with H_2SO_4 and weigh as $CoSO_4$.

NOTES. (1) Interferences are Fe, Cu, Bi, Ag, Pd, Cr, Ti, V, Sn, Mo, W and HNO_3. No interference is caused by Al, Be, Pb, Cd, Hg, As, Sb, Zn, Mn, Ca, Mg, PO_4^{3-}, AsO_4^{3-}, NH_4^+. If much Ni is present, dissolve the ignited oxide in HCl and reppt. as described in Note 2. Fe^{3+} does not interfere[12] if a dil. HNO_3 soln. is used with a reagent soln. in H_3PO_4. The method given above has been applied to steels and various alloys.[13]

(2) Various other procedures have been recommended. For 0·1–30 mg. Co in 20 ml. slightly acidic soln.[1, 11, 14] add 5–10 drops 30% H_2O_2 followed by 2*N* NaOH until a ppt. appears. Add 10–20 ml. AcOH, heat, add 200 ml. hot H_2O and 10–20 ml. 2% reagent in 50% AcOH and boil. Filter on a glass crucible, wash with hot 33% AcOH 3–4 times and with hot H_2O 3 times, dry at 130°C (81–140°C) and weigh as $Co(C_{10}H_6O_2N)_3 \cdot 2H_2O$. With this method, Co can be sepd. from Ni, Cr, Zn in 20–30% AcOH, and from large amts. of Ni in 30–40% AcOH.

(3) For 0·005–0·5 g. Co in 100–150 ml. acidic soln. (AcOH),[15] add 0·2 g. β-naphthol, boil, add 5% KNO_2 until the ppt. settles (if Ni is present, add HCl in a vol. equal to that of KNO_2 and boil), filter on paper and ignite.

(4) For amperometric titration, see Chapter 22, p. 180. For a colorimetric method see Note 4 below.

(b) *m*-Methoxy-*o*-nitrosophenol seems to be the best colorimetric reagent for Co.[16] For 5–50 μg. Co, transfer the soln. to a 100 ml. separatory funnel, add some drops 30% H_2O_2, 1 ml. citrate soln. (400 g. citric acid in 300 ml. H_2O adjusted to pH 8·5 with NH_4OH, dild. to 1 l. with H_2O, extd. with 0·01% dithizone in CCl_4 and then with CCl_4 and finally filtered) and 5 ml. satd. reagent soln. (40·2 mg./100 ml. at 18°C). If necessary, adjust to pH 7–8·5. After 15 min. shake for 1 min. with 5 ml. CCl_4, wash with 2 ml. CCl_4, and ext. with 5 ml. portions of CCl_4 until colorless. Combine the exts., shake with 10 ml. 10% Na_2CO_3, sep., dil. to 25 ml. with CCl_4 and measure at 400 mμ. The final soln. should contain 0·02–2·5 μg. Co/ml.

NOTES. (1) 1000-fold amts. of Ni or Fe^{2+} and 5000-fold amts. of Fe^{3+} can be tolerated. If Cu is present, thiourea or $Na_2S_2O_3$ should be added.

(2) Nitroso-R salt is suitable for 1–10 μg. Co.[9, 11] Evap. to dryness with 1 ml. HNO_3, add 5 ml. H_2O, 0·25 ml. 1:1 HCl and 0·25 ml. 1:10 HNO_3 and boil if necessary. Add 0·5 ml. 0·2% reagent and adjust to pH 5·5 with 1 g. NaOAc using bromocresol green as external indicator. Boil for 1 min., add 1·0 ml. HNO_3 dropwise, boil for 1 min., cool, dil. to 10 ml. with H_2O and measure at 420 mμ or at 500–550 mμ if 5 mg. Fe is present. Interferences are CN^-, peroxides, $S_2O_8^{2-}$, reductants, large amts. of Fe (sep. by ether extn.), more than 0·5 mg. Ni, and large amts. of NH_4^+. With 2 μg. Co, up to 1 or 40 mg. of Cu or Fe^{3+} can be tolerated; small amts. of Mn, Zn, Pb, Sn, Ti, V, Cr, Al, W, Ca, etc. can be present. The method has been applied to Ni and Ni alloys.[13] Fe does not interfere if NaF is added;[17, 18] addn. of KF after boiling with Br_2 prevents the interference of many elements.[19]

For < 5 μg. Co, treat the soln. with 1 ml. 33% NaOAc, 0·1 ml. AcOH, 0·85 ml. 0·5% reagent, 0·5 ml. 3% $KBrO_3$ and boil; add 0·5 ml. HNO_3, cool, dil. to 5 ml. with H_2O and measure at 425 mμ.[20] For > 5 μg. Co, add buffer solns. as in the previous method and 1 ml. reagent, boil, add 1 ml. HNO_3, cool, dil. to 25 ml. with H_2O and measure at 525 mμ.[20]

For biol. materials,[21] ext. the α-nitroso-β-naphthol complex with $CHCl_3$, wash with dil. HCl, ignite and proceed as above.

The reagent can be destroyed[22] by treatment with $NaBO_3$.

(3) β-Nitroso-α-naphthol is suitable for 0·5–10 μg. Co in 20 ml. soln. at pH 5–7.[9, 11, 23] Add 5 ml. 1% reagent in 2:3 CCl_4–EtOH, shake for 5 min., sep., wash the CCl_4 layer twice with 10 ml. HCl and then with H_2O, 10 ml. 1*N* NaOH and H_2O; filter through paper and measure at 530 mμ. Fe, Cu, Cr, etc., can be tolerated.

(4) Many other nitroso reagents have been proposed for colorimetric detn. of Co. 3-Nitrososalicylic acid in benzine permits the simultaneous detn. of Co, Ni and Cu.[24] *o*-Nitrosocresol is very sensitive, so that less than 1 μg. Co can be detd., but it is troublesome.[25] α-Nitroso-β-naphthol can be used in solns. contg. NH_4OH and citrate;[9, 26] alternatively, for 0·2–2 p.p.m., the complex is extd. with CCl_4 or $CHCl_3$ from soln. at pH 4 and the absorbance is measured at 400 or 317 mμ.[27, 36] 2-Nitroso-1-naphthol-4-sulfonic acid,[28] *o*-nitrosophenol,[11] isonitrosodimedone,[29] 4-nitrosoresorcinol,[11] 4-nitrosochromotropic acid[30] and isonitrosomalonylguanidine[31] have also been suggested.

(5) Isonitrosodimedone,[32] 1-nitroso-2-hydroxy-3-naphthoic acid,[33] dinitrosoresorcinol[30] and dinitroso-orcinol[30] have also been used for gravimetric detns.; the latter 2 reagents are particularly inaccurate.

(c) H_2S is useful[1, 34] for gravimetric detn. of < 5 mg. Co in soln. of pH 5·2 (adjusted with NaOH or AcOH to the disappearance of the purple color of bromocresol purple); place the soln. in a flask, sat. with H_2S, stopper and digest at 70°C for 1 hr. Filter, wash, ignite, add 1:1 HCl, evap to dryness, wash the flask with 1:1 HNO_3 and combine; add 2–8 drops 1:1 H_2SO_4, evap. to dryness and ignite to $CoSO_4$ at 500–600°C (700–820°C).

(d) NH_4SCN is satisfactory for colorimetric detn. of 1–50 μg. Co.[1, 9, 35] Treat the soln. with 3 ml. 50% reagent, 6 ml. acetate buffer (pH 1–4·5) and dil. with H_2O to 10 ml. Ext. with 5 ml. 1:5 iso-AmOH–EtOAc and measure at 320 mμ for 1–10 μg. Co or at 620 mμ for 10–50 μg. Co. (ϵ = 21 300 or 3900). For 0·2–10 p.p.m. Co, ext. with AmOH satd. with NH_4SCN from a soln. contg. 25 ml. 44% NH_4SCN/50 ml. at pH 3·0–5·0 and measure at 312 mμ.[36]

NOTES. (1) No interference occurs with the following amts. of the ions mentioned:

	Bi	Fe ($+PO_4^{3-}$)	Hg	Cu	Mn, Cr, Pb, Ni
320 mμ	100 μg.	500 μg.	∞	150 μg.	1 mg.
620 mμ	20 μg.	500 μg.	10 μg.	30 μg.	

V does nct interfere if NH_4OAc and tartrate are added.
(2) Addn. of Me_2CO or extn. with hexone improves the method and Cu can be masked with thiourea.[37] Me_2CO deepens the color.[9, 38] For 3–350 μg. Co in neutral or slightly acidic soln. add reagent to give at least a 5% soln. and Me_2CO to give at least a 50% v/v soln. and measure at 600–620 mμ. Fe interferes but can be detd. simultaneously (see Chapter 33, p. 259) or decolorized with NH_4F or $SnCl_2$; $SnCl_2$ also prevents Cu interference. Bi, Ni and U interfere.
(3) Thiocyanate can also be used in conjunction with arsonium salts and org. bases.[39, 40, 41] The tetraphenylarsonium chloride method is suitable for 25 ml. soln. contg. 50–1500 μg. Co.[39] Add 5 ml. 50% NH_4SCN, 15 drops 0·05*M* arsonium soln. and ext. with 10 ml. $CHCl_3$, add 5 drops arsonium reagent, ext. with 5 ml. $CHCl_3$ and repeat this process once. Filter on a small paper, dil. with $CHCl_3$ to 25 ml. and measure the blue color at 620 mμ. Fe^{2+}, Cr^{3+}, Mn and Ni can be tolerated; Cu interference is prevented by addn. of KI until 0·5 g. is present in excess of the amt. required to dissolve CuI, followed by a 3–5 drop excess of 10% $Na_2S_2O_3$ and 0·5 g. NH_4F. Fe^{3+} interference is avoided by addn. of NH_4F so that 0·2–0·3 g. is present in excess after the disappearance of the red color; interference of Mo is avoided by 0·5 g. NH_4F and that of V by 1·5 g. NH_4F and 0·35 g. Mohr's salt. 10–100 μg. Co/ml. can be detd.[41] with triphenylmethylarsonium thiocyanate after extn. with *o*-$C_6H_4Cl_2$; the error is ±2%.
(4) Antipyrine and SCN^- is used for 1–100 μg. Co in 4 ml. soln.[42] Add 10 ml. 0·1*N* HCl or H_2SO_4, 15 ml. 30% NH_4SCN, 5 ml. 10% antipyrine, ext. with 20 ml. 1:5 C_6H_6–EtOAc and measure at 630 mμ. Hg, Pb, Mn, Sn, Cr, As, Al, Zn, Ca, Mg can be tolerated, as can 1 mg. Fe or Cu if 15 ml. 15% $H_2C_2O_4$ is added, and 0·5 g. Ni if a correction is applied.
(5) Pptn. as Hg or Zn double thiocyanate may be applied for detn. of $<$ 200 μg. Co.[43] Dissolve in 5 ml. 10% w/v NH_4SCN in Me_2CO and MeOH and measure at 625 mμ; reflectance spectrophotometry with measurement at 60 mμ allows simultaneous detn. of Cu which is measured at 500 mμ. The Zn double salt can also be dissolved in 50% Me_2CO.[44]
(6) $HgCl_2$ and NH_4SCN are utilized gravimetrically.[45] Evap. the soln. to dryness, add $HgCl_2$ soln. (27 g./500 ml.) and NH_4SCN soln. (30 g./500 ml.) in a 1:2 ratio, adding more of the latter if the Co color persists; filter on a glass crucible, wash with H_2O and EtOH, dry at 90°C (50–200°C) for 10 min., and weigh as $Co[Hg(SCN)_4]$.
(7) HCl can be used colorimetrically.[9, 46] Evap. the soln. to dryness with HCl twice, add more HCl and 5 ml. 15% $SnCl_2$ in HCl, dil. to 50 ml. with HCl and measure at 625 mμ. Interferences are Cr, V, 126-fold amts. of Ni, and 100-fold Cu or Fe^{3+}.

(e) Electrodeposition is applied as described for Ni (see p. 265).[1, 14] See Chapter 4 for the controlled potential method. To det. 0·01 g. Co in 100 ml. soln. at pH 5 contg. AcOH and NaOAc, use this soln. as the anolyte and 2*N* HNO_3 as the catholyte, heat at 90–95°C and pass 0·5 amp. for 10 min. and then 1 amp.; weigh as Co_2O_3.[47]

(f) $(NH_4)_2HPO_4$ permits detn. of 0·25–0·6 mg. Co in 2–3 ml. neutral soln.[14, 48] Heat, add 1–2 ml. hot 5% reagent dropwise while air is passed slowly, heat for 10 min. and then cool; filter on paper, wash with hot 1% NH_4NO_3 and 50% EtOH, and ignite above 600°C to $Co_2P_2O_7$; alternatively, dry at 105–170°C and weigh as $NH_4CoPO_4 \cdot H_2O$. A little Ni can be tolerated. The ppt. should be red; it must be discarded if it is violet. See also under Separation, p. 269.

NOTE. Pptn. as $(NH_4)_3Co_6(AsO_4)_5$ and iodometric titration of the ppt. has been suggested.[49]

(g) Isonitrosothiocamphor is suitable for gravimetric detn. of 10–40 mg. Co in 200 ml. neutral soln.[50] Boil the soln., add 50 ml. 10% NaOAc, 1% reagent until pptn. is complete and 30 ml. 2*N* HCl if Ni is present; filter on a glass crucible after 30–40 min., wash with hot H_2O, 0·2*N* NaOH, 2*N* HCl and hot H_2O (red ppt.), dry at 105–110°C and weigh as $Co(C_{10}H_{14}SNO)_3$; alternatively, treat with H_2SO_4, etc. and weigh as $CoSO_4$. Cu interferes but Ni, Fe, Al, Cr, Zn, Mn, Mg and Ba do not.

(h) Miscellaneous gravimetric methods. Na-anthranilate can be used for 0·1–4 mg. Co in 2 ml. neutral soln.[14, 51] Add 1 drop 1:200 HCl, boil, add a 7-fold excess of reagent (0·2 g. anthranilic acid in 1·0 ml. 1*N* NaOH, mixed with 5 ml. H_2O, filtered, acidified with 6–7 drops 5% AcOH and dild. to 10 ml. with H_2O), boil and leave to cool for 10 min.; filter on a glass crucible, wash once with 0·2% reagent and then with

EtOH, dry the pink ppt. at 110°C (108–290°C) and weigh as $Co(C_7H_8O_2N)_2$. Alternatively, dissolve the ppt. and titrate with $KBrO_3$–KBr soln. Interferences are Ni, Cu, Zn, Cd, Mn, NO_3^-, tartrate, AcO^-, and much KCl or Na_2SO_4. 5-Bromo-2-aminobenzoic acid may also be applied.[51]

3,5-Dimethylpyrazole is suitable for 0·1 g. Co in 20 ml. neutral soln.[52] Add 25 ml. 2% reagent and 5 ml. 0·5*N* NaOH, filter on a glass crucible, wash with H_2O, dry the blue ppt. at room temp. and weigh as Co-$(C_5H_7N_2)_2$. Pb, Mn, Ni, etc. interfere.

Benzimidazole is used[53] in 100% excess in 150 ml. sample soln. contg. 2 g. K_2SO_4, the pH being adjusted to 10 with NH_4OH; the ppt. is dried at 105°C and weighed as $Co(C_7H_4N_2)_2$.

Phenylthiohydantoic acid may be utilized (see under Separation, p. 269) but the ppt. must be ignited at 511–946°C and weighed as Co_2O_3.

K-xanthate is applied in solns. contg. 1 g. citric acid and excess NH_4OH;[54] add 1 g. reagent and 1 g. AcOH, filter on paper, wash, return to the original beaker, add NH_4OH, filter again and wash with NH_4OH until colorless. Finally, ignite to Co_2O_3. Ni ppts. on acidification of the filtrate from the NH_4OH treatment.

K-xanthate is also used colorimetrically for 0·03–1 mg. Co in dil. HCl soln. also contg. 0·1–2 mg. Ni.[55] Add 1*M* reagent, ext. with 10 ml. CCl_4, wash the org. layer with 20–30 ml. 1:1 NH_4OH, add $(NH_4)_2$-tartrate and sep.; measure the Co in the dark green org. layer and Ni in the yellow-green aq. phase.

Oxanilic acid thioamide is applied gravimetrically[56] in solns. contg. some HCl; the ppt. is washed with H_2O, ignited, treated with H_2SO_4 and weighed as $CoSO_4$.

α-Nitroso-β-naphthylamine or the β-α analog is used for < 40 mg. Co in 300 ml. soln.[57] Add a slight excess of 1% reagent in EtOH, boil for 20 min. cool for 15 min., filter on a glass crucible, wash with dil. HCl, dil. NH_4OH and hot H_2O, dry at 110°C (80–179° for the α-β compd. and 72–218° for the β-α compd.) for 2 hr. and weigh as $Co(C_{10}H_7OH_2)_3$. Ni and Cu interfere but Zn, Al, Cr do not.

$H_2C_2O_4$ is suitable for < 0·5 g. Co in 10 ml. soln.[58] Add an equal vol. of AcOH, heat, add 4 ml. 0·5*M* reagent, place in boiling H_2O for 30 min., and filter after 12 hr.; wash with 50% EtOH, dry at 110–105°C and weigh as $CoC_2O_4\cdot 2H_2O$, or dissolve the ppt. and titrate with $KMnO_4$ soln. Large amts. of Na, K and NH_4^+ interfere.

(i) $K_3Fe(CN)_6$ provides a reliable titrimetric procedure for 0·05–25 mg. Co with a potentiometric end-point.[59] Add 50 ml. 20% $(NH_4)_3$-citrate and a 70 ml. excess of NH_4OH, dil. to 250 ml. with H_2O and titrate below 25°C with 1/300–1/30*M* reagent. Ethylenediamine may be added.[60]

NOTES. (1) 0·2 mg. Mn interferes but can be removed with $KBrO_3$. No interference is caused by 10 g. Ni; 100 mg. Zn, Sb^{3+}, Cr, Cu, Bi, Cd, Sn, Al, Fe^{3+}, As^{5+} or Mg; 10 mg. W or Mo; or by NH_4Cl or NH_4NO_3.

(2) Various other redox titrations have been suggested. For 0·05–0·1 g. Co in 100 ml. soln.[1] contg. < 5 ml. 6*N* H_2SO_4, add 1–2 g. $NaBO_3$ and a 10 ml. excess of 6*N* NaOH, boil out O_2 for about 10 min.; add excess 0·1*N* $FeSO_4$ keeping the soln. under CO_2, followed by 20–30 ml. 6*N* H_2SO_4, cool, add 10 ml. 25% H_3PO_4 and 5 drops 0·02% Ba-diphenylamine sulfonate, and finally titrate with 0·1*N* $K_2Cr_2O_7$. NO_3^-, oxidants, Mn, Cr and V and > 7 mg. Fe interfere, but Ni does not. Potentiometric titration is also applicable.[61]
Other redox titrations are: oxidation with H_2O_2 in bicarbonate soln. followed by iodometry;[62] oxidation with I_2 in NH_4OH soln. followed by titration with As^{3+} potentiometrically;[63] oxidation with PbO_2 in oxalate soln., addn. of excess Fe^{2+} and titration with $K_2Cr_2O_7$ with diphenylamine as indicator;[64] addn. of EDTA and Ce^{4+} or Cr^{6+} and titration with Cr^{2+} potentiometrically.[65]

(j) EDTA permits a rapid, if unselective, titrimetric detn. of Co in 50 ml. soln.[66] Add excess EDTA soln. (5·5 g./l.), adjust to pH 10 with 1:1 NH_4OH, add eriochrome black T indicator (0·2 g./100 ml. contg. some drops of NH_4OH) and back-titrate with Zn^{2+} soln. (1·4 g. ZnO in the min. amt. HNO_3 dild. to 1 l. with H_2O). NH_4SCN can also serve as indicator for detn. of Co in steels after sepn. with NH_4SCN and acridine.[67]

NOTES. (1) EDTA has also been applied colorimetrically. To 5 ml. soln., contg. Co to give a final concn. of 10–80 μg./ml.,[68] add 5 ml. 0·01*M* $K_2Cr_2O_7$, 5 ml. 2*N* AcOH and 5 ml. 0·01*M* EDTA and measure the purple color at 558 mμ. Interferences are (per ml.) 75 μg. Ni, 137 μg. Cu, 550 μg. Fe; Al, Zn, etc. require addn. of more EDTA; reducing agents interfere. The color is due to $[Co\text{–}EDTA]_7Cr_2O_7$.
For 0·1–0·5 mg. Co in neutral soln.[69] add 5% EDTA, 6 ml. 0·1*N* KOH, 20 ml. 30% H_2O_2, boil for 1 min., dil. to 100 ml. with H_2O and measure at 540 mμ. Interferences are Cu, Ni, Cr, Fe; Mn requires the addn. of 5 ml. 10% H_3PO_4 before the H_2O_2. It is also possible to use 5 ml. 0·1*M* EDTA, 2 ml. 7*M* NH_4OH and 10 ml. 30% H_2O_2 in a final vol. of 25 ml.[70]
(2) NTA has also been applied colorimetrically[71] for > 1·375 mg. Co in 25 ml. soln. at pH 4·8–5·7, the deep red color being measured at 510 mμ. If H_2O_2 is added, up to 10 mg. Co in 25 ml. can be detd.[70]

(k) Oxine is suitable for titrimetric or colorimetric detns. For detn. of < 0·2 g. Co in 150 ml. neutral soln.,[72, 73] add 5 g. NaOAc, 5 ml. 6*N* AcOH and excess 1% oxine in EtOH, boil, filter on a glass crucible, wash with hot H_2O, dissolve in 15% HCl and titrate with 0·1*N* $KBrO_3$ contg. KBr. Gravimetric detn. as Co $(C_9H_6OH)_2$ after drying at 155–295°C is inaccurate.

For colorimetry,[74] ext. with $CHCl_3$ from soln. of pH above 6·8 and measure at 420 mμ; this is suitable for 10 μg. Co/ml.

(l) KCN is used titrimetrically or gravimetrically. For titration of 2–50 mg. Co in 100 ml. of slightly acidic soln.,[75] add 20 ml. satd. borax soln. and 10 ml. 4% KI followed by KCN soln. (16·8 g. + ca. 10 g. NaOH in 3·5 l.) in such an amt. that if *V* ml. is needed to dissolve the ppt. almost completely so that a faint turbidity remains, then $1{\cdot}3V + 5$ ml. is added in excess. Then add 10 ml. 10% Na_2CO_3, pass air rapidly for 6 min., add 10 ml. 1:1 NH_4OH and 25 ml. 20% NH_4Cl followed by $AgNO_3$ soln. (5·792 g./l.) until a turbidity appears. Then add KCN reagent until clear (X ml.), add ($X - 0{\cdot}5$) ml. KCN reagent, make turbid with $AgNO_3$ soln., clear with KCN and continue alternate addn. to ascertain the end-point. If in all X ml. KCN and Y ml. $AgNO_3$ are required, then Co = $(X - Y) \times 0{\cdot}803$ mg.

NOTES. (1) Ni, Cu, etc. interfere and must be sepd. by extn. of the nitrosonaphthol complex.
(2) For gravimetry,[76] treat the neutral or slightly acidic soln. with KCN until the ppt. dissolves, evap. to dryness, add H_2O and some HNO_3, evap. to dryness, add hot H_2O and $AgNO_3$, filter, dry at 130°C (98–252°C) and weigh as $Ag_3[Co(CN)_6]$. Ni does not interfere.

(m) $NaNO_2$ is utilized to ppt. Co as $K_3Co(NO_2)_6$ which can then be detd. by redox titration.[77] Treat the neutral soln. with satd. $NaNO_2$, AcOH and K_2SO_4; after 12 hr., filter on a glass crucible and wash. Add a known excess of $K_2Cr_2O_7$, 10 ml. 1:1 H_2SO_4, 15 ml. of a soln. contg. 150 ml. H_2SO_4 and 150 ml. H_3PO_4/l., 2 drops 0·025M ferroin, dil. to 200 ml. with H_2O and titrate with 0·1N Fe^{2+}.

NOTE. Alternative finishes are available[1] (see also Chapter 54, p. 410). The ppt. can be treated with excess $KMnO_4$ soln. in H_2SO_4 medium, the excess being detd. with Fe^{2+} or $H_2S_2O_4$ soln. or iodometrically.

(n) Na-diethyldithiocarbamate provides a useful colorimetric procedure.[78] For 20–200 μg. Co in 100 ml. neutral soln., add 5% EDTA, make alk. with NH_4OH, add 6–20 ml. 0·1M $Ca(NO_3)_2$, boil, add 2 ml. 2% reagent, cool and ext. with 15 and 10 ml. portions of AcOEt; wash with H_2O and with H_2O contg. 1 ml. 2% $HgCl_2$, dil. with EtOH and measure the green color at 425 mμ. The error is ±5% for 40 μg. and ±1% for 140 μg. Co.

NOTE. Mo, W, V, U interfere. Interference by Cu or Ni is avoided by washing the ext. with 25% KCN or $HgCl_2$, that of Mn by addn. of $Na_4P_2O_7$ and those of Fe, Al, Cr, Ti by masking with tiron.

(o) β-Mercaptopropionic acid is used in soln. contg. NH_4OH and $Na_2S_2O_4$ for < 2·5 p.p.m. Co; Ni does not interfere.[79] Mercaptosuccinic acid is suitable[80] for 1–10 μg. Co/ml. with measurement at 520 mμ.

(p) Rubeanic acid may be used for Co at pH 9·5–10·5 with measurement at 530 mμ (see Chapter 18, p. 148). Diphenylrubeanic acid forms a complex which is measured at 410 mμ (see Chapter 22, p. 176).

(q) Tripyridyl is applied colorimetrically for 12·5–625 μg. Co.[9, 81] To 25 ml. soln. add 5 ml. 0·1% reagent (contg. the required amt. of HCl) and 1 drop 1:1 $HClO_4$, adjust to pH 2–11, dil. to 50 ml. with H_2O, add 20 ml. $PhNO_2$ and shake for at least 20 sec.; filter through glass wool and measure at 510 mμ (ϵ = 2900).

NOTES. (1) Interferences are (in p.p.m.) 1 p. VO_3^-, 2 p. Fe, 5 p. NO_2^-, $Cr_2O_7^{2-}$, 10 p. Ce^{4+}, 15 p. MoO_4^{2-}, 20 p. IO_4^-, CN^-, IO_3^-, 25 p. ZrO^{2+}, 30 p. Ni, 50 p. Zn, Ag, WO_4^{2-}, 100 p. Cu, UO_2^{2+}, 200 p. Cd, 300 p. Cr^{3+} or $S_2O_8^{2-}$ and 400 p. of many other ions.
(2) Several other procedures have been suggested in which Co-ammine complexes are formed. For colorimetric detn. with terosite, see Chapter 33, p. 256.
Pyridine and NH_4SCN allow gravimetric or titrimetric detns.[82, 83] For 0·1 g. Co in 50 ml. neutral soln., add pyridine until a ppt. appears, heat, dil. to 80 ml. with H_2O, add 0·5 g. NH_4SCN, boil, add 1 ml. pyridine, filter on a glass crucible and wash with the following solns.: (*i*) 855 ml. H_2O plus 130 ml. EtOH, 15 ml. pyridine and 1 g. NH_4SCN, (*ii*) 1 ml. pyridine and 10 ml. EtOH, (*iii*) 1 ml. pyridine and 10 ml. Et_2O. Dry in a vacuum desiccator below 45°C and weigh as $Co\,py_4(SCN)_2$ or dissolve the ppt. in HNO_3 and titrate by Volhard's method. Interferences are Cu, Cd, Ni, Mn, Zn; citric acid prevents interference of Fe or Cr. See also Chapter 23, p. 187 for the $Cr_2O_7^{2-}$ analog.
N_2H_4 and NH_4SCN allow pptn. of $Co(N_2H_4)_2(SCN)_2$ which can be dried at 110°C (< 79°C).[84] 10% K_2HgI_4 and NH_4OH are used to ppt. $[Co(NH_3)_6][HgI_3]_2$, which is dried below 35°C in a vacuum desiccator[85].

(r) $K_2S_2O_8$ in NH_4OH can be applied colorimetrically.[48] To 40 ml. neutral or slightly acidic soln., add 5 g. $(NH_4)_2HPO_4$, 5 g. NH_4Cl and excess reagent soln. (2 g. in 40 ml. 1:1 NH_4OH); heat to 80°C, add 2 g. $K_2S_2O_8$, boil for 1 min., cool, almost neutralize with HCl, dil. to 100 ml. with H_2O, filter after 12 hr. and compare the pink color. Ni (1 g.) does not interfere.

NOTES. (1) For 1 mg. Co in 10 ml. soln.,[9, 86] add 20 ml. 20% NH_4Cl, a small excess of NH_4OH and 0·6 g. Na_2O_2. H_2O_2 can be utilized at 500–530 mμ.[87]
(2) Diethylenetriamine is applied for 0·6–3·5 mg. Co/ml. in 10 ml. acidic (HNO_3) soln.[88] Add 2 ml. reagent, pass air for 15 min., filter if turbid, and measure the yellow Co complex at 460 mμ and the violet Ni complex at 850 mμ; a correction is required. Fe and Sn can be tolerated but Cu, Cr and Mn interfere.
Ethylenediamine forms a yellow-brown complex at pH 10 which can be measured at 365 mμ.[89]

(s) Miscellaneous colorimetric methods. A satd. soln. of $NaHCO_3$ contg. 0–8 p.p.m. Co forms a green color with 0·5 ml. H_2O_2, which can be measured at 260 mμ;[9, 90] Fe^{3+}, V^{5+}, U^{6+}, Cr, $Fe(CN)_6^{4-}$, Ti and Mo interfere. $NaBO_3$ and $NaHCO_3$ can be used for > 5 μg. Co/ml. with measurement at 645 mμ (Mori and Shibata[62]).

$K_2C_2O_4$ and PbO_2 allow detn. of 5–30 mg. Co in acidic (HCl) soln.[87, 91] Add 6N NaOH until a ppt. appears, add 2 ml. AcOH, 5 ml. 20% NH_4OAc, 10 ml. 1M $K_2C_2O_4$, 1 g PbO_2; dil. to 100 ml. with H_2O after 9 min., and measure the green complex at 605 mμ. Interferences are Cr, Cu, Fe, Mn, Ni, Ca.

$K_4Fe(CN)_6$ (2%) and 1% choline hydrochloride (freshly prepd.) can be used for 0·04–0·3 mg. Co in 3 ml. soln.;[92] add 1 ml. of each reagent, dil. to 6 ml. with H_2O and measure the green color with a S57 filter. For a titrimetric detn. with this reagent for 2·4–5·8 mg. Co in 50 ml. soln. at pH 6·0–6·4 (phenol red), add a few drops of M/20 $K_4Fe(CN)_6$, 0·02 ml. 0·1*N* I_2 and 2 ml. 0·2% starch and titrate until the blue-violet color becomes yellow-green; many elements interfere.[93]

$K_3Fe(CN)_6$ is applicable for 5–80 μg. Co/ml.[9, 94] in solns. contg. 5*N* NH_4OH, 1*N* $(NH_4)_3PO_4$, 2*N* $(NH_4)_3$-citrate, 0·5*N* $(NH_4)_2SO_4$ and 0·013*M* reagent; measure the red color at 500–540 mμ. WO_4^{2-}, CrO_4^{2-} and high concns. of electrolytes interfere.

Dimethylglyoxime in conjunction with *o*-tolidine allows detn. of < 0·25 mg. Co in 10 ml. neutral soln.[95] Add 0·5 ml. 1% dimethylglyoxime in EtOH and 0·2 ml. 1% *o*-tolidine and measure the orange-red color after 15 min. Ni does not interfere if the soln. is filtered; Al, Pb, Hg, Mn can be present.

Benzidine can replace *o*-tolidine;[96] 0·02–0·5 mg. Co can be detd. in 100 ml. soln. at pH 4·8–7·0 with measurement at 450 mμ. Dimethylglyoxime may also be applied titrimetrically with external indication with paper satd. with Ni^{2+} in NH_4OH;[97] W, Mo, V, Fe, Cr, Al can be tolerated, the last 3 if $P_2O_7^{4-}$ is added.

Diacetylmonoxime is suitable for 0·4–14 × 10^{-5}*M* Co soln.;[98] add 0·02*M* reagent, buffer of pH 8·75 (0·2*M* NH_4Cl and 1*M* NH_4OH) to give a vol. of 25 ml. and measure at 336 mμ. Interferences are Al, Fe, Cu, Ni.

α-Benzilmonoxime has been used for 0·2–5 × 10^{-5}*M* Co soln.;[98] add 0·02*M* reagent in iso-PrOH, dil. with buffer to 25 ml., add 25 ml. Me_2CO and measure at 380 mμ, or ext. with CCl_4 and measure at 386 mμ. Ni does not interfere.

α-Furilmonoxime has been suggested for < 200 μg. Co.[99] Adjust to pH 5–6 with NaOH, add 20 ml. satd. NaF and 5 ml. 10% reagent in pyridine and, after 10 min., 15–20 ml. 1:1 HCl. Ext. twice with 12 ml. $CHCl_3$, combine, add 1 ml. pyridine, dil. to 25 ml. with $CHCl_3$ and compare the reddish color. Al, Fe and 100 μg. Ni or Cu can be tolerated.

Cysteine hydrochloride may be applied for < 5 mg. Co;[100] evap. to dryness with 1·5 mg. H_2SO_4, cool, add 75 ml. buffer pH 7·5 and 10 mg. reagent and compare the brown color. Ni, Fe, Mn, Cu can be present.

NaCN and arsenophosphotungstic acid allow detn. of 0·25–0·5 mg. Co in 10 ml. neutral soln.;[101] 5 g. Ni can be tolerated. Add 3 ml. acid reagent (100 g. Na_2WO_4 in 100 ml., boiled for 20 min. with 50 g. As_2O_5, 25 ml. H_3PO_4 and 20 ml. HCl, cooled and dild. to 1 l. with H_2O) and 4 ml. NaCN soln. (50 g. in 1 l. H_2O contg. 2 ml. NH_4OH), stir, and compare the blue color after 2–10 min.

$NaHSO_3$ forms a yellow-red complex, $NaCo(NH_3)_4(SO_3)_2$, with 10 mg. Co in 80 ml. soln. after addn. of 5 ml. NH_4OH and 1 g. reagent; the soln. is dild. to 100 ml. before comparison.[102]

Up to 300 mg. Co can be detd. in 100 ml. dil. H_2SO_4 soln. by measuring at 505 mμ.[103] Interference of Fe or Cu is prevented by boiling with Na_3PO_4 and $Na_2S_2O_3$; 50 mg. W and 30 mg. Ni can be present but Mo, Cr, V and > 10% HCl interfere.

S-Methylthiourea sulfate forms a complex with Co in dil. NH_4OH soln. at pH 8·72–9·60 which can be measured at 495 mμ after 2 hr. (cf. Chapter 34, p. 267).

o-Mercaptoacetamido-*p*-nitrophenol is suitable for detn. of 1·2–30 mg. Co/l. at pH 10;[104] Ni does not interfere if KCN is added (see also Chapter 8, Section 2.6).

References

1. Hillebrand and Lundell, 322 (417); Scott and Furman, 305; Kimura, 242; Pigott, 166; Young, R. S., *Cobalt*, Reinhold, New York (1948).
2. Hoffman, J. I., *J. Research Natl. Bur. Standards*, **8**, 659 (1932).
3. Mashima, M., *Japan Analyst*, **5**, 319 (1956).
4. Kallmann, S., *Anal. Chem.*, **22**, 1519 (1950).
5. Broughton, D. B., *et al.*, *Anal. Chem.*, **19**, 72 (1947).
6. Welcher. **IV**, 137.
7. Bayliss, N. S. and Pickering, R. W., *Ind. Eng. Chem., Anal. Ed.*, **18**, 446 (1946).
8. Young, R. S. and Hall, A. J., *Anal. Chem.*, **18**, 262, 264 (1946).
9. Sandell, 274 ff.
10. Iwasaki, I. and Katsura, K., *Japan Analyst*, **2**, 305 (1953).
11. Welcher, **III**, 300, 303.
12. Evans, B. S., *Analyst*, **62**, 371 (1937).
13. A.S.T.M., 118 ff.
14. Hecht and Donau, 195.
15. Takagi, S. and Nagase, Y., *J. Pharm. Soc. Japan*, **56**, 574 (1936).
16. Torii, T., *J. Chem. Soc. Japan*, **76**, 328, 333, 675, 680, 707, 825 (1955); *Japan Analyst*, **4**, 177 (1955).
17. Pascual, J. N., *et al.*, *Anal. Chem.*, **25**, 1830 (1953).
18. Willard, H. H. and Kaufman, B., *Anal. Chem.*, **19**, 474 (1947).
19. Shipman, W. H., *et al.*, *Anal. Chem.*, **27**, 1240 (1955).
20. Shipman, W. H. and Lai, J. R., *Anal. Chem.*, **28**, 1151 (1956).
21. Saltzman, B. E., *Anal. Chem.*, **27**, 284 (1955).
22. Oka, Y. and Miyamoto, M., *Japan Analyst*, **2**, 322 (1953).
23. Boyland, E., *Analyst*, **71**, 230 (1946); also see Almond, H., *Anal. Chem.*, **25**, 166 (1953) (CCl_4 extn., shake with KCN; field analysis); Claassen, A. and Daamen, A., *Anal. Chim. Acta*, **12**, 547 (1955) (in metals); Baron, H., *Z. anal. Chem.*, **140**, 173 (1953) (toluene extn.).
24. Perry, M. H. and Serfass, E. J., *Anal. Chem.*, **22**, 565 (1950).
25. Gregory, R. L., *et al.*, *J. Assoc. Offic. Agr. Chemists*, **34**, 710 (1951).
26. Yoe, 173.
27. Nichol, W. E., *Can. J. Chem.*, **31**, 145 (1953); Oi, N., *J. Chem. Soc. Japan*, **76**, 413 (1955).
28. Brandt, W. W. and Wise, W. W., *Anal. Chem.*, **25**, 520 (1953); **26**, 693 (1954).

29. SHOME, S. C., *Anal. Chim. Acta*, **3**, 679 (1949).
30. WELCHER, **III**, 292 ff.
31. JEAN, M., *Anal. Chim. Acta*, **6**, 278 (1952).
32. GUHA-SIRCAR, S. S. and BHATTACHARJEE, S. C., *J. Indian Chem. Soc.*, **18**, 155 (1941).
33. DATTA, S. K., *J. Indian Chem. Soc.*, **34**, 238 (1957).
34. FAIRCHILD, J. G., *Ind. Eng. Chem., Anal. Ed.*, **11**, 326 (1939).
35. IKEDA, S., *Japan Analyst*, **2**, 218 (1953); also see HIRANO, S. and SUZUKI, M., *ibid.*, 316 (in steel).
36. LUNDQUIST, R., *et al.*, *Anal. Chem.*, **27**, 1731 (1955).
37. KINNUNEN, J., *et al.*, *Chemist Analyst*, **43**, 21 (1954).
38. PUTSCHÉ, H. M. and MALOOLY, W. F., *Anal. Chem.*, **19**, 236 (1947).
39. AFFSPRUNG, H. E., *et al.*, *Anal. Chem.*, **23**, 1680 (1951); PEPKOWITZ, L. P. and MARLEY, J. L., *ibid.*, **27**, 1330 (1955) (in steel); also see BANE, R. W. and GRIMES, W. R., *Natl. Nuclear Energy Ser., Div. VIII*, **1**, 429 (1950).
40. ZIEGLER, M., *et al.*, *Mikrochim. Acta*, 1526 (1956); *Angew. Chem.*, **28**, 436 (1956) (Bu_3NHOAc); SHINAGAWA, M., *et al.*, *Japan Analyst*, **5**, 29, 80 (1956) (tetraphenylphosphonium or triphenylsulfonium chloride).
41. ELLIS, K. W. and GIBSON, N. A., *Anal. Chim. Acta*, **9**, 275 (1953).
42. SUDO, E., *J. Chem. Soc. Japan*, **74**, 658 (1953); YOKOSUKA, S., *Japan Analyst*, **6**, 690 (1957) (in Ni).
43. SAKURABA, S., *Japan Analyst*, **3**, 417 (1954); **4**, 372 (1955).
44. PONOMAREV, V. D., *J. Gen. Chem. U.S.S.R.*, **15**, 151 (1954).
45. LAMURE, J., *Bull. soc. chim. France*, 661 (1946).
46. CLARKE, W. W., *Iron Age*, **153**, (23) 45 (1942).
47. TORRANCE, S., *Analyst*, **64**, 109 (1939); also see SALYER, D. and SWEET, T. R., *Anal. Chem.*, **28**, 61 (1956) (study using radioactive tracer).
48. SCHOELLER, W. R., *Analyst*, **69**, 8 (1944).
49. SHAKHTAKHTINSKIĬ, G. D. and TURCHINSKIĬ, M. L., *Trudy Azerbaidzhan. Ind. Inst. im M. Azizbekova*, No. 11, 64, 70 (1955).
50. SEN, D. C., *J. Indian Chem. Soc.*, **25**, 473 (1948); WELCHER, **III**, 284.
51. WELCHER, **II**, 197 ff.
52. HEIM, O., *Ind. Eng. Chem., Anal. Ed.*, **2**, 38 (1930).
53. GHOSH, S. P. and GHOSH, H. M., *J. Indian Chem. Soc.*, **33**, 899 (1956).
54. SCOTT and FURMAN, 310; WELCHER, **IV**, 104.
55. PILIPENKO, A. T., *et al.*, *Zhur. Anal. Khim.*, **10**, 299 (1955); *Ukrain. Khim. Zhur.*, **22**, 97 (1956).
56. WELCHER, **IV**, 135.
57. WELCHER, **III**, 410, 411; OKÁČ, A. and GRÁCOVÁ, L., *Chem. listy*, **47**, 367 (1953) (microdetn. with α-β-compd.).
58. MATSUMOTO, T., *Japan Analyst*, **3**, 307 (1954); KAWAGAKI, K., *J. Chem. Soc. Japan*, **77**, 1461 (1956).
59. YOKOSUKA, S., *Japan Analyst*, **6**, 690 (1957) (in Ni); also see IWASE, S. and SAI, K., *ibid.*, **1**, 145 (1952).
60. DIEHL, H. and BUTLER, J. P., *Anal. Chem.*, **27**, 777 (1955).
61. BAKER, L. C. W. and MCCUTCHEON, T. P., *Anal. Chem.*, **27**, 1625 (1955).
62. LAITINEN, H. A. and BURDETT, L. W., *Anal. Chem.*, **23**, 1268 (1951); also see MORI, M. and SHIBATA, M., *J. Chem. Soc. Japan*, **75**, 1044 (1954) ($NaBO_3$ oxidation).
63. YALMAN, R. G., *Anal. Chem.*, **28**, 91 (1956).
64. CARTLEDGE, G. H. and NICHOLS, P. M., *Ind. Eng. Chem., Anal. Ed.*, **13**, 20 (1941).
65. PŘIBIL, R. and ŠVESTKA, L., *Collection Czechoslov. Chem. Communs.*, **15**, 31 (1950); PŘIBIL, R. and MALIČKÝ, V., *ibid.*, **14**, 413 (1949).
66. HARRIS, W. F. and SWEET, TH. S., *Anal. Chem.*, **26**, 1648 (1954) (α-nitroso-β-naphthol sepn.); also see MUSIL, A. and PIETSCH, R., *Z. anal. Chem.*, **142**, 81 (1954) (atoxyl sepn.).
67. WAKAMATSU, S., *Japan Analyst*, **6**, 426 (1957).
68. GOTO, H. and KOBAYASHI, J., *J. Chem. Soc. Japan*, **75**, 964 (1954).
69. PŘIBIL, R. and MALÍK, J., *Chem. listy*, **45**, 237 (1951).
70. CHENG, K. L. and LOTT, D. F., *Anal. Chem.*, **28**, 462 (1956).
71. NIELSCH, W. and BÖLTZ, G., *Z. anal. Chem.*, **142**, 329 (1954).
72. ISHIMARU, S., *J. Chem. Soc. Japan*, **56**, 67 (1935).
73. WELCHER, **I**, 308.
74. MOELLER, T., *Ind. Eng. Chem., Anal. Ed.*, **15**, 346 (1943).
75. EVANS, B. S., *Analyst*, **62**, 363 (1937) (1 mg. Co in 5 g. steel); AGNEW, W. J., *ibid.*, **65**, 643 (1940).
76. SALTIKOVA, V. S., *Compt. rend. acad. sci., U.S.S.R.*, **49**, 34 (1945); NENADKEVICH, K. A. and SALTIKOVA, V. S., *Zhur. Anal. Khim.*, **1**, 123 (1946).
77. LÉONTOVICH, N. and BÉNARD, J., *Bull. soc. chim. France*, 157 (1946).
78. PŘIBIL, R., *et al.*, *Chem. listy*, **46**, 607 (1952); **47**, 842 (1953); BANE, R. W. and GRIMES, W. R., *Natl. Nuclear Energy Ser., Div. VIII*, **1**, 429 (1950).
79. LYONS, E., *Anal. Chem.*, **27**, 1813 (1955).
80. ROSELLI, M. E., *Anales direc. nacl. quím. (Buenos Aires)*, **7**, 35 (1954).
81. MILLER, R. R. and BRANDT, W. W., *Anal. Chem.*, **26**, 1968 (1954).
82. WELCHER, **III**, 9.
83. SPACU, G. and GHEORGHIU, C., *Commun. acad. rep. populare Romîne*, **5**, 385 (1955).
84. SARKAR, P. B. and DATTA-RAY, B. K., *J. Indian Chem. Soc.*, **7**, 251 (1931); TANII, K. and HASHIMOTO, J., *J. Chem. Soc. Japan*, **60**, 1119 (1939).
85. TAURINŠ, A., *Z. anal. Chem.*, **101**, 357 (1935).
86. HEINZ, W., *Z. anal. Chem.*, **78**, 432 (1929).
87. DLUGACH, R. E., *Nauch. Zapiski Dnepropetrovsk. Gosudarst. Univ.*, **43**, 67, 73 (1953).
88. WHEALY, R. D. and COLGATE, S. O., *Anal. Chem.*, **28**, 1897 (1956).
89. MICHAL, J. and DOLEŽAL, J., *Chem. listy*, **50**, 911 (1956).
90. TELEP, G. and BOLTZ, D. F., *Anal. Chem.*, **24**, 945 (1952).
91. MEHLIG, J. P. and ZEAGAS, G. J., *Chemist Analyst*, **40**, 76 (1951).
92. WELCHER, **II**, 502.
93. FUJITA, Y., *J. Chem. Soc. Japan*, **75**, 1235 (1954).
94. OKA, Y. and AYUZAWA, S., *Kinzoku-Gakkai-Shi*, **18**, 224 (1954) (in steel).
95. WELCHER, **III**, 199.
96. LEE, F. T. and DIEHL, H., *Proc. Iowa Acad. Sci.*, **57**, 187 (1950); POLYA, J. B. and WILSON, B., *Australian J. Sci.*, **13**, 26 (1950).

97. BABKO, A. K. and KOROTUN, M. V., *Zhur. Anal. Khim.*, **10**, 100 (1955).
98. CALZOLARI, C. and DONDA, A., *Ann. chim.*, **44**, 280 (1954).
99. MARTÍNEK, J. and HOVORKA, V., *Chem. listy*, **50**, 1450 (1956).
100. WELCHER, **IV**, 121.
101. LIEBERSON, A., *J. Am. Chem. Soc.*, **52**, 464 (1930).
102. HEINZ, W., *Z. anal. Chem.*, **78**, 434 (1929).
103. GAGNON, J., *Chemist Analyst*, **43**, 15 (1954).
104. BUSCARÓNS, F. and ARTIGAS, J., *Anales real soc. españ. fís. y quím. (Madrid)*, **48B**, 140 (1952).

36

ZINC

The principal sources for this chapter are given in refs. 1 and 2. As a general precaution in the determination of zinc, contamination from glassware or from sieves must be checked.

Attack

(a) Minerals. Treat with HCl, HCl and HNO_3 or HNO_3; fuse the residue with Na_2CO_3 and dissolve in HCl or HNO_3.

(b) Alloys. Treat with HNO_3, aqua regia or H_2SO_4, etc.

Separation

H_2S allows sepn. of Zn from group II metals in $2N$ H_2SO_4 media if the ppt. is filtered immediately, or in $9N$ H_2SO_4 media if the soln. is allowed to stand. Zn may coppt. with Cu or Cd unless 0·05 ml. crotonaldehyde is added.[3] $Na_2S_2O_3$ seps. Zn from Cu (see p. 172.) In formic acid soln. H_2S allows sepn. of Zn, Ga, In, Tl from Mn, Ni, Co, Fe, V, W, Al and group IV metals (see under Determination, p. 278). With this procedure Zn can be collected with Cu or Hg in slightly acidic soln. In very dil. AcOH solns. contg. KCN, H_2S seps. Zn from large amts. of Ni.[4] Sepn. from Ni and Co is obtained as follows:[5] add NaOH to the dil. H_2SO_4 soln. until a ppt. appears, then add 6–8 g. $(NH_4)_2SO_4$, dil. to 200–300 ml. with H_2O, add 0·2 ml. acrolein soln. (4 ml. acrolein, 10 mg. hydroquinone and 1 drop HCl in 100 ml.), pass H_2S for 30 min., add 10 ml. 0·02% gelatin, leave for 20 min. and filter. In this method the appearance of a white turbidity can be ignored; Ni and Co can be detd. in the filtrate after acid addn. and evapn. to 1/3 of the initial vol.

$(NH_4)_2S$ allows sepn. of Zn from group IV and V metals; if $(NH_4)_2$-tartrate is also added, Zn is sepd. from Al, Ti, Zr, Nb, etc. Na_2S or K_2S seps. Zn from Sn, Sb, As; the ppt. formed with Zn alone in alk. media tends to pass through the filter.

Small amts. of Zn can be sepd. from Fe, Al, etc. by addn. of excess NH_4OH and NH_4Cl and eventual repptn.; SiO_2 interferes. If Br_2 is also added to the pptn. mixt., Zn is sepd. from Mn. In both these cases, if much Cr or Ca is present, $Zn(CrO_2)_2$ or $CaH_2Zn_2O_4 \cdot 4H_2O$ may ppt. When 84·3–18·71% Zn is present, the loss with $Fe(OH)_3$ is 7–11·1%; with 90·68–12·20% Zn, the loss with $Cr(OH)_3$ is 4·6–7·6%.[6]

Treatment with $BaCO_3$ or NaOAc, etc. seps. Zn from Fe, In, etc. Zn and Cu are sepd. from Fe, Al, Mn, Pb, Cd with $(NH_4)_2CO_3$. Cupferron seps. Zn from Fe, Ti, Zr, V, Sn.

Complete sepn. from Cu, Pb, As, Sb, Bi, etc. and incomplete sepn. from Cd is possible by boiling with Al in 0·5–1% HCl or H_2SO_4 media. Treatment with Cu in soln. contg. KCN and tartrate allows sepn. from Cd.[7] Electrolysis allows sepn. of Zn from Cu.

Extn. with ether seps. Zn from Fe.

Digestion with HNO_3 allows sepn. from Sn, while evapn. with HBr seps. Zn from Sn and Sb. Treatment with KI seps. Zn from Tl.

Dimethylglyoxime allows sepn. from Ni, and α-nitroso-β-naphthol from Co.

Extn. with $CHCl_3$ of the soln. contg. 20 mg. Na-diethyldithiocarbamate in 50 ml. at pH 8·8–9·0 seps. Zn from Pb, Cd, Tl. Sepn. from Pb, Cu, Ag, Cd, Hg, Ni, Co, Bi is done by extn. with diethylammonium diethyldithiocarbamate in CCl_4 from soln. at pH 7·5–8·0 followed by shaking with 10% NaOH contg. citrate.

Methyldioctylamine (8% w/v) or tribenzylamine (5%) in $CHCl_3$ seps. Zn (and partly Fe) from Co, Ni and, partly, Cu and Cr on extn. with 8 ml. reagent from 4 ml. of 3–4N HCl soln. (see Chapter 16, p. 138).

For extn. of thiocyanate complexes, see p. 184.

Zn can be sepd. from Fe, Al, etc. by extn. with dithizone in CCl_4 from soln. at pH 8·3 contg. NH_4OH and citrate. Zn is stripped completely into the aq. phase on shaking the ext. with 0·01–0·02N HCl; it is thus sepd. from Cu and Co but is accompanied by Bi, Pb, Cd, Ni; this procedure of stripping has not been verified for the $CHCl_3$ ext. If fairly large amts. of Ag, Cu and Hg are present, they should be removed previously from 0·1N mineral acid soln. Extn. is complete from soln. at below pH 10·5 contg. diethyldithiocarbamate if di-β-naphthylthiocarbazone is used; shaking with 0·2N HCl allows sepn. from Cu, Ni and Co.

Treatment of 2–3M HCl solns. with Amberlite IRA-400 resin seps. Zn from Al, Mg, Cu, Co, Ni, Mn, Cr,

Fe, Th, Zr, Ti, U, Be, Ca (see Chapter 13, p. 111) $(NH_4)_2Hg(SCN)_4$ can be used to conc. Zn.

Heating the sample with carbon black at 1100°C in a stream of H_2 seps. Zn from other elements.[8]

Determination

The best method consists of pptn. as sulfide from formic acid soln. Quinaldic acid is a good reagent for mg. amts. of Zn and oxine is also satisfactory. For smaller amts. dithizone or zincon provide the best methods. Titration with EDTA is satisfactory if combined with an ion exchange sepn.

(a) H_2S is generally used gravimetrically but titrimetric and nephelometric methods are also possible.[9, 10] For gravimetric detn. of < 0·2 g. Zn, place the acidic soln. in an Erlenmeyer flask, add NH_4OH until a ppt. appears, add 25 ml. 20% citric acid and neutralize to methyl orange with NH_4OH. Add 25 ml. formic acid mixture (200 ml. 23·6*N* HCOOH, 250 g. $(NH_4)_2SO_4$ and 30 ml. 15*N* NH_4ON/l.), dil. to 200 ml. with H_2O (pH 2–3), heat the soln. and pass H_2S. Use a 2-hole stopper carrying an outlet tube flush with the stopper and an inlet tube extending almost to the liquid. Displace air, remove from the heat, close the outlet tube and allow to cool for 20–40 min. with occasional shaking. Filter on paper, wash with H_2S in 1*N* HCOOH, transfer to a porcelain crucible, heat slowly, ash below 500°C, then heat at 950–1000°C and weigh as ZnO.

NOTES. (1) Interferences are group II metals, Ga, In and Tl. Sepn. from Fe and Ni in the cold has been studied with radioisotopes.[11] No interference arises from Fe, Ni, Mn, V, Al or group IV metals or from small amts. of Co. The method has been applied to Al and its alloys and to Ag solders.[12]

When Fe, Ni or Co is present, add excess HCOOH and reppt.; complete sepn. from Co is difficult. Gelatin, agar-agar, $(NH_4)_2SO_4$ and NH_4SCN promote sepn. and coagulation of the ppt. Acrolein can also serve this purpose (see also p. 277).

(2) Many acids have been suggested for the control of pH: 0·01*N* H_2SO_4 has been used in the analysis of brasses, etc.;[12] AcOH, $CH_2ClCOOH$, CCl_3COOH, $H_2C_2O_4$, succinic acid, benzenesulfonic acid, HSCN, etc. have also been used.[10, 13] Citric acid solns. have been proposed;[14] treat the soln. with NH_4OH until a ppt. appears, add 25 ml. 20% citric acid, neutralize with NH_4OH, add 25 ml. 20% $(NH_4)_2SO_4$ and 20–25 ml. citric acid, dil. to 200 ml. with H_2O, pass H_2S, etc.

(3) Various other weighing forms are possible.[10] If the ZnS ppt. is treated with HCl and H_2SO_4 and heated at 500°C (300–788°C), it can be weighed as $ZnSO_4$, the heating being repeated after addn. of a few drops of H_2O. ZnS can be ignited to ZnO which is then distilled in H_2 and the vol. of Zn is detd. under the microscope.[15] The ZnS ppt. may also be heated to redness with S in H_2 and weighed as ZnS.

(4) For a titrimetric finish,[10] suspend the ZnS ppt. in H_2O, add excess I_2 in HCl and back-titrate with $Na_2S_2O_3$ (cf. Chapter 23, p. 185 and Chapter 58, p. 437). Alternatively, titrate the neutral Zn soln. with 0·1*N* Na_2S using a potentiometric end-point, or visually with Fe^{2+} or methyl red indicator.[10, 16] NH_4OH and Fe, etc. interfere with the latter method, but Cu, Ag, Mn do not, nor do Co and Ni if KCN is added.

(5) For nephelometric detn. see ref. 10.

(b) Na-quinaldate is normally used gravimetrically but titrimetric and colorimetric detns. are also possible. For < 0·1 g. Zn in 200 ml. soln.[17] contg. 2–3 ml. AcOH (pH 5·2–5·6 adjusted to methyl red–methylene blue), add a slight excess of 3·5% reagent to the hot soln., reheat, filter on a glass crucible, wash with warm H_2O, dry at 125°C and weigh as $Zn(C_{10}H_6O_2N)_2 \cdot H_2O$. For amperometric titration, cf. Chapter 22, p. 179.

NOTES. (1) Interference of Fe^{3+}, Cr^{3+}, Ti, U, Be is prevented by addn. of 3 g. NH_4Cl and 5 g. NaK-tartrate. That of Cu is prevented by addn. of 2–5 ml. dil. AcOH to the neutral soln. followed by 4–8 g. thiourea, 4–8 g. $NaHSO_3$ and H_2O to give a vol. of 200–300 ml. before proceeding as above. The treatment if Ag or Hg is present is similar except that $NaHSO_3$ is not added. Alternatively, when Cu, Ag or Hg is present, treat the neutral soln. with 8 g. KI, 4–8 g. $NaHSO_3$, 4–8 g. thiourea, etc. For Cd interference, see Shennan.[17] Al and group IV metals can be present, as can Mn and PO_4^{3-} if 6 ml. AcOH is added.

(2) Colorimetric methods have been proposed but neither is very satisfactory. With Na-quinaldate,[18] treat the soln. contg. 10–100 μg. Zn in 100 ml. with 0·2 g. tartaric acid, 1 ml. 1% resorcinol in EtOH, adjust to pH 9 with NH_4OH, ext. with 10 ml. 0·1% dithizone in $CHCl_3$, strip with 0·1*N* HCl and sep. heavy metals with H_2S after addn. of some Cu. Destroy org. compds. with HNO_3 and $KClO_3$, evap. with HNO_3, ppt. with the reagent, centrifuge and wash with Me_2CO 3 times. Dry at 100°C, boil with 2 ml. AcOH, transfer to a 50 ml. Pyrex flask, add 1 g. phthalic anhydride and 1·5 g. Zn powder, boil for 20 min. under reflux, decant, wash with Me_2CO–EtOH (1:1), combine, cool, dil. to a definite vol. and compare the yellow color. Cd, Ni and Co interfere.

5-Nitroquinaldic acid may be used for 0·05–1 mg. Zn in 5–10 ml. acidic (HCl) soln.[10, 19] Make alk. to methyl red with 3*N* NH_4OH, adjust to pH 2–8 with AcOH, boil, add a slight excess of reagent (0·75 g. in 100 ml. EtOH) and place on a steam-bath for 30 min. Filter on an asbestos pad, wash with hot H_2O, dissolve in 5 ml. $SnCl_2$ soln. (12·5 g. in 100 ml. HCl dild. to 500 ml. with H_2O and stored over Sn) and compare the orange color.

(c) EDTA provides an excellent titrimetric procedure[20] with eriochrome black T (mixed 1:500 with NaCl) as indicator. Treat the dil. HCl soln. with 2 ml. 50% citric acid and 10 ml. NH_4OH, add indicator and titrate at 30°C to the color change from red to dark violet.

Other indicators which have been applied are pyrocatechol violet (see Chapter 34, p. 266), zincon[21] and 3,3′-dimethylnaphthidine[22] in presence of $Fe(CN)_6^{3-}$ and $Fe(CN)_6^{4-}$. Photometric titration with eriochrome black T indicator has also been used.[23]

If the soln. is treated with KCN and HCHO before titration, Ni and Cu do not interfere; Fe can be present, if ascorbic acid is also added.[24] The $ZnHg(SCN)_4$ ppt. can be titrated after addn. of KI or KCN.[25]

(d) Dithizone is applied colorimetrically, either by a mixed color method which can be used photometrically or visually, or by a monocolor method which is used with a Duboscq colorimeter.

(*i*) Mixed color method (photometric). For < 5 μg. Zn in 10 ml. 0·01–0·03*N* HCl soln.,[26, 27] add 5 ml. buffer (equal vols. of 2*N* AcOH and 2*N* NaOAc shaken with 0·005 or 0·01% reagent and filtered through dry paper), 1·00 ml. 25% $Na_2S_2O_3$, 5·0 ml. 0·001% w/v dithizone in CCl_4, shake for 2 min. and measure at 520–540 mμ or at 620 mμ.

(*ii*) Mixed color method (visual). In a preliminary test, treat 1–2 ml. soln. with 2–3 ml. H_2O, acetate buffer (pH 4·5–4·75), 5 drops $Na_2S_2O_3$ and 5 ml. reagent; 1 μg. Zn forms a blue color, 2 μg. gives red-violet, 3 μg. violet and 4–5 μg. violet-red. For the actual comparison, treat the soln. contg. 2–4 μg. Zn with acetate buffer, 1·00 ml. $Na_2S_2O_3$, 5·0 ml. reagent, shake for 2 min. and compare the colors.

NOTES. (1) Cu interferes in amts. above twice that of Zn; up to 200 μg. Fe, Pb, Ni, Co, Bi, Cd can be tolerated.
(2) Dithizone can also be dissolved in methyl cellosolve.[28] For 3 μg. Zn in 1·5 ml. soln., add dil. HCl or NH_4OH to give pH 4 (thymol blue paper) and then add 0·2 ml. Na_3-citrate (25% citric acid adjusted to pH 4 with NaOH). Add 2 ml. buffer (1730 g. $Na_2S_2O_3$, 298 g. NaOAc and 20 g. KCN in 2 l. H_2O adjusted to pH 5·5 with AcOH, dild. to 4 l. with H_2O, extd. with dithizone in CCl_4 and adjusted to pH 4 with AcOH just before use). Then dil. to 4 ml. with H_2O, add 3·5 ml. methyl cellosolve, cool, add 0·5 ml. 0·01% dithizone in methyl cellosolve and measure in a 5 cm. cell at 525 mμ. Up to 1 p.p.m. Ni or Co, 3 p. Cd or Ag, 4 p. Cu or Hg^{2+}, 5 p. Bi, 10 p. Sn^{2+}, 30 p. Al, 50 p. Fe^{3+} or Hg^{+} and 40 p. Mn can be tolerated.

(*iii*) Monocolor method. For 10–30 μg. Zn in 10 ml. soln. (5–60 μg. Zn is the widest range),[29] add 1 ml. 7% cuprethol and buffer (2*M* AcOH and 2*M* NaOAc adjusted to pH 4·5 and extd. with 0·001% reagent in CCl_4). Adjust to pH 5·5–6·0 using methyl red paper, ext. with 5 ml. portions of 0·001% dithizone in CCl_4 until no color change occurs, and combine the exts. Wash with 0·05% Na_2S until no color is left in the aq. phase, dil. to a definite vol. and measure in a colorimeter. The error is ±2%.

NOTES. (1) No interference arises from 100 μg. Hg, 300 μg. Pb, 400 μg. Cu, 700 μg. Ag, 1 mg. Bi or Co and 2 mg. Cd.
(2) Di-β-naphthylthiocarbazone is generally better than dithizone but Cd interferes; for details, see ref. 26.

(e) Oxine acetate can be applied gravimetrically, titrimetrically or colorimetrically.[10, 30] For < 50 mg. Zn in 50 ml. neutral or slightly acidic soln., add 1–5 g. NaOAc, AcOH to give a 2–3% soln. (pH 4·6–5·5), heat to 60°C, add 2% reagent and boil; filter on a glass crucible (G3), wash with warm H_2O, dry at 105–125°C (< 65°C) and weigh as $Zn(C_9H_6ON)_2 \cdot 1\frac{1}{2}H_2O$; alternatively, dry at 195–230°C (127–284°C) and weigh as the anhydrous salt. For a titrimetric finish, dissolve the ppt. in HCl and titrate with 0·1*N* $KBrO_3$–KBr soln.

NOTES. (1) Interference of Al, Cr, Fe, Sb, As, Bi, Co, Ni and, partly, Mn can be prevented by addn. of 2–5 g. tartaric acid, neutralization with NaOH, addn. of 10–15 ml. 2*N* NaOH and reagent, etc. If Co, Ni or Mn is present, repptn. is necessary. No interference arises from Pb, group IV metals, Mg, PO_4^{3-} or tartrate. Thiourea can be added to sep. Zn from Cu.[31]
(2) 1–3 mg. Zn can be detd. with an error of ±5 μg.[32] The theoretical factor for the hydrated ppt. is 0·1718 and that for the anhydrous ppt. is 0·1849; after the ppt. has been dried at 125°C, a factor of 0·1861 should be applied.[11]
(3) The detn. from NaOH soln. contg. Na_2-tartrate is said to be inaccurate[33] but titrimetric detn. is possible by means of 2% quinosol.[34]
(4) Titrimetric finishes other than the bromometric one are available. Titration of the ppt. with $KMnO_4$ is suitable for <5 mg. Zn.[35] Amperometric[35] and other[10] procedures have also been suggested.
(5) Several colorimetric methods are possible. For 8–80 μg. Zn oxinate, Folin–Denis reagent may be utilized.[10, 36] For 5–10 μg. Zn oxinate, add 1·2*N* HCl, sulfanilic acid, $NaNO_2$ and NH_4OH and measure the red-brown color.[37] The fluorescence of 1–10 p.p.m. Zn oxinate can be measured.[26, 36]

Reagents which are analogous to oxine have been proposed. 8-Hydroxyquinaldine (5 g. in 12 g. AcOH dild. to 100 ml. with H_2O) is used in slightly acidic soln.[36, 38] Add 1 g. $(NH_4)_2$-tartrate and 2 ml. reagent for each 10 mg. Zn and dil. to 200 ml. with H_2O. Heat to 60–80°C, add 1:5 NH_4OH until the ppt. almost disappears, adjust to pH > 5·5 with 45 ml. 2*N* NH_4OAc added dropwise and leave for at least 10–20 min. Filter on a Gooch crucible, wash with hot H_2O, dry at 130–140°C (100–220°C) and weigh as $Zn(C_{10}H_8NO)_2$. Alternatively, pass 30 ml. hot 1:3 HCl through the filter, wash with this acid and H_2O, add 3 g. KBr, dil. to 150 ml. with H_2O, add methyl red and titrate with 0·1*N* $KBrO_3$, etc. Al and Mg can be tolerated.

4-Hydroxybenzothiazole (4% in MeOH) is suitable for 15–20 mg. Zn in 20 ml. soln.[36] Add 1 g. NaOAc and reagent, filter, wash with 10 ml. hot H_2O, dissolve in warm 10% HCl, and titrate with 0·1*N* $KBrO_3$ after addn. of 0·5 g. KBr.

Iodooxine can be applied colorimetrically[39] for 0·1–1 μg. Zn in soln. of pH 7·5; add 3 ml. reagent, dil. to 100 ml. with H_2O and measure after 15 min.

8-Hydroxyquinoline-azo-*p*-nitrobenzoic acid has been used gravimetrically.[40]

(f) Salicylaldoxime may be used gravimetrically.[41] To 50 ml. soln. contg. < 100 mg. Zn, add 60 ml. reagent (1 g. in 5 ml. EtOH dild. to 100 ml. with H_2O), adjust to pH 8·1–8·5 with NH_4OH, digest at 90–100°C for 10 min., filter on a glass crucible, wash with 20% EtOH, dry at 110°C and weigh as $ZnC_7H_6NO_2$. A 1:2 complex is formed at pH 6·8 and a 1:1 complex at pH 8·5; a mixt. is pptd. at intermediate pH values but this is converted to the 1:1 complex by heating. The 1:2

complex obtained by pptn. from NaOH soln. at pH 7·4–8·2 and at room temp. can also be weighed.[42]

(g) Na-anthranilate is suitable[10, 43] for gravimetric or titrimetric detn. of < 0·1 g. Zn in 150 ml. acetate buffered soln. at pH 5·5–7·0. Add 20–25 ml. 3% reagent (a small excess), filter on a glass crucible after 20 min., wash with 0·15% reagent and with EtOH, dry at 105–110°C and weigh as $Zn(C_7H_6O_2N)_2$ or dissolve the ppt. and titrate with $KBrO_3$–KBr soln. There is doubt about the drying temp.

NOTES. (1) Ni, Co, Cd, Mn, Cu interfere; 0·3 g. Na_2-tartrate prevents Sn interference. Group IV metals can be tolerated. (2) The stoichiometric factor is 0·1937, but on pptn. from hot soln. the empirical factor is 0·1951 and from cold soln. 0·1924.[11] A large excess of reagent should always be avoided.
(3) 5-Bromo-2-aminobenzoic acid forms a complex with Zn which can be dried below 123°C and weighed.[44]

(h) $(NH_4)_2HPO_4$ is predominantly used for gravimetric detn. but titrimetry and colorimetry are also possible. For detn. of 0·1–0·2 g. Zn in 200 ml. acidic (to methyl orange) soln.,[1, 11, 45] add 2 g. NH_4Cl for each 0·1 g. Zn and boil; add a 10–15-fold excess of reagent (dissolve 15 g. in H_2O, make just alk. to phenolphthalein with NH_4OH and dil. to 140 ml. with H_2O) and place on a steam-bath until the ppt. settles. Allow to cool for 2–4 hr., filter on a Gooch crucible, wash with 1% reagent and with 50% EtOH, dry at 130–170°C and weigh as $ZnNH_4PO_4$, or ignite above 550°C and weigh as $Zn_2P_2O_7$.

NOTES. (1) Cd, Bi, etc. interfere, as do large amts. of group V metals and NO_3^-. Cu does not interfere if tartrate is added, and some Ni can be present.
(2) The optimum pH is 6·4–6·9.[46] The ppt. is sol. in both acids and alkalies; it also adheres to the vessel wall and this amt. must be dissolved in AcOH, after being washed, and ignited in a tared crucible. Some Zn (<0·3 mg. as phosphate) passes into the filtrate. If filter paper is used for the filtration, the ppt. and paper must be ignited separately. Results are low if the ignition temp. is too high.[47]
Ni can be previously detd. as dimethylglyoxime; the filtrate is then treated with Br_2 water before proceeding as above.
(3) The ppt. can be treated with $HClO_4$ and $BiClO_4$, etc., for a titrimetric finish (see Chapter 23, p. 186). Other titrimetric finishes are also available.[10]
(4) A colorimetric procedure based on reaction with $(NH_4)_2HPO_4$ has been suggested.[48]
(5) In a similar method, Zn is pptd. as the arsenate which can be detd. iodometrically.[10]

(i) Electrodeposition is suitable for the detn. of 0·01–0·2 g. Zn in 15 ml. acidic soln.[9, 10, 49] Add 5*N* NaOH until a ppt. appears, clear the soln. with AcOH and dil. to 100 ml. with H_2O; add 15 g. Na_3-citrate, warm and, if necessary, make alk. to methyl red with NaOH. Add 15 ml. Me_2CO, insert a Pt anode and Pt gauze plated with Cu as cathode, stir and electrolyze for 1·5 hr. at 6 v. Wash with H_2O and EtOH, dry at 110°C for 1 min. and weigh as Zn.

(j) $K_2[Hg(SCN)_4]$ can be utilized in gravimetric, titrimetric and colorimetric detns. of Zn.[9, 10, 50] For gravimetric detn. of < 0·05 g. Zn in 100 ml. soln. contg. less than 1 ml. HNO_3 or HCl, or less than 0·5 ml. H_2SO_4, add 30 ml. reagent soln. (27·1 g. $HgCl_2$ and 42·6 g. KSCN/l.), filter on a glass crucible after 1 hr., wash with a soln. contg. 20 ml. reagent/l, dry at 105°C (50–270°C) and weigh as $Zn[Hg(SCN)_4]$. For a titrimetric finish, dissolve in dil. HNO_3 and titrate with $AgNO_3$ or $Hg(NO_3)_2$ (Volhard method), or dissolve in HCl and titrate with KIO_3.

NOTES. (1) Interferences are Cu, Co, Ni, Fe^{2+}, Mn, Bi, Cd, halides. Ag and Hg interfere in the gravimetric, but not in the titrimetric method. No interference arises from Fe^{3+}, Pb, As, Sb, Sn^{4+}, Al, Ca, etc. The above procedure has been applied to detn. of Zn in Al and its alloys.[12]
(2) For the colorimetric method $(NH_4)_2Hg(SCN)_4$ (8·0 g. $HgCl_2$ and 9·0 g. NH_4SCN in 100 ml. H_2O, filtered before use) is used as reagent[51] with $CuSO_4$ (0·2 g. in 100 ml. H_2O contg. a drop of H_2SO_4). For 0·1–3 mg. Zn in 5 ml. soln. add 1 drop satd. NaOAc soln., 1 drop $CuSO_4$ soln. and 0·5 ml. reagent and compare the color after 80 min. Cu and Fe interfere but 2 g. Cd and Pb, Mn, Cr, Al do not.

(k) Miscellaneous gravimetric methods. Picrolonic acid (15 ml. 0·01*N*) can be used[52] to ppt. 10 ml. 0·01*N* $ZnSO_4$ at 50°C; the ppt. is filtered after 2 hr. on a glass crucible, washed and dried at 105°C. Fe, Al, Ti, Cr can be tolerated.

Mercaptobenzothiazole ppts. Zn at pH 5–6, the $Zn(C_7H_4NS_2)_2$ being dried at 115–120°C.[53] Diallyldithiocarbamidohydrazine ppts. Zn at pH 7·5–8·6 (see Chapter 22, p. 180). For the use of morpholine, see Chapter 22, p. 179.

$H_2C_2O_4$ may be utilized for detn. of Zn.[10, 54] Make the soln. slightly acidic in H_2SO_4, add an equal vol. of AcOH, heat to boiling and add 0·5*M* reagent; place on a steam-bath for 1 hr., allow to cool, adjust to pH 3·1–4·4 (methyl orange) with dil. NH_4OH and leave for 12 hr. Filter on a glass crucible, wash with 50% EtOH, dry at 105°C and weigh as $ZnC_2O_4{\cdot}2H_2O$, or dissolve the ppt. in dil. H_2SO_4 and titrate with $KMnO_4$ soln. Large amts. of Na, K, etc. interfere. Ethyl oxalate can be used[11, 55] if the ppt. is titrated with $KMnO_4$.

The ppt. formed with Na_2CO_3 can be ignited to ZnO, or weighed as $5ZnO{\cdot}2CO_2$ after drying at 370–879°C.[10]

Cyanamide can be used to ppt. < 0·1 g. Zn.[10] Add 1–2 g. NH_4OAc, clear the soln. with NH_4OH, dil. and add 5% reagent contg. some drops of AcOH. Digest the soln., filter, wash with dil. NH_4OH soln. and ignite.

Satd. $Ca(OH)_2$ can be used to conc. 1 mg. Zn in 500 ml. soln.[10] Add 50 ml. reagent, followed by NH_4OH to make its concn. 10–15% by vol.; boil, cool, filter and treat the ppt. with HCl. Evap. the soln., add H_2O, $(NH_4)_2C_2O_4$ and NH_4OH, filter, treat the filtrate with H_2SO_4 and finally weigh as $ZnSO_4$.

(l) $K_4Fe(CN)_6$ is generally applied titrimetrically.[10, 56] For 0·25–0·35 g. Zn in 25 ml. soln. contg. 10 ml. 4*N* H_2SO_4 and 1–5 g. $(NH_4)_2SO_4$, add 2 drops 1% diphenylamine indicator in H_2SO_4, heat to 60°C and titrate with M/40 $K_4Fe(CN)_6$ (contg. 150 mg. $K_3Fe(CN)_6$/l. and standardized against ZnO) to the color change to olive-green. Back-titration is needed for smaller amts. of Zn. Several other indicators have been proposed. Even 0·001*M* Zn solns. can be titrated with 3,3′-dimethylnaphthidine as indicator.[57] Diphenylcarbazone,[58] diphenylbenzidine,[12, 59] *o*-dianisidine,[60] dithizone[61] and $FeSO_4 + K_3Fe(CN)_6$[12] have been used internally, while $UO_2(OAc)_2$[1, 12] and $(NH_4)_2MoO_4$[62] may be applied externally. Methyl orange can be used as an adsorption indicator.[63] For coulometric titration, see ref. 64, and for potentiometric, see ref. 56.

NOTES. (1) Interferences are NO_3^-, oxidants, heavy metals, Cu, Ni, Cd, Mn, large amts. of Al; KF prevents Fe interference.

(2) Alternative procedures have been suggested. Excess of $K_4Fe(CN)_6$ can be back-titrated[65] with Ce^{4+} or with $K_2Cr_2O_7$ in presence of benzidine indicator.[66] Iodometric titration is also possible:[67, 68] treat 50 ml. sample soln. which is 1*N* in HCl, with 100 ml. H_2O, 2 g. KCl, 20 ml. 0·2*M* $K_3Fe(CN)_6$ and, after 3 min., add 10 ml. 0·5*M* $Ba(OAc)_2$, 5–10 drops 0·5*M* Na_2SO_4 and 2 ml. 1*N* KI and titrate with 0·05*N* $Na_2S_2O_3$. This method can be used for as little as 0·3 mg. Zn.[59]

(3) Nephelometric detn. of Zn with $K_4Fe(CN)_6$ has been suggested[10, 69] and applied to detn. of Zn in Pb.[12]

(4) For colorimetric detns. $K_3Fe(CN)_6$ is used with diethylaniline, *p*-aminophenol[70] or *o*- or *p*-toluidine.[71]

(m) KCN can be used in presence of AgI indicator.[10]

(n) Zincon provides a useful colorimetric method[72] for 25–100 μg. Zn in 100 ml. neutral soln. Add 10 ml. Clark and Lubs buffer pH 9·0 and 3 ml. reagent (0·130 g. in 2 ml. 1*M* NaOH dild. to 100 ml. with H_2O), dil. to 50 ml. with H_2O and measure at 620 mμ.

NOTE. Interference of Al, Be, Bi, Cd, Co, Cr, Fe, Mn, Mo, Ni, Ti can be avoided by previous sepn. on Dowex 1 resin (see Chapter 13, Section 2.2). Cu and Zn can be detd. simultaneously by the above procedure with measurement at 600 mμ; Cu alone is detd. at 600 mμ if Clark and Lubs buffer pH 5·2 is used.

(o) Salicylaldehyde acetylhydrazone is suitable for fluorimetric detn. of 5–500 μg. Zn.[73] Add 10 ml. 0·1*M* acetate buffer, 10 ml. EtOH, 0·5 ml. 0·01*M* reagent and dil. to 50 ml. with H_2O before measuring the fluorescence. Interferences of Al and Fe can be prevented by NaF addn.

(p) NH_4SCN and rhodamine B permit the colorimetric detn. of 2–20 μg. Zn.[74] Add 0·5 ml. 20% NH_4SCN, 0·5 ml. buffer (13% NaOAc adjusted to pH 5 with AcOH and extd. with dithizone), 0·5 ml. 20% $Na_2S_2O_3$, dil. to 5 ml. with H_2O and add 1 ml. 0·02% rhodamine B; ext. with 5 ml. Et_2O and measure the green color at 555 mμ. Cu and Fe do not interfere.

Various similar reactions have been utilized in detn. of Zn. Methyl violet can replace rhodamine B.[75] For 5–25 ml. soln. add 5 ml. 1*N* HCl, dil. to 35 ml. with H_2O, add 2 ml. 0·06% dye soln. and 5 ml. 25% NH_4SCN soln. and dil. to 50 ml. with H_2O before comparing the color.

Pyridine and NH_4SCN have been used for gravimetric or titrimetric detn. of 3–33 mg. Zn in 100 ml. neutral soln.[10, 76] Add 1 g. NH_4SCN, 1 ml. pyridine and filter on a glass crucible after 1 hr.; wash the ppt. (see Chapter 34, p. 266), dry in a vacuum desiccator below 71°C and weigh as Zn $py_2(SCN)_2$. Alternatively, titrate the ppt. iodometrically with KIO_3 soln. or argentometrically with diphenylcarbazone as indicator, or apply Volhard's method to the filtrate. Isoquinoline (see Chapter 22, p. 178) or 2,7-diaminofluorene[77] may replace pyridine.

Methylene blue and NH_4SCN can serve for gravimetric detns. of 11 mg. Zn in 10 ml. soln.[78] Add 10 ml. HCl, 9·0 g. NH_4OAc, boil, add 15 ml. 1% dye soln., boil, add 5 ml. 10% NH_4SCN and dil. to 100 ml. with H_2O; filter, wash with H_2O contg. some HCl and ignite to ZnO. Al and Ca do not interfere. Methyl orange or methyl red may be applied similarly.

Nephelometry is possible with diantipyrinylmethylmethane and NH_4SCN.[79] To 10 ml. soln. contg. 0·3 ml. 1*N* HCl, add 0·03–0·05 g. ascorbic acid or 0·2 g. hydroquinone and filter; to a 5 ml. aliquot add 9 ml. reagent soln. (1 ml. 2% diantipyrinylmethylmethane in EtOH mixed with 1·52 g. NH_4SCN in 98 ml. H_2O) and measure after 15 min. Al, Cd, Ca, Mg can be tolerated, as can 10 μg. Fe^{3+}, 5 μg. Ni or Co and 1 μg. Cu.

Tetraphenylarsonium chloride ppts. Zn from NaCl-contg. soln. and the excess in the filtrate can be titrated with I_2 soln. potentiometrically.[10]

(q) Na-diethyldithiocarbamate can be used nephelometrically.[10, 80] For 20–100 μg. Zn, add 7·83 ml. 0·1*N* NH_4OH and 12·17 ml. 0·1*N* AcOH (pH 4·8) and 10 ml. 0·1% reagent and dil. to 50 ml. with H_2O. Measure the white turbidity at 434 mμ.

NOTES. (1) Cu, Ni, Co, Bi, CN^- interfere. $Na_4P_2O_7$ prevents interference of Fe and Mn. Pb interference can be corrected for by subtracting the absorbance remaining after addn. of 2 ml. 1*N* KOH.

(2) Photometric titration of 0·2–0·4 mg. Zn is also possible.[81]

(r) Miscellaneous colorimetric methods. α,β,γ,δ-Tetraphenylporphine has been suggested for detn. of 10–50 μg. Zn in AcOH soln.[82] Add 5 ml. reagent (0·1075 g./l. AcOH refluxed for 8 hr.), dil. to 25 ml. with AcOH and measure at 551 mμ (ϵ = 14 000). Cu interferes; interference of other ions can be obviated by addn. of an equal amt. to the reference soln. The method has been applied to detn. of Zn in Mg, Be and Cd.

Thiourea is used in conjunction with picric acid[83] for 3–30 mg. Zn in 5–40 ml. 1*N* acid soln. Add 0·4 g. thiourea, heat to 50–60°C, add an equal vol. of 1%

picric acid soln. and filter after 1 hr.; wash with a soln. of 3·5 g. thiourea and 0·5 g. picric acid in 100 ml., then 2 or 3 times with 1:3 Et_2O–C_6H_6, and finally with C_6H_6 at 40–50°C until there is no yellow color. Dissolve the ppt. in 20 ml. buffer soln. (118 g. NaOAc and 56·5 g. AcOH/l.), dil. to 50 ml. with H_2O and compare the colors.

Resorcinol may be used for 0·005–3 mg. Zn.[84] Add 5% reagent in EtOH, followed by NH_4OH and compare the blue color. The error is −6% and Cd, Cu, Co, Ni, Mn, Ca interfere. The blue color is also formed in HCl solns. But Beer's law is not obeyed.

Urobilin forms a fluorescent complex with 1 μg. Zn in slightly alk. ethanolic soln. under UV light.[10, 85] Interferences are Cd, Co, Ni, Cu, Ca, Mg, Na, K.

References

1. HILLEBRAND and LUNDELL, 328 (425); SCOTT and FURMAN, 1054; KIMURA, 218; PIGOTT, 535; FRESENIUS–JANDER, IIb (1945).
2. WILSON, H. N., *Ann. Repts. on Progr. Chem.* (*Chem. Soc. London*), **41**, 272 (1944) (Review).
3. CALDWELL, J. R. and MOYER, H. V., *J. Am. Chem. Soc.*, **59**, 90 (1937).
4. EVANS, B. S., *Analyst*, **60**, 464 (1935).
5. WELCHER, **I**, 372.
6. MASHIMA, M., *Japan Analyst*, **5**, 319 (1956).
7. BRYSON, A. and LOWY, L., *Analyst*, **78**, 299 (1953).
8. GEILMANN, W., *et al.*, *Z. anal. Chem.*, **154**, 418 (1957).
9. HILLEBRAND and LUNDELL, 328 (425).
10. FRESENIUS–JANDER, **IIb**, 1 ff (1945).
11. VANCE, J. E. and BORUP, R. E., *Anal. Chem.*, **25**, 610 (1953).
12. A.S.T.M., 292 ff.
13. MELLOR and THOMPSON, 385 (1938).
14. COLEMAN, S. A. and SMITH, G. B. L., *Ind. Eng. Chem., Anal. Ed.*, **13**, 377 (1941).
15. LUX, H., *Z. anorg. u. allgem. Chem.*, **226**, 1 (1935).
16. STEUER, H., *Z. anal. Chem.*, **118**, 396 (1939).
17. WELCHER, **II**, 214; HECHT and DONAU, 200; SHENNAN, R. J., *Analyst*, **64**, 14 (1939); BARTRAM, J. H. and KENT, P. J. C., *Metallurgia*, **33**, 179 (1946); LOWEN, J. and CARNEY, A. L., *Anal. Chem.*, **27**, 1965 (1955) (after ion exchange).
18. ALLPORT, N. L. and MOON, C. D. B., *Analyst*, **64**, 395 (1939).
19. LOTT, W. L., *Ind. Eng. Chem., Anal. Ed.*, **10**, 335 (1938).
20. FALLER, F. E., *Z. anal. Chem.*, **139**, 15 (1953) (in Al); UENO, K., *Anal. Chem.*, **24**, 1363 (1952); CHEW, B. and LINDLEY, G., *Metallurgia*, **53**, 45 (1946) (in Cu alloy, cellulose column sepn.); KODAMA, K. and KANIE, T., *Japan Analyst*, **4**, 627 (1955) (in Al, ion exchange).
21. KINNUNEN, J. and MERIKANTO, B., *Chemist Analyst*, **44**, 50 (1955).
22. BROWN, E. G. and HAYES, T. J., *Anal. Chim. Acta*, **9**, 6 (1953).
23. HUNTER, J. A., *Anal. Chem.*, **27**, 1206 (1955); HUNTER, J. A. and MILLER, C. C., *Analyst*, **81**, 79 (1956).
24. FLASCHKA, H., *Z. anal. Chem.*, **138**, 332 (1953); FLASCHKA, H. and PÜSCHEL, R., *ibid.*, **149**, 185 (1956).
25. FLASCHKA, H., *Chemist Analyst*, **42**, 84 (1953).
26. SANDELL, 619 ff.
27. WELCHER, **III**, 528; SHIRLEY, R. L., *et al.*, *J. Assoc. Offic. Agr. Chemists*, **32**, 276 (1949); BARNES, H., *Analyst*, **76**, 220 (1951); MALMSTROM, B. G. and GLICK, D., *Anal. Chem.*, **23**, 1699 (1951) (0·002–0·01 μg).
28. VALLEE, B. L., *Anal. Chem.*, **26**, 914 (1954).
29. KATO, T. and TAKEI, N., *Japan Analyst*, **2**, 208 (1953); also see SANDELL, 623 ($Na_2S_2O_3$ as masking agent); WELCHER, **III**, 527; BRICKER, L. G., *et al.*, *Ind. Eng. Chem., Anal. Ed.*, **17**, 661 (1945) (in steel); BRAMMELL, W. S., *J. Assoc. Offic. Agr. Chemists*, **39**, 429 (1956); YOKOSUKA, S., *Japan Analyst*, **6**, 431 (1957) (in Ni).
30. WELCHER, **I**, 281; HECHT and DONAU, 198; ISHIMARU, S., *J. Chem. Soc. Japan*, **56**, 64 (1935); **53**, 567 (1932).
31. HAIDER, S. Z. and KHUNDKAR, M. H., *Analyst*, **79**, 783 (1954).
32. CIMERMAN, C. and WENGER, P., *Mikrochemie*, **24**, 148, 162 (1938); **27**, 716 (1939).
33. GOTO, H. and KAKITA, Y., *J. Chem. Soc. Japan*, **62**, 925 (1941).
34. VAISMAN, G. A., *Compt. rend.*, **36**, 3117 (1942).
35. RAS'KIN, L. D., *Zavodskaya Lab.*, **5**, 1129 (1936); also see ISHIBASHI, M. and FUJINAGA, T., *Bull. Chem. Soc. Japan*, **23**, 27, 229 (1950) (amperometric).
36. WELCHER, **I**, 209 ff.
37. FOGEL'SON, E. I. and KALMYKOVA, N. V., *Zavodskaya Lab.*, **13**, 114 (1947).
38. KRAMER, H., *J. Assoc. Offic. Agr. Chemists*, **33**, 371 (1950).
39. SVOBODA, O. and PRODINGER. W., *Mikrochim. Acta*, 122 (1954).
40. DAS, R. and GUHA SIRCAR, S. S., *J. Indian Chem. Soc.*, **32**, 679 (1955).
41. SIMONSEN, S. H. and CHRISTOPHER, P., *Anal. Chem.*, **26**, 681 (1954); RYNASIEWICZ, J. and FLAGG, J. F., *ibid.*, 1506.
42. DUCRET, L., *Bull. soc. chim. France*, 392 (1946).
43. WELCHER, **II**, 194; HECHT and DONAU, 199; ANDERSON, C. W., *Ind. Eng. Chem., Anal. Ed.*, **13**, 369 (1941).
44. WELCHER, **II**, 204.
45. KAMBARA, T., *Radioisotopes* (*Tokyo*), **4**, No. 1, 21 (1955).
46. BALL, T. R. and AGRUSS, M. S., *J. Am. Chem. Soc.*, **52**, 120 (1933).
47. PAN, Z. H. and CHIANG, C. H., *J. Chinese Chem. Soc.*, **3**, 118 (1935).
48. HIBBARD, P. L., *Ind. Eng. Chem., Anal. Ed.*, **6**, 423 (1934).
49. FURMAN, N. H. and JENSEN, K. J., *Natl. Nuclear Energy Ser., Div. VIII*, **1**, 392 (1950); also see THEURER, K. and SWEET, T. R., *Anal. Chem.*, **25**, 119 (1951) (study using radioisotope); WINCHESTER, R. and YNTEMA, L. F., *Ind. Eng. Chem., Anal. Ed.*, **9**, 254 (1937); KARSHULIN, W. and BAN, S., *Z. anal. Chem.*, **120**, 244 (1940) (acetate buffer); HECHT and DONAU, 202 (NaOH soln.); LINGANE, *Electroanalytical Chemistry*, p. 341 (1953); TREADWELL, W. D., *Tabellen*, 121 (1938).
50. SIERRA, F. and HERNÁNDEZ CAÑAVATE, J., *Anales real soc. españ. fis y quim.* (*Madrid*), **49B**, 687 (1953); RULFS, C. L. and KIBBY, L. J., *Anal. Chem.*, **27**, 1438 (1955) (in brass after electrolysis of Cu).
51. ISHELL, H. G., *Ind. Eng. Chem., Anal. Ed.*, **4**, 284 (1932).
52. GUSEV, S. I., *Zhur. Anal. Khim.*, **1**, 114 (1946).
53. SPACU, G. and PIRTEA, TH. I., *Acad. rep. populare Romîne, Studii cercetâri chim.*, **2**, 183 (1954).
54. MATSUMOTO, T., *Japan Analyst*, **3**, 221 (1953).

55. Caley, E. R., *et al.*, *Anal. Chem.*, **22**, 1060 (1950); Prasad, B. and Nanda, R. K., *Current Sci.* (*India*), **26**, 148 (1957).
56. Richardson, M. R. and Bryson, A., *Analyst*, **78**, 291 (1953); Kolthoff *et al.*, *Volumetric Analysis*, **II**, 301 **III**, 659 (1957).
57. Belcher, R., *et al.*, *J. Chem. Soc.*, 1520 (1951).
58. Evans, B. S., *Analyst*, **71**, 455 (1946).
59. Sylvester, N. D. and Hughes, E. B., *Analyst*, **61**, 734 (1936).
60. Segar, G. A., *Analyst*, **81**, 65 (1956).
61. Mehlig, J. P. and Guill, A. P., *Anal. Chem.*, **23**, 1876 (1951).
62. Knetsch, M., *Gesundh.-Ing.*, **76**, 211 (1955).
63. Tananaev, I. and Georgobiani, M., *Z. anal. Chem.*, **106**, 92 (1936).
64. Lingane, J. J. and Hartley, A. M., *Anal. Chim. Acta*, **11**, 475 (1954).
65. Miller, L. C., *et al.*, *Ind. Eng. Chem.*, *Anal. Ed.*, **16**, 256 (1944).
66. Burriel, F. and Sierra, F., *Anales fis. y quim.* (*Madrid*), **32**, 87 (1934).
67. Meulen, J. H. van der, *Chem. Weekblad*, **38**, 125 (1941).
68. Castro, C. C. and Boyle, A. J., *Ind. Eng. Chem.*, *Anal. Ed.*, **15**, 623 (1943).
69. Boggs, H. M. and Alben, A. O., *Ind. Eng. Chem.*, *Anal. Ed.*, **8**, 97 (1936).
70. Iijima, S. and Hashimoto, J., *J. Chem. Soc. Japan*, **73**, 900 (1952); **74**, 256 (1953).
71. Iijima, S., *et al.*, *J. Chem. Soc. Japan*, **73**, 675 (1952).
72. Rush, R. M. and Yoe, J. H., *Anal. Chem.*, **26**, 1345 (1954); *Anal. Chim. Acta*, **6**, 526 (1952).
73. Holzbecher, Z., *Chem. listy*, **49**, 684 (1955).
74. Martin, G., *Bull. soc. chim. biol.*, **34**, 1174 (1952); Zaĭchikova, L. B. and Lutchenko, N. N., *Zavodskaya Lab.*, **21**, 1304 (1955).
75. Kochneva, E. G., *Zavodskaya Lab.*, **16**, 1170 (1950); Ramanov, D. V., *ibid.*, **21**, 782 (1955).
76. Spacu, G. and Pirtea, Th. I., *Commun. acad. rep. populare Romîne*, **5**, 859 (1955).
77. Welcher, **II**, 339.
78. Platunov, B. A. and Mikhaĭlovskaya, E. P., *Uchenye Zapiski Leningrad. Gosudarst. Univ. im A. A. Zhdanova.*, *Ser. Khim. Nauk*, No. 13, 189 (1953).
79. Gusev, S. I., *et al.*, *Biokhimiya*, **18**, 348 (1953).
80. Murakami, Y., *Bull. Chem. Soc. Japan*, **23**, 150 (1950); also see Mayne, J. E. O. and Noordhof, G. H., *Analyst*, **78**, 625 (1953) (polyvinyl alcohol as stabilizer).
81. Bobtelsky, M. and Rafailoff, R., *Anal. Chim. Acta*, **15**, 457 (1956).
82. Banks, C. V. and Bisque, R. E., *Anal. Chem.*, **29**, 522 (1957).
83. Mahr, C. and Denck, W., *Z. anal. Chem.*, **133**, 54 (1951).
84. Yoe, 396.
85. Welcher, **IV**, 310.

37

MANGANESE

The principal references for this chapter are given in ref. 1. The analysis of manganese has been reviewed.[2]

The composition of manganese oxides depends largely on the temperature,[3] the conversion of one oxide to another proceeding as follows:

$$MnO_2 \overset{530°C}{\rightleftharpoons} Mn_2O_3 \overset{950°C}{\rightleftharpoons} Mn_3O_4 \overset{1080°C}{\rightleftharpoons} MnO$$

Attack

(a) Silicates. Treat with HCl (with or without HF addn.), evap. to fumes with H_2SO_4 and fuse the residue with Na_2CO_3 or $Na_2S_2O_7$.

(b) Oxides. Treat with dil. HNO_3 and H_2O_2; fuse the residue with $Na_2S_2O_7$ and dissolve the melt in dil. HNO_3 or HCl.

(c) Sulfides. Treat with HNO_3 and $KClO_3$, evap. and then boil with HNO_3.

(d) Mn metal and alloys. Dissolve in 1:1–1:2 HNO_3. For Si–Mn, add HF and HNO_3, evap. to a few ml., digest at 80°C with HNO_3 and 1·5 g. H_3BO_3 for 10 min. and then apply the bismuthate method.

(e) Steels. If Co is absent, boil with 1:1 HNO_3, treat with persulfate or bismuthate, boil, add $NaNO_2$ or H_2SO_3, boil and apply the bismuthate method. If Co is present, add 30 ml. mixed acids (100 ml. H_2SO_4, 125 ml. H_3PO_4, 250 ml. HNO_3 and 525 ml. H_2O), boil out NO_2, etc. Finally det. Mn by the As^{3+} method. If much Cr is present, dissolve in 1:4 HCl and $HClO_4$, heat and then fume, add NaCl in small portions, then mixed acids and proceed as before; alternatively, apply a ZnO or $NaHCO_3$ sepn. after dissoln. in dil. H_2SO_4.

With Fe–W or Fe–Si, treat with HF and HNO_3, evap. to white fumes with $HClO_4$, add HNO_3 and boil. For Fe–V, Fe–Ti, Fe–Cr, Fe–W and Si–Mn (if they are insol. in acids), fuse with 2:1 Na_2CO_3–MgO, leach with H_2O and treat with H_2O_2; alternatively, fuse with Na_2O_2.

For 0·2 g of ferro-alloys,[4] heat with 5 ml. HF, 7 ml. 30% H_2O_2 and 10 ml. 1:3 H_2SO_4.

Separation

Mn is normally detd. on a separate sample.

Treatment with $KClO_3$ seps. Mn from many elements but large amts. of W, Mo, P interfere as do Co and NH_4^+. Boil 50 ml. of the HNO_3 soln. gently and add 5 g. reagent gradually over 10–20 min.; boil until effervescence has almost ceased but a little $HClO_3$ remains, then add 40 ml. H_2O, cool and filter.

If the soln. is evapd. to dryness on a steam-bath after addn. of $KClO_3$ and filtered after addn. of 50–100 ml. H_2O, less NO_3^- remains in the filtrate and Zn, Ca and Mg can be detd.[5] $NaClO_3$ in $HClO_4$ solns. has also been recommended.

In the above procedure about 0·1–3 mg. Mn passes into the filtrate, and can be detd. colorimetrically if required. To remove impurities, such as SiO_2, W, Nb, Ta, possibly Fe, Co, Sb, V, and, if much is present, Zn or Mg as manganates, proceed as follows: treat the ppt. with 10–40 ml. satd. SO_2 water, filter, boil with 2–3 ml. HCl, then with Br_2 water, make alk. with 1:1 NH_4OH to methyl orange, boil for 2 min., filter, wash with hot H_2O, add 1:3 HCl and reppt. Combine the filtrates, acidify with AcOH, boil and pass H_2S for 10–15 min. at room temp. and then for 15 min. at 90°C.

Various other oxidants can be used instead of $KClO_3$. $KBrO_3$ has been recommended for 20–150 mg. Mn in 50 ml. 0·8–1*N* H_2SO_4 or HNO_3 soln.[6] Add 1–2 g. reagent, boil for 10–20 min. and filter. The amts. of Fe and Mn present should be about equal; if no Fe is present, add 3–5 g. $ZnSO_4$. The sepn. obtained is better than that with $KClO_3$. $K_2S_2O_8$ allows complete sepn. from Fe but the pptn. of Mn is incomplete; treat the 0·5–1*N* H_2SO_4 soln. with 3–4 g. reagent, boil for 10 min., add another 2 g. reagent, boil for 5 min. and filter. Treatment with $(NH_4)_2S_2O_8$ is not satisfactory.

Sepn. of Mn from Ni, Co, Zn, etc. can be achieved by treatment with Br_2, $(NH_4)_2S_2O_8$, NaOCl, NaOBr, $K_3Fe(CN)_6$, etc. in acetate-buffered or alk. soln. if repptn. is carried out; manganates of group IV metals may coppt.

Treatment with PbO_2 in slightly acidic soln. is useful before a colorimetric finish; shake with 0·5 g. PbO_2, leave for 1 hr., remove the mother liquor, add HNO_3 and det. Mn.

Mn can be sepd. from Fe, Al, etc. by treatment with NH_4OH and NH_4Cl, or by the basic acetate method, or with ZnO, $BaCO_3$, etc. The mixture should not be boiled for over 3 min. $NaHCO_3$ seps. Mn from large amts. of Cr, W, etc. (see also Chapter 45, p. 332). NaOH seps. Mn from Mo and W. For concn. purposes, add a few mg. of Fe^{3+} and NaOH, stir for 1–2 min. and boil. Copptn. with $Mg(OH)_2$ serves a similar purpose. Treatment with NaOH and H_2O_2 or fusion with Na_2O_2 seps. Mn from Cr, V, W and Mo.

H_2S allows several sepns. under different conditions. Sepn. from group II metals is possible in 4% HCl soln., sepn. from Zn in HCOOH soln., sepn. from Ni and Co in acetate-buffered or pyridine soln. (see Chapter 2, Section 3.2), and sepn. from Ca, Mg, etc. in NH_4OH–NH_4Cl soln. In this last sepn. CaS_2O_3 may coppt. if very large amts. of Ca are present. A readily filterable ppt. is obtained[7] by treating the slightly acidic soln. with 2 g. hexamine (for less than 0·5 g. Mn) and passing H_2S at 60°C.

Cupferron seps. Mn from Fe, Ti, Zr, V, etc. Extn. with Et_2O seps. Mn from Fe and Mo. Extn. with $CHCl_3$ from solns. contg. oxine at pH 9 is useful for concn. Volatilization as CrO_2Cl_2 is useful for sepn. from Cr.

Determination

Macro amounts of Mn are best detd. by the bismuthate method so long as Co is absent; the phosphate method is also satisfactory. For mg. amounts of Mn, the best methods are gravimetric detn. as sulfate after pptn. of sulfide, and the arsenite method; the latter is suitable when Co is present. Of the colorimetric methods, by far the best involves oxidation to MnO_4^- with $NaIO_4$; the sensitivity of this procedure can be increased by addition of tetrabase, etc.

(a) Redox titrations. (*i*) $NaBiO_3$ is the best oxidant to use before the titrimetric finish.[1] For 50 mg. Mn^{2+} in 100 ml. soln. (< 1 mg. Mn/ml.) contg. 11–22% w/w HNO_3 or 6–11 ml. H_2SO_4 at 10–20°C, add $NaBiO_3$ (0·26 g./10 mg. Mn), shake for 1 min., add 100 ml. cold H_2O, filter on a glass crucible and wash with cold 3% HNO_3. Collect the filtrate in 0·1*N* Fe^{2+} soln. (an excess of about 10 ml.) contg. 2 ml. H_3PO_4 and back-titrate to a faint pink color with 0·1*N* $KMnO_4$.

NOTES. (1) Interferences are HNO_2, Cl^-, Ce, Co, > 2 mg. Cr, > 1 mg. V, large amts. of Sb or Ag and > 1 g. P_2O_5/100 ml. No interference is caused by $(NH_4)_2SO_4$, Fe, W, Mo, U, Ti, Pd, Pt; if very large amts. of Ni are present, Co^{2+} should be added after the oxidation.
The method has been applied to steels, Fe–Mn, Ni–Cr, Ni–Cr–Fe, Ni, brasses, bronzes and Mg and its alloys.[8, 9]
(2) For a coulometric titration, see Chapter 45, p. 333.
(3) When much Mn is present, add solid $FeSO_4$. After filtration, add 2 drops ferroin indicator and titrate with Fe^{2+} soln. For simultaneous detn. of Mn and Cr, add 10 ml. 1:1 H_2SO_4/100 ml. soln. and 2 ml. 0·025*M* $MnSO_4$ and titrate with standard $H_2C_2O_4$ soln. from brown-red to deep yellow (Mn); then add 5 ml. H_3PO_4 and titrate $Cr_2O_7^{2-}$ with Fe^{2+} soln. in presence of diphenylbenzidine indicator.[10]
(4) Oxidation with $NaIO_4$ is suitable for < 30 mg. Mn in 100 ml. soln. contg. 10–15 ml. H_3PO_4 (or 3–4 ml. H_3PO_4 and 5–4 ml. H_2SO_4).[11] Add 0·3–0·5 g. $NaIO_4$, boil for 15 min., cool, dil. to 150 ml. with H_2O, add 2–5 g. $Hg(NO_3)_2$ in a little H_2O, filter on a glass crucible and wash with H_2O, etc.

(*ii*) In an alternative method, which is often used in steel analysis, $(NH_4)_2S_2O_8$ is used as oxidant and As^{3+} as titrant.[1, 8] Treat 1 g. steel contg. 1–5 mg. Mn with 30 ml. mixed acids (see under Attack, p. 284) by heating slowly to boiling. Add 100 ml. hot H_2O, 10 ml. 0·8% $AgNO_3$ and 10 ml. 25% $(NH_4)_2S_2O_8$, boil for 1 min., cool below 25°C, add 75 ml. cold H_2O and titrate rapidly with 0·01*N* As^{3+} to the yellow end-point. Standardize the titrant against $KMnO_4$ or, preferably, against a standard steel similar to the sample.

NOTES. (1) No interference arises from Co, Ni, Sb, small amts. of V, Mo, or H_2SO_4 or H_3PO_4. Cr can be tolerated if the steel contains < 1%; if more is present, add more persulfate and heat for longer, or boil the $HClO_4$ soln. after adding NaCl. Fe can be compensated for by adding an equal amt. to the standard or by adding 3–4 ml. H_3PO_4/g. Fe. H_3PO_4 also prevents interference of W. Ti does not interfere if the steel contains < 5%.
The procedure has been used for steels (with a potentiometric end-point for high Mn contents) and a variety of metals and alloys.[8, 9]
If the soln. is cooled below 5·25°C, it is unnecessary[13] to add NaCl to remove Ag^+.
(2) If more than 15 mg. Mn is present, the end-point may be obscure. If a ppt. of $MnO(OH)_2$ appears, which may happen even in H_3PO_4 solns., discard the detn.; this pptn. can be prevented[12] by addn. of HF, HPO_3 or $H_4P_2O_7$. An iodometric finish is possible.[12]
PbO_2 can be used instead of persulfate.
(3) If OsO_4 or KIO_3 is added as catalyst, the end-point occurs when Mn^{2+} is formed.[14] After oxidation with persulfate and Ag^+, add 3 drops 0·01*M* OsO_4 and excess 0·0316*N* As^{3+} and titrate with 0·0316*N* $KMnO_4$ to det. Cr + Mn. Then boil, add 5 ml. 50% $(NH_4)_2S_2O_8$, boil for 8–10 min., add 4–5 ml. 1:3 HCl, boil for 5 min. after the pink color has disappeared, cool, add 3 drops 0·025*N* KIO_3 and titrate with the As^{3+} soln. to det. Cr. Mn and Cr can also be detd. by titration with V^{4+} soln.[15]
(4) The end-point of the titration is sharper if a mixt. of equal vols. of 0·05*N* As^{3+} and 0·05*N* $NaNO_2$ is used as titrant, and the results are then practically stoichiometric.[16] After the above oxidation, cool, add 5 ml. 0·2*N* NaCl and 10 ml. 12*N* H_2SO_4 and then titrate with the mixed reagent, allowing 2 min. between drops near the end-point, to the color change from purple to clear.

(*iii*) If $MnO(OH)_2$ is pptd. by $KClO_3$ from acidic soln., or by $KMnO_4$ in alk. soln. at 80°C, the detn. can be completed[1, 8] by addn. of excess $FeSO_4$, $H_2C_2O_4$ or H_2O_2 and H_2SO_4 and final titration with $KMnO_4$.

(*iv*) In Volhard's method for Mn,[17] treat 10 ml. neutral soln. with 50 g. K_2SO_4 or 90 g. Glauber's salt/500 ml. near the b.p., boil the mixture and titrate with $KMnO_4$ until the pink color remains for 4 min. If the initial soln. is acidic, neutralize with ZnO. Interferences are Fe^{2+}, Cl^-, NO_2^- and large amts. of Co, Cr, Mo, W.

(*v*) PbO_2 and EDTA or CyDTA are used with an iodometric titration or with a potentiometric titration with Fe^{2+} soln.[18] Treat the slightly acidic soln. with EDTA, adjust to pH 5 with NaOH, add 10–20 ml. AcOH and 10 ml. $Ca(OAc)_2$ soln. and treat with 0·3–1·5 g. PbO_2 to obtain Mn^{3+}. Filter on a G4 crucible, wash with H_2O, add 1 g. KI and titrate with $Na_2S_2O_3$ soln.

(*vi*) For another iodometric finish[6, 19] ppt. $MnO(OH)_2$ as described under (*iii*), treat with 50–70 ml. H_2O, 5 ml. 20% KF, 5 ml. 4*N* H_2SO_4, 1–2 g. KI and titrate with 0·1*N* $Na_2S_2O_3$; if Zn but no Fe is present, 1 ml. titrant is equivalent to 2·801 mg. Mn but if Fe is present, 1 ml. is equivalent to 2·774 mg. Mn. Cr, Fe, Co, Pb, Ni, Bi can be tolerated but > 50 mg. Mo, W and large amts. of PO_4^{3-} interfere.

(*vii*) Oxidation with $K_2Cr_2O_7$ soln. can be followed by titration with Fe^{2+} soln. if As^{3+} is present.[20] To the Mn^{2+} soln. contg. 5–40 ml. H_2SO_4 or 15–50 ml. HNO_3 in 180 ml., add HPO_3 dissolved in 25 ml. H_2O, 0·1 ml. diphenylamine indicator, $K_2Cr_2O_7$ soln. (15 g./l.) and As^{3+} soln. (15 g. As_2O_3 and 10 g. Na_2CO_3/l.) as indicated below; finally titrate with 0·1*N* Fe^{2+} from violet through blue to green.

Amt. Mn present (g.)	0·08	0·2	0·25
HPO_3 (g.)	5	8	10
$K_2Cr_2O_7$ (ml.)	35	60	75
As^{3+} (ml.)	45	65	80

No interference arises from Ni, Co, Ti, Pb, Cu, W, Fe (up to 0·6 g.) or Cl^-.

(*viii*) $Na_2S_2O_3$ can be used for detn. of 0·3–2 mg. Mn in 0·2 g. steel.[21] Dissolve the sample in 30 ml. 1:1 HNO_3 heat, add 50 ml. H_2O and 10 ml. 0·5% $AgNO_3$, boil, add 10 ml. 25% $(NH_4)_2S_2O_8$, boil for 1 min., dil. to 150 ml. with H_2O, cool, add 10 ml. 1% NaCl and titrate with 0·004*N* $Na_2S_2O_3$ (1 g./l.). H_3PO_4 interferes but 50% Ni, 2·5% Cr, 3% Co and 0·5% Cu can be present.

(*ix*) For titration in alk. soln.,[22] treat 1–7 ml. 0·02*N* Mn^{2+} soln. with 5 ml. 0·05*N* $KMnO_4$, 0·2 g. H_2TeO_4 and sufficient NaOH to give a 1*N* soln. and titrate with 0·03*N* TlOAc to a potentiometric end-point.

(b) H_2S can be used gravimetrically for 1–3 mg. Mn.[3, 23] Ppt. as described on p. 285 for separation, filter on paper and wash; pass dil. H_2SO_4 through the paper, wash with H_2O and collect in a porcelain crucible. Evap. the soln., heat to 250°C and then ignite at 450–700°C (200–940°C) for 20–30 min. before weighing as $MnSO_4$.

NOTES. (1) If the ignited ppt. is dark, repeat the heating after addn. of H_2SO_3 and H_2SO_4.
(2) If, after the above heating, the ppt. is cooled, mixed with some H_2O, evapd. to dryness and dried at 110°C for 30 min., it can be weighed as the monohydrate, which is less hygroscopic.[24] Heating above 950°C (1000°C) and rapid cooling permits weighing as Mn_3O_4 (which should be brown with no black spots). Heating with S at 900°C under H_2 and weighing as MnS gives unsatisfactory results.

(c) $NaIO_4$ provides an excellent colorimetric method.[1, 23, 25, 26, 27] For < 2 mg. Mn in 100 ml. soln. contg. 10 ml. H_2SO_4, or 15–20 ml. HNO_3 and 5–10 ml. H_3PO_4, or 2 ml. HNO_3, 15 ml. H_2SO_4 and 5–10 ml. H_3PO_4, add 0·2–0·4 g. reagent, boil for 1 min., maintain just below the b.p. for 10 min. (or for 1 hr. if only traces are present) and cool; dil. to 100 ml. with H_2O and measure the purple color at 525 mμ.

NOTES. (1) Large amts. of Fe or Hg interfere since the periodates are difficultly sol.; if Fe is present, add H_3PO_4. UO_2^{2+}, Co, Ni, Cu can be compensated by addn. of an equal amt. to the standard. Sn and Bi form a white turbidity. Cl^-, Br^- and I^- interfere. See below for detn. in presence of Cr. The procedure has been applied to a wide variety of metals and alloys.[8]
(2) For < 3 μg. Mn, oxidation is complete if 20 mg. $AgNO_3$ is added to the 2*N* H_2SO_4 soln.[28] $AgIO_4$ is said[29] to be better than $NaIO_4$.

Cr does not interfere if the measurement is made in alk. soln.[30] For 10–150 μg. Mn in 2*N* HNO_3 soln., add a few ml. cupferron, ext. with $CHCl_3$, evap. to dryness, add a few drops $HClO_4$ and 2*N* H_2SO_4, heat, add 5 ml. 5*M* H_2SO_4 and 0·2 g. reagent and maintain near the b.p. for 10 min. Cool, make just alk. with NaOH, dil. to 50 ml. with H_2O, centrifuge if turbid and measure at 525 mμ in a 5 cm. cell. No interference arises from 500 μg. Cr/ml., or from Fe, Cu, Al.

For simultaneous detn. of Cr and Mn[31] boil 1 g. steel in a 300-ml. Kjeldahl flask with 300 ml. H_2O and 10 ml. H_2SO_4 (and 10 ml. H_3PO_4 if W is present), then add 5 ml. HNO_3 gradually; if a dark residue appears, add another 5 ml. Boil to white fumes, dil. to 100 ml. with H_2O, boil, cool and dil. to 250 ml. with H_2O. Pipet 25–50 ml. into an Erlenmeyer flask (centrifuge or filter if necessary) and add 5 ml. H_2SO_4, 5 ml. H_3PO_4 and 1–2 ml. 0·1*N* $AgNO_3$. Dil. to 80 ml. with H_2O, add 5 g. $K_2S_2O_8$, maintain near b.p. for 5–7 min., cool slightly, add 0·5 g. KIO_4, boil gently for 5 min., cool, dil. to 100 ml. with H_2O and measure at 440 mμ (for Cr) and 545 mμ (for Mn). Apply corrections for each element as well as for V, Co, Ni, Fe.

Various other oxidants can replace periodate. $(NH_4)_2S_2O_8$ has been applied for 0·005–5 mg. Mn:[19,25,26] add 5 ml. mixed reagent (75 g. $HgSO_4$ in 600 ml. 2:1 HNO_3 mixed with 200 ml. H_3PO_4 and 0·035 g. $AgNO_3$ and dild. to 1 l. with H_2O), dil. to 90 ml. with H_2O, add 1 g. oxidant and bring to the boil within 2 min.; remove from the heat for 1 min., cool, dil. to 100 ml. and measure at 525 mμ. Org. compds. and 0·1 g. NaCl interfere unless more oxidant is added and heating is prolonged.

In the $S_2O_8^{2-}$ method, the catalytic power decreases in the order Co, Ag, Fe, Cu; the action of Co is increased by V and decreased by Ti.[32] $NaBiO_3$ can be used with[33] or without[25] $AgNO_3$; PbO_2 is not satisfactory. Ag_2O_2 is used at room temp.;[34] prep. the reagent from 10 g. $AgNO_3$ in 100 ml. H_2O by shaking vigorously with 10 g. $(NH_4)_2S_2O_8$, decanting and washing with H_2O. For a detn. treat the sample soln. (200 ml. contg. 1:10 H_2SO_4) with 0·1 g. Ag_2O_2 for 10 min.; add $HgSO_4$ if Cl^- is present.

The sensitivity of these reactions can be increased by addn. of aromatic amines (see below).

(d) $(NH_4)_2HPO_4$ is suitable for gravimetric detn. of < 100 mg. Mn in 100 ml. acidic soln.[1, 35, 36] Add 20 g. NH_4Cl, 2 g. reagent and 2% NH_4OH to give complete pptn. during 30 min. followed by 0·5 ml. in excess. Boil the soln., place in an ice-bath for 2–3 hr. (or cool ordinarily for over 12 hr.), filter on paper and wash with 0·25% reagent and then with 60–65% EtOH. Transfer to a porcelain crucible, dry below 90°C, heat slowly to above 700°C and weigh as $Mn_2P_2O_7$.

NOTES. (1) Interferences are Zn, Ni, Cu, etc., and large amts. of SO_4^{2-}. Fe and Al require addn. of sulfosalicylic acid, and Co addn. of 2 g. citric acid.
(2) 0·2 mg. Mn passes into the filtrate in the method described by Hillebrand and Lundell.[23]
(3) For a titrimetric detn. of the ppt. with $BiOClO_4$, see Chapter 23, p. 186.
(4) It is possible[37] to ppt. as $MnNH_4AsO_4$ and titrate the ppt. iodometrically.

(e) Miscellaneous gravimetric methods. Na-anthranilate is applicable for 0·1 g. Mn in 80 ml. neutral soln.[38] Add 60 ml. 3% reagent, filter after 1 hr. on a glass crucible, wash with 0·5% reagent and then with EtOH, dry at 105–120°C and weigh as $Mn(C_7H_6O_2N)_2$; alternatively, titrate the ppt. with $KBrO_3$ soln.

Pyridine and NH_4SCN are also suitable for 0·1 g. Mn in neutral soln.[39] Add 1·5 g. NH_4SCN, 4 ml. pyridine, filter on a glass crucible and wash as described for Ni (p. 266); dry in a vacuum desiccator and weigh as $Mn\,py_4(SCN)_2$.

For detn. with picrolonic acid, see Chapter 36, p. 280.

Tetraphenylphosphonium chloride has been applied gravimetrically and titrimetrically.[40] $BiOClO_4$ ppts. Mn as $Bi_3O_2H_2MnO_4$.[41]

(f) EDTA can be used for titrimetric detns. of Mn.[42] To the Mn^{2+} soln. add 0·1 g. KCN, 1 g. NaK-tartrate, 0·1 g. ascorbic acid, 2 ml. buffer (13·5 g. NH_4Cl, 88 ml. NH_4OH in 250 ml.), eriochrome black T indicator (1:400 with NaCl), boil the soln. and titrate with EDTA to a blue color. Co, Ni, Cu, Zn, Cd, Hg, Pd do not interfere. Pyrocatechol violet can also be used as indicator (see Chapter 34, p. 266).

(g) Oxine is generally applied titrimetrically for detn. of Mn.[43] For 5–30 mg. Mn in 100 ml. acidic soln., add 6 g. NH_4Cl, boil, add 10 ml. 3% oxine in 0·2*N* HCl followed by 2*N* NH_4OH until a ppt. appears, 4–5 ml. 1*N* HCl and 2–3 drops 30% H_2O_2. Boil for 1 min., add 10 ml. buffer (28 g. $KBrO_3$, 120 g. KBr and 250 g. $Na_2S_2O_3$/l.), boil for 1 min., filter on a glass crucible and wash with hot H_2O. Dissolve the ppt. in 120 ml. 1:3 HCl by heating, cool, add a small excess of 0·1*N* $KBrO_3$ (contg. 12 g. KBr and 2·5 ml. 0·5% indigo carmine/l.) and KI and titrate with $Na_2S_2O_3$ soln.

NOTES. (1) No interference arises from group IV or V metals; if > 10 mg. Mg is present, repptn. is needed.
(2) For gravimetric detn.[44] dry the ppt. at 180–280°C (117–250°C) and weigh as $Mn(C_9H_6ON)_2$.

(h) $K_4Fe(CN)_6$ may be used titrimetrically in presence of starch–iodine indicator.[45] For 3–55 mg. Mn in 50 ml. soln. at pH 6·0–6·7, add 0·2% starch and 0·02–0·03 ml. 0·1*N* I_2 and titrate with reagent soln. at 20–25°C to the disappearance of the blue color. For 0·5–2 m*M* Mn soln.[46] add 20 ml. 5% EDTA, 70 ml. H_2O, 20 ml. AcOH, 4 drops 1% $K_3Fe(CN)_6$ and 4 drops diphenylamine indicator and titrate with 0·05*M* reagent from purple to colorless. Ni, Co, Mo, UO_2^{2+} interfere, but Al, Fe, W, Pb, Ca, etc. do not.

(i) 4,4′-Tetramethyldiaminotriphenylmethane has been proposed[26] for colorimetric detn. of 0·05–0·5 μg. Mn in 10 ml. mixed acids (600 ml. 1*N* HNO_3 and 75 ml. H_3PO_4/l.). Add 50 mg. periodate and place in a water-bath for 1·5 hr. Pipet 3 ml., maintain at 80 ± 1°C, add 3 drops 0·1% reagent in 5% w/w H_3PO_4, shake for 5 min., and measure the yellow color at 575 mμ. Beer's law is not obeyed.

NOTES. (1) Interferences are Cr, V, Ce and Cl^-.
(2) Other org. bases may replace the above reagent. Benzidine (2·3 g. in 100 ml. 5% HCl) is suitable for 0·1–1 μg. Mn^{7+} in 100 ml. soln.[47] *o*-Tolidine allows detn. of 0·1 mg. Mn in 100 ml. neutral soln.;[47] make alk. to phenolphthalein with 1% NaOH, pass air for 30 min., add 5 ml. reagent (1 g. in 5 ml. 7% HCl, dild. to 500 ml. with H_2O and to 1 l. with 7% HCl) and compare the yellow color after 20 min. Fe does not interfere if 5 ml. H_3PO_4 is added.
Tetrabase is suitable for 2–30 μg. Mn in 100 ml. soln. after addn. of KIO_4, etc.[48] *p*-Amino-*N*,*N*-dimethylaniline sulfate can also be applied.[49]

(j) Formaldoxime has been suggested for the detn. of 10–50 μg. Mn in 30 ml. acidic soln.[50] Add 5 ml. 10% HEEDTA, neutralize with NaOH and add 1 ml. reagent (20 g. paraformaldehyde and 55 g. $NH_2OH \cdot H_2SO_4$ boiled with H_2O, dild. to 100 ml. with H_2O and then dild. to a 1:10 soln.) followed immediately by 2 ml. 10% NaOH. Heat at 65°C for 2 hr., cool, dil. to 50 ml. with H_2O and measure in a 4 cm. cell at 450 mμ. No interference arises from Cu, Cd, Pb, Mo, Zn, Al, Ti; Fe^{3+} requires HEEDTA addn. and 100 μg. Ni or Co is equivalent to 2 μg. Mn under the above conditions.

(k) Miscellaneous colorimetric methods. Na_2TeO_4 has been proposed[51] for the detn. of 60–800 μg. Mn^{2+}; add reagent equiv. to 4 times the amt. of Mn present, make the soln. 2·5*M* in NaOH, add an equiv. amt. of H_2O_2, dil. to 25 ml. with H_2O, heat for 10 min. at 60°C and measure the orange complex at 400 or 420 mμ. The 1:4 complex is formed.

CyDTA or EDTA may be employed with PbO_2 for detn. of 0·21–2·74 mg. Mn in 50 ml. soln., the red color being measured at 500 mμ (see under Redox titrations, p. 286).

Mn^{2+} (> 0·5 μg.) can be detd.[52] by its catalytic effect on the reaction of $C_2O_4^{2-}$ with $Cr_2O_7^{2-}$. Add 0·5 ml. 10% Na_2CO_3, 0·3 ml. satd. $Na_2C_2O_4$, 0·3 ml. H_3PO_4, 0·2 ml. 1% $K_2Cr_2O_7$, place in boiling H_2O for 10 min. and measure the green color at 470 mμ. Interferences are Cu, Fe, etc.

Triethanolamine may be used for 5–30 μg. Mn/ml.[53] Add 5 ml. reagent, adjust to pH 12 with 20% KOH, filter if turbid and measure the green complex at 625 mμ. Interferences are Cu, Co, Cr^{3+}, Fe^{3+}, CN^-, citrate, $C_2O_4^{2-}$, etc.

Satd. pyrophosphoric acid is used in conjunction with $KBrO_3$ for 2–40 mg. Mn in 40 ml. soln.[54] Add 6 ml. acid, 10 ml. 1:1 H_2SO_4, 1 ml. 3·3% KCN, 4–6 ml. 3% $KBrO_3$, dil. to 100 ml. with H_2O and compare the violet color. Cr and Br^- interfere but Fe, Al, Mg and small amts. of Zn, Cu, Co, Ni, Ca can be tolerated. In a similar method, which is suitable for 2–70 mg. Mn in 50 ml. soln.,[55] add H_2SO_4 to give an 8*M* soln., 2 ml. 0·5*M* KCN, 5 ml. 0·17*M* $KBrO_3$, dil. to 100 ml. with 8*M* H_2SO_4 and measure the red color at 500 mμ. CrO_4^{2-} and reducing agents interfere; Pb and Ba can be filtered off as sulfates.

Use of *o*-phenanthroline with $KBrO_3$ allows detn. of < 2 μg. Mn/ml.[56] Treat the neutral soln. with 5 ml. 0·5% reagent and 2 ml. 3% $KBrO_3$, boil gently for 5 min., cool, dil. to 25 ml. with H_2O and measure at 334 mμ.

Na-diethyldithiocarbamate forms a brown-violet complex with Mn, after $CHCl_3$ extn., which can be measured at 578 mμ.[57] Fe, Cu, Co and V interfere.

(l) Flame photometry. Such detns. are possible at 403·3 mμ but PO_4^{3-} interferes and attention must be paid to the K line at 404·6 mμ.[58]

References

1. Hillebrand and Lundell, 339 (439); Scott and Furman, 554; Kimura, 245; Pigott, 237.
2. Fuchs, O., *Z. anal. Chem.*, **118**, 359 (1939–40).
3. Ugai, T., *J. Chem. Soc. Japan*, **52**, 461 (1931).
4. Kawamura, K., *Japan Analyst*, **2**, 417 (1953).
5. Evans, R. L., *Anal. Chem.*, **20**, 87 (1948).
6. Kolthoff, I. M., and Sandell, E. B., *Ind. Eng. Chem., Anal. Ed.*, **1**, 189 (1929).
7. Ostroumov, E. A., *Zavodskaya Lab.*, **7**, 1233 (1938).
8. A.S.T.M., 80 ff.
9. Chemists of U.S. Steel Corp.: *Sampling and Analysis of Carbon and Alloy Steels*, 81 (1938).
10. Rao, G. G., and Muralikrishna, U., *Anal. Chim. Acta*, **13**, 8 (1955).
11. Willard, H. H., and Thompson, J. J., *Ind. Eng. Chem., Anal. Ed.*, **3**, 399 (1931); Smith, G. F., *et al.*, *ibid.*, **7**, 427 (1935); **8**, 350 (1936).
12. van der Meulen, J. H., *Chem. Weekblad*, **31**, 633 (1934).
13. Bright, H. A., and Larrabee, C. P., *J. Research Natl. Bur. Standards*, **3**, 573 (1939).
14. Pigott, 237.
15. Zharova, L. P., *Metody Analiza Chern. i Tsvet. Metallov.* 70 (1953).
16. Sandell, E. B., *et al.*, *Ind. Eng. Chem., Anal. Ed.*, **7**, 256 (1935).
17. Leroide, J., and Bruiltet, A., *Bull. soc. chim. France*, **2**, 740 (1935); also see Scott and Furman, 561; Kimura, 249 (acetate buffer + 1 g. $ZnSO_4$ soln.).
18. Přibil, R., and Vulterin, J., *Chem. listy*, **48**, 1132 (1954).
19. Scott and Furman, 554.
20. Lang, R., *Z. anal. Chem.*, **102**, 8 (1935); also see Lang and Faude, E., *ibid.*, **108**, 181 (1937) (detn. of Mn, Ce, Cr, V); Lang and Kurtz, F., *Z. anorg. u. allgem. Chem.*, **181**, 111 (1929) (in fluoride soln.); also see Lingane, J. J., and Karplus, R., *Ind. Eng. Chem., Anal. Ed.*, **18**, 191 (1946) (+ $P_2O_7^{4-}$, to Mn^{3+}, potentiometric); Huber, C. O., and Shain, I., *Anal. Chem.*, **29**, 1178 (1957) (potentiometric); Goffart, G., *Anal. Chim. Acta*, **1**, 393 (1947) (amperometric).
21. Mukoyama, T., *et al.*, *Japan Analyst*, **4**, 80 (1955).
22. Issa, I. M., and Issa, R. M., *Chemist Analyst*, **44**, 99 (1955).
23. Hillebrand and Lundell, 399 (439).
24. Brinkmann, G., and Schmedding, W., *Z. anal. Chem.*, **114**, 161 (1938).
25. Yoe, 273.
26. Sandell, 430.
27. Mehlig, J. P., *Ind. Eng. Chem., Anal. Ed.*, **11**, 274 (1939).
28. Nydahl, F., *Anal. Chim. Acta*, **3**, 144 (1949).
29. Ito, T., *et al.*, *Japan Analyst*, **4**, 353 (1955).
30. Sherwood, R. M., and Chapman, F. W., Jr., *Anal. Chem.*, **27**, 88 (1955).
31. Lingane, J. J., and Collat, J. W., *Anal. Chem.*, **22**, 166 (1950); also see Lacroix, S., and Labalade, M., *Anal. Chim. Acta*, **3**, 262 (1949).
32. Kuznetsov, V. I., and Budanova, L. M., *Zhur. Anal. Khim.*, **8**, 55 (1953).
33. Kiyota, H., and Yamamoto, T., *J. Chem. Soc. Japan*, **76**, 1179 (1955).
34. Tanaka, M., *J. Chem. Soc. Japan*, **72**, 29, 32, 136 (1951).
35. Nuka, P., *Z. anal. Chem.*, **87**, 7 (1932); Njegovan, V. N., and Morsan, B., *ibid.*, **131**, 187 (1950).
36. Hecht and Donau, 203; Welcher, **II**, 135.
37. Daubner, W., *Z. anal. Chem.*, **116**, 309 (1939).
38. Welcher, **II**, 201.
39. Welcher, **III**, 27; Spacu, G., and Lupan, S., *Analele Acad. Rep. populare Rumâne, Ser. Mat. Fis. Chim.*, **3**, *Mem.* 25 (1950).
40. Medoks, H. V., and Maskelowa, N. N., *Zhur. Anal. Khim.*, **1**, 319 (1946).
41. Hein, F., and Arvay, D., *Angew. Chem.*, **A60**, 157 (1948).
42. Flaschka, H., *et al.*, *Chemist Analyst*, **43**, 67 (1954); Přibil, R., *Chem. listy*, **48**, 382 (1954).
43. Smith, J. S., *Analyst*, **64**, 787 (1939).
44. Ishimaru, S., *J. Chem. Soc. Japan*, **56**, 66 (1935); Neelakantam, K., *Proc. Indian Acad. Sci.*, **27A**, 202 (1949).

45. Fujita, Y., and Kayamori, H., *J. Chem. Soc. Japan*, **75**, 655 (1954).
46. Cheng, K. L., *Anal. Chem.*, **27**, 1594 (1955); Sajó, I., *Magyar Kém. Folyóirat*, **61**, 196 (1956) (3,3′-dimethylnaphthidine).
47. Welcher, **II**, 280, 470.
48. Prodinger, W., and Gurski, A., *Mikrochemie ver. Mikrochim. Acta*, **36/37**, 580 (1950); also Welcher, **IV**, 565.
49. Welcher, **II**, 258.
50. Bradfield, E. G., *Analyst*, **82**, 254 (1957); also see Eckert, G., *Z. anal. Chem.*, **148**, 14 (1955) (in Ni metal).
51. Tourky, T. R., *et al.*, *Anal. Chim. Acta*, **16**, 151 (1957).
52. Almássy, Gy, and Dezsö, I., *Magyar Kém. Folyóirat*, **60**, 249 (1954).
53. Bruno, S., *Accad. pugliese sci.*, *Atti e relaz*, **11**, (2) 409, (1953).
54. Tomula, E. S., and Aho, V., *Ann. Acad. Sci. Fennicae*, **A55**, No. 1 (1940).
55. Purdy, W. C., Hume, D. N., *Anal. Chem.*, **27**, 256 (1955).
56. Kodama, K., *Research Repts. Nagoya Munic. Ind. Research Inst.*, (17), 27 (1957).
57. Specker, H., *Z. anal. Chem.*, **143**, 425 (1954).
58. Dippel, W. A., and Bricker, C. E., *Anal. Chem.*, **27**, 1484 (1955); Ikeda, S., *J. Chem. Soc. Japan*, **78**, 913 (1957) (in Fe–Mn).

38

VANADIUM

The principal references for this chapter are given in ref. 1. The gravimetric determination of vanadium has been fully described[2] and the general determination of vanadium has been reviewed.[3]

The reduction of vanadium to different valency states can be accomplished with different reagents. Reduction of V^{5+} to V^{4+} (blue) is possible with Fe^{2+}, SO_2, H_2S, H_2O_2, HBr, EtOH, HCOOH, $H_2C_2O_4$, sucrose in acidic soln. or by evapn. with HCl. Reduction to V^{3+} (green) can be done by boiling with HI or with Hg in acidic soln. Reduction to V^{2+} (violet to pale blue–violet) is done with Zn, Al, Cd, etc. in acidic soln.

Oxidation of V^{4+} to V^{5+} is carried out with $KMnO_4$ or $(NH_4)_2S_2O_8$ in dil. H_2SO_4 soln., with Br_2 or $KBrO_3$ in dil. HCl soln., or with Na_2O_2 in alk. soln. Oxidation with $K_2Cr_2O_7$ is not possible in cold acidic soln.

The composition of precipitates may vary according to the pH. Barium vanadate has the formula $Ba(VO_3)_2$ at pH 3·5–4·5, $(BaO)_{1-3}(V_2O_5)$ at pH 4·5–10·8 and $Ba_3(VO_4)_2 + BaCO_3$ at pH 10·8–11·4. $AgVO_3$ exists at pH 4–4·6 whereas $Pb_3(VO_4)_2$ exists at pH 4·3–5.

If WO_3 is pptd. by acid treatment, about 0·1% V may coppt. To avoid error from this source, treat the ignited oxide with 15 ml. 4% NaOH, filter, add H_2O and a 5 ml. excess of H_3PO_4 and determine the V colorimetrically. Alternatively, boil the ignited oxide with NH_4OH, filter, treat the ppt. with HCl and add to the main solution; treat the filtrate with 10 ml. HF, neutralize with NH_4OH, add 25 ml. HCl, dil. to 300 ml. with H_2O, add 50 g. NH_4Cl, filter, ignite, add H_2SO_4 and add to the main solution.

It should be noted that VF_5 is volatile, so that ignition should not be carried out after treatment with HF and H_2SO_4.

Attack

(a) Minerals (vanadates). Treat with HCl and HNO_3 (or HCl and $KClO_3$) and evap. to white fumes with H_2SO_4. Ext. the residue with 25% NH_4OAc and NH_4OH and then ignite. Treat with 5 ml. HF and 2 ml. HNO_3 and evap. to white fumes with 1 ml. 1:1 H_2SO_4. Combine the solns. If Pb is absent, fuse the residue with Na_2CO_3, leach with HCl and combine.

If much SiO_2 is present, evap. to white fumes with HF and H_2SO_4, add hot H_2O and a little H_2SO_4 and fuse the residue with $K_2S_2O_7$.

Minerals can also be dealt with by fusion with Na_2CO_3 (or K_2CO_3) and KNO_3 (10:1, adding more KNO_3 if required), or by fusion with Na_2O_2.

If the valency state of V is to be detd., heat the mineral in a sealed tube with H_2SO_4.

For analysis of black sand,[4] heat with H_3PO_4, heat to fumes after adding dil. H_2SO_4, etc. For sulfides, roast at a low temp. and then fuse with Na_2CO_3 and KNO_3.

(b) Steels. Treat with 1:9 H_2SO_4 and use $NaHCO_3$ sepn.; then fume with H_2SO_4 and HNO_3, apply Hg-cathode electrolysis, etc. (see also Chapter 45, p. 332). If very small amts. of V and large amts. of Cr or Ni are present, cupferron sepn. is advisable. Any Se or Te present should be removed with SO_2 in 10% HCl soln.

For treatment of steels with $HClO_4$, etc., see under Determination, p. 291.

For steels or Fe–V, heat with dil. H_2SO_4 and H_3PO_4 and add H_2O_2 if a black residue remains.[4] Alternatively,[5] treat 0·5 g. Fe–V of below 150 mesh with 5 ml. HF and 20 ml. 30% H_2O_2 and, after dissoln., add 10 ml. 1:3 H_2SO_4; cool, dil. to 200 ml. with H_2O, etc.

Steels may also be treated with aqua regia or HNO_3 or $HNO_3 + H_2SO_4 + HF$; fusion with Na_2CO_3 and KNO_3 or with Na_2O_2 may be required in certain cases.

Separation

Treatment with NH_4OH in presence of 0·1 g. Fe^{3+} is useful for concn. of V and is most satisfactory in presence of PO_4^{3-}; if over 10 mg. V is present, pptn. is incomplete.

$(NH_4)_2MoO_4$ treatment of 0·5*N* HNO_3 soln. contg. a 5–10-fold amt. of P (see p. 427) seps. V from Fe, U, etc. and is also useful for concn. $(NH_4)_2MoO_4$ also allows sepn. of V from PO_4^{3-}: pass SO_2 through the dil. H_2SO_4 soln., boil while passing CO_2, cool, add NH_4NO_3 and a little HNO_3 followed by 50 ml. reagent (75 g. in 500 ml. poured slowly into 500 ml. HNO_3); dissolve the ppt. in NH_4OH and reppt.

Extn. with 20:1 AcOH–HNO_3 seps. V from U, but P interferes.[6] Evap. the HNO_3 soln. to dryness and bake until NO_2 evolution ceases but do not ignite; add 15–20 ml. reagent, filter on a Gooch crucible and wash 5–6 times with reagent. Evap. the filtrate to dryness, bake, add 10 ml. reagent, etc. This procedure is preferable to the $Pb(OAc)_2$ method described below.

V, Cr^{6+}, Mo, W, P, As can be sepd.[1] from Fe, etc. with $Hg_2(NO_3)_2$. Ext. the Na_2CO_3 melt with H_2O, almost neutralize with HNO_3, add reagent, etc. Cl^- interferes.

Treatment with $Pb(OAc)_2$ seps. V, Mo, W and Cr from U, etc. Heat the soln. contg. 4 ml. HNO_3/100 ml. with 10 ml. 10% reagent and 20 ml. NH_4OAc soln. (1:1 NH_4OH neutralized with AcOH) on a steam-bath for 1 hr., filter and wash with hot H_2O; add H_2SO_4, heat to white fumes and filter. Sepn. from U is better if $(NH_4)_2CO_3$ is added. Sepn. from Cr is achieved by boiling with H_2O_2 for 2 min., before addn. of $Pb(OAc)_2$. U can be detd. in the filtrate from the above method: add NH_4OH and filter but do not wash, and pour into hot satd. $(NH_4)_2CO_3$ and NH_4OH; wash with dil. $(NH_4)_2CO_3$ + NH_4OH, add satd. H_2S water, boil, filter, wash with H_2S water contg. $(NH_4)_2CO_3$; finally boil, add NH_4OH, etc.

Treatment of the soln. with $MnSO_4$ in presence of NH_4Cl and NH_4OH seps. V from Mo^{7+} (see also Chapter 29, p. 214).

V can be sepd. incompletely from U by pouring the hot soln. into a boiling soln. of NH_4NaHPO_4 (5 g. + 15 g. NH_4OAc in 5 ml. AcOH and 95 ml. H_2O) followed by boiling for 2 min.; after decantation, dissolve in HNO_3 and reppt. U can be detd. titrimetrically after dissoln. of the ppt. in 15 ml. of hot 1:3 H_2SO_4.

$Pb(ClO_4)_2$ in hot dil. $HClO_4$ soln. seps V from Cr^{6+} (see under Determination, below).

Sepn. from Cr is best achieved by volatilization of CrO_2Cl_2: evap. the $HClO_4$ soln. in a covered Erlenmeyer flask until $HClO_4$ condenses on the walls, remove the cover, swirl and add 1–2 ml. HCl or some NaCl at intervals until no more brown fumes are evolved; cover and evap., repeat this process 3–4 times, cool, add 20 ml. H_2O, etc.

V is also sepd. from Cr by treatment of the soln. contg. 10 ml. satd. NH_4OAc with 10 ml. satd. Na_2S soln. (pH 9–12); dil. Na_2S soln. is used for washing.[8] Another method is to treat the dil. HNO_3 soln. with SO_2, pour into boiling 10% NaOH, boil for 2 min. and filter; Cl^- must be previously removed by evapn. with HNO_3. Treatment with H_2O_2 followed by extn. with EtOAc also seps. V from Cr (see p. 332).

Cupferron seps. V, Fe, Zr, Ti, etc. from U^{6+}, Cr^{3+}, Al, Mn, Zn, Ni, As, P by treatment of the soln. contg. < 4% H_2SO_4 or < 15% HCl at 0–20°C. This reagent is also used for concn. purposes with a little Fe^{3+}. Extn. with $CHCl_3$ of the complex serves for concn. and for sepn. from Al, etc. Sepn. from W is possible in dil. HCl soln. contg. NH_4Cl or NH_4F.[9]

Fusion with Na_2CO_3 and KNO_3 followed by extn. with H_2O or pptn. with NaOH seps. V, P, As, Mo, Cr, U and partly Si and Al from Fe, Ti, Zr, etc.

Treatment with 8% $NaHCO_3$ seps. V from large amts. of Fe^{2+} and Mn; the small amt. of V in the ppt. is recovered by fusion with Na_2O_2 and extn. with hot H_2O. For oxides, fuse with a 6-fold amt. of Na_2CO_3, dissolve in 500 ml. H_2O, boil, add NH_4NO_3 (10 times the amt. of oxides) in small amts. while boiling but do not remove all the CO_2; then filter, wash with NH_4NO_3 and reppt. This process seps. V from Al.[7]

H_2S treatment of acidic solns. contg. tartrate seps. V from group II metals and particularly from As and Mo. Treatment of ammoniacal solns. contg. tartrate gives a sepn. from Fe, Co, Ni, Zn, Mn.

Electrolysis of a dil. H_2SO_4 soln. with a Hg-cathode seps. V, U, Al, P (and partly As) from Fe, Cr, Co, Ni, Cu, Mo.

Ether extn. of an HCl soln. seps V from Fe and Mo but some V is also extd. Phenarsazinic acid seps. V from Ni, Cr, Mg, Zn (see Chapter 14, Section 2) but is not satisfactory.

$VOCl_2$, Mo, As and some Fe volatilize on heating the sample in a stream of HCl gas or CO_2 + CCl_4 and are thus sepd. from SiO_2, etc.

Treatment with tannin seps. V from Ti in $(NH_4)_2C_2O_4$ soln. and from Zr in slightly acidic (HCl) NH_4Cl soln. Hydrolysis in tartaric acid soln. gives a sepn. from Nb, Ta, W. For further details of these methods, see pp. 355, 361, 374 and 378.

Extn. of the oxinates with $CHCl_3$ at pH 3·5–4·5 seps. V from Cr, Al, F^- and PO_4^{3-} but Fe, Mo and W interfere; this is also used for concn. Sepn. of V^{4+} from V^{5+} is possible with oxine in solns. of pH 4·5–5 contg. EDTA.[10]

Determination

It is important to remember that minerals may contain U and that steels contain Cr and W. Titration with $KMnO_4$ is the most used method; the procedure given below may not be the best available, for details of the procedures are rarely given. Of the colorimetric methods, those involving H_2O_2, oxine or phosphotungstate are probably the best.

(a) Redox titrations. (*i*) Titration with $KMnO_4$ in presence of ferroin indicator is used for detn. of V in steels.[11] Dissolve 2 g. steel with 20–25 ml. HCl and 35 ml. 55% $HClO_4$ by boiling to white fumes in a covered 400 ml. beaker and maintain for 10 min. at a temp. such that $HClO_4$ refluxes gently down the wall. Slide the beaker on to a cold plate for 10–20 sec., remove the cover and cool by dipping the beaker, whilst rotating it, intermittently into cold water. Add 70 ml. H_2O, boil for 3 min., remove from the heater and add 5 drops 0·5*M* $AgNO_3$ followed by 0·5*M* $Pb(ClO_4)_2$ (6 ml./100 mg. Cr and 5 ml. for each addnl. 100 mg. Cr). Heat for 30 sec., cool in running water, filter and wash with cold H_2O. Add 7 ml. H_3PO_4, 2 ml. satd. ferroin perchlorate and excess Fe^{2+} soln. (6 g. $FeSO_4$ crystals in 6·8 l. H_2O and 1·2 l. H_3PO_4) and back-titrate with 0·01*N* $KMnO_4$ until the red color disappears; the red color may return and the first decolorization should be taken. (If the end-point is overrun, add more Fe^{2+} and again decolorize with $KMnO_4$; if the amt. of $KMnO_4$ needed is below 1 ml., add more Fe^{2+} and proceed as before so that the amt. needed will be above 1 ml.) Then add 20 ml. H_3PO_4 and 35 ml. K_2HPO_4 (450 g./220 ml.) and titrate with 0·01*N* $KMnO_4$ to the red to violet end-point.

NOTES. (1) If W is present, V may coppt. (see p. 291). No interference arises from Cr, Ni, Co, Mo, As, U, Fe.

(2) Various similar procedures have been suggested.

(*i*) Reduction with SO_2 can be followed by potentiometric titration with 0·02–0·03*N* $KMnO_4$.[11] Heat the 2:98 H_2SO_4 soln. to boiling and add concd. $KMnO_4$ until pink. Pass SO_2 for 5–10 min. and then pass CO_2 while boiling, until 1 drop 1:1 H_2SO_4 and 1 drop 0·1*N* $KMnO_4$ in 5 ml. soln. is not decolorized by the evolved gases. Cool to 70°C, titrate potentiometrically and repeat the process if desired. The method is suitable for low Cr steels[11] and a visual end-point is possible.[1, 12] Fe, As, Sb, Pt, Cr interfere and must be sepd. by treatment with $NaHCO_3$, electrolysis at a Hg-cathode, H_2S sepn. etc.

(*ii*) Fe^{2+} reduction can also be applied differently from the main procedure given above.[1, 11, 12] If Fe^{3+} is present, add H_3PO_4 to the 1:9 H_2SO_4 soln. Add $KMnO_4$ to give a pink color followed by 0·1*N* Fe^{2+} until a drop of soln. gives a blue color with $K_3Fe(CN)_6$ and then 3–5 ml. in excess. Stir for 1 min., cool below 18°C, add 8 ml. 15% $(NH_4)_2S_2O_8$ and titrate with 0·03*N* $KMnO_4$ until the soln. stays pink for 30 sec. W interferes but Ni, Co, Mo, As, U and Cr do not (Cr can be detd. previously if desired). For steels[11] dissolve in HCl and $HClO_4$, volatilize Cr with HCl or NaCl and titrate with $KMnO_4$ after addn. of Fe^{2+} (preoxidation with $KMnO_4$ is unnecessary). Excess Fe^{2+} in the above method can also be removed with $K_2Cr_2O_7$ using $K_3Fe(CN)_6$ as external indicator.

(*iii*) Reduction with Zn–Hg may be utilized. Shake the 1–2*N* H_2SO_4 soln. for at least 3 min. with Zn–Hg under CO_2 (to form V^{2+}), sep., titrate with 0·1*N* $KMnO_4$ until near the end-point, transfer to a beaker, heat and complete the titration. Since the equivalent of V is small, the accuracy is increased if no other elements are present. Fe and V can be detd. if the SO_2 reduction method precedes this procedure.[6] Alternatively, after the reduction with Zn–Hg, transfer to a beaker, add 30 ml. satd. Ag_2SO_4 soln. for 0·1 g. V, boil for several min. (to form V^{4+}), filter and titrate. For other amalgams and oxidants, see ref. 13. For use of the Jones reductor, see ref. 6.

(*iv*) Evapn. with HCl in presence of an amt. of Fe^{3+} equivalent to the V present is suitable for minerals; none of the elements present in V minerals interfere, nor do Zn, Cu, As, etc.[6, 7] Treat 2–3 g. 100-mesh mineral with 40–60 ml. HCl at 50–60°C, add 2 g. $KClO_3$ gradually and evap. to fumes with 20 ml. 1:1 H_2SO_4. Add 100 ml. H_2O, boil, filter, treat the residue with HF and H_2SO_4, after removal of $PbSO_4$, and then combine with the main soln. Add 5 ml. HNO_3, evap. to 40 ml., make pink with 2·5% $KMnO_4$, evap. to fumes and add 20 ml. 1:1 H_2SO_4, 50 ml. HCl and $Fe_2(SO_4)_3$ (so that Fe = V). Evap. to 30 ml., add 25 ml. HCl, heat rapidly to fumes and fume for 10 min. Cool, add 50 ml. H_2O, 5 ml. H_3PO_4 and hot H_2O to give a vol. of 350 ml., warm, cool to 20–25°C and titrate with 0·05–0·1*N* $KMnO_4$ until pink for 30 sec. Deduct a blank obtained by adding 1 drop 0·1*N* Fe^{2+}, stirring for 1 min. with 8 ml. 15% $(NH_4)_2S_2O_8$ and titrating with $KMnO_4$. If a very large amt. of Fe is present, ext. the bulk with Et_2O.

(*v*) Reduction with H_2O_2 is rapid.[6, 7] Heat the soln. to fumes with H_2SO_4, cool, add H_2O_2 gradually until brown, heat for 4–5 min., add 100 ml. H_2O, heat to 80°C and titrate with $KMnO_4$. V in steels is sepd. as phosphovanadomolybdate which is dissolved in H_2SO_4 and treated as above.[6] Reduction with H_2S or $H_2C_2O_4$ is also possible.[7]

(*vi*) For reduction with Hg,[14] shake the dil. H_2SO_4 soln. for 5 min. with 20 ml. Hg and add NaCl; filter on a glass crucible, wash with H_2O, dil. to 250 ml. with H_2O, heat to 80–90°C and titrate with $KMnO_4$. Fe interferes but As and U do not.

(*ii*) Titration with Fe^{2+} is best with ferroin indicator.[15] Titrate the 5*M* H_2SO_4 soln. of V^{5+} with 0·1*M* Fe^{2+} in 1*M* H_2SO_4. No interference arises from Fe, Cr^{3+} or Mo. Potentiometric titration is suitable for 5 μg. Cr or V.[16] For analysis of steels,[7, 17] diphenylamine-sulfonic acid or diphenylamine can be used as indicator after oxidation of V with $KMnO_4$, excess of which is removed with $NaNO_2$ and urea or with NaN_3. Potentiometric titration is also suitable after oxidation with HNO_3.[11, 12] For photometric and coulometric titrations, see Chapter 45 (p. 333).

(*iii*) Other methods. Reduction with Fe^{2+} can be followed by treatment with $K_2Cr_2O_7$ and As^{3+} and titration with Fe^{2+} in presence of diphenylamine indicator as for Mn (p. 286).[18]

Reduction with Zn–Hg is followed by titration with 0·1*N* Ce^{4+} in presence of ferroin indicator.[19] This titration is also used after treatment of V^{4+} in 0·1–1*N* alk. soln. with a 1·5–2-fold excess of $K_3Fe(CN)_6$ for 30 min.; the soln. is acidified with 9*N* H_2SO_4 before titration.[20] The titration of V^{4+} with $K_3Fe(CN)_6$ can also be done in Na_2CO_3 soln. contg. pyro- or triphosphate at pH 12. Titration of V^{5+} is done with 0·1*N* $K_4Fe(CN)_6$ with diphenylamine as indicator in 2*N* H_2SO_4 soln. contg. pyro- or triphosphate.[21]

V in steels can be titrated with hydroquinone soln. using diphenylamine indicator in 20% H_2SO_4 medium.[22]

Titration with 0·01*N* $Na_2S_2O_3$ with *p*-aminodimethylaniline as indicator is suitable for 0·015–2 mg. V in 100 ml. slightly acidic (HNO_3) soln.[23] Add 1 g. NH_4F, 20 drops H_3PO_4, 0·5 g. NH_4F, 2 ml. 1% indicator, and titrate to the disappearance of the pink color; then add another 1 ml. indicator and complete the titration. No interference is caused by U, U + Fe or PO_4^{3-}.

For a coulometric titration with Cu^{+} or Ti^{3+}, see Chapter 45, p. 333, and ref. 24. For iodometric titration, see p. 294.

(b) Oxine is generally used colorimetrically,[25] but gravimetric and titrimetric procedures are also available.

For 1–50 μg. V in 50 ml. soln., neutralize to methyl orange with NH_4OH or HNO_3, and ext. 3 times by shaking for 2·5 min. with 5 ml. 0·5% oxine in $CHCl_3$ (purified by shaking 6 times with 0·25 times its vol. of H_2O). Combine the exts., shake with 50 ml. buffer soln. (200 ml. 4*N* NH_4OH and 100 ml. 4*N* HNO_3 in 2 l.; pH 9·4), discard the org. layer and shake with 5 ml. portions of $CHCl_3$ until no color remains. Then add 1 drop methyl orange, neutralize with 4*N* HNO_3, add 2 ml. buffer soln. (12·77 g. KH-phthalate in 250 ml.) and ext. twice with 5·00 ml. portions of 0·1% oxine in $CHCl_3$ (purified as above). Measure at 550 or 365 mμ, using 0·1% reagent as reference.

NOTES. (1) Some time is needed for the reaction of oxine with V. If much Fe or Al is present, use more oxine. This procedure is twice as sensitive as the phosphotungstate method.

(2) In an alternative method,[26] heat the acidic (H_2SO_4) soln. to 50°C and, if Cr is present, add Na_2SO_3, heat, add 1 drop satd. Br_2 water and heat; then treat with oxine in AcOH, adjust to pH 3·5–4·5 (3·5 if Al is present) with NH_4OAc and ext. with $CHCl_3$.

(3) For detn. of V in natural waters,[27] add HCl and Fe^{3+} (10 mg./l.) to a 5–20 l. sample, make alk. to bromocresol purple with NH_4OH, filter and ignite. Heat with 5 ml. 6*N* HCl, dil. to 50 ml. with H_2O and add 15 ml. of a soln. contg. 30 g. tartaric acid and 200 g. NaOH/l. Heat on a steam-bath for 30 min. until clear, centrifuge and decant. Neutralize with 4*N* H_2SO_4 to *p*-nitrophenol, add 3 ml. in excess, heat, add 2 ml. oxine soln. (2 g. oxine and 5 g. malonic acid/100 ml.), neutralize with NH_4OH and add 4 ml. in excess (if the ppt. is large, centrifuge). Then ext. twice with 20 ml. C_6H_6, neutralize with 4*N* H_2SO_4, add 3 ml. in excess, 4 ml. acetate buffer pH 4 and 10 ml. oxine soln., ext. twice with AmOH, dil. to 10 ml. with AmOH and measure at 475 mμ.

(4) For gravimetric or titrimetric detn.,[28] treat the 0·2–2*N* AcOH soln. with 5 g. NH_4OAc and 4% oxine in Me_2CO, boil out most of the Me_2CO, cool, filter on a glass crucible and wash with H_2O. Dry at 120–130°C (< 195°C) and weigh as $V_2O_3(C_9H_6ON)_4$, or titrate the ppt. with $KBrO_3$–KBr in the usual way. No interference is caused by As^{5+}, Cr^{3+}, Be, Cu, Zn, Cd, Hg, Al, Pb, Mn, Ca, etc. or by PO_4^{3-}. The ppt. can be weighed as $VO(OH)Ox_2$ after drying at 140–200°C or as $V_2O_3(Ox)_4$ at 250–270°C. Pptn. is said to be incomplete (Duval).

(5) Bromoxine or iodoxine ppt. V at pH 4–5;[29] the ppts. can be dried to $VO(C_9H_4ONX_2)_2$ at 150–160° and 170–180°C resp.

8-Hydroxyquinoline-5-sulfonic acid can be used colorimetrically for 2·5–20 μg. V/ml.:[30] treat the acetate-buffered soln. with satd. reagent soln. and measure the brown complex at 510 mμ. Fe, Cu, Pb, Cd, Al, Zn interfere.

(c) Na_2WO_4 and H_3PO_4 are applied[12, 31, 32] for colorimetric detn. of 1–5 μg. V in 10 ml. 0·5*N* mineral acid soln. Add 1·0 ml. 1:2 H_3PO_4 and 0·5 ml. 0·5*M* Na_2WO_4 (16·5 g./100 ml.), boil, cool, dil. to 15 ml. with H_2O, and measure the yellow-orange color at 400 mμ. If Fe is absent or only traces of V are present, it is unnecessary to heat.

For steels,[33] dissolve in 1:9 H_2SO_4 or 30% $HClO_4$, apply $NaHCO_3$ sepn. and filter on paper; digest with H_2SO_4 or $HClO_4$ and HNO_3, electrolyze using a Hg cathode, treat with HF and $HClO_4$, etc. Cr can be sepd. with 0·5*M* $Pb(ClO_4)_2$.

For rocks,[31, 34] fuse 1 g. with 4–5 g. Na_2CO_3 over a Méker burner for 30 min., ext. with H_2O, filter and wash with 20% Na_2CO_3. Dil. to 100 ml. with H_2O, and pipet 10 ml. for basic rocks or 25 ml. for acidic rocks. Neutralize with 4*N* H_2SO_4 to methyl orange (if much Fe is present, acidify, treat with $KMnO_4$, filter and make alk. with NaOH) and add 2 ml. $CHCl_3$ and 0·1 ml. 2·5% oxine in 2*N* AcOH (redistd. AcOH, dild. to 1:8). Shake, sep. and repeat the extn. twice. Combine the exts., add 0·1 g. Na_2CO_3, evap., ignite, add H_2O, filter if turbid, add 1 ml. 4*N* H_2SO_4 and proceed as above.

NOTES. (1) Interferences are Cr, SCN^-, I^-, 1 mg. Zr, 4 mg. Mn, 10 mg. Mo, Cu, Co, Sb, Th, 15 mg. Bi, 20 mg. Fe or Ti and 25 mg. Sn. No interference is caused by Na, Mg, Ca, Sr, Ba, Cd, Hg^{2+}, Al, Pb, As^{5+}, Ag, 0·1 g. U, 75 mg. K or 50 mg. SiO_2; AcO^-, Br^-, tartrate, $C_2O_4^{2-}$, citrate, CN^-, BO_2^- and F^- can be present.

(2) Several minor modifications have been suggested. The salt formed can be extd. with iso-BuOH.[35] Alternatively, the NH_4VO_3 is pptd., dissolved in NaOH, NH_3 boiled out and the solution neutralized with H_2SO_4 before proceeding as above.[36] Reduction of the salt with $SnCl_2$ has been suggested.[37] Molybdate can replace tungstate[38] or the yellow color formed with molybdate alone can be utilized.[39]

(d) H_2O_2 forms a yellow-brown color with up to 1 mg. V in 10 ml. 1–2*N* H_2SO_4 soln.[1, 31, 40] Add 0·25 ml. 3% reagent and measure at 460 mμ (or at 530 mμ if U is present). The optimum acidity is 0·6–6*N* H_2SO_4 or 3 ml. 1:1 HCl in 50 ml. soln. The color depends on the amt. of H_2O_2 added and fades if too much is added.

NOTES. (1) Simultaneous detn. of Mo, Ti, V in $HClO_4$ soln. is possible (see Chapter 50, p. 362). Differential spectrophotometry can be used to det. 2–5 mg. V in Al alloys with solns. contg. 5 ml. $HClO_4$ and 1 ml. 5% H_2O_2 per 25 ml. soln.[41]

(2) Mo interference is avoided by extn. with Et_2O from HCl soln. Fe requires PO_4^{3-} or F^- addn., Ti needs HF addn. and W needs $H_2C_2O_4$ addn. Co, Ni, Cu, etc., much Ce and I^- and Br^- interfere. If much Cr is present, EtOAc extn. is necessary. F^- and PO_4^{3-} do not interfere. The tolerance for Cr^{6+} or Ti is better at 290 mμ and the sensitivity is also better; but if Fe^{3+} or NO_3^- is present, 460 mμ is the preferred wavelength.[42]

(e) Cupferron can be applied gravimetrically or colorimetrically.[7, 43] For the gravimetric detn. see under Separation, p. 291. The ppt. is ignited at 900°C (581–946°C) and weighed as V_2O_5.

For colorimetry, use a 1% reagent soln. decolorized with active charcoal.[43] To 10 ml. soln., add 1 ml. H_2SO_4, 2 ml. 25% K_2SO_4 (if Cr > V add a little H_2O_2 and boil), 1 ml. 2% gum arabic and 1 ml. reagent and compare the colors.

NOTES. (1) For 40 μg. V in soln. of pH 1·8, add reagent and ext. with $CHCl_3$; Fe and Ti interfere, while Ce requires addn. of NH_4OH and H_2O_2, and Cu is removed with H_2S.[43]

(2) For 0·6–6 mg. V in 150 ml. soln. at pH < 1, add 10 ml. 10% EDTA, cool to 0–10°C, add paper pulp and reagent and adjust to pH < 1; after 5–10 min. filter through 2 layers of Whatman No. 40 paper, wash with 10% H_2SO_4, dissolve the ppt. from the paper with Me_2CO, dil. to 100 ml. and measure the green color after 20–30 min.[44]

(3) Benzoylphenylhydroxylamine is suitable for colorimetric detn. of 0·05–0·75 mg. V.[45] Add 0·2–2 ml. H_2SO_4 to give a final pH of 1·9–2·8, 10 ml. 0·2% reagent in EtOH, 15 ml. EtOH, and dil. to 50 ml. with H_2O; measure the reddish color at 510 mμ after 10 min. Fe, Al, W, Cr, Ti, etc. interfere.

(f) Tannin can be applied gravimetrically.[7, 46] Adjust the soln. with NH_4OH or AcOH so that it is slightly acidic, heat and add 5–10 g. NH_4Cl, 5–10 g. NH_4OAc and reagent in a 10-fold amt. (at least 0·2 g.). Add paper pulp and filter on paper, washing with 2% NH_4NO_3 contg. some tannin. Ignite to V_2O_5. Tartrate does not interfere.

(g) $AgNO_3$ can also be used gravimetrically.[47] To 200 ml. neutral soln. add 3 g. NaOAc, 0·5 ml. NH_4OH (s.g. 0·95) and excess reagent, boil and heat on a steam-bath for 30 min. Filter on a porcelain filter, wash with hot H_2O, dry at 110°C, transfer to a porcelain crucible and ignite at 350–650°C to Ag_3VO_4. Results are usually 1% low but the method is said[47] to be accurate for 0·5–10 mg. V_2O_5. According to Duval, pptn. from acidic soln. and drying at 60–500°C leads to $AgVO_3$.

Many other cations have been recommended for detn. of V. With $UO_2(OAc)_2$, which is used for 0·05 g. V_2O_5 in 25 ml. soln.,[48] neutralize to neutral red–methylene blue with NH_4OH, acidify with AcOH, add 2 g. NH_4OAc, boil, add 0·1N reagent in excess and allow to cool; filter on a glass crucible, wash, dry at 105°C and weigh as $NH_4UO_2VO_4 \cdot 1\frac{1}{2}H_2O$, or ignite at 450–700°C (560–950°C) and weigh as $(UO_2)_2V_2O_7$.

$Hg_2(NO_3)_2$ ppts. 0·1 g. V from 110 ml. soln. contg. 0·2 ml. HNO_3: heat, add 3 ml. 10% H_2O_2 and 40 ml. of a satd. soln. of reagent in hot H_2O and boil for 30 min. Filter on paper, wash with cold H_2O, burn the paper and ppt. separately, ignite at 900°C (371–950°C) and weigh as V_2O_5. NH_4^+ interferes.[7, 47]

$Pb(OAc)_2$ ppts. V from slightly alk. (Na_2CO_3) soln.[6, 7] Add 10% reagent, heat until the ppt. turns white, filter on paper and wash with very dil. AcOH. Evap. to fumes with HNO_3 and H_2SO_4, add H_2O, filter on paper, wash, evap. and ignite to V_2O_5. Alternatively (Moser *et al.*[47]), adjust the pH with $KBrO_3$ and KBr, ignite at 350–400°C and weigh as $Pb_2V_2O_7$. The method is said to be inaccurate (Duval).

$BiOClO_4$ can also be applied.[49] Add 5 ml. $HClO_4$ and excess reagent (10 g. Bi dissolved in 20 ml. HNO_3 evapd. to fumes twice with 30 ml. $HClO_4$ and dild. to 500 ml. with H_2O), dil. to 80 ml. with H_2O and boil until the ppt. crystallizes; dil. to 200 ml. with hot H_2O, boil for 1 hr., allow to cool, filter on paper and wash with 2% NH_4NO_3 contg. some HNO_3, before igniting. An empirical factor of 0·245 is needed for conversion to V_2O_5. Most cations can be tolerated in amts. up to 10 mg. but Sb, Sn, Cl^-, SO_4^{2-}, PO_4^{3-}, AsO_3^{3-}, AsO_4^{3-}, $Cr_2O_7^{2-}$, MoO_4^{2-}, WO_4^{2-} and much NO_3^- interfere.

$[Co(NH_3)_6]Cl_3$ forms a yellow ppt. with V from AcOH–NaOAc soln. which can be dried at 110°C (58–143°C) and weighed as $[Co(NH_3)_6](VO_3)_3$ or ignited and weighed as $4CoO \cdot 9V_2O_5$. Fe, Cu, Ca, PO_4^{3-} and AsO_4^{3-} can be tolerated but WO_4^{2-}, MoO_4^{2-} and Pb interfere.[50] If the ppt. is formed from acidic soln. and dried below 127°C, it can be weighed as $[Co(NH_3)_6](V_6O_{17})_3$ (Duval). Conductometric titration based on this reaction is also possible.[51]

NH_4Cl can be used to ppt. V.[7] Sat. 50 ml. of the soln. with NH_4Cl, evap. to 25 ml. adding some NH_4OH occasionally, filter on a Gooch crucible after 12 hr., wash with satd. NH_4Cl and ignite.

(h) Miscellaneous gravimetric methods. The ppt. formed with strychnine nitrate or brucine acetate in AcOH soln. can be ignited to V_2O_5; CrO_4^{2-} interferes.[52] Strychnine can also be applied colorimetrically for 10 μg. V in 20 ml. 50% H_2SO_4 soln.; Fe interferes but Ti, Mo, W and Al do not.[52]

The ppt. formed with diantipyrinylphenylmethane can be dried at 105°C and weighed as $[(C_{11}H_{11}ON_2)_2$-$CHC_6H_5] \cdot H_4V_6O_{17}$ or dissolved in 0·1N NaOH and titrated.[53]

Dicyanodiamidine sulfate[54] and quinoline[55] are other possible reagents for V; CrO_4^{2-} does not interfere in the quinoline method.

Reduction with Na_2SO_3 can be followed by pptn. with cinnamate or benzoate.[55] For 0·13 g. V_2O_5 in 25 ml. soln., heat, add 10 ml. 2N HCl, boil, add Na_2SO_3 until the soln. becomes blue, followed by 8% NH_4-cinnamate or benzoate and boil for 3 min.; after 4 hr. filter on paper, wash with satd. cinnamic acid soln. and ignite.

V can also be pptd. by treating the 2N HCl soln. under CO_2 with Zn–Hg, pouring into NH_4OH and filtering on paper; after ignition, the ppt. is evapd. with H_2O_2 and ignited to V_2O_5 at 700°C.[56]

(i) Iodometric titration is suitable for detn. of 1–10 mg. V in 2–3 ml. soln.[57] Make alk. with NaOH, add 5 ml. of freshly prepd. 10% $K_4Fe(CN)_6$ and 50 ml. 6N HCl and pass CO_2; add 20 ml. 4% KI, 1 ml. 10% $ZnSO_4$ and titrate with 0·01N $Na_2S_2O_3$ after 5 min. Blank values must be detd. This method is better than titration with $KMnO_4$ for the amt. specified.

Other iodometric titrations have also been proposed. Direct titration with 0·05N $Na_2S_2O_3$ can be used in 1:3 H_3PO_4 soln. at 19–22°C after addn. of 2–10 ml. 0·2N KI; Fe does not interfere.[58] A CO_2 atmosphere is advisable and this titration can be applied after distn. with KBr and HCl.[7] In another method,[59] 25 ml. 0·054N KI is added to the 6–7N HCl soln. under CO_2 and excess is back-titrated with 0·025M KIO_3 to a

$CHCl_3$ end-point. Cd reduction of V^{5+} can be followed by titration with KIO_4 in presence of starch, *p*-ethoxychrysoidine, safranine T or neutral red as indicator or with a potentiometric end-point.[60]

For titration of V^{4+}, treat the soln. with 2 g. tartaric or oxalic acid, boil, cool, almost neutralize with $KHCO_3$, add excess 0·1*N* I_2, add more $KHCO_3$ and back-titrate with 0·1*N* As^{3+} to starch indicator; Sb and As do not interfere.[6] Borax-buffered soln. at pH 9–10 has also been used for this titration.[61] Reduction with Zn–Hg in H_2SO_4 or HCl soln., followed by addn. of excess I_2, excess As^{3+} and back-titration with I_2 is also possible[62]

Reduction with As^{3+} followed by titration with $KBrO_3$ in presence of ICl and CCl_4 has been proposed.[63]

EDTA titration is possible with Cu-pyridylazonaphthol indicator at pH 3·5–4·5 after boiling with ascorbic acid.[64]

$VOSeO_3 \cdot 3H_2O$ can be pptd. with H_2SeO_3.[65] Treat the sulfate soln. with excess 0·1*N* H_2SeO_3, add EtOH to give a 50% soln., adjust to pH 4–4·5 with 5% NH_4OAc, filter on Whatman No. 42 paper and wash with abs. EtOH. Dissolve in HCl, dil. to 250 ml. with H_2O, pipet 50 ml. and titrate iodometrically.

(j) *p*-Amino-*N*,*N*-dimethylaniline provides a colorimetric detn. of 0·2 mg. V in 10 ml. soln.[66] Add 0·3 ml. 50% v/v HCl, 0·5 ml. H_3PO_4, 40 ml. EtOH, 4 ml. glycerol and HCl until the turbidity disappears; then add 1 ml. 0·5% reagent and compare the red color after 4 min. U does not interfere.

Other amines can be applied similarly. Na-diphenylamine sulfonate is suitable for 0·3 mg. V^{5+} in 4 ml. 1:1 H_2SO_4 and 15 ml. H_3PO_4: add 2·0 ml. 0·05% reagent, dil. to 100 ml. with H_2O and measure the blue color at 562 mμ.[67] This procedure can be used for detn. of V in NaCl electrolytes after concn. with $FeCl_3$ and H_2O_2, as well as in iron sands, steels, etc.

Diphenylamine,[66] benzidine,[68] diphenylbenzidine (1–10 μg. V/ml.),[69] aniline[70] and phenylthiosemicarbazide[71] have also been suggested.

$K_4Fe(CN)_6$ is suitable for detn. of $< 0{\cdot}05$ mg. V/ml. of acidic soln.;[72] add 3 ml. reagent soln. (42 mg./ml.), dil. to 100 ml. with H_2O and measure using a blue filter.

(k) Formaldoxime is suitable for colorimetric detn. of 0–5 μg. V/ml. in dil. HCl soln.[73] Add 5–10 mg. Na_2SO_3, heat for some min. on a steam-bath, cool, add 1 ml. reagent and make alk. with 3*N* NH_4OH; measure the yellow color after 15 min. at 410 mμ. None of the elements extd. with H_2O after fusion with Na_2CO_3 interfere.

(l) Benzohydroxamic acid can be used to det. 0·026–5·1 mg. V^{5+} colorimetrically.[74] Add 10·0 ml. 0·2*M* reagent, adjust to pH 2·0 with 6*M* H_2SO_4, dil. with H_2O to 30–90 ml., ext. with 20·0 ml. 1-hexanol and centrifuge; measure at 450 mμ.

NOTES. (1) Interferences are Ti, Fe, Bi, Sb, $C_2O_4^{2-}$, IO_4^-, CN^-, S^{2-}, NO_2^- and more than 10-fold amts. (compared to V) of Nb, Co, Ni, I^-, $Cr_2O_7^{2-}$, Mo, SO_3^{2-}; Zr, Mn, Th, Al, W require addn. of more reagent. No interference arises from Cu, Zn, Cd, Ta, Ca, Cr^{3+}, UO_2^{2+}, PO_4^{3-}, F^-, tartrate, citrate or other anions.

(2) Salicylhydroxamic acid has been used colorimetrically for 50–250 μg. V:[75] add 30 ml. 0·5% reagent and buffer pH 3–3·5, ext. with EtOAc and measure the violet color at 475 mμ. This can be used for steel analysis. The reagent has also been applied gravimetrically.[76]

(m) Catalytic reactions may be used for very small amts. of V. The reaction of $KBrO_3$ with *p*-phenetidine and pyrocatechol is suitable for $> 0{\cdot}0006$ μg. V/ml.[77] Add 1 ml. 0·1% *p*-phenetidine, 1 ml. 1% pyrocatechol and H_2O to give a vol. of 4 ml.; then add 1 ml. 5% $KBrO_3$ rapidly and measure the time required from this moment until the absorbance in the violet region attains a fixed value. A method with $KClO_3$ and aniline in presence of oxine has been studied (Almássy and Nagy[70]).

The reaction between $KClO_3$ and KI can also be utilized.[78] Mix 2·0 ml. 4% $KClO_3$, 2 ml. 4% KI, 1·0 ml. 1*N* H_2SO_4, 1 ml. 0·5% starch with H_2O and add the soln. contg. 5–50 μg. V^{4+} (boil V^{5+} with SO_2); measure the time required until the transmittance at 572 mμ decreases from 60% to 10%. Interferences are NH_4^+, Mn, Ni and > 2 mg. NO_3^-.

(n) *o*-Phenanthroline with $FeCl_3$ is used for colorimetric detn. of 10–40 μg. V.[79] Treat the dil. H_2SO_4 soln. with 1 ml. 30% H_2O_2, boil and add 0·1*N* $KMnO_4$ to give a pink color. Add HCl, evap. to dryness, repeat this process thrice, add HCl and dil. to 100 ml. with H_2O. Pipet 20–25 ml., add 1 ml. $FeCl_3$ soln. contg. 100 μg. Fe/ml., 5 ml. 0·5% *o*-phenanthroline, 10 ml. 2% NH_4OAc and adjust to pH 5–6 with NH_4OH. Dil. to 50 ml. with H_2O and measure at 520 mμ after 1 hr. If much Fe is present, add 1–2 ml. 5*N* H_3PO_4.

Dipyridyl[80] or dimethylglyoxime[81] can be used analogously in conjunction with Fe^{3+}.

(o) Miscellaneous colorimetric methods. The color of V^{5+} itself in alk. soln. at 270 mμ can be used to det. 0·435–43·5 μg. V/ml.[82] For 1 g. mineral, fuse with 5–6 g. Na_2CO_3, heat with 5–10 ml. H_2O and boil with 3–5 ml. MeOH; filter and wash with hot H_2O. Dil. to 100 ml. with H_2O, pipet 10–20 ml. and neutralize with 4*N* H_2SO_4. Add a few drops of 2·5% oxine in dil. AcOH, ext. completely with 2–3 ml. portions of $CHCl_3$, combine and evap., and ignite with 0·1 g. Na_2CO_3. Dissolve in 10–15 ml. H_2O, add 4 g. NaOH, dil. to 100 ml. with H_2O and measure.

1–16 μg. V^{5+} in 75–85 w/w % H_2SO_4 can be detd. at 340–440 mμ after $KMnO_4$ oxidation in 50% H_2SO_4 soln.[83] H_3PO_4 must be added if Fe is present. Up to 140 μg. V/ml. can be measured at 445 mμ; this can be used for analysis of $TiCl_4$ or Ti.[84] Up to 1·5 mg V/ml. can be detd. at 390 mμ in a soln. of 3 ml. $HClO_4$, 5 ml. H_3PO_4 and 10 ml. H_2SO_4; interference of Fe is avoided by compensation, that of Cr by removal as CrO_2Cl_2, that of Ni by Hg-cathode electrolysis and that of W or Si by removal as oxides.[85]

SO_2 can be used for 0·5–3 mg. V/ml. of soln. which is $< 10N$ in H_2SO_4 and $< 1N$ in HCl,[86] the blue color being measured at 760 mμ; small amts. of Fe^{2+}, CrO_4^{2-} and UO_2^{2+} can be tolerated.

Pyrocatechol may be employed with Na_2SO_3: to 10–25 ml. neutral soln. contg. $<$ 0·4 mg. V, add 10 ml. satd. Na_2SO_3, 5 ml. 10% pyrocatechol, 1–2 g. NaOAc and 0·5–1 ml. 10% NH_4F, dil. to 50 ml. with H_2O, and measure after 10 min. at 600 mμ.[87] Interferences are Cu, Ni, Co, Cr and large amts. of Fe or Mn; Ti, Nb, W, U, Al, F^-, PO_4^{3-} and tartrate can be tolerated. Mo can be detd. simultaneously by measuring at 400 or 430 mμ.

$(NH_4)_2S$ forms a red color with V in alk. soln.[88]

NH_4SCN in Me_2CO can also be utilized.[89] To 0·5 ml. H_2SO_4 soln. add 1 ml. HCl (and if no H_2SO_4 is present in the sample soln., add 2 ml.) followed by 200 mg. cryst. $SnCl_2$; after 10 min., add a few ml. H_2O and 15 ml. 3·0*M* NH_4SCN in Me_2CO, dil. to 25 ml. with H_2O and measure at 396 mμ (ϵ = 11 750). For 5–15 mg. V in 5 ml. soln. contg. 0·1 ml. H_2SO_4, add 1 ml. of $>$ 6% SO_2 water, 15 ml. Me_2CO and 3 ml. 8·33*M* reagent, dil. to 25 ml. with H_2O and measure at 750 mμ.[90]

Fast grey RA is suitable for 0·02–1 μg. V in 1 ml. neutral soln.[91] Add 2 ml. 0·05*N* HCl, 3·5 ml. 0·01% dye, dil. to 10 ml. with H_2O and measure at 560 mμ. Zr interferes, Fe^{3+} must be reduced by heating with ascorbic acid, and Cu removed with NH_4SCN.

Hydrazinophthalazine can be applied at pH 5·5 with measurement at 442 mμ, the sensitivity being almost as good as that of the H_2O_2 method.[92]

References

1. Hillebrand and Lundell, 352 (452); Scott and Furman, 1030; Kimura, 444; Schoeller and Powell, 178; Pigott, 520.
2. Morette, A., *Bull. soc. chim. France*, 526 (1950).
3. Hartmann, W. M., *Z. anal. Chem.*, **87**, 119, 459 (1932); **88**, 206 (1932).
4. Wakamatsu, S., *Japan Analyst*, **6**, 19 (1957).
5. Kawamura, K., *Japan Analyst*, **2**, 417 (1953).
6. Scott and Furman, 1031 ff.
7. Schoeller and Powell, 178 ff.
8. Tsubaki, I., and Tominaga, K., *Japan Analyst*, **3**, 242 (1954).
9. Clarke, S. G., *Analyst*, **52**, 466, 527 (1927).
10. Rehák, B., and Malínek, M., *Z. anal. Chem.*, **153**, 166 (1956).
11. Chemists of the U.S. Steel Corporation, *Sampling and Analysis of Carbon and Alloy Steels*, 160 (1938).
12. A.S.T.M., 109 ff.
13. Ishimaru, S., *Kagaku-Zikken-Gaku*, **X**, 32 (1942).
14. McKay, L. W., and Anderson, W. T., Jr., *J. Am. Chem. Soc.*, **44**, 1018 (1922).
15. Walden, G. H., Jr, *et al.*, *J. Am. Chem. Soc.*, **56**, 57 (1934).
16. Parks, T. D., and Agazzi, E. J., *Anal. Chem.*, **22**, 1179 (1950); Gale, R. H., and Mosher, E., *ibid.*, 942.
17. Willard, H. H., and Young, P., *Ind. Eng. Chem., Anal. Ed.*, **5**, 158 (1933); Bagshawe, B., *et al.*, *J. Iron Steel Inst.* (*London*), **170**, 343 (1952).
18. Lang, R., and Kurtz, F., *Z. anal. Chem.*, **86**, 288 (1931).
19. Shiokawa, T., *J. Chem. Soc. Japan*, **67**, 61 (1946).
20. Suseela, B., *Anal. Chim. Acta*, **13**, 543 (1955).
21. Kiboku, M., *Japan Analyst*, **6**, 11 (1957).
22. Simon, V., and Zýka, J., *Chem. listy*, **49**, 1646 (1955).
23. Nikitina, E. I., *Zavodskaya Lab.*, **11**, 1033 (1945).
24. Malmstadt, H. V., and Roberts, C. B., *Anal. Chem.*, **27**, 741 (1955).
25. Talvitie, N. A., *Anal. Chem.*, **25**, 604 (1953); also see Sandell, 611; Welcher, **I**, 297.
26. Motojima, K., *J. Chem. Soc. Japan*, **78**, 533 (1957).
27. Naito, H., and Sugawara, K., *Bull. Chem. Soc. Japan*, **30**, 799 (1957); Sugawara *et al.*, *ibid.*, **26**, 417 (1953).
28. Welcher, **I**, 297; Ishimaru, S., *J. Chem. Soc. Japan*, **56**, 72 (1935); also Borrel, M., and Pâris, R., *Anal. Chim. Acta*, **4**, 267 (1950).
29. Alimarin, I. P., and Kryukov, V. G., *Zhur. Anal. Khim.*, **10**, 56 (1955).
30. Molland, J., *Compt. rend.*, **210**, 144 (1940).
31. Sandell, 607 ff.
32. Wright, E. R., and Mellon, M. G., *Ind. Eng. Chem., Anal. Ed.*, **9**, 251 (1937).
33. Cooper, M. D., and Winter, P. K., *Anal. Chem.*, **21**, 605 (1949).
34. Murakami, Y., *Bull. Chem. Soc. Japan*, **23**, 153 (1950).
35. Sherwood, R. M., and Chapman, F. W., Jr., *Anal. Chem.*, **27**, 88 (1955).
36. Morachevskiĭ, Yu. V., and Gordeeva, M. N., *Vestnik Leningrad. Univ.*, **10**, No. 11, *Ser. Mat. Fis. i Khim.*, No. 4, 139 (1955).
37. Romashchenko, V. A., *Zavodskaya Lab.*, **11**, 104 (1945); Tikhonova, A. A., *ibid.*, **16**, 1168 (1950).
38. Bogatzki, G., *Arch. Eisenhüttenw.*, **12**, 539 (1939); Erdey, L., *et al.*, *Acta Chim. Acad. Sci. Hung.*, **4**, 259 (1954).
39. Woodman, A. G., and Cayvan, C. C., *J. Am. Chem. Soc.*, **23**, 105 (1901).
40. Wright, E. R., and Mellon, M. G., *Ind. Eng. Chem., Anal. Ed.*, **9**, 375 (1937).
41. Freeland, M. Q., and Fritz, J. S., *Anal. Chem.*, **27**, 1737 (1955).
42. Telep, G., and Boltz, D. F., *Anal. Chem.*, **23**, 901 (1951).
43. Welcher, **III**, 381.
44. Willard, H. H., *et al.*, *Anal. Chem.*, **25**, 1863 (1953).
45. Shome, S. C., *Anal. Chem.*, **23**, 1186 (1951).
46. Schoeller, 152, 161.
47. Moser, L., and Brandl, O., *Monatsh.*, **51**, 172 (1929); Kroupa, E., *Mikrochemie*, **32**, 245 (1944) (accurate for 0·5–10 mg. V_2O_5).
48. Lewis, P. T., *Analyst*, **65**, 560 (1940); Tashiro, M., *J. Chem. Soc. Japan*, **52**, 728 (1931) (inaccurate).
49. Kodama, K., *Japan Analyst*, **5**, 628 (1956).
50. Parks, W. G., and Prebluda, H. J., *J. Am. Chem. Soc.*, **57**, 1676 (1935).
51. Murgulescu, I. G., and Alexa, V., *Z. anal. Chem.*, **123**, 341 (1942).
52. Welcher, **IV**, 214, 267, 269.
53. Gusev, S. I., *et al.*, *Zhur. Anal. Khim.*, **6**, 43 (1951).
54. Fidler, J., *Collection Czechoslov. Chem. Communs.*, **14**, 28 (1949).

55. WELCHER, **II**, 32, 52.
56. TSUBAKI, I., *J. Chem. Soc. Japan*, **68**, 92 (1947).
57. EVANS, B. S., *Analyst*, **63**, 870 (1938).
58. WERZ, W., *Z. anal. Chem.*, **83**, 161 (1931); **81**, 448 (1931).
59. SWIFT, E. H., and HOEPPEL, R. W., *J. Am. Chem. Soc.*, **51**, 1366 (1929).
60. MÁZOR, L., and ERDEY, L., *Acta Chim. Acad. Sci. Hung.*, **2**, 331 (1953).
61. DESHMUKH, G. S., *Chem. Ber.*, **88**, 615 (1955).
62. SOMEYA, K., *Sci. Repts. Tôhoku Imp. Univ., First Ser.*, **16**, 521 (1927); **17**, 131 (1928).
63. DESHMUKH, G. S., *Z. anal. Chem.*, **148**, 347 (1955).
64. FLASCHKA, H. and ABDINE, H., *Chemist Analyst*, **45**, 58 (1956).
65. SUSEELA, B., *Z. anal. Chem.*, **144**, 329 (1955).
66. WELCHER, **II**, 255 ff.
67. HIRANO, S., *et al.*, *Japan Analyst*, **4**, 616 (1955); **5** 7, 336 (1956).
68. BERTRAND, D., *Bull. soc. chim. France*, 128 (1942).
69. ECKHOUT, J. and WEYNANTS, A., *Anal. Chim. Acta*, **15**, 145 (1956).
70. ZILBERMINTZ, V. A., and FLORENZKIÍ, K. P., *Mikrochemie*, **18**, 154 (1935); ALMÁSSY, GY., and NAGY, Z., *Acta Chim. Acad. Sci. Hung.*, **6**, 339, 639 (1955).
71. KOMATSU, S., and KUMAGAI, N., *J. Chem. Soc. Japan*, **78**, 1558 (1957).
72. VORONTSOV, R. V., *Zavodskaya Lab.*, **13**, 1155 (1947).
73. TANAKA, M., *Japan Analyst*, **3**, 75 (1954); *Mikrochim. Acta*, 701 (1954).
74. WISE, W. M., and BRANDT, W. W., *Anal. Chem.*, **27**, 1392 (1955) (in steel and soil); DAS GUPTA, A. K., and SINGH, M. M., *J. Sci. Ind. Research (India)*, **11B**, 268 (1952).
75. BHADURI, A. S., and RÂY, P., *Z. anal. Chem.*, **154**, 103 (1957).
76. BHADURI, *Z. anal. Chem.*, **151**, 109 (1956).
77. SZEBELLÉDY, L. and AJTAI, M., *Mikrochemie*, **26**, 87 (1939); WELCHER, **I**, 158.
78. SHIOKAWA, T., *J. Chem. Soc. Japan*, **70**, 418 (1949).
79. GOTTLIEB, A., *Mikrochemie ver. Mikrochim. Acta*, **36/37**, 370 (1951); JANTSCH, G., and ZEMEK, F., *Z. anal. Chem.*, **139**, 249 (1953); ROSOTTE, R., and JAUDON, E., *Chim. anal.*, **36**, 160 (1954) (in steel).
80. PONOMAREV, A. I., and RETINA, L. L., *Zavodskaya Lab.*, **21**, 918 (1955).
81. OI, N., *J. Chem. Soc. Japan*, **75**, 841 (1954).
82. GOTTLIEB, I. M., *et al.*, *Anal. Chim. Acta*, **11**, 376 (1954).
83. LENCH, A., *Australia Commonwealth Dept. Supply, Defense Standards Lab., Rept. No. 218*, 1, 13 (1955).
84. OWENS, W. H., *et al.*, *Anal. Chem.*, **29**, 243 (1957).
85. WAKAMATSU, S., *Japan Analyst*, **6**, 273 (1957).
86. SANTINI, R., *et al.*, *Anal. Chim. Acta*, **6**, 368 (1952).
87. PATROVSKÝ, V., *Chem. listy*, **48**, 622 (1954); **49**, 854 (1955).
88. STENGEL, E., *Tech. Mitt. Krupp, A. Forschungber.*, **2**, 93 (1939).
89. CROUTHAMEL, C. E., *et al.*, *Anal. Chem.*, **27**, 507 (1955).
90. FEINSTEIN, H. I., *Anal. Chim. Acta*, **15**, 141 (1956).
91. KHALIFA, H. and FARAG, A., *Z. anal. Chem.*, **158**, 1 (1957).
92. RUGGIERI, R., *Anal. Chim. Acta*, **16**, 242 (1957).

39

URANIUM

The classical sources for this chapter are given in ref. 1. The analytical chemistry of uranium has been thoroughly discussed by Rodden and Warf[2] and analytical methods for the determination of uranium and fluorine have been reviewed.[3] Several shorter reviews on methods for uranium are also available[4, 5, 6] and the difficulties encountered in the determination of small amounts have been described.[7]

It should be noted that some uranium minerals contain so much helium that the total percentage value obtained in a complete analysis may not equal 100% unless great care is taken.

Attack

(a) Minerals. Treat with HNO_3 (and HCl) and then treat the residue with HF and HNO_3 (and possibly HCl) or fuse the residue with Na_2CO_3. If a titrimetric detn. of U is to follow, the soln. should be converted to H_2SO_4. Dissolve uraninite in HNO_3 and H_2SO_4, and carnotite in HNO_3 and HF (4:1) (see also Chapter 38, p. 290).

Titanoniobates can be fused with $K_2S_2O_7$ (see p. 366) but fusion with Na_2O_2 is better.[8]

(b) Metal. Dissolve in HNO_3, or HCl with addn. of H_2O_2, Br_2 or HNO_3.

(c) Steels.[9] Treat with dil. H_2SO_4 and cupferron, ignite, digest with HF and H_2SO_4, ignite, fuse with Na_2CO_3 and $NaNO_3$ and leach with H_2O. Filter, boil with H_2SO_4 and H_2O_2, add cupferron and evap. Fume with HNO_3 and $(NH_4)_2S_2O_8$, dil. with H_2O, reduce with Zn, filter, treat with cupferron, etc.

Separation

V and CO_3^{2-} interfere seriously in most methods for sepn. of U.

H_2S treatment of 1:20 HCl solns. seps. U from group II metals; it is preferable to have tartrate present and to use a pressure bottle for sepn. from Mo.

$(NH_4)_2S$ allows sepn. from the As group. If $(NH_4)_2CO_3$ is also present, U is sepd. from Fe, Al, Ti, Co, Ni, Zn, Ca, etc.; if $(NH_4)_2$-tartrate is also present, U is sepd. from Fe, Co, etc.

Evapn. with HBr from H_2SO_4 soln. allows sepn. from As, Sb, Sn, Ge.

If the sample soln. is poured into hot 2·5% $(NH_4)_2CO_3$ in $3N$ NH_4OH, U is sepd. from Al, Fe, small amts. of Pb and from Be if NH_2OH is added. Treatment with Na_2CO_3 seps. U from Fe, Ti, Co, Ni, Mn, Zn, Be, Ca, etc.; traces of Fe accompany U. Treatment with Na_2CO_3 and H_2O_2 yields incomplete sepn. from Fe.[10] Treatment with $(NH_4)_2CO_3$ seps. U^{4+} from U^{6+} and Fe^{2+}; also U^{6+} can be sepd. from Fe^{3+}, Cr, V and Mo. This is useful for detn. of U in steel.[11]

Treatment with H_2O_2 can be used to remove large amts. of U; add NH_4OH to 5 g. U in 500 ml. soln. until a turbidity appears, clarify with $2N$ HNO_3, add 5 ml. 30% H_2O_2 and centrifuge.

$K_4Fe(CN)_6$ in pH 3–6 soln. seps. U from P, As and partly Be and Al, but is not very satisfactory.

Extn. with EtOAc from slightly acidic soln. contg. NH_4SCN is useful for concn. of U.

Extn. with Et_2O from 1:1 HCl soln. seps. U from Fe, Mo, etc. but traces of Fe remain. Extn. with Et_2O from nitrate soln. seps. U from most elements.[2, 12] For 1–20 mg. U_3O_8, add $Fe(NO_3)_3$ to give a $1M$ soln., HNO_3 to give $3N$, and ext. 3 times with equal vols. of Et_2O. Combine the exts. in a beaker contg. 30–50 ml. H_2O, evap., almost neutralize with NaOH and add Na_2CO_3 to give a 1–5% soln. Heat, boil for 1 min., cool, add H_2O and filter. Interferences are SO_4^{2-}, PO_4^{3-} and Cl^-. Some modifications have been suggested: extn. with Et_2O from $3N$ HNO_3 soln. satd. with NH_4NO_3 is said to be better.[13] Extn. with 10 ml. EtOAc from 10 ml. of $< 3\%$ HNO_3 soln. contg. $10{\cdot}0 \pm 0{\cdot}5$ g. $Al(NO_3)_3{\cdot}9H_2O$ is also possible.[14] For possible extns. with tributyl phosphate in *n*-hexane or with other solvents, see p. 138.

Cellulose columns permit sepn. of U from many elements; see Chapter 13, p. 116.

Specially treated silica in a column seps. U from several elements.[15] For the silica, mix 20 g. ignited SiO_2 and 5 g. $NaNO_3$ with a little H_2O, evap. to dryness, ignite in a porcelain vessel and powder to 100 mesh. For a sepn. evap. the nitrate soln. contg. 50–500 μg. U to dryness, warm with 1 ml. 20% HNO_3 and mix with 0·9 g. anhyd. NaOAc and 1·5 g. pure SiO_2. Transfer to the top of a column of 4 g. of treated SiO_2 which has been pretreated with 1% HNO_3 in Et_2O, and wash with 150 ml. 1% HNO_3 in Et_2O at a rate of 2 drops/3 sec. Strip U with 3 × 10 ml. H_2O, evap. to dryness and dil. with H_2O to 100 ml. Det. U in a 25 ml. aliquot by the 2-acetoacetylpyridine method (p. 301). U can be sepd. from Th, from Zn (if 60 mg. $Na_2C_2O_4$ is added), from 50 mg. Fe, etc. and from PO_4^{3-} if Fe^{3+} is added.

Sepn. of U from Fe, Mo etc. is best done by Hg-cathode electrolysis from 2–3% H_2SO_4 soln. at 8 v. and 0·3–0·5 amp./cm.² for 2·5 hr.[10]

Extn. with $CHCl_3$ from $(NH_4)_2CO_3$ soln. contg. oxine seps. U from Fe, Al, etc.

Cupferron can be applied under various conditions. U^{6+} is sepd. from Fe, V, Ti, Zr, etc. by treating the 10% v/v H_2SO_4 soln. with $KMnO_4$ to give a pink color, followed by 6% cupferron soln., filtration on paper and washing with a soln. contg. 0·2 g. reagent/100 ml. 10% H_2SO_4. U^{4+} is sepd. from U^{6+}, Al, Cr, Mn, Zn, Ca, Mg, PO_4^{3-} as follows: cool the soln. contg. 5 ml. H_2SO_4/100 ml. and 5 g. $NH_2OH \cdot HCl$ to 5–10°C, stir for 2 min. with cupferron and repeat with a second addn.; filter after 5 min. on paper and wash with a freshly prepd. mixture of 100 ml. 7·5% H_2SO_4 and 50 ml. H_2O contg. 0·8 g. cupferron and 3 g. $NH_2OH \cdot HCl$. If necessary, U^{6+} is reduced by passing through a Jones reductor and then passing air through the soln.

Cupferron in Et_2O permits sepn. of U from Al, etc.[2] For 0·5–5 mg. U_3O_8 in 30 ml. soln. contg. 2·5 ml. H_2SO_4, dil. to 50 ml. in a separatory funnel with 1:200 H_2SO_4, add 3 ml. 2·4% Zn–Hg, shake for 5 min., add 1·5 ml. Et_2O and 1·5 ml. reagent (2 g. cupferron in 25 ml. H_2O, filtered into a separatory funnel, mixed with 5 ml. 6*N* H_2SO_4 and extd. with 25 ml. Et_2O) and shake for 1 min. Allow to settle for 1 min., sep. and repeat four times. Collect the ethereal layers in a Pt dish and evap. to dryness. If Fe^{3+}, etc. are extd. previously from the U^{6+} soln. and the org. matter in the aq. layer is destroyed before the above procedure is applied, U is sepd. from nearly all elements.

HF allows sepn. of a little U^{4+} from U^{6+}, Fe, V, Zr, Ta, etc.

U^{4+} is sepd. from U^{6+} by treatment with 10% KIO_3 in 10% H_2SO_4: to 25–40 ml. 5% H_2SO_4 soln. under CO_2 add an equal vol. of hot reagent followed by 2 vols. of 0·8% KIO_3 in 2% H_2SO_4; heat, cool, filter on paper and wash with hot NH_4OH; then treat with HNO_3, NH_4OH, etc.

U^{4+} is pptd. by $Na_2H_2P_2O_6$ from dil. acidic soln. and thus sepd.[16] from U^{6+}.

H_3AsO_4 seps. U from Fe, Al and rare earths. For 50 mg. U in 100 ml. 10–20% AcOH soln., add 1 g. NH_4Cl, 25 ml. 8% (w/v) reagent, boil, cool and filter. If much Fe is present, reduce first with SO_2 and add NH_4OAc.

U can be sepd. from V by extn. with AcOH and HNO_3 or with $Pb(OAc)_2$; for details, see Chapter 38, p. 291.

Treatment with $Ca(NO_3)_2$ seps. traces of U from large amts. of V. Treat the sample with H_2O, 30 ml. 50% NaOH and 300 ml. H_2O, add glass beads, cover and evap. to 150 ml.; then add 150 ml. H_2O, boil, add 10 ml. 1·2% (w/v) reagent and filter after some time on Whatman No. 42 paper.

$H_2C_2O_4$ seps. U^{6+} from rare earths (see p. 348). Sepn. from many elements is possible as follows: treat the U^{4+} in 2–3*N* HCl soln. with Zn–Hg, filter on a Whatman No. 52 paper and collect in a beaker contg. 2–6 g. reagent; after at least 1 hr., filter on Whatman No. 42 paper and wash with 1% reagent in 3*N* HCl.

Tannin allows sepn. of U from Ti, Nb, Ta in slightly acidic soln. contg. $C_2O_4^{2-}$ and NH_4Cl (see p. 374).

α-Nitroso-β-naphthol can be used to sep. U from V^{4+} and Fe by AmOH extn. of the complex from neutral soln. contg. EDTA.

U can be concd. by extn. of the diethyldithiocarbamate complex with $CHCl_3$ from soln. of pH 6 contg. EDTA and Ca^{2+}, and stripped by shaking with dil. $(NH_4)_2CO_3$ soln.[17] Fe^{3+} or Al and NH_4OH or $(NH_4)_2HPO_4$ can also be used to conc. U.

For possible separations with ion exchange resins, see Chapter 13, Section 2.2.

Determination

Gravimetric detn. with NH_4OH and titrimetric detn. with $KMnO_4$ or $K_2Cr_2O_7$ are probably the most suitable methods for macro amounts of U. $K_2Cr_2O_7$ or oxine is more appropriate for mg. amounts. Of the available colorimetric methods, that involving NH_4SCN is the most convenient; the fluorescence method is very often used and the dibenzoylmethane method seems to be satisfactory.

(a) NH_4OH provides the classical gravimetric method for detn. of U.[1] For UO_2SO_4 soln. contg. $< 1\%$ UO_2^{2+}, add 5–10 g. NH_4NO_3/100 ml. soln., make alk. to methyl orange with NH_4OH, add filter pulp, boil for 5 min., filter on Whatman No. 40 paper and wash with 2% NH_4NO_3 contg. some NH_4OH. Ignite at 700–900°C (745–946°C) and weigh as U_3O_8; alternatively, dry at 480–610°C and weigh as UO_3.

NOTES. (1) Interferences are CO_3^{2-}, org. compds., Fe, etc. and PO_4^{3-}. If EDTA is present, sepn. of U from Fe, etc. is possible.[18]

(2) The following methods are said to be better, that involving tannin being especially suitable for small amts. of U.

Pyridine or hexamine can replace NH_4OH, pyridine being preferable.[19] Add NH_4Cl or NH_4NO_3 to the slightly acidic soln., boil and add 20% pyridine until the soln. is alk. to methyl red; then add 10 ml. in excess and place on a steam-bath for 30–40 min. until the ppt. settles (if the ppt. turns red, add more reagent). Filter on paper, wash with hot 3% NH_4NO_3 contg. a few drops of pyridine and ignite. If sulfate is present a larger excess of reagent is necessary.

With tannin,[20] treat the acidic (AcOH) soln. with 5 g. NHCl, make slightly alk. with NH_4OH, boil, add 1 g. tannin and 5 g. NH_4OAc and filter. No interference arises from CO_3^{2-}, $C_2O_4^{2-}$ or tartrate.

(3) A titrimetric check on the gravimetric result is possible by dissoln. of the ignited ppt. in HF, evapn. with H_2SO_4 and titration. It is said[11] to be easier to dissolve the ppt. in H_2SO_4 and NH_4VO_3 before titration with $KMnO_4$.
(4) Interferences of V and Al can be corrected for by dissoln. of the ppt. in HNO_3; V is detd. by the H_2O_2 method and Al with $(NH_4)_2CO_3$ and the amts. are subtracted.
(5) A titrimetric detn. on this principle is possible.[21] Adjust the soln. to pH 4·2–4·3 with NaOH, add 0·1*M* KIO_3, 3–5 g. KI and 5–10 ml. CCl_4 and reflux at 60–70°C for 20 min.; cool and titrate with $Na_2S_2O_3$ or with As^{3+} in presence of a borax buffer.

(b) Redox titrations. (*i*) $KMnO_4$ is best used with Ba-diphenylaminesulfonate indicator.[1, 10] Pass the sulfate soln. in 5% v/v H_2SO_4 through a Jones reductor and pass air through the effluent for 5 min. after the olive-green color changes to green. Add 3–4 drops 0·05*M* indicator and titrate with 0·1*N* $KMnO_4$ to the violet end-point.

NOTES. (1) HNO_3 interferes and is difficult to remove even by fuming with H_2SO_4; Fe, etc., Mo, Cu and large amts. of PO_4^{3-} (over 0·4 g./0·5 g. U) also interfere.
(2) For reduction with amalgams, add 150 g. Zn–Hg to the 2–3*N* H_2SO_4 soln., shake for 1 min., sep., shake with air and titrate as above. For other amalgams and titrants, see refs. 2, 22.

(*ii*) $K_2Cr_2O_7$ is also best used with Ba-diphenylaminesulfonate indicator.[23] Reduce and oxidize with air as described above; then add 25 ml. 2% $FeCl_3$, 15 ml. H_3PO_4 and 10–12 drops 0·2% indicator and titrate with 0·1*N* $K_2Cr_2O_7$. NO_3^- interferes.

NOTES. (1) *N*-Phenylanthranilic acid is said to be a better indicator.[24]
(2) The method can be applied to HCl solns. Small amts. of U can be titrated with 0·01*N* soln. and this can be applied for detn. of 0·08–0·8 mg. Na.
(3) Reduction with $SnCl_2$ produces U^{4+} only.[25] To 10 ml. soln. add 2 ml. Fe soln. (0·5585 g. Fe in 20 ml. HCl with a few drops of H_2O_2, dild. to 500 ml. with H_2O) as catalyst, followed by 20–25 ml. HCl, 4 ml. 1:1 H_3PO_4, and heat to 96–99°C. Add 5% $SnCl_2$ in 1:10 HCl (1 ml./50 mg. U and 1 ml. in excess) and heat for 10–15 min. Cool, add 20 ml. satd. $HgCl_2$ soln. and, after 2 min., 20 ml. 8% $FeCl_3$ and dil. to 250–300 ml. with H_2O. Add some dry ice, 15 ml. 3:1 H_3PO_4–H_2SO_4, 0·25 ml. 0·005*M* Ba-diphenylamine-sulfonic acid and titrate with 0·02*N* $K_2Cr_2O_7$. Mo, Cu, V, Ti interfere but As, W, Mn, Ce, Bi, Co and 5 mg. NO_3^- do not. Ti^{3+} can also be used for the reduction in presence of $CuSO_4$ as catalyst.

(*iii*) Ce^{4+} is applied with ferroin indicator.[26] Pass the soln. contg. 20 ml. HCl/80 ml. soln. through a Pb reductor and wash with 80 ml. 1*N* HCl. Add 1 ml. 0·001*M* ferroin, 1 drop H_3PO_4 and titrate with 0·01*N* Ce^{4+} until an appreciable color change is observed. Then add 2 ml. H_3PO_4 and titrate slowly to the end-point. If much U is present, use 0·1*N* Ce^{4+}, 2 drops 0·025*M* ferroin and 2 ml. 20% Fe-alum in 5% H_2SO_4 instead of 2 ml. H_3PO_4. 12–120 μg. U in 0·5 ml. 1*M* H_2SO_4 soln. can be detd. after reduction with Cr^{2+} with an error of ±12%.[27] Reduction with Ti^{3+} is possible.[28] The titration can also be done coulometrically[29] or with diphenylbenzidine or *N*-phenylanthranilic acid as indicator.[30]

(*iv*) $NaVO_3$ can be used with diphenylbenzidine or *N*-phenylanthranilic acid as indicator.[31]

(*v*) $K_3Fe(CN)_6$ can be used with a potentiometric end-point;[32] Mn, V, Ce, Ag, Cd interfere. Other potentiometric titrations are possible: Fe^{3+} has been used.[33] $TiCl_3$ is applied in solns. contg. KNa-tartrate and 12·5% (v/v) HCl at 60°C.[34] Cr^{2+} is best in 8*N* HCl soln. contg. tartaric acid.[35]

(*vi*) Some coulometric methods, other than those mentioned above, have been described.[36]

(c) Oxine acetate allows gravimetric, titrimetric or colorimetric detns. of U. For the gravimetric method,[37] treat the acidic soln. with NH_4OH until a ppt. appears, make clear with 2*N* HCl and adjust to pH 5–9 (if tartrate is present, adjust to pH 6 with NH_4OH). Add 20–25 ml. 20% NH_4OAc, dil. to 100–200 ml. with H_2O, heat nearly to b.p., add 4% reagent (0·5 ml./10 mg. U and 4–5 ml. in excess) and an equal vol. of 2*N* NH_4OH, boil for 1–2 min. and cool to 40°C. Filter on a glass crucible, wash with 0·04% reagent, dry at 110–140°C for 1–2 hr. and weigh as $UO_2(C_9H_6ON)_2{\cdot}C_9H_7ON$. (Below 157°C the ppt. is said to be $U(C_9H_6ON)_6{\cdot}2UO_3{\cdot}C_9H_7OH$ and at 252–346°C, $U(C_9H_6ON)_6{\cdot}2UO_3$.) Alternatively, dissolve the ppt. in 2*N* HCl and det. it with 0·1*N* $KBrO_3$ and KBr.

NOTES. (1) Groups IV and V do not interfere. Large amts. of Na interfere, as do CO_3^{2-} and mixtures of Zr and PO_4^{3-}. Interference of Th, rare earths, V, Al, Cu, Co, Ni, Zn, Cd, Pb, Mn and Fe^{3+} is avoided by addn. of 10 ml. 10% EDTA to the pH 5·3 soln. Interference of V, Mo, W is avoided by EDTA addn. at pH 8·4 and that of Zr by EDTA addn. and extra reagent. PO_4^{3-} interference is prevented by EDTA addn. at pH 5·3 after addn. of reagent.
Prior sepn. of U (0·04–0·25 g.) as phosphate from HEEDTA-contg. soln. at pH 8 ± 1 can be followed by dissoln. in H_2SO_4, diln., adjustment with AcOH and NH_4OH, oxine addn., HEEDTA addn. and pH adjustment to 5·3, etc.
(2) For colorimetric detn. of 0·05–2·5 mg. U,[2, 38, 39] adjust to pH 8·7–8·9 and ext. with 5 ml. portions of 2·5% (w/v) oxine in $CHCl_3$; dil. to 10 ml. (0·05 mg. U) or 25 ml. (2·5 mg. U) and measure at 400–440 mμ. Fe interference is prevented by addn. of KI and $Na_2S_2O_3$ to the HCl soln. which is then poured into NaCN soln. before proceeding as above; most other elements can be sepd. by extn. with Et_2O. If the absorbance is measured at 470 mμ and 500 mμ after extn. of the pH 7·2–8·1 soln., a good criterion of purity can be attained.[40] The method can be used for detn. of U in Th, Bi, monazite, phosphate rocks, carnotite or low-grade pitchblende after extn. with tributyl phosphate.[40]
(3) Of oxine derivs. 8-hydroxyquinaldine (see Chapter 20, p. 161) and iodoxine (see Chapter 22, p. 174), can be applied gravimetrically.

(d) NH_4SCN in Me_2CO is useful for colorimetric detn. of 0·05–0·8 mg. U.[41] Evap. to fumes with 1 ml. HCl and 0·5 ml. H_2SO_4, cool, add H_2O and 20 drops 10% $SnCl_2$ in 1:10 HCl and dil. to 10 ml. with H_2O. Add 15 ml. of freshly prepd. satd. reagent and measure at 375 mμ.

NOTES. (1) Fe, Pb and Co in amts. half that of U can be tolerated; 2-fold amts. of Ni, 10-fold Hg, Sn, MnO_4^-, 25-fold F^-, 50-fold Zr, 70-fold SiF_6^{2-}, 100-fold PO_4^{3-} and 250-fold Al can also be present.
(2) Ascorbic acid is said[42] to be a better reductant than $SnCl_2$. Extn. with 32·5% tributyl phosphate in CCl_4 from solns. at pH 3·5–3·9 contg. EDTA and NH_4SCN has been suggested.[43]
(3) For 0·4–2 mg. U_3O_8 in <3 ml. soln.,[44] adjust to pH 0–3 with HNO_3 or NaOH and add 15 ml. $Al(NO_3)_3$ soln. (1880 g. in 500 ml. H_2O by warming, add 200 ml. 1:1 NH_4OH and dil. to 2 l. with H_2O; if the sample contains Ti, add 60 g. tartaric acid and an extra 60 ml. NH_4OH). Shake for 2 min. with 20 ml. hexone, centrifuge. pipet out 10 ml. of the org. phase and shake with 5 ml. reagent (46 g. NH_4SCN and 2 g. ascorbic acid in 150 ml. 11:4 butyl cellosolve–H_2O). Measure at 375 mμ for 0·4–2 mg. U_3O_8, and at 420 mμ for >2 mg. U_3O_8. Up to 5 mg. Ti, 20 mg. V, 40 mg. Zr and 100 mg. Hg, as well as most other elements can be tolerated.

(e) Dibenzoylmethane is suitable[14, 45] for colorimetric detn. of 2·5–9 p.p.m. UO_2^{2+}. Pour 5–10 ml. sample soln. into 28 ml. EtOH, dil. to 45 ml. with H_2O and adjust to pH 5·0–5·5 using a glass electrode. Add 1 ml. 1% reagent in EtOH, adjust to pH 7, transfer to a 50 ml. measuring flask, wash twice with 1 ml. portions of EtOH, dil. to 50 ml. with H_2O and measure at 395 mμ. Interferences of V, Fe, Cu, etc. are avoided by Et_2O sepn. With addn. of 5% EDTA, 1% $Ca(NO_3)_2$ and NH_4OH to give pH 7 and with final extn. with EtOAc, up to 0·5 mg. of any element can be tolerated.[46] A reagent contg. 2 g. dibenzoylmethane, 12·5 g. acid-EDTA and 500 ml. pyridine/l. has been recommended;[47] to 5 ml. alk. (Na_2CO_3) sample soln. add 1 ml. 50% tartaric acid, dil. to 25 ml. with reagent and measure at 415 mμ after 30 min.

NOTES. (1) 2-Acetoacetylpyridine in BuOAc can be used to det. <200 μg. U in 15 ml. soln.[15] Adjust to pH 5·0–6·5 with AcOH or NaOH, add 10 ml. 0·4*N* NH_4OAc, 1–2 drops 0·2*N* NaOH and dil. to 50 ml. with H_2O (pH 7–7·7). Add 10 ml. 1·2% reagent, shake and sep. and measure at 382·5 mμ. The many interferences can be avoided by sepn. on a SiO_2 column.
(2) 2-Furoylbenzoylmethane is the most sensitive deriv. and can be used to det. 1–120 μg. U in 10 ml. 50% EtOH soln.[48]

(f) NaF fusion can be combined with spectrographic measurement with a microphotometer attachment under UV light (argon lamp).[2, 49] Evap. the soln. to dryness with 1 g. NaF (+ HF) and grind the cooled melt in an agate mortar. Fuse a 25 mg. portion (10^{-6} – 5×10^{-3} mg. U; lowest limit 10^{-7} mg.) on a Pt loop until just clear, cool in plate form (if possible) and measure.

NOTE. Interferences are SiO_2, Ti, Th, rare earths, Fe, Nb, SO_4^{2-}, Ca and large amts. of Mn; K, Mg and Ba do not interfere.

(g) $(NH_4)_2HPO_4$ is applied gravimetrically for < 5 mg. U in dil. H_2SO_4 soln.[2, 8, 50] Add NH_4OH to the hot soln. until a ppt. appears, then add a few drops of dil. HNO_3, a 10-fold excess of 10% reagent and 1:1 NH_4OH until pptn. is complete. Boil for 30 min., filter on paper and wash with 5% NH_4NO_3. Ignite, cool, add a little HNO_3, ignite at 700–900°C (673–946°C) and weigh as $(UO_2)_2P_2O_7$.

NOTES. (1) Interferences are CO_3^{2-}, Fe, etc.
(2) $(NH_4)_2S_2O_3$ and NaH_2PO_2 can be used similarly.[51] Warm the soln. contg. 8–10 ml. HCl/200 ml., add 20 ml. 20% NaH_2PO_2, boil, add 20–25 ml. 20% $(NH_4)_2S_2O_3$, stir for 2 min., let settle, filter on Whatman No. 41 paper and wash with warm 1% HCl and hot H_2O. Ignite and weigh as $(UO_2)_2P_2O_7$. Interference from group II metals is avoided by H_2S treatment; Zr and Ti can be sepd. by boiling with NaH_2PO_2 and filtering before the above procedure.
(3) Detn. of U as vanadate is inaccurate. Pptn. as arsenate from acetate-buffered soln. followed by ignition allows weighing as U_3O_8.[2]

(h) Miscellaneous gravimetric methods. Atoxyl can be used to det. 100 mg. U^{6+} in dil. HNO_3 or HCl solns.[52] Add 0·5 g. reagent, boil, adjust to pH 4–7 with NH_4OH, filter, wash with hot H_2O and ignite to U_3O_8. Tartrate, $C_2O_4^{2-}$, SO_4^{2-} and K interfere.

β-Isatoxime is utilized to det. 9–240 mg. UO_2^{2+} in 50–100 ml. slightly acidic soln.[53, 54] Add 6–60 ml. 1% reagent in 50% EtOH to the boiling soln., followed by 5–15 ml. 10% NaOAc, cool, filter after 3 hr. on paper, wash with a soln. contg. 25 ml. reagent/500 ml. and ignite to U_3O_8. Groups IV and V and Mn and Zn do not interfere but Ag, Pb, Hg, Cu, Fe^{2+} do; NaK-tartrate and NH_4SCN prevent Ni or Co interference.

Salicylhydroxamic acid ppts. U from soln. of pH 4·46–5·4 as $UO_2(C_7H_6O_3N)_2$, which can be dried at 105°C and weighed.[55] This reagent can also be applied colorimetrically for 5–20 p.p.m. U at pH 8·5–9·5 with measurement at 400 mμ.[56] Interferences are V, Mo, Th, Ce^{3+}, Fe^{3+}, F^-, PO_4^{3-}, $C_2O_4^{2-}$, citrate and tartrate.

Na-quinaldate can be used to ppt. U as nitrate from 120 ml. soln. at pH 6–7.[57] Add 3·5% reagent to the boiling soln. contg. 5–7 g. NH_4Cl, filter on paper, wash with a mixture of 5% hexamine and 5% NH_4Cl and ignite to U_3O_8 above 850°C.

α-Nitroso-β-naphthol also requires ignition to U_3O_8.[58] Adjust the soln. to alk. with NH_4OH, make clear with HNO_3 and add 1–2 drops NH_4OH and excess 10% reagent; filter, wash and ignite at 800–900°C. 1-Nitroso-2-hydroxy-3-naphthoic acid ppts. U at pH 3·4–4·5.[59] Add 1% reagent soln. to the boiling 50 ml.

sample soln., place on a steam-bath for 20 min., filter, wash with hot H_2O, dry at 120°C and weigh as $H_2UO_2[C_{10}H_5O(NO)CO_2]_2$. Hg, Pb, Fe, Ce^{4+} and Pd interfere, but Cu, Cd, Bi, Ti, V, Pt do not; Al, Be, Cr necessitate repptn., Co hexone extn., and Th or Zr a modified procedure.

Cupferron forms a ppt. (see under Separation, p. 299) which can be ignited at 800–946°C and weighed as U_3O_8.[1]

Electrodeposition can be used to det. 200 mg. U in 100 ml. soln. at pH above 6 (0·5*M* NH_4OAc).[2] Place the soln. in a Pt dish and electrolyze with a rotating Pt anode at 80–90°C, 2–6 v. and 0·2 amp./cm.^{2} for 1–2 hr. Wash with dil. NH_4OAc, ignite and weigh as U_3O_8.

H_2O_2 ppts. U from nitrate or acetate soln. at pH 2·0–2·5.[2] Add a 2-fold excess of 30% reagent at 0°C, cool to −45°C (solid CO_2 and EtOH) for at least 1 hr., filter on Whatman No. 42 paper at 0°C and wash with a 3% soln. of NH_4NO_3 in 3% H_2O_2 at pH 2·0–2·5 below 2°C; ignite to U_3O_8. No interference arises from Na, Mg, Ca, Al, rare earths, Ti, Ni, Co, Mn, Cu, Cd; V, Zr, Hf, Th, K, NH_4^+, F^-, Cl^- and large amts. of SO_4^{2-} or alk. earths interfere. Lactic acid prevents Fe interference.

$H_2C_2O_4$ forms a ppt.[2] which can be dried at 100–180°C and weighed as $U(C_2O_4)_2$ or ignited at 700–946°C and weighed as U_3O_8.

$NaIO_3$ ppts. 6–60 mg. U in acetate soln.[60] Add satd. reagent soln. at 60–65°C, cool, filter on a Gooch crucible and wash with H_2O; dry at 120°C and weigh as $UO_2(IO_3)_2$, or titrate the filtrate iodometrically. Mineral acids, Cl^- and NO_3^- interfere.

Hexamine is applied in conjunction with H_2S.[61] Add 2 g. hexamine to 100 ml. neutral soln. at 60°C, pass H_2S for 15 min., heat nearly to b.p. and pass for another 15 min.; allow to cool for 15 min., filter on paper, wash with 3% NH_4NO_3 contg. some NH_4OH and ignite to U_3O_8. The actual ppt. is $NH_4SS(OH)^{2-}U^{4-}(OUO_2ONH_4)_2$.

(i) Miscellaneous titrimetric methods. Certain redox titrations can be used after reduction of U^{6+} with org. materials under UV light; such methods have not been much studied and are thus listed here. For < 1 mg. U, add 10 ml. 0·1*M* $H_2C_2O_4$, place under UV light (2537 Å) for 2 hr., add 5–10 ml. 18*N* H_2SO_4, dil. to 100 ml. with H_2O and titrate with 0·002*N* $KMnO_4$; the error is ±5% for 0·1 mg. U/l.[62] Reduction with lactic acid under UV light in 1–2*N* H_2SO_4 can precede titration with V^{5+} soln. using phenylanthranilic acid indicator.[63]

Pptn. with H_2SeO_3 at pH 4–5 in 50% EtOH soln. can be followed by iodometric titration of the uranyl selenite ppt. after dissoln. in HCl.[64] U^{4+} in boiling HCl soln. reduces H_2SeO_3 to Se, which can be weighed, or the excess SeO_3^{2-} can be titrated iodometrically.[64]

(j) l-Ascorbic acid provides a useful colorimetric method.[2] Evap. the Et_2O ext. after adding 10 ml. H_2O, add 8 ml. buffer (160 ml. 1*N* NH_4OAc, 10 ml. 5*N* AcOH and 180 ml. H_2O), 2 ml. 10% pyridine, 10 ml. 12% ascorbic acid and adjust to pH 4·6 ± 0·1 with NH_4OH or HCl; dil. to 50 ml. with H_2O and measure the red-brown color at 410 mμ. Fe, Cr^{3+}, Pb and Cu do not interfere.

(k) Na_2O_2 is suitable[2, 8, 65] for colorimetric detn. of 1–25 mg. U_3O_8. Ext. with Et_2O, evap., add 2 ml. H_2SO_4, 3 ml. HNO_3, 3 ml. $HClO_4$, evap. to fumes, cool and rinse the vessel walls. Neutralize with 1:1 NaOH, add 1 g. Na_2O_2 and add NaOH to give a final concn. of 10%. Dil. to 100 ml. with H_2O, filter on double Whatman No. 1 paper and measure at 425 mμ.

NOTES. (1) PO_4^{3-} and small amts. of F^- can be tolerated. Th requires filtration and repptn. while V, Cr, Mn, Ce, Fe, Co, Ni, Mo, Cu must be sepd. by Et_2O extn. If V is present, neutralize the soln., add 20 ml. 1:1 NaOH, dil. to 100 ml. with H_2O, add 0·5 g. Na_2O_2, filter on double Whatman No. 1 paper, receiving into a 250 ml. flask; heat almost to b.p., cool and measure at 425 mμ.

(2) If H_2O_2 replaces Na_2O_2, measurement is done at 370 mμ.[12] H_2O_2 can also be used in a differential method for 100–150 mg. U_3O_8 with measurement at 400 mμ after double Et_2O extn.[12]

(3) The Na_2O_2 method has been used after other sepns.[66] It is also applicable in acetate-buffered solns. at pH 4–5·5.

(l) Miscellaneous colorimetric methods. Resacetophenoneoxime forms a red-brown complex with U at pH 5·6 in NH_4OAc-buffered soln. and this can be measured at 420 mμ;[67] Fe interferes but Al, Zr and Th do not.

Salicylamidoxime forms an orange-yellow complex with 7–145 p.p.m. U at pH 7·9–9·1, which can be measured at 400 mμ; most cations interfere.[68]

Salicylamide has been used to det. 1–150 p.p.m. U at pH 6·6–7·2 with measurement at 430–440 mμ;[69] Th, Ce, Zn, Al, Pb, Mo, V, tartrate, citrate, AcO^-, $C_2O_4^{2-}$ and F^- interfere.

Na-salicylate is suitable for detn. of 1 mg U in 25 ml. soln. with measurement at 360 mμ;[70] interferences are Fe, mineral acids, many org. acids and org. solvents.

Tiron is used to det. 4–400 p.p.m. U;[71] add 5 ml. 5% tiron, 5 ml. 10% NaOAc and 1*N* HCl to give pH 3, and dil. to 25 ml. with H_2O before measurement at 373 mμ.

Sulfosalicylic acid,[72] resorcylic acid,[72] chromotropic acid,[2] R-salt,[73] and tannin[74] have also been proposed.

Quinalizarin forms a blue complex with 3·5–9·5 p.p.m. UO_2^{2+} in EtOH soln.;[75] adjust to pH 7·2, add reagent in EtOH and measure at 620 mμ. Alizarin S can be applied at pH 8·2 and 570 mμ.[2, 76]

Quercetin is suitable for 0·1–0·8 mg. U in 5 ml. neutral soln.:[77] add the sample soln. to 10 ml. 0·1*N* NH_4OAc (pH 7·0) and 8 ml. EtOH, then add 2 ml. reagent, dil. to 25 ml. with H_2O and compare the brown color after 10 min.

Morin can be used for 50–400 μg. U in 15 ml. neutral soln.[78] Add 0·5 ml. 1*N* HCl, 2 ml. 25% NH_4Cl, 2 ml.

1·5% EDTA and 0·6 ml. 0·33% morin in EtOH; after 5 min., add 1 ml. NH_4OH, dil. to 25 ml. with H_2O and compare after 10 min. Moderate amts. of Fe^{3+}, MoO_4^{2-} Al, Cu, Mg, Ca, TiO^{2+} can be tolerated.

NH_4-thioglycolate allows detn. of 0·1–1·6 mg. U.[79] Add 4 ml. reagent soln. (10 ml. thioglycolic acid in 50 ml. H_2O, neutralized with 1:1 NH_4OH and dild. to 100 ml.), adjust to pH 10 with 1:1 NH_4OH, dil. to 25 ml. with H_2O and measure the orange-yellow color at 380 mμ. Fe interference can be corrected for by detg. Fe at 600 mμ and subtracting the absorbance found; other interferences are Cu, Ni, Pb, Co and over 1 mg. CO_3^{2-} or PO_4^{3-}. No interference is caused by Al, Th, Ti, Zr if 3 ml. 10% tartrate/50 mg. metal is added; 0·5 g. Cl^-, ClO_3^-, NO_3^-, SO_4^{2-}, 0·2 g. F^-, tartrate, 0·4 g. AcO^-, 50 mg. $C_2O_4^{2-}$ and 20 mg. citrate can be tolerated.

Diethyldithiocarbamate can be applied in solns. contg. below 0·1 ml. 6*N* HCl or H_2SO_4 in 10 ml. soln.[2, 80] Add 5 ml. 20% NH_4OAc, 1 ml. 1% reagent, dil. to 50 ml. with H_2O and measure the yellow color with a blue filter after 5 min. Fe, Cu, etc. interfere.

The color of UO_2^{2+} or U^{4+} itself can be used for colorimetric detn. of 0·75–0·15% U in solns. contg. $<$ 10% H_2SO_4 and $<$ 4% H_3PO_4; U^{4+} is measured at 360 mμ and U^{4+} and U^{6+} at 410 mμ.[81] Fe in amts. equal to U requires addn. of 10% H_3PO_4; if more is present, it must be detd. with thioglycolic acid and deducted. Cu ($<$ 6U) and V (+ SO_2) require the use of a blue filter. Cr does not interfere. A differential technique can be used for 20–60 mg. U/ml. of sulfate soln. with measurement at 418 mμ.[82] A similar technique (at 420 mμ) has been applied in 50% v/v H_2SO_4 soln. to Nb–U alloys.[83] It is also applicable (at 430 mμ) in 7·2*N* H_2SO_4 soln.[84] in presence of Zr, Mo, Ti but Ta or Nb require addn. of 0·4*N* $H_2C_2O_4$.

Several similar procedures have been described. 0·5*M* $FeSO_4$ in 1*N* H_2SO_4 has been used for 10–50 mg. U_3O_8 in 20 ml. soln.[85] Add 20 ml. H_3PO_4 and 0·5 ml. 30% H_2O_2, boil for 10 min., cool, add 0·1 g. Na_2SO_3, 10 ml. reagent and boil for 10 min.; dil. to 50 ml. with H_2O, filter and measure at 600 and 700 mμ in a 4 cm. cell against a reference soln. prepd. as above from 10 ml. 1*N* H_2SO_4. V can be corrected for, but NO_3^- and moderate amts. of Cu, Ni, Co, Bi,Mn, Cr, Mo, TiO_2, Fe_2O_3 interfere.

A differential method is suitable for 10–70 mg. U/ml. in 2–65% $HClO_4$ (s.g. 1·67) soln. with measurement at 415–420 mμ; Fe, Al, Th, Zr, Pb, Cd do not interfere.[86] Detns. in nitrate soln. at 410 mμ,[87] in chloride soln.,[88] and in Na_2CO_3–$NaHCO_3$ soln. at 320 mμ[89] are also possible.

The diethylcellosolve ext. of the nitrate from satd. NH_4NO_3 soln. can be measured at 430 mμ.[90] 25% Tributylphosphate in iso-octane satd. with H_2O has been used for 0·1–1 mg. U in 10 ml. soln.:[91] add 5·1 g. $NaNO_3$, adjust to pH 3·0 with HNO_3 or NaOH, add 10 ml. solvent, stir for 4 min., sep. and measure at 250 mμ. A similar process is applicable for 0·04–0·2 mg. U in 20 ml. soln.[91]

$K_4Fe(CN)_6$ allows detn. of 0·1–0·5 mg. U in 10–15 ml. soln. contg. $<$ 0·02*N* H_2SO_4 (pH 6·3);[2, 80, 92] add 5 ml. 10% reagent in 1% Na_2SO_3, dil. to 25 ml. with H_2O, and measure the brown color after 15 min. with a blue filter. Interferences are Cu, Fe and AcO^-.

Fe^{3+}-*o*-phenanthroline allows detn. of 50–400 μg. U^{4+} in 50 ml. soln.[93] Cacotheline forms a violet complex[94] with U^{4+}.

Morellin can be used for 2–6 or 12–51 p.p.m. U in EtOH soln. at pH 5–7 with measurement at 540 mμ.[95]

Thoron is suitable for $<$ 50 μg. U in 2 ml. 3*N* HCl soln.[17] Reduce with 0·15 g. Pb, decant, wash, add 20 ml. Me_2CO and 1 ml. 0·5% thoron, dil. to 25 ml. with H_2O and measure at 535 mμ in a 4 cm. cell; a 1:2 complex is formed.

NaN_3 has been proposed for 0–2 mg. U:[96] add 5 ml. 7% HNO_3 and 20 ml. 3*M* reagent, dil. to 25 ml. with H_2O and measure at 360 mμ.

EDTA forms a complex in neutral soln. with UO_2^{2+}; 1–2 × $10^{-6}M$ solns. are measured at 290 mμ, and 5–25 × $10^{-6}M$ solns. at 340 mμ.[97] A high-frequency titration with EDTA is also possible.[98]

References

1. HILLEBRAND and LUNDELL, 364 (464); SCOTT and FURMAN, 1017; SCHOELLER and POWELL, 296; PIGOTT, 513.
2. RODDEN, C. J. and WARF, J. C., *Natl. Nuclear Energy Ser., Div. VIII*, **1**, 3–159 (1950).
3. FLAGG, J. F., *et al.*, *Natl. Nuclear Energy Ser., Div. VI*, **1**, 147–93 (1949).
4. RODDEN, C. J., *Anal. Chem.*, **25**, 1598 (1953).
5. GRIMALDI, F. S., *et al.*, *U.S. Geol. Survey Bull.* No. 1006 (1954); *Profess. Papers*, No. 300, 605 (1956).
6. EINECKE, E. and HARMS, J., *Z. anal. Chem.*, **99**, 120 (1934); HARTMANN, W. M., *ibid.*, **93**, 373 (1933); IWASE, E., *et al.*, *Japan Analyst*, **6**, 261, 390, 469, 531 (1957).
7. LJUNGGREN, G., *et al.*, *Svensk Kem. Tidskr.*, **61**, 170 (1949).
8. SCHOELLER and POWELL, 311.
9. PIGOTT, 518.
10. BENNETT, W. R., *J. Am. Chem. Soc.*, **56**, 277 (1934).
11. TSUBAKI, I., *Japan Analyst*, **4**, 77, 357 (1955).
12. GUEST, R. J. and ZIMMERMAN, J. B., *Anal. Chem.*, **27**, 931 (1955).
13. NORSTRÖM, A. and SILLÉN, L. G., *Svensk Kem. Tidskr.*, **60**, 227, 232 (1948).
14. ADAMS, J. A. S. and MAECK, W. J., *Anal. Chem.*, **26**, 1635 (1954).
15. HARA, T., *J. Chem. Soc. Japan*, **78**, 333 (1957).
16. HECHT, F. and KRAFFT-EBING, H., *Z. anal. Chem.*, **106**, 321 (1937).
17. FOREMAN, J. K., *et al.*, *Analyst*, **82**, 89 (1957).
18. PŘIBIL, R. and VORLÍČEK, J., *Chem. listy*, **46**, 216 (1952).
19. WELCHER, **III**, 15, 30.
20. SCHOELLER, 139, 157; WELCHER, **II**, 156.
21. DESHMUKH, G. S. and JOSHI, M. K., *Chem. Ber.*, **87**, 1446 (1954).

22. ISHIMARU, S., *Kagaku-Zikken-Gaku*, **X**, 34 (1942).
23. KOLTHOFF, I. M. and LINGANE, J. J., *J. Am. Chem. Soc.*, **55**, 1871 (1933); COOKE, W. D., *et al.*, *Anal. Chem.*, **22**, 654 (1950); SCHREYER, J. M. and BAES, JR., C. F., *ibid.*, **25**, 644 (1953).
24. RAO, V. P., *et al.*, *Z. anal. Chem.*, **147**, 99 (1955).
25. MAIN, A. R., *Anal. Chem.*, **26**, 1507 (1954); GUEST, R. J. and LALONDE, C. R., *Can. Dept. Mines and Tech. Surveys, Mines Branch, Radioactivity Div., Topical Rept.* TR-135/56 (1956).
26. SILL, C. W. and PETERSON, H. E., *Anal. Chem.*, **24**, 1175 (1952).
27. ALLEN, K. A., *Anal. Chem.*, **28**, 1144 (1956).
28. WAHLBERG, J. S., *et al.*, *Anal. Chem.*, **29**, 954 (1957).
29. FURMAN, N. H., *et al.*, *Anal. Chem.*, **25**, 482 (1953).
30. RAO, V. P., *et al.*, *Z. anal. Chem.*, **150**, 401 (1956).
31. RAO, V. P., *et al.*, *Z. anal. Chem.*, **147**, 161 (1955).
32. SIMON, V. and PŘIPLATOVÁ, E., *Chem. listy*, **50**, 907 (1956).
33. CELLINI, R. F. and LÓPEZ, J. A., *Anales real soc. españ. fís. y quím.* (*Madrid*), **52B**, 163 (1956).
34. STEUER, H., *Z. anal. Chem.*, **118**, 389 (1939/40); LINGANE, J. J. and IWAMOTO, R. T., *Anal. Chim. Acta*, **13**, 465 (1955) (coulometric).
35. EL-SHANY, H. K. and EL-DIN ZAYAN, S., *Analyst*, **80**, 65 (1955).
36. CARSON, W. N., *et al.*, *Anal. Chem.*, **25**, 466 (1953) (Br_2); BOOMAN, G. L., *et al.*, *ibid.*, **29**, 219 (1957) (reduction).
37. CLAASSEN, A. and VISSER, J., *Rec. trav. chim.*, **65**, 211 (1946); SEN SARMA, R. N. and MALLIK, A. K., *Z. anal. Chem.*, **148**, 179 (1955); *Anal. Chim. Acta*, **12**, 329 (1955) (interfering elements); WENDLANDT, W. W., *Anal. Chem.*, **28**, 499 (1956) (230–380°C, $UO_2(C_9H_6ON)_2$); CARTER, J. A. and WEBER, C. W., *U.S. Atomic Energy Comm.*, TID-7516, 186 (1956); HECHT and DONAU, 205; WELCHER, **I**, 302.
38. SILVERMAN, L., *et al.*, *Anal. Chem.*, **25**, 1389 (1953); RULFS, CH. L., *et al.*, *ibid.*, **27**, 1802 (1955) (pH 5·8–8·0).
39. HÖK, B., *Svensk Kem. Tidskr.*, **65**, 106 (1953).
40. EBERLE, A. E. and LERNER, M. W., *Anal. Chem.*, **29**, 1134 (1957).
41. CROUTHAMEL, C. E. and JOHNSON, C. E., *Anal. Chem.*, **24**, 1780 (1952); also see CURRAH, J. E. and BEAMISH, F. E., *ibid.*, **19**, 609 (1947); SANDELL, 601; GERHOLD, M. and HECHT, F., *Mikrochemie ver. Mikrochim. Acta*, **36/37**, 1100 (1951) (AmOH, Et_2O extn.); SILVERMAN, L. and MOUDY, L., *Nucleonics*, **12**, No. 9, 60, 62 (1954) (tetraethylene glycol/dibutyl ether extn.); KIMBALL, R. B. and REIN, J. E., *U.S. Atomic Energy Comm.*, IDO-14380 (1956) (+EtOH).
42. TUCHER, H. T., *Analyst*, **82**, 529 (1957).
43. CLINCH, J. and GUY, M. J., *Analyst*, **82**, 800 (1957).
44. NIETZEL, O. A. and DESESA, M. A., *Anal. Chem.*, **29**, 756 (1957).
45. YOE, J. H., *et al.*, *Anal. Chem.*, **25**, 1200 (1953); **26**, 424 (1954).
46. PŘIBIL, R. and JELINÉK, M., *Chem. listy*, **47**, 1326 (1953).
47. BLANQUET, P., *Anal. Chim. Acta*, **16**, 44 (1957).
48. YAMANE, Y., *J. Pharm. Soc. Japan*, **77**, 400 (1957).
49. SANDELL, 597; also see NORTHUP, M. A., *Ind. Eng. Chem., Anal. Ed.*, **17**, 664 (1945); NAKANISHI, M., *J. Chem. Soc. Japan*, **68**, 42 (1947); *Bull. Chem. Soc. Japan*, **23**, 198, 201 (1950); **24**, 33, 36 (1951); ERLENMEYER, H., *et al.*, *Helv. Chim. Acta*, **33**, 25 (1950); PRICE, E. R., *et al.*, *Anal. Chem.*, **25**, 322 (1953); CENTANNI, F. A., *et al.*, *ibid.*, **28**, 1651 (1956) (2% LiF + 98% NaF fusion); THATCHER, L. I. and BARKER, F. B., *ibid.*, **29**, 1575 (1957) (9% NaF + 45·5% Na_2CO_3 + 45·5% K_2CO_3 flux; 0·1 μg. in natural water).
50. TILLU, M. M., *Current Sci.* (*India*), **24**, 45 (1955) (pH 5 + EDTA soln.).
51. RÂY, H. N. and BHATTACHARYA, N. P., *Analyst*, **82**, 164 (1957).
52. PIETSCH, R., *Z. anal. Chem.*, **152**, 168 (1956).
53. HOVORKA, V., *et al.*, *Chim. anal.*, **29**, 268 (1947).
54. WELCHER, **III**, 351.
55. BHADURI, A. S., *Sci. and Culture* (*Calcutta*), **18**, 95 (1952); *Z. anal. Chem.*, **151**, 109 (1956).
56. BHADURI, A. S. and RÂY, P., *Sci. and Culture* (*Calcutta*), **18**, 97 (1952); *Z. anal. Chem.*, **154**, 103 (1957).
57. WELCHER, **II**, 214.
58. TANII, K., *et al.*, *J. Chem. Soc. Japan*, **61**, 269 (1940).
59. DATTA, S. K., *Z. anal. Chem.*, **155**, 241 (1957).
60. VENUGOPALAN, M., *Z. anal. Chem.*, **153**, 187 (1956).
61. WELCHER, **III**, 128.
62. PAIGE, H. H., *et al.*, *Science*, **120**, 347 (1954).
63. RAO, G. G., *et al.*, *Anal. Chim. Acta*, **15**, 97 (1956); *Z. anal. Chem.*, **150**, 178 (1956) (EtOH).
64. JOSHI (DZHOSHI), M. K., *Zhur. Anal. Khim.*, **11**, 495 (1956); see also DESHMUKH, G. S. and JOSHI, M. K., *Chem. Ber.*, **88**, 186 (1955).
65. SCOTT, T. R., *Analyst*, **74**, 486 (1949).
66. SEIM, H. J., *et al.*, *Anal. Chem.*, **29**, 443 (1957) (after ion exchange sepn.); KURAMA, T., *et al.*, *Japan Analyst*, **6**, 3 (1957) (pH 12·4, after cellulose column sepn.).
67. URS, M. K. and NEELAKANTAM, K., *J. Sci. Ind. Research* (*India*), **11B**, 79 (1952).
68. BANDYOPADHAYAY, D. and RÂY, P., *Sci. and Culture* (*Calcutta*), **19**, 466 (1954); *J. Indian Chem. Soc.*, **33**, 269 (1956).
69. CHAKRABURTTY, A. K., *et al.*, *J. Indian Chem. Soc.*, **30**, 496 (1953).
70. WELCHER, **II**, 126; THOMASON, P. F., *et al.*, *U.S. Atomic Energy Comm.*, ORNL-1641 (1955).
71. SARMA, B. and SAVARIAR, C. P., *J. Sci. Ind. Research* (*India*), **16B**, 80 (1957).
72. WELCHER, **II**, 116, 138.
73. RAO, M. N. and RAO, BH. S. V. R., *Z. anal. Chem.*, **142**, 161 (1954).
74. DAS-GUPTA, P. N., *J. Indian Chem. Soc.*, **6**, 763 (1929).
75. MAJUMDAR, A. K., *Sci. and Culture* (*Calcutta*), **13**, 468 (1948); PÉREZ, T. P. and CHABANNES, J., *Anales edafol. y fisiol. vegetal* (*Madrid*), **10**, 595 (1951).
76. VENKATESWARLU, K. S. and RAO, BH. S. V. R., *Anal. Chim. Acta*, **13**, 79 (1955).
77. KOMENDA, J., *Chem. listy*, **47**, 531 (1953).
78. ALMÁSSY, G., *et al.*, *Magyar Tudományos Akad. Kém. Tudományok Osztályanak Közleményei*, **5**, 257 (1954); also see BECK, M. and HANTOS, E., *Magyar Kém. Folyóirat*, **60**, 244 (1954) (in EtOH soln., 430 mμ); TOMIČ, E. and HECHT, F., *Mikrochim. Acta*, 896 (1955) (in Me_2CO soln., fluorescence).
79. DAVENPORT, JR., W. H. and THOMASON, P. F., *Anal. Chem.*, **21**, 1093 (1949); KOSTA, L., *Sloven. Acad. Sci. Arts*, "*J. Stefan*" *Inst. Phys. Repts.*, **1**, 12 (1953).
80. SANDELL, 603.

81. SCOTT, T. R. and DIXON, P., *Analyst*, **70**, 462 (1945).
82. SUSANO, C. D., *et al.*, *Anal. Chem.*, **28**, 1072 (1956).
83. BANKS, C. V., *et al.*, *Anal. Chem.*, **29**, 995 (1957).
84. BACON, A. and MILNER, G. W. C., *Atomic Energy Research Estab.* (*Gt. Brit.*), *Rept.* C/R-1637, 1749 (1955).
85. CANNING, R. G. and DIXON, P., *Anal. Chem.*, **27**, 877 (1955).
86. SILVERMAN, L. and MOUDY, L., *Anal. Chem.*, **28**, 45 (1956).
87. WATERS, D. E., *U.S. Atomic Energy Comm.*, CC-1110 (1943).
88. CARVALHO, A. H. DE and VIDEIRA, F. M., *Rev. fac. ciên. Univ. Lisboa*, **3**, 55 (1954).
89. WESSLING, B. W. and DESESA, M. A., *U.S. Atomic Energy Comm.*, WIN-43 (1956).
90. PRICE, T. D., *et al.*, *U.S. Atomic Energy Comm.*, CD-B-S-518 (1944).
91. PAIGE, B. E., *et al.*, *Anal. Chem.*, **29**, 1029 (1957).
92. AHRLAND, S., *Svensk. Kem. Tidskr.*, **61**, 197 (1949).
93. MANNING, D. L. and WHITE, J. C., *U.S. Atomic Energy Comm.*, ORNL-1476 (1953).
94. GRIMES, W. R., *et al.*, *U.S. Atomic Energy Comm.*, CD-2270 (1945).
95. RAO, B. R. L. and PATEL, C. C., *Proc. Indian Acad. Sci.*, **43A**, 276 (1956).
96. FEINSTEIN, H. I., *Anal. Chim. Acta*, **15**, 288 (1956).
97. RAO, G. G. and SOMIDEVAMMA, G., *Z. anal. Chem.*, **157**, 27 (1957).
98. HARA, R. and WEST, P. W., *Anal. Chim. Acta*, **12**, 285 (1955).

40

THALLIUM

The main sources for this chapter are given in ref. 1. Anderson[2] has described the detection and determination of thallium in some detail, and the rapid and accurate determination of thallium has also been discussed.[3]

Thallium(I), which is similar in reactions to potassium and lead, can be converted to thallium(III) by treatment with Cl_2, Br_2 or aqua regia; the reverse reaction is accomplished by SO_2, H_2O_2, Na_2SO_3 or H_2S on boiling. Thallium(III) is somewhat similar to iron(III) in reactions. Some Tl^{3+} may be reduced to Tl^+ on heating with Br_2 in absence of Cl^-.

The flame test for Tl gives a blue-green color with maximum luminescence at 535·1 mμ.

Attack

(a) Minerals. Heat with 10 ml. H_2SO_4 and 2 g. K_2SO_4, cool, add 100 ml. H_2O, boil, cool and filter. Neutralize with Na_2CO_3, add 2 g. in excess, dil. to 200 ml. with H_2O, boil with 5 g. NaCN and leave for 12 hr. Filter on paper, wash with 1% Na_2CO_3 and add $(NH_4)_2S$. Filter, dissolve the ppt. in hot 10% H_2SO_4, add SO_2, almost neutralize with Na_2CO_3, and apply the K_2CrO_4 or KI method.

For pyrites or sphalerite, treat 25–100 g. with HCl, HNO_3 and H_2SO_4, evap. to fumes, add H_2O and excess Zn and leave for 12 hr. Add 2–3 ml. HCl, filter on paper contg. Zn, wash and treat the ppt. with H_2SO_4, Na_2CO_3, NaCN, etc. as described above.

(b) Silicates, glass. Fuse with Na_2CO_3.

(c) Org. materials. Heat almost to boiling with 1:1 HCl, and add $KClO_3$ in small portions. Alternatively, digest with H_2SO_4 and HNO_3, or with $HClO_4$, H_2SO_4 and HNO_3.

Separation

Treatment with H_2S in acidic soln. allows sepn. of Tl from group II elements; there is danger of copptn. with As, Sn, Sb or Cu sulfide. In dil. AcOH solns. H_2S seps. black Tl_2S from group IV metals; Na_2S can be used similarly and is said to be better than H_2S.[4] Concn. is possible by copptn. with Hg, Pb, Ag, etc. The ppt. of Tl_2S is readily oxidized.

Treatment with HCl (and Cl_2) seps. Tl from Ag; Tl is sepd. from Pb with H_2SO_4.

Na_2CO_3 and NaCN in conjunction with $(NH_4)_2S$ (see above) seps. Tl from Pb, Bi, Cu, As, Sb, Sn.

KI in slightly acidic (H_2SO_4) solns. allows sepn. from Hg, Pb, Bi, Cd, As, Sb, Sn, Fe, Al, Cr, Co, Ni, Zn, Mn and groups IV and V; interferences are Ag and Cu (which is sol. in NH_4OH). Prior treatment with SO_2 is required.

Tl and Sn can be sepd. by neutralization of the acidic soln. with NH_4OH, addn. of some AcOH and 2–3 g. NH_4NO_3, diln. to 500 ml. with H_2O, boiling and filtration. NH_4OH and SO_2 treatment seps. Tl from Ga.

Tl can be sepd. from Fe, Al, Cr with NH_4NO_2: almost neutralize the acidic soln. with Na_2CO_3, heat to 40°C, add 20 ml. 7% NH_4NO_2 and 20 ml. MeOH and boil for 20 min. before filtration on paper and washing with 5% NH_4NO_3.

$(NH_4)_2HPO_4$ in NH_4OH soln. contg. 20 ml. 50% sulfosalicylic acid/0·1 g. Pb seps. Tl from Pb and Mn. $(NH_4)_2HPO_4$ in neutral soln. seps. Tl from Bi.

K_2CrO_4 allows sepn. from many elements (see under Determination, p. 307) and concn. is possible with Ba present.

Zn or Mg in HCl or H_2SO_4 soln. also allows sepn. from many elements; it is essential to use boiled H_2O.

Electrolysis at a Zn–Hg electrode in dil. H_2SO_4 soln. seps. Tl from V, Al and Zr.

Extn. with Et_2O from small vols. of solns. contg. 6*N* HCl (and some Cl_2) seps. Tl from many elements; triple extn. with equal vols. of Et_2O pre-equilibrated with 6*N* HCl is needed. Interferences are Fe, Au, Sb, Sn, Ga. If the ext. is shaken with SO_2 water, 99% Fe is sepd. If this extn. is combined with a dithizone extn., sepn. from practically all elements becomes feasible. Extn. with iso-Pr_2O from 1:1 HCl soln. contg. Br_2 seps. Tl from Pb, and from Fe if H_3PO_4 is present.[5] Extn. with Et_2O from Br_2-contg. 1*N* HBr soln. and shaking the ext. with 1*N* HBr seps. Tl from Ga and In. Iso-Pr_2O extn. is said to be better.

Dithizone extn. from solns. of pH 10 contg. citrate and CN^- allows sepn. of Tl from many elements.[6, 7]

For a 1 g. sample, heat with 10 g. Na_2SO_4 and 5 ml. H_2SO_4 in a 250 ml. Erlenmeyer flask until no S remains and a fused mass is left (if SiO_2 is present add some NaF). Cool, add 75 ml. H_2O and some $NaHSO_3$, boil, cool, filter and wash with 2% H_2SO_4. Add 5 ml. Na_3-citrate soln. (200 g. citric acid in H_2O, neutralized with NaOH until blue to thymol blue, and dild. to 600 ml. with H_2O) and 5–6 drops 0·04% thymol blue. Add NaOH to the color change from red to yellow and then neutralize with NH_4OH from yellow to blue adding 2–3 ml. in excess. (If it is necessary to add more or less than 3–5 ml. NH_4OH, add a suitable amt. of H_2SO_4 and repeat the neutralization.) Then add 15 ml. NaCN soln. (200 g. NaCN in 400 ml. H_2O treated with a min. amt. of 1·83% $Pb(OAc)_2$ until the brown color becomes no deeper, heated and filtered). Add 5 ml. $NH_2OH \cdot \frac{1}{2}H_2SO_4$ soln. (20 g. in 50 ml. H_2O, neutralized with NaOH to thymol blue and dild. to 100 ml. with H_2O). After 2–3 min., when the soln. becomes blue (if it does not, heat at 90°C for 5 min. and then cool rapidly), transfer to a separatory funnel. Shake for 20–30 sec. with 10 ml. dithizone (1·5 g./l. $CHCl_3$). Repeat this extn. until the soln. is completely green; 3 times is normally enough but, if not, add more NaCN and repeat. Combine the exts. and wash with 50 ml. 0·5% $(NH_4)_3$-citrate (5 g. in 1 l. H_2O, neutralized with NH_4OH to thymol blue and 1 ml. NH_4OH and 25 ml. NaCN soln. added). After this sepn. wash twice with H_2O, combine the washings, ext. with 5 ml. dithizone soln. and combine with the org. phase. Evap. with 1 ml. H_2SO_4 until charring occurs, add 1 ml. $HClO_4$, heat slowly for 10–15 min. evap. to white fumes, cool, add H_2O and 2–3 drops $HClO_4$ and fume again. Finally, add 25 ml. H_2O and apply an iodometric titration. Alternatively, carry out the extn. similarly to the above method, wash the exts. with 10–20 ml. 1:1000 NH_4OH and H_2O, strip twice with 10 ml. 1:100 HNO_3, evap. to fumes with 0·5 ml. 1:5 H_2SO_4, fume with 20 mg. $(NH_4)_2S_2O_8$, repeat until colorless and finally apply the rhodamine B colorimetric finish (p. 308).

Thionalide also allows the sepn. of Tl from many elements (see under Determination, p. 308).

Thiourea seps. Tl^+ from Hg, Ag, Cu, Cd, Fe, Ni, Co, Zn, Mn, Al, Cr, Ba, Sr, Ca.[8, 9] Add an equal vol. of 10% reagent to the 2% $HClO_4$ soln., filter on a glass crucible after 30 min., and wash with slightly acidic ($HClO_4$) 5% reagent soln. Sepn. from Pb is possible by dissoln. of the ppt. in hot H_2O, addn. of $HClO_4$ and repptn.

Several concn. procedures have been mentioned above. Others involve copptn. with K or Rb on addn. of H_2PtCl_6, $Na_3Co(NO_2)_6$ or phosphotungstate; or copptn. with Fe^{3+} on addn. of NH_4OH.

Determination

In a comparison of 15 gravimetric methods, Chretien and Longi[3] found the K_2CrO_4 procedure the most accurate. Of the titrimetric processes, the $KBrO_3$ method is very accurate while the Ce^{4+} method seems promising.[3] The K_2CrO_4, $KBrO_3$, KIO_3 and thionalide methods are all reliable for macro or semi-micro amts. of Tl. Of the various colorimetric procedures, the rhodamine B method is satisfactory, while the KI method seems convenient.

(a) K_2CrO_4 can be applied gravimetrically or titrimetrically.[1, 10] For gravimetric detn. of $< 0·1$ g. Tl^+ in 100 ml. soln. contg. 3 ml. 2:1 NH_4OH, heat to 70–80°C, add 10% K_2CrO_4 to give a 2 g. excess of reagent, cool and leave for 12 hr. Filter on a Gooch crucible, wash with 1% reagent soln. and 50% EtOH, dry at 120–130°C (97–745°C) and weigh as Tl_2CrO_4.

NOTES. (1) No interference arises from Ag, Hg, Cu if KCN is added; from Ga, In, Al, Fe, Cr if 10 ml. 50% sulfosalicylic acid/0·1 g. metal is added; from As or Sb if H_2O_2 is added; from V^{4+} if tartaric acid is added; from Zn, Cd, Ni, Co if more NH_4OH is added; or from Mo or W.
(2) For the detn. of mg. amts. add 50% EtOH after cooling. Tl^{3+} can be reduced with SO_2 in H_2SO_4 soln. or with H_2O_2 in HCl soln.
(3) The CrO_4^{2-} ion in the ppt. or filtrate can be detd. iodometrically but this is less accurate than gravimetry.
(4) Na_2CrO_4 can replace the K salt.[11] For 35 mg. $<Tl^+$ in $1F$ $HClO_4$ soln. add $0·5F$ reagent to give a final concn. of $0·125F$ and a final vol. of 100 ml.; keep at 0°C for 12 hr., filter on a glass crucible and wash with a mixt. of $0·5F$ $HClO_4$ and $0·125F$ Na_2CrO_4. Dip the ppt. for 45 min. in a soln. of 2 g. Na_2CrO_4 in 150 ml. $1F$ NH_4OH and $1F$ NaCN, wash with EtOH and dry at 110°C. No interference arises from <40 mg. Fe or Tl^{3+}; if Tl^{3+} is absent, >35 mg. Tl can be detd.

(b) $KBrO_3$ provides an excellent titrimetric detn.;[12] a visual methyl orange or a potentiometric end-point can be applied. For $> 5\,\mu$g. Tl in ca. 5% HCl soln., use a direct titration as indicated, or add excess of $KBrO_3$ and det. the excess iodometrically. Fe^{3+} interference is avoided by addn. of 100 mg. $(NH_4)_2HPO_4$/5 mg. Fe. Hg, Pb, Bi, Cu, Cd, As^{5+}, Sb^{5+}, Sn^{4+} do not interfere.

Many other redox titrations have been proposed. KIO_3 is suitable for 0·078–0·42 g. Tl^+ in 100 ml. 3–5N HCl soln.[13] Add 4 ml. CCl_4, 5 ml. ICl soln. and titrate with 0·1N reagent until the org. layer is colorless. This method cannot be applied in presence of KCN.

$KMnO_4$ can be used for 6–100 mg. Tl^+ in 60 ml. 1·2N HCl which is also 1·2N in NaF; 0·005M reagent is added to the pink end-point.[14] KCl can be added instead of NaF but this is less accurate (Scott and Furman[1]). Titration of $5 \times 10^{-5}N$ Tl in alk. soln. with a potentiometric end-point is possible.[15] $KMnO_4$ is also applicable with addn. of KBr.[16]

Titration with 0·1N Ce^{4+} in solns. contg. 40–50 ml. HCl in 200 ml. at 50°C in presence of ICl catalyst and ferroin indicator gives high results.[17] Chloramine-T may be used potentiometrically to det. 10 ml. ca. 0·1N $TlNO_3$ after addn. of 10 ml. 10% KBr, 5 ml. 2N HCl and 35 ml. H_2O.[18] KIO_4 (0·1–0·001N) allows detn. of 25 μg.–50 mg. Tl in 5–100 ml. 28% HCl soln., the end-point being potentiometric.[19] Br_2 may be applied coulometrically[20] as can $Fe(CN)_6^{3-}$, the latter allowing detn. of 8–20 mg. Tl in 125 ml.[21]

For iodometric methods, see the next column.

(c) Thionalide provides gravimetric, titrimetric, nephelometric and colorimetric methods for Tl. For detn. of 10–50 mg. Tl^+ in neutral soln.[22, 23] add 10–15 ml. 20% Na_2-tartrate, neutralize to phenolphthalein with NaOH, add 20% KCN to give a 5% soln. and 2*N* NaOH to give a 1*N* soln. and dil. to 100 ml. Add a 4–5-fold excess of 5% thionalide in Me_2CO, boil, cool, filter on a G4 crucible, wash with H_2O and Me_2CO, dry at 110°C (69–156°C) and weigh as $Tl(C_{12}H_{10}ONS)$. Alternatively, dissolve the ppt. in AcOH and 2*N* H_2SO_4 (3:1), add excess 0·02*N* I_2 and titrate with 0·02*N* $Na_2S_2O_3$.

NOTES. (1) No interference is caused by Ag, Cu, As, Sb, Sn, W, Mo, Zn, Al, Co, Ni, Fe^{2+}. In presence of group IV metals, det. Tl directly in 1*N* NH_4OH; NH_4Cl is also added if Mg is present. For Fe^{3+}, V, Au, Pt, Pd, add $NH_2OH \cdot \frac{1}{2}H_2SO_4$, boil, filter if necessary, and proceed as above. For UO_2^{2+}, add $(NH_4)_2CO_3$ to the soln. and to the wash water. For Hg, add KCN to give a 9% soln. and Me_2CO to give a 30% soln.; for Bi or Pb, omit KCN but add Me_2CO as for Hg.

(2) For colorimetric detn.[22, 24] of the thionalide ppt. obtained from 5–300 μg. Tl, centrifuge, add 2 drops H_2SO_4 and 1 ml. EtOH, warm and transfer to a Nessler tube with EtOH and H_2O. Add 1–3 drops Folin–Denis reagent (1 g. phosphomolybdic acid, 5 g. Na_2WO_4, 5 ml. H_3PO_4, 18 ml. H_2O, boiled for 2 hr. under reflux and dild. to 25 ml. with H_2O) followed by 1·5–2·5 ml. formamide, heat for 15 min. at 40°C, dil. and compare the blue color. The error is −5% for 5 μg. Tl.

(d) Rhodamine B provides an excellent colorimetric procedure.[7] For 1–10 μg. Tl in 0·5 ml. H_2SO_4 soln. add 5·0 ml. 2*N* HCl, 1·0 ml. Br_2 water and heat to remove all Br_2. Cool, dil. to 10 ml. with 2*N* HCl, add 1·0 ml. 0·2% reagent and 10·0 ml. C_6H_6, shake for 1 min., sep., centrifuge and measure at 560 mμ. A correction of +10% is required. Dithizone extn. removes Sb, Fe, W, and Au can be removed by reduction.

Several similar reagents have been recommended. Crystal violet is suitable for detn. of Tl^{3+} in 25 ml. 1·2*N* HCl soln.[25] Add 0·5 g. $Na_4P_2O_7$, 10 drops 0·2% reagent and 10 ml. toluene, shake for 30 sec. and measure at 540–570 mμ.

Methyl violet or brilliant green may be used to det. 0·05 μg. Tl/ml. in 0·08–0·16*N* acid, with AmOAc extn. and measurement at 630 mμ.[26] For detn. of < 50 μg. Tl in 4–5 ml. soln.[27] add 2 ml. 10% $NaNO_2$, 5 ml. HCl and, after 5 min., 0·5 g. urea; dil. to 100 ml. with H_2O, add 2 ml. 0·2% methyl violet and ext. twice with 25 ml. C_6H_6. If extn. is done with toluene, $\epsilon = 48\,000$ at 570 mμ and 64 000 at 620 mμ.[28] Turquoise blue, crystal violet or malachite green may be applied similarly.

A variety of procedures utilize the formation of halide complexes. $[Co(NH_3)_6]Cl_3$ is used for detn. of 0·1 g. Tl^{3+} in 100–400 ml. soln. contg. 4–6 ml. HCl and some $KClO_3$;[29] boil, cool and add a small excess of reagent (100 g. $CoCl_2 \cdot 6H_2O$ and 30 g. NH_4Cl in a little H_2O, treated with AgCl in 20% NH_4OH for 2 days, filtered, extd. with H_2O at 25°C, mixed with a small excess of HCl, cooled, filtered and recrystd. from H_2O). After settling, filter on a G4 crucible, wash with 2% HCl, then 6–7 times with a 2–3 ml. EtOH and 4–5 times with Et_2O; dry in a vacuum desiccator and weigh as $[Co(NH_3)_6][TlCl_6]$. Hg, Pb, Bi interfere; Ag interference is avoided by boiling with HCl and $KClO_3$ and filtering before the above procedure.[29] This method is said to be easier and more accurate than the K_2CrO_4 method. The ppt. may be detd. colorimetrically using nitroso-R salt[30] or titrimetrically[31] by Volhard's method or absorptiometrically at 420 mμ (1–50 mg. Tl) after dissoln. in hot H_2O.

Tetraphenylarsonium chloride provides a gravimetric method.[32] Make the 20–50 ml. soln. contg. Tl^+ alk. with NaOH, add 2 ml. 30% H_2O_2 and HCl to give a 0·5–2*N* HCl soln., add 1 ml. H_2O_2 and excess 6·7% reagent and boil. Filter on a glass crucible after 12 hr., wash with 1*N* HCl, dry at 110°C (50–218°C) and weigh as $(C_6H_5)_4AsTlCl_4$. Interferences are heavy metals, Re, MnO_4^-, ClO_4^-, IO_4^-, SCN^-, NO_3^-, I^-, Br^-, F^-,

Tetraphenylammonium bromide and KI can be applied nephelometrically.[33]

HCl alone forms a complex with 8–40 p.p.m. Tl^+ which can be measured at 245 mμ;[34] add 50 ml. HCl to the soln. and dil. to 100 ml. with H_2O before measuring. Interferences are Fe, Cu, Sb, V, Cr, Hg, Bi, Sn, Pb, I^- and NO_3^-.

(e) KI can be applied colorimetrically, titrimetrically or gravimetrically for detn. of Tl. For colorimetric detn.[24] of 5–200 μg. Tl^{3+} in 35 ml. soln. add 5 ml. 0·2% KI and 1 ml. starch–glycerol soln. (10 g. sol. starch in 50 ml. H_2O poured into 450 ml. boiling H_2O, boiled for 5 min. after addn. of 500 ml. glycerol and dild. to 1 l. with H_2O). Stir for 5 min. below 18°C and measure the blue-violet color at 600 mμ; the color deepens with time.

In an alternative method for 40–100 μg. Tl^{3+} in 60 ml. 1*N* HCl soln.[35] add 5 ml. 0·2% KI, shake for 30 sec. with 20 ml. CS_2 and compare the violet color in the org. layer; the accuracy is ±3–5%. Fe can be present if H_3PO_4 is added, and Cu, Pb, As, Hg, W, Mo require preliminary extn. with Et_2O.

For iodometric detn. of 2 mg. Tl in 25 ml. soln.,[6, 9, 36] add 1 ml. H_2SO_4, 25 ml. Br_2 soln. (100 g. $NaH_2PO_4 \cdot H_2O$ and 100 g. NH_4Cl in 900 ml. satd. Br_2 water), heat to boiling within 3 min. and boil until the soln. is yellow. Cool rapidly, add 0·2 ml. 25% w/v phenol in AcOH, 5 ml. 0·5% w/v KI and after some sec., 1 ml. indicator (1 g. starch in 5 ml. H_2O poured into 40 ml. boiling H_2O, mixed with 50 ml. glycerol and boiled down to ca. 75 ml.). Titrate with 0·001*N* $Na_2S_2O_3$.

For titration of 25 ml. 0·002–0·2*N* $TlCl_3$, add up to 3 ml. AcOH and 1–2 g. KI and titrate with $Na_2S_2O_3$ to a potentiometric or visual $CHCl_3$ end-point (the visual method is suitable only for > 0·04*N* soln.).[37] Alternatively, add KI and $NaHCO_3$ as above and titrate with As^{3+} to a similar end-point.[37]

Several colorimetric procedures which utilize the oxidative power of Tl^{3+} have been suggested. *p*-Phenetidine is suitable for $0{\cdot}25$–$2{\cdot}0 \times 10^{-4}M$ Tl at pH 3·1;[38] add 5 drops reagent (0·5 ml. in 25 ml. EtOH) and measure the purple color after 20 min. at 540 mμ with a green filter. Interferences are Fe^{3+}, Au^{3+} and Pb. The color formed with pyramidone can be measured at 510 mμ.[39]

Diphenylamine forms a violet color with $Tl(OH)_3$ ppts.[40] Benzidine,[41] *p*-aminophenol[42] and 3-(*p*-dimethylaminophenylazo)chromotropic acid[43] have also been applied.

KI can be used for pptn. of Tl^+. For gravimetric detn.[1, 44] of < 0·5 g. Tl in 50–150 ml. soln. contg. 2 ml. AcOH, boil with 10% KI until pptn. is complete, then add 1 g. solid KI/100 ml. soln., filter on a glass crucible after 18 hr., wash with 1% KI–1% AcOH soln. and then with 80% Me_2CO, dry at 100°C (70–473°C) and weigh as TlI. Results tend to be low. Cl^-, Ag, Pb, Ti, etc. interfere, but Cd, Fe, Al, Cr, Co, Ni, Zn, Mn, Ca do not. If EDTA is added, Pb, Cu, Bi, Fe do not interfere.[45] NaI should be used if Re is present. The method is also applicable in solns. contg. 2 ml. 20% NH_4OH/50 ml.

For a titrimetric finish,[46] add a known excess of KI, filter and titrate the filtrate with $Hg(NO_3)_2$ with diphenylcarbazone indicator (see Chapter 59, p. 446). Potentiometric titration is possible in presence of EDTA.[45] In another method[47] treat the Tl^+ soln. with excess 20% NaOH and excess I_2, filter after 15 min., wash, acidify the filtrate with HCl and titrate with $Na_2S_2O_3$ soln.

For colorimetric detn.[48] of the ppt. from 0·05–10 mg. Tl, add 5 ml. H_2SO_4, $NaNO_2$ and 0·5 ml. $CHCl_3$ and shake.

(f) Oxine acetate can be applied gravimetrically for 1–200 mg. Tl^{3+} (1 mg./10 ml.) in dil. H_2SO_4 soln.[49] Add oxine acetate or oxine in EtOH, adjust to pH 4–8 with NH_4OH and store at 20–30°C for 2 hr. Filter on a glass crucible, wash with hot H_2O, and dry at 120°C for 1·5–2 hr. The temp. of drying is uncertain and the ppt. seems to be a mixt. of anhydrous oxinate and monohydrate.

NOTES. (1) For colorimetric detn. dissolve the ppt. in $CHCl_3$ and measure at 400–402 mμ.[49]
(2) Bromoxine is also utilized gravimetrically, the ppt. being dried at 93–156°C (Duval).

(g) Mercaptobenzothiazole provides a gravimetric detn. of 0·1 g. Tl_2O in 30 ml. neutral soln.[50] Add a 5-fold excess of 1% reagent in 2·5% NH_4OH, filter on a glass crucible, wash with 2·5% NH_4OH, dry at 110°C (52–217°C) and weigh as $Tl(C_7H_4NS_2)$.

Bismuthiol II may be used rather similarly at pH 1–13; interferences are Sn, Hg, Ag, Au, Pt and Pd.[51]

(h) $Na_3[Co(NO_2)_6]$ may be used gravimetrically[52] for Tl^+ in 50 ml. 5% HCOOH soln. Heat to 30–50°C, add a small excess of reagent at 30–40°C (28·6 g. $Co(NO_3)_2{\cdot}6H_2O$ in 50 ml. 50% HCOOH, dild. to 500 ml. with H_2O; 180 g. $NaNO_2$ in 500 ml. H_2O; equal vols. of the 2 solns. are mixed as needed). After 30 min. filter on a glass crucible, wash with cold H_2O, dry at 120°C and weigh as $Tl_3[Co(NO_2)_6]$.

NOTES. (1) Interferences are Ag, Pb, Hg, K and NH_4^+.
(2) The above method, and the temp. of drying are said to be unsatisfactory.[53] Weighing as $Tl_2Na[Co(NO_2)_6]$ is not recommended.[53]

(i) Reinecke's salt ($NH_4[Cr(SCN)_4(NH_3)_2]{\cdot}H_2O$) allows gravimetric detn. of < 2 mg. Tl/ml. soln.[54] Add H_2SO_4 to give a final concn. of < 2*N*, add 2–3 ml. 2·5% reagent, heat at 40–50°C for 20 min., cool, filter on a G4 crucible, wash 3–4 times with 5 ml. portions of H_2O, dry at 110°C or *in vacuo* and weigh as $Tl[Cr(SCN)_4(NH_3)_2]$. No interference occurs from Fe, Al, Cr, Sn^{2+}, Ti, Th, Mn, Co, Ni, U^{6+}, Mo, W, V, As, P; from Ag, Cu, Cd, Hg if KCN is added; or from Sb, Bi if tartrate is added.

(j) Electrodeposition is used to det. < 0·2 g. Tl in sulfate soln.[3] Use a Hg-cathode prepd. by electrolysis of $HgNO_3$ soln. with a Pt cathode to cover it with 0·5 g. Hg, wash with EtOH, dry and weigh. Boil the soln. after addn. of 1 g. C_6H_5COOH (add gallic acid if Pb is present), add 5 ml. HNO_3, dil. to 175 ml. with H_2O, heat to 40°C and electrolyze with a rotating cathode at 5 amp. for 15 min. Wash with Me_2CO (EtOH-free), dry for 20 min. under CO_2 and weigh as Tl. The error is < +6·25% for 16–160 mg. Tl.

NOTES. (1) Other procedures have been suggested but none is suitable for detn. purposes. Electrolysis may be done with a Wood's metal cathode in soln. contg. 2–3 ml. HCl/80 ml. soln. and 3–5 g. $NH_2OH{\cdot}HCl$, for 2 hr. at 80°C with 2–6 v. and 2–3 amp.[55]
(2) Below 0·25 g. Tl^+ as nitrate can be electrolyzed with a Pt dish as anode and a Pt gauze rotating cathode in soln. contg. 1–2 g. 40% HF and 1 ml. 30% H_2O_2 for 1 hr.[56] After repetition of the electrolysis, wash with EtOH, dry at 110°C (156–283°C) and weigh as $Tl_2O_3{\cdot}HF$. An empirical factor of 0·8444 (theor. 0·8573) is required.
(3) Internal electrolysis as Tl_2O_3 has been proposed.[57]
(4) For controlled potential electrolysis[58] use Pt electrodes and 0·70 v. *vs.* N.H.E. in a soln. contg. 0·1 g. Tl_2SO_4, 0·2 g. $AgNO_3$, 4 g. NH_4NO_3, 8 ml. NH_4OH in 25 ml. soln. at pH 9·5. Weigh Ag and calc. Tl.

(k) Miscellaneous gravimetric methods. Mg can be used to det. Tl in slightly acidic soln.[59] in a flask fitted with a Bunsen valve. Boil the soln. with Mg, cool, add NH_4Cl and shake until no Mg remains; decant, add a weighed amt. of Wood's alloy, warm gently to melt the alloy, cool, decant, wash with H_2O and weigh to find the increase in wt.

H_2S ppts. Tl_2S (see under Separation, p. 306),[60] which can be treated with H_2SO_4, etc., ignited at 740–770°C (92–355°C) and weighed as Tl_2SO_4. Weighing as $TlHSO_4$ is not recommended. Na_2S may be used colorimetrically in alk. soln. contg. KCN; Bi and Pb interfere.[24]

Br_2 water and NaOH allow detn. in 10 ml. nitrate soln.[61] Add a small excess of Br_2 water, followed by NaOH to give pH 2–5, filter on a Gooch crucible, wash with hot H_2O, dry at 200°C (100–230°C) for 1 hr. and weigh as Tl_2O_3 (protected from CO_2). Low results are obtained with NH_4OH. Methods with KOH and $K_3Fe(CN)_6$ (Hillebrand and Lundell[1]) and NaOH and I_2 (p. 309) have also been proposed. The reaction with Br_2 and NaOH can also be used nephelometrically for 6–920 μg. Tl/ml. if gelatin is added.[62]

Na-tetraphenylboron is applied[63] in $< 1N$ H_2SO_4 soln., the ppt. being dried at 100–105°C and weighed as $Tl[B(C_6H_5)_4]$; conductometric titration is also possible. Interferences are K, Rb, Cs, Zn, Hg, Ag, Ce^{4+}, Zr, Co, Ni, Mn, Pt, Sb^{3+}, Bi, NH_4^+.

H_2PtCl_6 ppts. Tl^+. Add reagent to boiling soln.,[64] cool, filter on a Gooch crucible, dry at $<$ 250°C (65–155°C) and weigh as Tl_2PtCl_6. The ppt. is difficult to filter and is of indefinite compn.

Na_4SnS_4 ppts. Tl from slightly acidic soln.[65] Add reagent to the boiling soln., add H_2O, filter on a glass crucible after 3 hr., wash with H_2O, dry at 105°C and weigh as Tl_4SnS_4; the drying temp. is unreliable.

$K_4Fe(CN)_6$ and $CaCl_2$ ppt. Tl as $Tl_2Ca[Fe(CN)_6]$.[66]

H_2SeO_3 can be utilized by refluxing the $4N$ HCl soln. with excess reagent for 20–30 min., filtering on glass, washing with H_2O, EtOH and Et_2O, drying at 90°C and weighing Se.[67]

(l) EDTA can be applied titrimetrically with eriochrome black T indicator.[68] To the Tl^{3+} soln. add 5 ml. $0{\cdot}1M$ Mg–EDTA, neutralize with NaOH to methyl red paper, add 2 ml. buffer pH 10 and indicator and titrate with $0{\cdot}1M$ EDTA. Photometric titration of Tl^+ at 222 mμ is possible.[58] Tl^{3+} can be detd. at pH 3·5 by back-titration of EDTA with Th^{4+} soln. and alizarin S indicator.[58]

(m) Volhard's method for $< 0{\cdot}4$ g. Tl^+ is as follows.[69] Add 50 ml. $0{\cdot}1N$ $AgNO_3$, 5 ml. $2N$ HCl, 10 ml. 15% NaOH and place on a steam-bath protected from light for 30 min. Filter on paper, wash with hot H_2O; warm the ppt. with 2 ml. HNO_3, dil. to 50 ml. with H_2O, cool and titrate with NH_4SCN using Fe-alum indicator. The reaction is $TlNO_3 + 2AgCl + 3NaOH \rightarrow Tl(OH)_3 + 2NaCl + NaNO_3 + 2Ag$.

(n) Miscellaneous colorimetric methods. Zn–dibenzyldithiocarbamate can be used[58] for 0·5–10 mg. Tl^{3+} in acidic soln.; shake with 50 ml. 0·3% reagent in $CHCl_3$, sep. and measure at 430 mμ. Interferences are Cu, Sb, Bi, Co, Hg, Ni, Ag.

Na-diethyldithiocarbamate along with iso-Pr_2O extn. allows measurement at 315 mμ.[70]

Phosphomolybdic acid can be used for 10–50 μg. Tl^+ in 5 ml. neutral soln.[24] Add some drops of 1:1 HNO_3, 4 drops 5% reagent, dil. to 10 ml. with H_2O and compare the yellow color after 5 min. K and NH_4^+ interfere but moderate amts. of Pb, Bi, Hg^{2+} and Cd are tolerated.

Dithizone can also be used colorimetrically for Tl.[71]

(o) Flame photometry is possible at 377·6 mμ.[72]

References

1. Hillebrand and Lundell, 373 (474); Scott and Furman, 942; Kimura, 452; Schoeller and Powell, 88; Fresenius–Jander, **IIIaβ/IIIb**, 81 (1956).
2. Anderson, J. R. A., *Anal. Chem.*, **25**, 108 (1953).
3. Chrétien, A. and Longi, Y., *Bull. soc. chim. France*, **11**, 241, 245 (1944).
4. Jílek, A. and Lukas, J., *Collection Czechoslov. Chem. Communs.*, **1**, 426 (1929).
5. Lounamaa, K., *Z. anal. Chem.*, **147**, 196 (1955).
6. Sill, C. W. and Peterson, H. E., *Anal. Chem.*, **21**, 1268 (1949).
7. Onishi, H., *Bull. Chem. Soc. Japan*, **30**, 567 (1957); **29**, 945 (1956).
8. Welcher, **IV**, 183.
9. Mahr, C. and Ohle, H., *Z. anal. Chem.*, **115**, 254 (1938/39).
10. Hecht and Donau, 209; Welcher, **II**, 136.
11. Forchheimer, O. L. and Epple, P. R., *Anal. Chem.*, **23**, 1445 (1951).
12. Zintl, E. and Rienäcker, G., *Z. anorg. u. allgem. Chem.*, **153**, 276 (1926); Rienäcker, G. and Knauel, G., *Z. anal. Chem.*, **128**, 459 (1948); Evans, B. S., *Analyst*, **58**, 450 (1933).
13. Swift, E. H. and Garner, C. S., *J. Am. Chem. Soc.*, **58**, 113, 165 (1936); Berry, A. J., *Analyst*, **64**, 28 (1939).
14. Beale, R. S., *et al.*, *Ind. Eng. Chem., Anal. Ed.*, **13**, 240 (1941).
15. Issa, I. M. and Issa, R. M., *Analyst*, **79**, 771 (1954); *Anal. Chim. Acta*, **13**, 108 (1955).
16. Jílek, A., *et al.*, *Chem. zvesti*, **9**, 546 (1955).
17. Willard, H. H. and Young, P., *J. Am. Chem. Soc.*, **55**, 3268 (1933).
18. Welcher, **IV**, 319.
19. Simon, V., *Chem. listy*, **49**, 1727 (1955).
20. Buck, R. P., *Anal. Chem.*, **24**, 1199 (1952); Songina, O. A. and Vaĭloshnikova, A. P., *Zavodskaya Lab.*, **22**, 19 (1956).
21. Hartley, A. M. and Lingane, J. J., *Anal. Chim. Acta*, **13**, 183 (1955); also see Deshmukh, G. S., *ibid.*, **12**, 586 (1955) (As^{3+}; potentiometric).
22. Welcher, **IV**, 173.
23. Berg, R. and Fahrenkamp, E. S., *Z. anal. Chem.*, **109**, 305 (1937); **115**, 214 (1938/39); Cimerman, C. and Selzer, G., *Anal. Chim. Acta*, **15**, 213 (1956) ($< \pm 0{\cdot}4\%$ for 3–6 mg.).
24. Sandell, 562.
25. Gur'ev, S. D. and Shkrobot, E. P., *Analiz Rud Tsvetn. Metal. i Produktov ikh Pererabotki, Sbornik Nauch. Trudov*, No. 12, 79 (1956).
26. Voskresenskaya, N. T., *Zhur. Anal. Khim.*, **11**, 585 (1956).
27. Efremov, G. U. and Galibin, V. A., *Uchenye Zapiski Leningrad. Gosudarst. Univ. im A. A. Zhdanova, Ser. Khim. Nauk*, No. 15, 83 (1957).

28. Gur'ev, S. D., *Sbornik Nauch. Trudov Gosudarst. Nauch.-Issled. Inst. Tsvetn. Metal.*, No. 10, 317 (1955).
29. Spacu, G. and Pop, A., *Z. anal. Chem.*, **120**, 322 (1940); Murakami, Y., *Bull. Chem. Soc. Japan*, **22**, 206 (1949); **23**, 1 (1950); also see Ishimori, T., *ibid.*, **26**, 336 (1953); *J. Chem. Soc. Japan*, **76**, 858 (1955) (radiometric using radioactive Co; 5–50 μg; in rock).
30. Nozaki, T., *J. Chem. Soc. Japan*, **77**, 493 (1956).
31. Ishimori and Ueno, K., *Japan Analyst*, **5**, 329 (1956).
32. Smith, Jr., W. T., *Anal. Chem.*, **20**, 937 (1948).
33. Castagnou, R. and Michelet, M., *Bull. soc. pharm. Bordeaux*, **90**, 347 (1952).
34. Merritt, Jr., C., *et al.*, *Anal. Chem.*, **25**, 572 (1953).
35. Shaw, P. A., *Ind. Eng. Chem., Anal. Ed.*, **5**, 93 (1933).
36. Pohl, F. A. and Kokes, K., *Mikrochim. Acta*, 318 (1957).
37. Hollens, W. R. A. and Spencer, J. F., *Analyst*, **60**, 675 (1935).
38. Iijima, S. and Kamemoto, Y., *J. Chem. Soc. Japan*, **75**, 1294 (1954).
39. Kamemoto, Y., *J. Chem. Soc. Japan*, **78**, 604 (1957).
40. Haddock, L. A., *Analyst*, **60**, 399 (1935).
41. Křepelka, J. H. and Houda, M., *Chem. listy*, **41**, 173 (1947).
42. Gladyshev, V. P. and Tolstikov, G. A., *Zavodskaya Lab.*, **22**, 1166 (1956).
43. Korenman, I. M., *et al.*, *Zhur. Anal. Khim.*, **11**, 307 (1956).
44. Takeno, R., *J. Chem. Soc. Japan*, **54**, 741 (1933).
45. Přibil, R. and Zábranský, *Chem. listy*, **46**, 16 (1952).
46. Trtílék, J., *Z. anal. Chem.*, **111**, 10 (1937).
47. Deshmukh, G. S., *Z. anal. Chem.*, **145**, 249 (1955).
48. Kluge, N., *Z. Untersuch.-Lebensm.*, **76**, 158 (1938).
49. Moeller, T. and Cohen, A. J., *Anal. Chem.*, **22**, 686 (1950); see also Feigl, F. and Baumfeld, I., *Anal. Chim. Acta*, **3**, 83 (1949).
50. Welcher, **IV**, 113.
51. Majumdar, A. K. and Singh, B. R., *Z. anal. Chem.*, **154**, 262 (1957).
52. Nishifuku, S., *J. Soc. Chem. Ind., Japan*, **37**, 411 (1934)
53. Nakano, S., *J. Chem. Soc. Japan*, **70**, 60 (1949).
54. Bagbanly, L. and Mirzoeva, T., *Doklady Akad. Nauk Azerbaĭdzhan. S.S.R.*, **9**, 373 (1953); Spacu, P. and Hlevea, G., *Acad. rep. populare Romîne, Studii cercetări chim.*, **3**, 207 (1955).
55. Powek, H. and Sticks, W., *Z. anal. Chem.*, **79**, 124 (1930).
56. Jílek, A. and Lukas, J., *Chem. listy*, **24**, 223, 245 (1930).
57. Liptschinsky, A., *Zhur. Anal. Khim.*, **12**, 83 (1957).
58. Foley, W. T. and Pottie, R. F., *Anal. Chem.*, **28**, 1101 (1956).
59. Schoeller and Powell, 91.
60. Umemura, T., *J. Chem. Soc. Japan*, **6**, 28 (1940).
61. Browning, P. E., *Ind. Eng. Chem., Anal. Ed.*, **4**, 417 (1932).
62. Zolotukhin, V. K. and Molotkova, A. S., *Zhur. Anal. Khim.*, **11**, 248 (1956).
63. Wendlandt, W. W., *Anal. Chim. Acta*, **16**, 216 (1957); *Chemist Analyst*, **46**, 8 (1957).
64. Jílek, A. and Lukas, J., *Collection Czechoslov. Chem. Communs.*, **1**, 88 (1929).
65. Hawley, L. F., *J. Am. Chem. Soc.*, **29**, 1011 (1907).
66. Gaspar y Arnal, T., *Anales fís. y quím. (Madrid)*, **30**, 398 (1932).
67. Deshmukh, G. S., *Anal. Chim. Acta*, **12**, 319 (1955).
68. Flaschka, H., *Mikrochemie ver. Mikrochim. Acta*, **40**, 42 (1952).
69. Troítzki, M. W., *Chem. J., Ser. B., J. Gen. Chem.*, **1**, 1083 (1931).
70. Pohl, H., *Z. Erzbergbau u. Metallhüttenw.*, **9**, 530 (1956) (in Pb, Zn, Cd).
71. Welcher, **III**, 543; also see Amer, M. M., *et al.*, *Proc. Pharm. Soc. Egypt, Sci. Ed.*, **37**, No. 12, 69 (1955) (titration method).
72. Barret, P., *Compt. rend.*, **226**, 470 (1948).

INDIUM

The principal references for this chapter are given in ref. 1. The extraction of indium from cylindrite, chalcopyrite and metallic tin has been discussed in detail.[2] A bibliography on indium chemistry covering 1863–1933 has been published[3] and the analysis of indium has been reviewed.[4]

It should be noted that $InCl_3$ is volatile, hence if a precipitate must be ignited, chloride must be removed previously.

Indium gives a blue flame reaction with lines at 4511·55 and 4101·95 Å.

Attack

Dissolve sphalerite in HCl and HNO_3, pyrite in aqua regia; fuse Sn minerals with Na_2O_2. Subsequent treatment is the same in all cases. Add HCl, evap., filter, add Zn in excess and filter. Evap. the ppt. to fumes with HNO_3 and H_2SO_4. Boil the filtrate with NH_4OH, filter, dissolve the ppt. in HCl and almost neutralize with NH_4OH. Add 5 g. $NaHSO_3$, boil for 15 min., treat the ppt. with HCl, etc.

Alternatively, after the Zn addn., add HNO_3, filter and evap. the ppt. to fumes with H_2SO_4. Add NH_4OH and filter pulp to the filtrate and then reppt. Dissolve in $< 0{\cdot}05N$ HCl, treat with H_2S, etc.

Separation

H_2S in $< 3{\cdot}6N$ H_2SO_4 soln. seps. In from group II metals; many elements coppt. in 0·5*N* soln. Treatment with H_2S of solns. contg. AcOH and NaOAc (or 0·005*N* H_2SO_4 or 0·03–0·5*N* HCl) for 2 hr. at 80°C seps. yellow In_2S_2 from Fe and Mn, and from Al if sulfosalicylate is added; this can be used for concn. purposes with Zn or Sb^{3+}. Treatment of alk. soln. with H_2S or treatment with $(NH_4)_2S$ seps. white In_2S_3 from group IV metals, etc. $(NH_4)_2S$ and $(NH_4)_2$-tartrate seps. In from Zr, Ti, Al, etc.

Tannin in chloride soln. seps. In from Sn, Sb, Bi, which ppt.; add 3 g. $H_2C_2O_4$, NH_4OH until the soln. is just acid to methyl red, add reagent and filter.

KI allows sepn. of In from As: add HCl and 1 g. KI, evap. to dryness and then evap. twice with HCl.

Repptn. with NH_4OH and NH_4Cl (pH 5–6) seps. In from Cd, Ni, Mn, Zn, and partly from Co. Concn. of In and sepn. from Ga is possible with $KMnO_4$, NH_4OH and EtOH.

Addn. of 10% KCNO to a slightly acidic soln. contg. a very large excess of NH_4Cl, until the mixt. is yellow to methyl orange, followed by boiling seps. In from Zn and CrO_4^{2-}, and from Ni and Co if KCN is present.

Treatment with $BaCO_3$ or with AcOH and NH_4OAc seps. In from Zn, Ni, Co, Mn. NaOH and Na_2O_2 allow sepn. from Al, Be, V and U. NaOH alone gives incomplete sepn. from Ga.

Pptn. or extn. with cupferron allows sepn. from Fe, Ga, etc.

$NaHSO_3$ in boiling neutral soln. seps. In as $In_2(SO_3)_3{\cdot}2In(OH)_3{\cdot}5H_2O$, from many elements, but Sn, Ti and Zr interfere.

Zn in slightly acidic (H_2SO_4) soln. seps. In, Cu, Pb, Cd, Sn, Tl, etc. from Ga, Al, Zr, Fe, etc. Mg or Al can replace Zn.[5] Electrolysis in 1:4 H_2SO_4 soln. seps. In from Fe but deposition of In is incomplete.

Treatment with H_2SO_4 seps. In from Pb;[6] and with $K_2Hg(SCN)_4$ seps. In from Zn. Both sepns. are incomplete.

Hexamine seps. In from Pb, which appears in the filtrate.[6] Add NH_4OH until a turbidity appears, then add 10 g. NH_4OAc and 0·5–1 g. reagent and boil; treat the ppt. with HNO_3, NH_4OH, 5 g. NH_4NO_3, hexamine, etc.

Extn. with Et_2O of a 6*N* HCl soln. seps. In from Tl and Ga. Extn. of a 4·5*N* HBr soln. seps. In, Tl, Fe, Au, Sb, Mo, Re (and partly Zn and Te) from many elements. Extn. with iso-Pr_2O of the bromide from 0·5–6*N* HBr soln.[7] and extn. with Et_2O of the iodide[8] have also been utilized.

Extn. with $CHCl_3$ of the oxine-contg. soln. at pH 3·2–4·5 allows sepn. of In from Ag, Hg^{2+}, Pb, Sn^{4+}, Cd, Fe^{2+}, Cr^{3+}, Mn, Zn, Ca, Sr, Mg; interferences are Bi, Sn^{2+}, Cu, Fe^{3+}, V^{5+}, Al, Ga, Tl^{3+}.

A detailed procedure has been described for the sepn. of In from cylindrite.[9] Heat 100 mg. sample with 2 ml. HCl, and then with 1 ml. HNO_3, 5 ml. 72% $HClO_4$ and 1 ml. H_2SO_4. Pass N_2 at a rate of 6 bubbles/sec., heat to 230°C and add 10 ml. HBr dropwise during 30 min.

Cool, rinse, evap. to fumes of SO_3, cool and rinse. Centrifuge and wash with 10–15 ml. H_2O by centrifugation. Evap. to 10–15 ml., cool and transfer to a separatory funnel. Dil. to 25 ml. with H_2O, add 2 ml. 10% $(NH_4)_3$-citrate and NH_4OH until the soln. is yellow to thymol blue; then add 5 ml. 1:9 $HClO_4$ and ext. twice or more (a green org. layer should be obtained) with 5 ml. portions of 0·1% dithizone in $CHCl_3$. Wash with 5 ml. $CHCl_3$ and discard the org. phases. Treat the aq. phase with NH_4OH until purple to thymol blue (pH 9·0–9·3), add 5 ml. 10% NaCN and 10 ml. 0·1% dithizone and ext. 3 times or more; wash with 5 ml. $CHCl_3$, combine the exts. and strip In with 4 portions of 5 ml. 2*N* H_2SO_4. Wash with H_2O, combine the aq. phases and wash with 5 ml. $CHCl_3$. Add 5 ml. KI soln. (100 g. in 100 ml. H_2O) and ext. thrice with 10 ml. Et_2O. Combine the exts., strip with 4 portions of 5 ml. 0·1*N* HCl, add 1 ml. $NaHSO_3$ and ext. with 5 ml. portions of $CHCl_3$ until colorless. Then add 5 ml. buffer, oxine, etc. (see below).

Determination

Hydrolysis with NH_4OH is suitable for detn. of 0·1 g. amts. of In. Oxine is the best reagent for less than 1 mg. In. Dithizone provides a good colorimetric method.

(a) NH_4OH provides the classic gravimetric detn.[1] For acidic (HNO_3) solns. contg. $<$ 0·5 mg. In/ml., add a small excess of NH_4OH, boil for 1 min., digest at 60°C, add some filter paper pulp, filter on paper and wash with slightly ammoniacal 1% NH_4NO_3 until no Cl^- remains. Heat slowly to 700–830°C and ignite at this temp. before weighing as In_2O_3, which is reddish when hot and yellow when cold. Alternatively, ignite above 850°C (above 345°C) and weigh as In_3O_4.

NOTES. (1) Interferences are Fe, etc., org. compds. and large amts. of Cl^-.
(2) The ppt. is volatile above 1000°C.[10]
(3) Instead of NH_4OH, it is possible to use KCNO (see under Separation, p. 312) or NH_4NO_2 (see Chapter 40, p. 306), but not $KBrO_3$ and KBr or KIO_3 and KI.[11]

(b) Oxine provides gravimetric, titrimetric and colorimetric procedures. For 1 mg. In[6, 12] add 1 drop HCl and 0·5 ml. 5% oxine in 12% AcOH, warm and add 2*N* NH_4OAc until a ppt. appears, followed by another 0·5 ml. to give pH 2·5–3·0. Filter on a glass crucible after 10 min., wash with hot H_2O, dry at 120°C (100–285°C) and weigh as $In(C_9H_6NO)_3$. Alternatively, dissolve the ppt. in HCl and titrate with $KBrO_3$ and KBr.

For colorimetric detn.[9, 12, 13] of 0·015–1 mg. In in 25 ml. acetate-buffered soln. at pH 3·5, add 5 ml. 0·01*M* oxine in $CHCl_3$ contg. 1% EtOH and ext. 5 times with 5 ml. portions of $CHCl_3$. Dil. to 25–50 ml. with $CHCl_3$ and measure at 400 mμ.

NOTES. (1) Interferences in the colorimetric method are Al, Ga, Tl^{3+}, Sn^{2+}, Bi, Cu, Fe^{3+}, V^{5+}, Mo^{6+}, Ni and Co; Mg, Ca, Sr, Zn, Cd, Hg^{2+}, Sn^{4+}, Pb, Mn, Ag and Cr^{3+} can be present. The method has been applied to analysis of Ge.[14] It has been compared with a radioactivation method.[9]
(2) For fluorimetric detn. of 60 μg. In,[15] add 1 ml. 0·5% oxine in 7% AcOH, 2 ml. 20% NH_4OAc, dil. to 50 ml. with H_2O, adjust to pH 5·1 with NH_4OH and ext. thrice with 10 ml. portions of C_6H_6 or $CHCl_3$. Dil. to 50 ml. with solvent, filter through a dry filter and measure the fluorescence at 535 mμ with a Hg lamp (365 mμ) as light source. Interferences with C_6H_6 are Cu, Fe, Al, Be, Zr, and with $CHCl_3$ are Fe, Al, Cd, Zn, Ni, Zr, V; Cu requires KCN addn. in the latter case.
(3) 8-Hydroxyquinaldine can be applied gravimetrically (see Chapter 20, p. 161). This reagent can also be used fluorimetrically as a 1% soln. in 1*N* AcOH in a procedure similar to that given in Note 2 except that the pH is 7·5 and the measurement is done at 520 mμ; interferences are Cu, Ni, Mn, Th, Fe, Zn, Be, Ga[15] (cf. Chapter 42, p. 317).

(c) Dithizone provides an excellent colorimetric detn. of 1–10 μg. In.[13, 16] Evap. the soln. to dryness with HNO_3 (add HCl and Br_2 if Sn is present), and then add some drops of HNO_3 or HCl followed by 1 ml. 20% citric acid and 10 ml. H_2O (add 1 ml. 20% $NH_2OH{\cdot}HCl$ if Tl^{3+} is present). Adjust to pH 4 (methyl orange) with 3*N* NH_4OH, add 25 ml. AcOH–NH_4OAc buffer of pH 4 and ext. with 5 ml. portions of 0·02*M* oxine in $CHCl_3$. Wash the $CHCl_3$ phase with buffer soln., ext. the buffer phase with 5 ml. oxine soln. and combine the $CHCl_3$ phases in a 100 ml. Kjeldahl flask. Add 1 ml. H_2SO_4, remove the $CHCl_3$ by heating, add 1 ml. HNO_3, heat, add 1 ml. $HClO_4$ and heat slowly to fumes. Add 25 ml. H_2O and 1 ml. 20% Na_3-citrate (if Fe is present, add 1 ml. 20% $NH_2OH{\cdot}HCl$, boil gently for some min. and cool). Make alk. to cresol purple with NH_4OH, transfer to a separatory funnel, add 5 ml. 1% cupferron and ext. with 5 ml. portions of 0·001% (w/v) dithizone in $CHCl_3$ until there is no further color change. Combine the exts., shake for 1 min. with 50 ml. 1% HNO_3, discard the org. phase, wash the aq. phase with 5 ml. $CHCl_3$ and sep. Add 5 ml. of a 2:1·5 mixt. of 10% KCN and NH_4OH followed by 15 ml. dithizone soln., shake for 1 min., sep. and measure at 510 mμ.

NOTES. (1) No interference is caused by 10 mg. Zn, Cu or Pb. Removal of Pd, Au, Pt, Hg, Cu and Ag at pH 2·5 has been recommended.[17]
(2) The optimum pH for extn. is 5·2–6·3 with CCl_4 and 5·3–9·6 with $CHCl_3$.

(d) Electrodeposition can be used in a Clarke-Hermance cell to det. 2 mg. In in 2 ml. soln.[6, 18] Add 0·1 g. $H_2C_2O_4$, make alk. to methyl orange with NH_4OH, dil. to 5 ml. with H_2O and heat to 70–80°C. Electrolyze at 3 v. for 3 hr. while passing air (previously bubbled through NH_4OH) through the soln. Wash with H_2O and EtOH, switch off the current, dry in air and weigh as In. The method is said to be accurate. For the apparatus, see ref. 19.

(e) $[Co(NH_3)_6]Cl_3$ may be used gravimetrically[20] to det. In as chloride in 75 ml. > 2·4*N* HCl soln. Add hot 4% reagent, leave for 12 hr., filter and wash with a satd. soln. of the ppt. in 2·4*N* HCl, then with EtOH and Et_2O. Dry at 105°C (< 95°C) and weigh as $[Co(NH_3)_6]$-$InCl_6$. Al and Zn can be tolerated but Ag, Hg, Tl, Cd and large amts. of Fe or Cu interfere.

Nitroso-R salt can be used colorimetrically to det. 0·01–1 mg. In (see Chapter 40, p. 308).[21]

(f) Miscellaneous gravimetric methods. $(NH_4)_2HPO_4$ ppts. $InPO_4$ from dil. AcOH soln.;[20] the method is accurate but time-consuming.

Na-diethyldithiocarbamate is suitable for < 100 mg. In in neutral or slightly acidic soln.[20, 23] The ppt. is filtered on a glass crucible after 8 hr., washed with H_2O, dried at 105°C (100–210°C) and weighed as $In(C_5H_{10}NS_2)_3$, or ignited above 600°C and weighed as In_2O_3. Pb, Cd, Zn, Cu and Fe interfere. Small amts. of Zn, Fe, Cu, Al, W, Sn, Sb are tolerated[22] if pptn. is done at pH 8–10 in soln. contg. NaOH, tartrate and CN^-.

H_2S ppts. In from 140 ml. soln. contg. 30 ml. 2*N* AcOH and 10 ml. 2*N* NH_4OH.[1] Filter on a Gooch crucible, wash, dry at 350°C (94–221°C) in a H_2 atmosphere, cool under CO_2 and weigh as In_2S_3; alternatively, dry at 320–544°C and weigh as InS, or ignite in air above 690°C and weigh as In_2O_3.

(g) EDTA has been applied for In detn. with many indicators. For 50 ml. 0·05–0·2m*M* In, add 1*N* NaOH until a turbidity appears, then add 2 ml. AcOH and 2 drops 0·01% 1-(2-pyridylazo)-2-naphthol in MeOH as indicator and titrate with 0·01*M* EDTA to the color change from red to yellow.[24]

NOTES. (1) Bi, Pb, Ga and Sn interfere but Al, Mn, Ca, etc. do not. Cu, Zn, Cd, Ni, Ag, Hg can be tolerated at pH 7–8 in presence of KCN and tartrate; and Fe at pH 7–8 in presence of NaF.

(2) Eriochrome black T[25] and morin[26] have also been used in direct titrations. Eriochrome black T may also be utilized with back-titration of excess EDTA with Zn^{2+} or Mg^{2+} soln.[27] Pyrocatechol violet allows back-titration with Cu^{2+} soln.[27] or with Bi^{3+} soln. (see Chapter 33, p. 260).

(h) $K_4Fe(CN)_6$ is applicable for titrimetric detn. of 10–15 mg. In in 40% v/v AcOH soln. with 2% diphenylbenzidine in H_2SO_4 as indicator.[28] Add 2 drops indicator and titrate with reagent soln. (2·5 g. $K_4Fe(CN)_6$ and 0·2 g. $K_3Fe(CN)_6$/l.) until the green color remains for 10 sec. If Fe is present, titration is done in 60% AcOH soln. contg. 5 ml. 10% HF. Cl^- and NO_2^- interfere. For other indicators, see Chapter 36, p. 281 and Chapter 42, p. 317.

(i) Flame photometry can be used for analysis of alloys.[29] Dissolve 0·1 g. alloy (85% Cu, 11% Al and 0·5–2·5% In) in HNO_3, dil. to 100 ml. with H_2O (the HNO_3 concn. must be below 1*N*) and use a H_2–O_2 flame with measurement at 451·1 mμ. Zn does not interfere; Cu and Al can be compensated for by addn. to the standard.

References

1. HILLEBRAND and LUNDELL, 379 (481); SCOTT and FURMAN, 445; KIMURA, 451; SCHOELLER and POWELL, 83; FRESENIUS–JANDER, **III**a*β*/**III**b, 51 (1956).
2. BREWER, F. and BAKER, E., *J. Chem. Soc.*, 1290 (1936).
3. POTORATZ, H. A. and EKELEY, J. B., *Univ. Colorado Studies*, **21**, 151 (1934).
4. EINECKE, E., *Z. anal. Chem.*, **93**, 129 (1931); with HARMS, J., *ibid.*, **98**, 428 (1934).
5. BARLOT, J., *Mikrochim. Acta*, 179 (1956).
6. SCHOELLER and POWELL, 84.
7. KOSTA, L. and HOSTE, J., *Mikrochim. Acta*, 790 (1956).
8. HOSTE and BERGHE, H. VAN DER, *Mikrochim. Acta*, 797 (1956).
9. IRVING, H. M., *et al.*, *Analyst*, **82**, 549 (1957).
10. TAKENO, R., *J. Chem. Soc. Japan*, **54**, 742 (1933).
11. MOSER, L. and SIEGMANN, F., *Monatsh. Chem.*, **55**, 14 (1930).
12. WELCHER, **I**, 292.
13. SANDELL, 357.
14. LUKE, C. L. and CAMPBELL, M. E., *Anal. Chem.*, **28**, 1340 (1956) (in Ge).
15. ISHIBASHI, M., *et al.*, *J. Chem. Soc. Japan*, **77**, 1479 (1956); also see BOCK, R. and HACKSTEIN, K. G., *Z. anal. Chem.*, **138**, 337 (1953).
16. MAY, I. and HOFFMAN, J. I., *J. Wash. Acad. Sci.*, **38**, 329 (1948).
17. KLEĬNER, K. E. and MARKOVA, L. V., *Zhur. Anal. Khim.*, **8**, 279 (1953).
18. ROYER, G. L., *Ind. Eng. Chem., Anal. Ed.*, **12**, 439 (1940).
19. HECHT and DONAU, 142.
20. ENSSLIN, F., *Metall u. Erz*, **38**, 305 (1941).
21. NOZAKI, T., *J. Chem. Soc. Japan*, **77**, 1751 (1956).
22. PATROVSKÝ, V., *Chem. listy*, **48**, 1047 (1954).
23. WELCHER, **IV**, 90.
24. CHENG, K. L., *Anal. Chem.*, **27**, 1582 (1955).
25. FLASCHKA, H. and AMIN, A. M., *Z. anal. Chem.*, **140**, 6 (1953); *Mikrochim. Acta*, 410 (1953).
26. PATROVSKÝ, V., *Chem. listy*, **47**, 1338 (1953).
27. DOLEŽAL, J., *et al.*, *Chem. listy*, **50**, 903 (1956).
28. HOPE, H. B., *et al.*, *Ind. Eng. Chem., Anal. Ed.*, **8**, 51 (1936); NIMER, E. L., *et al.*, *Anal. Chem.*, **22**, 790 (1950) (amperometric).
29. MELOCHE, V. M., *et al.*, *Anal. Chem.*, **26**, 1387 (1954).

42

GALLIUM

The principal sources for this chapter are given in ref. 1. A series of papers on the separation and determination of gallium has been published,[2] the chemistry of gallium has been described in detail[3] and the analysis of gallium has been reviewed.[4]

$GaCl_3$ is volatile; nevertheless, HCl solutions can be evaporated almost to dryness on a steam-bath, and to fumes if H_2SO_4 is present, without loss of gallium. Some gallium may be lost as Ga_2O from precipitates with organic reagents if ignition is not done under proper oxidizing conditions. A porcelain crucible is preferable to metal crucibles for ignitions.

Attack

(a) Sphalerite. Evap. a 100 g. sample with aqua regia, then evap. with HCl and repeat several times. Add HCl and a moderate amt. of Zn (not an excess) and filter. Add excess Zn to the filtrate and boil. Heat the ppt. with HCl and HNO_3, add NH_4OH and filter. Dissolve this ppt. in 6*N* HCl and ext. with Et_2O. Add H_2SO_4 to the org. phase, evap., etc. (see also ref. 5).

(b) Fe or Mn minerals. Treat with HCl and Zn, etc.

(c) ZnO. Add the sample gradually to HCl until it is neutralized and filter.

(d) Bauxite. Fuse with $Na_2S_2O_7$, leach with dil. HCl and filter. Treat the filtrate with NH_4OAc, As^{3+} and H_2S. Treat the ppt. with aqua regia, evap. with HCl, add more HCl, etc. (see also ref. 5).

(e) Kaolin. Fuse with Na_2CO_3, leach with HCl, evap., treat the filtrate with NH_4OAc and continue as in (d).

(f) Al. Dissolve a 100 g. sample in HCl, evap. to a thick syrup, add 300 ml. HCl and 300 ml. Et_2O while cooling, filter and evap. the filtrate to a thick syrup. Add 200 ml. 1:1 HCl–Et_2O, sat. with HCl gas in the cold and filter. Repeat the removal of Al with 50 ml. of the mixt. Evap. the filtrate to dryness, dissolve in a min. amt. of 10% HCl and sat. with H_2S. Add HCl to the filtrate to give a 6*N* soln. and ext. with Et_2O. Evap. the org. phase, add 10% HCl and Br_2 and treat with NaOH. Acidify the filtrate with AcOH and ppt. Ga with tannin.[5]

(g) Ga metal. Dissolve in $HClO_4$ or in 1:2 $HClO_4$–H_2SO_4.

(h) Rocks. Treat with HF and H_2SO_4.

Separation

Treatment with HCl seps. Ga from Ag.

H_2S treatment of 0·6*N* HNO_3 soln. followed by 1:1 diln. and repeated treatment seps. Ga from Pb and Cd. Sepn. from group II elements is better in a soln. contg. over 10% H_2SO_4 or HCl; sepn. from Cd is incomplete but Ga can be pptd. from the filtrate with tannin.[5] H_2S treatment of solns. contg. As^{3+}, AcOH and NH_4OAc seps. Ga from group IV elements, etc.; concn. is also possible in contg. NH_4OH–$(NH_4)_2$-tartrate solns. a little Fe.

Treatment with NH_4OH and NH_4Cl seps. Ga from Ni, Mn, group IV elements, etc. Concn. with Al is feasible. Sepn. from Fe is possible if thioglycolic acid is added. A small amt. of $Ga(OH)_3$ is sol. in NH_4OH.

NaOH ($> 0{\cdot}3N$) seps. Ga from small amts. of Fe, Ti, etc. Sepn. is incomplete if the amt. of Ga is small, although addn. of Al may help. Fusion and extn. with H_2O is preferable. Sepn. from In is incomplete with 0·2*N* NaOH; results are better if MnO_2 is used as a collector. 1·5*N* KOH seps. Ga from Fe, but sepn. is incomplete if > 20 mg. Ga is present. Treatment with hexamine and $N_2H_4{\cdot}HCl$ followed by NaOH allows sepn. from Fe.[5]

Boiling for 5 min. with 5% Na_2CO_3 seps. Ga from In. $BaCO_3$ seps. Ga from Mn, but Zn, Ni and Co interfere and some Ga may be lost by adsorption.

$K_2Hg(SCN)_4$ allows sepn. from Zn (see Chapter 36, p. 280).

Cd seps. Ga from Pb, Cu, Sn, Sb, Pt; add Cd powder to the slightly acidic soln., stir and filter. Evap. the filtrate to fumes with 2 ml. H_2SO_4, add 75–100 ml. H_2O, electrolyze and then treat with H_2S.

Treatment with Cu and $Cu(OH)_2$ gives incomplete sepn. from Pb, Cd, Co, Ni, Mn, Zn, Te, Be and rare earths, and from Tl if SO_2 is added.

$K_4Fe(CN)_6$ seps. Ga from Al, Cr, Mn, Cd, Hg, Pb, Bi, Tl but Zn, Zr, In, NO_3^- and oxidants interfere.

Heat the 1:3 HCl soln. with reagent for 30 min. at 60–70°C, leave for 5 hr.–5 days, filter, heat the ppt. with NH_4NO_3 and treat with dil. NaOH.

Treatment with HCl gas of Et_2O–HCl solns. allows sepn. from Al.

With NaF, sepn. from Al is incomplete but the method is useful for removing the bulk.

Extn. with Et_2O pre-equilibrated with an equal vol. of 1:1 HCl allows sepn. from Al, Fe^{2+}, Zn, etc.[2, 6, 7] The procedure is tabulated below.

Ext. 25 ml. 5·5*N* HCl (s.g. 1·093) soln. 3 times with 25 ml. portions of Et_2O, combine and wash 3 times with 5 ml. portions of 5·5*N* HCl

→ Evap. the org. layer to dryness, add HNO_3, evap., repeat several times, then add 100 ml. H_2O

→ Evap. the washings to dryness, add 50 ml. H_2O, 5 ml. 2*N* NH_4OAc and 5 ml. 6*N* AcOH, boil and filter → Acidify the filtrate with 6*N* AcOH

Combine, add 15 ml. 6*N* AcOH and 3 g. Na-camphorate, etc. (see next column).

Sepn. from Fe is complete if the soln. for extn. contains $TiCl_3$ and if the org. layer is washed with $TiCl_3$ soln. The optimum acidity for extn. with iso-Pr_2O is 7*N*; this extn. is better than Et_2O for small amts.[8, 9] Back-extn. can be done with H_2O. See also Chapter 16, (pp. 135 and 138).

Camphoric acid allows sepn. from many elements (see below).

α-Nitroso-β-naphthol (2% in 50% AcOH) seps. Ga from Fe in AcOH media on 12 hr. standing.

Cupferron seps. Ga from Al, Cr, In, rare earths, U, Be and Fe^{2+} by pptn. or by extn. with $CHCl_3$ from 2*N* H_2SO_4 media; large amts. of NH_4^+ interfere. Cupferron in 1*N* $H_2C_2O_4$ soln. contg. $(NH_4)_2C_2O_4$ seps. Ga from Ti, Zr, Th.

Phenylarsonic acid allows sepn. from Ti and Zr.

Tannin seps. Ga from Co, Ni, Mn, Cd, Zn, Tl and Be (see the next column).

Oxine allows sepn. from V, Mo and W (see p. 317). Extn. of oxinate with $CHCl_3$ at pH 2 allows sepn. from large amts. of Al.

Ion exchange resins are useful for certain sepns. (see Chapter 13, Section 2.2).

Heating at 230–255°C in a stream of Cl_2 seps. $GaCl_3$ (b.p. 215–220°C) from $InCl_3$ (b.p. > 600°C) and $ZnCl_2$ (b.p. 738°C).

Determination

Camphoric acid seems to be the best gravimetric reagent for Ga, although the oxine and tannin methods are also accurate. Oxine or rhodamine B are the best reagents for colorimetric detns.

(a) Na-camphorate is excellent for gravimetric detn. of 1–100 mg. Ga_2O_3 as nitrate or sulfate in 100 ml. neutral soln.[2, 10] Add 10 ml. 6*N* AcOH, 20 ml. 10% $NaNO_3$ and 2 g. reagent, boil for 10 min. and leave for 2–3 hr. Filter on paper, wash with a satd. camphoric acid soln., dry and ignite at 1000°C (> 478°C) to Ga_2O_3. The ppt. can also be weighed as $Ga_2(O_2CC_8H_{14}CO_2)_3$ after drying at 94–125°C.

NOTES. (1) If Zn, Cd, Pb, Mn, Ni, Co, Mg, groups IV and V and rare earths are present, $NaNO_3$ in the above procedure is replaced by NaOAc. If Tl is present, reduce with SO_2, H_2O_2 or $Na_2S_2O_3$ and add reagent; halides interfere in this case. With Cr, V or U, treat the ppt. obtained as above, with 5 ml. 2*N* NaOH, 0·5 g. Na_2O_2, boil, add AcOH and reppt.; alternatively, ext. with Et_2O. With Fe, ignite the ppt., add aqua regia, evap. to dryness, add 50 ml. H_2O and some drops HNO_3, add NaOH to give a 1*N* soln., boil and filter; acidify the filtrate with AcOH, add 10 ml. 6*N* AcOH, dil. to 100 ml. and continue as above.
(2) If pptn. is done from formic acid-buffered soln. the ppt. can be dried at 110°C but an empirical factor (0·213) is required.[6]

(b) Tannin provides a useful gravimetric detn.[1, 11] For 0·1 g. Ga_2O_3 in 100 ml. soln. contg. NH_4OAc and 1% AcOH, add 2 g. NH_4NO_3, boil, add 10% tannin soln. in 10-fold excess (at least 0·5 g.), add filter pulp and cool. Filter on Whatman No. 41 paper, wash with hot H_2O contg. some NH_4NO_3 and AcOH, ignite at 1000°C and weigh as Ga_2O_3.

NOTES. (1) If Ni, Co, Zn, Mn, Cd, Be, Tl is present, dissolve the ppt. in hot dil. HCl and reppt.
(2) Straightforward hydrolytic methods without tannin are less satisfactory because $Ga(OH)_3$ is more sol. than $Al(OH)_3$ and hard to filter. $KBrO_3$ with KBr cannot be used. NH_4OH has been used with a dil. H_2SO_4 sample soln.;[1] add reagent until the soln. is alk. to cresol red, boil, add filter pulp, filter on paper, wash with 2% NH_4NO_3 and ignite above 408°C. Pyridine can be used[12] somewhat similarly in solns. contg. NH_4Cl.
Urea is suitable for detn. of 50–200 mg. Ga as sulfate in 150–200 ml. soln.[13] but a correction is needed. Add 3 g. reagent, dil. to 500 ml. with H_2O and add NH_4OH until a ppt. appears. Boil until the pH is 4–5·5, filter on a porcelain crucible, wash with H_2O, ignite at 850°C and weigh as Ga_2O_3. Transfer the bulk of the ppt. to a porcelain crucible, weigh, ignite at 1200°C for 1 hr., weigh and apply the correction. Alternatively, filter on paper, heat below 500°C until the ppt. is white, ignite at 1100–1200°C for 1 hr. and weigh.
NH_4HSO_3 (a satd. soln. of SO_2 in NH_4OH) is suitable for <0·1 g. Ga in 100–200 ml. acidic (HCl or H_2SO_4) soln. (Hillebrand and Lundell[1]). Add NH_4OH until alk. to litmus, then add 5 ml. reagent, make acid to litmus with dil. HCl, dil. to 200 ml. with H_2O, boil for 5 min., etc.

(c) Oxine allows gravimetric, titrimetric or colorimetric detns. For gravimetric detn. of 15–100 mg. Ga in neutral soln.[14] add 2 g. NaOAc, make alk. with NH_4OH, dil. to 200 ml. with H_2O, heat to 70–80°C and add excess 1% oxine in EtOH. Make just acid to thymol blue–bromothymol blue with HCl, heat for 1 hr. on a steam-bath and leave to cool for 1–2 hr. Filter on a glass crucible, wash with cold H_2O, dry at 120°C and weigh as $Ga(C_9H_6ON)_3$. The temp. of drying is doubtful. Alternatively, dissolve the ppt. in hot 1·5*N* HCl and titrate with $KBrO_3$ and KBr. V, Mo and W interfere but can be sepd. in concd. NH_4OH soln.

For fluorimetric detn.[7, 15] of 0·5–10 μg. Ga in 5 ml. soln. contg. 2 ml. 0·2*N* HCl, add 1 ml. 20% NH_2OH·HCl, 6·0 ml. 0·2*M* KH-phthalate (20·41 g. in 500 ml. H_2O) and, after 20 min., 0·25 ml. reagent (0·1 g. oxine in H_2O contg. 0·6 ml. 6*N* AcOH dild. to 100 ml. with H_2O). Shake for at least 30 sec. with 2·0 ml. $CHCl_3$ and compare the yellow fluorescence under UV light with that of a solution prepared similarly to the above.

NOTES. (1) Mo interferes if it gives a color to the $CHCl_3$ layer. If Et_2O extn. precedes the above method, few of the elements present in rocks interfere. With In, if 0·05 mg. is present, ext. from a soln. at pH 5; if 0·05–1 mg. is present, ext. from a soln. of pH 2·6.

(2) In the colorimetric process, the optimum pH range for extn. is 3·0–6·2 and the complex can be measured at 392·5 mμ.[16] Simultaneous detn. of Al is possible with measurement at 520 mμ using light excitation of wavelength 365·0 and 435·8 mμ.[17] An absorptiometric method has been applied in the analysis of Ge (see Chapter 41, p. 313).

(3) Several similar reagents have been suggested. 8-Hydroxyquinaldine allows a fluorimetric detn. of 0–30 μg. Ga in 40 ml. soln.[18] Add 1 ml. 1% reagent in 1*N* AcOH, 5 ml. 20% NH_4OAc, adjust to pH 3·9–4·1 with 1*N* HCl and ext. thrice with 10 ml. $CHCl_3$; combine the exts., dil. to 50 ml. with $CHCl_3$, filter through a dry filter and measure. Interferences are Cu, citrate, >100 μg. Tl or In and >5 mg. Al; V^{5+} requires addn. of 1–2 ml. 1% NH_2OH·HCl. It is possible to ext. successively <30 μg. Ga at pH 3·9, <100 μg. In at pH 5·5 (12% In is coextd. with Ga), and <6 μg. Be at pH 8·1; Ga and In are measured absorptiometrically or fluorimetrically and Be fluorimetrically.

Bromoxine can be applied gravimetrically[19] or fluorimetrically.[20] To det. <30 μg. Ga/ml. of 0·06*N* HCl soln. add Me_2CO to give a 30% soln., boil and add satd. bromoxine in Me_2CO; finally dry at 100–224°C and weigh. Fe interferes but Al does not. For fluorimetry[20] of 0·25–1 μg. Ga in CN^--contg. soln. at pH 9, ext. with 6 ml. $CHCl_3$, and measure under UV light.

o-(Salicylideneamino)-phenol forms a yellow-green fluorescence with Ga at pH 4·5–5·5; Al interference is avoided by BF_4^- addn.[21]

(d) **Rhodamine B** is applicable for colorimetric detn. of 0·1–10 μg. Ga.[9] To 5 ml. 6*N* HCl sample soln. add 0·40 ml. 0·5% reagent in 1:1 HCl, and 0·1 ml. 10% NH_2OH·HCl, ext. with 10 ml. C_6H_6 (extn. coeff. = 0·57) and measure the absorbance at 565 mμ (1–10 μg.) (ϵ = 60 000) or the fluorescence under UV light (0·1–10 μg.). Interferences are Fe, Tl^{3+}, Sb, Au, In, W, but can be avoided by preliminary iso-Pr_2O extn. with $TiCl_3$ addn.

(e) **Miscellaneous gravimetric methods.** Cupferron can be used for 0·01–0·3 g. Ga in 200 ml. 7:93 H_2SO_4 soln.[1] Add 6% reagent, ignite above 745°C and weigh as Ga_2O_3. No interference is caused by Al, etc.

Electrodeposition can be applied.[22] Treat the soln. with 25 ml. $CuSO_4$ soln. (2 mg. Cu/ml.), 10 ml. 5*N* NaOH or KOH and 3–5 g. $(NH_4)_2SO_4$ and dil. to 100 ml. with H_2O. Electrolyze with a Cu-plated Pt electrode at 2 v. and 4–5 amp., wash with H_2O, EtOH and Me_2CO and weigh Ga + Cu.

(f) **EDTA** provides a satisfactory titrimetric detn. For 0·25–50 mg. Ga, add 10 ml. AcOH, adjust to pH 2·8 with NH_4OH, add 5 drops gallocyanine indicator (1% in AcOH) and titrate to the color change from blue to red.[23] Morin can serve as indicator in a direct titration (see Chapter 41, p. 314).[24] Back-titration of excess EDTA with Zn^{2+}, Mg^{2+}, Cu^{2+} or Pb^{2+} soln. in presence of eriochrome black T, naphthidine or murexide indicator is possible.[25] Pyrocatechol violet can serve as indicator (see Chapter 33, p. 260) or EDTA can be back-titrated with Fe^{3+} soln. in presence of benzohydroxamic acid indicator.[26]

(g) **$K_4Fe(CN)_6$** is suitable for titration of 3 mg. Ga.[27] Add 1 drop 0·5% $K_3Fe(CN)_6$, 2 drops 0·2% 3,3′-dimethylnaphthidinedisulfonic acid and titrate with 0·0075*M* reagent to the color change from red to pale green.

(h) **Quinalizarin** provides a colorimetric detn. of 0·1–10 μg. Ga.[15, 28] Treat the soln. with NH_4OH until a turbidity appears, clear with 6*N* HCl, add 4 ml. in excess followed by 7·7 g. NH_4OAc and 2·7 g. NH_4Cl and dil. to 70–80 ml. with H_2O. Heat to 70–80°C, add satd. NaF soln. until pptn. of Al is complete and add 0·5 g./l. in excess. After 1 hr., add filter pulp, filter on paper and wash with dil. NaF soln. Dil. the soln., adjust the pH to 5·0 and dil. to 100 ml. with H_2O. Take an aliquot contg. 0·1–10 μg. Ga, add 1·0 ml. 0·01% quinalizarin in EtOH (this is stable for a week) and compare the pink-violet color.

NOTE. V, Mo, Ni, Co interfere. Fe^{3+} or In requires sepn. with $KMnO_4$, NaOH and EtOH. Ge must be sepd. by distn. Pb, Cu, Sn, Sb, Pt are sepd. with Cd. If <15 mg. Al/l. is present, the filtration described above can be omitted. NaF prevents interference from Be, Ti, Zr, Th, rare earths, Sn^{4+} and Tl^{3+}. No interference arises from Mg, Mn, Fe^{2+}, Hg, Tl^+, Cd, W, U, As^{5+}, Ag, Bi, Nb, PO_4^{3-}, $C_2O_4^{2-}$, citrate or tartrate.

(i) **Miscellaneous colorimetric methods.** Alumocreson can be used for < 25 μg. Ga at pH 4·37 and at 60–70°C with measurement at 530 mμ (see Chapter 43, p. 322). Aluminon reacts at pH 3·8, the measurement being made at 525 mμ; Fe, Al and Be interfere.[29]

Cupferron in conjunction with morin allows detn. of 1–6 μg. Ga.[30] Pass the soln. through an Ag reductor, wash, add HCl to give a 6*N* soln. and 8 ml. satd. $TiCl_3$ soln. and leave for 12 hr.; ext. with 25 ml. Et_2O pre-equilibrated with 6*N* HCl, sep., evap., add KH_2PO_2 and

$3N$ HCl and evap. to dryness. Add 2 ml. $3N$ HCl, 10 drops 6% cupferron, 2 drops 0·2% morin in MeOH, and 6 ml. $CHCl_3$ and compare the fluorescence under UV light after 3 min.

Na-pyrrolidinedithiocarbamate can be used nephelometrically or gravimetrically.[31] For 10–130 μg. Ga in 5 ml. soln. add 50 mg. tartaric acid, 0·5 ml. 0·1% gum arabic and 2 ml. buffer (50 ml. $1N$ NH_4OH and 100 ml. $1N$ AcOH in 500 ml.) and adjust to pH 3–4 with HCl or Na_2CO_3. Add 1 ml. reagent (200–250 mg. in 10 ml. H_2O), dil. to 10 ml. with H_2O and measure with a blue filter within 20 min. For gravimetry of 5 mg. Ga, add reagent, filter, dry at 110–120°C and weigh as $(C_5H_8NS_2)_3Ga$. Fe interferes but Al, F^- and SO_4^{2-} do not.

Eriochrome red E is suitable for 1–4 μg. Ga/ml.;[32] to 5 ml. 0·1N HCl soln., add 1 ml. 1M NaOAc, 4 ml. H_2O, 0·075 ml. 0·075% reagent in EtOH, shake for 2 min. and measure the fluorescence after 5 min.

Eriochrome black has been applied for 3–8 μg. Ga/ml.:[32] treat the soln. as above, add 0·2 ml. 0·05% reagent, shake, add 6 ml. AmOH, shake, pipet out 3 ml. of the org. phase, add 3 ml. AmOH and compare the fluorescence; for 0–1 μg. Ga, use 0·05 ml. reagent.

(j) Flame photometry can be used to det. 0–10 p.p.m. in a H_2–O_2 flame with measurement at 417·2 mμ. For detn. of 100–1000 p.p.m. Ga, add an equal amt. of Cu. Interferences are Fe, Al, In, Zn.[33]

References

1. HILLEBRAND and LUNDELL, 383 (486); SCOTT and FURMAN, 426; KIMURA, 449; SCHOELLER and POWELL, 75; FRESENIUS–JANDER, **IIIa**β/**IIIb**, 1 (1956).
2. ATO, S., *Sci. Papers Inst. Phys. Chem. Research* (*Tokyo*), **12**, 225 (1930); **14**, 35 (1930); **15**, 289 (1931); **24**, 270 (1934); **29**, 71 (1936); **40**, 228 (1943).
3. EINECKE, E., *Das Gallium*, L. Voss, Leipzig (1937).
4. EINECKE, E., *Z. anal. Chem.*, **93**, 110 (1933).
5. SCHOELLER and POWELL, 76 ff.
6. MILNER, G. W. C., *et al.*, *Analyst*, **79**, 272 (1954).
7. SANDELL, E. B., *Anal. Chem.*, **19**, 63 (1947).
8. NACHTRIEB, N. H. and FRYXELL, R. E., *J. Am. Chem. Soc.*, **71**, 4035 (1949).
9. ONISHI, H. and SANDELL, E. B., *Anal. Chim. Acta*, **13**, 159 (1955).
10. WELCHER, **II**, 32.
11. WELCHER, **II**, 159.
12. OSTROUMOV, E. A. and IVANOV-EMIN, B. N., *Zavodskaya Lab.*, **11**, 1034 (1945); **12**, 674 (1946).
13. WILLARD, H. H. and FOGG, H. C., *J. Am. Chem. Soc.*, **59**, 1197, 2422 (1937).
14. WELCHER, **I**, 293; ROLLINS, O. W. and DREISCHER, C. K., *Anal. Chem.*, **26**, 769 (1954) (titrimetry).
15. SANDELL, 324.
16. MOELLER, T. and COHEN, A. J., *Anal. Chem.*, **22**, 686 (1950).
17. COLLAT, J. W. and ROGERS, L. B., *Anal. Chem.*, **27**, 961 (1955).
18. ISHIBASHI, M., *et al.*, *J. Chem. Soc. Japan*, **78**, 1139 (1957).
19. GASTINGER, E., *Z. anal. Chem.*, **126**, 373 (1944); WELCHER, **I**, 327.
20. LADENBAUER, I. M. and SLAMA, O., *Mikrochim. Acta*, 1219, 1238 (1955/56).
21. PATROVSKÝ, V., *Chem. listy*, **48**, 537 (1954).
22. TERREY, H. and THABIT, J., *J. Chem. Soc.*, 3064 (1957); also see REICHEL, R., *Z. anal. Chem.*, **87**, 321 (1932); CARRARA, G., *Aluminnio*, **23**, 255 (1954).
23. MILNER, G. W. C., *Analyst*, **80**, 77 (1955).
24. PATROVSKÝ, V., *et al.*, *Chem. listy*, **49**, 1517 (1955).
25. FLASCHKA, H. and ABDINE, H., *Mikrochim. Acta*, 655 (1954).
26. MILNER, *Analyst*, **81**, 367 (1956).
27. BELCHER, R., NUTTEN, A. J. and STEPHEN, W. I., *J. Chem. Soc.*, 2438 (1952); also see ATO, S., *Sci. Papers Inst. Phys. Chem. Research* (*Tokyo*), **10**, 1 (1929); FETTER, N. R. and SWINEHART, D. F., *Anal. Chem.*, **28**, 122 (1956) (0·001M Ga, potentiometric).
28. WELCHER, **IV**, 462.
29. RINCK, E. and FESCHOTTE, P., *Bull. soc. chim. France*, 230 (1957).
30. BRADACS, L. K., *et al.*, *Mikrochim. Acta*, 269 (1954).
31. GEILMANN, W., *et al.*, *Z. anal. Chem.*, **148**, 161 (1955).
32. LADENBAUER, I. M., *et al.*, *Mikrochim. Acta*, 1076 (1955/56).
33. MELOCHE, V. M. and BECK, B. L., *Anal. Chem.*, **28**, 1890 (1956).

43

ALUMINUM

The principal sources for this Chapter are given in ref. 1.

Attack

(a) Bauxite. Treat with HF, HNO_3 and H_2SO_4 and evap. to fumes, or fuse with Na_2CO_3, Na_2O_2 or Na_2CO_3 and borax and leach with HCl, treating the residue with HF and H_2SO_4 or fusing it with $Na_2S_2O_7$.

For cryolite add 5–10 ml. 2*N* HCl, 50 ml. H_2O and 0·5–1·0 g. $Be(NO_3)_2$ and heat for 5 min.; filter, add NH_4OH until a ppt. appears, make clear with 2*N* AcOH, add 4% oxine acetate, etc.[2]

Fuse refractories with Na_2CO_3, Na_2O_2 or $Na_2S_2O_7$, or heat with NH_4F for detn. of alkali.[3]

Fuse Al_2O_3 with Na_2O_2 (see Chapter 2, Section 2.3). Alternatively, digest it with HCl and HNO_3 in a sealed tube at 250–300°C; or fuse with Li_2CO_3 and H_3BO_3 (1:1) at 500–800°C for 10 min., treat with 1:2 HCl and sep. as $AlCl_3{\cdot}6H_2O$.

Dissolve Al metal or light alloys in HCl, in $HClO_4$, in HNO_3 contg. a little H_2O, or in H_2SO_4; dissoln. is rapid if a trace of $HgCl_2$ is added.

(b) Steels. Dissolve in dil. H_2SO_4 and sep. with $NaHCO_3$; add dil. HCl. Ignite the residue, heat with HF and H_2SO_4 and fuse with $Na_2S_2O_7$ (if acid-insol. Al is to be detd., treat this portion separately, otherwise combine it with the first soln.). Treat with H_2S, boil, add HNO_3, evap. and sep. with NaOH. Add HCl and NH_4OH and reppt. Ignite, examine the ppt. for Fe, P, Cr and V and make appropriate corrections. A study of the detn. of Al in steels has been made.[4]

With Fe–V, dissolve in dil. H_2SO_4 and HNO_3 (and if necessary HF), fume and add $KMnO_4$ and cupferron. Reppt. if much Al is present. Then treat with H_2SO_4, HNO_3 and $HClO_4$, add NH_4OH and finally weigh as phosphate.

With Fe–Ti, treat with dil. H_2SO_4 and HF, add HNO_3, evap., add dil. H_2SO_4 and dil. HCl and ppt. with cupferron. Treat with HNO_3 and $HClO_4$, add NH_4OH, etc. Det. P_2O_5 in the ppt. and deduct.

(c) Ni–Cr or Ni–Cr–Fe. Heat with HCl and HNO_3, fume with $HClO_4$ and pass HCl gas to remove Cr; filter, ignite, etc. Combine with the first filtrate, add tartaric acid, NH_4OH and NaCN and pass H_2S. Boil and add oxine. Treat with HNO_3 and $HClO_4$, etc., then add dil. H_2SO_4 and cupferron. Treat with HNO_3 and $HClO_4$, fume, add NH_4OH, etc.

With Ni, dissolve in HNO_3 and $HClO_4$, evap. and add H_2O. Apply Hg-cathode electrolysis, add cupferron, ext. with $CHCl_3$ and use the aluminon method (p. 321).

With Ni–Cu, treat with HNO_3, fume with $HClO_4$ and H_2SO_4, add H_2O and filter. Apply Hg-cathode electrolysis, add cupferron followed by a known amt. of Al (10 mg.), tartaric acid, NH_4OH, HCOOH and more cupferron. Treat the ppt. with HNO_3, $HClO_4$, fume, add H_2O, tartaric acid, H_2SO_3, NH_4OAc and oxine. If small amts. of Al are present, recover traces from the residue of the acid treatment by concn. with Fe^{3+} and NH_4OH, etc.

(d) Brasses and bronzes. Dissolve in HCl and HNO_3. (If Si or Pb is present, fume with H_2SO_4, add H_2O, filter and recover Al from the SiO_2 residue.) Add Fe^{3+} and NH_4OH if the amt. of Al is small. Use Hg-cathode electrolysis; then add NH_4OH if Be and P are absent, or oxine if they are present.

(e) Mg and Mg alloys. Add H_2O followed by HCl dropwise. If much Al is present, take an aliquot of the soln. and ppt. with benzoate; then apply the oxine method. If the amt. of Al is small, add NH_4OH, dissolve the ppt. in H_2SO_4, apply Hg-cathode electrolysis and then the NH_4OH method.

(f) Ti. Dissolve in 1:1 HCl, boil with H_2O_2, cool, add cupferron and ext. with $CHCl_3$. Fume with H_2SO_4 and HNO_3, add H_2O and filter. Apply Hg-cathode electrolysis, sep. with NaOH and H_2O_2 and apply the oxine method.

(g) Zn-base die-casting alloys. Dissolve in H_2SO_4, use Hg-cathode electrolysis, add NH_4OH, H_2SO_4 and H_2S, boil and use the NH_4OH or oxine method.

Separation

NH_4OH and NH_4Cl sep. Al from Ni, Mn, group IV elements, etc.; interferences are F, P, B, As, etc. Sepn. from Zn, Co and Cu is incomplete. Pptn. of Al with NaOAc, $(NH_4)_2S$ or $(NH_4)_2CO_3$ is incomplete. The ppt. is readily filtered when $Na_2S_2O_3$, KI and KIO_3, or NH_4NO_2 is used as reagent. Urea and succinate give the best result, sepn. from Zn, Co and Ni being complete. Concn. of Al by addn. of some mg. of Fe, Zr, etc. is possible.

Phenylhydrazine allows sepn. of Al, P, Cr, Ti, Zr, Th, etc. from Fe, etc.

Boiling with 5% NaOH seps. Al, P, V, W, Mo from Fe^{3+}, Ti, Zr, Mn and rare earths; Mg, Ni and large amts. of Ti interfere. The sepn. is incomplete if Al is < 5 mg. and if the Fe:Al ratio is large. If PO_4^{3-} is present, the method is accurate if Fe:P_2O_5 ≑ 2. Sepn. is almost complete on addn. of Na_2S and Cu^{2+}.

Fusion with Na_2CO_3 and extn. with H_2O seps. Al from Fe, Ti, Zr, etc. and is suitable before a colorimetric finish.[5]

$(NH_4)_2S$ in $(NH_4)_2$-tartrate soln., or Et_2O extn. from 6*N* HCl soln. seps. Al from Fe. $(NH_4)_2CO_3$ and 2,2′-dipyridyl in EtOH sep. Al from large amts. of Fe.[6]

NaOH and Na_2CO_3 or Na_2HPO_4 seps. Al from Ca, etc.; Mn and Mg interfere. Al can be concd. with Fe^{3+} on addn. of NH_4OH and phosphate.

Evapn. with H_2SO_4 seps. Al from SiO_2; this is more effective than HCl evapn. but some Al may coppt. if Pb or Ba is present.

Electrolysis with a Hg-cathode from dil. H_2SO_4 soln. seps. Al, Be, etc. from Fe, Ni, Co, Cr, Zn, Ga, Cu, Sn, Mn, Mo, Pb, Sb, Cd.

Oxidation with $HClO_4$ followed by treatment with NH_4OH and NH_4Cl allows sepn. from Cr. Treatment of alk. soln. with Br_2 followed by HNO_3, NH_4OH, etc., serves the same purpose. Volatilization as CrO_2Cl_2 is also useful.

HCl gas and Et_2O permit sepn. from Fe, Ti, Be, rare earths, Zn, Cu, Hg, Bi, P_2O_5; Ba and alk. metal chlorides interfere. Add 12–25 ml. HCl to 5–10 ml. soln., sat. with HCl gas below 15°C, add an equal vol. of Et_2O and pass HCl gas while cooling; filter on a Gooch crucible, wash with 1:1 HCl–Et_2O satd. with HCl gas.

p-Hydroxyphenylarsonic acid seps. Al from Ti, Zr, Sn (see Chapter 50, p. 361). Tannin in $(NH_4)_2C_2O_4$ soln. seps. Al from Nb, Ta, Ti (see Chapter 51, p. 374). Cupferron seps. large amts. of Al from small amts. of Fe, Ti, Zr, V, Sn, etc. Et_2O and C_6H_6 or $CHCl_3$ can be used for extn. in this case. Al can be pptd. from the cupferron filtrate with NH_4OH at pH 5 after addn. of cupferron; pptn. is also possible from dil. HCOOH soln. but not from dil. $H_2C_2O_4$ soln.; this allows sepn. from Be (see p. 326).

Oxine provides a sepn. from Be, Mg, etc. (see under Determination, below). If the oxine complex is extd. at pH 4·5–5·0, sepn. from Ca, Mg, Be, Mn, Cr and rare earths is possible; at pH 9, sepn. from W, Mo, V, Ta, Cr, Mg, Si and from Cu, Zn, Ni and Fe (if CN^- is present), is possible. Sepn. from Nb, Th, U is done by extn. after H_2O_2 addn. Shaking the oxine ext. with Na_2SO_4, seps. Al from Ce.[7]

8-Hydroxyquinaldine followed by extn. of the complex formed at pH 9·2 with $CHCl_3$ seps. Al from Cd, Co, Cu, Fe, Mn, Ce, Ni, Pb, Sb, Sn, Zn, Ti.

Diethyldithiocarbamate and extn. with $CHCl_3$ seps. Al from many elements.

Ion exchange resins or cellulose columns allow sepns. from Fe, etc. (see Chapter 13, p. 107, et. seq.).

Determination

Precipitation with NH_4OH is the predominantly applied method. The oxine or phosphate method is better for mg. amts. of Al. The best colorimetric methods are those involving lake formation with aluminon, or extraction of the oxinate with $CHCl_3$.

(a) NH_4OH provides the classical gravimetric procedure for Al.[1] To 200 ml. slightly acidic soln., add 5 g. NH_4Cl, 2 drops methyl red and dil. NH_4OH until the soln. is yellow (pH 6·5–7·5). Boil the soln., add some filter paper pulp, filter on paper and wash with 2% NH_4NO_3 or NH_4Cl. Ignite above 1200°C (> 475°C) and weigh as Al_2O_3.

NOTES. (1) Many elements interfere. The procedure has been applied to steels, ferrous alloys, Ni–Cr, brasses, bronzes and Zn-base die-casting alloys.[8] Repptn. is necessary if groups IV or V or Mn are present; in this case, the soln. should be boiled only briefly after the appearance of the ppt.

(2) When only small amts. of Al are present, better results can be obtained[9] by treating the slightly acidic (HCl) soln. with tannin, NH_4OAc, etc.

(3) A correction for SiO_2 can be detd. by treatment with HF and H_2SO_4; see Hillebrand and Lundell[1] for a detailed discussion of sources of error.

(4) Many reagents can be used for pH adjustment (see Chapter 2, Section 3.3); urea and succinate or phenylhydrazine is most satisfactory. Pyridine and hexamine have been recommended.[10]

(b) Oxine acetate is suitable for gravimetric, titrimetric or colorimetric detns. For gravimetric detn. of < 0·1 g. Al in 100 ml. slightly acidic (mineral acid) soln.,[1, 11] add excess 5% reagent, boil, add 2–10 ml. 2*N* NaOAc (pH 4·7–9·8). Filter on a glass crucible, wash with warm and cold H_2O successively, dry at 105–115°C (102–220°C) and weigh as $Al(C_9H_6OH)_3$. If Al is > 50 mg., add $H_2C_2O_4$, ignite and weigh as Al_2O_3. Alternatively, dissolve the ppt. in 15–20 ml. warm HCl and titrate with 0·1*N* $KBrO_3$ and KBr.

NOTES. (1) If a little Fe is present, add Na_2SO_3 or NH_2OH and *o*-phenanthroline. Interference from Fe, Ni, Co, Cu, Cr, Mo is avoided as follows: add 5 ml. 40% tartaric acid/0·1 g. metal, neutralize with 40% NaOH, add a 20-fold excess of KCN (for Fe), heat slowly to boiling and boil gently for 15–20 min.; cool, acidify to litmus with 1:1 AcOH, add a 2-drop excess, heat to 80–90°C for 10–15 min., cool to 40°C, filter if the soln. is turbid and wash with warm 10% NaCl. Heat to 60°C, add 1% reagent in 0·3% NaOH, etc. If V, Mo, Nb or Ti is present, add H_2O_2 and NH_4OH to the acidic soln. before adding reagent. Interference of U is prevented by addn. of 3–6 g. $(NH_4)_2CO_3$ and repptn. H_3BO_3 prevents interference of F^-. No interference arises from Be, Mg, P, As, B or tartrate.

(2) Many modifications and applications have been suggested. For 20–50 mg. Al in 150–200 ml. soln. a better ppt. is obtained by addn. of 5–6 ml. 10% reagent in 20% AcOH and 5 g. urea followed by heating for 2–3 hr. on a steam-bath.[12] It is possible to det. Al in 5 mg. silicate rocks,[13] in steels[14] and in many alloys.[8]
Sepn. from Cu, Sn, Fe, Mn, Zn, Pb, Co is possible in NH_4OH solns. contg. EDTA, tartaric acid and KCN.[15]
Sepn. of 10 mg. Al from large amts. of Mg is done as follows:[16] to 100 ml. slightly acidic soln., add 5–10 g. NH_4Cl and 10 ml. 3% reagent in 0·2*N* HCl, boil and add NH_4OH until a ppt. appears; add 3 ml. 1*N* HCl, warm, add 10 ml. buffer soln. (28 g. $KBrO_3$, 120 g. KBr and 250 g. $Na_2S_2O_3$/l.), boil for 1 min., filter, etc.

For the colorimetric detn. extn. with $CHCl_3$ is most satisfactory.[5, 17] To 50 ml. acidic soln. contg. 50 μg. Al, add 2 ml. 2% oxine in 1*N* AcOH and 2 ml. buffer (200 g. NH_4OAc and 70 ml. NH_4OH/l.), adjust to pH 8·0 ± 1·5 with 6*N* NH_4OH and transfer to a 125 ml. separatory funnel. Ext. with 3 10–15 ml. portions of $CHCl_3$ (previously shaken with an equal vol. of 2*M* NH_4OH + 2*M* NH_4Cl and distd.), then sep., filter on Whatman No. 40 paper, dil. to 50 ml. with $CHCl_3$ and measure at 390 mμ.

NOTES. (1) Over 50 μg. Fe interferes but can be removed by extn. at pH 2–2·5. Fe, Mo, Sb, Co, Cu, Ni, Sn can be removed by electrolysis at a Hg-cathode. Ti and V can be sepd. with cupferron. F^- interference is prevented by H_3BO_3. Large amts. of tartrate or PO_4^{3-} interfere.
Very few of the elements in steel interfere[18] if the soln. contains tartrate, CN^- and H_2O_2 at pH 9. For analysis of alloys,[7] only Zr accompanies Al if Hg-cathode electrolysis is followed by treatment with 8-hydroxyquinaldine, extn. with $CHCl_3$ at pH 9·2, extn. with oxine at pH 9·2 after H_2O_2 addn., and shaking with anhyd. Na_2SO_4; Zr can be sepd. by extn. with cupferron. After extn. from NH_4OH soln. contg. EDTA, CN^- and H_2O_2, only Zr, Ga, Bi, Sb and In interfere.[19]
(2) 0·2 μg. Al in 50 ml. soln. can be detd. by comparison of fluorescence under UV light.[20] Fluorimetric detn. has been applied to phosphate rocks.[21]
(3) Some oxine may be extd. from acidic soln.;[22] this can be corrected for, or removed by shaking with H_2O.
(4) Sepn. of Al from Fe is possible by extn. of solns. contg. $NH_2OH{\cdot}HCl$ and phenanthroline.[23] Fe and Al can be detd. simultaneously;[24] Be^{2+} is added if F^- is present (see also Chapter 50, p. 363).
(5) In alternative finishes, the ppt. is treated with mineral acid and measured at 252[5] or 365 mμ.,[25] or treated with Folin–Denis reagent (see Chapter 53, p. 397).[26] Treatment with $NaNO_2$ and sulfanilic acid or naphthionic acid is also possible.[26]

Several derivs. or analogs of oxine have been proposed for detn. of Al. Bromoxine is suitable[27] for gravimetric detn. of 6–8 mg. Al_2O_3. Add 3 g. NH_4NO_3, sufficient Me_2CO to give a 15% v/v soln. and NH_4OH to give a slightly alk. soln.; boil, add 5–20 ml. satd. bromoxine in Me_2CO, filter on a G4 crucible, wash with 10% Me_2CO contg. 1·5% NH_4OAc and some NH_4OH and then with warm H_2O, dry at 110–156°C and weigh as $Al(C_9H_4Br_2ON)_3$.

Ferron is used colorimetrically for 10–60 μg. Al (+Fe) in 5–10 ml. neutral soln.[28] Add 1 ml. 1:9 HCl, 1 ml. 1:9 HNO_3, 5 ml. 10% NH_4OAc and 2 ml. 0·2% reagent and dil. to 25 ml. with H_2O; measure at 370 mμ. If necessary, det. Fe at 600 mμ and subtract the absorbance of an equal amt. of Fe at 370 mμ.

o-(Salicylideneamino)-phenol allows detn. of Al in 5 ml. soln.[29] Add 0·5 ml. 5% NaOAc, 1 drop 5% AcOH, 3–5 drops 0·05% reagent and 0·1–1 ml. 0·2*N* HNO_3; measure the fluorescence under UV light after 5 min.

(c) $(NH_4)_2HPO_4$ permits gravimetric detn. of < 10 mg. Al in 400 ml. soln. contg. 10 ml. HCl.[1, 30] Add 1 g. reagent and some filter pulp, make alk. to methyl orange with NH_4OH, add 0·5 ml. HCl, boil, add 30 ml. 25% NH_4OAc and boil for 5 min. Filter on paper, wash with 5% NH_4NO_3 until the filtrate is Cl^--free, ignite at 1000°C (> 743°C) and weigh as $AlPO_4$.

NOTES. (1) Interferences are Fe, Ti, Zr, etc., Mn, Zn, Ca, Mg and ClO_4^-. Fe^{3+} can be reduced[31] with 20 ml. 30% $(NH_4)_2S_2O_3$ or with 15 g. $Na_2S_2O_3$. Ca does not interfere at pH 4·0–4·5 (bromophenol blue).[32] The method has been applied to detn. of Al in Fe–V.[8]
(2) $(NH_4)_2HAsO_4$ can be used titrimetrically.[33] To the soln. contg. 5% NH_4Cl and 5% AcOH, add reagent to give a 0·38–0·53% soln. of As_2O_5; filter on a glass crucible, wash with 90% EtOH, dissolve the ppt. in 1*N* HCl, boil with SO_2, add some tartaric acid and $NaHCO_3$ and titrate with 0·1*N* I_2.

(d) Aluminon can be used colorimetrically for detn. of Al;[25] two different procedures are applicable. The first is suitable for 0–70 μg. Al and the second for 0–10 μg. Al.

(*i*) To 20 ml. soln. contg. 2·0 ml. 5*N* HCl, add 10 ml. H_2O, 1·0 ml. 5% gum arabic, 5·0 ml. buffer (156 g. NH_4OAc and 108 g. NH_4Cl/l.) and 2·0 ml. 0·2% reagent and boil gently for 5 min. Cool, add 4·0 ml. borate soln. (93 g. H_3BO_3 in 1 l. of 1*N* NH_4OH, filtered and adjusted to 0·8*N* NH_4OH with HCl), dil. to 50 ml. with H_2O and measure after 5 min. at 525 mμ or with a green filter. Use a 1 cm. cell for 10–70 μg. Al and a 4 cm. cell for 0–10 μg. Al.

NOTE. No interference arises from <1 mg. common heavy metals or from 10 mg. Ca, Mg or P_2O_5. Fe can be removed by extn. with cupferron–$CHCl_3$; boil the soln. after extn., cool, add 1 drop methyl red and make just alk. with NH_4OH; acidify with 5*N* HCl, add 5·0 ml. in excess followed by 2 drops Br_2 water and boil. If the color does not fade, then the removal of cupferron was incomplete; add 0·5 ml. 10% $NH_2OH{\cdot}HCl$, dil. to 100 ml. with H_2O, etc.

(*ii*) For < 10 μg. Al in 3 ml. slightly acidic soln. add 0·2 ml. 1% v/v thioglycolic acid, 1 ml. reagent soln. (0·75 g. reagent, 15 g. gum acacia, 200 g. NH_4OAc and 190 ml. HCl mixed, filtered and dild. to 1·5 l. with H_2O) and dil. to 5 ml. with H_2O. Place in boiling H_2O

for exactly 4 min., allow to cool for 1·5–2 hr., and measure with a green filter.

NOTES. (1) Interferences are Cr and rare earths; 0·2 mg. Fe or PO_4^{3-} and 2 mg. Mg do not interfere. To avoid interferences in a procedure involving aluminon and thioglycolic acid,[34] sepns. by electrolysis at a Hg-cathode, extn. with cupferron in $CHCl_3$ (sepn. from Ti, Zr, Hf), extn. with oxine in $CHCl_3$ (sepn. from Be and Sc), and back-extn. with acid have been examined.
(2) The technique has been used for detn. of Al in alloys after ion exchange sepn.,[35] in Ti by a differential method,[36] in Ni[8, 37] and in steels.[37]
(3) Very many different modifications of the basic method have been recommended.
(4) Similar reagents have been suggested. Eriochrome cyanine R is suitable for detn. of 0·2–0·6 mg. Al in acidic (HCl) soln.[25, 38] Dil. the soln. to 100–150 ml. with H_2O, add 10 ml. 0·1% reagent, and after 5–7 min., 5–10 ml. 40% NAOAc, dil. to 200 ml. with H_2O (pH 5·5–6·5) and measure the reddish complex at 530 mμ within 5 min. Alumocreson allows detn. of <12 μg. Al at 500 mμ. after reaction at pH 4·37 and at 60–70°C.[39]

(e) Cupferron can be applied gravimetrically.[8] Treat the acidic filtrate from the cupferron sepn. of Fe, etc. with 1 ml. 20% tartaric acid; add NH_4OH slowly until the soln. is alk. to litmus, then neutralize with HCOOH and add 5 ml. in excess. Cool to 10–15°C, add 5% reagent (freshly prepd. and filtered) allowing 0·4 ml./mg. Al and 10 ml. in excess, and add filter pulp. After 15–20 min. filter on Whatman No. 42 paper with suction, wash with H_2O contg. 1 ml. reagent and 1 ml. HCOOH/100 ml., ignite at 1250–1300°C and weigh as Al_2O_3.

NOTES. (1) Cupferron can also be used nephelometrically.[40] To the soln. at pH 0·3 add 2 ml. 5% cupferron in C_6H_6, and NH_4OAc–NH_4OH buffer, shake, add *o*-phenanthroline, shake and measure at 510 mμ. Fe, etc. in moderate amts. do not interfere; for large amts. Hg-cathode electrolysis can be applied for sepn.
(2) *N*-Benzoylphenylhydroxylamine also allows gravimetric detn. (see Chapter 33, p. 260).

(f) Miscellaneous gravimetric methods LiCl allows detn. of Al in 100 ml. soln.[41] Add 10% reagent in excess, phenolphthalein and 5 g. NH_4OAc, and make just alk. with NH_4OH. After 10 min., filter on paper, wash with 2% NH_4OAc, dissolve the ppt. in hot dil. HNO_3, add 5 g. NH_4OAc, phenolphthalein and 3 ml. reagent, etc. Repeat the repptn. Ignite at 900–950°C (> 1471°C) and weigh as $2Li_2O{\cdot}5Al_2O_3$. No interference is caused by Zn.

Na-anthranilate forms a ppt. with Al at pH 4·6; ignition to Al_2O_3 is required.[42]

Na-mercaptobenzothiazole can be used for 3–300 mg. Al.[43] Add 2–8 ml. 10–15% reagent to a neutral soln., filter on a G3 crucible, wash with 0·1% reagent and then with H_2O, dry at 105–110°C for 30–45 min. and weigh as $Al(C_7H_4NS_2)_3$.

(g) EDTA titration is best done in boiling soln. at pH 3 (NH_4OAc) with Cu-pyridylazonaphthol indicator.[44] Chrome azurol S is a suitable indicator for direct titration[45] of 100 ml. acidic soln. Add 3 drops 0·1% indicator, adjust to pH 4, boil and add $N_2H_4{\cdot}H_2SO_4$. Titrate with 0·05*M* EDTA until a red-orange color appears, then add 2*M* NaOAc to give a pink-violet color and titrate further to the color change to yellow. Zr and Zn interfere but Ca, Mg, Mn, Ti do not; $N_2H_4{\cdot}H_2SO_4$ prevents Fe^{3+} interference.

Several indirect titrations are available. 0·1*M* EDTA can be added in excess followed by pH adjustment to 6 and back-titration with 0·1*M* $FeCl_3$ with salicylic acid indicator.[46] For 0·2–0·5m*M* Al soln.,[47] excess (0·3–0·7m*M*) EDTA, 10 ml. buffer pH 4·5, EtOH to give a 40–50% soln. and 2 ml. 0·025% dithizone in EtOH are added, and the soln. is back-titrated with 0·05*M* $ZnSO_4$. $K_3Fe(CN)_6$, $K_4Fe(CN)_6$ and 3,3′-dimethylnaphthidine can also serve[48] as indicator in back-titration with Zn^{2+}. Back-titration with Th^{4+} soln. and alizarin S indicator[49] or with Zn^{2+} and Cu^{2+} soln. and variamine blue indicator[50] are other possibilities.

(h) NaF can be used for direct titration with morin as indicator.[50] This has been applied to Al-bronzes. Add some HCl, 30% H_2O_2, NH_4OH and boil the soln. Neutralize with 1:1 AcOH and add 25 ml. in excess followed by 2 ml. 1% gum arabic, 50 ml. MeOH, 10 drops 0·4% morin in MeOH and titrate with 0·6*M* NaF to the disappearance of fluorescence under UV light.

NOTES. (1) Neither Cu nor Fe interferes.
(2) Titration with HCl can be used after NaF addn.[51] For 5 mg. Al in 100 ml. soln. add 10 drops 2:1 0·1% thymolphthalein–0·1% alizarin yellow as indicator, adjust to violet with NaOH, adjust to green with HCl, add 20 ml. 7% NaF soln. (adjusted to pH 9·8), and titrate with HCl to a yellow color. Interference from CO_3^{2-} is avoided by $BaCl_2$ addn.; that from Cr^{3+} and Fe^{3+} by boiling and filtration; that from NH_4^+ by boiling. SiO_2 interferes.
KF can replace NaF in a similar method[52] for 25–250 mg. Al_2O_3. Add some 0·1% phenolphthalein and 50 ml. 20% Na-gluconate and dil. to 250 ml. with H_2O. Make just alk. with standard NaOH soln., add 25·0 ml. (for <105 mg. Al_2O_3) or 50·0 ml. (for 105–210 mg. Al_2O_3) of 0·3*N* HCl, add 25 ml. 50% KF soln. and titrate with NaOH to pH 8·3.
(3) Fe^{3+} soln. and SCN^- can serve as indicator in a direct titration with NaF soln. (see Chapter 52, p. 391).
(4) Fe^{3+}, SCN^- and $C_2O_4^{2-}$ can be applied colorimetrically for detn. of >1·2 mg. Al in 50 ml. soln.[53] $K_2C_2O_4$ has been used in conjunction with NaOH titration to neutral red indicator.[53]

(i) Alizarin S permits colorimetric detn. of < 150 μg. Al.[25, 54] Add 0·5 ml. H_2SO_4, evap. to fumes, add some H_2O and transfer to a 100 ml. measuring flask. Add 5·0 ml. 0·1% reagent, 10 ml. 3*N* NH_4OH and 5·0 ml. 5*N* AcOH, dil. to the mark and measure at 370 mμ.

NOTES. (1) Fe does not interfere at 370 mμ, although it does at 525 mμ. The color of the lake formed deepens[55] on addn. of Ca^{2+}.

(2) Quinalizarin (0·1% in 0·1*N* NaOH) is suitable for colorimetric detn. of Al in acetate-buffered soln. at pH 5·4–5·9 contg. gelatin, with measurement at 535 mμ.[56]
(3) Alizarin can be used[57] by extg. the excess of reagent with BuOH and Et_2O.

(j) Morin allows colorimetric detn. of 0·1–1 mg. Al.[58] To the soln. add 10 ml. 30% AcOH, dil. to 25 ml. with H_2O, add 0·5 ml. 1% morin in EtOH (filtered) and 20 ml. EtOH and dil. to 50 ml. with H_2O. After 30 min., measure at 420 mμ, or measure the yellow-green fluorescence under UV light at 546 mμ.

NOTES. (1) Interferences are Fe, UO_2^{2+}, Sn^{2+}, Mg, Mn, SO_4^{2-}, PO_4^{3-}, F^- and citrate. 10–80 μg. Al can be detd. in 60% EtOH media (Ishibashi *et al.*[58]).
(2) Similar reagents are cochineal, which forms a red fluorescence with 10–100 μg. Al,[59] and quercetin.[60]

(k) Miscellaneous colorimetric methods. Hematoxylin allows detn. of 2·5–15 μg. Al in 50 ml. neutral soln.[25] Add 1 ml. 2% starch, 1·0 ml. 0·05% reagent, 1 ml. 25% $(NH_4)_2CO_3$ and, after 10 min., 1 ml. 35% AcOH. The pH should be 4·5–4·6. Shake and measure the brownish or purple complex at 540 mμ. The color fades quite rapidly. Interferences are W, Cr, Co, Pb, La, Mn, Ag, Ti, V, Sn^{2+}. Fe can be corrected for after measurement at 660 mμ. Ca, Mg, As, Cd, Cu, Ni, U do not interfere.

Calcon can be used to det. 1–18 μg. Al.[25, 61] Add 1 ml. 0·1% calcon in EtOH (left to stand for some days before use) for 0·2–1 μg. Al, 1·5 ml. reagent for 1–12 μg. Al and 2 ml. reagent for 12–18 μg. Al. Dil. to 40 ml. with H_2O, adjust to pH 4·8, dil. to 50 ml., heat for 10 min. at 80°C, cool and measure the red fluorescence under UV light at 595–600 mμ. Interferences are Fe, 10 μg. V, Co, Ni or Ti, 20 μg. Cu and 50 μg. Ga.

Other azo dyes have been suggested. Diamine bright blue FFG can be used for 1·2–4·8 μg. Al.[62] Neothoron forms a violet complex with Al in solns. contg. hexamine.[63] Stilbazo is suitable for 0·1–5 μg. Al in 5 ml. soln. at pH 5·4 with measurement at 515 mμ.[64]

Xylenol orange forms a red color with Al.[65]

(l) Flame photometry can be applied for detn. of 100–200 p.p.m. Al by means of the interference on the Ca flame from 200 p.p.m. Ca; town gas or H_2–O_2 may be used.[66]

References

1. HILLEBRAND and LUNDELL, 389 (494); SCOTT and FURMAN, 1; KIMURA, 189; PIGOTT, 63.
2. FEIGL, F. and SCHAEFFER, A., *Anal. Chem.*, **23**, 351 (1951).
3. HILLEBRAND and LUNDELL, 389 (494) ff.
4. NARITA, K., *J. Chem. Soc. Japan*, **75**, 1037 (1954).
5. PARKS, T. D. and LYKKEN, L., *Anal. Chem.*, **20**, 1102 (1948).
6. SMITH, G. F. and CAGLE, JR., F. W., *Anal. Chem.*, **20**, 57 (1948)
7. HYNEK, R. J. and WRANGELL, L. J., *Anal. Chem.*, **28**, 1520 (1956).
8. A.S.T.M., 122 ff.
9. SCHOELLER, 161.
10. WELCHER, **III**, 15, 124.
11. HECHT and DONAU, 207; WELCHER, **I**, 285.
12. STUMPF, K. E., *Z. anal. Chem.*, **138**, 30 (1953).
13. MILLER, C. C. and CHALMERS, R. A., *Analyst*, **78**, 686 (1953).
14. ELLIOT, C. and ROBINSON, J. W., *Anal. Chim. Acta*, **13**, 235 (1955).
15. DETMAR, A. and VAN ALLER, H. C., *Rec. trav. chim.*, **75**, 1429 (1956).
16. SMITH, G. S., *Analyst*, **64**, 577 (1939).
17. WIBERLEY, S. E. and BASSETT, L. G., *Anal. Chem.*, **21**, 609 (1949); KENYON, O. A. and BEWICK, H. A., *ibid.*, **24**, 1826 (1952); GENTRY, C. H. R. and SHERRINGTON, L. G., *Analyst*, **71**, 432 (1946).
18. KASSNER, J. L. and OZIER, M. A., *Anal. Chem.*, **23**, 1453 (1951).
19. CLAASSEN, A., *et al.*, *Anal. Chim. Acta*, **10**, 373 (1954).
20. GOON, E., *et al.*, *Anal. Chem.*, **25**, 608 (1953).
21. GRIMALDI, F. S. and LEVINE, H., *U.S. Geol. Survey Bull.*, No. 922, 39 (1953).
22. MARGERUM, D. W., *et al.*, *Anal. Chem.*, **25**, 249 (1953).
23. SPRAIN, W. and BANKS, C. V., *Anal. Chim. Acta*, **6**, 363 (1952).
24. MOTOJIMA, K., *J. Chem. Soc. Japan*, **76**, 903 (1955); MOTOJIMA and HASHITANI, H., *Japan Analyst*, **6**, 642 (1957).
25. SANDELL, 146.
26. WELCHER, **I**, 288.
27. SANKO, A. M. and BURSSUK, A. J., *J. Applied Chem. (U.S.S.R.)*, **9**, 895 (1935).
28. DAVENPORT, JR., W. H., *Anal. Chem.*, **21**, 710 (1949).
29. HOLZBECHER, Z., *Chem. listy*, **47**, 680 (1953).
30. SAXER, E. T. and JONES, E. W., *Blast Furnace Steel Plant*, **39**, 445, 476, 549 (1951).
31. KLINGER, P., *Arch. Eisenhüttenw.*, **8**, 337 (1935).
32. GWYER, A. G. C. and PULLEN, N. D., *Analyst*, **57**, 704 (1932).
33. DAUBNER, W., *Angew. Chem.*, **48**, 589 (1935).
34. LUKE, C. L., *Anal. Chem.*, **24**, 1120 (1952).
35. HORTON, A. D. and THOMASON, P. F., *Anal. Chem.*, **28**, 1326 (1956).
36. BANERJEE, D. K., *Anal. Chem.*, **29**, 55 (1957).
37. ECKERT, G., *Z. anal. Chem.*, **153**, 261 (1956).
38. IKENBERRY, L. C. and THOMAS, A., *Anal. Chem.*, **23**, 1806 (1951); also see HILL, U. T., *ibid.*, **28**, 1419 (1956) (in iron ore, + thioglycolic acid); THRUN, W. E., *ibid.*, **20**, 1117 (1948); THALER, M. and MÜHLBERGER, F. H., *Z. anal. Chem.*, **144**, 241 (1955) (in bio-materials).
39. KUL'BERG, L. M. and MOLOT, L. A., *Ukrain. Khim. Zhur.*, **21**, 256 (1955).
40. ROSOTTE, R., *Chim. anal.*, **38**, 250 (1956); WELCHER, **III**, 394.
41. FISH, F. H. and SMITH, J. M., *Ind. Eng. Chem., Anal. Ed.*, **8**, 349 (1936); also see OKA, Y. and MURATA, A., *J. Chem. Soc. Japan*, **69**, 179 (1948) (from nitrate soln., $Li_2O{\cdot}2Al_2O_3$).
42. BHADURI, A., *J. Indian Chem. Soc.*, **27**, 281 (1950).
43. SPACU, G. and PIRTEA, TH. I., *Acad. rep. populare Rumâne, Bull. Ştiinţ., Ser. Mat. Fiz. Chim.*, **2**, 619 (1950).
44. FLASCHKA, H. and ABDINE, H., *Z. anal. Chem.*, **152**, 77 (1956).
45. THEIS, M., *Z. anal. Chem.*, **144**, 106 (1955); also see TAYLOR, M. P., *Analyst*, **80**, 153 (1955) (hematoxylin).

46. MILNER, G. W. C. and WOODHEAD, J. L., *Analyst*, **79**, 363 (1954); *Anal. Chim. Acta*, **12**, 127 (1955).
47. WÄNNINEN, E. and RINGBOM, A., *Anal. Chim. Acta*, **12**, 308 (1955).
48. FLASCHKA, H. and ABDINE, H., *Mikrochim. Acta*, 37 (1955); FLASCHKA *et al.*, *Mikrochim. Acta*, 345 (1953).
49. JOHANNSEN, W. and BOBOWSKI, E., *Metall*, **10**, 212 (1956).
50. KINNUNEN, J. and MERIKANTO, B., *Anal. Chem.*, **23**, 1690 (1951); also see STEUER, H., *Z. anal. Chem.*, **118**, 389 (1939/40) (potentiometric); RINGBOM, A. and WILKMAN, B., *Acta Chem. Scand.*, **3**, 22 (1948) (amperometric).
51. PAULSON, R. V. and MURPHY, J. F., *Anal. Chem.*, **28**, 1182 (1956); also see ELLIOTT, C. and ROBINSON, J., *Anal. Chim. Acta*, **13**, 309 (1955) (in steel, cresol red + thymol blue).
52. WATTS, H. L. and UTLEY, D. W., *Anal. Chem.*, **28**, 1730 (1956).
53. SZABÓ, Z. B. and BECK, M. T., *Anal. Chem.*, **25**, 103 (1953).
54. BARTON, C. J., *Anal. Chem.*, **20**, 1069 (1948); WELCHER, **IV**, 424.
55. PARKER, C. A. and GODDARD, A. P., *Anal. Chim. Acta*, **4**, 517 (1950).
56. BURRIEL-MARTI, F. and BOLLE-TACCHEO, S., *Anal. Chim. Acta*, **14**, 553 (1956); WELCHER, **IV**, 461.
57. BABKO, A. K. and NAZARCHUK, T. N., *Zhur. Anal. Khim.*, **9**, 96 (1954).
58. ISHIBASHI, M., *et al.*, *Japan Analyst*, **3**, 293 (1954); SZABÓ, Z. and BECK, M. T., *Acta Chim. Acad. Sci. Hung.*, **4**, 211 (1954); WELCHER, **IV**, 371.
59. GOTO, H., *J. Chem. Soc. Japan*, **60**, 938 (1939).
60. WELCHER, **IV**, 388.
61. ISHIBASHI, M., *et al.*, *Japan Analyst*, **6**, 568 (1957); WEISSLER, A. and WHITE, C. E., *Ind. Eng. Chem.*, *Anal. Ed.*, **18**, 530 (1946).
62. BARSKAYA, S. I., *Zavodskaya Lab.*, **16**, 278 (1950).
63. KUZNETSOV, V. I. and GOLUBTSOVA, R. B., *Zavodskaya Lab.*, **21**, 1422 (1955); **22**, 161 (1956).
64. KUZNETSOV *et al.*, *Zavodskaya Lab.*, **16**, 787 (1950); JEAN, M., *Anal. Chim. Acta*, **10**, 526 (1954) (in steel).
65. KÖRBL, J., *et al.*, *Chem. listy*, **50**, 1440 (1956).
66. KASHIMA, J. and MUTAGUCHI, M., *Japan Analyst*, **4**, 420, 445 (1955).

44

BERYLLIUM

The principal sources for this chapter are given in ref. 1. The analytical chemistry of beryllium has been discussed in several reviews,[2, 3, 4, 5] one of which deals particularly with analysis of small amounts.[3] A bibliography on the analysis of beryllium has been compiled.[6] A monograph on beryllium has been published.[7]

Attack

The general methods are similar to those used for Al. It should be noted that some beryls contain He.

(1) Minerals. Fuse with Na_2CO_3 and leach with HCl.

(2) Phosphates. Treat with aqua regia, add HNO_3 and evap.; repeat this process. Fuse the residue with Na_2CO_3 and combine the solutions.

(3) Org. matter. Ignite and take care that all the residue is dissolved completely in the later steps.

Separation

Sepn. methods for Be are also similar to those for Al. Table 39 (from Fresenius–Jander[1]) outlines the classical possibilities. Sepn. from phosphate is difficult.

Oxine allows sepn. from Al, Fe, Ti, Zr, Cu, Co, Ni

TABLE 39. Separation of Beryllium

Reagent \ Sepn. from	Pb	Cu	V^{5+}	Mo	Fe	Al	Ni	Co	Mn	Cr	Zn	Ti	Zr	Th	Others
NH_4OH		+	+	+	+(II)		+		+	+(VI)	+				groups IV, V, (Ga, U)
NH_4OH+ EDTA	+	+			+	+	+	+	+	+	+				Bi, Cd
NH_4NO_2				+			+	+	+		+				Cd, Tl, Mg, Ca, Sr
Guanidine carbonate		+	+	+	+	+				+(VI)			+	+	As, Sb, W, Tl, U
H_2S (acidic soln.)	+	+		+											Hg, Cd, Bi, As, Sb[a]
H_2S (feebly acidic soln.)							+				+				Ga (+As)
H_2S (NH_4OH+ $(NH_4)_2$-tartrate)	+	+			+		+	+	+						
Oxine		+	(+)	+	+	+	+	+			+	+	+		W, U. Also $CHCl_3$ extn.
Tannin			+	(+)	+	+			+			+	+	+	Sn, W, Ga, Nb, Ta
Cupferron		+	+		+	(+)						+	+	(+)	(Sn), U, Ga, Nb, Ta
H_2SeO_3												+	+	+	Bi
KOH					+				+					+	rare earths
Na_2CO_3 fusion, H_2O extn.			+			+				+					W, SiO_2, PO_4^{3-}, group V
Hg-cathode electrolysis	+	+		+	+		+	+		+	+				

[a] SnS_2 absorbs Be; sep. with tannin.

Zn and partly from V. Treat 200 ml. soln. contg. 10 ml. HCl with 15 ml. NH_4OAc soln. (30 g. in 75 ml.), add 8–10 drops bromocresol purple and make alk. with NH_4OH. Add a 15–25% excess of 2·5% oxine in 0·83*N* AcOH, boil for 1 min. and cool to 60°C before filtration. Alternatively, ext. with $CHCl_3$ from the soln. at pH 5. The detn. of Be with NH_4OH in the filtrate from the above method may give low results; this can be overcome by cooling more before filtration,[8] by treating the filtrate with HNO_3 and H_2SO_4,[8] or by removing oxine with $Cu(OAc)_2$.[9] If much Fe or Al is present, repptn. is done after dissoln. in 1:4 HCl, or the method is combined with $NaHCO_3$ sepn. If small amts. of Fe or Al are present, $CHCl_3$ extn. is better. Any Mn in the BeO must be detd. colorimetrically and subtracted.

NH_4OH in presence of EDTA allows sepn. from Al in amts. below 1·3 times that of Be; repptn. is needed if more is present. Sepn. from Fe, Cr, Bi, Pb, Cu, Cd, Ni, Co, Mn, Zn is also possible.[10] To 100 ml. soln. contg. 50–80 mg. BeO, add NH_4OH until a ppt. appears, HCl until the soln. is clear, and 2 ml. NH_4-EDTA soln. for each 27 mg. Al (29·21 g. EDTA acid in 40 ml. H_2O neutralized with NH_4OH to methyl orange and dild. to 200 ml.). After 2–12 hr., filter on paper, wash with 100–150 ml. hot NH_4NO_3 and ignite. Interferences are PO_4^{3-} and Ti. NH_4OH can also be applied in tartrate[11] or fluoride[12] soln. NH_4OH and thioglycolic acid sep. Be from Fe (*cf.* below).

Cupferron allows sepn. of Be from Al. To 200 ml. soln. add 10 g. tartaric acid, make alk. with NH_4OH, acidify with 8% $H_2C_2O_4$, cool and add 6% cupferron. Make the filtrate ammoniacal, add a 15 ml. excess of HCOOH and ppt. Al with cupferron (Pigott[1]).

Pptn. with 5% NaOH seps. Be, Al, etc. from Fe, Zr, Ti, etc. Sepn. is incomplete if Fe $\geqslant$ Be; this sepn. is better done with 10% NaOH and Na_2S. Be can be sepd. from Al by adding NaOH to the soln. until the ppt. dissolves, then dilg. to 400 ml. with H_2O and boiling for 40 min.; sepn. is complete if BeO $\geqslant$ Al_2O_3, and a known amt. of BeO should be added[13] if BeO $<$ Al_2O_3. Fusion with NaOH of the ppt. formed with NH_4OH and thioglycolic acid seps. Be from traces of Fe, Ti, etc. (*cf.* above).

Be can be partly sepd. from $>$ 0·1 g. Al and from W, V, Cr, SiO_2, PO_4^{3-} and F^- by Na_2CO_3 fusion above 1100°C, followed by addn. of H_2O and 1 g. Na_2CO_3 and boiling for 2–3 min. Sepn. from Al is complete if PO_4^{3-} is present.[14] A combination of this method with the tannin sepn. is said to be best for sepn. of Be from Al.[15] Boiling for 1 min. with 10% $NaHCO_3$ gives a partial sepn. from large amts. of Fe or Al but Ti, Zr and P interfere.

Extn. of the acetate with $CHCl_3$ also seps. Be from Al.[16] Treat the hydroxide ppt. with AcOH, add some H_2O, evap. and ext. with $CHCl_3$. For extn. of the butyrate with $CHCl_3$, see Chapter 16, p. 183.

Treatment with $(NH_4)_2CO_3$ gives incomplete sepn. from Al and Fe. If $NH_2OH{\cdot}HCl$ is added, sepn. from U is satisfactory.

Sepn. from Fe is also possible with HCl and Cl_2 gas at 200–300°C. Treatment with HCl gas of a HCl soln. contg. Et_2O seps. Be from Al and Ti (see Chapter 43, p. 320). Be is recovered from the filtrate by pptn. with NH_4OH after addn. of Fe, and then by fusion with NaOH. Be and Fe are sepd. by extn. of a HCl soln. with Et_2O.

$K_4Fe(CN)_6$ seps. Be from U.[15]

Ion exchange resins can be used to sep. Be from Fe and Al (see Chapter 13, Section 2.1).

Sepn. from Fe in minerals is possible by ignition in H_2, cooling and treatment with HCl. The residue (BeO) is dissolved in HF.

p-Chloraniline allows sepn.[17] of 5–40 mg. BeO from 2–50 mg. TiO_2. Treat 250 ml. soln. with NH_4OH until a ppt. appears, add 1–1·5 g. reagent, boil for 3 min., filter on paper and wash with hot H_2O.

Na_2SO_4 seps. Be from the Ce group (see p. 352) and $H_2C_2O_4$ allows sepn. from the Y group (see p. 348).

$(NH_4)_2MoO_4$ seps. Be from P. This sepn. is also possible by treatment with Bi^{3+} in 0·5*N* HNO_3 soln. followed by H_2S.

Tannin can be applied in several different ways. For the sepn. of $<$ 80 mg. Al + Be in slightly acidic soln.,[18] add 25 ml. satd. NH_4OAc soln., dil. to 500 ml. with H_2O, adjust to pH 4·6 with H_2SO_4 or NH_4OH, and boil; add 50 ml. 3% tannin dropwise, place on a steam-bath for 1 hr., cool, filter on paper and wash with 5% NH_4OAc contg. tannin at pH 4·6. Better results may be obtained by adding the sample soln. to the tannin–NH_4OAc soln. because of less adsorption.[19] The above method allows sepn. from Al, Fe, Cr, Th, V, Ti and Zr. The Al–tannin complex ppts. at pH 4·6 and the Be complex at pH 4·9; the pH is best adjusted[20] with NH_4OH to a blue-green color with 1 drop 0·1% methyl red and 6 drops 0·1% bromocresol green, followed by adjustment to a purple color with H_2SO_4.

Treatment with 5% tannin in $(NH_4)_2C_2O_4$ soln. seps. Be from Ti, Nb, Ta (see Chapter 51, p. 374). Sepn. from Sn is possible with tannin in 200 ml. soln. which is 0·05–0·08*N* in HCl.[15]

Concentration

Be can be sepd. from almost all elements and concd. by electrolysis with a Hg-cathode, followed by extn. of the acetylacetone complex.[21] After electrolysis, transfer the soln. to a separatory funnel and adjust the vol. to 40–45 ml. Add a few drops of AcOH, adjust to pH 4·5 with NH_4OH, add 4 ml. acetylacetone and stir for 5 min. Add 20 ml. C_6H_6, stir for 15 min. and check the pH; then rinse the vessel wall with 20 ml. H_2O and sep. (If much PO_4^{3-} is present, increase the stirring times and repeat the extn.). Then add 15 ml. 5*N* HCl, stir for 15 min., sep., wash the aq. layer with C_6H_6, evap. to dryness and ignite. Add 5 drops H_2SO_4, evap. nearly to dryness, add H_2O and apply the morin colorimetric finish. Extn. of the acetylacetone complex with CCl_4 from alk. soln. contg. EDTA is also possible.[22]

Copptn. with $AlPO_4$ can also be used to conc. Be.

Determination

The NH_4OH gravimetric procedure is most commonly applied. The tannin or 8-hydroxyquinaldine method is better for mg. amounts of Be. Guanidine carbonate is a useful reagent when Al is present, and the $(NH_4)_2HPO_4$ procedure is convenient if PO_4^{3-} is present. For colorimetric determination, morin provides the most sensitive method; quinalizarin and its analogs, 8-hydroxyquinaldine and acetylacetone appear to be satisfactory reagents for Be. The accuracy and sensitivity of several colorimetric methods have been compared;[3] the data are tabulated in Table 40.

TABLE 40. Comparison of Methods for Small Amounts of Be[3]

Method	Accuracy ($\pm x$ μg.)	
Quinizarin-2-sulfonic acid	0·1	
Aluminon	0·2	
Alkannin	0·06	
Naphthazarin	0·06	
Eriochrome cyanine R	0·05	
	Sensitivity (μg.)	
Colorimetric	0·2	± 30%
Fluorimetric (morin)	0·004	± 20%
Spectrographic (arc)	0·002	± 50%
(spark)	0·004	± 50%

(a) NH_4OH provides the classical gravimetric method for Be.[1, 23] For > 20 mg. Be in 200 ml. slightly acidic soln. add 5 g. NH_4Cl, boil, make alk. to bromophenol blue with NH_4OH, boil, add filter pulp, filter on paper and wash with 3% NH_4NO_3 which has been made alk. as above, until no Cl^- appears in the filtrate. Heat slowly to 700°C, then ignite at 1000°C and weigh as BeO.

NOTES. (1) After the filtration the vessel wall should be wetted with some hot dil. HNO_3, and the soln. pptd. with NH_4OH; this ppt. is filtered through the same paper as the bulk part. The weighed ppt. should be checked to ensure absence of Al, P, Ga or Ge. The ignited oxide may contain SO_3, alkalies, Al, SiO_2; these can be removed[15] by fusion with Na_2CO_3 and extn. with hot H_2O. For sepn. from Fe, Al, etc. in presence of EDTA or tartrate, see under Separation, p. 326.

(2) Various hydrolysis methods have been recommended; those involving tannin or guanidine carbonate seem preferable. With tannin[1, 15, 18] take a faintly acidic sample soln. contg. 10–100 mg. BeO (see under Separation, p. 326). Add at least a 10-fold excess of 5% tannin, make the soln. alk. to litmus with NH_4OH, filter on paper and wash with a 5% NH_4OAc soln. contg. tannin and made alk. to litmus.

Guanidine carbonate is suitable for <0·25 g. Be in 50 ml. of slightly acidic (HCl or HNO_3) soln.[24, 25] Add 50 ml. 3% $(NH_4)_2$-tartrate, 2·5 ml. 40% HCHO and 3*N* NaOH until alk. to phenolphthalein. Make acid to methyl orange with dil. HCl, add 150 ml. 4% reagent, filter on Whatman No. 42 paper after 12 hr. and wash with a mixt. contg. 50 ml. 3% $(NH_4)_2$-tartrate, 450 ml. reagent and 5 ml. 40% HCHO. Finally, ignite and weigh as BeO. Interference from large amts. of NH_4^+ is prevented by addn. of more HCHO. Up to 0·1 g. Al, Sb, Cu, Fe^{3+}, Tl, Th, UO_2^{2+}, Zr, Ti, As^{3+} or Cr^{3+} can be tolerated. If V or W is present, add tartrate, make definitely alk. with NaOH, neutralize to methyl orange with HCl and proceed as above. It is advisable to det. Be in the filtrate with quinalizarin and apply a correction.

NH_4NO_2 can be used for 20–100 mg. Be in 100 ml. of slightly acidic soln.[24] Add Na_2CO_3 until a ppt. appears, make clear with HCl, heat to 70°C and pass air through the soln. Add 50 ml. 6% reagent and 20 ml. MeOH, filter on paper, wash with 2% NH_4OAc contg. NH_4OH, etc. Other reagents which have been used are hexamine,[26] α-picoline[27] and KI with KIO_3.[24]

(3) For a titrimetric procedure,[24] add a small excess of NH_4OH, boil for 10 min., add 0·1*N* HCl until the soln. is colorless to thymolphthalein and then add a known excess of acid. Dil. to 200 ml. with H_2O (if F^- is present, add $CaCl_2$, boil for 1 min. and cool), then add 20 ml. satd. KIO_3 soln. and 20 ml. 4% KI, stir for 2–3 sec., add 4 g. $NaHCO_3$ and titrate with 0·1*N* As^{3+}.

(b) $(NH_4)_2HPO_4$ can be used gravimetrically, titrimetrically or colorimetrically. For gravimetric detn.[24, 28] of < 10 mg. BeO (as nitrate or sulfate) in slightly acidic soln., add 5 g. reagent, 20 g. NH_4NO_3, 30 ml. satd. NH_4OAc soln., boil and add 1:2 HNO_3 until the soln. is clear. Then add 1·5*N* NH_4OH at a rate of 5–6 drops per min. until the soln. is alk. to phenolphthalein. Filter on paper after 12 hr., wash with hot 5% NH_4NO_3 contg. a few drops of NH_4OH, ignite above 640°C and weigh as $Be_2P_2O_7$. An empirical factor of 0·255 is applied, the theoretical factor being 0·2605.

NOTES. (1) The method is accurate if Fe and Al are previously removed with oxine. If EDTA is added, none of the elements present in beryl interfere.[2, 29]

(2) For a titrimetric finish,[30] ppt. at pH 5–5·5 in presence of EDTA, dissolve the ppt. in $HClO_4$ and titrate with $BiOClO_4$ soln., using diallyldithiocarbamidohydrazine in $CHCl_3$ as indicator. Ti does not interfere if H_2O_2 is added; Fe, etc. do not interfere.

(3) For colorimetric detn.[31] ppt. at pH 5, dissolve the ppt. in 2*N* $HClO_4$, add molybdate soln. and measure at 390–420 mμ.

(4) In a similar procedure, Be is pptd. as arsenate and the ppt. is titrated iodometrically.[32] If EDTA is present, this method can be used for Be-bronze.[33]

(c) Morin provides a very sensitive fluorimetric procedure.[34, 35, 36] For 0·1–1 μg. Be in 5–10 ml. soln. add 5 ml. satd. $Na_4P_2O_7$ soln. followed by 1–2*N* NaOH to give a final concn. of 0·1*N* (if Al or Zn is present, add more) and add 2 ml. 5% KCN if Zn is present. Then add 0·20 ml. 0·05% w/v morin in Me_2CO, dil to 25 ml. and measure the yellow-green fluorescence under excitation at 365 mμ with a secondary filter which absorbs below 525 mμ. A mercury arc lamp is said to be too strong;[3] light from a motor-car headlamp has been recommended. If Be exceeds 1 μg., comparison in strong daylight is satisfactory.

NOTES. (1) 10 mg. Al_2O_3 can be tolerated; an equal amt. is added to the standard if more is present. Most common elements and Rb, Cs, SiO_2, PO_4^{3-} and BO_2^- do not interfere. Ti, Zr, Ce. La, Th, Nb, Ta, Ga, In, Tl, Mo, W, U, V should be sepd. with NH_4OH and thioglycolic acid followed by NaOH fusion. Interference of Ca or much Sc is prevented by $Na_4P_2O_7$ addn., that of Zn with KCN. Large amts. of Li (>5000 Be) interfere as do oxidants such as Cu^{2+}, CrO_4^{2-}, MnO_4^-, etc.
(2) The use of pure morin makes the method 10 times more sensitive than with impure reagent.

(d) Quinalizarin provides an excellent colorimetric method for 1–5 μg. Be in 5–10 ml. soln.[1, 15, 24, 34, 37] Add NaOH to give a final concn. of 0·25*N*, add 1 ml. 0·01% reagent in Me_2CO (stored in the dark) and compare the blue complex.

NOTES. (1) Elements which are pptd. by NaOH interfere. Interference of Zn, Cu, Ni is avoided by KCN addn. and that of Mg by NaOH addn. followed by Br_2 water. Up to 2 mg. Al and F^-, CN^- and PO_4^{3-} do not interfere.
(2) Several anthraquinone derivs. have been investigated for this detn.; Al does not interfere if EDTA is added.[38]
(3) Quinizarin-2-sulfonic acid is suitable[39] for colorimetric detn. of 1–20 μg. Be in 15 ml. soln. at pH 6. Add 2 ml. buffer (0·1*M* histidine-HCl·H_2O in 1% gum arabic soln. adjusted to pH 6·5 with 2*N* NaOH and a small crystal of thymol added) followed by 1 ml. 0·16% reagent, dil. to 20 ml. with H_2O, place for 10 min. in boiling H_2O, cool and compare the red complex at 575 mμ.
(4) Alkannin or naphthazarin can be used colorimetrically for 1–30 μg. Be in 9·5 ml. soln.[40] Add 5 ml. buffer (10% mannitol in 0·5*M* H_3BO_3 adjusted to pH 5·0 with NaOH and some thymol added) followed by 0·5 ml. 0·5% gum arabic, 5 ml. reagent (0·4 mg./ml. dioxane); dil. to 20 ml. with H_2O (pH 6·5) and measure the blue complex at 600 mμ. 1 μg. Zn, Cu, Fe or Al, 10 μg. Mg or PO_4^{3-}, and 1 mg. Ca can be tolerated. This method is said[3] to be preferable to the quinizarin-2-sulfonic acid method.

(e) 2-Hydroxy-1-naphthaldehyde can be applied gravimetrically.[41] Add a 5-fold excess of 2% reagent in EtOH, add EtOH to give a 50% soln. and boil. Add NH_4OH until NH_3 can be smelled, filter, wash with 50% EtOH, dry at 110°C and weigh. The conversion factor is 0·02565. EDTA prevents interference from Cu, Fe, Al.

(f) $BaCl_2$ and NaF provide a gravimetric detn. of 7–22 mg. Be.[42] Add 5 drops of Wesselow's indicator (?), 50 ml. 2·5% NaF, dil. to 300 ml. with H_2O, add 4 g. H_3BO_3 and HCl to give a violet color, boil and add 15 ml. 5% $BaCl_2$ dropwise. Place on a steam-bath for 1 hr., filter on a glass crucible, wash once with hot H_2O and twice with EtOH, dry at 110–120°C for 1 hr. and weigh as $BaBeF_4$.

NOTES. (1) Beryl can be analyzed as follows. Add $NaBF_4$, heat at 540°C and leach with hot H_2O. Adjust to pH 7·2–7·4 with Na_2CO_3, boil for several min., cool, filter and wash with Na_2CO_3. Add H_3BO_3, adjust to pH 3·5 with HCl, heat to remove CO_2, add $BaCl_2$, etc.
(2) A titrimetric method is possible with KF alone.[2, 43] Add a 3–16-fold excess of Na-salicylate, and neutralize with 0·1*N* NaOH to thymolphthalein. Add a 1·25–3-fold excess of 0·1*N* HCl and a 2–3-fold excess of KF, leave for 3–5 min., and titrate with 0·1*N* NaOH to phenol red indicator.

(g) H_2SeO_3 may be used gravimetrically for < 0·1 g. BeO in 100 ml. of slightly acidic soln.[24] Add 5 ml. 10% reagent, make slightly pink with 5% NH_4OH to phenolphthalein (warm if the amt. of Be is small), filter on paper, wash with hot H_2O, ignite and weigh as BeO. Zr, etc. interfere but can be removed in mineral acid soln.

(h) Curcumin is suitable for colorimetry of 0·5–10 μg. Be in 10 ml. slightly acidic soln.[24, 34, 44] Add 0·05 ml. 0·1% curcumin in EtOH, 0·5 ml. 4*N* NH_4Cl and 0·5 ml. 4*N* NH_4OH and compare the reddish color. Interferences are large amts. of group III elements, very large amts. of Mg, and F^-.

(i) 2-(*o*-Hydroxyphenyl)-benzothiazole provides a colorimetric detn. of 0–100 μg. Be in 5 ml. soln.[45] Add 10 ml. acetate buffer pH 4·3–5, 20 ml. EtOH, and 1 ml. 0·02*M* reagent in EtOH, dil. to 50 ml. with H_2O and measure the blue fluorescence under UV light at 435 mμ.

NOTES. (1) Cu and Zn interfere but Fe^{3+}, Cr, Al, Bi, Sb, Sn^{4+}, Zr, Ti do not if NaK-tartrate is added.
(2) 8-Hydroxyquinaldine can be applied gravimetrically, titrimetrically or colorimetrically.[46] For 2–10 mg. Be, add 5 ml. 4*N* NH_4Cl, 5 ml. 10% Na_2-tartrate, dil. to 50 ml. with H_2O, heat to 60–70°C, adjust to pH 7·8–9·2 with 2*N* NH_4OH and add a 20–30% excess of 1% reagent in 2% AcOH. After 30 min., filter, wash with 1:100 NH_4OH, dry at 110°C and weigh as $Be(C_{10}H_8NO)_2$. Alternatively, dissolve in HCl and titrate with $KBrO_3$–KBr soln. Al and SO_4^{2-} do not interfere, but Bi, Cd, Cr, Co, Cu, Fe, In, Mn, Ni, Ag, Zn require sepn. by Hg-cathode electrolysis. Ti and Mg interfere.
The reagent can also be applied colorimetrically for 2–30 μg. Be with extn. by 10 ml. $CHCl_3$ at pH 8·0 ± 0·2 and measurement at 380 mμ, or fluorimetrically for 0·3–4 μg. Be (see Chapter 42, p. 317). In this case Al, Fe, etc. interfere, but can be removed by extn. with oxine in $CHCl_3$ at pH 5.
(3) Oxine can be applied gravimetrically or titrimetrically for 5–15 mg. Be.[47] Heat the soln. to 70°C, add NH_4OH until a turbidity appears, followed by a 2–5-fold excess of 2% oxine in 5% AcOH and digest at 65°C for 3 hr. (pH 8·0 ± 0·2). Filter on a glass crucible, wash with warm H_2O, dry at 110°C and weigh as $Be_2O(C_9H_6NO)_2 \cdot 2H_2O$. Be can be sepd. from Al in solns. of pH 4·5–5·2. Ext. the reagent from the filtrate with CCl_4, add NH_4OH and NH_4Cl, filter, dissolve in HCl and proceed as above.

(j) Miscellaneous colorimetric methods. Naphthochrome green G may be used[48] for > 0·1 μg. Be in 5 ml. soln. at pH 11·5–12·3 contg. PO_4^{3-}; add 0·2 ml. reagent (0·15 g. in 100 ml. EtOH; the commercial material is first dissolved in H_2O, pptd. with HCl at 30°C, dried at 70°C). Store at 30°C for 20 min. and measure at 650 mμ.

Eriochrome cyanine R is suitable for 1–15 μg. Be in 1 ml. soln.[49] Add 10 ml. 5% NaK-tartrate, 10 ml. 0·05*M* borax, leave for 1 hr. and add 1 ml. 0·5% reagent. Measure at 527 mμ after 3 hr. Interferences (in p.p.m.) are 4·5 Zr, 9 Th, 12 Fe, Al, Ti or Ca, 14 Mg or SiO_2 and 45 U^{6+} or F^-.

Aluminon provides a method for 4–90 μg. Be in 80 ml. acidic (HCl) soln.[50] Prep. the reagent as follows: dissolve 500 g. NH_4OAc in 1 l. H_2O, add 80 ml. AcOH and filter if turbid; dissolve 1 g. aluminon in 50 ml. H_2O, mix with the first soln., add 3 g. benzoic acid in 20 ml. EtOH, mix, dil. to 2 l. with H_2O, add 10 g. gelatin in 250 ml. hot H_2O dild. to 500 ml. and cooled, mix and finally dil. to 4 l. with H_2O. For a detn. add 2 ml. EDTA soln. (2·5 g. acid in 30 ml. H_2O, neutralized to methyl red with 1:1 NH_4OH, warmed, cooled and dild. to 100 ml. with H_2O) followed by 15 ml. reagent, dil. to 100 ml. with H_2O and measure in a 2 cm. cell at 515 mμ. Fe and Cu do not interfere.

Chrome azurol S is applicable for 0·2–1·6 μg. Be/ml.;[51] interferences are Cu, Bi, Sn, Sb, Al, Fe, Ni, Ti.

p-Nitrobenzeneazo-orcinol allows detn. of 5–80 μg. Be in 10 ml. soln.[2, 15, 34, 52] Add 2·7 ml. 2·0*N* NaOH, 5 ml. 0·64*M* H_3BO_3, dil. to 19 ml. with H_2O, add 6 ml. reagent (0·025% in 0·1*N* NaOH shaken for several hr. and filtered) and measure at 525 mμ in a 2 cm. cell. Al, Cu, Fe, Ni, Ca do not interfere if EDTA is added. A differential method for 1·0–1·6 mg. Be in 50 ml. soln. at pH 12·7 (Na_3-citrate, Na-borate and NaOH buffered) is applicable.[53] Be can be detd. in Ti.[54]

Plasmocorinth is suitable for 0–100 μg. Be in 1*N* NaOH soln.[55] Pour the soln. into 0·6 ml. 0·05% reagent in 1*N* NaOH, dil. to 10 ml. with 1*N* NaOH, and measure the red color at 619 mμ. Interferences are Ca, Fe^{3+} and Co.

Beryllon I or II forms a blue complex with Be at pH 12–13·2 in presence of EDTA.[56] The EDTA prevents interference from Ca, Mg, Al, Ni, Cu, Co, Mn, Mo, Cr; ascorbic acid is required if Fe^{3+} is present.

Thoron forms a complex with Be at pH 12·4.[57]

Sulfosalicylic acid can be used for 3–450 μg. Be in 100 ml. slightly acidic soln.[58] Add 10·0 ml. 0·01*M* reagent, 50 ml. 0·5*M* EDTA, adjust to pH 9·2–10·8 with NH_4OH, dil. to 200 ml. with H_2O and measure at 317 mμ. No interference is caused by Al (0·2 g.), Pb, Sb, As, Cd, Co, Zn, Mn, Cr, Ti, La, Ca, ClO_4^-, SO_4^{2-}, Cl^- or F^-. Interferences are Cu, Zr, Hf, Ni, Sn^{4+}, PO_4^{3-}, NO_3^-, AcO^-. Fe can be removed by extn. with bis-2,2′-chloroethyl ether.

Acetylacetone provides a detn. of < 10 μg. Be in soln. of pH 0·5–1.[59] Add 2·0 ml. 10% EDTA, adjust to pH 7–8 with 0·1*N* NaOH, add 5 ml. acetylacetone (5% in H_2O), readjust the pH and ext. after 5 min. with 3 10·0 ml. portions of $CHCl_3$. Combine the exts. in a beaker, add 15 ml. H_2O, 2 ml. HNO_3 and 2 ml. $HClO_4$ and evap. to dryness. Repeat this addn. and evapn. Then add 15 ml. 0·1*N* HNO_3, bromothymol blue and 1–2 ml. 10% EDTA and adjust to pH 7 with 0·1*N* NaOH. Add 2 ml. acetylacetone reagent, readjust the pH and after 5 min. ext. 3 times with 8 ml. portions of $CHCl_3$. Dil. to 25 ml. with $CHCl_3$, shake for 1 min. with 50 ml. 0·1*N* NaOH twice and finally measure at 295 mμ (ϵ = 31 000). Citrate and large amts. of AcO^- interfere but Fe, Cr, Zn, Cu, Mn, Pb, Ag, Ce, U can be tolerated in amts. up to 1 mg., and Al in amts. up to 100 mg.

L*

References

1. HILLEBRAND and LUNDELL, 402 (516); SCOTT and FURMAN, 137; SCHOELLER and POWELL, 54; PIGOTT, 97; FRESENIUS–JANDER, **II**a, 1 (1940).
2. VINCI, F. A., *Anal. Chem.*, **25**, 1580 (1953).
3. TORIBARA, T. Y. and SHERMAN, R. E., *Anal. Chem.*, **25**, 1594 (1953).
4. MOTOJIMA, K., *J. Chem. Soc. Japan*, **77**, 95, 97, 100 (1956); *Bull. Chem. Soc. Japan*, **29**, 29, 71, 75 (1956).
5. AKIYAMA, T., *Japan Analyst*, **1**, 133 (1952); **2**, 13, 116, 354, 460 (1953); **3**, 35, 127, 410, 467 (1954); **4**, 417 (1955); **5**, 212 (1956); **6**, 26 (1957).
6. *U.S. Atomic Energy Comm., Bibliography, Analytical Chemistry of Beryllium*, AECU-10 (1948).
7. WHITE, JR., D. W. and BURKE, J. E., *The Metal Beryllium*, Am. Soc. Metals, Cleveland (1955).
8. BARBOSA, P. E. F., Chem. Abstracts, **41**, 5050 (1947).
9. CASTELLO, L., *Eng. e quím.* (*Rio de Janeiro*), **3**, 229 (1951).
10. PŘIBIL, R. and KUCHARSKÝ, J., *Collection Czechoslov. Chem. Communs.*, **15**, 132 (1950); BREWER, P. I., *Analyst*, **77**, 539 (1952); A.S.T.M. 350.
11. MILLER, H. S., *Ind. Eng. Chem., Anal. Ed.*, **9**, 221 (1937).
12. RUML, V., *Chem. průmysl*, **5**, 480 (1955).
13. DEWER, J., *Analyst*, **61**, 536 (1936).
14. STEVENS, R. E. and CARRON, M. K., *U.S. Geol. Survey Bull.*, No. 950, 91 (1946).
15. SCHOELLER and POWELL, 54.
16. TREADWELL, F. P. and HALL, W. T., *Analytical Chemistry*, **I**, 507 (1932).
17. WELCHER, **II**, 334.
18. NICHOLS, M. L. and SCHEMPF, J. M., *Ind. Eng. Chem., Anal. Ed.*, **11**, 278 (1939); also see SCHOELLER, 155 and WELCHER, **II**, 163.
19. TSCHERNICHOW, J. A., *Chem. Zentr.*, **107**, 3573 (1936).
20. SEARS, G. W. and GUNG, H., *Ind. Eng. Chem., Anal. Ed.*, **16**, 598 (1944).
21. TORIBARA, T. Y. and CHEN, JR., P. S., *Anal. Chem.*, **24**, 539 (1952).
22. ALIMARIN, I. P. and GIBALO, I. M., *Zhur. Anal. Khim.*, **11**, 389 (1956).
23. A.S.T.M., 130 ff.
24. FRESENIUS–JANDER, **II**a, 1.
25. WELCHER, **II**, 389.
26. WELCHER, **III**, 131.
27. OSTROUMOV, E. A. and BOMSHTEĬN, R. I., *Zavodskaya Lab.*, **11**, 146 (1945).

28. SÉGUIN, M. and GRAMME, L., *Bull. soc. chim. France*, 28 (1950).
29. HURÉ, J., *et al.*, *Anal. Chim. Acta*, **7**, 37 (1952).
30. DAS, M. S. and ATHAVALE, V. T., *Anal. Chim. Acta*, **12**, 6 (1955).
31. SUNDARESAN, M. and DAS, M. S., *Analyst*, **80**, 697 (1955).
32. AIROLDI, R., *Ann. chim.*, **43**, 15 (1953).
33. GORYUSHINA, V. G. and ARCHAKOVA, T. A., *Zavodskaya Lab.*, **22**, 532 (1956).
34. SANDELL, 199.
35. WELCHER, **IV**, 373.
36. SANDELL, E. B., *Anal. Chim. Acta*, **3**, 89 (1949); KLEMPERER, F. W. and MARTIN, A. P., *Anal. Chem.*, **22**, 828 (1950); LAITINEN, H. A. and KIVALO, P., *ibid.*, **24**, 1467 (1952); RILEY, J. M., *U.S. Bur. Mines, Rept. Invest.*, 5282 (1956).
37. FISCHER, W. and WERNER, J., *Angew. Chem.*, **A60**, 729 (1948); FURUHATA, T., *Repts. Sci. Research Inst.* (*Tokyo*), **26**, 12 (1950).
38. PRZHEVAL'SKIĬ, E. S., *Vestnik Moskov. Univ.*, **11**, *Ser. Mat. Mekhan. Astron. Fiz. i Khim.*, No. 1, 191 (1956); FLETCHER, M. H., *et al.*, *Ind. Eng. Chem., Anal. Ed.*, **18**, 179 (1946) (quinizarin; fluorimetry).
39. CUCCI, M. W., *et al.*, *Anal. Chem.*, **21**, 1358 (1949).
40. UNDERWOOD, A. L. and NEUMAN, W. F., *Anal. Chem.*, **21**, 1348 (1949).
41. GUSEV, S. I., *et al.*, *Zhur. Anal. Khim.*, **12**, 55 (1957).
42. DATTA, R. K. and GUPTA, A. K. S., *J. Indian Chem. Soc.*, **33**, 146 (1956); GUPTA, *ibid.*, **34**, 725 (1957).
43. ZLOLOTUKHIN, V. K., *Naukovi Zapiski L'vis. Derzhav. Univ. im I. Franka*, **34**, *Ser. Khim.*, (4) 115 (1955); MCCLURE, J. H. and BANKS, C. V., *Proc. Iowa Acad. Sci.*, **57**, 193 (1950).
44. WELCHER, **IV**, 404; FURUHATA, T., *Repts. Sci. Research Inst.* (*Tokyo*), **26**, 15 (1950).
45. HOLZBECHER, Z., *Chem. listy*, **48**, 1156 (1954); *Collection Czechoslov. Chem. Communs.*, **20**, 193 (1955).
46. MOTOJIMA, K., *Bull. Chem. Soc. Japan*, **29**, 29, 71, 75 (1956).
47. MOTOJIMA, *J. Chem. Soc. Japan*, **77**, 95 (1956).
48. ALDRIDGE, W. N. and LIDDELL, H. F., *Analyst*, **73**, 607 (1948) (in bio-materials).
49. UMEMOTO, S., *Bull. Chem. Soc. Japan*, **29**, 545 (1956); WOOD, C. H. and ISHERWOOD, H., *Metallurgia*, **39**, 321 (1949) (in Mg-metal).
50. LUKE, C. L. and CAMPBELL, M. E., *Anal. Chem.*, **24**, 1056 (1952); A.S.T.M. 350 (in Cu–Be); also see GOTO, H, and KAKITA, Y., *Sci. Repts. Research Inst. Tohoku Univ., Ser. A.*, **5**, 163 (1953); KOSEL, G. E. and NEUMAN, W. F., *Anal. Chem.*, **22**, 936 (1950).
51. WOOD, J. H., *Mikrochim. Acta*, 11 (1955).
52. WELCHER, **IV**, 384; FURUHATA, T., *Repts. Sci. Research Inst.* (*Tokyo*), **26**, 18 (1950).
53. WHITE, J. C., *et al.*, *Anal. Chem.*, **28**, 956 (1956).
54. COVINGTON, L. C. and MILES, M. J., *Anal. Chem.*, **28**, 1728 (1956).
55. FURUHATA, T., *Repts. Sci. Research Inst.* (*Tokyo*), **26**, 139 (1950).
56. LUKIN, A. M. and ZAVARIKHINA, G. B., *Zhur. Anal. Khim.*, **11**, 393 (1956); KARANOVICH, G. G., *ibid.*, 400.
57. ADAMOVICH, L. P. and YUTSIS, B. V., *Ukrain. Khim. Zhur.*, **22**, 523, 805 (1956).
58. MEEK, H. V. and BANKS, C. V., *Anal. Chem.*, **22**, 1512 (1950); MEEK, H. V., *Iowa State Coll. J. Sci.*, **25**, 295 (1951).
59. ADAM, J. A., *et al.*, *Anal. Chim. Acta*, **6**, 462 (1952).

45

CHROMIUM

The principal sources for this chapter are given in ref. 1. The complete analysis of chromite has been considered in detail.[2] The chemistry of chromium has been dealt with in a monograph.[3]

Chromium(III) can be oxidized to the hexavalent state in alkaline solution with Cl_2, Br_2, Na_2O_2 or H_2O_2, and in acidic solution by boiling with $KMnO_4$, $AgNO_3$ and $(NH_4)_2S_2O_8$, PbO_2, Ag_2O_2, $KClO_3$, $KBrO_3$ or by fuming with $HClO_4$. The reduction of chromium(VI) to chromium(III) can be accomplished with H_2S, SO_2, Fe^{2+}, EtOH, H_2O_2, HBr or HI in acidic solution, and with NH_2OH in alk. soln.

Attack

(a) Chromite. A very wide variety of fluxes has been recommended.[4]

(*i*) Add 0·5 g. chromite to 15 g. $K_2S_2O_7$ in a 50 ml. SiO_2 crucible, fuse for 30 min., cool, add 5 ml. dil. HCl, heat and transfer with hot H_2O to a beaker contg. 20 ml. HCl. Heat, add 200 ml. H_2O and boil. Filter on paper, wash with hot H_2O and fuse the residue with Na_2CO_3. Det. SiO_2 by treatment with HCl and then with HF and H_2SO_4. Fuse the residue with $K_2S_2O_7$ and combine it with the main soln.[2]

(*ii*) Mix 0·5 g. chromite (200 mesh) with 4–5 g. Na_2CO_3, mix, cover with 1 g. Na_2CO_3, fuse over a Méker burner under a stream of O_2.[5]

(*iii*) Treat 0·1–0·15 g. chromite with 8:3 H_2SO_4–H_3PO_4, add $HClO_4$ and heat at 215°C for 5 min., etc.[6]

(*iv*) Fuse 0·2 g. chromite with 0·5 g. soda-lime (or 0·4 g. MgO) and 0·4 g. Na_2CO_3.[7]

(*v*) Mix 0·5 g. chromite with 5–6 g. Na_2O_2 in a heavy-walled porcelain crucible, cover with 1–2 g. Na_2O_2 and fuse for 5 min. at 600–700°C stirring with a Pt wire. Cool, transfer to a 600 ml. beaker, add 200 ml. H_2O and if the soln. is purple, add H_2O_2 and boil for 10 min. Almost neutralize the soln. with dil. H_2SO_4. Filter on paper, wash with H_2O, fuse the residue, etc. Alternatively, after the fusion, cool, add H_2O, neutralize with 20% H_2SO_4, add 2 g. $K_2S_2O_8$ or 3–5 g. $(NH_4)_2S_2O_8$, heat rapidly to 80°C, boil gently, add $\frac{1}{4}$ of the soln. vol. of 20% H_2SO_4, boil for 30 min., cool, etc. Complete dissoln. is difficult.

(*vi*) For detn. of Fe, SiO_2, etc. in chromite, fuse with 4:1 Na_2CO_3–KNO_3.

(b) Ores contg. large amts. of SiO_2. Evap. almost to dryness with HF and H_2SO_4, fuse with a 5–10 g. excess of Na_2CO_3 for 30 min., adding small amts. of KNO_3 to the center of the crucible from time to time. Cool and add hot H_2O. If much Fe is present, dissolve in HCl, pour into hot NaOH and H_2O_2 soln. and filter. H_2O_2 is difficult to remove by boiling unless a trace of MnO_2 or Ni salt is added; alternatively, almost neutralize the soln. with dil. H_2SO_4 (brown) and boil with $KHSO_4$.

(c) Steels. For steel contg. $< 2\%$ Cr, heat with dil. H_2SO_4 and H_3PO_4, and then boil with dil. HNO_3. If much Cr is present, add H_2SO_4, evap. until salts begin to sep., add HNO_3 and apply persulfate oxidation. For high Ni–Cr steels, treat with HCl and HNO_3, add $HClO_4$ and some HF, evap. to fumes and fume for 10 min.; then add H_2O, H_2SO_4, etc. For low Cr steels, dissolve in dil. H_2SO_4, sep. with $NaHCO_3$, ignite, fuse with Na_2O_2 and ext. with H_2O and Na_2O_2 soln.

A general method is as follows.[8] To 1 g. steel, add 10 ml. H_2O and 20 ml. $HClO_4$ (use another 10 ml. for each extra 1 g. sample and 1 ml. for each 10 mg. Cr). Cover the vessel, heat and boil for 10 min. so that the acid condenses about halfway up the wall. Place on a cold plate for 20–30 sec., dip in cold H_2O several times and hold in the H_2O for 10 sec. Add 50–60 ml. H_2O, boil for 5 min., add 5 drops 20% $AgNO_3$, cool rapidly and dil. to 200 ml. with H_2O before applying a $KMnO_4$ titration. If the steel is not dissolved by the above method, dissolve in HNO_3 (d = 1·20), in HCl, or in 2:1 HCl–HNO_3; then add 20 ml. H_2O, 20 ml. HNO_3, evap., add $HClO_4$, etc. Oxidation is complete in presence of $AgNO_3$.[9] If over 0·02% P is present, add 2 drops HCl before boiling the soln., in order to reduce Mn_2O_3. If W is present, see p. 332.

In another method for 1 g. steel,[10] dissolve in 10 ml. HF, add 30 ml. 30% H_2O_2 gradually and use a colorimetric finish; or evap. with $HClO_4$ and use a titrimetric finish. Treatment with 1:1 HCl, or with 1:3 H_2SO_4 with 15% H_2O_2 is satisfactory for steels, and Na_2O_2 fusion is satisfactory for Fe–Cr.

(d) Ni–Cr or Ni–Cr–Fe. Fume with $HClO_4$ and

H_3PO_4, add H_2O, boil, add H_2SO_4, etc. For Cu–Cr, dissolve in HNO_3 contg. a little HF, add H_2SO_4 and evap.

(e) Ti. Dissolve in dil. H_2SO_4 and HF, add HNO_3 and H_3BO_3 and evap.

Separation

It should be noted that complete separation is rarely essential.

Fusion with Na_2O_2 or Na_2CO_3 and KNO_3 followed by leaching with H_2O (plus EtOH if Mn is present) seps. Cr, Al, As, Mo, W, V, U, P from Fe, Ti, Zr, Ni, Co, Mn, Cu, etc. Treatment with Na_2O_2 or H_2O_2 in alk. soln. serves the same purpose.

Cr is sepd. from Fe, Al, etc. by boiling the acidic soln. with $(NH_4)_2S_2O_8$ or $NaBrO_3$ and then adding NH_4OH; sepn. is more complete if PO_4^{3-} is added. Treatment with NH_4OH and NH_4Cl seps. Cr^{3+} from Ni, Mn, etc.; excess reagent dissolves Cr as $[Cr(NH_3)_6]^{3+}$, and $Zn(CrO_2)_2$ or $Mg(CrO_2)_2$ may ppt. Treatment with NH_4OH and $(NH_4)_2CO_3$ seps. Cr from U. Cr can be sepd. from Al, etc. with NaOH.

For sepns. with $Hg_2(NO_3)_2$, see Chapter 38, p. 291.

H_2S in acidic soln. seps. Cr from group II elements; in alk. soln. Cr is sepd. from Mg and the As group, while if tartrate is added, Cr is sepd. from Fe, Ni, Co, Zn.

Extn. with Et_2O from HCl solns. seps. Cr from Fe and Mo.

Extn. with EtOAc seps. Cr from V and Mo.[11] To 40 ml. neutral soln. contg. Cr^{6+}, add 2 drops 1:1 H_2SO_4, 80–150 ml. solvent, 0·5 ml. 3% H_2O_2, shake, sep., repeat the extn. and combine the exts., washing with 10–20 ml. H_2O. Cr is stripped by shaking with 10% KOH.

Extn. with hexone from dil. HCl soln. seps. Cr^{6+} from V (see Chapter 16, p. 137). For extn. with tri-octylphosphine oxide in cyclohexane, see p. 138. Extn. with $CHCl_3$ or pptn. with cupferron seps. Cr from V, Fe, Zr, Ti, Nb, Ta. For extn. of the oxine complex with $CHCl_3$, see Chapter 38, p. 291.

Electrolysis at the Hg-cathode is useful for removal of Cr.

For the possibilities of vaporization as CrO_2Cl_2, and treatment with $Pb(ClO_4)_2$ in $HClO_4$ soln. or treatment with NH_4OAc and Na_2S, see Chapter 38, p. 291.

Evapn. with H_2SO_4 seps. Cr from small amts. of SiO_2.

Determination

Reduction with excess Fe^{2+} and titration with $KMnO_4$ solution is the best method for macro or semimicro amounts of Cr, particularly if V is present, since this can be determined simultaneously. For semimicro amounts of Cr, colorimetric methods are also available for the chromate, dichromate and Cr^{3+} ions. Diphenylcarbazide is the most sensitive reagent for colorimetry.

(a) Redox titrations provide the most popular methods. For detn. of $Cr_2O_7^{2-}$ in 200 ml. dil. $HClO_4$ soln. (see under Attack)[8] add a known vol. of Fe^{2+} soln. (10 g. $FeSO_4 \cdot 7H_2O$ in 1 l. 15% H_3PO_4) and 2 ml. ferroin perchlorate as indicator and titrate rapidly with 0·01–0·1N $KMnO_4$ (standardized against $Na_2C_2O_4$) to the color change from red to faint violet or colorless. When V is present, the red color returns quickly; in this case, add 1–2 ml. Fe^{2+} and titrate with 0·1N $KMnO_4$ to the disappearance of the red color. Record this buret reading as the zero reading for the V detn. Then add 20 ml. H_3PO_4, and 1·3 ml. K_2HPO_4 soln. (5 lb. in 1·1 l. H_2O) for each ml. $HClO_4$ present; if V is present the red color returns and the soln. can be titrated further to a second end-point. The first titration gives Cr or Cr + V, and the second gives V alone. A correction is required for the diln. effect.

NOTES. (1) W in steel requires modification of the above method.[11] Warm 1 g. steel with 20 ml. H_3PO_4 and $HClO_4$ (2:1), add 25 ml. $HClO_4$ and heat for 20 min. after the soln. has become orange at a temp. where $HClO_4$ gently refluxes on the vessel wall. Place momentarily on a cold plate, dip into cold H_2O 2–3 times briefly and then for 1 min. Add 50 ml. H_2O, boil for 3 min., add 5 drops 20% $AgNO_3$, cool, dil. to 200 ml. with H_2O, add 50 ml. Fe^{2+} soln. (15 g. $FeSO_4 \cdot 7H_2O$ in 950 ml. H_2O and 50 ml. 55% $HClO_4$) and 2 ml. ferroin indicator and titrate with 0·1N $KMnO_4$ until the red color starts to fade. Complete the titration rapidly with 0·01N $KMnO_4$ to an amber shade. Titrate an equal vol. of Fe^{2+} soln. similarly. The difference between the amts. corresponds to Cr + V + Mn^{3+}. Dil. to 325 ml. with H_2O, add 20 ml. H_3PO_4 and 40–45 ml. K_2HPO_4 soln., add indicator to give a red color and titrate with 0·01N $KMnO_4$ to colorless. Det. Mn by another method and calc. the amts. of Cr and V. This method is less accurate than that described above.

(2) In an alternative method,[12] treat the sample with 20–25 ml. $HClO_4$, etc., cool rapidly, add 25 ml. H_2O, boil for 3 min. and dil. to 200–300 ml. with H_2O. Cool rapidly, add 15 ml. H_3PO_4 and a known excess of Fe^{2+} soln. (0·05N in 20 ml. H_2SO_4 and 980 ml. H_2O) followed by ferroin, cool and titrate rapidly with 0·05N $KMnO_4$ until the soln. remains green for 1 min. (Cr + V). Add solid NaOAc (if a heavy ppt. of $FePO_4$ appears, remove it with H_2SO_4), heat to 50°C, add 1 drop of indicator if necessary and titrate further to a blue-green shade (V).

If much Cr is present, oxidation with $HClO_4$ may be incomplete. Oxidation with $KMnO_4$ is liable to give high results. If much Mn is present, it is best to oxidize with $KBrO_3$. If oxidation is done with $(NH_4)_2S_2O_8$, $AgNO_3$ is not necessary if the final acidity is below 1·8 ml. H_2SO_4/100 ml.; the contribution of $(NH_4)_2S_2O_8$ to the acidity (theoretical 0·242 ml./1 g. for 90% decompn.) must be considered. If the final acidity is over 1·6 ml. H_2SO_4/100 ml., formation of MnO_2 does not occur even when H_3PO_4 is absent.[13] Many oxidation methods have been recommended.

$AgNO_3$ and $(NH_4)_2S_2O_8$ are used as follows.[1] To 300 ml. soln. contg. 15–18 ml. H_2SO_4 and 3 ml. HNO_3, add 2·5% $AgNO_3$ (10 mg./10 mg. Cr) and 20 ml. 10% $(NH_4)_2S_2O_8$, boil, etc. If much Cr is present, then a violet color or a darkening of the clear green color indicates the end-point of the final titration. Interference from Mn can be prevented by oxidation in presence of H_3PO_4, addn. of 5 ml. 1:3 HCl or NaN_3, and boiling for 10 min.; alternatively, decompn. with $NaNO_2$ and urea is used. This method has been applied to steels and many alloys.[14] The optimum concn. of H_2SO_4 is said to be 19–20 ml./300 ml.[15]

With $KMnO_4$ as oxidant,[12] boil 300 ml. soln. contg. 3 ml. H_2SO_4 and 15 ml. H_3PO_4, add 2% $KMnO_4$ to give a purple color, boil for 2 min. and add 0·1*M* NaN_3 to the boiling soln. gradually until it becomes clear. Then boil for 5 min., add 10 ml. H_2SO_4, cool below 15°C, etc. W and V interfere.

Other methods include boiling with PbO_2; or treatment with $KClO_3$ or $KBrO_3$ in acidic soln.; or boiling with $AgNO_3$ in 1*N* NaOH soln.[16] Fusion with Na_2CO_3 and KNO_3 is suitable for small amts. of Cr, and fusion with Na_2O_2 for large amts.

Many alternative modifications of the above titration have been suggested. V interferes in all the methods described below.

Direct titration with Fe^{2+} soln. after oxidn., as on p. 331, is possible, the ferroin indicator being added near the end-point.[6] It is possible to titrate Cr alone after oxidation with $HClO_4$ and then titrate Cr + Ce after oxidation with $K_2S_2O_8$ and Ag^+ catalyst.[17] Diphenylamine can be used instead of ferroin in direct titration with Fe^{2+} soln. (see Chapter 38, p. 292); this has been applied in steel analysis.[14] Phenylanthranilic acid indicator may be used after oxidation of Cr with bismuthate.[18] Diphenylamine can serve in the back-titration of excess Fe^{2+} with $K_2Cr_2O_7$ soln. (Scott and Furman[1]). Fe^{2+} can also be back-titrated with Ce^{4+} soln.[19]

Potentiometric methods have been used in analysis of steels and metals[14] and coulometric titration is another possibility.[20] Photometric titration at 350 mμ is suitable for detn. of Cr and V in steels.[21]

Titration of Cr^{6+} with Ti^{3+} or hydroquinone soln. in presence of diphenylamine indicator has been proposed (see Chapter 38, p. 292).

If much Cr is present, reduction with As^{3+} is preferable[11] to Fe^{2+}. Oxidize the soln. with 25 ml. 55% $HClO_4$, dil. to 50 ml. with H_2O, add 6 drops 0·01*M* OsO_4 and then add 0·01–0·03*N* As^{3+} to the color change from yellow to violet, adding 2 ml. 0·03*N* soln. (or its equivalent) in excess. Dil. to 200 ml. with H_2O, add 1 ml. ferroin perchlorate indicator and titrate with 0·01*N* $KMnO_4$ from red to colorless. When the red color returns, titrate to colorless and subtract a blank. V does not interfere in this method. For a simultaneous detn. of Cr and V,[22] take a soln. contg. < 75 mg. Cr^{6+} in 1–2*N* H_2SO_4; add 5–8 ml. H_3PO_4 if Fe is present, excess As^{3+} soln. contg. 10 g. NaCl/l., and 1–2 drops 0·0025*N* KI. Titrate with $KMnO_4$ soln. to det. Cr. Remove the MnO_4^- color with As^{3+} and titrate with Fe^{2+} soln. using diphenylbenzidine indicator to det. V. KBr can replace KI as catalyst in the above method.[13]

For a simultaneous detn. of Mn and Cr, see Chapter 37, p. 285.

Direct titration with As^{3+} soln. is also feasible.[23] Add 5–6 ml. H_2SO_4 to the Cr^{6+} soln. and dil. to 50–60 ml. with H_2O. Cool, add 5 ml. catalyst (20 mg. KI and 5 mg. $MnSO_4$ in 250 ml. H_2O) and 1 drop 1% diphenylamine in H_2SO_4 and titrate with As^{3+} soln. (4·948 g. As_2O_3 in H_2O contg. 5 g. NaOH, boiled, dild., mixed with 10 ml. H_2SO_4 and dild. to 1 l. with H_2O) until the soln. remains pale green for 5 min. Fe interference is prevented by NaF addn.; Hg and SCN^- interfere.

Cr^{3+} in 0·2–2·5*N* HCl soln. can also be detd.[24] by reduction with Zn–Hg and titration with $KMnO_4$ soln. under CO_2. Similar methods are available but SO_4^{2-} interferes in all of them. Titration with $K_3Fe(CN)_6$ using cacotheline indicator has been suggested (see Chapter 29, p. 215).

NaOBr is also applicable;[25] treat the neutral soln. of Cr^{3+} with 10 ml. 1*N* NaOH and excess 0·1*N* NaOBr and back-titrate after 5 min. with oxine-contg. H_2O_2 using 0·5% lucigenin indicator.

(b) Diphenylcarbazide provides the best colorimetric procedure.[26, 27, 28] For 0–16 μg. Cr in 10 ml. 0·5*N* H_2SO_4, add 0·5 ml. 1*N* $KMnO_4$, place on a steam-bath for 20 min. (add more $KMnO_4$ if the color fades) and add 5% NaN_3 at a rate of 1 drop/10 sec. until the brown color disappears, followed by 3–5 drops in excess. Cool rapidly, filter if turbid, transfer to a 25 ml. measuring flask and add 1 ml. reagent soln. (10·0 g. phthalic anhydride in 150 ml. EtOH warmed and cooled; mix with 0·625 g. diphenylcarbazide in 50 ml. EtOH, dil. to 250 ml. with EtOH and store in a brown bottle). After 1 min., add 2·5 ml. 4*M* NaH_2PO_4, dil. to 25 ml. with H_2O and measure at 546 mμ within 30 min.

NOTES. (1) Interferences are 5 mg. Fe or Cu, 1 mg. Mo and 0·5 mg. V; these metals cause a +ve error if the amt. of Cr is small and a −ve error if it is large. The interference is avoided by extn. of the oxine complexes with $CHCl_3$; Fe can be sepd. with NaOH. Hg interference is prevented by NaCl and that of MoO_4^{2-} with $C_2O_4^{2-}$.

(2) The method has been applied to a variety of metals[26] and alloys[14] as well as to biol. materials.[29]

(3) Results are said to be better with 0·5% reagent in 1:9 AcOH and in $HClO_4$ media.[13] Oxidation of Cr^{3+} with Ag_2O_2 in H_2SO_4 soln.[30] or with $KBrO_3$ [31] can precede the above method.

(4) For detn. of Cr in rocks[27, 31] decomp. by the method described for V (p. 293). Neutralize a 10 ml. aliquot with 4*N* H_2SO_4 (pH 5, the required amt. being already known from the detn. of V); add 0·1 ml. oxine soln. and ext. 3 times with $CHCl_3$ (previously shaken with a soln. contg. 0·35 mg. $K_2Cr_2O_7$/ml.). If V is <Cr, this extn. can be omitted. Filter on moist paper, make slightly alk. with NaOH, add 0·05–0·1 g. Na_2O_2 and boil for 10 min. Add some MnO_2, boil, cool, filter on paper washed with 20% Na_2CO_3, wash, add 1·5 ml. 4*N* H_2SO_4, etc.

(c) Chromate or dichromate can be measured colorimetrically without addnl. reagent.[1, 27] For a soln. contg. 5–100 μg. Cr/ml., measure the yellow color at

365–370 mμ after fusion of the sample with 10:1 Na_2CO_3–KNO_3, extn. with H_2O, and filtration on asbestos. U and Ce interfere; EtOH bleaches $KMnO_4$. Cu and Fe form colloids which interfere; this is prevented by digestion for 1 hr. on a steam-bath. Low Cr steels can be analyzed.[14]

For detn. of Cr in steel[32] heat a 0·5 g. sample with 20 ml. mixed acids (600 ml. $HClO_4$ and 300 ml. H_3PO_4/l.), fume for 3 min. (add H_2O if the fumes become brown), cool, add H_2O, cool, dil. to 100 ml. with H_2O and measure at 440 mμ using an aliquot with some Fe^{2+} added as reference soln. This method is said to be 5 times more sensitive if $Fe(ClO_4)_3$ is present.[33]

Again, many oxidants have been applied. Oxidation with Br_2 is suitable[34] in alk. soln.; acidify with H_2SO_4, boil, cool, add 1·5 ml. H_3PO_4, dil. to 25 ml. with H_2O and measure in a 5 cm. cell after 1·25 hr. Other oxidants are KIO_4 (see Chapter 37, p. 286), $(NH_4)_2S_2O_8$ with $AgNO_3$, $KMnO_4$ and $NaBiO_3$ with $AgNO_3$.[35]

(d) NH_4OH is suitable for the gravimetric detn. of Cr^{3+} in acidic soln.[36] Boil with NH_4Cl and NH_4OH for 10 min., filter on a Gooch crucible, wash, ignite in H_2, or above 1000°C in air, cool rapidly and weigh as Cr_2O_3.

Pyridine can replace NH_4OH in the above procedure.[37] If little Cr is present, tannin should be added.[38] The compn. of the ppt. may be indefinite if it is ignited in air. Cr^{6+} can be reduced with H_2S, SO_2, NH_2OH, EtOH, etc. Hexamine,[37] thiosemicarbazide,[39] N_2H_4·H_2SO_4 and $C_6H_5N_2H_3$ can act as both reductants and precipitants.

(e) Miscellaneous gravimetric methods. $Ba(OAc)_2$ or $BaCl_2$ ppts. Cr^{6+} from neutral soln.[36] Boil the soln., add 10 ml. 10% reagent very slowly and boil for 2–3 hr.; filter on a Gooch crucible, wash with 10% EtOH, heat above 300°C (> 60°C) and weigh as $BaCrO_4$ (repeat the ignition if the ppt. is yellow-green). Interferences are NO_3^-, ClO_3^-, SO_4^{2-}, VO_3^-, AcO^-, etc.

$Pb(NO_3)_2$ can be used in acidic soln.[40] Boil 200 ml. soln. contg. 10–15 ml. 2*N* HNO_3, add reagent (3–5 g. $Pb(NO_3)_2$/30 ml.) and leave for 12 hr. Filter on a G3 crucible, wash with cold, then hot H_2O, dry at 160–180°C (91–904°C) and weigh as $PbCrO_4$. Cl^- interferes but Ba, Sr, Ca, Fe, Al, Cd, Cu, Mn, Zn, Mg, K, Na, NH_4^+ and AcO^- do not. In an alternative method,[41] treat the neutral soln. with 10 ml. acetate buffer, 10 ml. 3·5% $Pb(NO_3)_2$, $KBrO_3$, etc. (see Chapter 20, p. 159).

$Hg_2(NO_3)_2$ is also applicable.[36] Boil the neutral soln., add 2 g. Na_2CO_3 and a small excess of reagent (satd. $Hg_2(NO_3)_2$ soln. mixed 10:1 with HNO_3), boil, filter on a Gooch crucible, wash with hot H_2O and dry below 180°C (52–256°C) before weighing as Hg_2CrO_4, or ignite above 1000°C (>671°C) and weigh as Cr_2O_3.

H_2SeO_3 is suitable for < 0·1 g. Cr^{3+} in 50 ml. neutral soln.[42] Add 15 ml. 33·3% NH_4NO_3, 10 ml. 10% NH_4OAc and 20 ml. 10% reagent and neutralize with NH_4OH to methyl orange. After 12–24 hr., filter on Whatman No. 42 paper, wash with a soln. of 3 ml. 33·3% NH_4NO_3 and 2 ml. 10% NH_4OAc in 120–140 ml. H_2O, dry at 100°C, ignite and weigh as Cr_2O_3.

Oxine (2% in 2*N* AcOH) ppts. Cr^{3+}. Add NH_4OH to 10 ml. soln.[43] until a ppt. appears, remove the ppt. with H_2SO_4, heat to 70°C and add 20 ml. reagent, 20 ml. 1*N* NaOH and 20 ml. 4*N* NH_4Cl. Boil for 1 min., filter on a glass crucible, wash with hot H_2O, dry at 105–110°C (70–156°C) and weigh as $Cr(C_9H_6ON)_3$.

Either oxine or 8-hydroxyquinaldine can be applied colorimetrically.[44] Add Fe^{3+} (> 2 Cr), ppt. with reagent, filter and dry the ppt. Dissolve in $CHCl_3$, add an equal vol. of C_6H_6, pass through an alumina column and measure at 425 or 410 mμ. Al, Co, V do not interfere with the 8-hydroxyquinaldine method. Fe, U, Ti, Ce, Ni, Cu, Mo, Mn, Th, Zn, Ga, In, Tl do not interfere in either method.

KF ppts. Cr^{3+} at 70–80°C on addn. of hot reagent soln.[45] After 15–20 min., the ppt. is filtered, washed with 2% reagent, EtOH and Et_2O, air-dried and weighed as K_2CrF_5·H_2O.

(f) Iodometric titration has been applied in numerous modifications. The classical method[46] is as follows: to 100 ml. Cr^{6+} soln. contg. 20 ml. 1*N* HCl or H_2SO_4, add 2 g. KI, place in the dark for 10 min., add starch indicator and titrate with $Na_2S_2O_3$ soln. Cu, As, V, Mo interfere; Fe interference is avoided by H_3PO_4 addn.

For 1 mg. Cr^{6+} in 10 ml. neutral soln.,[47] add 10 ml. 4*N* H_2SO_4, 10 ml. 0·001*N* $AgNO_3$, dil. to 100 ml. with H_2O, pass CO_2 through the soln. for 30 min., add 1 g. KI, place in the dark for 30 min., add 3 ml. starch and titrate with 0·01*N* $Na_2S_2O_3$ soln., comparing with a soln. contg. an equal amt. of $AgNO_3$ under orange light.

For 0·2–3·5 mg. Cr^{3+} in 20 ml. soln.,[48] make the soln. alk. with NaOH, add 2–6 drops 3% H_2O_2, boil, cool, add 3–7 ml. Cl_2 water and shake. After several min., add 1–2 ml. 5% KCN, shake, leave for 2 min., dil. to 40 ml. with H_2O, add 10 ml. 50% H_2SO_4, 2 g. $KHCO_3$ in a large lump and 0·2 g. KI and titrate after 5 min.

NOTES. (1) Fe and Cu do not interfeɪe if EDTA is added.[49]
(2) The end-point is not very sharp. It is said to be better to use C_6H_6 as indicator.[50]
(3) It is possible to det. Cr and V simultaneously (Scott and Furman[1]). To 100 ml. soln. contg. Cr^{6+}, V^{5+} and 15–20 ml. HCl, add 1–2 g. KBr and distil while passing H_2 through the soln. Collect the distillate in alk. soln. contg. KI, acidify slightly with HCl, titrate with 0·1*N* $Na_2S_2O_3$ until colorless, add starch and back-titrate with 0·1*N* I_2 ($V^{5+} \rightarrow V^{4+}$ and $Cr^{6+} \rightarrow Cr^{3+}$). Then remove air by passing H_2 through the soln., add 2 g. KI, 10–15 ml. HCl and 3 ml. H_3PO_4 and distil under a stream of H_2 until 10 ml. soln. remains. Complete the titration as before ($V^{4+} \rightarrow V^{3+}$, Cr^{3+}).

(g) Methyl orange can be used in daylight in a direct titration with $C_2O_4^{2-}$ and Fe^{3+} as catalysts.[51] Dil. 0·1–1·0 ml. 0·001*N* $K_2Cr_2O_7$ to 2 ml. with H_2O, add 0·1 ml. 10% Na_2CO_3, 0·1 ml. 5% $FeCl_3$, 0·5 ml. H_3PO_4

and 0·5 ml. satd. $Na_2C_2O_4$ soln. and titrate with 0·001% methyl orange in clear daylight, which catalyzes the reaction. Interferences are large amts. of Mo, V and Mn; Al, Cu, Ni, Zn, Ca can be tolerated.

(h) Cr^{3+} like Cr^{6+} can be detd. colorimetrically by its own color.[52] For 16–24 mg. Cr^{3+} in 150 ml. 1:3 H_2SO_4 soln., measure at 580 mμ. Ni can be corrected for but Co interferes. H_3PO_4 prevents interference of Fe. Al, Mo, W, Mn^{2+}, V, Ti do not interfere. Cu, Pb can be removed by reduction with Zn; subsequent oxidation of Mo, W, etc. with H_2O_2 is then needed.

(i) EDTA can be applied colorimetrically or titrimetrically. For colorimetric detn.[53] of 0·1–8 mg. Cr^{3+} in 30–50 ml. acetate-buffered soln. at pH 2–4, add 5 ml. 5% EDTA, boil for 5 min., cool, dil. to 100 ml. with H_2O and measure the blue-violet color at 550 mμ. No interference arises from Zn, Al, Mn, Mg, H_2O_2; Fe, Co, Ni must be sepd. with KOH and H_2O_2, the soln. neutralized, and 2 ml. 0·1% $MnSO_4$ added before proceeding as above.

Direct titration of Cr^{3+} with EDTA is not feasible. If excess EDTA is added to the pH 3 soln. and the soln. is boiled and cooled, back-titration with $FeCl_3$ soln. using Bindschedler's green as indicator is satisfactory.[54] Alternative back-titrations include Zn^{2+} with eriogreen B–congo red indicator,[55] Fe^{3+} with a potentiometric end-point[55] and Ni^{2+} with murexide indicator.[56]

(j) Miscellaneous colorimetric methods. $CoSO_4$ and EDTA can be used for detn. of 5–30 μg. Cr^{6+} (see Chapter 35, p. 272).

Chromotropic acid allows detn. of 0·8–400 μg. Cr^{6+} in 100 ml. alk. soln.[57] Add 2 ml. H_3PO_4, 8 ml. H_2SO_4 and 2 ml. 1% reagent and measure the reddish color after 15 min. V in amts. greater than or equal to Cr interferes. The chrome dyeing of wool can be measured with Chromotrope F4B.[58]

p-Phenetidine–HCl is suitable[59] for about 0·1 ml. 0·1*N* $K_2Cr_2O_7$. Add 0·3 ml. reagent (10 ml. 1% *p*-phenetidine–HCl and 1 ml. 0·5*N* HCl) and dil. to 100 ml. with H_2O after 1 min. Interferences are SiO_2, PO_4^{3-}, oxidants and reductants. Aniline,[59] α-naphthylamine[59] and *o*-dianisidine[60] can be applied similarly.

$H_2C_2O_4$ can be used for 0·01–0·05 g. Cr in 25 ml. soln.[61] Add 2 g. reagent, boil for 3 min., cool, dil. to 50 ml. with H_2O and measure at 420 or 560 mμ. Fe does not interfere at 520 mμ.

H_2O_2 may be used for 50–250 μg. Cr^{6+} in 5 ml. soln. at pH 1·7.[62] Add 6 ml. EtOAc, cool to 10°C, add 3% H_2O_2, shake for 30 sec., and measure at 580 mμ after 2 min. Fe, Mn, V, W, Mo do not interfere.

Na-*o*-aminophenyldithiocarbamate is sensitive enough to allow detn. of 0·1–1·0 μg Cr^{6+}/ml. in 0·03–0·07*N* HCl or HNO_3 or 0·02–0·08*N* H_2SO_4 soln.,[63] the yellow color being measured at 480 mμ. No interference arises from moderate amts. of Fe, Co, V, Ag, Hg or from Ni, Mn, Cu, Pb, Zn, Cd, U, Mo, Ti, etc.

(k) Flame photometry can be applied for $<$ 20 μg. Cr/ml. hexone after extn. from aq. soln. with this solvent.[64] An O_2–C_2H_2 flame is used with measurement at 357·9, 359·4 and 425·4 mμ; this is 50 times more sensitive than in aq. soln. Up to 200 μg. Cr/ml. can be detd. with measurement at 425 or 427·5 mμ.[65] Fe, Mn, Al, Co, Cu do not interfere.

References

1. HILLEBRAND and LUNDELL, 408 (524); SCOTT and FURMAN, 282; KIMURA, 197; PIGOTT, 142.
2. VAN DER WALT, C. F. J., *Analyst*, **63**, 176 (1938).
3. UDY, M. J., *Chromium*, Vols. I–II, Reinhold, New York (1956).
4. MELLOR and THOMPSON, 527 (1938).
5. MALHOTRA, P. D., *Analyst*, **79**, 785 (1954).
6. SMITH, G. F. and GETZ, C. A., *Ind. Eng. Chem., Anal. Ed.*, **9**, 518 (1937).
7. USATENKO, YU. I. and KLIMKOVICH, E. A., *Ukrain. Khim. Zhur.*, **22**, 670 (1956).
8. Chemists of U.S. Steel Corporation: *Sampling and Analysis of Carbon and Alloy Steels*, 141 (1938).
9. LYNN, S. and MASON, D. M., *Anal. Chem.*, **24**, 1855 (1952).
10. KAWAMURA, K., *Japan Analyst*, **2**, 417 (1953).
11. FOSTER, M. D., *U.S. Geol. Survey Bull.*, No. 950, 15 (1946).
12. WILLARD, H. H. and YOUNG, P., *Ind. Eng. Chem., Anal. Ed.*, **6**, 48 (1934).
13. PIGOTT, 147 ff.
14. A.S.T.M., 104 ff.
15. DÖRING, TH., *Z. anal. Chem.*, **111**, 49 (1937/38).
16. KOMATSU, S. and HIROAKI, Z., *J. Chem. Soc. Japan*, **77**, 1166 (1956).
17. BANKS, C. V. and O'LAUGHLIN, J. W., *Anal. Chem.*, **28**, 1338 (1956).
18. AGAFONOV, P. F., *Zhur. Anal. Khim.*, **11**, 752 (1956).
19. RODDEN, C. J. and WARF, J. C., *Natl. Nuclear Energy Ser.*, Div. VIII, **1**, 445 (1950).
20. MEIER, D. J., *et al.*, *J. Am. Chem. Soc.*, **71**, 2340 (1949) (Cu^+); MEITES, L., *Anal. Chem.*, **24** 1057 (1952) (Fe^{2+}).
21. MILES, J. W. and ENGLES, D. T., *Anal. Chem.*, **27**, 1996 (1955).
22. KOLTHOFF, I. M. and SANDELL, E. B., *Ind. Eng. Chem., Anal. Ed.*, **2**, 140 (1930).
23. SZABÓ, Z. and CSÁNYI, L., *Anal. Chem.*, **21**, 1144 (1949).
24. ISHIMARU, S., *Kagaku-Zikken-Gaku*, **X**, 36 (1942).
25. ERDEY, L. and BUZÁS I. *Acta Chim. Acad. Sci. Hung.*, **6**, 77 (1955).
26. SALTZMAN, B. E., *Anal. Chem.*, **24**, 1016 (1952); also see CAHNMANN, H. J. and BISEN, R., *ibid.*, 1341; NORWITZ, G. and CODELL, M., *Anal. Chim. Acta*, **9**, 546 (1953) (in Ti); KITAGAWA, H. and AKIMOTO, Y., *Japan Analyst*, **4**, 144 (1955) (in Cu metal).
27. SANDELL, 258 ff.
28. WELCHER, **III**, 433.
29. GROGAN, CH, H., *et al.*, *Anal. Chem.*, **27**, 983 (1955).
30. NAKANISHI, M., *Bull. Chem. Soc. Japan*, **23**, 165 (1950).
31. MURAKAMI, Y., *Bull. Chem. Soc. Japan*, **23**, 157 (1950).
32. WOOD, A. A. R., *Analyst*, **78**, 54 (1953).
33. SINGER, L. and CHAMBERS W. A., *Ind. Eng. Chem., Anal. Ed.*, **16**, 507 (1944).
34. SHERWOOD, R. M. and CHAPMAN, JR., F. W., *Anal. Chem.*, **27**, 88 (1955).

35. KIYOTA, H. and YAMAMOTO, T., *J. Chem. Soc. Japan*, **76**, 1746, 1749 (1955).
36. SCOTT and FURMAN, 286.
37. WELCHER, **III**, 65, 124.
38. SCHOELLER, 161.
39. WELCHER, **IV**, 191.
40. TSCHAWDAROW, D. and TSCHAWDAROWA, N., *Z. anal. Chem.*, **110**, 348 (1937).
41. HOFFMAN, A. and BRANDT, W. W., *Anal. Chem.*, **28**, 1487 (1956).
42. JÍLEK, A. and KOT'A, J., *Chem. listy*, **32**, 30 (1938).
43. WELCHER, **I**, 302.
44. BLAIR, A. J. and PANTONY, D. A., *Anal. Chim. Acta*, **14**, 545 (1956).
45. TALIPOV, SH. T. and FEDOROVA, T. I., *Trudy Sredneaziat. Gosudarst. Univ. (Tashkent), Khim. Nauki*, **40**, No. 5, 57 (1953).
46. KOLTHOFF and BELCHER, *Volumetric Analysis*, Vol. III, 237, 332 (1957).
47. HAGEN, S. K., *Z. anal. Chem.*, **95**, 414 (1933).
48. SCHULEK, E. and SZAKÁCS, M., *Acta Chim. Acad. Sci. Hung.*, **4**, 457 (1954).
49. PŘIBIL, R., *et al.*, *Collection Czechoslov. Chem. Communs.*, **16**, 573 (1951).
50. WA, N., *J. Chem. Soc. Japan*, **42**, 454 (1921).
51. ALMÁSSY, GY. and KOVÁCS, E., *Acta Chim. Acad. Sci. Hung.*, **8**, 1 (1955).
52. KASLINE, C. T. and MELLON, M. G., *Ind. Eng. Chem., Anal. Ed.*, **8**, 463 (1936); also see KAHN, M. D. and MAYER, F. J., *Anal. Chem.*, **26**, 1371 (1954) (in steel and bronze); MIZOGUCHI, S., *Japan Analyst*, **5**, 452 (1956).
53. PŘIBIL, R. and KLUBALOVÁ, J., *Collection Czechoslov. Chem. Communs.*, **15**, 42 (1950); CELLINI, R. F. and VALIENTE, E. A., *Anales real soc. españ. fís. y quím. (Madrid)*, **B51**, 47 (1955); NIELSCH, W. and BÖLTZ, G., *Metall*, **10**, 916 (1956) (in Cu–Cr); USATENKO, YU. I. and KLIMKOVICH, E. A., *Zavodskaya Lab.*, **22**, 279 (1956) (in chromite).
54. WEHBER, P., *Z. anal. Chem.*, **150**, 186 (1956).
55. DOPPLER, G. and PATZAK, R., *Z. anal. Chem.*, **152**, 45 (1956).
56. WEINER, R. and NEY, E., *Z. anal. Chem.*, **157**, 104 (1957).
57. YOE, 165; WELCHER, **I**, 246; BAKER, E. H., *Foundry*, **75**, 92, 182 (1947).
58. WELCHER, **IV**, 558.
59. WELCHER, **II**, 269, 410.
60. BUSCARÓNS, F. and ARTIGAS, J., *Anal. Chim. Acta*, **16**, 452 (1957).
61. THEIS, E. R., *et al.*, *J. Am. Leather Chemists' Assoc.*, **41**, 449 (1946).
62. GLASNER, A. and STEINBERG, M., *Anal. Chem.*, **27**, 2008 (1955); also see CASTAGNOU, R. and BUJARD, J., *Bull. trav. soc. pharm. Bordeaux*, **88**, 49 (1950).
63. GAGLIARDI, E. and HAAS, W., *Z. anal. Chem.*, **147**, 321 (1955).
64. BRYAN, H. and DEAN, J. A., *Anal. Chim. Acta*, **29**, 1289 (1957).
65. IKEDA, S., *J. Chem. Soc. Japan*, **78, 1228** (1957).

46

THORIUM

The principal sources for this chapter are given in ref. 1. The analytical aspects of thorium chemistry have been reviewed.[2] Important information is given by Rodden and Warf[3] and by Grimaldi.[4] A paper has been published on the determination of impurities in thorium.[5] A selective bibliography covering 1951–1955 is available.[6]

It should be noted that thorium compounds usually dissolve slowly in solvents. $ThCl_4$ is volatile, hence any precipitate which is to be ignited must be thoroughly washed previously. $Th(C_2O_4)_2$ is soluble in oxalate-containing alkaline solutions and in mineral acids. $Th(OH)_4$ is rather soluble in alkaline solutions containing carbonate. Unfortunately, none of these properties can be utilized for the separation of thorium from rare earths. Care is required in mineral analysis, since He is usually present.

Attack

(a) Monazite and thorianite. Several methods are available.

Heat 50 g. mineral with 75 ml. H_2SO_4 above 250°C (slight evolution of fumes) for 5–8 hr. Then pour into 4 vols of ice-cold H_2O, keeping the temp. below 20°C. Alternatively,[7] boil for 1–1·25 hr. with 200 ml. $HClO_4$, cool slightly, add 50 ml. $HClO_4$, 300 ml. H_2O, and 18 g. $N_2H_4{\cdot}2HCl$ in small portions, digest for 1 hr., cool, add 3 g. siliceous earth, filter on a 15 cm. paper and wash with 1:3 $HClO_4$. Transfer the paper to a beaker, decant several times with 1:3 $HClO_4$ through a small paper, combine, dil. to 1 l. with 1:3 $HClO_4$ and apply the methyl oxalate sepn.

The following method is suggested for monazite.[8] Boil a 1 g. sample with 5 ml. HNO_3 and 30 ml. $HClO_4$ in a 250 ml. Erlenmeyer flask, fume for 1–1·5 hr., cool, add 15 ml. H_2O and 5 ml. 3% H_2O_2 and warm; if dissoln. is difficult, add 5–10 ml. HCl. Then cool, filter and wash with 1:3 HNO_3. Evap. the filtrate to fumes, add 50 ml. H_2O and 5 ml. 3% H_2O_2, warm; add 100 ml. H_2O, NH_4OH until a ppt. appears and then 10 ml. HCl. After 5 min., add 6 g. methyl oxalate, stir mechanically and digest at 70–80°C for 30 min. after the appearance of the ppt. Then add a hot soln. of 8 g. $H_2C_2O_4$ in 200 ml. H_2O, warm for 30 min., cool, adjust to pH 0·7–0·9, filter and wash with cold 2% $H_2C_2O_4$ contg. HCl to give pH 1·0. Return the ppt. to the original beaker, add 20 ml. HNO_3 and 5 ml. $HClO_4$ and heat slowly to fumes. Cool, add 200 ml. H_2O and 6 g. methyl oxalate, warm for 30 min., add 8 g. $H_2C_2O_4$ in 200 ml. H_2O, warm for 30 min., cool, filter on paper and wash. Treat the ppt. with 20 ml. HNO_3 and 10 ml. $HClO_4$ and continue as in the previous step, finally detg. Th and sepg. it from rare earths with tetrachlorophthalic acid or urea (see p. 339).

For a 1 g. sample of thorianite,[9] fuse with 8 g. $KHSO_4$, ext. with a hot soln. contg. 5 g. $(NH_4)_2C_2O_4$, filter and wash with hot 1% $(NH_4)_2C_2O_4$. Ignite the residue, add HCl, NH_4OH and hexamine, filter, dissolve in hot dil. HCl, filter, almost neutralize the filtrate with NH_4OH, combine it with the bulk soln. and acidify with HCl.

For monazite or rare earth minerals, fuse 0·5 g. with 0·5 g. NaF and 10 g. $K_2S_2O_7$ and leach with 1:10 HCl.

(b) Thorite and silicates which contain little rare earths. These are treated as follows: heat with HCl for 1–2 hr. near the b.p., fuse the residue with $K_2S_2O_7$, leach with HCl and combine.

ThO_2 can be dissolved in hot H_2SO_4.

Separation

HF gives a sepn. of Th and rare earths from most other elements and from PO_4^{3-}. Stir 5–50 mg. Th soln. in a celluloid tube with reagent, centrifuge and wash with 1:5 HNO_3. When only small amts. of Th are present,[3] treat the soln. with 10 ml. HF, evap. to 8 ml., add 30 ml. H_2O, warm and add 10 ml. $HgNO_3$ (0·95 g. in 100 ml. H_2O contg. 3 drops HNO_3) and 1 ml. 7% v/v HCl. Leave to cool for 4 hr., filter on Whatman No. 40 paper and wash with two 10 ml. portions of 5% HF and twice with H_2O. Place the ppt. and paper in a 20 ml. Pt crucible, heat below 500°C, add a little H_2O and 8 ml. HF, place for 20 min. on a steam-bath, dil. to 40 ml. with H_2O and reppt.

Satd. $H_2C_2O_4$ soln. seps. Th and rare earths from other metals of groups III and from PO_4^{3-}. Pour 1 l. of sample soln. contg. $< 4\%$ HCl into a 10–40-fold excess of reagent and filter after 15 hr. Neutralize the filtrate with NH_4OH, add 10–15 ml. HCl and $H_2C_2O_4$, filter after 15 hr., ignite, dissolve in HCl, ppt. with $H_2C_2O_4$ and combine with the main ppt. Alternatively, mix 100 ml. sulfate soln. with 15 ml. HNO_3, pour into hot concd. reagent soln. and filter after at least 6 hr. Treat the filtrate with 25 ml. HNO_3, evap. to 15 ml., add 10 g. $H_2C_2O_4$, dil. to 200 ml. with H_2O and filter after at least 6 hr. Interferences are alkali metal oxalates, Ca, Sr, Ba and Zr. The optimum pH for the sepn. is blue to methyl violet.

For sepn. with methyl oxalate see above. An easily filtered ppt. can be obtained as follows.[9] Almost neutralize the soln. with NH_4OH (avoid a permanent ppt.), dil. to 100 ml. with H_2O, heat to boiling, add a hot soln. of 4 g. $(NH_4)_2C_2O_4$ and HCl dropwise until a turbidity appears followed by 10 ml. 1:1 HCl in excess. Filter after 12 hr. Extn. of the bisulfate melt with hot $(NH_4)_2$-C_2O_4 soln. seps. the bulk of Th from small amts. of rare earths.[9]

Extn. with mesityl oxide seps. Th from all elements except U, V, Zr.[10] Heat 0·2 g. monazite (200-mesh) with 3 g. KHF_2 for 3–5 min. on a Méker burner, add 100 ml. H_2O, 20 ml. HF and place on a steam-bath for 30 min. Centrifuge and wash with H_2O and a few ml. HF. Transfer the ppt. to a mixt. of 19 g. $Al(NO_3)_3 \cdot 9H_2O$ and 2·5 ml. HNO_3 with a min. amt. of H_2O, heat and evap. to 20 ml. if necessary. Transfer to a separatory funnel, add 20 ml. mesityl oxide and shake. (A white ppt. at the boundary is unimportant and can be removed by addn. of up to 1 ml. HNO_3.) Sep. and ext. again with 10 ml. solvent. Combine the exts., wash thrice with 20 ml. portions of a mixt. of 30 ml. HNO_3 and 380 g. $Al(NO_3)_3 \cdot 9H_2O$ in 170 ml. H_2O; then strip Th by shaking twice with H_2O. Combine the aq. layers, evap. with HNO_3 and $HClO_4$, dissolve in dil. HCl, dil. to 200 ml. and take a 25 ml. aliquot for detn. by the thoron method (p. 340).

Extn. with cyclohexanone takes up Th, UO_2^{2+}, Ce^{3+}, 2·2% Fe^{3+}, 2·9% Zr and 2·0% Ti.[11] Add Al^{3+} to the soln. followed by $NH_2OH \cdot HCl$ if Fe^{3+} is present. Adjust to pH 3·4–4·5 and centrifuge. Add HNO_3 and 1 g. $Al(NO_3)_3 \cdot 9H_2O$, sat. the soln. with NH_4NO_3 and adjust to pH 0·65 with HNO_3. Ext. 3 times with equal vols. of cyclohexanone, combine, shake with a 1/3 vol. of H_2O and sep.

Extn. with 0·25*M* thenoyltrifluoroacetone in C_6H_6 from HNO_3 soln. at pH 2·5 seps. Th from Ra, Ac, etc.[12] Th can be stripped with $HClO_4$ soln. at pH 1. See also Chapter 10, Section 2.

Treatment with KIO_3 in HNO_3 soln. (see p. 339) seps. Th, Ti, Zr, Ce^{4+} from rare earths and PO_4^{3-}. If the filtered ppt. is boiled with 50 ml. 10% $H_2C_2O_4$, Th is sepd. from Ti and Zr. A small modification allows sepn. of Th from Sc (see p. 344). A very dense ppt. can be obtained by homogeneous pptn. with $NaIO_4$ and β-hydroxyethyl acetate.[13] Copptn. has been studied by tracer methods.[14] Sepn. from Zr, Ti, Bi is possible[15] with KIO_3 in solns. contg. 30% HNO_3 and 10% $H_2C_2O_4$. Th can be concd. by copptn. with Hg^{2+} in dil. HNO_3 soln. contg. H_2O_2, tartaric acid and oxine; this also allows sepn. from Zr, W, Sc, Bi, Ti, Nb, Ta and Fe.[16]

Tetrachlorophthalic acid seps. Th from rare earths (see under Determination, p. 339). Phenylarsonic acid seps. Th, Ti, Zr from rare earths; sepn. from Sc is incomplete (see under Determination, p. 340).[17] *m*-Nitrobenzoic acid seps. Th from Ti, rare earths and small amts. of Zr; sepn. from Zr is possible in 0·2*N* HNO_3 soln. For analogous compounds, see Chapter 11, Section 2.

Quinaldic acid (see p. 341) seps. Th from rare earths and Zr. Alizarin S allows sepn. from rare earths (see Chapter 47, p. 345).

H_2O_2 seps. Th, Ti, Zr from La, etc. and partly from Ce. For 10–30 mg. Th in 50 ml. soln. contg. H_2SO_4 to give a final concn. of 1–2*N*, add excess reagent, heat to 55–60°C and allow to cool for over 1 hr.; filter on paper and wash with H_2O. PO_4^{3-} interferes. The ppt. formed is $ThOOSO_4$. If pptn. is done from neutral or slightly acidic soln. the ppt. is difficult to filter and is of indefinite compn.[3] For pptn. from a neutral nitrate soln., add 10 g. NH_4NO_3, dil. to 100 ml. with H_2O, heat to 60–80°C and add 20 ml. 3% H_2O_2; filter on Whatman No. 41 paper, wash with 2% NH_4NO_3, dissolve in HNO_3, evap., add 100 ml. 10% NH_4NO_3, etc. See also Fresenius–Jander.[18]

$Na_4P_2O_7$ allows sepn. of Th, Ti, Zr from Ce^{3+}, La, Pr, Nd, Fe, etc. Treat 450 ml. soln. contg. 5 ml. HCl with satd. SO_2 water until it is colorless. Add 15 ml. 5% $Na_4P_2O_7$ soln., boil for 10 min., filter on paper and wash with H_2O contg. 1 drop HCl. Remove H_2O by wrapping the paper with the ppt. in filter paper, transfer the filter to a Kjeldahl flask, heat with H_2SO_4 and a little NH_4ClO_4 added in 2 portions, cool to 0°C, add 100 ml. H_2O at 0°C and pour into the original beaker contg. 30 g. NaOH in 125 ml. H_2O. Boil, leave for 5 min., filter on paper and wash with hot H_2O. Return the ppt. to the beaker, add 10 ml. HCl and 150 ml. H_2O and boil; filter on paper and wash. Dil. the filtrate with 400 ml. H_2O, add satd. SO_2 water and reagent and reppt. See also ref. 18. Sepn. with hypophosphate is less satisfactory than the above method. For a study using radioactive P, see ref. 19.

$(NH_4)_2MoO_4$ seps. Th from rare earths, U and Ca in AcOH soln. (see under Determination, p. 341) but sepn. is not complete.

$Na_2S_2O_3$ seps. Th, Sc, Al, Ti and Zr from the Ce group.[18] Add 20% reagent to 150 ml. soln. contg. 2 drops HCl, boil for 1 hr., filter on Whatman No. 41 paper and wash with warm H_2O; reppt. HNO_3 and PO_4^{3-} interfere; sepn. from the Y group is incomplete.

Urea or hexamine allows sepn. from rare earths (see under Determination, p. 339). Heating with $PbCO_3$ at 60°C for 2 hr. seps. Th, Zr, Ce^{4+}, Fe^{3+} from Ce^{3+}, La, Nd, Pr, Y, Sm and the Y group; U, Cr and Al divide between the phases and the sepn. with urea or hexamine is preferable.

Extn. of the oxine complex with $CHCl_3$ seps. Th from rare earths.[2]

Treatment with NH_4F seps. Th from Sc (see p. 345).

H_2S in strongly acidic media seps. Th from group II metals; add satd. H_2S water, dil. with H_2O, pass H_2S, etc. $(NH_4)_2S$ and $(NH_4)_2$-tartrate sep. Th from Fe.

Treatment with NH_4OH and NH_4Cl allows sepn. from groups IV and V and from Mg. NaOH yields a sepn. from Al and Be. $BaCO_3$ is suitable for sepn. from Ni and Co.

Cupferron in AcOH–NaOAc soln. seps. Th from Al. Tannin in $(NH_4)_2C_2O_4$ media seps. Th from Nb, Ta, Ti (see p. 374).

Passage through a cellulose column seps. Th from many other elements (see Chapter 13, Section 6). Ion exchange columns also provide useful sepns. (see Chapter 13, Section 4.3).

Determination

$H_2C_2O_4$ provides one of the classical methods for determination of Th. However, tetrachlorophthalic acid seems to be a better reagent, for the precipitate formed is crystalline and separation from rare earths is possible. KIO_3, urea or hexamine are also useful reagents. Ferron is the best reagent for mg. amounts of Th and thoron is the best colorimetric reagent.

(a) Tetrachlorophthalic acid is the best gravimetric reagent for Th.[8] Dil. the $HClO_4$ soln. obtained from sepn. (see p. 337) with 200 ml. H_2O, add 1 g. NaI, adjust to pH 1·5–1·6, add 20 ml. 0·3% reagent soln., adjust to pH 1·0–1·1, heat to 70–80°C, stir mechanically and keep hot for 1·5 hr. after the ppt. begins to appear. Filter, wash with cold 0·1% reagent soln. at pH 1·5, suspend the ppt. in hot 2% NaOH, filter and wash at least 10 times with 2% NaOH. Dissolve the ppt. in hot 2*N* HCl, reppt., filter on paper and wash. Dry at 110°C, heat at 350°C for 45 min., and at 850°C for 1 hr. and weigh as ThO_2. Rare earths do not interfere.

Many other carboxylic acids have been suggested for Th detn. $H_2C_2O_4$ has been applied gravimetrically, titrimetrically and colorimetrically. For gravimetric detn.[1, 20] use 200–500 ml. soln. contg. $< 4\%$ (v/v) HCl (the optimum is 3 ml. HCl/100 ml.). Boil the soln., add hot 10% $H_2C_2O_4$ (an excess of 20 ml./100 ml. soln.), heat for 2–3 hr., leave for 12 hr., filter on paper, wash with H_2O contg. 2 drops HCl and some $H_2C_2O_4$, ignite above 800°C ($>$ 600°C) and weigh as ThO_2. Interferences are Sc, rare earths and large amts. of PO_4^{3-} and SO_4^{2-}.

Colorimetric detn. is possible by measuring the fading of the color of $KMnO_4$ soln. on addn. of the ppt.[21] $KMnO_4$ soln. can also be used to titrate the ppt.[22] Other titrimetric methods use alizarin S,[23] di-SNADNS or nitroso-SNADNS or dinitrosochromotropic acid as indicator.[24]

m-Nitrobenzoic acid is suitable for gravimetric detn. of 0·1 g. Th in 25 ml. neutral soln.[18, 25] Add 150 ml. 0·4% reagent, heat for 15 min. at 80°C, filter on a glass crucible and wash with a soln. of 5 ml. reagent in 100 ml. H_2O. Dissolve the ppt. in 3 ml. dil. HNO_3, add 25 ml. reagent and neutralize to methyl orange with NH_4OH. Filter on paper, wash, heat above 413°C and weigh as ThO_2, or heat at 70–153°C and weigh as $Th(O_2NC_6H_4CO_2)_4$. No interference arises from rare earths, Fe, U, etc. or from small amts. of Zr. The ppt. can be dissolved in H_2SO_4, and treated with excess Ti^{3+} soln. which is back-titrated with Fe^{3+}.[26]

Detns. with other carboxylic acids are discussed in Chapter 11, p. 88.

(b) Urea allows a gravimetric detn.[7, 18] To the acidic soln. contg. $HClO_4$ from the sepn. add 1 g. KI/25 ml. followed by reagent (8 g. urea, 10 g. NH_4Cl and 3 ml. 87–90% HCOOH in 150 ml. H_2O, filtered), dil. to 350 ml. with H_2O, adjust to pH 4·45 $\pm$ 0·02 using a glass electrode and boil gently for 95–97 min. (pH 5·4–6·2). Filter on paper, wash with a soln. contg. 20 g. NH_4NO_3 and 8 ml. HCOOH/l. adjusted to pH 5·6 with NH_4OH. Dissolve the ppt. in hot 2*N* HCl, add 1 g. KI, etc. Filter on paper, wash, heat the beaker with 10 ml. 1:1 HCl, add NH_4OH and pass through the same filter. Ignite and weigh as ThO_2. Rare earths do not interfere.

Hexamine can be applied also.[18, 27] Heat 100 ml. soln. at pH 2–4 to 30°C, add 5 g. NH_4Cl and 10% hexamine gradually to give a small excess and a pH value of 5·8. Filter on Whatman No. 41 paper, wash with 2% NH_4NO_3, dissolve in hot 2% HCl, dil. to 100 ml. with H_2O, neutralize to methyl red with NH_4OH, acidify with HCl, heat to 30°C, add NH_4Cl, etc.

NH_4OH gives a ppt. which can be dried to $ThO_2{\cdot}2H_2O$ at 260–380°C,[18] but addn. of tannin is said to be better.[18, 27] Pyridine, quinoline, piperidine,[28] aniline and toluidine[18] are other reagents which have been proposed.

(c) KIO_3 is best used titrimetrically,[18, 29] although gravimetric and colorimetric methods are also available. For detn. of 0·175 g. ThO_2 in 100 ml. soln. add 50 ml. HNO_3 and, if Ce^{4+} is present, add a few drops of 30% H_2O_2, boil and cool. Cool in ice and add ice-cold reagent (15 g. KIO_3 in 50 ml. HNO_3 and 30 ml. H_2O). Stir occasionally during 30 min., filter on Whatman No. 50 paper, and wash with 20 ml. of a soln. contg. 2 g. KIO_3 in 25 ml. HNO_3 and 225 ml. H_2O. Return the ppt. to the original beaker with hot H_2O, boil, add 30 ml. HNO_3, cool, add 4 g. KIO_3 in 7 ml. HNO_3 and 20 ml. H_2O. After 30 min., filter on the same paper and wash with $<$ 100 ml. H_2O at 0°C. Transfer to an Erlenmeyer flask along with the paper, dissolve in 100 ml. 4*N* H_2SO_4, add 50 ml. H_2O, 30–35 ml. 10% KI and titrate with 0·2*N* $Na_2S_2O_3$ using starch as indicator.

NOTES. (1) Interferences are HCl, Zr, Ti and Sn. Rare earths, PO_4^{3-} and SO_4^{2-} do not interfere.

(2) The ppt. is $Th(IO_3)_4$ but the compn. depends strongly on the conditions of pptn. The HNO_3 concn. must be <40%. Small amts of ppt. should be centrifuged rather than filtered. Ce can be detd. in the filtrate after oxidation with $KBrO_3$.
(3) Gravimetric detn. is possible from 4*N* HNO_3 solns. contg. 3·5% HIO_3; the ppt. is weighed as $Th(IO_3)_4$ after drying at 105°C (200–300°C).[30]
(4) For colorimetry,[3] dissolve the ppt. in 1:1 H_2SO_4, add H_3PO_2, ext. I_2 with CCl_4 and measure at 520 mμ.

(d) Ferron can be used gravimetrically for < 10 mg. Th in 10 ml. slightly acidic soln.[18, 31] Add 2 drops bromophenol blue indicator, adjust to blue with 10% NH_4OAc and then to yellow with dil. HCl (pH 2–2·5). Heat on a steam-bath and add reagent (0·2% ferron, filtered) until a ppt. appears, followed by 25 ml. in excess. Heat for 30 min., filter on a Whatman No. 42 paper and wash with reagent soln. Ignite above 570°C and weigh as ThO_2 or dry at 110–216°C and weigh as $Th(C_9H_3O_4NSI)_2$.

NOTES. (1) Ag, Cu, Hg and SO_4^{2-} interfere but La, Ce, Ti, Ni, Co, W do not. If >30 mg. U is present, the ppt. must be dissolved in 2*N* HCl and repptd.
(2) Oxine can be applied gravimetrically for small amts. of Th or titrimetrically for large amts.;[18, 32, 33] the former method is not recommended. For 20–100 mg. Th as nitrate in 30–200 ml. soln., add NH_4OH until a turbidity appears, clear the soln. with 1:10 HNO_3 and add AcOH to give a 2·5% v/v soln. Boil and add 3 ml. reagent soln. (4 g. in 8 ml. AcOH dild. to 160 ml. with H_2O) for each 10 mg. Th. Then add 50% NH_4OAc until a turbidity appears, add the same amt. of reagent as before, followed by more NH_4OAc (5–10 ml. in all), and allow to cool. Filter on a G3 crucible, wash with warm H_2O, dissolve in HCl and titrate with 0·1*N* $KBrO_3$–KBr soln. For a gravimetric finish, dry in air and weigh as $Th(C_9H_6ON)_4 \cdot (C_9H_7ON)$, or heat slowly to 150–200°C and weigh as $Th(C_9H_6ON)_4$. La, etc. do not interfere but Ce requires addn. of 1 g. $NH_2OH \cdot HCl$; if PO_4^{3-} is present, add 5 g. $(NH_4)_2C_2O_4$ and 5 g. NH_4OAc to 300 ml. soln. followed by reagent and NH_4OH until the soln. is slightly alk.
For a colorimetric finish,[34] dissolve the ppt. in 0·1*N* HCl and measure at 320 mμ, or in Me_2CO and measure at 330 mμ; this is suitable for 2 μg. Th/ml.
(3) Hydroxyquinaldine also ppts. Th (see Chapter 20, p. 161).
(4) Bromoxine has been tested for colorimetric detn. at 390 mμ but is not satisfactory.[35] Iodoxine allows detn. of <6 μg. Th/ml.[36] Add 2 ml. 0·005% iodoxine in EtOH to 2 ml. 0·01*N* HNO_3 sample soln., dil. to 10 ml. with acetate buffer pH 5·6 and measure at 650 mμ.

(e) Thoron provides an excellent colorimetric detn.[10, 37] For 5–80 μg. Th in soln. of pH 0·5–0·6 (HCl) add 1·0 ml. 0·1% thoron, dil. to 10 ml. with H_2O and measure the red complex at 545 mμ; subtract a blank value.

NOTES. (1) 1 mg. of Fe^{2+} or U^{6+} and rare earths, Ti, Al, Ca, etc. do not interfere. Fe^{3+} can be reduced with 1 ml. 10% $NH_2OH \cdot HCl$ by boiling for some min. Interferences are U^{4+}, Zr, Nb, Ta, Sn, F^-, $C_2O_4^{2-}$, PO_4^{3-} and large amts. of SO_4^{2-}. Zr does not interfere if mesotartaric acid is added;[16, 38] this method has been used for detn. of Th in zircon, etc. For a study of ion exchange concn. using ^{234}Th as tracer, see ref. 39.
(2) Neothoron is suitable for detn. of 0–40 μg. Th.[11] Add $NH_2OH \cdot HCl$ if Fe^{3+} is present; add 2 ml. 0·5% reagent and 10 ml. buffer (7·6 g. KCl and 17 ml. 12*N* HCl/l.), dil. to 20 ml. with H_2O and measure at 600 mμ. The method has been used in rock analysis.
(3) Pararsonic acid may be used to det. 0·5–500 μg. Th in 43 ml. soln. contg. 4 drops HCl.[3] Add 2 drops methyl red, neutralize with NH_4OH, and add 7:100 HCl until the soln. is just red followed by 1·2 ml. in excess. Add 5 ml. reagent (0·1 g. pararsonic acid and 10 g. NH_4OAc in 50 ml. 1:1 EtOH) and heat for 10–20 min. on a steam-bath. Filter on a Gooch crucible, wash with 10 ml. portions of a mixt. of 10 g. NH_4OAc, 12 ml. 7:100 HCl and 488 ml. H_2O, pour 30 ml. warm *N* NaOH through the filter, wash with H_2O, dil. the filtrate to 250 ml. with H_2O and measure at 480 mμ. Ti, Zr, Hf must be previously sepd. in strongly acidic soln.
(4) Phenylarsonic acid is applied gravimetrically.[2, 40] Add SO_2 to 300 ml. soln. contg. 30 ml. 1:1 HCl, boil, add 30 ml. 10% reagent, 75 ml. AcOH and 5 ml. satd. NH_4OAc and heat for 10 min. Filter on a glass crucible, wash, dissolve the ppt. in 30 ml. 1:1 HCl, dil. to 300 ml. with H_2O, add SO_2, boil, add a few ml. reagent, etc. Then dissolve in 10 ml. 1:1 HCl, dil. to 400 ml. with H_2O, add 5 g. $H_2C_2O_4$, filter after 12 hr. and ignite to ThO_2. PO_4^{3-}, Zr, etc. interfere but Ce^{3+}, rare earths and U do not. The method can be applied after the $H_2C_2O_4$ sepn.; sepn. from Ce is said to be incomplete.[2]

(f) Picrolonic acid allows a gravimetric detn.[18, 41] of 2–100 mg. Th (< 10 mg./5 ml.) in 2·5–3% v/v AcOH; the final pH of the soln. should be 2–3·2. Boil the soln. and add a 2·5-fold excess of reagent (2·7 g./l. H_2O, heated on a steam-bath, left for 12 hr. and filtered), i.e. 2·5 ml./mg. Th. Keep at 0°C for 1 hr., filter on a glass crucible and wash with ice water. Dry by suction below 25°C and weigh as $Th(C_{10}H_7O_5N_4)_4 \cdot H_2O$ or heat slowly to 100–180°C (60–200°C) and weigh as the anhydrous salt. The ppt. is difficult to dry to const. compn. If only a little Th is present, evap. the soln. after addn. of reagent. Interferences are NH_4^+, group V elements, Ca, Pb and rare earths.

(g) Miscellaneous gravimetric methods. Benzenephosphonic acid is suitable for 20–200 mg. Th in 150 ml. 1:3 HCl soln.[42] Boil, add a 5-fold excess of 2·5% reagent, boil for 1 hr., dil. to 400 ml. with H_2O, adjust to pH 0·5–1·0 with NH_4OH, leave for several hr. and filter on a porcelain crucible. Dry at 150°C and weigh as $Th(C_6H_5PO_3)_2 \cdot 3H_2O$.

Na-phenylsulfinate can be applied[18, 43] for detn. of 1–4 mg. $ThCl_4$. Evap. to dryness, add 1 drop 1:1 HCl and transfer to a beaker with one 2 ml. portion and 3 × 0·5 ml. portions of H_2O. Heat the soln., add a 2·5-fold excess of reagent (2 g. in 100 ml. H_2O and 1 drop of HCl, filtered), place on a steam-bath for 30 min. and leave for 12 hr. Filter, wash with 1:3 reagent soln. and with cold H_2O, dry at 120°C and weigh as $Th(C_6H_5SO_2)_4$.

The *p*-bromo or *p*-iodo deriv. can be used in a slight modification of the above method, the iodo deriv. being suitable for < 1 mg. Th. α- or β-Naphthylsulfinic acid has also been suggested (Welcher[43]).

Quinaldic acid ppts. Th from dil. AcOH solns.[44] Al, Be, Cr, U interfere but La, Ce, Pr, Nd, Y, the Y group and Zr do not interfere. 5,6-Benzoquinaldic acid ppts. Th at pH > 3·0,[45] the ppt. being dried at 110°C and weighed as $Th(C_{14}H_{18}O_2N)_4$; rare earths do not interfere.

KIO_4 ppts. Th from hot neutral soln. on addn. of hot reagent;[46] the ppt. is filtered on glass after 3–4 hr., dried at 110°C and weighed as $ThHIO_6{\cdot}5H_2O$ or titrated iodometrically. A small amt. of rare earths can be tolerated in pptn. from 4*N* HNO_3 soln.

Na-mercaptobenzothiazole allows detn. of 20–200 mg. $Th(NO_3)_4$ in 5–20 ml. soln., the ppt. being weighed as $Th(C_9H_4NS_2)_4$; see Chapter 43, p. 322.

H_2SeO_3 can be used to det. 0·1 g. ThO_2 in 100 ml. soln. which contains 5 g. NH_4OAc and is neutral to methyl red.[47] Add 20 ml. 10% reagent, filter after 2 hr. and ignite to ThO_2. For a titrimetric finish,[48] dissolve the ppt. in HCl, dil. with H_2O to give a 1–2*N* HCl soln., add KI and titrate with $Na_2S_2O_3$ soln.

H_2O_2 ppts. Th from solns. contg. EDTA;[49] Fe does not interfere but Al necessitates repptn. (see also under Separation, p. 338).

Phytic acid ppts. Th from 6*N* HNO_3 soln.,[50] the ppt. being ignited at 1000°C and weighed as ThP_2O_7. Interferences are caused by Zr, Ti, U, Fe unless $H_2C_2O_4$ is added; other elements in monazite do not interfere.

(h) EDTA has been used for titration of Th with many different indicators. For titration of 6–50 mg. Th in 25 ml. 0·02–0·03*N* HNO_3 soln., add 4 drops 0·05% alizarin S soln., make alk. with NH_4OH and titrate with 0·025*M* EDTA (standardized against $CaCO_3$) until fading begins. Adjust to pH 3·1 and titrate further to the color change from pink to yellow (Fritz and Ford[10]).[51]

NOTES. (1) Interferences are Pb, Cu, Ni, Bi, Fe, Zr, Sn, Ce, Ti, V; La, Mn, Co, Cd, Zn, Ca, etc. can be tolerated. If chrome azurol S is used as indicator, Ce^{3+}, Al, Cr, Ag and U can be present.[10]

(2) Pyrocatechol violet is a good indicator.[52] For < 100 mg. Th in 100 ml. soln., adjust to pH 2·5–3·5, add a few drops of 0·1% indicator, heat to 40°C and titrate. The error is −0·04 mg. for 0·5–2·2 mg. Th. Interferences are Fe^{3+}, Zr, Bi, Sb, Al; U, Pb, Cu, Ag, Co, Mn, Zn, Nd, Pr, Ce, La, Ca, etc. can be tolerated.

(3) SPADNS, SNADNS, di-SNADNS, nitroso-SNADNS and dinitrosochromotropic acid can serve as indicators at pH 3·09.[53] Fe^{2+} soln. and cacotheline have also been proposed.[54]

(4) Photometric titration can be applied[55] at 290 mμ after addn. of Cu^{2+}. High frequency titration of 0·0002–0·001*M* Th soln. has been recommended.[56]

(i) $(NH_4)_2MoO_4$ can be used in conjunction with a reductor column and an oxidimetric titration.[18, 57] For 0·2 g. ThO_2 in 7% AcOH soln., add 0·76% (w/v) $(NH_4)_2MoO_4$ until 1 ml. 0·25% diphenylcarbazide used as an external indicator gives a pink color. Filter the ppt. on a glass crucible and wash. Dissolve the ppt. in HCl, pass the soln. through a Jones reductor and titrate with Ce^{4+} soln. using ferroin indicator or with $KMnO_4$ soln. Rare earths and Ca interfere. Direct titration with a potentiometric end-point[58] or with diphenylcarbazide as visual indicator in 50% EtOH soln.[59] are other possibilities.

(j) NaF can be used to titrate Th with thoron as indicator.[60] For < 100 mg. Th, add 10 ml. acetate buffer (100 ml. 1*N* NaOAc and 97 ml. 1*N* HCl dild. to 500 ml.) and 2 ml. 0·02% thoron, dil. to 50 ml. with H_2O and titrate with 0·1385*M* NaF to the color change from violet to scarlet-red. Zr and large amts. of most ions interfere. A gravimetric procedure has also been described.[18]

(k) Oxalohydroxamic acid and $FeCl_3$ can be used colorimetrically or titrimetrically.[61] For colorimetry of 25–250 μg. Th in soln. add an equal vol. of 1% oxalohydroxamic acid, 1 ml. 5% NH_4Cl and a few drops of 9*N* NH_4OH and boil. Filter on a glass crucible, and wash 5 times with a soln. of 20 g. NH_4Cl and 10 ml. NH_4OH/l. Dissolve the ppt. in 3·5 ml. 10% AcOH, add H_2O and 1 ml. $FeCl_3$ soln. (5·8 g. $FeCl_3{\cdot}6H_2O$ in 200 ml.), dil to 25 ml. with H_2O and measure at 500 mμ.

For titration of 1–5 or 10–50 mg. Th, add hot 2% reagent and 0·5 g. NH_4Cl and make alk. to litmus with NH_4OH, adding 0·5 ml. in excess. Boil for 1–2 min., filter on Whatman No. 41 paper and wash. Dissolve the ppt. in 50 ml. hot 6*N* HCl, boil for 10 min., add a 2-fold excess of 0·02 or 0·1*N* $TiCl_3$, pass CO_2 for 10 min., add 5 ml. 10% KSCN and titrate with Fe^{3+} soln. in 5% v/v H_2SO_4 until the soln. becomes red.

(l) Miscellaneous colorimetric methods. Morin can be utilized for detn. of < 60 μg. Th at pH 2.[62] Treat the soln. with 1·0 ml. 0·63*N* HCl or HNO_3, dil. to 20 ml. with H_2O, add 2·0 ml. 0·1% morin in EtOH, dil. to 50 ml. with H_2O and measure the yellow color at 410 mμ after 1 hr. in a 5 cm. cell. This method can be applied[63] after copptn. with LaF_3 and extn. with thenoyltrifluoroacetone in C_6H_6.

Quercetin is suitable for 10–150 μg. Th in 15 ml. soln.[64] Adjust to pH 2·8–3·0 with Na_2CO_3, add 4 ml. EtOH and 2 ml. 0·1% quercetin in EtOH, dil. to 25 ml. with H_2O and measure after 15 min. at 422 mμ (ϵ = 33 000). Interferences are Fe, Al, V, Cr^{6+}, U^{6+}; SO_4^{2-}, F^-, AcO^- and PO_4^{3-} can be removed by ion-exchange.

Quinalizarin allows detn. of 0–10 ml. $1{\cdot}66 \times 10^{-4}M$ Th soln.[65] Add the sample soln. to 10 ml. $2{\cdot}54 \times 10^{-4}M$ quinalizarin in Me_2CO, dil. to 50 ml. with Me_2CO and measure at 580–600 mμ. Ce earths in amts. up to 15 times that of Th can be tolerated.

Alizarin S forms a pink complex with 0·2–0·5 mg.

Th.[66] Zr, Ti, Ce interfere but Ce earths (< 10 Th) can be tolerated. Carmine red forms a reddish complex with $< 130\,\mu$g. Th/ml. at pH 2·5 which can be measured at 560 mμ. Fe^{3+} and Sn^{2+} interfere but moderate amts. of rare earths, U and Fe^{2+} can be present.[67] Naphthazarin is suitable for 2–66 $\times 10^{-6}M$ Th in EtOH soln.,[68] the purple complex being measured at 620 mμ; rare earths, U, Zr and Ti interfere.

Di-SNADNS forms a blue complex at pH 2·5–3·5 and this is measurable at 640 mμ.[69] Interferences are Fe, Zr, Au, Cu, Ni, PO_4^{3-} and F^-. SPADNS[70] and dinitrosochromotropic acid[71] have also been recommended.

Pyrocatechol violet forms a complex at pH 2–4 which can be measured at 480 mμ (see Chapter 21, p. 169).

Nitroso-R salt forms a yellow complex with max. absorbance at 380 mμ.[72] Morellin can be used to det. 1·4–25 p.p.m. Th at pH 5–7 in $> 50\%$ EtOH media with measurement at 515 mμ; PO_4^{3-}, $C_2O_4^{2-}$, F^- and CO_3^{2-} interfere.[73] $NaNH_4HPO_4$ can be applied[74] colorimetrically in conjunction with molybdate and $SnCl_2$.

References

1. Hillebrand and Lundell, 416 (533); Scott and Furman, 946; Schoeller and Powell, 156; Fresenius–Jander, **IV**b, 288 (1950).
2. Moeller, T., *et al.*, *Chem. Revs.*, **42**, 63 (1948).
3. Rodden, C. J. and Warf, J. C., *Natl. Nuclear Energy Ser., Div. VIII*, **1**, 160–207 (1950).
4. Grimaldi, F. S., *et al.*, *U.S. Geol. Survey Bull.*, No. 1006 (1954); *Profess. Paper*, **300**, 605 (1956).
5. Burelbach, J. P. and March, R. J., *U.S. Atomic Energy Comm.*, ANL-5240 (1953).
6. Basil, H., *Selective Bibliography 1951–1955*, Crane Co., Chicago (1955).
7. Willard, H. H. and Gordon, L., *Anal. Chem.*, **20**, 165 (1948).
8. Gordon, L., *et al.*, *Anal. Chem.*, **21**, 1323 (1949).
9. Schoeller and Powell, 156 ff.
10. Banks, C. V. and Byrd, C. H., *Anal. Chem.*, **25**, 416 (1953); also see Banks *et al.*, *ibid.*, 952; Fritz, J. S. and Ford, J. J., *ibid.*, 521, 1540; Banks and Edwards, R. E., *ibid.*, **27**, 947 (1955).
11. Ishibashi, M. and Higashi, S., *Japan Analyst*, **4**, 14 (1955); **5**, 135 (1956).
12. Meinke, W. W. and Anderson, R. E., *Anal. Chem.*, **24**, 708 (1952).
13. Stine, C. R. and Gordon, L., *Anal. Chem.*, **25**, 1519 (1953).
14. Shaver, K. J., *Anal. Chem.*, **28**, 2015 (1956).
15. Tillu, M. M. and Athavale, V. T., *Anal. Chim. Acta*, **11**, 62 (1954).
16. Grimaldi, F. S., *et al.*, *Anal. Chem.*, **29**, 848 (1957).
17. Fischer, W. and Bock, R., *Z. anorg. u. allgem Chem.*, **249**, 146 (1942).
18. Fresenius–Jander, 288 ff.
19. Moeller, T. and Schweitzer, G. K., *Anal. Chem.*, **20**, 1201 (1948).
20. Hecht and Donau, 210; Welcher, **II**, 61.
21. Rider, B. F. and Mellon, M. G., *Anal. Chim. Acta*, **2**, 370 (1948).
22. Majer, V., *Chem. listy*, **44**, 68 (1950).
23. Venkateswarlu, P. and Ramanathan, A. N., *Current Sci.* (*India*), **31**, 45 (1952).
24. Datta, S. K., *Z. anal. Chem.*, **156**, 270 (1956); *Anal. Chim. Acta*, **15**, 415 (1956).
25. Welcher, **II**, 225; Osborn, G. H., *Analyst*, **73**, 381 (1948).
26. Dutt, N. K. and Chowdhury, A. K., *Anal. Chim. Acta*, **12**, 515 (1955).
27. Welcher, **III**, 129, 170.
28. Welcher, **III**, 30, 51, 151.
29. Moeller, T. and Fritz, N. D., *Anal. Chem.*, **20**, 1055 (1948); Tillu, M. M. and Athavale, V. T., *Anal. Chim. Acta*, **11**, 62, 324 (1954).
30. Venkataramaniah, M. and Rao, Bh. S. V. R., *J. Indian Chem. Soc.*, **26**, 487 (1950).
31. Ryan, D. E., *et al.*, *Anal. Chem.*, **19**, 416 (1947).
32. Berg, R. and Becker, E., *Z. anal. Chem.*, **119**, 1 (1940).
33. Ishimaru, S., *J. Chem. Soc. Japan*, **53**, 571 (1932); **56**, 70 (1935).
34. Eswaranarayana, N. and Rao, Bh. S. V. R., *Anal. Chim. Acta*, **11**, 339 (1954).
35. Rao, K. V. S. R. and Rao, Bh. S. V. R., *Z. anal. Chem.*, **150**, 21 (1956).
36. Tomic, E. and Khalifa, H., *Z. anal. Chem.*, **156**, 326 (1957).
37. Thomason, P. F., *et al.*, *Anal. Chem.*, **21**, 1239 (1949); Taylor, A. E. and Dillon, R. T., *ibid.*, **24**, 1624 (1952); Mayer, A. and Bradshaw, G., *Analyst*, **77**, 154 (1952); Clinch, J., *Anal. Chim. Acta*, **14**, 162 (1956).
38. Grimaldi, F. S. and Fletcher, M. H., *Anal. Chem.*, **28**, 812 (1956); Fletcher *et al.*, *ibid.*, **29**, 963 (1957).
39. Ishimori, T., *et al.*, *J. Chem. Soc. Japan*, **77**, 1705 (1956).
40. Scott and Furman, 952; Welcher, **IV**, 58.
41. Welcher, **IV**, 44; Kiba, T. and Ikeda, T., *J. Chem. Soc. Japan*, **60**, 912 (1939).
42. Banks, C. V. and Davis, R. J., *Anal. Chim. Acta*, **12**, 418 (1955).
43. Hecht and Donau, 214; Welcher, **IV**, 202.
44. Erämetsä, O., *Suomen Kemistilehti*, **17B**, 30 (1944).
45. Majumdar, A K. and Banerjee, S., *Anal. Chim. Acta*, **14**, 306 (1956).
46. Venkataramaniah, M. and Rao, Bh. S. V. R., *Current Sci.* (*India*), **18**, 170 (1949); *J. Indian Chem. Soc.*, **26**, 287 (1950).
47. Kot'a, J., *Chem. listy*, **27**, 79, 100, 128, 150, 194 (1933).
48. Deshmukh, G. S. and Swamy, L. K., *Anal. Chem.*, **24**, 218 (1951).
49. Schneider, P., *Chem. listy*, **50**, 81 (1956) (in W).
50. Ryabchikov, D. I., *et al.*, *Zhur. Anal. Khim.*, **11**, 658 (1956).
51. See also Haar, K. ter and Bazen, J., *Anal. Chim. Acta*, **10**, 108 (1954).
52. Suk, V., *et al.*, *Chem. listy*, **48**, 533 (1954); *Chemist Analyst*, **45**, 61 (1956).
53. Banerjee, G., *Z. anal. Chem.*, **148**, 349 (1955); Datta, S. K., *ibid.*, **149**, 328 (1956); *Anal. Chim. Acta*, **16**, 115 (1957).
54. Rao, V. N. and Rao, G. G., *Z. anal. Chem.*, **155**, 334 (1957).
55. Malmstadt, H. V. and Gohrbandt, E. C., *Anal. Chem.*, **26**, 442 (1954).

56. HARA, R. and WEST, PH. W., *Anal. Chim. Acta*, **13**, 189 (1955).
57. BANKS, C. V. and DIEHL, H., *Anal. Chem.*, **19**, 222 (1947); BANKS, *Nuclear Sci. Abstr.*, **4**, 15 (1950).
58. GORDON, L. and STINE, R., *Anal. Chem.*, **25**, 192 (1953).
59. DESHMUKH, G. S. and BOKIL, I., *Bull. Chem. Soc. Japan*, **29**, 449 (1956).
60. BANERJEE, G., *Z. anal. Chem.*, **146**, 417 (1955); also see SUNDARESAN, M. and KARKHANAVELA, M. D., *Current Sci.* (*India*), **23**, 258 (1954) (amperometric).
61. DHAR, S. K. and DAS GUPTA, A. K., *J. Sci. Ind. Research* (*India*), **12B**, 518 (1953).
62. FLETCHER, M. H. and MILKEY, R. G., *Anal. Chem.*, **28**, 1402 (1956).
63. PERKINS, R. W. and KARKWARF, D. R., *Anal. Chem.*, **28**, 1989 (1956).
64. MENIS, O., *et al.*, *Anal. Chem.*, **29**, 1426 (1957); TOMIC, E. and KHALIFA, H., *Mikrochim. Acta*, 668 (1957).
65. PURUSHOTTAM, A., *Z. anal. Chem.*, **145**, 245 (1955).
66. MURTHY, T. K. S. and RAO, BH. S. V. R., *Current Sci.* (*India*), **18**, 248 (1949); SARMA, D. V. N. and RAO, *Anal. Chim. Acta*, **13**, 142 (1955).
67. ESWARANARAYANA, N. and RAO, BH. S. V. R., *Z. anal. Chem.*, **146**, 107 (1955).
68. MOELLER, T. and TECOTZKY, M., *Anal. Chem.*, **27**, 1056 (1955).
69. DATTA, S. K., *Z. anal. Chem.*, **150**, 347 (1956).
70. BANERJEE, G., *Anal. Chim. Acta*, **16**, 56 (1957).
71. DATTA, S. K., *Anal. Chim. Acta*, **15**, 421 (1956).
72. RAO, K. V. S. and RAO, BH. S. V. R., *J. Sci. Ind. Research* (*India*), **14B**, 278 (1955).
73. RAO, B. R. L. and PATEL, C. C., *Proc. Indian Acad. Sci.*, **42A**, 317 (1955).
74. NOZAKI, T., *J. Chem. Soc. Japan*, **76**, 996 (1955).

47

SCANDIUM

The principal references for this chapter are given in refs. 1 and 2. The chapter on the determination of rare earths should also be consulted.

The chemistry of scandium contains several peculiarities. The K_2SO_4 double salt is insoluble in saturated K_2SO_4 solution (this is similar to the behavior of yttrium) while the corresponding Na-salt is soluble in saturated Na_2SO_4 solution. Similarly to the yttrium and lanthanum compounds, scandium oxalate and fluoride are insoluble in H_2O. Scandium behaves similarly to thorium in that its oxalate is soluble in $(NH_4)_2C_2O_4$ solution, its carbonate is soluble in cold alkali metal carbonate solution, and its basic thiosulfate is insoluble in H_2O. Similarly to zirconium, scandium fluoride is soluble in alkali fluoride.

Attack

(a) Thortveitite. Fuse with Na_2CO_3, add HCl, $Na_2S_2O_3$, etc.

(b) Rare earth minerals. See p. 348. For Nb and Ta minerals, add H_2O and HF, evap. to dryness, add dil. HF, filter on paper and wash with 1:99 HF.

(c) Wolframite. Fuse 10–100 g. with a 2–3-fold amt. of Na_2CO_3 and ext. with H_2O. Evap. the residue with HCl, etc. Treat the filtrate with Na_2SiF_6. Alternatively, dissolve the sample in aqua regia and filter; to the filtrate add 5 g. Na_2SiF_6, boil for 1 hr., filter on paper, wash with hot H_2O; evap. the residue to fumes with H_2SO_4, cool, add H_2O and $(NH_4)_2$-tartrate.

Separation

Cupferron in $CHCl_3$ seps. Sc from Fe, Zr, Ti, V. Treatment with Hg^+ and iodate seps. Sc from Th. Extn. with tributyl phosphate from HCl soln. seps. Sc (and partly U, Th, Fe) from Al, Be, Cr, rare earths and from Ti if H_2O_2 is added (see p. 138). Treatment with tartrate and Y seps. Sc from U, Co, Cu, Ni, Fe, Al, Mg.

The combined following procedure seps. Sc from most elements;[3] it is suitable for $< 120\ \mu$g. Sc_2O_3 in 100 ml. 10% H_2SO_4 or HCl soln. Add 10 ml. 6% cupferron and ext. 3 times with 25 ml. portions of $CHCl_3$, add 5 ml. cupferron and ext. 4 times with 25 ml. portions of $CHCl_3$. Repeat if necessary. Dil. to 300 ml. with H_2O, boil and make slightly alk. with NH_4OH. If no ppt. appears, acidify and add 200 mg. $Al(NO_3)_3$, NH_4OH and some filter pulp. Filter on a glass crucible, dissolve the ppt. in 100 ml. warm 20% HNO_3 and reppt. if HCl was present originally. Otherwise, add 2·0 ml. 2·5% w/v $Hg_2(NO_3)_2$ in 20% HNO_3, and 75 ml. satd. KIO_3 in 10% HNO_3, stir for 15 min., filter on a glass crucible and wash with KIO_3 soln. Dil. to 300 ml. with H_2O, make alk. with NH_4OH, heat to 80°C, add filter pulp and filter. Dissolve the ppt. in 25 ml. HCl and wash the filter with another 25 ml. HCl. Transfer the first 25 ml. of solution to a separatory funnel, add 0·5 ml. 30% H_2O_2 and ext. with 25 ml. tributyl phosphate. Sep., add the 25 ml. HCl used for washing, shake, sep., and then shake twice more with 25 ml. portions of HCl. Add 70 ml. H_2O to the org. phase, shake for 30 sec. and sep. into another funnel. Shake the transferred aq. phase with 25 ml. Et_2O, shake, sep., evap. to 30 ml. and add 25 mg. Y_2O_3 as chloride, followed by 25 ml. 40% $(NH_4)_2$-tartrate in 8% NH_4OH and 10 ml. NH_4OH. Heat just to boiling, stir, filter on a glass crucible and wash with 8% $(NH_4)_2$-tartrate. Dissolve the ppt. in 50 ml. 20% HCl and reppt. twice more. Dissolve the ppt. in 25 ml. HCl and wash with 25 ml. HCl. Ext. with tributyl phosphate as described above. Shake for 30 sec. with 50 ml. H_2O, sep., add 25 ml. Et_2O, sep., add 8·0 ml. NH_4OH, heat, add 2·0 ml. 0·1% alizarin S, etc. If Zr or Ti is absent, the cupferron and iodate sepns. can be omitted.

Na_2SiF_6 allows sepn. of Sc (and some Th or rare earths) from W, etc. Boil the 1:10 HCl soln., add reagent soln. gradually to give a concn. of 2%, boil for 30 min., maintaining the vol., and allow to cool. Filter on paper and wash with 1% Na_2SiF_6 in 1:99 HCl. The ppt. is difficult to filter.

H_2S seps. Sc from group II elements in acidic soln. Copptn. of Sc with Pb should be noted.

Sc can be sepd. from most group III elements, etc., by treatment with 20 ml. satd. $H_2C_2O_4$ soln. of 50–60 ml. slightly acidic (HCl) soln. Interferences are mineral acids and $(NH_4)_2C_2O_4$. The soly. of the Sc salt is larger than the soly. of Th or rare earth oxalates. Sepn. from Zr and Ti is incomplete.

Sc, Th and rare earths can be sepd. from many other elements by treatment of 100 ml. soln. contg. 2–4 ml. HCl with HF. An excess of HF should be avoided. ScF_3 is less sol. in H_2O than Th or rare earths but it is more sol. in excess of HF or NaF. The ppt. is difficult to filter and to decomp. with H_2SO_4.

$Na_2S_2O_3$ serves to sep. Sc and Th from rare earths (see Chapter 46, p. 338). Sc is pptd. incompletely from slightly acidic soln.; it is pptd. completely from neutral soln. but is accompanied by the Y earths. Treat the acidic soln. with Na_2CO_3 until it is almost neutral, add 10 g. $Na_2S_2O_3$ and boil for 1 hr. Add 1 ml. hydrazine carbonate soln. (13 g. $N_2H_4 \cdot H_2SO_4$ and 10·6 g. Na_2CO_3 in 200 ml. hot H_2O), filter on Whatman No. 41 paper and wash with hot H_2O contg. some hydrazine carbonate soln. Dissolve the ppt. in 10 ml. HCl, boil, filter, ignite, dissolve in hot HCl, combine with the first soln. and apply the tartrate method.[2]

Alizarin S in dil. HCl soln. serves to sep. Sc and Th from rare earths.[4]

NH_4F seps. Sc from Th and rare earths but the ppt. is hard to filter and sepn. from Th is incomplete. Pour the almost neutral chloride soln. into an 8-fold excess of hot reagent soln., boil for 10 min., filter on paper and wash with hot H_2O.

KIO_3 also allows sepn. of Sc from Th. To 5 ml. of slightly acidic (HNO_3) soln. add 5–10 ml. 10% reagent in 1:2 HNO_3, stir, add 10–20 ml. 0·8% reagent in 1:9 HNO_3, digest at 60–80°C for 15 min. and allow to cool. Filter on paper and wash with the second reagent soln.

Sepn. of Sc from Th, rare earths, Zr, etc., is possible with NH_4OH and $(NH_4)_2$-tartrate (see above and under Determination below). Sepn. from the Y earths is incomplete but the ppt. is easily filtered. Evap. the chloride soln. to dryness, add 50–100 ml. H_2O, almost neutralize with NH_4OH, pour into 100 ml. 20% $(NH_4)_2$-tartrate and add a few drops of HCl if the soln. is turbid. Heat, add NH_4OH until a faint odor appears, cool, filter and wash with 2% $(NH_4)_2$-tartrate.[2]

Extn. of the thiocyanate with Et_2O seps. Sc from Th, Zr, Ti and the Ce group.[5] Place 30 ml. 0·5*N* HCl sample soln. in a separatory funnel, add 26·5 g. NH_4SCN and dil. to 50 ml. with H_2O. Ext. with 50 ml. Et_2O, sep. and ext. twice with 25 ml. Et_2O, adding 2·5 ml. 2*N* HCl for each extn. Combine the exts., shake with 10 ml. NH_4SCN soln. (53 g. in 60 ml. 0·1*N* HCl) and repeat this twice. (See also below under Determination). Sepn. from the Y earths is incomplete. Sepn. from Ti is possible[2] at pH 3 with tropaeolin OO.

Boiling with 20% Na_2CO_3 gives incomplete sepn. from Th.

Determination

Gravimetric determination of Sc with $(NH_4)_2$-tartrate is the most convenient method. $H_2C_2O_4$ or NH_4OH can be applied gravimetrically after separation of Sc from other elements by one of the above methods. The best colorimetric methods for Sc are those involving quinalizarin or morin.

(a) $(NH_4)_2$-tartrate can be used gravimetrically for > 30 μg. Sc in dil. HCl soln.[1, 2, 6] Add 50 mg. Y as YCl_3 and 20 g. reagent and neutralize with NH_4OH to neutral red indicator. Add NH_4OH to give a final concn. of 0·2–1*N*, dil. to 100 ml. with H_2O, boil for 30 min. and leave for at least 24 hr. Filter on paper and wash with 3·5% $(NH_4)_2$-tartrate in 0·3–0·5*N* NH_4OH. Ignite, dissolve in 30 ml. 0·5*N* HCl and apply the method for extn. of thiocyanate with Et_2O (see above). Evap. the org. layer with a little HCl, add some HNO_3 and evap. to dryness. Evap. to fumes with H_2SO_4 twice, then evap. to dryness with aqua regia, add a few drops of HCl and reppt. Ignite at 1000°C and weigh as Sc_2O_3.

(b) Quinalizarin is suitable for colorimetric detn. of > 0·1 μg. Sc.[7] Ext. with EtOAc or iso-AmOH from ammoniacal soln. contg. $(NH_4)_2CO_3$ and measure the blue complex at 650 mμ. No interference is caused by Be, Mg, rare earths or Fe^{2+}, but Al, Ti, Th, Zr interfere.

Alizarin S is suitable for 10–120 μg. Sc_2O_3 in acidic (HCl) soln.[3] Heat the soln. with NH_4OH, add 2·0 ml. 0·1% reagent and make the soln. pink with NH_4OH (if the end-point is overshot, add HCl and repeat). Then add 5·0 ml. NH_4OAc soln. (100 g. in 300 ml. H_2O adjusted to pH 3·5 with HCl and dild. to 500 ml.), cool, dil. to 100 ml. with H_2O, and measure in a 5 cm. cell at 520 mμ.

(c) Morin provides a fluorimetric detn. of 0·2–5 μg. Sc in 5–10 ml. neutral soln.[8] Add 2·0 ml. 50% w/v NH_4OAc, 1·0 ml. 25% Na-benzoate and 2·0 ml. EtOAc and shake. Add 0·05 ml. 0·01% morin in EtOH and measure the fluorescence under UV light. Interferences are Fe, Al, Be, Ga, In, PO_4^{3-} and F^-.

(d) Miscellaneous gravimetric methods. $H_2C_2O_4$ ppts.[9] Sc as $Sc_2(C_2O_4)_3 \cdot 10H_2O$, which can be dried at 67°C (Duval). NH_4OH can also be used gravimetrically.[2, 9]

Oxine is applicable for 0·03m*M* Sc in 110 ml. soln.[10] Add 5 drops 0·005% aerosol, heat to 75°C and add 10 ml. 5% oxine in 2*N* AcOH and 45 ml. buffer (30 ml. 2*N* NH_4OAc, 15 ml. 2*N* NH_4OH). Filter on a glass crucible after 2 hr., wash with H_2O, dry at 105–110°C for 3 hr. and weigh as $Sc(C_9H_6NO)_3 \cdot C_9H_7NO$. Interferences are Fe, Al, etc.

Hydroxyquinaldine can also be utilized (see Chapter 20, p. 161).

(e) EDTA allows a titrimetric detn. with 1-(2-pyridylazo)-2-naphthol as indicator.[11] Add NaOH to the soln. contg. 3–10 mg. Sc until a turbidity appears, adjust to pH 2·5 with AcOH, add excess 0·01*M* EDTA and 6 drops 0·01% indicator in MeOH and titrate with 0·01*M* $CuSO_4$ from yellow to red.

References

1. HILLEBRAND and LUNDELL, 426 (543); SCOTT and FURMAN, 773.
2. SCHOELLER and POWELL, 69 ff.
3. EBERLE, A. R. and LERNER, M. W., *Anal. Chem.*, **27**, 1551 (1955).
4. BECK, G., *Mikrochemie*, **27**, 47 (1939).
5. FISCHER, W. and BOCK, R., *Z. anorg. u. allgem. Chem.*, **249**, 146 (1942).
6. FISCHER, W. *et al.*, *Z. anal. Chem.*, **133**, 57 (1951).
7. BECK, G., *Mikrochemie ver. Mikrochim. Acta*, **34**, 282, 423 (1948/49).
8. SANDELL, 536; WELCHER, **IV**, 374.
9. HILLEBRAND and LUNDELL, 429.
10. POKRAS, L. and BERNAYS, P. M., *Anal. Chem.*, **23**, 757 (1951).
11. CHENG, K. L. and WILLIAMS, JR., T. R., *Chemist Analyst*, **44**, 96, 98 (1955).

48

RARE EARTH ELEMENTS

The principal references for this chapter are given in refs. 1 and 2. Monographs on the chemistry of the rare earths (lanthanons) have been published[3, 4] and reports on their analytical chemistry have been made.[5, 6]

The rare earths are classified as shown in Table 41; certain physical properties are also given. When a mixt. of rare earths is ignited it may be difficult to attain const. weight (see under Determination).

Some properties which are important for the sepn. of rare earths are mentioned in Table 42. The Tb group is situated between the Ce and Y groups, but the platinocyanides resemble those of the Y group.

The order of basicity of the rare earths is La–Ce^{3+}–Pr–Nd–Y–Eu–Gd–Sm–Tb–Dy–Ho–Er–Tm–Yb–Lu–Sc–Ce^{4+}. Ce^{4+} can be sepd. from the others.

The tendencies of the valency states are shown in Fig. 5.

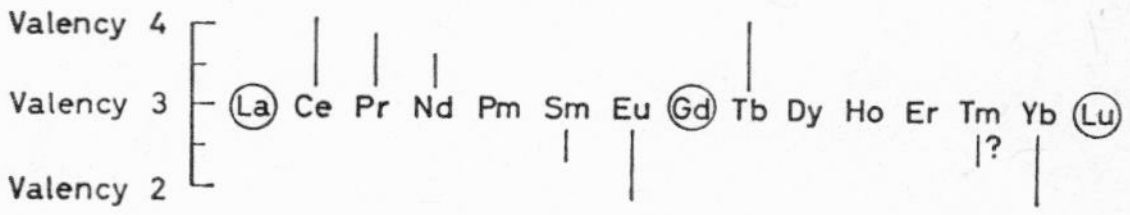

FIG. 5. Tendencies of valency states.

TABLE 41. Classification of Rare Earth Elements into Groups

	Group	Oxides (ions) and their color	$\lambda_{max.}$ (ϵ) (Interf.)
	Ce group	yellow-brown	
	La	La_2O_3 white	
	Ce	Ce_2O_3 white; CeO_2 pale yellow; (Ce^{4+} red-brown)	Ce^{3+} 253·6, 295·5 (59·0); Ce^{4+} 320.
	Pr	Pr_2O_3 green-yellow; Pr_6O_{11} brown; PrO_2 black; (Pr^{3+} green)	444·2 (10·49)
	Nd	Nd_2O_3 purple; (Nd^{3+} lilac-rose with bluish fluorescence)	521·6 (4·41), 575·5 (6·93) (Pr), 354·0 (5·20), 739·5 (7·20), 794·0 (11·78)
	Pm	?	
	Sm	Sm_2O_3 light yellow; (Sm^{3+} yellowish)	401·5 (Eu)
	Tb group		
	Eu	Eu_2O_3 pale pink; (Eu^{3+} pink; Eu^{2+} colorless)	394·2 (3·06) (Sm)
	Gd	Gd_2O_3 white	272·8 (4·20) (Er)
	Tb	Tb_2O_3 white; Tb_2O_7 dark brown; (Tb^{3+} pale rose)	
	Y group	white–pale yellow (Er group absent) yellow–pale red (Er group present)	
	Y	Y_2O_3 white	
Er group	Dy	Dy_2O_3 yellow-white: (Dy^{3+} yellowish)	908·0 (2·46) (Er, Yb), 350·4 (2·54) (Ho), 365·0 (2·10)
Er group	Ho	Ho_2O_3 pale yellow; (Ho^{3+} yellowish)	537·0 (5·16), 640·4 (3·53) (none), 287·0 (3·59), 361·1 (2·34), 450·8 (4·16)
Er group	Er	Er_2O_3 rose; (Er^{3+} rose-pink)	379·6 (7·18), 523·5 (3·20), 487·1 (1.92) (Ho band for all)
Er group	Tm	Tm_2O_3 pale green; (Tm^{3+} green)	683·0 (2·56), 777·5 (1·07)
	Yb	Yb_2O_3 white	974·0 (Er)
	Lu	Lu_2O_3 white	

TABLE 42. Some Properties Important for Separation into Groups

	Ce group	Y group
Hydroxide	slightly sol. in H_2O	barely sol. in H_2O
Carbonate	insol. in H_2O, $(NH_4)_2CO_3$ soln.	insol. in H_2O, sol. in $(NH_4)_2CO_3$ soln.
Oxalate	as above	as above, soly. greater
Fluoride	insol.	insol.
Double sulfate	insol. in satd. K_2SO_4	sol. in satd. K_2SO_4
Basic nitrate	slightly sol.	barely sol.
Double nitrate	easy to crystallize	hard to crystallize
Phosphate	insol.	insol.
Formate	barely sol.	considerably sol.
Platinocyanide	$R_2[Pt(CN)_4]_3 \cdot 18H_2O$, yellow, monoclinic	$R_2[Pt(CN)_4]_3 \cdot 21H_2O$, red, triclinic

It should be noted that the soly. of many salts of rare earth elements decreases as the temp. increases, hence it is not advisable to heat in order to obtain dissoln.

Attack[1, 7]

(a) Uraninite, bröggerite, cleveite, nivenite, pitchblende or thorianite is dissolved in HNO_3. Allanite, cerite, gadolinite, thorite or yttrialite dissolves in HCl. Niobates, tantalates or titanates require HF or fusion with KHF_2 (see below for treatment of filtrate). Monazite, xenotite, cerite, aeschenite, allanite, euxenite, gadolinite, thorianite, yttrotitanite are dissolved in H_2SO_4 or $HClO_4$ (see Chapter 46, p. 337). Euxenite, fergusonite, polyclase, samarskite, yttrotantalite require $Na_2S_2O_7$ fusion, particularly for detn. of Th.

(b) Na_2CO_3 fusion is applied in the detn. of SiO_2, P, B and F. H_2SO_4 may be used for dissoln. before detn. of F.

Separation

Sepn. of rare earths from silicates in absence of Nb, Ta and Ti is carried out as follows. Dissolve in HCl or HNO_3, or fuse with Na_2CO_3 and leach with HCl. Filter off SiO_2, ppt. with NH_4OH and reppt. (if much Ca is present, 3 repptns. may be needed). Filter, dissolve in HCl, evap. to dryness, add H_2O and treat with $H_2C_2O_4$ to sep. rare earths and Th from Fe, etc. which appear in the filtrate.

Sepn. of rare earths from niobates and tantalates (cf. p. 370) is outlined below.

Evapn. with HCl, H_2SO_4, or $HClO_4$ seps. rare earths from SiO_2.

H_2S allows a sepn. from group II elements.

Treatment with NH_4OH and NH_4Cl seps. rare earths from group IV elements and Mg. The rare earths of strong basicity ppt. incompletely. It is best to use the procedure applied for pptn. of $Al(OH)_3$, then decompose the NH_4^+ salts with HNO_3, evap. to dryness, add H_2O followed by NH_4OH until colorless to malachite green, etc. Tannin gives complete pptn.

HF allows sepn. of small amts. of rare earths from large amts. of other elements, but large amts of Al interfere.[8] The ppt. is readily sol. in HNO_3 contg. H_3BO_3 and rare earths are pptd. with $H_2C_2O_4$.

Tartaric acid hydrolysis seps. rare earths from large amts. of Nb or Ta (see p. 374). Sepn. is incomplete. hence the filtrate is treated with tannin, the ppt. is ignited, fused with $Na_2S_2O_7$ and extd. with $H_2C_2O_4$, The latter fusion and extn. is general for sepn. from small amts. of Nb, Ta or Ti oxides.

Digestion with NaOH, or leaching with H_2O following Na_2CO_3 fusion, allows sepn. from P, As, Sb, Sn, W and partly from SiO_2, Al and U.

Sepn. of rare earths from many elements (cf. Chapter 46, p. 337) is possible by gradual addn. of satd. $H_2C_2O_4$

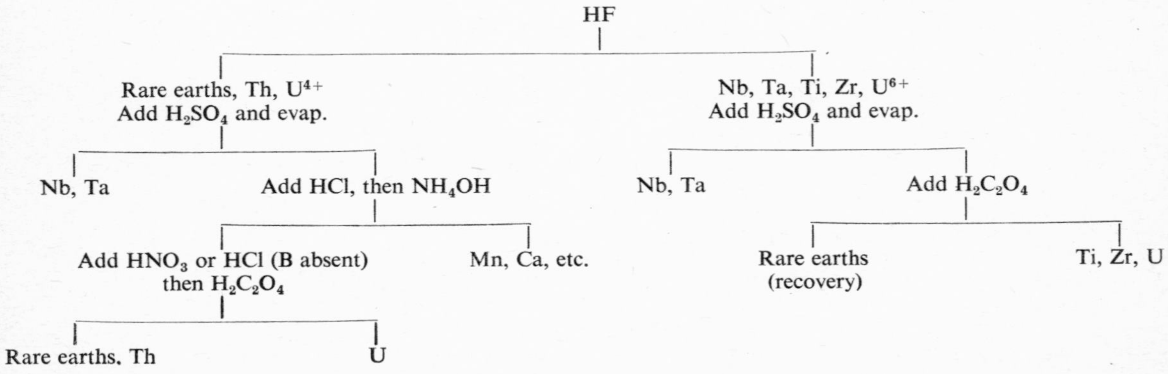

soln. to a soln. contg. 3–4 ml. HCl/100 ml. until 3 g $H_2C_2O_4$/100 ml is present in excess; the soln. is then maintained at 60°C for 12 hr. or placed on a steam-bath for 3 hr. Sepn. from U is incomplete if U exceeds 25 times the amt. of rare earths. If much U is present, the bulk is removed by ether extn. Sepn. from U is incomplete even in the presence of salicylate.[9] The reaction can be applied for concn. of rare earths with Ca or Sr. The best ppt. is obtained as follows:[10] to < 1·5 g. oxides in soln. contg. < 5 ml. H_2SO_4 or HCl/100 ml., add an equal vol. of reagent all at once without stirring; after 0·5–1 hr., stir vigorously, leave for 12 hr., filter, wash with 2% $H_2C_2O_4$ contg. a little HNO_3 and ignite; add HCl or digest with hot 10% NaOH, filter, wash with hot H_2O. If large amts. of other metals or PO_4^{3-} are present, dissolve the ppt. in HCl and reppt.

KIO_4 allows sepn. of Ce^{4+} from Th, other rare earths and Ce^{3+} (see below). Ce is sepd. from other rare earths by treatment with KIO_3 and $KBrO_3$ (see below), or by means of oxidants in alk. soln., e.g. $KBrO_3$ and marble or Na_2CO_3, $NaBrO_3$ and pyridine.[11] 1:4 $KMnO_4$–Na_2CO_3, KOH–Br_2, H_2O_2–NH_4OH or trinitrotriammine cobalt complex can be applied similarly.[2] The use of KIO_3 and other reagents allows sepn. of rare earths from Th or Sc (see Chapter 46, p. 338).

Rare earths are sepd. from Th by treatment of the soln. contg. NH_4NO_3 and AcOH with salicylic acid followed by extn. with 1:9 Et_2O–EtOAc.

For extn. of Ce^{4+} with hexone from 8–10*M* HNO_3 soln., see Chapter 16, p. 136. Extn. with thenoyltrifluoroacetone in xylene seps. Ce from other rare earths (see Chapter 10, Section 2).

Oxine sulfonic acid allows sepn. of Ce from La (see Chapter 8, Section 1.2).

The Ce group is sepd. from the Y group by treatment with K_2SO_4 (see p. 351). Electrolysis at a K–Hg or Hg electrode in presence of SO_4^{2-} seps. Eu, Yb and partly Sm from other rare earths.[12] Eu can be sepd. from Sm and both sepd. from other rare earths by shaking their acetate-contg. soln. with 0·5% Na–Hg and then shaking the amalgam with AcOH and H_2SO_4 mixt.[13]

If a sample is mixed with 25% its wt. of C and heated to 1400°C at 10^{-3} mm. Hg, then Sm, Eu and Yb volatilize.[14]

For sepn. into individual elements, see Mellor[15] or Shibata.[2] For ion exchange sepns., see Chapter 13, Section 4.1.

Determination

After separation from other elements, the total rare earths can be determined by means of $H_2C_2O_4$; alternatively, Ce can be separated and determined first and the other earths weighed as the oxides, being ignited in H_2 if required. As necessary, the mean atomic weight is determined and then separation into the Ce and Y groups is carried out, or the separation can precede the atomic weight determination.

Apart from Ce, only a few individual elements, e.g. Eu, Yb, can be determined by chemical methods, although recently advances have been made in this field. The other earths are generally determined by X-ray analysis, etc. (see refs. 2, 16). The chemical methods are summarized below for each element.

CERIUM

Of the gravimetric methods, determination with $H_2C_2O_4$ after separation with KIO_3 and $KBrO_3$ is accurate; the KIO_4 procedure is also useful. In general, redox titrations are most convenient. For colorimetric determination, the use of persulfate with or without brucine seems most satisfactory. For semimicro amounts the photometric determination of Ce^{3+} is convenient.

(a) KIO_3–$KBrO_3$ provides a good sepn. and is followed[1] by pptn. with $H_2C_2O_4$. For < 0·15 g. Ce as nitrate in 75 ml. soln. contg. 25 ml. HNO_3, add 0·5 g, $KBrO_3$ and a 10–15-fold excess of KIO_3 soln. (100 g. KIO_3 in 333 ml. HNO_3 and 666 ml. H_2O). Let stand, filter on Whatman No. 42 paper, decant and wash with a soln. contg. 8 g. KIO_3 in 50 ml. HNO_3 and 950 ml. H_2O. Return to the original beaker, boil, add HNO_3 until the ppt. just dissolves (avoid any excess), then add 0·25 g. $KBrO_3$, KIO_3, etc., and allow to cool. Filter on the same paper, decant three times and transfer the ppt. with paper to the original beaker. Add 5–8 g. $H_2C_2O_4$ and 50 ml. H_2O, heat, boil out I_2 and leave to stand for at least 5 hr. Filter on paper, wash with cold H_2O, ignite at 670–765°C and weigh as CeO_2; alternatively, ignite above 1040°C and weigh as Ce_2O_3. The actual ppt. is $2Ce(IO_3)_4 \cdot KIO_3 \cdot 8H_2O$.

NOTES. (1) Other rare earths are detd. as follows: combine the filtrates, treat with NaOH, filter, dissolve in HCl, add $H_2C_2O_4$, ignite the ppt., heat in H_2, cool and weigh as R_2O_3.

(2) Homogeneous pptn. of Ce has been studied[17] with NH_4IO_3 and $(NH_4)_2S_2O_8$ or with $KBrO_3$, using direct ignition of the ppt.

(3) For a titrimetric finish,[18] filter the ppt. on a glass crucible, wash as above and then with EtOH 4 times and Et_2O twice, dry at 40–45°C for 10–15 min., add KI and HCl and titrate with 0·1*N* $Na_2S_2O_3$.

(b) KIO_4 provides a useful gravimetric method.[19] For < 0·5 g. oxides in 10 ml. soln. add 120 ml. 1:5 HNO_3 and 70 ml. satd. KIO_4 in 1:5 HNO_3, place on a steam-bath for 10–15 min. and allow to cool. Filter on a G4 crucible, wash with 1:10 HNO_3, return to the original beaker, dissolve in the min. amt. of HNO_3 and add H_2O until the soln. is 2*N* in HNO_3. Reppt., filter, wash with 200 ml. 1:10 HNO_3 and 100 ml. cold H_2O, heat at 100–110°C for 3–4 hr. and weigh as $CeHIO_6 \cdot H_2O$. Th, Ce^{3+} and other rare earths do not interfere. In 0·08–0·13*N* HNO_3 soln. repptn. allows sepn. of Ce from 750-fold amts. of other rare earths.[20]

(c) Redox reactions. These can be applied titrimetrically, colorimetrically or gravimetrically.

(*i*) Titrimetric methods. Oxidation with $(NH_4)_2S_2O_8$ usually precedes[1] titration with Fe^{2+} and $KMnO_4$. To the Ce^{3+} soln. contg. 2·5–10 ml. H_2SO_4 or 5 ml. HNO_3 in 200 ml., add 2–5 ml. 0·25% $AgNO_3$ and 1–5 g. $(NH_4)_2S_2O_8$ and boil for 10 min. Cool, add a known excess of Fe^{2+} and back-titrate with $KMnO_4$. Th, Zr, Ti and other rare earths do not interfere.

NOTES. (1) For a comparison of titrimetric methods, see ref. 21. The above titration can be done potentiometrically or coulometrically (see Chapter 45, p. 333) or visually with ferroin indicator.[22] H_2O_2 can replace Fe^{2+}.
(2) With $NaBiO_3$ as oxidant[10] in solns. contg. 20 ml. H_2SO_4/100 ml., add 2 g. $(NH_4)_2SO_4$ and 1 g. $NaBiO_3$, boil, filter on a glass crucible contg. asbestos, wash with 100–150 ml. 2% H_2SO_4, add Fe^{2+} and titrate with $KMnO_4$. For trace amts. of Ce, the filtrate can be titrated with 0·005*M* ferroin.[23]
(3) For photometric titration,[24] add 1–10 ml. sample soln. to 15 ml. $K_4P_2O_7$ soln. (86 g. in 750 ml. H_2O and filtered) adjusted to pH 5·5–7·0 with H_2SO_4; readjust the pH and titrate with $KMnO_4$ measuring at 525 mμ. Interferences are Hg^+, V^{4+}, Cr^{3+}, As^{3+}, Sb^{3+}, I^-, F^-, Tl and Mn (if >Ce); Ce^{4+}, Fe^{3+}, Fe^{2+} (after aeration), Al, Co, Mo, V^{5+}, W, Th, Bi, Sn^{2+}, Ni, Cu, Cl^- and Br^- do not interfere.
(4) A catalytic oxidation method has been advanced.[25] For <0·63 g. Ce in 200 ml. soln. contg. 5–30 ml. HCl, 3–40 ml. H_2SO_4 or 5–50 ml. HNO_3, add 4–5 g. HPO_3 in 10–20 ml. H_2O and 3 drops 1% diphenylamine in H_2SO_4. Then for <0·63 g. Ce, add 50 ml. $K_2Cr_2O_7$ soln. (15 g./l.) and 55–60 ml. As^{3+} soln. (15 g. As_2O_3 and 10 g. Na_2CO_3/l.); for <0·35 g. Ce, add 30 ml. and 35–40 ml. of these solns. resp. After 30 sec. titrate with 0·1*N* Fe soln. (28 g. $FeSO_4$ and 10 ml. H_2SO_4/l.) from blue-violet to green. Deduct 0·015 ml. 0·1*N* Fe^{2+} as blank.
(5) Oxidation of Ce^{3+} can be done with $KMnO_4$; excess is decomposed by boiling with HCl, and Ce^{4+} is titrated with Fe^{2+} and $KMnO_4$ with diphenylamine indicator.[26]
(6) Reaction with KSCN can be followed[27] by detn. of SCN^- by Volhard's method, by means of 0·01*N* $Hg(NO_3)_2$ with diphenylcarbazone indicator or by potentiometric titration with $AgNO_3$. Other procedures which have been suggested include titration[28] with H_2O_2 in presence of Ti^{4+}, titration with hydroquinone using ferroin indicator (see Chapter 38, p. 292), titration with ascorbic acid using variamine blue indicator,[29] amperometric titration[30] with $K_3Fe(CN)_6$, or coulometric titration[31] with Ti^{3+}.

(*ii*) Colorimetric methods. Persulfate oxidation is most satisfactory.[32] For 0·04–0·2 mg. Ce in 10 ml. 1*N* H_2SO_4 soln., add 0·2 ml. 0·25% $AgNO_3$, 1 ml. 2·4% $K_2S_2O_8$ and some SiC; boil for 5–10 min. maintaining the vol. at 6–10 ml. by H_2O addn. Place in H_2O at 15°C for 5 min., dil. to 10 ml. with H_2O and measure at 320 mμ. Cl^-, F^- and PO_4^{3-} interfere; interferences of Fe, UO_2^{2+}, Mn, Cr, V can be prevented or corrected for. Cu and Th do not interfere.

Of the other available methods, the most sensitive is that involving brucine.[33] For 0·2 mg. Ce in 10 ml. 1*N* H_2SO_4 soln., treat with $(NH_4)_2S_2O_8$ in presence of $AgNO_3$, cool, add 0·25 ml. 0·1% brucine in 1*N* H_2SO_4 and measure the red-brown color using a blue filter. Benzidine can replace brucine.[34]

PbO_2 can also serve as oxidant.[35] For 0·02–1 mg. Ce, add 2–4 ml. H_2SO_4, dil. to 10–25 ml. with H_2O, add 0·5 g. PbO_2 and stir for 5 min. Filter on a glass crucible, receive in Fe^{2+} soln. (4·2 g. Mohr's salt in 1 l. 0·5*N* H_2SO_4; dil. 5 ml. (for 20–150 μg. Ce) or 20 ml. (for > 150 μg.) to 100 ml. before use). Add 10 ml. 0·1% *o*-phenanthroline, adjust to red with NH_4OH, cool, adjust to pH 2·5–2·8, dil. to 100 ml. with H_2O and measure at 505 mμ. Interferences are Mn, V and Cl^-; Th and other rare earths do not interfere.

H_2O_2 can be used along with methylene blue.[36] To 4 ml. of slightly acidic soln. add 1 drop 30% H_2O_2 and 1 drop 0·05% methylene blue, make alk. with NaOH, dil. to 50 ml. with H_2O and compare the green color. KCN prevents interference of Cd, Co, Ag and Zn.

In a similar method,[37] make the soln. acid to litmus, add 25 ml. K_2CO_3 soln. (100 g./100 ml.) and 10 ml. 6*N* HCl to give pH 10·1–10·5 and dil. to 50 ml. with H_2O; add 1 ml. 3% H_2O_2 and measure the yellow or reddish color at 304 mμ. This is suitable for 4–25 p.p.m. Ce. V, Cr, U and $Fe(CN)_6^{4-}$ interfere.

An oxalate ppt. can be detd. by treatment with H_2O_2 in presence of K_3-citrate and NaOH[38] or in presence of NH_4OH and EDTA.[39]

Veratrole can be used[40] to det. Ce^{4+} in 5 ml. soln. Add 5 ml. 50% H_2SO_4, and 0·2 ml. reagent soln. in EtOH, shake, add 1 ml. C_6H_6, shake and measure the orange color in the C_6H_6 layer.

(*iii*) Gravimetric method. Treat the soln. with KOH to give an excess of 2 g./200 ml. soln. Pass Cl_2 or Br_2 until there is no alk. reaction, leave for 12 hr., filter on paper, wash and repeat the pptn. several times. Finally ignite to CeO_2 and weigh.[41]

(d) Ce^{3+} can be measured absorptiometrically.[42] For 1–5 mg. Ce in H_2SO_4 soln., evap. to fumes, cool, add 3 ml. 10% H_2O_2 in dil. H_2SO_4, heat just to fumes, dil. to 25 ml. with 1*N* H_2SO_4 and measure at 253·6 mμ. 40–200 mg. Ce/l. can be measured in 0·05–3·5*N* H_2SO_4 solns. Interferences are NO_3^-, U^{6+}. Moderate amts. of Cu, Th, Zr, Hf, La, Pr, Nd, Sm, Eu, Gd, Dy, Ho, Er, Yb and Y can be tolerated. Ce at concns. of 10^{-3}–$2 \times 10^{-2}M$ can be measured at 295·5 mμ ($\epsilon = 59{\cdot}0$).[43]

(e) Oxine can be applied gravimetrically or titrimetrically.[44] To the filtrate from the detn. of Th (see p. 340) add 1 g. $NH_2OH{\cdot}HCl$ and 10 ml. concd. Na_2-tartrate soln. Heat to 60°C and add NH_4OH until an odor appears. Add 2% oxine in EtOH, boil and leave for 30 min.; filter on a G4 crucible, wash with dil. NH_4OH, dry at 110°C (128–233°C) and weigh as $Ce(C_9H_6ON)_3$. Alternatively, dissolve the ppt. and titrate with 0·1*N* $KBrO_3$–KBr soln.

NOTES. (1) Other rare earth elements can be detd. in the same way but addn. of $NH_2OH{\cdot}HCl$ is unnecessary.[45] The La ppt. can be titrated[46] with $KMnO_4$, and the Y ppt.[47] with $KBrO_3$

(2) For colorimetry of $>0{\cdot}5$ μg. Ce in soln. contg. NH_4OH and tartrate (pH 10·2–11·1),[48] add reagent and ext. with AmOH, measuring at 470 mμ. Fe, Mn, V and F^- interfere. For detn. of Ce in steels, ext. with $CHCl_3$ and measure at 505 mμ.[33]
(3) To det. 0–50 μg. Y, add 1·00 ml. 0·5 or 1% oxine in $1N$ AcOH, 50 ml. 20% NH_4OAc and adjust to pH 9·55 with $1N$ NH_4OH. After 2–3 min., ext. 3 times with 10 ml. portions of $CHCl_3$, dil. to 50 ml. with $CHCl_3$, filter on a dry paper and measure the fluorescence at 500 mμ under the 365 mμ Hg line within 15 min. of the start of the extn. process.[49] La interferes (100 μg. corresponds to 11·5 μg. Y) but 10 μg. Ce can be tolerated.
Oxine can be used gravimetrically for Y at pH 5–6; or colorimetrically at 330 or 340 mμ in CCl_4 or Me_2CO media.[50]

(f) $K_4Fe(CN)_6$ may be employed gravimetrically or titrimetrically. For the former,[51] treat 40 ml. neutral soln. with $0{\cdot}1M$ reagent, filter on a glass crucible after 30 min., wash with 50% EtOH, EtOH and Et_2O, dry in a vacuum desiccator and weigh as $KCeFe(CN)_6\cdot 4H_2O$. Th and La interfere but Er does not.

Potentiometric titration is possible at 70°C in neutral soln. contg. 30% EtOH.[52] I_2-starch can be used as indicator for titration of 6–95 mg. Ce in 50 ml. soln. contg. 20–30% EtOH at pH 4·6–6·2.[53] If a known excess of $K_4Fe(CN)_6$ is used, the filtrate can be titrated[54] with Ce^{4+} soln. in presence of ferroin after addn. of 20 ml. 4–$5N$ H_2SO_4.

(g) Miscellaneous colorimetric methods. Cupferron allows detn. of 5–35 μg. Ce^{4+} in 0·1–$0{\cdot}15N$ H_2SO_4 soln.;[55] add 0·5 ml. 2% cupferron, ext. with 5 ml. AmOAc and measure the red-brown color under a blue filter. Other rare earths do not interfere.

NH_4-anthranilate is used for 1 mg. Ce in 10 ml. soln.;[56] add NH_4OH until a ppt. appears, add 2–3 ml. 2% reagent, heat to 70–80°C, add $7{\cdot}5N$ HNO_3, heat to 70–80°C, add NH_4OH and HNO_3 and measure the pink color.

Gallic acid is applicable for 30–70 μg. Ce in 2·7 ml. neutral soln.[57] Add an equal vol. of 0·02% gallic acid, cover with white mineral oil or ether, add 5·3 ml. of a mixt. of 1% Na_2SO_4 and 0·2% NH_4OH, dil. to 10 ml. with H_2O and measure the violet to yellow-brown color. Pyrogallol can be used similarly.[57].

Tiron allows detn. of 4–60 p.p.m. CeO_2 at pH 7·0–10·5;[58] add 0·5–1% reagent and $1N$ NaOAc and measure the blue color at 500 mμ. Other rare earths, Th, F^-, $C_2O_4^{2-}$, PO_4^{3-}, etc. can be tolerated.

Chrome fast pure blue B forms a color with Ce at pH 7·5.[59]

TOTAL AMOUNT OF OTHER RARE EARTH METALS

(a) $H_2C_2O_4$ is used gravimetrically (see under Separation, p. 348). The ppt. is ignited, heated in H_2, cooled and weighed as R_2O_3. If it is ignited in air only, the ppt. contains Pr_6O_{11} and Tb_2O_7 (also CeO_2 if Ce has not been sepd.). The acid liberated on addn. of $0{\cdot}1M$ Na_2-tartrate to a neutral soln. of rare earths can be titrated with alkali.[60]

(b) Tannin also permits a gravimetric detn.[61] Boil 200 ml. of slightly acidic sample soln., add 25 ml. satd. NH_4Cl, 5 g. NH_4OAc and 0·5 g. tannin followed by NH_4OH until the odor is detectable. Heat on a steam-bath, filter on paper, wash with 2% NH_4NO_3, ignite, etc., and weigh as R_2O_3. Tartrate does not interfere. If only NH_4OH is added, results may be low, particularly if much NH_4^+ is present.

(c) Mean atomic weight can be detd. as follows.[62] For 0·1–1 g. R_2O_3 (Pr^{3+} and Tb^{3+} with no Ce present), add 50 ml. $0{\cdot}1N$ H_2SO_4, heat, add 8 ml. $0{\cdot}2N$ $K_2C_2O_4$, boil and cool; add phenolphthalein and titrate with $0{\cdot}1N$ NaOH to the pink end-point. Calc. the mean at. wt. from the weight of the oxide and the amt. of $0{\cdot}1N$ H_2SO_4 consumed.

In an alternative method for 1 g. oxide,[63] add 7 ml. $15N$ HCl/50 ml., dil. to 100 ml. with H_2O, boil, add 50 ml. 10% $H_2C_2O_4$ and filter on paper. Decant twice with 100 ml. hot H_2O and then wash further with decantation. Dry at 110°C for 8–12 hr., weigh out 0·2 g., ignite at 900°C and weigh as R_2O_3. Weigh out 0·15 g. of the oxalate ppt., add 20 ml. $10N$ H_2SO_4 and 100 ml. H_2O, heat to 90°C and titrate with 0·025–$0{\cdot}04N$ $KMnO_4$.

(d) EDTA titration is suitable for detn. of rare earths.[64] To the slightly acidic soln. add a few crystals of NaK-tartrate, 5 ml. pH 8–9 buffer per 50 ml. soln., and eriochrome black T indicator and titrate the boiling soln. with $0{\cdot}01M$ EDTA until the color becomes blue. Back-titration with Zn^{2+} using eriochrome black T, or dimethylnaphthidine with $K_3Fe(CN)_6$, as indicator has also been used. Alizarin S with methylene blue is another indicator combination.[65]

(e) Alizarin S permits colorimetric detn. of 1–20 μg. rare earths in 10 ml. soln.[33, 66] Add 1 ml. $2N$ NH_4OAc and AcOH, followed by 0·4 ml. 0·1% alizarin S and measure the violet color at 550 mμ. 0·6 μg. La can be detd. in 60% Me_2CO soln. at 520 mμ and 0·4 μg. Y at 510 mμ.[67]

(f) Miscellaneous colorimetric methods. Hematein is applicable for simultaneous detn. of 0·5 mg. La_2O_3/l. at 600 mμ and 0·2 mg. Y_2O_3/l. at 650 mμ.[68]

Aluminon is used [69] with thioglycolic acid to det. 6 μg. rare earths/ml. in ammoniacal soln. The molybdenum blue procedure can be applied after pptn. of the earths as phosphates.[70]

SEPARATION INTO CERIUM AND YTTRIUM GROUPS

Satd. K_2SO_4 soln. is generally used for this sepn.[1, 71] For $>0{\cdot}5$ g. R_2O_3, evap. to dryness with HCl, add 1–2 drops HCl and dissolve in the min. amt. of H_2O. Add 200–300 ml. satd. K_2SO_4 soln. and 5 g. K_2SO_4 powder, stir for 5 min. and leave for 12 hr. Filter on paper and wash twice with reagent soln. (filtrate 1). Boil the ppt. with 100 ml. 10% NaOH, dil. to 250 ml. with H_2O, boil, filter, add HCl, etc. and reppt. (filtrate 2). Again treat the ppt. with NaOH and add H_2O, boil and filter, as before. Then add HCl and $H_2C_2O_4$, etc. Ignite the ppt. which contains the Ce group (along with the bulk of the Tb group and a small amt. of the Y group).

Combine filtrates 1 and 2, add NaOH, filter, add HCl and $H_2C_2O_4$, etc.; finally ignite the ppt. which contains the Y group along with a trace of the Ce group (particularly Nd and Sm).

NOTES. (1) Th and Sc appear with the Ce group. If Na_2SO_4 is used, Sc appears with the Y group.
(2) With Na_2SO_4 as reagent, the Tb group divides itself between the Ce and Y groups.[72] Other reagents which have been applied are sulfamic acid[73] and oxalate with EDTA.[74]

EUROPIUM

Iodometric titration can follow reduction.[10, 41] To the R_2O_3 ppt. add HCl and dil. with H_2O to give a 0·1–0·2*N* HCl soln. Pass through a Jones reductor and collect in a known excess of 0·04*N* I_2 under CO_2; back-titrate with $Na_2S_2O_3$ soln. Other rare earths do not interfere but SO_4^{2-}, PO_4^{3-}, NO_3^-, Fe, etc. interfere. Titration with $KMnO_4$ in presence of Zimmermann–Reinhardt soln. is also feasible.[41] The potential of the Eu^{3+}/Eu^{2+} couple is −0·710 v.

NOTE. In an alternative method,[75] dissolve the R_2O_3 ppt. in HCl, evap. to a syrup, dil. to 20 ml. with H_2O and pass through a Jones reductor. First pass 150 ml. 0·5*N* HCl, then pass the sample soln., and 150 ml. 0·05*N* HCl. Collect in 20 ml. 0·02*N* $FeCl_3$ under CO_2. Add 4 ml. HCl, 5 ml. H_3PO_4 and 3 drops 0·3% Na-diphenylaminesulfonate indicator and titrate with 0·04*N* $K_2Cr_2O_7$. The error is −3%.

YTTERBIUM

Electrolytic reduction can be followed by $KMnO_4$ titration.[76] For 50–200 mg. Yb/50 ml. 1*N* H_2SO_4 soln., electrolyze at 0·1 amp./cm.^{2} for 1 hr, add a known excess of Fe^{3+} and titrate with $KMnO_4$ soln., using ferroin indicator. The potential of the Yb^{3+}/Yb^{2+} couple is −1·430 v. Eu interferes.

Yb^{2+} can be measured colorimetrically.[77] For 2–100 mg. Yb as chloride in 5 ml. neutral soln., add 5 ml. 0·1% Na/Hg, shake for 15 sec., add 10 drops HCl, shake for a few sec. and measure the green color. The final shaking period should be 1–2 sec. for 2 mg. Yb and 2–5 min. for 0·1 g. Pr interferes but is rarely present; NO_3^-, etc. interfere.

PRASEODYMIUM, NEODYMIUM, SAMARIUM, EUROPIUM, GADOLINIUM, YTTERBIUM, THE ERBIUM GROUP

These earths can be detd. colorimetrically.[78] For 1–3 g. oxide (free from Ce), add H_2O and HCl (or $HClO_4$) in excess and evap. to dryness. Add H_2O, evap. to dryness, dil. to a definite vol. and measure the absorbances at the wavelengths listed in Table 41 at a definite slit width.

Nd can be detd. in Sm in a 10% $HClO_4$ medium by differential spectrophotometry at 575 mμ.[79] Sm chloride can be measured at 401·6 mμ.[80]

LANTHANUM

La can be detd. by flame photometry[81] using the lines at 790·0, 438·3, 442·3 or 560·0 mμ.

NEODYMIUM

Chloroxine allows a colorimetric detn.[82] For 4·3–8·6 mg. Nd in 25 ml. soln. add a 2-fold excess of reagent in 3*N* HCl followed by NH_4OAc and 0·2*N* NH_4OH until the ppt. becomes yellow. Adjust to pH 9·5 with 15*N* NH_4OH, add 100 ml. $CHCl_3$, ext. and measure at 581·8 mμ. Other rare earths do not interfere. Nd is extd. completely above pH 9·4 Er is extd. above pH 8·3 and can be detd. at 520·8 mμ.

TERBIUM

UV fluorescence can be used to det. 0·05–2·0 mg. Tb in 10 ml. 0·5*N* HCl soln. in a borosilicate glass tube.[83] An Allen hydrogen arc at 1 amp. below 2500 Å is used with measurement at 545 mμ. No interference arises from Y, Gd, Dy, Ho; up to 10% Ce, Al, Ca, K, Mg, Na, or Ni; up to 5% Co or Mn, 1% Cr, 0·5% Cu or UO_2^{2+}, 0·2% Fe, or 0·1% NO_3^-.

PRASEODYMIUM

Iodometric titration of the mixed oxides obtained by heating the oxalate ppt. at 803°C for 3 hr. is possible. La and Nd do not interfere.[84]

References

1. HILLEBRAND and LUNDELL, 430 (547); SCOTT and FURMAN, 245; SCHOELLER and POWELL, 94; PIGOTT, 133; FRESENIUS–JANDER, **IIIaβ/IIIb**, 113 (1956).
2. SHIBATA, Y., *Mukikagaku-Zensho*, **IX**, Maruzen, Tokyo (1948/49).
3. VICKERY, R. C., *Chemistry of Lanthanons*, Butterworths, London (1953).
4. YOST, D. M., *et al.*, *The Rare Earth Elements and their Compounds*, Wiley, New York (1947).
5. RYABCHIKOV, D. I., *et al.*, *Trudy Komissii Anal. Khim., Akad., Nauk S.S.S.R., Inst. Geokhim. i Anal. Khim.*, **3**, 23–88 (1951).
6. LEDICOTTE, G. W., *U.S. Atomic Energy Comm.*, ORINS-12 (1956).
7. See KIMURA, 458.
8. SANDELL, 506.
9. DUTT, N. K., *J. Indian Chem. Soc.*, **22**, 75 (1945).
10. SCHOELLER and POWELL, 98 ff.
11. OSTROUMOV, E. A., *Zhur. Anal. Khim.*, **2**, 111 (1947).
12. BRUKL, A., *Angew. Chem.*, **49**, 159 (1936); **50**, 15 (1937).
13. MARSH, J. K., *J. Chem. Soc.*, 398, 523 (1942); 8, 531 (1943).
14. ARCHARD, J. C., *Compt. rend.*, **244**, 3059 (1957); **245**, 1064 (1957).
15. MELLOR, V., 561 (1924).
16. HOPKINS, B. S. and TAEBEL, W. A., *Trans. Illinois State Acad. Sci.*, **31**, 136 (1939).
17. WILLARD, H. H. and YU, S. Ts., *Anal. Chem.*, **25**, 1754 (1953); KIMURA, K., *et al.*, *Japan Analyst*, **6**, 719 (1957).
18. CHERNIKOV, YU. A. and USPENSKAYA, T. A., *Zavodskaya Lab.*, **9**, 276 (1940).

19. Venkataramaniah, M. and Rao, Bh. S. V. R., *Current Sci. (India)*, **18**, 248 (1948).
20. Aleksandrov, G. P. and Tikhonova, V. S., *Ukrain. Khim. Zhur.*, **22**, 379 (1956).
21. Weiss, L. and Sieger, H., *Z. anal. Chem.*, **113**, 305 (1938).
22. Axt, M. O., *J. Soc. Chem. Ind.*, **60**, 229 (1941).
23. Charlot, G., *Bull. soc. chim. France*, **6**, 1126 (1939).
24. Marple, T. L., *et al.*, *Anal. Chem.*, **28**, 1892 (1956); Edwards, J. W. and Milner, G. W. C., *Analyst*, **82**, 593 (1957); also see Goffart, G., *Anal. Chim. Acta*, **2**, 150 (1948) (amperometric).
25. Lang, R., *Z. anal. Chem.*, **97**, 395 (1934).
26. Pigott, 136.
27. Deshmukh, G. S. and Sant, B. R., *Proc. Indian Acad. Sci.*, **37A**, 504 (1953); Deshmukh, *Z. anal. Chem.*, **145**, 251 (1955); Sant, *Rec. trav. chim.*, **76**, 590 (1957).
28. Beck, M. T., *Acta Chim. Acad. Sci. Hung.*, **5**, 209 (1955).
29. Jach, Z., *et al.*, *Z. anal. Chem.*, **154**, 185 (1957).
30. Leonard, G. W., *et al.*, *Anal. Chim. Acta*, **16**, 185 (1957).
31. Lingane, J. J. and Kennedy, J. P., *Anal. Chim. Acta*, **15**, 465 (1956).
32. Medalia, A. T. and Byrne, B. J., *Anal. Chem.*, **23**, 453 (1951); also see Sandell, 251; Freedman, A.-J. and Hume, D. N., *Anal. Chem.*, **22**, 932 (1950) (study using radioisotope); Huré, J. and Saint James-Schonberg, R., *Anal. Chim. Acta*, **9**, 415 (1953).
33. Sandell, 251.
34. Murthy, T. K. S. and Rao, Bh. S. V. R., *J. Indian Chem. Soc.*, **27**, 383 (1950).
35. Gordon, L. and Feibush, A. M., *Anal. Chem.*, **27**, 1050 (1955).
36. Welcher, **IV**, 214.
37. Telep, G. and Boltz, D. F., *Anal. Chem.*, **25**, 971 (1953); also see Plank, J., *Z. anal. Chem.*, **116**, 312 (1939); *Magyar Kém. Folyóirat*, **50**, 141 (1944); Conca, N. and Merritt, Jr., C., *Anal. Chem.*, **28**, 1264 (1956).
38. Ryabchikov, D. I. and Strelkova, Z. G., *Zhur. Anal. Khim.*, **3**, 226 (1948).
39. Malínek, M. and Klír, L., *Chem. listy*, **50**, 1317 (1956).
40. Antoniades, H. N., *Chemist Analyst*, **44**, 34 (1955).
41. Hillebrand and Lundell, 438 (556).
42. Greenhaus, H. L., *et al.*, *Anal. Chem.*, **29**, 1531 (1957).
43. Holleck, L., *et al.*, *Angew. Chem.*, **68**, 522 (1956).
44. Berg, R. and Becker, E., *Z. anal. Chem.*, **119**, 1 (1940).
45. Pirtea, Th. I., *Z. anal. Chem.*, **107**, 191 (1936); Welcher, **I**, 310.
46. Misumi, S., *J. Chem. Soc. Japan*, **74**, 453 (1953).
47. Murthy, A. S., *et al.*, *Z. anal. Chem.*, **145**, 418 (1955).
48. Misumi, *J. Chem. Soc. Japan*, **74**, 67 (1953).
49. Ishibashi, M., *et al.*, *J. Chem. Soc. Japan*, **77**, 1474 (1956).
50. Sitaramachandra, A., *et al.*, *Z. anal. Chem.*, **145**, 418 (1955).
51. Spacu, P., *Z. anal. Chem.*, **104**, 28 (1936).
52. Atanasiu, J. A., *Z. anal. Chem.*, **108**, 329 (1937).
53. Fujita, Y., *J. Chem. Soc. Japan*, **78**, 1761 (1957).
54. Deshmukh, G. S. and Venugopalan, M., *J. Indian Chem. Soc.*, **33**, 299 (1956).
55. Hagiwara, Z., *Technol. Repts., Tôhoku Univ.*, **18**, 32 (1953); *J. Chem. Soc. Japan, Ind. Chem. Sect.*, **57**, 26 (1954).
56. Shemyakin, F. M., *et al.*, *Trudy Komissii Anal. Khim., Akad. Nauk S.S.S.R., Inst. Geokhim. i Anal. Khim.*, **3**, 246 (1951).
57. Welcher, **I**, 166, 202.
58. Sarma, B., *J. Sci. Ind. Research (India)*, **15B**, 696 (1956).
59. Misumi, S., *J. Chem. Soc. Japan*, **73**, 171, 173 (1952).
60. Oshchapovskiĭ, V. V., *Ukrain. Khim. Zhur.*, **22**, 383 (1956).
61. Schoeller, 166, 168.
62. Scott and Furman, 259.
63. Barthauer, G. L., *et al.*, *Ind. Eng. Chem., Anal. Ed.*, **15**, 548 (1943).
64. Flaschka, H., *Mikrochim. Acta*, 55 (1955).
65. Brunisholz, G. and Cahen, R., *Helv. Chim. Acta*, **39**, 324 (1956).
66. Rinehart, R. W., *Anal. Chem.*, **26**, 1820 (1954).
67. Rao, Bh. S. V. R., *et al.*, *J. Sci. Ind. Research (India)*, **14B**, 190 (1955).
68. Sarma, T. P. and Rao, Bh. S. V. R., *J. Sci. Ind. Research (India)*, **14B**, 450 (1955).
69. Holleck, L., *et al.*, *Angew. Chem.*, **65**, 347 (1953); *Z. anal. Chem.*, **146**, 103 (1955) (aluminon + sulfosalicylic acid).
70. Bamann, E. and Heumüller, E., *Ber.* **75B**, 1514 (1942).
71. Beydon, J., *Compt. rend.*, **224**, 1715 (1947) (study using radioisotope).
72. Moeller, T. and Kremers, H. E., *Ind. Eng. Chem., Anal. Ed.*, **17**, 44 (1945).
73. Kleinberg, J., *et al.*, *Ind. Eng. Chem., Anal. Ed.*, **11**, 368 (1939).
74. Gordon, L. and Shaver, K. L., *Anal. Chem.*, **25**, 784 (1953).
75. Foster, D. C. and Kremers, H. E., *Anal. Chem.*, **25**, 1921 (1953).
76. Brukl, A., *Angew. Chem.*, **50**, 25 (1937).
77. Moeller, T. and Kremers, H. E., *Ind. Eng. Chem., Anal. Ed.*, **17**, 798 (1945).
78. Moeller, T. and Brantley, J. C., *Anal. Chem.*, **22**, 433 (1950); Holleck, L. and Hartinger, L., *Angew. Chem.*, **67**, 648 (1955) (chlorides); Banks, Ch. V. and Klingman, D. W., *Anal. Chim. Acta*, **15**, 356 (1956) (in 1M $HClO_4$); also see Sandell, 506 (nitrates); Rodden, C. J., *J. Research Natl. Bur. Standards*, **26**, 557 (1941); **28**, 265 (1942); Schoeller and Powell, 105 (nitrates).
79. Banks, Ch. V., *et al.*, *Anal. Chem.*, **28**, 1894 (1956).
80. Rasin-Streden, R., *et al.*, *Mikrochim. Acta*, 512 (1956).
81. Albinati, J. F. P. de., *Anales asoc. quim. Arg.*, **43**, 106 (1955) (in U).
82. Moeller, T. and Jackson, D. E., *Anal. Chem.*, **22**, 1393 (1950).
83. Fassel, V. A. and Heidel, R. H., *Anal. Chem.*, **26**, 1135 (1954).
84. Misumi, S., *J. Chem. Soc. Japan*, **77**, 786 (1956).

ZIRCONIUM AND HAFNIUM

The principal references for this chapter are given in ref. 1. A number of special papers and reviews on the analytical chemistry of these metals has been published.[2, 3, 4, 5]

It should be noted that PO_4^{3-} ions may cause difficulties owing to the precipitation of Zr in strongly acidic solution. Zr compounds hydrolyze readily. A complex is formed between Zr and SO_4^{2-} ions and this can interfere in some methods of determination.

As a rule Zr contains 1–3% Hf. If the percentage of Hf is unknown, Zr should be weighed as the oxide. The ignition of Zr compounds must be done very slowly.

Attack

(a) Zirconium minerals. Fuse 4 g. borax in a Pt crucible, add a 0·3 g. sample of the powdered mineral gradually, heat on a Meker burner, stir with a Pt wire and cool. Add 150 ml. 1:5 HCl, followed, after dissoln., by 20 ml. H_2SO_4; evap. to fumes, cool, dil. to 100 ml. with H_2O and filter (ppt. 1). Leave the filtrate for 2 hr., filter on paper and wash with 5% NH_4NO_3 (ppt. 2). Treat the filtrate with 5 g. NH_4Cl and NH_4OH, filter on paper and wash with 2% NH_4NO_3. Treat this ppt. with 100 ml. 5% H_2SO_4 and filter (residue A and filtrate A). Combine ppts. 1 and 2 with residue A, ignite in the original Pt crucible, add HF and H_2SO_4 and evap. to dryness. Fuse with Na_2CO_3 and ext. with H_2O. Fuse the residue with $K_2S_2O_7$ and ext. with 5% H_2SO_4. Combine this extract with filtrate A, add H_2O until the H_2SO_4 concn. is 1%, pass H_2S and filter. Then add tartaric acid and NH_4OH, pass H_2S again and filter. Acidify the filtrate with H_2SO_4, add cupferron, etc. (see under Determination, p. 357).

For minerals contg. $< 0{\cdot}25$ g. ZrO_2, fuse with Na_2CO_3, ext. with H_2O (for detn. of P or F), and fuse the residue with $K_2S_2O_7$. Treat the residue and the soln. separately. Fusion with 1:1 Na_2CO_3–borax may be preferable. With ferruginous samples, evap. to dryness with 10 ml. HCl on a steam-bath, add 25 ml. of hot 1*N* HCl, filter and wash; ignite the residue and fuse as above before combining the filtrates.[6]

Zircon is fused with Na_2CO_3 or $Na_2S_2O_7$. Baddeyelite is fused with $K_2S_2O_7$.

Fusion with Na_2O_2 is done as follows: fuse a layer of Na_2CO_3 to the inner wall of a Pt or Ni crucible, coat this with a layer of fused Na_2O_2, add the sample and Na_2O_2 and fuse for 5–10 min.

Fusion with KOH, KHF_2, $KHF_2 + K_2S_2O_7$ (1:10), NH_4F (for detn. of alk. metals) or B_2O_3 has been suggested but all these methods are troublesome.

ZrO_2 can be dissolved with HF contg. some H_2SO_4.

Rocks are best dissolved in HF and $HClO_4$.

(b) Steels. Add 5–10 g. H_3BO_3 and 40–60 ml. HCl (s.g. 1·19) and heat at 80–90°C. Add 8–15 ml. 30% H_2O_2 and 25 ml. H_2O, heat for 1–2 min., add 350 ml. hot H_2O, enough NH_4OH to give a turbidity and then HCl to clear the soln. Add 10–20 g. Na_2SO_3 in 50 ml. hot H_2O followed by 20 ml. HCl and stir. Then add 8–10 g. $(NH_4)_2HPO_4$ in 50 ml. H_2O, etc.[7]

In another method, dissolve the steel in 1:4 HCl and ppt. with cupferron. Fuse the ppt. with $K_2S_2O_7$, filter, add H_2O_2 and $(NH_4)_2HPO_4$, etc.

With Fe–Zr, evap. to fumes with HF and H_2SO_4, add dil. HCl and a little HNO_3, boil, ext. with Et_2O, etc.

For Fe–W, treat with HCl and HNO_3, evap. the residue to dryness with HF and H_2SO_4, fuse with Na_2CO_3 and ext. with H_2O. Then fuse with $K_2S_2O_7$, add dil. H_2SO_4, ppt. with NH_4OH, treat the ppt. with HCl, etc.

(c) Zr metal. Heat a 5 g. sample with 3 ml. H_2SO_4 and 20 g. $(NH_4)_2SO_4$.

Separation

Zr and Hf can be sepd. from nearly all other elements by means of H_2SeO_3, $(NH_4)_2HAsO_4$, $(NH_4)_2HPO_4$, phenylarsonic acid or mandelic acid (see under Determination). For the sepns. possible with arsonic acids, see p. 357.

Sepn. from P, V, Cr and Mo is possible by fusion with Na_2CO_3 or Na_2O_2 and leaching with H_2O. Sepn. from W is obtained[8] by fusion with K_2CO_3 and leaching with H_2O; leaching with dil. KOH allows sepn. from Nb and Ta (see p. 378). Sepn. from Nb can be done by fusion with KOH or with K_2CO_3 and Na_2CO_3 followed by leaching with H_2O; here, sepn. from Ta is incomplete and Ti is divided between the phases.

Sepn. from group II follows from H_2S treatment of acidic solns. below 40–50°C. The filtrate must not be boiled; H_2 is passed to remove H_2S.

Treatment with NH_4OH and NH_4Cl seps. Zr and Hf from group IV metals and Mg. $(NH_4)_2S$ and $(NH_4)_2$-tartrate seps. them from a little Fe.

Sepn. from large amts. of Fe is possible by extn. with Et_2O. Electrolysis at the Hg-cathode from dil. H_2SO_4 solns. seps. Zr, Hf from Fe and other metals.

Cupferron seps. Zr, Hf from Fe^{2+}, Al, UO_2^{2+}, Cr, Bi, Mn, Ni, Co, Zn. (see p. 357).

Rare earths and Th are sepd. from Zr, Hf by HF or $H_2C_2O_4$; Th is sepd. with *m*-nitrobenzoic acid.

Sepn. from Ti is possible with KIO_3; Th interferes. To the $0{\cdot}3N$ H_2SO_4 soln. add 35 ml. 3% H_2O_2, dil. to 200 ml. with H_2O, add KIO_3 soln. (10 g. in 100 ml. H_2O contg. some drops of HNO_3), filter on a glass crucible after 3 hr. and wash with a soln. contg. 3 g. KIO_3 and 3 ml. H_2O_2 in 150 ml. H_2O. Incomplete sepn. of Zr and Hf from Ti is obtained with NH_4OH and NH_4-salicylate (see Chapter 50, p. 361). Complete sepn. is possible with NH_4F; treat the soln. with NH_4OH until a turbidity appears, add excess NH_4F, boil and add more NH_4OH. Zr is detd. in the filtrate after evapn. with H_2SO_4.

Treatment with $Ba(NO_3)_2$ and HF allows sepn. from U and Nb. To 40 ml. soln. contg. HNO_3, add 1 ml. HF, 20 ml. 5% $Ba(NO_3)_2$ for each 0·1 g. Zr and 3 ml. HF, allow to stand, add a little $Ba(NO_3)_2$ soln. and HF, filter on Whatman No. 42 paper and wash with H_2O. To det. Zr, dissolve the $BaZrF_6$ ppt. in 20 ml. HCl, 20 ml. 5% H_3BO_3 and 150 ml. H_2O and treat with cupferron.

Tannin allows sepn. of Zr, Hf from Al, Fe, Cr, rare earths, U, Be and Ni in chloride solns. (see p. 357). In $(NH_4)_2C_2O_4$ solns. sepn. from Ti, Nb and Ta is obtained (see Chapter 51, p. 374).

For extn. with tributylphosphate in *n*-Bu_2O, see p. 138. Zr is sepd. from Hf by extn. with thenoyltrifluoroacetone in C_6H_6 from $2M$ $HClO_4$ soln. (see Chapter 10, Section 2). Ion exchange resins also allow this sepn. (see Chapter 13, Section 4.3). For other sepns. of Zr from Hf, see refs. 9, 10, 11.

Determination

The gravimetric method with phosphate is the rapid and specific classical procedure but is said to be unreliable. The arsenate or H_2SeO_3 methods are greatly superior. Probably the arsenate procedure is the best gravimetric one, since it is accurate, reliable and relatively selective.[2] However, the *p*-bromomandelic acid procedure is described first below, because Hf can be determined simultaneously and Th and Ti do not interfere. Arsonic acids provide convenient gravimetric and colorimetric determinations in certain cases. Alizarin S or flavanol provides an excellent colorimetric procedure.

(a) ***p*-Bromomandelic acid** is employed gravimetrically or titrimetrically. For the former,[12] use a soln. contg. < 0·1 g. ZrO_2 in 50 ml. 1:5 HCl or in < 5% w/w H_2SO_4. Add 50 ml. $0{\cdot}1M$ reagent, heat at 80°C for 15–20 min., filter on paper and wash with cold H_2O. Ignite to ZrO_2 and weigh. For titrimetry[13] dissolve the ppt. in hot NH_4OH, add HCl and excess Ce^{4+}, boil and back-titrate with Fe^{2+} using ferroin indicator.

NOTES. (1) No interference arises from Fe, Al, Ti, Th, Ce, V, Cr, Sn, Bi, Sb, Cu, Cd, Ca, Ba, BO_2^-, tartrate or citrate.

(2) For detn. of Hf,[14] treat the soln. contg. 50–100 mg. oxides with 15 ml. HCl, dil to 40 ml. with H_2O, add 2 ml. H_2SO_4, heat to 85–95°C and add 20 ml. $0{\cdot}1M$ *p*-bromomandelic acid from a buret. Heat at 85–95°C for 10 min., add 30 ml. reagent, heat at the same temp. for 15–20 min. and leave for 10–20 min. Rinse the beaker wall with 10–15 ml. EtOH, leave for 30–40 min., transfer to a 50 ml. centrifuge tube, wash with 25 ml. $1N$ HCl and 1–2 ml. EtOH and centrifuge. Decant the supernate, add 25 ml. $1N$ HCl, stir for 1 min., add 1–2 ml. EtOH, centrifuge and decant. Add 25 ml. $1N$ HCl, stir and suck through a small Hirsch funnel contg. Whatman No. 40 paper. Wash twice with 20 ml. EtOH and twice with 20 ml. Et_2O, transfer to a Pt crucible, heat at 120–130°C for 1 hr. and weigh. Then ignite at 900–1000°C for 1–2 hr. and reweigh. For calculation, % HfO_2 = 274·2 − 33·40 × (wt. of salt/wt. of oxide). The error is ± 0·5% for > 10% HfO_2. For smaller amts. the H_2SeO_3 procedure is preferable. Interferences in the above method are Fe, Ti, Al.

(3) Several analogous reagents have been proposed. *p*-Chloromandelic acid is less satisfactory than the bromo compd. while mandelic acid itself is less satisfactory still, although the latter method is said to be accurate for 0·2 mg. Zr. With mandelic acid,[15, 16] treat 20 ml. HCl soln. with 50 ml. 16% reagent and dil. to 100 ml. with H_2O. (The optimum acidity is $2M$, the range being $0{\cdot}1$–$8M$). Heat slowly and digest at 80°C for 20 min. Filter on paper and wash with 2% HCl contg. 5% reagent. Ignite and weigh as ZrO_2, or dry at 110–120°C (60–188°C) and weigh as $Zr(C_6H_5CHOHCO_2)_4$. In an alternative procedure,[17] boil the soln., which is > $5M$ in HCl, add reagent dropwise, cool, filter, wash with EtOH and Et_2O and weigh as $Zr(C_8H_7O_3)_4$. If the acidity is less than $5M$, some basic salt ppts.

Mandelic acid can also be applied[18] colorimetrically by dissoln. of 0·5–50 mg. of the Zr ppt. in NH_4OH and measurement at 258 mμ.

(4) 1-Naphthylglycolic acid[19] ppts. Zr from $0{\cdot}1$–$0{\cdot}5N$ HCl or $0{\cdot}36$–$2{\cdot}5N$ H_2SO_4. *m*-Azo-β-naphtholmandelic acid may be used colorimetrically for 0·1–10 μg. Zr.[20]

(5) Various other carboxylic acids can be applied. Tetrachlorophthalic acid can be used similarly to mandelic acid.[21] With *m*-cresoxyacetic acid, SO_4^{2-} interferes. Ti interferes in the benzilic acid method. For other possibilities, see Chapter 11, Section 2.

(6) KH-phthalate allows a nephelometric detn. of 10–125 p.p.m. Zr.[22] To 5 ml. $0{\cdot}25N$ HCl soln. add 10 ml. reagent (7 g./l. $0{\cdot}25N$ HCl), stopper, place in boiling H_2O for 10 min., cool rapidly, shake, leave for 3–4 min. and measure at 430 mμ. Interferences in p.p.m. are 1 F^-, 1 PO_4^{3-}, 60 Fe, 100 Ti, 200 Cr, 500 ClO_4^- and 100 Th, etc. This reagent can also be used gravimetrically.[23]

(b) H_2SeO_3 provides an excellent gravimetric procedure;[1, 24] a titrimetric finish is also available. For < 0·1 g. Zr in 100–400 ml. soln. which is < 0·6*N* (< 0·3*N* for small amts. of Zr) in HCl or H_2SO_4 or < 0·38*N* in HNO_3, add 0·5–2 g. reagent, boil and place on a steam-bath for 5–12 hr. Filter on a G4 crucible, wash with 3:97 HCl, hot H_2O and cold H_2O, dry at 120–200°C and weigh as $Zr(SeO_3)_2$. Alternatively, filter on paper, heat with 6 ml. 1:1 H_2SO_4 and 5–10 ml. 3% NaF, filter on paper and wash with dil. H_2SO_4 contg. NaF. Dil. the filtrate to 200–300 ml. with H_2O, add 10–15 ml. 2% starch, some $NaHCO_3$ and 2–4 g. KI in soln. and titrate with 0·05–0·1*N* $Na_2S_2O_3$. The results of the gravimetric method are slightly high. The titrimetric finish is accurate for ZrO_2 but the error varies from +1% to +1·4% for HfO_2. The HfO_2 content can be calcd. from the 2 detns. if required.

NOTES. (1) No interference is caused by Al, Cr, Fe, Co, Ni, Cu, U, V^{4+} and some of the rare earths. Interference of Ti or Ce is prevented by H_2O_2, that of V^{5+} by EtOH. Th, Nb, Ta, Sn, WO_4^{2-}, PO_4^{3-}, $C_2O_4^{2-}$ and large amts. of SO_4^{2-} interfere; 0·5 g. Na_2SO_4 is permissible in 400 ml. 0·6*N* H_2SO_4 soln.

(2) It is usually necessary to reppt. when other elements are present. If desired, the ppt, can be ignited to ZrO_2 in the same way as the arsenate ppt. If Th is present, the above method can be combined with the phosphate method.[25] Ppt. as above, add 40 ml. 10% $H_2C_2O_4$ and filter (this is unnecessary if Th is absent); then add 50 ml. 1:1 H_2SO_4, heat, add 50 ml. 20% $(NH_4)_2HPO_4$, leave for 2 hr., filter, etc.

(c) $(NH_4)_2HAsO_4$ also allows a good gravimetric detn.[1, 26] For 0·1 g. Zr as chloride in 360 ml. 2·75*N* HCl or 3·75*N* HNO_3 soln. add 50 ml. 1% reagent soln. dropwise, boil, add 15 ml. 10% reagent. Boil for 20 min., filter on paper, decant and wash with 1*N* HCl and then with hot H_2O. Return to the original beaker with H_2O, evap. to a syrup, wash the filter paper with a mixt. of 82 ml. HCl and 100 ml. H_2O and add this soln. Warm, dil. to 360 ml. with H_2O, cool and reppt. as above using 10 ml. 10% reagent. Filter on double paper, wash with hot 1*N* HCl and hot H_2O and place in a porcelain crucible. Dry at 110°C, heat slowly over a Bunsen and finally on a Meker burner for 1 hr. Weigh as ZrO_2.

NOTES. (1) No interference arises from Cu, Cd, Fe, Al, Ni, Co, Zn, Mn, Cr, V, Mo, U, Ce^{3+}, Mg or group IV or V elements. Interferences are W, Nb, Ta and large amts. of SO_4^{2-}. Th, Sn, Bi, Be require repptn. H_2O_2 prevents interference of Ce^{4+} and Ti; Ti should be detd. colorimetrically in the ppt. and a correction made.

(2) Pptn. can also be done with 10% H_3AsO_4 in a soln. contg. 2*N* HCl finally.[27] Ignite the ppt. to a moderate heat, weigh, transfer to a Pt crucible, treat with HF and H_2SO_4, ignite above 1100°C, weigh as ZrO_2 and apply a correction.

(3) Filtration through a double paper is unnecessary if the ppt. is ignited with sugar carbon.[2] The ppt. can also be weighed as $(ZrO)_2As_2O_7$ (Sarudi[26]). If W is present, ppt. with NH_4OH, filter, ignite, fuse with Na_2CO_3, leach with hot H_2O, filter, ignite, fuse with $K_2S_2O_7$, add hot H_2O and NH_4OH, filter, return to the beaker, dissolve in HCl and proceed as above.

(d) $(NH_4)_2HPO_4$ is the classical gravimetric method;[1, 7, 28, 29] the ppt. tends to be very difficult to filter. For 0·5 mg. ZrO_2 in 25 ml. 20% w/v (10% v/v) H_2SO_4 soln. or for 0·1 g. ZrO_2 in 200 ml. soln., add H_2O_2 and 10% reagent in a 10–100-fold excess. Add some filter paper pulp and digest at 40–50°C for 2–12 hr. Filter on Whatman No. 40 paper and wash 3–4 times with 100 ml. H_2SO_4 (s.g. 1·20) contg. 0·5 g. $(NH_4)_2HPO_4$ and several drops of 30% H_2O_2; then wash 6–10 times with 5% NH_4NO_3. Heat very slowly, ignite at 1200°C (> 850°C) and weigh as ZrP_2O_7.

NOTES. (1) Th and Ce require repptn. No interference is caused by Al, V, U, Co, Ni, Zn, Mn, Cu, As, Mo. Interferences are Nb, Ta, and much Cr. Fe^{3+} (> 0·1 g.) needs reduction with Na_2SO_3. With Sn or W present, fuse the ppt. with Na_2CO_3, leach with H_2O, fuse with $K_2S_2O_7$, leach with H_2O and reppt. Ti requires addn. of 10 ml. 30% H_2O_2 and colorimetric detn. in the ppt. The method is used for analysis of various alloys.[28, 30]

(2) When Zr exceeds 2 mg., some P_2O_5 is lost by washing unless the above wash soln. is used. It may be better to weigh as the oxide: treat the ppt. with HF, add dil. NaOH, filter and repeat this process before adding HCl and NH_4OH and igniting. Alternatively, fuse the ppt. with Na_2CO_3, ext. with H_2O, repeat several times, fuse with $K_2S_2O_7$, add dil. H_2SO_4, pass H_2S, filter, add NH_4OH and reppt.; then ignite to ZrO_2. It is possible to det. Hf from the weights of the phosphate and oxide.[30, 31]

(3) For titrimetric detn.[32] of 50–100 mg. ZrO_2 in dil. $HClO_4$ soln., ppt. with alkali phosphate and titrate the PO_4^{3-} in the filtrate with $BiOClO_4$ soln. using diallyldithiocarbamidohydrazine indicator in $CHCl_3$.

(4) For colorimetry,[33] treat the soln. with excess KH_2PO_4 and det. PO_4^{3-} in the filtrate by the molybdate method. Alternatively, for 1·7 μg.–1·7 mg. of the Zr ppt., add satd. NaK-tartrate soln. and 1*N* KOH (if Zr < 10 μg., add 10–20 μg. P), neutralize with HCl to *p*-nitrophenol indicator, add molybdate and apply the $SnCl_2$ reduction method.

(5) Metaphosphoric acid can be applied gravimetrically.[34] For 0·2–200 mg. Zr in 150–200 ml. 3·6*N* H_2SO_4 soln. add 5 g. reagent in 25 ml. H_2O, and 5 ml. 30% H_2O_2 if Ti is present; after 12 hr., heat near the b.p. for 1 hr., allow to cool, filter on Whatman No. 40 paper, wash with 300–500 ml. 5% NH_4NO_3, ignite at 900–950°C (> 700°C) and weigh as ZrP_2O_7. Interferences are Bi, Sn, ClO_4^-, and moderate amts. of Fe, Ti, Th (repptn. is needed). No interference arises from Al, As^{5+}, B, Cd, Cr, Ce^{3+}, Ca, Cu, Mg, Mn, Hg, Ni, K, Na, V, Y, Zn; Sb requires tartrate addn. Pptn. is possible from HNO_3 media; results are low with HCl media.

Trimethyl phosphate can be used similarly to metaphosphoric acid; interferences are similar.[34]

(e) Alizarin S is probably the best colorimetric reagent for Zr and Hf.[35, 36] For 20–250 μg. Zr in 90 ml. soln., add HCl to give a final concn. of 0·20*N*, 1 ml. 10% thioglycolic acid, wait 1–2 min., add 2·00 ml. 0·05% alizarin S, dil. to 100 ml. with H_2O, leave for 1 hr. and measure at 525 mμ.

NOTES. (1) No interference arises from Th, Ti, Al, Fe^{2+}, Mn, Ca, etc. Interferences are F^-, PO_4^{3-}, SiO_2, Mo, Sb, W and org. acids contg. OH groups, and > 20 mg. SO_4^{2-}.
(2) For 1·0–1·6 mg. Zr in 15 ml. 1*M* $HClO_4$ soln.,[37] add 3 ml. 0·05% reagent in 0·1*M* $HClO_4$ and 5 ml. Me_2CO, dil. to 25 ml. with 1*M* $HClO_4$ and measure after 30 min. at 530 mμ using a differential method. In another procedure,[38] add Me_2CO, adjust to pH 0·7 and heat at 70–90°C for 10–30 min. Various other modifications have been suggested.[39]
(3) Several analogous reagents may be applied. Chloranilic acid is suitable for detn. of 0·18–4·6 μg. Zr/ml. in 1–2*M* $HClO_4$ soln. with measurement at 340 mμ.[40] Alizarin allows detn. of 5–100 μg. Zr in 1 ml. 2*N* HCl soln.;[41] add 0·50 ml. 0·125% alizarin in EtOH, make alk. with NH_4OH, neutralize after 2 min. with 1*N* HCl, add 0·1 ml. 7*N* HCl, dil. to 25 ml. with EtOH and measure at 650 mμ.
Quinalizarin yields a complex which is measured at 620 mμ; the reagent is 2–3 times more sensitive than alizarin but Beer's law is not obeyed.[41]

(f) Flavanol is a satisfactory colorimetric reagent for Zr and Hf.[42] For 10–50 μg. Zr in 0·2*N* H_2SO_4 soln. add 1 ml. 0·01% flavanol in EtOH, dil. to 25 ml. with 0·2*N* H_2SO_4 and measure the fluorescence after 20 min. at the Hg-line 365 mμ. In 55% MeOH media contg. 0·8*M* $HClO_4$, the complex can be measured at 385 mμ ($\epsilon = 2 \times 10^4$).

NOTES. (1) Very few elements interfere; 0·25 mg. Al gives an interference corresponding to 1 μg. Zr. Fe^{3+} is best removed by Hg-cathode electrolysis. F^- and PO_4^{3-} are removed by fusion with 3:1 Na_2CO_3–borax glass and extn. with H_2O.
(2) Quercetin is suitable for 5–50 μg. Zr in 15 ml. soln. contg. 5·2 ml. HCl[43]. Add 5 ml. EtOH and 3 ml. 0·1% reagent in EtOH, dil. to 25 ml. with H_2O and measure at 440 mμ. Interferences are $C_2O_4^{2-}$, F^-, PO_4^{3-}, Sc, Ga, Hg^+, Ti, Hf, Th, Ge, Sn, V, Cr, Mo, W, Fe, Sb, Nb, Ta and Pt metals, hence sepn. with pararsonic acid is necessary.
(3) Myricetin allows measurement of the Zr complex at 425 mμ ($\epsilon = 2 \cdot 5 \times 10^4$) (Hörhammer[42]). Morin is applied fluorimetrically for < 4 μg. Zr in 25 ml. 2*M* HCl soln.[44] Thioglycolic acid prevents interference of Fe^{3+}; Al, Ga, Th, U, Sn, Sb, are corrected for by deducting the residual absorbance after EDTA addn. Ge and Se interfere but most other elements do not. In an alternative procedure,[45] the color formed with < 5 μg. Zr/ml. in 0·4–0·7*N* HCl soln. is measured at 436 mμ.
(4) Phenylfluorone provides a detn. of < 50 μg. Zr in 20 ml. of at least 0·1*N* HCl soln.[46] Add 10 ml. EtOH, 5 ml. cyclohexanol, 10 ml. reagent soln. (0·6 mg./ml. EtOH) and 0·1*N* HCl to give a vol. of 50 ml.; measure at 540 mμ after 2 hr. Small amts. of Fe, Ti, Ge, Sn, Sb^{3+}, F^-, $C_2O_4^{2-}$ and HPO_4^{2-} interfere. The procedure is 40–50 times more sensitive than that with alizarin S.

(g) *n*-Propylarsonic acid can be applied gravimetrically.[30, 47] For < 0·1 g. Zr in 100 ml. 1·2*N* HCl soln., boil, add 5% reagent, place on a steam-bath for 0·5–1 hr., filter on paper, wash with H_2O, ignite above 960°C and weigh as ZrO_2.

NOTES. (1) No interference arises from Al, Be, Fe, Ti, V, U, Ce, Th, Cr, Co, Zn, Mn, Tl, Mo, Cu, Cd, Mg or a little W. Sb, Bi, Nb, Ta and large amts. of H_2SO_4 interfere; Sn interference is avoided by heating the ignited oxide with NH_4I (see Chapter 27, p. 206).
(2) Other arsonic acids can be used but the number of interfering elements increases. Phenylarsonic acid is used gravimetrically or nephelometrically.[30, 47] For < 0·1 g. Zr in 200 ml. 10% v/v HCl or H_2SO_4 soln., add 10 ml. 10% phenylarsonic acid, boil for 1 min., filter on paper, wash with 1% HCl, ignite in air and then in H_2 and weigh as ZrO_2. Interferences are Nb, Ta, Sn, W, SiO_2, and large amts. of Fe^{3+}; Ti requires addn. of H_2O_2 and more reagent; PO_4^{3-} requires pptn. from 10% H_2SO_4 soln., dissoln. in 1:1 H_2SO_4 and repptn.
p-Hydroxyphenylarsonic acid is used gravimetrically for pptn. of Zr from 2·5–3*N* HCl soln.[30, 47] Interferences are Ce^{4+}, Th, Sn, W, PO_4^{3-}, much SO_4^{2-}, Ti (add H_2O_2) and large amts. of Fe (add NH_4SCN).
Other reagents applied gravimetrically are arrhenal and atoxyl.[30, 47]
(3) Pararsonic acid is useful colorimetrically for Zr in slightly acidic (HCl) soln.[47] Add 15 ml. reagent (0·25 g. in 10 ml. HCl, dild. to 250 ml. with EtOH), boil for 1 min. leave for 30 min., filter on triple Whatman No. 42 paper, wash with a soln. of 10 ml. HCl/1. H_2O, dissolve in 1:2 NH_4OH by passing it 3–4 times through the filter, pass through a cotton layer and measure at 450 mμ. A procedure suitable for 1–10 μg. of the Zr ppt. can be used to det. Zr in U.[48]
(4) Thoron allows colorimetric detn. of 10–100 μg. Zr.[49] To the soln. add 5 drops 20% $NH_2OH{\cdot}HCl$, 7 drops HCl and 1·0 ml. 0·2% thoron, dil. to 10 ml. with H_2O, heat at 75–80°C for 5 min., cool and measure at 555 mμ. No interference arises from Co, Al, Cu, Cd, SO_4^{2-}, Fe^{2+} or Sn^{2+}. Interferences are Hf (2·1 μg. = 1 μg. Zr), 1 μg. Ce_4^+, 1 μg. F^-, 10 μg. PO_4^{3-}, 100 μg. Ti, 1 mg. Sn^{4+}, U, Fe, Cr^{3+}, and Mo in 10-fold amts.
Neothoron is also applicable colorimetrically.[50]

(h) Cupferron may be used gravimetrically, titrimetrically or colorimetrically. For gravimetry,[1] add excess of cold 6% cupferron to the 10% v/v H_2SO_4 soln. at 5–6°C, then add filter pulp, filter on paper and wash with 1:10 HCl. The ppt. should be white; a yellow color indicates Ti and brown shows Fe or V. Ignite the ppt. above 745°C and weigh as ZrO_2. Interferences are Ti, Th, rare earths, Fe, V, Nb, Ta, W, U^{4+}, SiO_2, group II elements and large amts. of group V elements. Al, Cr, U^{6+}, Be, BO_2^-, tartrate and a little PO_4^{3-} can be tolerated; F^- requires addn. of more reagent.

Amperometric titration of Zr with cupferron is possible.[51] Colorimetry is possible with a nitrate soln. and cupferron;[52] a special procedure allows detn. of the Hf–Zr ratio.

(i) Tannin is applied gravimetrically.[53] For 0·1 g. ZrO_2 as chloride, add 20 ml. satd. NH_4Cl soln., dil. to

200 ml. with H_2O and add HCl to give a concn. of 0·25*N* (if V or Th is present, add HCl to give a 0·5*N* soln.). Boil, add 1 g. tannin in soln., boil for 1 min., cool and leave for 2 hr. Filter on Whatman No. 41 paper contg. paper pulp and wash with a soln. contg. 50 ml. satd. NH_4Cl and 25 ml. HCl in 500 ml. Treat the filtrate with 7·5*N* NH_4OH until only 2–3 ml. HCl is unneutralized, cool, combine the ppts., ignite and weigh as ZrO_2.

NOTES. (1) Ti, Sn and SO_4^{2-} interfere but U, V, Th and di- and tri-valent elements can be tolerated. If Ti is present, adjust the acidity of the filtrate to 0·01–0·05*N* HCl (pH 2–3), combine the ppts., ignite and det. Ti in the oxide. If V is present, moisten the filter paper with 2% NH_4Cl in 0·5*N* acid and remove V by fusing the ignited oxide with Na_2CO_3.
(2) Hydrazine sulfate ppts. Zr at pH 2·8; Fe, Ti, Al, U, Sn interfere but Th, Be, Ni and rare earths do not.[54] NH_4OH and several other reagents can, of course, be used.[30]

(j) Miscellaneous gravimetric methods. Oxine allows detn. of 12 mg. Zr as nitrate in 50 ml. soln.[30, 55] Heat to 50–60°C, add 3% oxine in EtOH and 50–70 ml. 2*N* NH_4OAc and heat. Filter on a G4 crucible, wash with hot NH_4OAc soln. and cold H_2O, dry at 115–140°C (?) and weigh as $Zr(C_9H_6ON)_4$. No ppt. is formed in HCl or H_2SO_4 solns.

Benzoquinaldic acid ppts. Zr above pH 1·8; the ppt. must be ignited (see Chapter 46, p. 341).

(k) EDTA titration can be used with several indicators. For 0·003–0·005*M* Zr soln.,[56] adjust to pH 1·4, add 2 drops 0·4% eriochrome cyanine R indicator and titrate slowly with 0·05*M* EDTA. Alternatively, add the above indicator or alizarol cyanine R and a small excess of EDTA, adjust to pH 1·4, heat almost to boiling and back-titrate with 0·05*M* Zr soln.

NOTES. (1) With eriochrome cyanine R indicator, interferences are Cu, Hf, Th, Ag, Bi, Mo, Sb, W, F^-, SO_4^{2-}, PO_4^{3-}, $C_2O_4^{2-}$ and tartrate; if Ti or Sn is present, add excess reagent at pH 0·5. A soln. contg. 0·15–0·25 m*M* Zr and < 1m*M* Fe in 50 ml. soln. is analyzed by adjusting to pH 1, passing the soln. through a Jones reductor and titrating under N_2. Al interferes with alizarol cyanine RC as do most of the ions indicated above.
(2) Excess EDTA can be titrated with Bi^{3+} soln. in presence of thiourea indicator.[56] Chrome azurol S may be used in a direct titration.[57] Back-titration with Fe^{3+} soln. using salicylic acid[58] or benzohydroxamic acid (photometrically)[59] are other possibilities. SPADNS can serve as indicator in 0·01*N* HCl soln.[60]

(l) Miscellaneous titrimetric methods. The ppt. formed by Zr with oxalohydroxamic acid (> 10 mg.) can be dissolved in dil. HCl, heated with $TiCl_3$ soln. and back-titrated with Fe^{3+} soln.[61] For < 10 mg. ppt., dissolve in 10% AcOH, add Fe^{3+} and measure the purple color at 500 mμ.

1-Nitroso-2-naphthol is suitable for an amperometric titration;[62] interferences are Cu, Co, Fe, Pd, Ni and large amts. of F^-.

Pptn. with KIO_3 can be followed by iodometric titration.[63, 64] For 1–4 mg. Zr in 10 ml. 5*N* HNO_3 soln., add 10 ml. 10% KIO_3 in 5*N* HNO_3, filter after 30–40 min. and wash 3–4 times with 15–20 ml. 0·8% KIO_3 in 0·75*N* HNO_3, 3–4 times with 10–15 ml. EtOH, and finally with 2–4 ml. EtOH. Dry at 40–45°C for 10–15 min., wash into a flask, add 20 ml. 2·5*N* HCl and 10 ml. 10% KI, dil. to 60–80 ml. with H_2O and titrate with 0·1*N* $Na_2S_2O_3$. The ppt. formed is $2Zr(IO_3)_4 \cdot KIO_3 \cdot 8H_2O$. The method is inaccurate if Zr is < 1 mg.

Zr can be titrated in HNO_3-contg. soln. with 0·526*M* NaF to a potentiometric end-point with a Zr electrode.[65] For other methods, see ref. 64.

(m) Miscellaneous colorimetric methods. Hematoxylin allows colorimetric detn. of 0·04–0·20 mg. Zr.[66] Add 10 ml. HCl, dil. to 95 ml. with H_2O, add 2 ml. 0·1% hematoxylin (adjusted to pH 5·8), dil. to 100 ml. with H_2O and measure at 500 mμ after 2–3 hr. Interferences are Fe, Ti, F^- and PO_4^{3-}.

SPADNS is suitable for 7–56 μg. ZrO_2 in 0·5*N* HCl soln.[67] Add 3 ml. 0·1% reagent, dil. to 25 ml. with H_2O and measure at 580 mμ.

Fast grey RA is used for 0·2–10 μg. Zr in 1 ml. 0·1*N* HCl soln.;[68] add 5 ml. 0·4*N* HCl, 3 ml. 0·005% reagent and H_2O to give a vol. of 10 ml., and measure at 570 mμ after 20–50 min. Cu and Ni interfere but U, Co, Al, Th, Bi, Zn and rare earths can be tolerated; Fe^{3+} must be reduced with ascorbic acid.

Pyrocatechol violet allows detn. of 3–60 μg. Zr.[69] Add 3 ml. 0·1*M* EDTA (or more if large amts. of other metals are present) and 1 drop methyl red. Make alk. with NH_4OH, acidify with HCl, add buffer soln. (27 g. NaOAc/l. adjusted to pH 5·2 with AcOH) and 2 ml. 0·001*M* pyrocatechol violet, dil. to 25 ml. with buffer and measure at 620 mμ after 30 min., using a similar soln. contg. 1–2 drops 1% NH_4F as reference. U, Ti, Cr, Th, Y can be present, but Sb, Sn, Hg^+ and F^- interfere.

References

1. HILLEBRAND and LUNDELL, 442 (564); SCOTT and FURMAN, 1093; SCHOELLER and POWELL, 134; PIGOTT 538; FRESENIUS–JANDER **IVb**, 170 (1950).
2. COPPIETERS, I. V., *Ing. chim.* (*Milan*), **22**, 179, 233 (1938).
3. CLAASSEN, A., *et al.*, *Rec. trav. chim.*, **61**, 103, 299 (1942).
4. CHERNIKOV, YU. A. and DOBKINA, B. M., *Zavodskaya Lab.*, **23**, 1019 (1957).
5. EINECKE, E. and HARMS, J., *Z. anal. Chem.*, **99**, 113, (1934); HARTMANN, W. M., *ibid.*, **92**, 430 (1933).
6. SCHOELLER and POWELL, 148.
7. CUNNINGHAM, T. R. and PRICE, R. J., *Ind. Eng. Chem., Anal. Ed.*, **5**, 334 (1933).
8. SCHOELLER, 92
9. GMELIN, PT. **43**, 9 (1941).
10. WILLARD, H. H. and FREUND, H., *Ind. Eng. Chem., Anal. Ed.*, **18**, 195 (1946).

11. FUJIWARA, S., *Analysis and Reagents* (*Japan*), **2**, 245 (1948).
12. OESPER, R. E. and KLINGENBERG, J. J., *Anal. Chem.*, **21**, 1509 (1949); KLINGENBERG and PAPUCCI, R. A., *ibid.*, **24**, 1861 (1952); **27**, 835 (1955) (in Mg alloy); PAPUCCI *et al.*, *ibid.*, **25**, 1758 (1953) (Al alloy).
13. VERMA, M. R., and PAUL, S. D., *Nature*, **173**, 1237 (1954).
14. HAHN, R. B., *Anal. Chem.*, **23**, 1259 (1951).
15. HAHN, *Anal. Chem.*, **21**, 1579 (1949); KUMINS, C. A., *ibid.*, **19**, 376 (1947).
16. GAVIOLI, G. and TRALDI, E., *Met. ital.*, **42**, 179 (1950); ASTANIN, A. A. and OSTROUMOV, E. A., *Zhur. Anal. Khim.*, **6**, 27 (1951); JONCKERS, M. D. E., *Chim. anal.*, **32**, 207 (1950); MILLS, E. C. and HERMON, S. E., *Analyst*, **78**, 256 (1953) (low results when Zr <3 mg.; heat on steam bath for 18 hr.); BELCHER, R., *et al.*, *Anal. Chim. Acta*, **10**, 37 (1954).
17. HAHN, R. B. and BAGINSKI, E. S., *Anal. Chim. Acta*, **14**, 45 (1956).
18. HAHN and WEBER, L., *Anal. Chem.*, **28**, 414 (1956).
19. HAHN and JOSEPH, P. T., *Anal. Chem.*, **28**, 2019 (1956).
20. OESPER, *et al.*, *Anal. Chem.*, **24**, 1492 (1952).
21. MURTY, P. S. and RAO, BH. S. V. R., *Z. anal. Chem.*, **141**, 93 (1953).
22. LEONARD, JR., G. W., *et al.*, *Anal. Chem.*, **26**, 1621 (1954).
23. PURUSHOTTAM, A. and RAO, BH. S. V. R., *Analyst*, **75**, 684 (1950).
24. CLAASSEN, A., *Z. anal. Chem.*, **117**, 252 (1939); SCHUMB, W. C. and PITTMAN, F. K., *Ind. Eng. Chem., Anal. Ed.*, **14**, 512 (1942); LARSEN, E. M., *et al.*, *Inorg. Syntheses*, **3**, 69 (1950).
25. SIMPSON, S. G. and SCHUMB, *Ind. Eng. Chem., Anal. Ed.*, **7**, 36 (1935).
26. SCHUMB, W. C. and NOLAN, E. J., *Ind. Eng. Chem., Anal. Ed.*, **9**, 371 (1937); GUMP, J. R. and SHERWOOD, G. R., *Anal. Chem.*, **22**, 496 (1950) (homogeneous pptn.); also see SARUDI, I., *Z. anal. Chem.*, **131**., 416 (1950).
27. CLAASSEN, A. and VISSER, J., *Rec. trav. chim.*, **62**, 172 (1943).
28. A.S.T.M., 121, 216.
29. CLAASSEN, A. and VISSER, J., *Rec. trav. chim.*, **61**, 103 (1942).
30. FRESENIUS–JANDER, **IV**b, 170 ff.
31. FUJIWARA, S., *Analysis and Reagents* (*Japan*), **2**, 241 (1948).
32. SUBBARAMAN, P. R. and RAJAN, K. S., *J. Sci. Ind. Research* (*India*), **13B**, 31 (1954).
33. KIEFER, K. W. and BOLTZ, D. F., *Anal. Chem.*, **24**, 542 (1952); NOZAKI, T., *J. Chem. Soc. Japan*, **75**, 582 (1954).
34. WILLARD, H. H. and HAHN, R. B., *Anal. Chem.*, **21**, 293 (1949).
35. SANDELL, 638.
36. GREEN, D. E., *Anal. Chem.*, **20**, 372 (1948); WENGERT, G. B., *ibid.*, **24**, 1449 (1952).
37. MANNING, D. L. and WHITE, J. C., *Anal. Chem.*, **27**, 1389 (1955).
38. SILVERMAN, L. and HAWLEY, D. W., *Anal. Chem.*, **28**, 806 (1956).
39. MEYER, A. and BRADSHAW, G., *Analyst*, **77**, 476 (1952); MILLS, E. C. and HERMON, S. E., *Metallurgia*, **51**, 157 (1955) (in Al metal); GÜBELI, O. and JACOB, A., *Helv. Chim. Acta*, **38**, 1026 (1955); DEGENHARDT, H., *Z. anal. Chem.*, **153**, 327 (1956) (in rock).
40. THAMER, B. J. and VOIGT, A. F., *J. Am. Chem. Soc.*, **73**, 3197 (1951); FROST-JONES, R. E. U. and YARDLEY, J. T., *Analyst*, **77**, 460 (1952); MENIS, O., *Anal. Chem.*, **26**, 1854 (1954); BRICKER, C. E. and WATERBURY, G. R., *ibid.*, **29**, 558 (1957) (in Pu, etc.); HAHN, R. B. and JOHNSON, J. L., *ibid.*, 902 (in steel, Hg-cathode electrolysis).
41. WELCHER, **IV**, 417, 467; FRESENIUS–JANDER, **IV**b, 239.
42. ALFORD, W. C., *et al.*, *Anal. Chem.*, **23**, 1149 (1951); HÖRHAMMER, L., *et al.*, *Z. anal. Chem.*, **148**, 251 (1955).
43. GRIMALDI, F. S. and WHITE, C. E., *Anal. Chem.*, **25**, 1886 (1953).
44. GEIGER, R. A. and SANDELL, E. B., *Anal. Chim. Acta*, **16**, 346 (1957).
45. TŮMA, H. and TIETZ, N., *Chem. listy*, **51**, 722 (1957).
46. KIMURA, K. and SANO, H., *Bull. Chem. Soc. Japan*, **30**, 80 (1957).
47. WELCHER, **IV**, 52 ff.
48. RUSSEL, E. R., *U.S. Atomic Energy Comm.*, DP-161 (1956).
49. HORTON, A. D., *Anal. Chem.*, **25**, 1331 (1953).
50. KUZNETSOV, V. I., *et al.*, *Zavodskaya Lab.*, **22**, 406 (1956).
51. OLSON, E. C. and ELVING, P. J., *Anal. Chem.*, **26**, 1747 (1954); **27**, 1817 (1955); **28**, 251 (1956) (in Mg alloy).
52. FUJIWARA, S., via *Kagaku-Shusho*, **X**, 130, Kawade, Tokyo (1948).
53. SCHOELLER, W. R., *Analyst*, **69**, 260 (1944); HOLNESS, H. and KEAR, R. W., *ibid.*, **74**, 505 (1949); PURUSHOTTAM, A. and RAO, BH, S. V. R., *ibid.*, **75**, 555 (1950); *Rec. trav. chim.*, **70**, 555 (1951); WELCHER, **II**, 169.
54. VENKATESWARLU, C. and RAO, BH, S. V. R., *J. Indian Chem. Soc.*, **27**, 395 (1950).
55. WELCHER, **I**, 295.
56. FRITZ, J. S. and FULDA, M. O., *Anal. Chem.*, **26**, 206 (1954); FRITZ and JOHNSON, M., *ibid.*, **27**, 1653 (1955).
57. MUSIL, A. and THEIS, M., *Z. anal. Chem.*, **144**, 427 (1955).
58. MILNER, G. W. C., *et al.*, *Analyst*, **79**, 475 (1954); **80**, 879 (1955).
59. MILNER and BARNET, G. A., *Anal. Chim. Acta*, **14**, 414 (1956).
60. BANERJEE, G., *Z. anal. Chem.*, **147**, 105 (1955).
61. DHAR, S. K., and DAS GUPTA, A. K., *J. Sci. Ind. Research* (*India*), **11B**, 500 (1952).
62. WILSON, R. F. and RHODES, TH., *Anal. Chem.*, **28**, 1189 (1956).
63. CHERNIKHOV, YU, A. and USPENSKAYA, T. A., *Zavodskaya Lab.*, **10**, 248 (1941); CHERNIKHOV and KUCHMISTAYA, G. I., *ibid.*, **23**, 14 (1957).
64. FRESENIUS–JANDER, **IV**b, 244.
65. MEGREGIAN, S., *Anal. Chem.*, **29**, 1063 (1957).
66. TAKETATSU, T., *J. Chem. Soc. Japan*, **74**, 1011 (1953).
67. BANERJEE, G., *Naturwissenschaften*, **42**, 177 (1955); *Anal. Chim. Acta*, **16**, 62 (1957).
68. KHALIFA, H. and ZAKI, M. R., *Z. anal. Chem.*, **158**, 1 (1957).
69. FLASCHKA, H. and SADEK, F., *Z. anal. Chem.*, **150**, 339 (1956); FLASCHKA, H. and FARAH, M. Y., *ibid.*, **152**, 401 (1956).

50

TITANIUM

The principal sources for this chapter are given in ref. 1. Several monographs on the chemistry of titanium have been published.[2, 3, 4] The analytical chemistry of the element has been reviewed.[5, 6] Very many papers have appeared dealing with the analysis of titanium metals and alloys.

It should be noted that titanium compounds are usually readily hydrolyzed. TiF_4 is volatile but it can be heated in presence of H_2SO_4. The hydroxide is very difficult to dissolve completely from filter paper. Titanium phosphate is insoluble.

Attack

The relevant sections of the chapters on Nb, Ta and Zr should be referred to (p. 365 and 354).

(a) Minerals. Treat with HF, H_2SO_4 and a few drops of HNO_3; evap. to fumes until no F^- remains. Fusion with NaOH, NaOH + Na_2CO_3, or with Na_2O_2 is used in ind. analysis. Fusion with 10:1 Na_2CO_3–KNO_3 is suitable for detn. of P, Cr, V and S or if much SiO_2 is present. Fusion with KHF_2, 1:6 KF–$Na_2S_2O_7$, or with borax is also possible.

For bauxite, evap. to fumes with 50 ml. mixed acids (100 ml. HNO_3, 300 ml. HCl and 60 ml. H_2SO_4), treat the residue with H_2SO_4 and HF, evap. and fuse with $Na_2S_2O_7$. With rutile or ilmenite, fuse with $Na_2S_2O_7$ (1:12·5 for rutile and 1:35 for ilmenite) and ext. with acid; some Ti is retained by Nb and Ta oxides. For the tannin method, see ref. 7.

(b) Ti metal. Dissolve in dil. HCl. Heating with concd. HCl may be necessary. Pure TiO_2 is dissolved by heating with H_2SO_4 and $(NH_4)_2SO_4$.

(c) Iron ores. Dissolve in HCl and H_2SO_4; treat the residue with HF and H_2SO_4. Alternatively, heat the sample with H_2SO_4 and H_3PO_4.

(d) Steels. Dissolve in 1:1 HCl; treat the residue with HF and $HClO_4$. 55% $HClO_4$, HNO_3, aqua regia, or HCl, HNO_3 and H_2SO_4 may also be used.

For Ni–Cr steels, treat with dil. HCl, ppt. with cupferron, ignite and fuse with $K_2S_2O_7$; if Cu or V is present, sepn. with NH_4OH or NaOH resp. is necessary. This process is followed by H_2O_2 treatment and colorimetry.

For Fe–Ti, treat 0·5 g. with dild. aqua regia, add H_2SO_4 and evap. to fumes. Cool, add H_2O and some HCl, and filter. Ignite, treat with HF and H_2SO_4, fuse with $KHSO_4$, add dil. H_2SO_4 and combine with the initial filtrate.

(e) Ni metal. Dissolve in dil. HNO_3, add Fe^{3+} and NH_4OH and apply a colorimetric finish with tiron.

(f) Al metal. Treat with NaOH and then with HNO_3 and H_2SO_4.

Separation

Ti can be sepd. from Sn by heating in a stream of H_2, or by fusion with $KHSO_4$, extn. with dil. tartaric acid soln. and treatment with H_2S (see Chapter 51, p. 373).

Treatment with H_2S of the 0·3N H_2SO_4 soln. contg. 0·2 g. TiO_2 and 1 g. tartaric acid in 100 ml., seps. Ti from group II elements. Treatment of a soln. contg. NH_4OH, $(NH_4)_2$-tartrate and $NaHSO_3$ seps. Ti, Al, Be, Nb, Ta, Cr, Zr from Fe, Co, Ni, Zn and partly from Mn. If much Fe is present, the ppt. is fused with $KHSO_4$ after ignition and then repptd.

Ti is sepd. from Mn, Mg and group IV elements by treatment with NH_4OH and NH_4Cl. Sulfosalicylic acid and NH_4OH seps. Ti from Fe, Al, Cr. NH_4OH treatment of solns. contg. excess EDTA seps. Ti from Fe, Al, Cr, Mn, Hg, Cu, Pb, Bi, Cd, Ni.[8] This sepn. is also obtained as follows.[9] Add excess EDTA and 1 g. NH_4Cl, cool, dil. to 50 ml. with H_2O, add 10–20 ml. 10% $MgSO_4$ and then NH_4OH; allow to stand, filter and wash with dil. NH_4OH.

Sepn. of Ti from Fe, etc. is possible with $Na_2S_2O_3$. Treat the soln. with H_2S, almost neutralize with Na_2CO_3, add 10 g. reagent and boil for 30 min. maintaining the vol. with H_2O. Filter, wash with hot H_2O, ignite, fuse with $KHSO_4$ and reppt.

Boiling of a moderately concd. HCl soln. seps. Ti from Mn, Mg and group IV elements but Zr, rare earths, etc. interfere. Treatment of a dil. HCl soln. with SO_2 and boiling seps. Ti from Fe, Al, Zn, etc.; Zr, rare earths, etc. again interfere. Sepn. from Fe is obtained by Et_2O extn. of dil. HCl soln.

Small amts. of Ti can be sepd. from Fe by treatment with KOH and H_2O_2 but Mn interferes. Fusion with Na_2O_2 and extn. with cold H_2O seps. Ti from Fe.

Electrolysis at a Hg-cathode allows a better sepn. Copptn. with Zr arsenate from 1*N* HCl soln. seps. Ti from Fe, V, Mo, Cr.[10]

KIO_3 seps. Ti from Al, Mn, Ca, etc. (see p. 363); Fe must be extd. with Et_2O and Zr interferes.

Cupferron allows sepn. of Ti from Fe^{2+}, Be, Cr^{3+}, Mn, Ni, Co, Zn, U, P, B. Concn. can be done with Fe^{3+} or by extn. with $CHCl_3$. For sepn. from Nb, Ta, see p. 378.

Treatment with $Pb(ClO_4)_2$ in $HClO_4$ soln. seps. Ti from large amts. of Cr (see Chapter 38, p. 291).

Incomplete sepn. of Ti from Zr and Th is obtained with NH_4-salicylate.[11] Treat the dil. HNO_3 soln. with Na_2CO_3 until a turbidity just appears, pour into 50 ml. H_2O contg. 10 g. NH_4-salicylate, boil for 0·5–1 hr., dil. to 200 ml. with H_2O, filter on paper and wash with hot concd. reagent soln.

Ti is sepd. from Zr by treatment with $(NH_4)_2HPO_4$, mandelic acid, etc. (see Chapter 49, pp. 355 and 356).

Sepn. of Ti from Mo, W, V, P, B, Al, Be, Cr^{6+}, etc. is achieved by boiling with 5% NaOH, or by fusing with Na_2CO_3 and KNO_3, or with NaOH, in presence of Fe. The ppt. should be ignited and then fused with $Na_2S_2O_7$. For sepn. from W, better results are obtained as follows.[7, 11] Fuse 0·25 g. oxide with 3 g. Na_2CO_3, transfer to a Ni dish contg. 20% NaOH and place on a steam-bath for several hr. while maintaining the vol. with H_2O. Remove the original crucible from the Ni dish, wash it with 50 ml. hot H_2O, leave for 12 hr., filter on paper and wash with half-satd. NaCl soln. Neutralize the filtrate to phenolphthalein with HCl, heat, neutralize again, filter on paper and wash with NaCl soln. Combine the ppts., dissolve in HCl, add NH_4OH, etc., and finally ignite.

p-Hydroxyphenylarsonic acid allows sepn. of Ti and Zr from Fe, V, Mo (see below).

$H_2C_2O_4$ or HF allows sepn. of Ti from Th and rare earths (see p. 337). H_2SeO_3 seps. Ti from Nb, Ta (see p. 378).

Several sepns. are possible with tannin. When it is used along with antipyrine in H_2SO_4-contg. soln., Ti is sepd. from Fe, Al, Cr, Ni, Co, Mn, Zn and PO_4^{3-}; W interferes. Sepn. from Al, Fe and V is possible in $< 0{\cdot}02N$ HCl soln.[12] Sepn. from U is obtained with tannin in NH_4Cl and $(NH_4)_2C_2O_4$ soln.[11] In $(NH_4)_2C_2O_4$ soln. Ti, Nb and Ta are sepd. from V, Zr, Hf, Th, Al, Be, U, Mn and up to 50 mg. Fe.[11] Fusion with $Na_2S_2O_7$ followed by extn. with tannin soln. seps. Ti from Nb and Ta (see p. 378).

Determination

Ti is normally determined by titration with $KMnO_4$ or Fe^{3+} solution or by colorimetry with H_2O_2. *p*-Hydroxyphenylarsonic acid provides a convenient method if Fe, etc. are present; the vanadate method is suitable for Ti^{3+} in minerals and slags. Tiron is the best of the various phenolic reagents which have been proposed. The method involving alizarin S and $SnCl_2$ seems to be satisfactory.

(a) Redox titrations.[13] (*i*) $KMnO_4$ is the commonest titrant used.[1] For 0·05–0·1 g. TiO_2 in 150 ml. 3–5% H_2SO_4 soln., pass the soln. through a Jones reductor, collect in Fe^{3+} soln. and titrate with 0·1*N* $KMnO_4$ to a pink color.

NOTES. (1) Interferences are org. compds., HNO_3, Sn, As, Sb, Mo, Fe, Cr, V, W, U and Nb.

(2) Alternatively, shake the 2*N* H_2SO_4 soln. under CO_2 with Zn–Hg for at least 1 min. and titrate.[14] Various other amalgams can be applied.[14] For detn. of Ti in ilmenite, treat a 0·2 g. sample with 6 ml. H_3PO_4, cool, add 10 ml. H_2SO_4, dil. to 100 ml. with H_2O, add Zn–Hg, pass CO_2 for 2 min., shake for 15 min., sep., add 5 ml. 0·5% Na_2WO_4 and titrate with $KMnO_4$ from blue to colorless (Ti) and then to violet (Fe).[15]

(*ii*) $FeCl_3$ is suitable with KSCN as indicator.[7, 13, 14, 16] Treat the hydroxide with HF and 10 drops 1:1 H_2SO_4, add 60 ml. HCl and 50 ml. 5% NaF dropwise, and dil. to 250 ml. with H_2O. After 1–2 hr. pipet out 100 ml., add 200 g. Zn–Hg, shake for 8–10 min., collect under CO_2 in a flask contg. 30 ml. 1:1 HCl, add indicator and titrate.

NOTES. (1) Nb, Ta and Fe do not interfere.

(2) If only a little Ti is present, add 60 ml. NaF and 70–75 ml. HCl and allow to stand for 4–5 hr. This method is especially useful for detn. of large amts. of Ti in Nb and Ta compds. When Nb or Ta is absent, addn. of HF or NaF is unnecessary.

Ti^{3+} can be titrated in H_2SO_4 soln. after reduction with Fe.[17] A Cd reductor may also be applied.[18]

(*iii*) Ce^{4+} is used with diphenylamine or ferroin indicator.[13, 14] Reduce Ti in 2*N* H_2SO_4 with Zn–Hg under CO_2, sep., add indicator and titrate. $KBrO_3$, KIO_3 or $K_2Cr_2O_7$ can be applied similarly.

(*iv*) Methylene blue can serve as indicator and titrant.[13, 19] Titrate 150 ml. soln. contg. 30 ml. HCl under CO_2 at 35°C with 0·35% methylene blue; Ti is first reduced with Zn. Interferences are H_2SO_4, HNO_3, Mo, V, W, Cr and Sn; Fe, Al, Sb, As, P and SiO_2 can be tolerated.

(*v*) V^{5+} is generally added in excess and back-titrated with Fe^{2+} soln.[20] For 0·5 g. slag, add 10 ml. V soln. (50 g. V_2O_5 in 500 ml. H_2O and 150 ml. H_2SO_4, filtered on glass wool, cooled and dild. to 1 l. with H_2O) and 30 ml. 1:3 H_2SO_4; boil, add 10 ml. HF, cool, pour into a mixt. of 300 ml. H_2O and 10 ml. H_3PO_4, add 5 drops Ba-diphenylamine sulfonate indicator and titrate with 0·1*N* Fe^{2+} soln. The content of Fe^{2+} in the slag must be detd. independently and deducted.

(*vi*) Coulometric titration of Ti^{3+} is possible[21] after passing the soln. through a Cd reductor, and adding excess Fe^{3+}. Potentiometric titration with Cr^{2+} is also available.[13]

(b) Na-*p*-hydroxyphenylarsonate provides a suitable gravimetric method, especially if Fe is present.[13, 22] For 20–100 mg. Ti in 100 ml. of 1·5*N* HCl or 1·6*N*

H_2SO_4 soln., add 1 g. NH_4SCN, 4 ml. 10% reagent (5% for small amts. of Ti) and boil for 15 min. After 2 hr., filter on Whatman No. 42 paper, wash first with a hot soln. contg. 50 g. NH_4NO_3, 3 g. NH_4SCN and 1 g. reagent/l., and then with hot 2% NH_4NO_3. Transfer to an unglazed porcelain crucible, ignite above 555°C for 2–3 hr. and weigh as TiO_2.

NOTES. (1) No interference arises from Fe, Al, Be, Ce^{3+}, Cr^{3+}, Co, Mn, Ni, Zn, U, V, Te, group IV or V elements, CrO_4^{2-}, MoO_4^{2-}, PO_4^{3-}, MnO_4^-, VO_3^-. The method is very useful for sepn. of Ti from Fe and Al, which can be detd. in the filtrate by addn. of tartaric acid, NH_4OH, oxine, etc. Interferences are Ce^{4+}, Th, Sn and H_2O_2. Zr must be sepd. from 2·5–3·0*N* HCl soln. contg. H_2O_2.
(2) The acidity limits for pptn. are 0·9–1·5*N* HCl or 0·8–2·5*N* H_2SO_4.

(c) H_2O_2 provides the classical colorimetric method.[1, 23, 24] For 0·1–13 mg. Ti in soln. add 15 ml. 6*N* H_2SO_4 (to give a final concn. of 1·5–3·5*N*), cool to 20–25°C, add 5 ml. 3% H_2O_2, dil. to 50 ml. with H_2O and measure the yellow color at 420–430 mμ. The method has been applied to steels, nichrome alloys and Al alloys.[25] The reaction has been studied in the pH range 0–13.[26]

NOTES. (1) Many ions interfere. If Fe^{3+} is present, add equal amts. of H_3PO_4 to the soln. and to the standard. For V, add 1 ml. 1% dihydroxymaleic acid in EtOH for 100 ml. of soln.; alternatively det. V simultaneously by its absorbance at 550–580 mμ. Large amts. of alkali salts interfere (4 g. K_2SO_4 0·4 ≡ mg. Ti) unless the acidity is doubled. Interference of much PO_4^{3-} is compensated by adding an equal amt. to the standard. Br^- and I^- require addn. of 3 ml. Me_2CO/100 ml. soln. Other interferences are Nb, Ni, Co, U, Mo, Ce, Cr^{6+}, F^- and citrate. H_2O_2 may contain F^-. Fe, Co, Ni do not interfere if the absorbance is measured against the untreated sample soln.
A simultaneous detn. of Ti, V and Mo is possible in 3·5*M* $HClO_4$ soln. with measurement at 410, 460 and 330 mμ resp.[27] Interference of Nb can be corrected for; the Ti complex color decreases gradually to up 25% acid and almost disappears in 100% acid soln., whereas the Nb color is weak in 25% acid soln. and is at a max. in 100% acid soln.
(2) For titrimetric detn. of 10 mg. Ti in 150 ml. soln.,[26] make alk. with satd. $KHCO_3$, add a few drops 30% H_2O_2, heat at 80°C for 2 hr., cool, add 50 ml. 6*N* H_2SO_4, leave for 30 min. and titrate with 0·1*N* $KMnO_4$.

(d) Tiron is often employed colorimetrically.[13, 23, 25, 28] For 0·5–40 μg. Ti in 30 ml. of slightly acidic soln., add 5 ml. 4% tiron, neutralize to congo red with NH_4OH, add 5 ml. buffer (1:1 1*N* AcOH and 1*N* NaOAc), dil. to 50 ml. with H_2O, add 10–20 mg. EDTA or 25 mg. $Na_2S_2O_4$ and measure the yellow color at 410 mμ.

NOTES. (1) Interferences are V^{4+}, MoO_4^{2-}, OsO_4^{2-}, U, W, Cr, Cu, oxidants and F^-. Fe^{3+} can be detd. simultaneously by its absorbance at 560 mμ before and after addn. of $Na_2S_2O_4$. Fe is said not to interfere if EDTA is added.[29]
(2) Many other phenols[30] and polyhydroxy acids have been proposed. Thymol is quite commonly used.[13, 23, 31] For 2–5 μg. Ti/ml. H_2SO_4 soln. add 0·25 ml. 1% w/w thymol in H_2SO_4 and measure at 440 mμ after 10 min. The absorbance is stable up to 2 hr. although the visual color may change. Interferences are F^-, NO_3^-, Sb, W, Cr, Nb, Ta; Fe, Al, Mg and SiO_2 do not interfere.
Chromotropic acid forms a purple complex measurable at 535 mμ in 75–95% H_2SO_4 soln.[32, 33] Interferences are F^-, Nb, Ta, Cr^{6+} and V. If the reaction is carried out at pH 6·2, the sensitivity is greater but more ions interfere.[33]
Salicylic acid forms a blood-red complex with 0·02–4 mg. TiO_2/100 ml. 87% H_2SO_4 soln. on addn. of 0·7–1·4 g. reagent.[13, 34] Sulfosalicylic acid is also applicable.[35]
Salicylhydroxamic acid forms a yellow complex, measureable at 390 mμ, with up to 10 μg. Ti in 6–11*N* H_2SO_4 soln.;[36] interferences are Fe, V, PO_4^{3-}, CrO_4^{2-}, WO_4^{2-}.
Gallic acid is suitable for 0·3–80 μg. Ti/ml. of neutral soln.[13, 37] Add 8 ml. 1% reagent, 4 ml. 5% NaOAc, dil. to 50 ml. with H_2O (pH 4·2–6·2) and measure the reddish color at 295 or 370 mμ. Interferences are Fe^{3+}, U, V, Ni, Co, Zn, Mn, Cr, W, Mo, Ce, Al, Be, Th, Zr, Ca.
Dihydroxymaleic acid forms a yellow-brown complex with Ti.[13, 38]
Ascorbic acid can be used to det. 5–120 μg. Ti in 25 ml. soln.[39] Add 10 ml. of reagent (2·5 g. ascorbic acid and 1·00 g. $NaHSO_3$/100 ml.), 5 ml. AcOH and 5*N* NaOH to give pH 5; dil. to 50 ml. with H_2O and measure at 360 mμ. Interferences are F^-, PO_4^{3-}, MoO_4^{2-}, VO_3^- and over 5 mg. SiO_2; Fe, Al, Co, Cr, Cu, Mn, Ni, W and NO_3^- can be tolerated.

(e) Alizarin S provides a satisfactory method for up to 50 μg. Ti.[40] Evap. the soln. almost to dryness, add 4 ml. HCl and 2 ml. satd. $(NH_4)_2C_2O_4$ followed by 0·7 ml. 0·2% alizarin S, 2 ml. 20% $SnCl_2$ in 6*N* HCl, and dil. to 10 ml. with H_2O; measure the green color after 30 min. at 760 mμ. No interference arises from 200 μg. Zr, Nb, Ta, Ge, Mg, Cu, Co, Ni, 0·5 mg. V, W, 1 mg. Cr, 5 mg. Mo, 50 mg. Mn, 100 mg. Al, Zn; for over 300 mg. Fe, add more $SnCl_2$ and leave for over 50 min.

Hydroquinone forms a measurable color with Ti.[41] To 4 ml. H_2SO_4 soln. add $SnCl_2$ and 40 ml. 5% reagent in H_2SO_4 and heat at 70°C for 3 min. Interference of W and Nb can be prevented by addn. of 2 ml. H_2O.

(f) Tannin and antipyrine are employed gravimetrically.[7, 11, 13, 42] For 2–50 mg. Ti in 100 ml. slightly acidic soln. add 10 ml. H_2SO_4 and 40 ml. 10% tannin and dil. to 400 ml. with H_2O. Add 20% antipyrine dropwise until pptn. of the orange ppt. is complete and a white ppt. appears; boil, add 40 g. $(NH_4)_2SO_4$, let cool, filter on paper and wash with a soln. of 10 g. $(NH_4)_2SO_4$ and 1 g. antipyrine in 100 ml. 5% H_2SO_4. Ignite the ppt., ext. with H_2O contg. a little acid, ignite and weigh as TiO_2.

NOTES. (1) Fe, Al, Cr, Co, Mn, Ni, Zn, PO_4^{3-}, SiO_2 and tartrate can be tolerated.
(2) Some other tannin methods are described on p. 361. For other hydrolytic methods, see under Separation (p. 360) and also ref. 13.

NH_4OH forms a ppt. which can be ignited above 750°C and weighed as TiO_2.[13, 43] Na_2SO_3 ppts. Ti from slightly acidic (AcOH) soln.; boil for 0·5–1 hr. after addn. of 10 g. reagent, etc.[7] In an alternative method,[44] add NH_4OH to the acidic soln. until a ppt. appears, then add 1 ml. 10% NH_4HSO_3, 5 ml. AcOH and 15 g. NH_4OAc, dil. to 300 ml. with H_2O, boil for 3 min., etc.

Guanidine carbonate is suitable for 0·2 g. Ti in 50 ml. soln.[13, 45] Add 50 ml. 2·5% $(NH_4)_2$-tartrate, add 10% NaOH until the soln. is just acid to methyl orange, add 75 ml. 8% guanidine carbonate, dil. to 400 ml. with H_2O and boil for 5 min. Filter on paper, wash with 1% NH_4OAc, ignite and weigh as TiO_2. Al, Cr, Mo, W, As, Tl, U can be tolerated.

(g) Oxine is applicable for gravimetric, colorimetric and titrimetric detns. For detn. of 2–70 mg. Ti in 100 ml. acidic soln.,[13, 46] add 0·5–1 g. tartaric acid, 0·5 g. NaOAc and 5–10 ml. 3% H_2O_2 and neutralize to phenolphthalein with NH_4OH. Add 1–2 ml. AcOH, heat to 60°C, add 3% oxine in EtOH, warm, add 5 g. Na_2SO_3 and boil for 10 min. Filter on a G3 crucible, wash with warm H_2O, dry at 110–130°C and weigh as TiO-$(C_9H_6OH)_2$; better, ignite above 718°C and weigh as TiO_2. Alternatively, dissolve the ppt. in 2*N* HCl and titrate with 0·1*N* $KBrO_3$–KBr soln.

NOTES. (1) No interference arises from group IV or V elements or from Mg. PO_4^{3-} does not interfere; if it is absent, H_2O_2 and Na_2SO_3 can be omitted from the above procedure.

(2) For small amts. of Ti, proceed in the same way as for Al (p. 321).

(3) Possible sepns. with oxine are as follows. In soln. contg. NaOH and Na_2-tartrate, Ti is sepd. from Cu, Cd, Zn, Mg, Al. Sepn. from Al and group IV elements is obtained by adding 1 g. NaOAc, 1 g. tartaric acid and 10 g. malonic acid, dilg. to 150 ml. with H_2O, neutralizing with NH_4OH, adding 1–2 ml. AcOH, reagent, etc.

(4) For colorimetric detn.,[47, 48] treat the soln. with 2 ml. 3% H_2O_2, neutralize with NaOAc, add 20 ml. 1*M* NaOAc, adjust to pH 3·0 with H_2SO_4 and dil. to 50 ml. with H_2O. Add 10 ml. 1% oxine in $CHCl_3$, shake for 5 min., sep., transfer to a flask contg. 1 g. anhyd. Na_2SO_4 and compare the colors. The method is suitable for up to 60 μg. Ti/ml. Interferences are Mo, V, Zr and over 35 μg. Fe, or 100 μg. Al; Be does not interfere.

(5) For gravimetric detn. of trace amts. of Ti, chloroxine is preferable to oxine.[13, 49] To the 0·025*N* HCl or HNO_3 soln. at 50°C, add satd. chloroxine in Me_2CO, dil. to 8 ml. with H_2O and place on a steam-bath for 3–5 min. Filter on a glass crucible, wash first with 0·04*N* HCl contg. 10–20% Me_2CO and then with warm H_2O, dry at 145–165°C (105–195°C) and weigh as $TiO(C_9H_4Cl_2ON)_2$. No interference arises from Ni, Co, Zn, Mn, Al, Be, Cr, U, Mg or Ca. Bromoxine does not form a suitable ppt.

(6) 8-Hydroxyquinaldine can be used for colorimetry of up to 50 μg. Ti.[48] Adjust to pH 5·3 with acetate buffer, add 10 ml. $CHCl_3$ and reagent, ext., add anhyd. Na_2SO_4 and measure at 380 mμ. Fe is measured at 580 mμ and Al can be detd. by extg. its oxinate with $CHCl_3$ from the aq. phase and measuring at 390 mμ. Interferences are Bi, Co, Cu, Ni, U, Zr and tartrate.

(h) Cupferron can also be used gravimetrically, titrimetrically and colorimetrically. For gravimetric detn.[1, 13, 50] add 6% cupferron soln. and paper pulp to the soln. contg. 10 ml. H_2SO_4 and 2·5 g. tartaric acid/100 ml.; filter on Whatman No. 42 paper, ignite and weigh as TiO_2. Fe interference is prevented by SO_2; Al, Cr, Co, Ni, Mn, Zn do not interfere. If EDTA is added, only Sn, U, Be and PO_4^{3-} interfere.[51]

For the titrimetric procedure, see Chapter 49, p. 357.

Colorimetric detn. is applied to 8–10% v/v HCl soln.[52] Add 2 vols. MeOH or 1 vol. butylene glycol and 20% excess of reagent.

N-Benzoylphenylhydroxylamine is used[53] gravimetrically for < 0·1 g. Ti in 400 ml. soln. contg. 4 ml. HCl. Add reagent at 25°C, wash with a soln. contg. 10 ml. reagent soln. and 3 ml. HCl/l. and ignite to TiO_2.

(i) Miscellaneous gravimetric methods. 3-Hydroxy-1-*p*-chlorophenyl-3-phenyltriazine allows detn. of 10 mg. TiO_2 in 10 ml. soln.[54] Add 4 ml. 1*N* HCl, 5 ml. 10% NaOAc (pH 2·3), 0·5 g. reagent as a 1% soln. in MeOH and 200 ml. hot H_2O. After 1·5–2 hr. on a steam-bath, filter on Whatman No. 40 paper, wash with hot H_2O and ignite to TiO_2. Interferences are Zr, Th, V, W, Mo, Fe, Pd, Cu, Ce^{4+}, PO_4^{3-}, F^- and tartrate.

5,6-Benzoquinaldic acid ppts. Ti above pH 3; the ppt. must be ignited.[55] Al interferes but rare earths do not; alk. earths and Mg require NH_4Cl addn. and Th, Zr, Fe are masked with Mg–EDTA complex.

KIO_3 ppts. 0·1 g. TiO_2 from 50 ml. < 1·2*N* H_2SO_4 soln.[13] Add 27 ml. HNO_3, dil. to 200 ml. with H_2O, add excess 10% KIO_3 soln. contg. a few drops HNO_3 and leave for 1 hr. Filter on paper, wash with 20 ml. portions of a soln. contg. 2 g. KIO_3 and 6 ml. HNO_3/100 ml.; return to the original beaker, add 15 ml. HCl and some H_2O, pass SO_2 until the soln. is colorless, dil. to 300 ml. with H_2O, add NH_4OH, etc. and finally weigh as TiO_2. Alternatively, dry the ppt. at 138–295°C and weigh as $Ti(IO_3)_4 \cdot 3KIO_3$. Fe and Zr interfere but Al, Mn, Ni, Ca and Mg do not.

$(NH_4)_2HPO_4$ ppts. Ti from 30 ml. 1:5 H_2SO_4 soln.[13, 56] Add 20 ml. H_2O, neutralize with NH_4OH, add 20 ml. 20% reagent, dil. to 400 ml. with hot H_2O and add H_2SO_4 until the ppt. almost disappears. Add 10 g. $Na_2S_2O_3$ and 15 ml. AcOH, boil for 30 min., filter on paper, wash, ignite and weigh as TiP_2O_7; ignition above 400°C may give $TiPO_4$ (Duval). Zr interferes but Fe, etc. do not. This reagent can also be applied colorimetrically for 5 μg.–1 mg. Ti (see Chapter 49, p. 356).[57]

H_2SeO_3 ppts. Ti from 100 ml. < 0·2*N* HCl.[13] Add a small excess of 5% reagent, filter on paper, wash with cold H_2O and ignite above 880°C to TiO_2. If Fe is present, add 10% $NaHSO_3$ in excess (NH_4SCN as indicator) to the warm soln. Al and Zn interfere.

(j) EDTA can be applied to detn. of Ti by addn. of excess and back-titration with Zn^{2+} soln. with ferri-ferrocyanide and benzidine as indicator.[58]

Colorimetric detn. of 4–40 p.p.m. Ti (in the final soln.) is possible at pH 0·4–4;[59] add 0·05*M* EDTA and H_2O_2 and measure at 365 mμ. Photometric titration is satisfactory at 450 mμ. The complex formed is $TiO(H_2O_2)Y^{2-}$. Interferences are Fe, Ni, Mo, Co, Cu, Cr^{6+}.

(k) Miscellaneous colorimetric methods. NH_4SCN provides an unselective method.[60] To 5 ml. soln. contg. 2·0 ml. H_2SO_4, add 2·0 ml. HCl and 15 ml. 3·0*M* NH_4SCN in Me_2CO, dil. to 25 ml. with H_2O, shake and remove the aq. phase with a pipet (0·5 ml. can be left). Add 5·0 ml. reagent and 1·0 ml. 6*M* HCl, dil. to 25 ml. with H_2O, maintain at 20°C for 5 min. and measure the yellow color at 417 mμ (ϵ = 78 000 ± 800).

Diantipyrinyl(*o*-hydroxyphenyl)methane allows detn.[61] of 30–120 μg. Ti in 6 ml. soln. Add 3 ml. EtOH and 1 ml. reagent soln. and compare the yellow complex after 30 min. Over 5% H_2SO_4 interferes; H_3PO_4 prevents interference of Fe or V.

References

1. HILLEBRAND and LUNDELL, 452 (576); SCOTT and FURMAN, 975; KIMURA, 454; SCHOELLER and POWELL, 113; FRESENIUS–JANDER, **IVb**, 1 (1950).
2. BARKSDALE, J., *Titanium: Its Occurrence, Chemistry and Technology*, Ronald, New York (1949).
3. SKINNER, G. B., *et al.*, *Titanium and its Compounds*, H. L. Johnson, Columbus (1954).
4. THORNTON, JR., W. M., *Titanium*, Chem. Catalog Co., New York (1927).
5. CLAASSEN, A., *Chem. Weekblad*, **39**, 23 (1942).
6. FRESENIUS, L. and HARTMANN, W. M., *Z. anal. Chem.*, **93**, 202 (1933).
7. SCHOELLER and POWELL, 120 ff.
8. PŘIBIL R. and SCHNEIDER, P., *Collection Czechoslov. Chem. Communs.*, **15**, 886 (1950).
9. PICKERING, W. F., *Anal. Chim. Acta*, **9**, 324 (1953); **12**, 572 (1955).
10. SIMMLER, J. R., *et al.*, *Anal. Chem.*, **26**, 1902 (1954).
11. SCHOELLER, 90 ff.
12. SCHOELLER, W. R. and HOLNESS, H., *Analyst*, **70**, 319 (1945).
13. FRESENIUS–JANDER, **IVb**, 1 (1950).
14. ISHIMARU, S., *Kagaku-Zikken-Gaku*, **X**, 28 (1942).
15. MIZOGUCHI, S., *Japan Analyst*, **5**, 229 (1956).
16. WINTERSTEIN, C., *Z. anal. Chem.*, **119**, 385 (1940); **117**, 81 (1939).
17. BISCHOFF, F., *Mikrochemie ver. Mikrochim. Acta*, **36/37**, 251 (1951).
18. CLAASSEN, A. and VISSER, J., *Rec. trav. chim.*, **60**, 213 (1941).
19. WELCHER, **IV**, 518.
20. MACCARDLE, L. E. and SCHEFFER, E. R., *Anal. Chem.*, **23**, 1169 (1951).
21. MALMSTADT, H. V. and ROBERTS, CH. B., *Anal. Chem.*, **28**, 1884 (1956).
22. RICHTER, F., *Z. anal. Chem.*, **121**, 1 (1941); WELCHER, **IV**, 66.
23. SANDELL, 572.
24. YOE, 377; PIGOTT, 492.
25. A.S.T.M., 120 ff.
26. MORI, M., *et al.*, *Bull. Chem. Soc. Japan*, **29**, 904 (1956).
27. WEISSLER, A., *Anal. Chem.*, **17**, 695, 775 (1945).
28. YOE, J. H. and ARMSTRONG, A. R., *Anal. Chem.*, **19**, 100 (1947); POTTER, G. V. and ARMSTRONG, C. E., *ibid.*, **20**, 1208 (1948); SHERWOOD, R. M. and CHAPMAN, JR., F. W., *ibid.*, **27**, 88 (1955).
29. SZARVAS, P. and CSISGÁR, B., *Magyar Kém. Folyóirat*, **61**, 50 (1955).
30. SOMMER, L., *Chem. listy*, **50**, 1702, 1711, 1729 (1956); **51**, 875 (1957).
31. GRIEL, J. V. and ROBINSON, R. J., *Anal. Chem.*, **23**, 1871 (1951).
32. BRANDT, W. W. and PREISER, A. E., *Anal. Chem.*, **25**, 567 (1953); also see ROSOTTE, R. and JAUDON, E., *Anal. Chim. Acta*, **6**, 149 (1952); KOCH, W. and PLOUM, H., *Arch. Eisenhüttenw.*, **24**, 393 (1953) (in steel).
33. WELCHER, **I**, 245.
34. WELCHER, **II**, 122.
35. SAARNI, K. and SUIKKANEN, S., *Z. anal. Chem.*, **143**, 112 (1954) (in steel); ZIEGLER, M. and GLEMSER, O., *ibid.*, **139**, 92 (1953).
36. XAVIER, J., *et al.*, *Sci. and Culture* (*Calcutta*), **20**, 146 (1954).
37. WELCHER, **I**, 203; VENKATESWARLU, CH., *et al.*, *Proc. Indian Acad. Sci.*, **40A**, 260 (1954).
38. WELCHER, **II**, 108.
39. HINES, E. and BOLTZ, D. F., *Anal. Chem.*, **24**, 947 (1952).
40. GOTO, H, *et al.*, *J. Chem. Soc. Japan*, **78**, 373, 1337, 1340, 1343 (1957) (in steels, ferro-alloys, Mn, Si, Cr).
41. JOHNSON, C. M., *Iron Age*, **157**, No. 14, 66 (1946).
42. WELCHER, **II**, 154; **III**, 107.
43. YAMAMURA, K., *J. Chem. Soc. Japan*, **51**, 786 (1930).
44. SCOTT and FURMAN, 981.
45. WELCHER, **II**, 388.
46. HECHT and DONAU, 218; ISHIMARU, S., *J. Chem. Soc. Japan*, **56**, 71 (1935).
47. GARDNER, K., *Analyst*, **76**, 485 (1951).
48. MOTOJIMA, K., *Bull. Chem. Soc. Japan*, **29**, 455 (1956); MOTOJIMA and HASHITANI, H., *ibid.*, 458.
49. HECHT and DONAU, 217; ISHIMARU, S., *J. Chem. Soc. Japan*, **55**, 205 (1934).
50. HECHT and DONAU, 217; WELCHER, **III**, 371.
51. MAJUMDAR, A. K. and CHOWDHURY, J. B. R., *Anal. Chim. Acta*, **15**, 105 (1956).
52. BUSCARÓNS, F. and MALUMBRES, J. L. M., *Anales real soc. españ. fís. y quím.* (*Madrid*), **51B**, 117, 124 (1955).
53. SHOME, S. C., *Analyst*, **75**, 27 (1950).
54. SOGANI, N. C. and BHATTACHARYA, S. C., *Anal. Chem.*, **28**, 1616 (1956).
55. MAJUMDAR, A. K. and BANERJEE, S., *Anal. Chim. Acta*, **14**, 427 (1956).
56. GHOSH, J. C., *J. Indian Chem. Soc.*, **8**, 695 (1931); TCHANG, T. D. and HOUONG, L., *Compt. rend.*, **200**, 2173 (1935).
57. NOZAKI, T., *J. Chem. Soc. Japan*, **75**, 937 (1954).
58. SAJÓ, I., *Magyar Kém. Folyóirat*, **60**, 331 (1954).
59. MUSHA, S. and OGAWA, K., *J. Chem. Soc. Japan*, **78**, 1686 (1957).
60. CROUTHAMEL, C. E., *et al.*, *Anal. Chem.*, **27**, 507 (1955).
61. GUSEV, S. I. and BEĬLES, R. G., *Trudy Komissi Anal. Khim., Akad. Nauk S.S.S.R., Otdel. Khim. Nauk*, **5**, No. 8, 68 (1954).

51

NIOBIUM AND TANTALUM

The main sources for this chapter are mentioned in ref. 1. A monograph on the analytical chemistry of niobium (columbium) and tantalum has been published.[2] Several reviews of the subject are available[3–6] but none is up to date. A bibliography on the analysis of the two metals has been compiled.[7]

The analysis of niobium and tantalum minerals is extremely difficult, particularly because the amount of sample available is generally small. The accuracy of the determinations depends essentially on the methods of separation used. Schoeller[2] developed a complicated and delicate system for analysis, but the technique is very demanding so that results tend to vary with different analysts.[5] The terminology and symbols suggested by Schoeller are used in the following paragraphs.

The behavior of the mass obtained by fusion of the minerals with $K_2S_2O_7$ on various treatments is of general interest. (When the fusion is done in a silica crucible, it is essential to separate SiO_2 at some appropriate point and to correct the weight of the oxide obtained finally.) Treatment of the mass with tartaric acid (10% soln.) in an amount about equal to that of $K_2S_2O_7$ requires vigorous stirring to prevent turbidity; if the solution does become turbid, evaporate the solution to foaming with 5 ml. H_2SO_4, add HNO_3 dropwise, evaporate to a fused mass and start again. Treatment of the mass with ammonium tartrate (10% tartaric acid, neutralized with ammonia and 10 ml. ammonia added) followed by acidification with H_2SO_4 yields better dissolution than tartaric acid alone. When the mass is treated with a saturated solution of $(NH_4)_2C_2O_4$, $x + 1$ g. of the oxalate should be added, x being the weight of $K_2S_2O_7$. Titanium can be determined colorimetrically with H_2O_2 after this treatment. Treatment of the mass with SO_2 water (pyrosulfate hydrolysis) yields incomplete precipitation of Nb and Ta and is unsuitable for quantitative purposes. The behavior of niobium and tantalum in various media is summarized below.

The potassium salts of niobate and tantalate are soluble in water, while the sodium salts are only sparingly soluble.

When niobium and tantalum are precipitated from solutions which contain non-volatile salts, it is necessary to heat the ignited oxide with 1*N* HCl on a steam-bath for 1 hr. in order to remove adsorbed salts, then to make alkaline with NH_4OH, filter and reignite.

	Contg. tartrate	Contg. oxalate
HCl	Nb, Ta ppt.	Nb, Ta ppt. incompletely
NH_4OH	Nb, Ta do not ppt.; Fe can be sepd. with H_2S	Nb, Ta ppt. partially; sepn. of Fe with H_2S is unsatisfactory
Tannin	Nb, Ta, Ti, Zr, Th, Fe, Al, U, rare earths ppt. from neutral soln.	Only Nb, Ta, Ti ppt. from neutral soln. which is half-satd. with NH_4Cl.

Attack

(a) Minerals. The best method of decomposition depends strongly on the type of sample. The preferred method for niobates, tantalates and titanates[8] is outlined in Tables 43 and 44. The analysis of rare earth minerals[8] is given in Table 45, and that of minerals akin to zircon[8] in Table 46.

Eudialite is analyzed as follows.[8] Evap. the sample with HCl repeatedly and filter. Ignite the residue and weigh, treat with H_2SO_4 and HF, ignite and weigh again; the difference corresponds to SiO_2. Fuse the residue with $Na_2S_2O_7$ and leach with H_2O. The ppt. contains the Nb and Ta. Combine this filtrate with the first filtrate, treat with NH_4OH and H_2O_2, and filter. The filtrate contains Mn, Ca and Mg. Treat the ppt. (Ti, Zr, rare earths, Fe, Mn) with HCl and $H_2C_2O_4$ and filter; the ppt. contains Th and the rare earths. Treat the filtrate with tartaric acid, H_2S, NH_4OH and H_2S and filter. The ppt. contains the Fe and Mn. Evap. the filtrate to dryness, ignite, fuse with $Na_2S_2O_7$, leach with dil. H_2SO_4 and add NH_4OH. The ppt. contains the Zr and Ti, and the filtrate contains the Ca.

Cassiterite, ainalite and similar minerals are analyzed as follows.[8] Heat the mineral in a combustion tube in a stream of H_2, ext. the residue with 1:3 HCl and filter. Ignite the residue and then repeat the above process (residue A). Combine the two filtrates, partly neutralize with NH_4OH and treat with H_2S; the ppt. is SnS while

TABLE 43. Analysis of Niobates, Tantalates and Titanates[8]

Fuse 0·5 g. sample in a SiO_2 crucible with 4 g. $K_2S_2O_7$, cool, add 0·5–1 ml. H_2SO_4, fuse at a low temp., cool, add 50 ml. hot 10% tartaric acid while stirring vigorously, warm, filter on Whatman No. 40 paper with pulp addn., wash with warm H_2O. If Pb is present, wash with 0·5% H_2SO_4. If needed, repeat this process on the residue. (Note 1)

- **Residue**
  Ext. with NH_4OAc
  - **Residue**
    Ignite, weigh, fuse with Na_2CO_3, add H_2O and HNO_3 and evap.
    - **Residue**
      Ignite, weigh, add $HF + H_2SO_4$, ignite, weigh. *SiO_2*

      SnO_2 is in the residue (Note 2)
    - **Filtrate**
      Det. metals if necessary
  - **Filtrate**
    Treat with $(NH_4)_2S$
    - PbS
      Add H_2SO_4
      $PbSO_4$
- **Filtrate**
  (If turbid, add the filter, evap. with $HNO_3 + H_2SO_4$, add 10% tartaric acid, etc.). Heat to 50°C, add H_2S, heat at 50° for 1 hr., filter on paper and wash with H_2S soln. contg. some H_2SO_4
  - **SP**[1]
    Evap. to fumes with 8 ml. H_2SO_4 and HNO_3, cool, add 10 ml. 20% tartaric acid, 25 ml. H_2O and make alk. with NH_4OH. Pour into $(NH_4)_2S_x$ soln., heat for 1 hr. on a steam-bath, filter on paper and wash with dil. $(NH_4)_2S$
  - **Filtrate**
    Evap. to 150 ml., reduce Fe with H_2S, boil, add 25 ml. HCl, boil for 3 min. filter on Whatman No. 40 paper and wash with 2% NH_4Cl

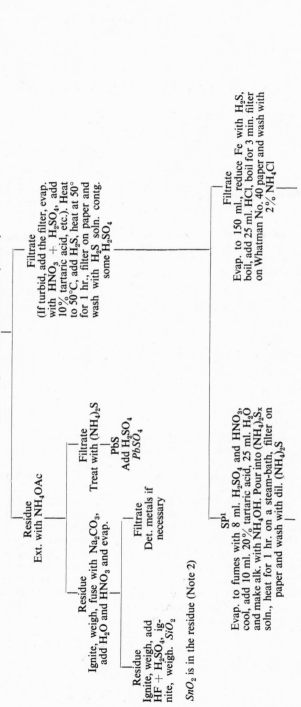

- **SP^2**
  Add dil. HNO_3, evap. to dryness, add hot 10% HNO_3, filter on paper and wash with 10% HNO_3
  - **Ppt.** Ignite → (combine, below)
  - **Filtrate** *Cu, Bi, Pb*
- **Filtrate**
  Acidify with AcOH, boil, add H_2S, filter
  - **SP^3**
    Add H_2SO_4, $KHSO_4$, heat, add H_2O; titrate Sb with $KMnO_4$. Treat with H_2SO_4 and Fe
    - **Ppt.** Sb + Cu. Det. *Cu*
    - **Filtrate** Add H_2S. *SnS*
  - **Filtrate**
    Boil, neutralize with NH_4OH, add 5 g. NH_4Cl and 5 g. NH_4OAc, boil, add 0·5 g. tannin (5% soln.), filter on Whatman No. 41 paper and wash with 5% NH_4Cl
    - **Ppt.** Ignite → (combine, below)
- **Ppt.** Ignite → (combine, below)

Combine, weigh (HP) and treat according to Table 44.
Bulk of earth acids, WO_3 and some TiO_2, UO_3, ThO_2.

- **Filtrate**
  Evap. to 20 ml., pass H_2S, add excess NH_4OH and 10 ml. $(NH_4)_2S$, warm for 1 hr., filter on Whatman No. 40 paper and wash with dil. NH_4Cl soln. contg. $(NH_4)_2S$
  - **Ppt.**
    Ignite in a porcelain crucible, add HCl and 0·2–0·5 g. NH_4Cl, evap. to dryness, add H_2O and NH_4OAc, dil. to 150 ml. with H_2O, boil, filter
    - **Ppt.** Add HCl and NH_4OH
      - **Ppt.** Ignite. *Fe_2O_3*
    - **Filtrate.** Add NH_4Cl and $(NH_4)_2HPO_4$
      - **Ppt.** Ignite. *$Mn_2P_2O_7$*
        - Det. Ni, Co if necessary
  - **Filtrate** (Note 3)

NOTES. (1) If group II, other than Pb and Sn, is absent, do not filter but add 5 ml. 10% H_2SO_4 and 2–3 ml. 1% $HgCl_2$, heat to 50°, pass H_2S, filter on paper and wash with H_2S soln. contg. some H_2SO_4. Treat the filtrate as described for SP^1 filtrate. Ignite the ppt. (P^1) in a porcelain crucible, weigh and repeat the entire treatment. Treat this filtrate as described for SP^2 filtrate. Ignite the ppt. (P^2) and weigh (*Sn*, *SiO_2*).

(2) If little SiO_2 is present, transfer to a porcelain boat, heat in a combustion tube in a stream of H_2, treat the residue with HCl and filter. Treat the filtrate with H_2S (*SnS*). Ignite the first ppt., weigh and det. SiO_2, etc. by the usual method.

(3) The treatment of the filtrate depends on the mineral. For microlite, samarskite, yttrotantalite, fergusonite, etc., evap. the filtrate, add H_2SO_4 and HNO_3, evap. to a fused mass, cool, add warm H_2O and NH_4OH, filter and reppt. The filtrates contain *Ca*, *Mg* and some *Mn*. The ppt. (AP) contains, some *earth acids*, a trace of *WO_3* as well as *TiO_2, ZrO_2, UO_3, ThO_2, rare earths, Al_2O_3 and BeO*.
For tantalite, columbite, stürveite, ilmenorutile, stibiotantalite, bismuthotantalite, boil the filtrate, acidify with AcOH, add NH_4Cl and NH_4OAc, boil, add tannin and filter. Ignite the ppt. (TP) and combine with the main ppt. from which WO_3 has been removed. Evap. the filtrate with H_2SO_4 and HNO_3, ppt. with NH_4OH, $(NH_4)_2S$ and $(NH_4)_2HPO_4$, etc. successively in the usual way.

(4) For the detn. of Nb and Ta only, see ref. 9. For a shorter method of analysis, again see ref. 9. A simpler method with 20 mg. samples has been described.[10]

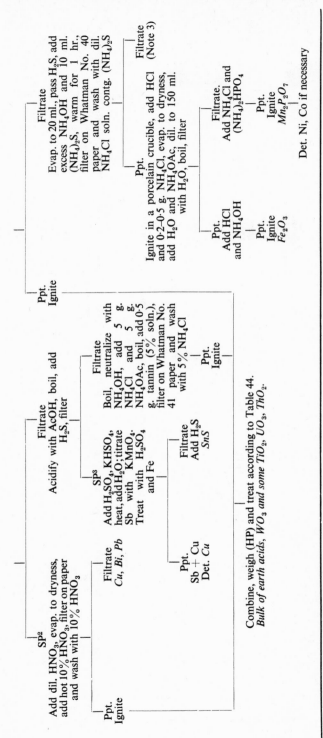

TABLE 44. Analysis of Tannin Group[8]

- Fuse HP (Table 43) with K_2CO_3 etc., treat with magnesia mixt. for little W, or fuse with NaOH, etc. for much W (see under Separation)
  - Ppt.
    Combine with recovery from filtrate or with TP. Ignite, fuse with $Na_2S_2O_7$, ext. with $(NH_4)_2C_2O_4$
    - Residue
      Th
    - Filtrate (→ Combine, below)
  - Filtrate
    Add tannin, cinchonine
    - Ppt.
      Ignite, fuse with NaOH, treat with NaCl
      - Ppt.
        Combine with main portion
      - Filtrate
        Acidify, add tannin and cinchonine
        - Ppt.
          Ignite
          WO_3
    - Filtrate
      Add NH_4OH
      - Ppt.
        Ignite
        UO_3
- Fuse AP (Table 43, Note 3) with $Na_2S_2O_7$ and ext. with $H_2C_2O_4$
  - Residue
    Th, rare earths
  - Filtrate (→ Combine, below)

Combine, apply the oxalo-tannin complex method (p. 374)

- Ppt.
  Use Na-salicylate method (p. 378)
  - Ppt.
    Use oxalo-tannin method (p. 374)
  - Filtrate
    Ti
- Filtrate
  Heat, add a 10-fold amt. of 5% tannin and 10 ml. 1:1 NH_4OH, boil for 30 min., leave for 5 hr., filter on paper and wash with 5% NH_4NO_3. (Note)
  - Ppt.
    Ignite, fuse with 2–3 g. $K_2S_2O_7$, treat with 4% v/v H_2SO_4, filter and wash with 4% H_2SO_4

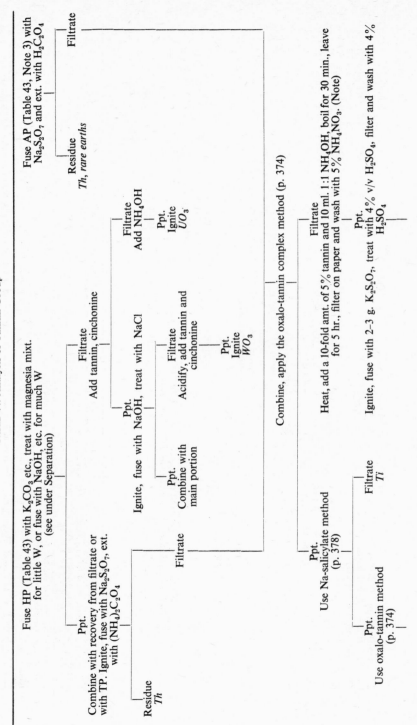

Ppt. *Ta*

Filtrate *Nb*

Filtrate

Cool to 10°C, add paper pulp and cupferron, filter on paper and wash with 4% H_2SO_4 contg. cupferron

- Ppt. *Zr*
- Filtrate
  Boil for 15 min., add HNO_3, boil, cool, make slightly alk. with NH_4OH, add 0·5 g. tannin in soln., cool for 1 hr., filter and wash with 5% NH_4NO_3 contg. NH_4OH and tannin
  - Ppt.
    Ignite, fuse with $Na_2S_2O_7$, add 20 ml. H_2O and filter
    - Filtrate
      Neutralize with NH_4OH, evap. almost to dryness, add 5 ml. 10% $(NH_4)_2CO_3$ and some warm H_2O, digest at 60°C for some min., cool, filter on paper and wash with cold H_2O contg. NH_4OH and $(NH_4)_2CO_3$
      - Ppt.
        Ignite
        (repeat pptn. if not white)
        Al
      - Filtrate
        Acidify with H_2SO_4, boil, cool, add NH_4OH until a ppt. appears, acidify with H_2SO_4, add $K_4Fe(CN)_6$
        - Ppt.
          Det. *U*
        - Filtrate
          Det. *Be* colorimetrically

NOTE. If much Zr is present, heat the filtrate with 100 ml. HNO_3 and 10 ml. H_2SO_4, evap. to fumes, cool, add H_2O, filter on paper and wash with hot H_2O. Almost neutralize the filtrate with NH_4OH, boil, add NH_4OH until its odor appears, add some tannin and paper pulp, filter on paper and wash with NH_4NO_3 soln. Repeat the tannin addn., etc. on the filtrate. Combine the ppts., ignite, fuse with $K_2S_2O_7$, etc.

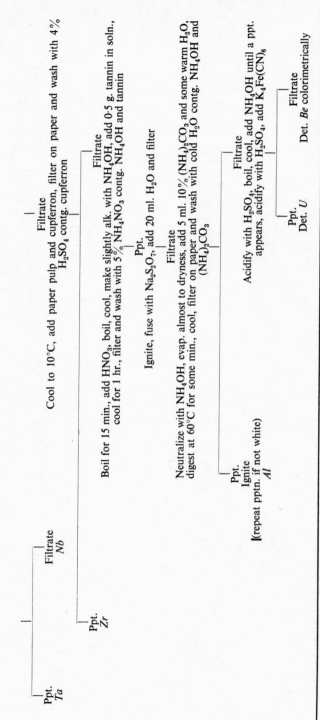

TABLE 45. Analysis of Rare Earth Minerals[8]

I. To 0·5 g. samarskite, etc. (325 mesh) in a Pt dish, add a little H_2O and 5–10 ml. HF and warm with occasional stirring. Evap. to 15 ml. and repeat if necessary. Dil. to 100 ml. with H_2O, filter on paper after 12 hr. and wash with 5% HF

- **Ppt.** (rare earths, Th, U^{4+}, Pb, Zr, Ca, Fe and some common metals)
  Return to the Pt dish, burn the paper and combine with the ppt. Evap. to fumes with 12 ml. 1:1 H_2SO_4 and some HNO_3, cool, dil. to 20 ml. with H_2O, evap. to fumes and pour into a beaker contg. 50 ml. H_2O. Rinse with 50 ml. H_2O, leave to stand and filter
  - **Ppt.** Treat with NH_4OAc and $(NH_4)_2S$
    - **Filtrate (A)**
    - **Ppt.** Treat with $HNO_3 + H_2SO_4$
      - Ppt. → *$PbSO_4$*
  - **Filtrate** Treat with H_2S
    - **Ppt.** Treat with $HNO_3 + H_2SO_4$
      - Ppt. → *$PbSO_4$*
    - **Filtrate** Boil, treat with HNO_3, boil, treat with $NH_4OH + NH_4Cl$. Reppt. twice
      - **Ppt.** (combined below)
      - **Filtrates** Acidify slightly with H_2SO_4, evap. to a small vol., add NH_4OH
        - **Ppt.** (combined below)
        - **Filtrate (B)**
      - Combined Ppts.: Add HNO_3, evap. almost to dryness, pour into $H_2C_2O_4$ soln.
        - **Ppt.** Treat with $Na_2S_2O_3$
          - **Ppt.** *Th*
          - **Filtrate** *Rare earths*
        - **Filtrate** Treat with $(NH_4)_2CO_3$ and $(NH_4)_2S$
          - **Ppt.** Ignite, fuse with $Na_2S_2O_7$, add dil. H_2SO_4 and add to filtrate (X). See below
          - **Filtrate** Evap. to dryness, ignite, treat with HNO_3, filter on paper, wash
            - **Residue** (Pt)
            - **Filtrate** Treat with NH_4OH. Ignite the ppt., weigh (U_3O_8), det. SiO_2 and BeO, deduct and calc. *UO_2*
- **Filtrate** (see below)

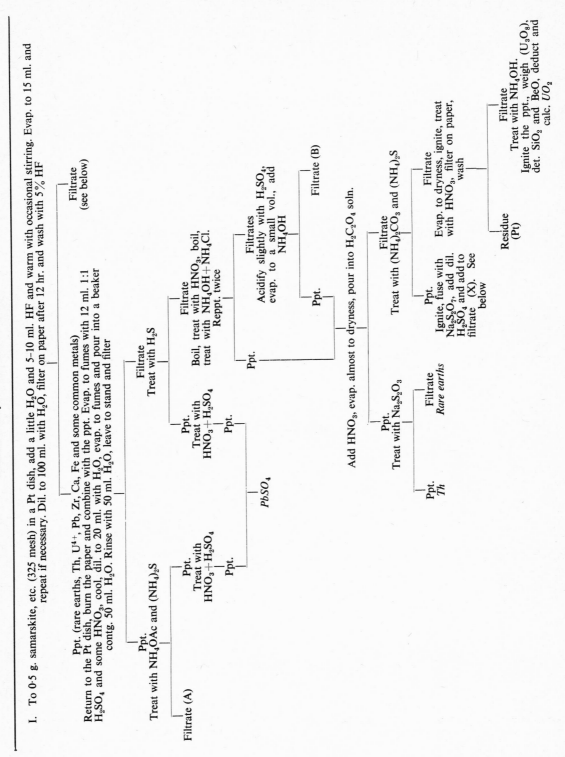

II. Treat the first filtrate (Nb, Ta, Ti, Zr, W, Sn, U^{6+}, Fe, Be, common metals) (Note) with 10 ml. 1:1 H_2SO_4, evap. to fumes, add H_2O, evap. to remove most SO_3, add H_2O, heat for 1 hr. on a steam-bath, add pulp, filter on paper and wash with H_2O contg. NH_4NO_3

- Ppt. (combined with the Ppt. from the NH₄OH treatment below)
- Filtrate. Treat with NH_4OH
  - Ppt. (combined with the first Ppt.)
  - Filtrate (D): *Ca, Mg, alkalies*

Combined Ppts.: Ignite, fuse with 4 g. $K_2S_2O_7$, add 10% tartaric acid, treat with H_2S, filter on paper and wash with H_2S in H_2O contg. some H_2SO_4

- Ppt. Evap. to fumes with H_2SO_4, add H_2O and some HCl, heat on a steam-bath, filter on paper and wash with hot NH_4OAc
  - Filtrate. Treat with H_2S
    - Ppt.: *Sn, Pb*
- Filtrate. Apply tartaric hydrolysis (p. 374)
  - Ppt. (HP): $(Nb, Ta)_2O_5$
  - Filtrate (X). Combine, treat with H_2S, NH_4OH and $(NH_4)_2S$
    - Ppt.: *Fe, Mn*
    - Filtrate. Evap. with $H_2SO_4+HNO_3$, etc., treat with NH_4OH and filter
      - Ppt.: *Ti, Zr, Al, U, etc.*
      - Filtrate (C)

III. Det. Ca and Mg in filtrates (A), (B), (C) and (D); det. SiO_2 in a separate portion

NOTE. If alkali metals can be detd. in a separate sample, add H_2SO_4, evap. to fumes, add 3 g. $KHSO_4$, evap. to a fused mass, add tartaric acid, H_2S, etc.

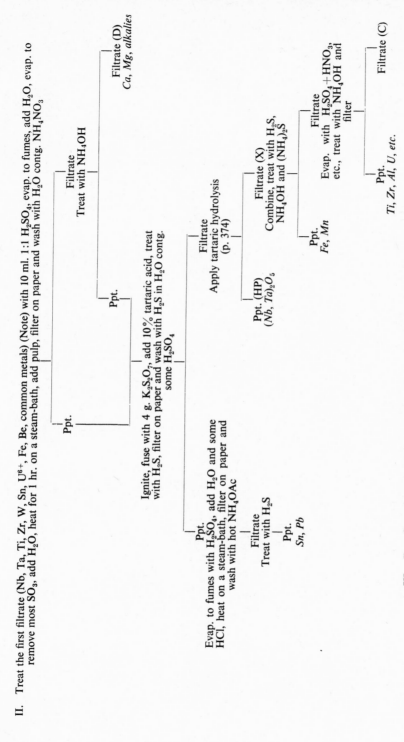

TABLE 46. Analysis of Minerals akin to Zircon[8]

Fuse 0·5 g. naegite, hagatalite, etc., with 5 g. Na_2CO_3, add hot H_2O and some NaOH, filter on paper and wash with 2% Na_2CO_3

- **Residue**: Wash into original beaker, add 1*N* HCl, digest, add NH_4OH, filter on original paper, wash with 0·5% NH_4Cl
  - **Residue**: Repeat the above process, ignite in SiO_2 crucible, fuse with 4 g. $K_2S_2O_7$, add 100 ml. 0·1*N* H_2SO_4, heat, filter and wash with slightly acidic H_2O
    - **Filtrate** (combined below with the ignition step)
    - **Ppt.** (combined with Ppts. below)
  - **Filtrate (b)**
- **Filtrate**: Add HCl, evap., filter and wash. Treat the filtrate again
  - **Ppts.**
  - **Filtrate**: Add citric acid + magnesia mixt.; reppt.
    - **Ppt.** Ignite — *P_2O_5*
    - **Filtrate**: Neutralize with HCl, boil, add tannin, NH_4OAc, etc.
      - Ppt. (e)

Ppt. + Ppts.: Ignite, weigh, treat with H_2SO_4 + HF, ignite, weigh; difference = *SiO_2*. Fuse the residue (f) with $K_2S_2O_7$, etc.

Filtrate + above: Treat with 5 g. NH_4Cl and NH_4OH, and reppt.

- **Ppt. (g)** (Th, rare earths, Fe, Zr, Nb, Ta, Ti, U, Al). Ignite, fuse with $K_2S_2O_7$, add 100 ml. warm 5% $H_2C_2O_4$, warm, filter after 12 hr. and wash
  - **Ppt.** — *Th, rare earths*
  - **Filtrate**: Treat with 2–3 g. tartaric acid, H_2S, NH_4OH and H_2S
    - **Ppt.** FeS → *Fe_2O_3*
    - **Filtrate**: Add 1:1 H_2SO_4 to give a 10% soln., boil, cool and add cupferron
      - **Ppt.** Ignite in a SiO_2 crucible and weigh — *Nb, Ta, Ti, Zr*
      - **Filtrate**: Add 10 ml. HNO_3, boil, add NH_4OH and tannin
        - **Ppt.** Combine with ppt. (e), ignite — *U, Al*
- **Filtrates**: Combine with filtrate (b). Det. *Mn, Ca and Mg*

NOTE. A method that does not require tannin has been described.[10]

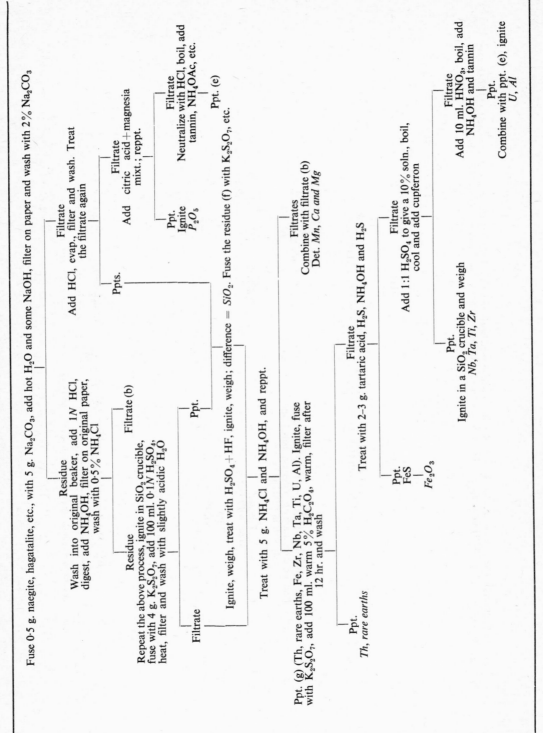

the filtrate contains Fe, etc. Ignite residue A in a silica crucible, fuse with $Na_2S_2O_7$ and treat with tartaric acid; the residue is SiO_2 and the filtrate contains Nb, Ta, etc.

Wolframite is analyzed as follows.[8, 11] Weigh a 10-g. sample, divide it into 3 parts and treat each separately. Heat the sample with 30–40 ml. HCl for 30 min., add 10–15 ml. HNO_3, heat for 2 hr. and add 2 vols. H_2O; filter on paper and wash with hot H_2O. Treat the residue with 30–40 ml. 10% NH_4OH and 15–20 ml. satd. NH_4NO_3 soln. and heat; filter on paper and wash with hot 2% NH_4NO_3 contg. some NH_4OH. Ignite the residue, crush it and repeat the above treatments. Then ignite the residue in a Pt crucible, add H_2SO_4 and HF, heat on a steam-bath, evap. to fumes, add 3–5 ml. H_2SO_4, evap. to fumes, add 20–30 ml. 10% HCl, heat on a steam-bath for 10–15 min., add 10% NH_4OH, boil, filter on paper and wash with 2% NH_4NO_3 contg. some NH_4OH. Ignite the ppt., fuse with a 10-fold amt. of $K_2S_2O_7$, add 50% tartaric acid soln. contg. tartaric acid equal to the wt. of $K_2S_2O_7$ used, then add a 10-fold wt. of H_2O, pass H_2S, filter on paper and wash with 2% tartaric acid contg. H_2S. Treat the filtrate with NH_4OH, pass H_2S for 5–10 min. and filter. Treat the filtrate with HCl to give a 3–5% v/v soln., cool and add 6% cupferron soln., filter, ignite the ppt. and weigh. This gives Nb and Ta. Remove 1–5 mg. of the ignited ppt. and det. W colorimetrically. Det. Ti in another portion of the ppt. The final method of analysis depends on the amt. of W and Ti (see under Separation, p. 374 and 378).

Minerals can also be decomposed by fusion with borax (see Chapter 2, Section 3). Fusion with KOH and extn. with HCl yields incomplete pptn. of Nb and Ta though it is better than pyrosulfate hydrolysis.

(b) Ta metal. This is dissolved with HF and HNO_3.

(c) Steels. Treat 1–2 g. with 20 ml. HCl, add HNO_3 dropwise and evap. to dryness; add 2 ml. 1:1 HCl, dil. to 200 ml. with H_2O, add 2 g. $NH_2OH{\cdot}HCl$, heat, add 5 g. NH_4Cl and 20 ml. 5% tannin, boil for 5 min., filter and wash with 2% NH_4Cl contg. 2 ml. HCl/l. Ignite, fuse with $K_2S_2O_7$, treat with $(NH_4)_2C_2O_4$, tannin, etc.

In another method, heat 2–3 g. steel with 25–50 ml. HCl and 10 ml. HNO_3 on a steam-bath, add 30 ml. $HClO_4$, evap. to fumes, boil for 10 min., cool slightly and add 175 ml. H_2O, 50 ml. H_2SO_3 and some filter pulp. Boil for 10 min., heat at 65–75°C for 15 min., filter on a filter pulp pad and wash 12–15 times with 1:49 HCl. Ignite. (If W is present, boil with 20 ml. 10% NaOH, dil. to 100 ml. with H_2O, add excess HCl, boil, add NH_4OH in excess, filter, wash and ignite.) Treat the ignited residue with 3–5 ml. HF, 2 ml. $HClO_4$ and 6 ml. H_2SO_4 and evap. to 2·5 ml. (if a ppt. appears, add 1 ml H_2SO_4 and heat). Cool slightly, transfer to a beaker with hot 1:49 HCl, add H_2SO_3, etc. Add 0·0500 g. TiO_2, fuse with 3 g. $K_2S_2O_7$, etc. and use a titrimetric finish, or fuse the ignited oxides with $KHSO_4$, dissolve in $(NH_4)_2C_2O_4$ and det. colorimetrically with pyrogallol and hydroquinone. $HClO_4$ alone can also be employed for dissoln. of steels.

For Fe–Ta or Fe–Nb, treat with HF and HNO_3, evap., add H_2SO_4, evap., add 5 g. Na_2SO_4, and evap. to a melt. Alternatively, fuse with $K_2S_2O_7$.

Decompn. of oxide samples and simultaneous sepn. is possible by heating at 310°C with octachloropropane.[12] Nb, Ta and Zr are sepd. from Ti and Sn but Fe interferes. TiO_2 alone cannot be chlorinated and chlorination is difficult when basic oxides such as BeO, ZnO, Fe_2O_3, etc. are present. The oxides should be dried at a low temp. and freed from K, etc.

Heating in a stream of S_2Cl_2 or SCl_4 + Cl_2 at 150–240°C for 1 hr., 240–280° for 1 hr. and 280–500° for 5 min. also achieves decompn. and sepn. In this way, Nb, Ta, Ti, W, Sn, Mo, Sb, As, (and partly Fe) are sepd. from Si, B, Pb, rare earths, Al, Ca, Mg and group V elements. Heating with Cl_2 + CCl_4 is applied similarly.[13]

Separation

n-Propylarsonic acid allows sepn. of Nb, Ta, Zr, Hf, Ti, Sn from other elements.[14] For steels, treat 0·5 g. with 50 ml. 1:1 HCl–HNO_3, evap. to fumes with 35 ml. $HClO_4$, dil. to 200 ml. with H_2O, boil and filter. Add $ZrOCl_2$ (10 mg. ZrO_2) and 30 ml. 5% *n*-propylarsonic acid and heat near boiling for 2 hr. Ignite, fuse with 2·5 g. $KHSO_4$, add 200 ml. 1·2*M* tartaric acid and dil. to 500 ml. with H_2O. Pipet 10·0 ml. and det. colorimetrically with KSCN. Phenylarsonic acid may be used similarly.

N-Benzoyl-*N*-phenylhydroxylamine seps. Nb and Ta from Fe, Al, Ni, Co, Cr, Sn and V^{4+} (see under Determination, p. 381).

Other sepn. processes are described below.

(a) Sepn. from SiO_2. Small amts. of Nb and Ta are sepd. from much SiO_2 by treatment with HF and H_2SO_4. For full treatment, fuse with $K_2S_2O_7$, add 15–20 ml. 20% tartaric acid soln., warm, rinse into a warm mixt. of 50–80 ml. H_2O and 5 ml. 10% H_2SO_4, warm, stir, filter on paper contg. paper pulp and wash with warm H_2O; ignite and treat with HF and H_2SO_4. Sepn. from SnO_2 is incomplete; for complete sepn. pass H_2S, filter, wash with 1% H_2SO_4 contg. H_2S, ignite, treat with the mixed acids and reignite.

(b) Sepn. from Sn and Pb. Treatment with H_2S of solns. contg. tartaric acid yields sepn. from group II elements and especially from small amts. of Sn (see above). If the ppt. is large, treat with H_2SO_4 and HNO_3, evap. to fumes, add 2–3 g. tartaric acid in 20 ml. H_2O, warm, make alk. with NH_4OH, pour into a hot soln. of yellow $(NH_4)_2S_X$, heat, filter and wash. Then acidify with AcOH, heat, filter and apply the tannin method.

Sepn. of large amts. of Sn is possible by heating in H_2, dissoln. in 1:1 HCl and treatment of the residue as above. Oxine allows sepn. of Nb from Sn and Sb (see p. 381).

(c) Sepn. from the tannin group B. Sepn. from Fe is done by H_2S treatment of tartaric acid soln. and further treatment after NH_4OH addn. If much Nb and Ta are present, the bulk is removed by tartaric hydrolysis (see below). If Mn is present, the tartaric hydrolysis filtrate is evapd. to a syrup, dild. to 25 ml. with H_2O, and H_2S is passed.

Oxine seps. Al from Nb and Ta in solns. contg. $(NH_4)_2$-tartrate, NH_4OH and H_2O_2.[15]

Sepn. from Fe and Mn can be done with guanidine carbonate and EDTA.[16] Zr divides between the phases. Glycerol, NH_4OH and EDTA allow sepn. of Nb, Ta and Ti from Fe, Co, W.[17] For 0·5 g. hard metal, treat with HF and HNO_3, add H_2O and 10 ml. glycerol, pour into a mixt. of 300 ml. 1:1 NH_4OH and 1 g. EDTA, boil for 5 min., filter, wash with very dil. NH_4OH and ignite. Alternatively,[18] fuse 0·25 g. oxides with 8–10 g. $K_2S_2O_7$, add 30 ml. satd. $H_2C_2O_4$, 10 ml. HCl and 100 ml. H_2O, filter and wash with H_2O contg. $H_2C_2O_4$ and a few drops HCl; then add 60–70 ml. satd. NH_4Cl soln., 0·5 g. tartaric acid and 25 ml. 10% EDTA, dil. to 400 ml. with H_2O, adjust to pH 5–6 (bromocresol green), boil, add 50 ml. 10% tannin, etc. In the latter process, only Sn, Sb, Ti and W accompany Nb and Ta.

Tartaric hydrolysis[8, 9] serves to sep. Nb, Ta and W from Ti, Zr, Th, Fe, Mn, V, rare earths, Al, Be, Ca and Mg; some Ti, Zr, Th, U and PO_4^{3-} accompany Nb, etc. and $H_2C_2O_4$ and large amts. of H_2SO_4 interfere. For the sepn., boil 200–300 ml. soln. contg. about 10% tartaric acid, add 25–35 ml. HCl or HNO_3, boil for 5 min. and add filter pulp; filter on Whatman No. 41 paper contg. filter pulp using slight suction, wash with 2% NH_4Cl and treat the filtrate with H_2S.

Small amts. of Nb and Ta pass into the filtrate but can be recovered with NH_4OAc and tannin. Pptn. of W is complete if much less W than Nb and Ta is present or if HNO_3 is used; if Ta is > W, pptn. of W is also complete with HCl media whereas if only Nb is present, pptn. is incomplete. Some Ti coppts., the amt. increasing with the size of the ppt. Some Zr and Th coppt.; if the amts. present are large, an increased amt. of Ta appears in the filtrate. Likewise, if much U is present, more Nb appears in the filtrate. A correction must be made for PO_4^{3-}, because most of it coppts.: fuse the ignited oxides with NaOH, ext. with a 50%-satd. soln. of NaCl, filter on paper and wash with the NaCl soln.; add tartaric acid, magnesia mixt., etc. to the filtrate, reppt., etc., det. PO_4^{3-} and apply the correction.

Treatment of the filtrate from tartaric hydrolysis seps. large amts. of Nb and Ta from small amts. of rare earths.[8] Make alk. with NH_4OH, boil, add 10 g. NH_4OAc and 0·7 g. tannin (as a 5% soln.), filter on paper and wash with 2% NH_4NO_3 contg. a little tannin; ignite, fuse with 2 g. $Na_2S_2O_7$, ext. with $H_2C_2O_4$ as described below, or dissolve the fused mass in tartaric acid, and add $H_2C_2O_4$.

Small amts. of Nb and Ta can be sepd. from small amts. of rare earths as follows.[8] Fuse with $Na_2S_2O_7$, heat for 15 min. on a steam-bath with 50 ml. 5% $H_2C_2O_4$, leave to cool for 12 hr., filter on paper and wash with 1% $H_2C_2O_4$.

HF allows sepn. from large amts. of rare earths.[8]

Cupferron seps. Nb, Ta, Ti, Zr, etc. from Al, U, rare earths, etc.;[8, 9] less than 1 mg. $(Nb, Ta)_2O_5$ passes into the filtrate. The medium should contain 10% H_2SO_4 and $H_2C_2O_4$ or tartaric acid.

(d) Sepn. from W. Bicarbonate hydrolysis allows sepn. from small amts. of W.[8, 9] Fuse the mixed oxides with 3 g. K_2CO_3, add 0·3–0·5 g. KOH, leach with warm H_2O, add 17 g. NaCl/50 ml. soln., filter on paper and wash with 50%-satd. NaCl (ppt. A). Neutralize the filtrate with 1*N* HCl using phenolphthalein, warm, neutralize again, repeat the process, filter on paper and wash with 50%-satd. NaCl (ppt. B). Treat the filtrate with tannin and cinchonine (see Chapter 56, p. 422), ignite and weigh WO_3. Combine ppts. A and B, add HCl until acid, place on a steam-bath for 30 min., neutralize to methyl orange with NH_4OH, heat for another 30 min., filter on paper and wash with 2% NH_4NO_3. Ignite the ppt. and weigh as $(Nb, Ta)_2O_5$.

Large amts. of Nb and Ta can be sepd. from a little W with magnesia mixt. (1 g. $MgSO_4$, 2 g. NH_4Cl and a few drops NH_4OH/25 ml.).[8, 9] The procedure is detailed in Table 47.

Small amts. of Nb and Ta can be recovered from large amts. of W as follows.[8, 9] Fuse 1 g. mixed oxides with 2 g. NaOH for 30 sec. at red heat in a Ni crucible, add 10 ml. 50%-satd. NaCl, heat for a few min. and allow to cool for 2–3 hr. Filter on paper after adding paper pulp, decant with 50%-satd. NaCl, return to the beaker, boil with dil. HCl, add NH_4OH, filter and wash with 2% NH_4Cl. This is useful for recovery of Nb and Ta from the filtrate obtained by treatment with magnesia.

Sepn. from W is also possible with NH_4OH, EDTA and glycerol (see above).[16] Sepn. from W and Mo can be done with cupferron, washing being done with 5:95 NH_4OH (see under Determination, p. 381).[19]

(e) Sepn. from Zr. The oxalo-tannin complex method allows sepn. of Nb, Ta, Ti from Zr, Th, Al, Be, U, V, Cr, Mn and < 0·05 g. Fe. W interferes by copptn. with Nb. A repptn. method is applied when little U is present or when Zr, Th, etc. exceed Nb and Ta. Fuse 0·2–0·4 g. mixed oxides with $K_2S_2O_7$, boil with 150–200 ml. satd. $(NH_4)_2C_2O_4$ soln., make turbid with 1*N* NH_4OH, clarify with dil. HCl, make red to litmus, add an equal vol. of satd. NH_4Cl soln., boil and add 5% tannin until the supernate becomes colorless or pale yellow. Then add tannin in an amt. 10–12-fold that of the oxide, heat on a hot plate for 30 min., filter on Whatman No. 40 paper and wash with 5% NH_4Cl contg. 1% $(NH_4)_2C_2O_4$. Ignite the ppt. in a silica crucible, fuse with $K_2S_2O_7$, treat with $(NH_4)_2C_2O_4$ soln., filter on paper and wash with hot H_2O. Treat the filtrate with NH_4OH until turbid, add HCl, etc., and an amt. of tannin 12-fold that of the oxide, etc. Treat the filtrate

TABLE 47. Separation of Earth Acids from W with Magnesia Mixture

Fuse 0·2–0·5 g. mixed oxides with 4 g. K_2CO_3, add 150 ml. hot H_2O and 20–40 ml. reagent dropwise, heat on a steam-bath for 30 min., filter on paper and wash with 5% NH_4Cl

- **Ppt.** Return to the original beaker, burn paper and add ash; add 150 ml. H_2O, acidify with HCl, heat for 1 hr. on a steam-bath, add 150 ml. satd. NH_4Cl, neutralize with NH_4OH, boil, add 2 g. NH_4OAc and 5% tannin, heat on a steam-bath, filter on paper and wash with NH_4Cl soln.
  - **Ppt. (TP[1])** Ignite, repeat above process
    - **Ppt. (TP[2])** → (to Combine, below)
    - **Filtrate** → (to combined filtrates, below)
  - **Filtrate** → (to combined filtrates, below)
- **Filtrate** → (to combined filtrates, below)

Combined filtrates: Add 50 ml. satd. NH_4Cl soln., acidify and treat with tannin and cinchonine

- **Ppt.** Ignite, fuse with NaOH, add 50%-satd. NaCl, etc. (see p. 374.). If only Ta is present, omit this process
  - **Ppt.** Ext. with HCl
    - **Residue** → Combine with Ppt. (TP[2]), ignite: $(Nb, Ta)_2O_5$
  - **Filtrate** Add tannin and cinchonine
    - **Ppt.** Ignite: WO_3
- **Filtrate** Add NH_4OH
  - **Ppt.** Ignite: U_3O_8

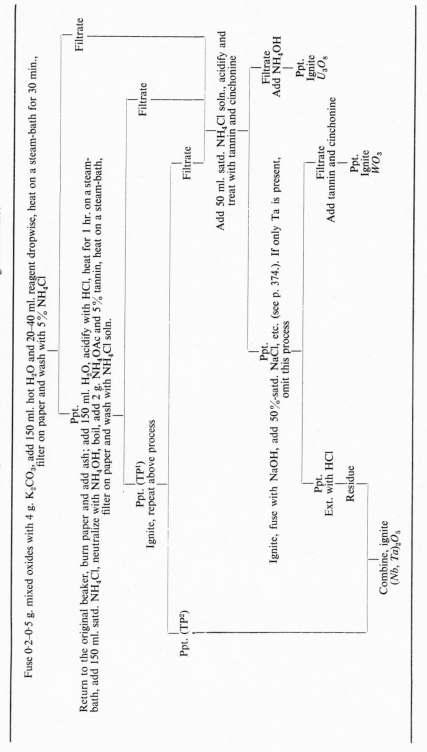

TABLE 48. Oxalate-salicylate–$CaCl_2$ Method

Fuse <0·25 g. mixed oxides with 3 g. $K_2S_2O_7$, add 2 g. $(NH_4)_2C_2O_4$ as a hot concd. soln., filter on paper and wash with hot H_2O. Treat the filtrate with 5 g. Na-salicylate/250 ml. soln. as a hot soln., add 40–50 ml. 10% $CaCl_2$ dropwise, place on a steam-bath for several min., filter hot through Whatman No. 40 paper and wash with hot 2% Na-salicylate until the filtrate is colorless

Ppt.
Return to original beaker, wash paper against side of beaker with hot H_2O, add 40–50 ml. hot 1:1 HCl, then hot H_2O. Burn the paper and add the ash. Add 60 ml. satd. $KMnO_4$ soln., boil till dark brown, add some tannin to reduce MnO_2, add 5% tannin soln. in an amt. up to 1 g., boil for 2 min., add paper pulp, filter and wash with NH_4Cl soln.

- **Ppt. (P^1)**
  Ignite in a SiO_2 crucible

- **Filtrate**
  Neutralize with 1:1 NH_4OH, acidify with AcOH, add 10 g. NH_4OAc and 10 g. NH_4Cl, boil down to 300 ml., add 0·5 g. tannin, filter after 12 hr.

  Ppt. (p^1)

Filtrate
Boil, add 10 g. NH_4OAc and 10 g. NH_4Cl, add 5% tannin soln. in amt. up to 1–2·5 g., heat on a steam-bath, filter on paper and wash with NH_4Cl soln.

Ppt. (P^{1a})

Ppt. (p^1) and Ppt. (P^{1a}): Combine, ignite, fuse with 1–3 g. $K_2S_2O_7$ add 1 g. tannin in 5% H_2SO_4, etc. (pyrosulfate tannin method), filter on paper and wash with 5% H_2SO_4

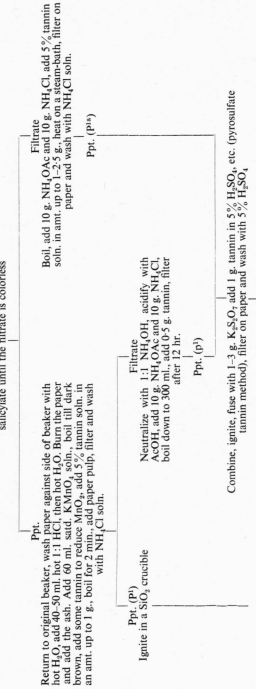

Ppt. (π^1)
Ignite

Fuse with $K_2S_2O_7$, add hot $(NH_4)_2C_2O_4$ soln., filter; treat the residue with $HF+H_2SO_4$, evap. to dryness, fuse with $K_2S_2O_7$, etc. Combine and repeat the above procedures

Ppt.
Treat with HCl, tannin, $KMnO_4$, etc.

Ppt. (P^2)

Filtrate
Treat with NH_4OH, AcOH, NH_4OAc, tannin, etc.

Ppt. (p^2)

Filtrate
Add NH_4OAc, NH_4Cl, tannin, etc.

Ppt. (P^{2a})

Ignite, fuse with $K_2S_2O_7$, add tannin soln., etc.

Ppt. (π^2)

Filtrate B
Combine with filtrate A

Combine, ignite
$(Nb, Ta)_2O_5$

Filtrate A
Combine with filtrate B, almost neutralize with NH_4OH, boil, filter on paper, wash with NH_4Cl soln. contg. some tannin

Ppt.
Ignite, ext. with H_2O, ignite, TiO_2. If much Ti is present, add $HNO_3+H_2SO_4$, heat, evap., filter, neutralize with Na_2CO_3, add Na_2SO_3, boil, etc.
TiO_2

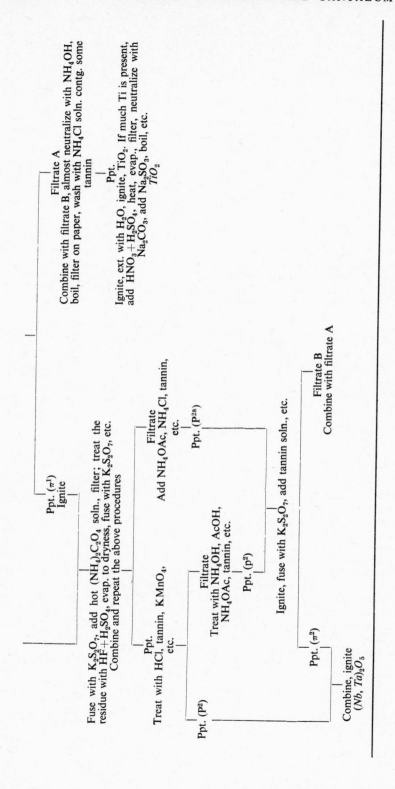

from the first filtration with 0·1 g. tannin and add 1*N* NH_4OH dropwise; when the ppt. which appears is orange, combine it with the first ppt. before ignition. When the ppt. which appears is grey-brown and dissolves on addn. of HCl, sepn. is complete.

A fractional pptn. method is applied when much U is present or when much Nb and Ta are present. For this, obtain the $(NH_4)_2C_2O_4$ soln. as above, treat with NH_4OH, HCl, NH_4Cl, etc. as above, boil and add tannin. Add less than the amt. used above and stop the addn. while the ppt. is orange. Filter on paper and wash (ppt. A). Evap. the filtrate to the original vol., and half the above amt. of tannin, add 1*N* NH_4OH until the orange color of the ppt. starts to change (if the color changes much, add 1 drop HCl), filter on paper and wash (ppt. B). Combine ppts. A and B, ignite and treat with $K_2S_2O_7$, $(NH_4)_2C_2O_4$, etc. as described above.

Nb and Ta can be sepd.[8, 9] from Zr by fusion with 1:6 K_2CO_3. Treat the melt with up to 0·5 g. KOH in hot H_2O, add filter pulp, filter on paper contg. paper pulp and wash with 2% K_2CO_3. Heat the ppt. with a little HCl, add NH_4OH, etc., ignite and apply the above tannin method. Some Ti accompanies Nb and Ta.

For the pyrosulfate–tannin method, see below.

Nb and Ta are sepd. from Zr, Ti and Fe by treatment of the mass from $K_2S_2O_7$ fusion with 5% pyrogallol in 1% HCl.[20] Small amts. are sepd. completely from Zr if the process is repeated. Sepn. from Zr is also obtained by extn. with butyl phosphoric acid in Bu_2O (see Chapter 16, p. 138).

(f) Sepn. from Ti. The pyrosulfate–tannin method seps. small amts. of Nb and Ta from much Ti and Zr.[8, 9] Treat the mass (contg. < 0·25 g. oxides) from $K_2S_2O_7$ fusion with 50–100 ml. 1% tannin in 5% H_2SO_4, boil, leave for 12 hr., filter on paper and wash with 5% H_2SO_4. When Ti is > 0·1 g., repeat the process. Det. Ti by the method given below. The filtrate contains < 0·3 mg. $(Nb, Ta)_2O_5$.

The oxalate–salicylate–$CaCl_2$ method[8] seps. Nb and Ta from Ti and is used when TiO_2:Ta_2O_5 exceeds 50; if < 0·1 g. Ti is present, the procedure need not be repeated. Details are given in Table 48. The TiO_2 contains 1–2 mg. $(Nb, Ta)_2O_5$; this is compensated by loss of TiO_2 in the $(Nb, Ta)_2O_5$ so that the TiO_2 value obtained as described is better than that obtained from the sum of the TiO_2 value and the TiO_2 detd. colorimetrically in the mixed oxides. No correction should be made for the TiO_2 as detd. colorimetrically in the mixed oxides, when Nb and Ta are detd.; it is better to add 0·8 mg. Ta_2O_5/0·2 g. Ta_2O_5 and 2·4 mg. Nb_2O_5/0·2 g. Nb_2O_5. A shorter procedure is given in Schoeller and Powell.[9]

For methods involving ion exchange resins and cellulose columns, see Chapter 13, Sections 4.3 and 6.

TiO_2 (200–250 mg.) can be sepd. from 50–100 mg. Nb_2O_5 with 1% tannin in 1:9 HCl.[21] Treat 0·3 g. oxides with 2–3 ml. HF, evap. to a syrup, transfer to a beaker with 100–200 ml. reagent, add 4–5 g. H_3BO_3/100 ml. soln., boil for 5 min., leave for 2–3 hr., filter on paper and wash with 1:2 reagent–H_2O. Ignite, add HF, etc. and repeat 3 times. If much Ti is present, add initially 1 g. tannin in 95 ml. 5:95 HCl.

To recover Nb from the filtrate, evap. to 400 ml., neutralize with NH_4OH, add 10–15 g. NH_4OAc and 2–3 g. tannin, leave to cool, filter on a Büchner and wash with 2% NH_4Cl contg. some tannin. Boil the ppt. for 10–15 min. with 35 ml. reagent, leave for 12 hr., filter on paper and wash. Ignite, add HF and H_2SO_4, evap., treat with NH_4OH and tannin, etc. and then ignite.

Sepn. from 85% Ti is possible[5] by repeated treatment of the mass from $K_2S_2O_7$ fusion with a little tannin after boiling with 2·5*N* HCl.

H_2SeO_3 allows[22] sepn. of Nb and Ta from Ti by boiling the soln. contg. < 0·1 g. Nb, Ta in 100 ml. 3*N* HCl soln. contg. 1% tartaric acid with reagent and then repptg. Extn. with cupferron in $CHCl_3$ from soln. contg. 2% $(NH_4)_2$-tartrate at pH 5 is also used;[23] citrate and $C_2O_4^{2-}$ interfere. Nb and Ta cupferrates extd. with $CHCl_3$, EtOAc, Et_2O, or iso-PrCHO from solns. contg. 2–3% $(NH_4)_2$-tartrate; iso-AmOH is most satisfactory for extn. of Nb, Ta and Ti from solns. contg. 2–3% $(NH_4)_2$-tartrate at pH 0–8.

(g) Sepn. from V.[8, 9] This is rarely necessary in mineral analysis.

For sepn. from V, fuse the mixed oxides with $K_2S_2O_7$, and boil with tartaric acid and HCl (tartaric hydrolysis); this gives ppt. A. Neutralize the filtrate with NH_4OH, add NH_4OAc, boil, add tannin, filter on paper and wash with NH_4NO_3 soln. Ignite the ppt., fuse with a little $K_2S_2O_7$, add 1% tannin in 2·5% H_2SO_4, heat for 1 hr. on a steam-bath (pyrosulfate–tannin method), add 1–2 drops 5% cinchonine–HCl soln., leave for 24 hr., filter on paper and wash with NH_4Cl soln. contg. a little H_2SO_4 and tannin; this is ppt. B. Neutralize the filtrate with NH_4OH, add NH_4OAc, boil, add tannin, filter on paper and wash with NH_4NO_3 soln. Ignite the ppt. and weigh; then fuse with $Na_2S_2O_7$, add dil. H_2SO_4, filter, ignite, weigh and deduct this wt. from the first to obtain V_2O_5 (check titrimetrically). Combine ppts. A and B, ignite and weigh as $(Nb, Ta)_2O_5$. Any W present appears in the ppt.

(h) Sepn. of Nb from Ta. This sepn. is possible by treatment of the $(NH_4)_2C_2O_4$ soln. with tannin, NH_4OH, etc. (see under Determination, p. 379). Interferences are Ti, W, Sb.

Extn. with 8% tribenzylamine in $CHCl_3$ or CH_2Cl_2 from 11*M* HCl soln. is also satisfactory. For this and other methods involving solvent extn., see p, 138.

Marignac's method with KF yields an accuracy of ±0·5% with 10–30 g. oxides.[24] K_2TaF_7 is difficultly soluble and the method is useful for detn. of small amts. of Nb in Ta.[8] Boil 100 ml. soln. contg. 5 g. Ta_2O_5 and HF, add ca. 3 g. KF (2·7 g. KOH and acidify with HF), evap. to 60 ml., allow to cool, filtei on paper and wash

4 times with 10 ml. portions of cold H_2O. To the filtrate add 15 ml. 1:1 H_2SO_4, evap. to fumes, cool, add H_2O and 4 g. $KHSO_4$, evap. to a fused mass, add 100 ml. satd. $(NH_4)_2C_2O_4$ soln. and tannin, etc. About 0·25 g. Ta appears in the filtrate.

Nb (and partly Ti) are extd.[24] from the mixed oxides with $SeOCl_2$ in H_2SO_4. Treatment of the oxalate soln. (after $K_2S_2O_7$ fusion and $(NH_4)_2C_2O_4$ extn.) with NaH_2PO_2 gives[25] a ppt. of $(Ta_2O_5)H(PO_2H_2)$.

n-Propylarsonic acid, *N*-benzoylphenylhydroxylamine and oxine are useful for this sepn. Details are given under Determination (see below and p. 381).

Ta and Ti can be extd. with BuOH after addn. of pyrocatechol to the oxalate soln. at pH 3; Ti is then stripped with 5% H_2SO_4; the error is ±10%.[26] Ferroin forms a dark red ppt. with Ta in HF-contg. soln., which must be recrystd. several times to remove Nb.[27]

H_2O_2 is used as follows.[28] Fuse the mixed oxides with 8–10 times their wt. of KOH in a Ni crucible, cool, add 50–100 ml. H_2O and 10 ml. 12% H_2O_2 and pour into a mixt. of 16 ml. H_2SO_4 and 20 ml. H_2O; boil for 30 min., filter and wash. Repeat the process and finally weigh as Ta_2O_5. Recover Nb_2O_5 from the filtrate by boiling with Na_2SO_3.

Another possibility is to heat the oxides *in vacuo* at 150, 200 or 230°C for 24, 48 or more hr. with $AlCl_3$, $AlBr_3$ or AlI_3 resp.; the iodide is best.[29]

For sepns. with ion exchange resins or cellulose columns, see Chapter 13, Sections 4.3 and 6.

Determination

Nb and Ta can be determined gravimetrically by the tannin method after separation as the mixed oxides. However, interferences may cause trouble (especially that of Ti) and the method is very troublesome in general, hence it may be preferable to apply a titrimetric procedure for Nb to a small tannin fraction as described below. In recent years, some methods for the separation of Nb from Ta have been proposed, notably the *n*-propylarsonic acid, *N*-benzoyl-*N*-phenylhydroxylamine, oxine and cellulose column methods, and these will probably supersede the tannin procedure.

Titrimetric determination of Nb is accurate, except for trace amounts. Pyrogallol seems satisfactory for colorimetry of Nb and Ta. Nb itself is readily determined colorimetrically with KSCN or with H_2O_2.

Apart from the methods mentioned above, other procedures which are given below for the precipitation of mixed oxides are not successful when other elements are present.

(a) Tannin is used for sepn. and gravimetric detn. of Nb and Ta.[1, 8, 30] Details are given in Table 49.

NOTES. (1) Ti, W and Sb interfere. If $Ta_2O_5:TiO_2$ is <80, Ti should be removed; the oxalate–salicylate–$CaCl_2$ method is suitable for ratios of less than 50:1. For colorimetry of Ti in the mixed oxides, remove a 10–20 mg. sample, fuse with 0·5 g. $K_2S_2O_7$, add 10 ml. satd. $(NH_4)_2C_2O_4$ soln., 5 ml. 10% H_2SO_4 and a little Na_2O_2 and measure the yellow color.

(2) Sepn. is incomplete if much Nb is present, unless at least 0·2 g. tannin is added for 1 g. mixed oxides. If much Ta is present, the bulk should be removed with KF previously (see under Separation, p. 378).

(3) The filtrate from P^{1a} (see Table 49) is more conveniently treated as follows.[31] To the ca. 400 ml. soln. add 2 drops bromophenol blue and 1–2 ml. H_2SO_4, boil and add 1:3 NH_4OH until just purple; if the color is pale, copptn. of Nb may be insufficient, while if it is too dark, copptn. may be excessive. Then add tannin and 10 g. NH_4Cl, boil for 20–30 min., etc. Filter on paper and wash with 2% NH_4Cl, ignite and weigh. Fuse the ppt. with $K_2S_2O_7$, add dil. H_2SO_4, pass through a Jones reductor into Fe^{3+} soln. and titrate with 0·1*N* $KMnO_4$. Then deduct the calcd. amt. of Nb_2O_5 from the wt. to obtain Ta_2O_5.

(4) Ta ppts. at pH 1·9 and Nb at 2·4, hence the sepn. is much easier if the pH is adjusted by means of a glass electrode.[32] Beneficially slow neutralization is obtained[33] by treating the oxalate soln. with 8 ml. 5% sulfosalicylic acid for each 0·05 g. oxides, then adding reagent, NH_4OH, etc.; however, this process may not be satisfactory.[34]

The sepn. is better if brucine is added.[35] Cinchonine and strychnine are less satisfactory, while antipyrine, pyramidone and hexamine have no effect at all. For the brucine reagents, suspend a weighed amt. in H_2O, heat, add > 0·1*N* HCl until just dissolved and dil. to give a 2·5% soln. For detn. fuse 37·7 mg. Nb_2O_5 and 42·4 mg. Ta_2O_5 with 5 g. $K_2S_2O_7$, add 100 ml. 1% $H_2C_2O_4$ and 50–55 ml. 0·1*N* NH_4OH, dil. to 200 ml. with H_2O, add 20 ml. 2% tannin, 50 ml. 20% w/v NH_4Cl and 10 ml. brucine soln. while heating and leave to cool for 12 hr. Filter on paper and wash with 0·2% brucine in 5% NH_4Cl. Ignite the ppt., fuse with 5 g. $K_2S_2O_7$, add 50 ml. $(NH_4)_2C_2O_4$ soln., heat and add 70–90 ml. 0·1*N* NH_4OH (the pH of the filtrate is 1·6); dil. to 200 ml. with H_2O, etc. This process must be repeated 3 times in all.

Morin or quercetin can be used to ppt. Nb and Ta.[36] Fuse 20 mg. oxide with 1 g. $KHSO_4$, add 30 ml. satd. $(NH_4)_2C_2O_4$ soln. or 10% tartaric acid soln. and 25 ml. H_2SO_4, dil. to 100 ml. with H_2O, heat to 50–60°C, add 2% reagent in EtOH, boil for 2–4 min., filter after 12 hr. and wash with 1% NaCl in 0·1*N* H_2SO_4. Ignite and weigh.

Pyrogallol and hexamine ppt. Nb and Ta from $H_2C_2O_4$-contg. soln.[37] Add 10 ml. reagent (equal vols. of 10% pyrogallol and 10% hexamine with a little HCl added) and 2·5 ml. 6*N* HCl, heat to 60–70°C, make alk. with NH_4OH to litmus, then make slightly acidic with HCl and add paper pulp; filter on paper, wash with H_2O, ignite and weigh.

(b) *n*-Propylarsonic acid is satisfactory for gravimetric detn. of Ta.[38] After pyrosulfate fusion, add 3% $(NH_4)_2C_2O_4$ soln., dil. to 95 ml. with H_2O, add 5 ml. H_2SO_4, boil, add 5% reagent soln. and digest for 1 hr. Filter, wash with 1% H_2SO_4, ignite and weigh as Ta_2O_5. Zr, Hf and Ti (> Ta) interfere, but Nb and W do not.

TABLE 49. Separation of Nb from Ta

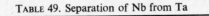

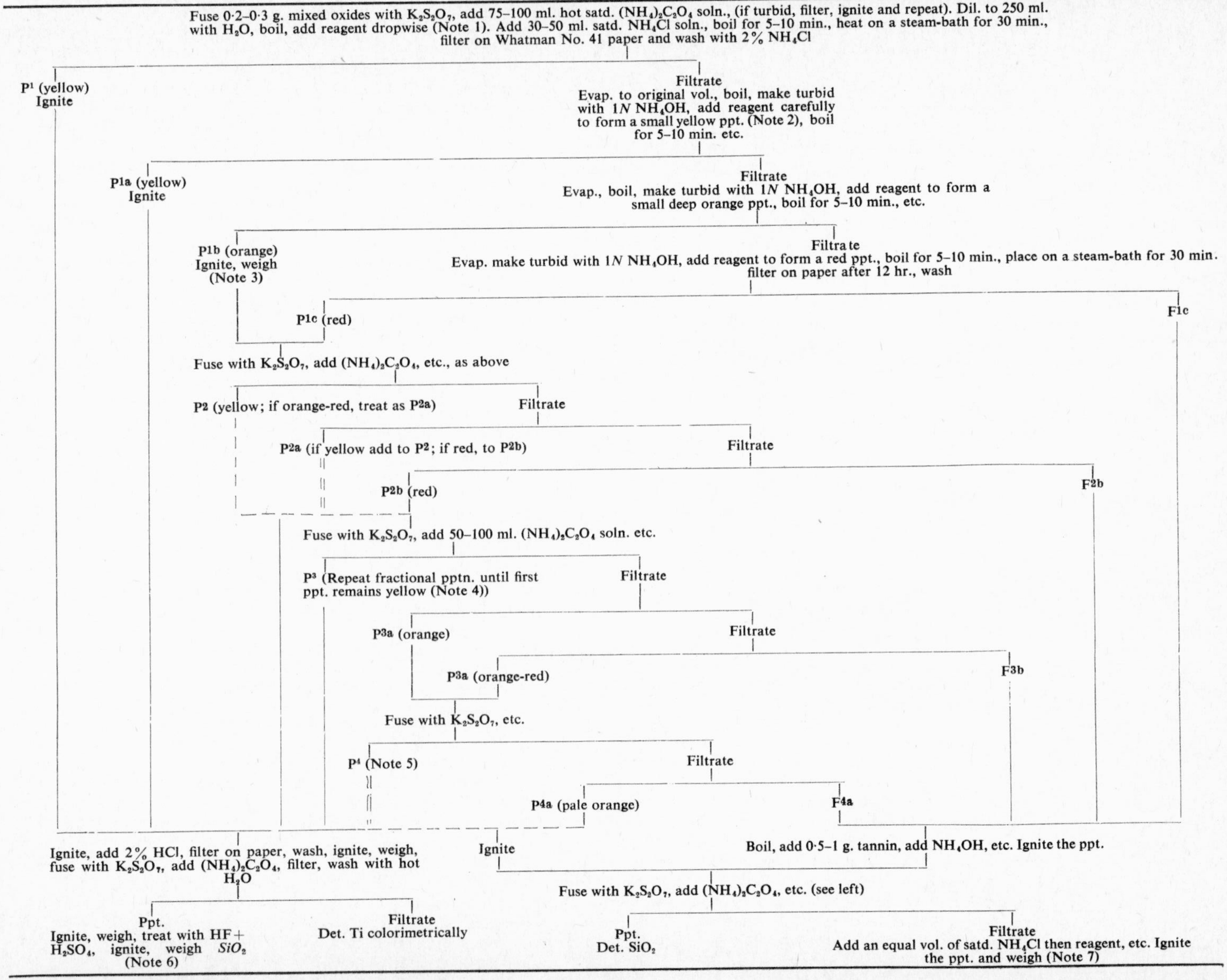
Fuse 0·2–0·3 g. mixed oxides with $K_2S_2O_7$, add 75–100 ml. hot satd. $(NH_4)_2C_2O_4$ soln., (if turbid, filter, ignite and repeat). Dil. to 250 ml. with H_2O, boil, add reagent dropwise (Note 1). Add 30–50 ml. satd. NH_4Cl soln., boil for 5–10 min., heat on a steam-bath for 30 min., filter on Whatman No. 41 paper and wash with 2% NH_4Cl
P^1 (yellow) Ignite
Filtrate
Evap. to original vol., boil, make turbid with 1N NH_4OH, add reagent carefully to form a small yellow ppt. (Note 2), boil for 5–10 min. etc.
P^{1a} (yellow) Ignite
Filtrate
Evap., boil, make turbid with 1N NH_4OH, add reagent to form a small deep orange ppt., boil for 5–10 min., etc.
P^{1b} (orange) Ignite, weigh (Note 3)
Filtrate
Evap. make turbid with 1N NH_4OH, add reagent to form a red ppt., boil for 5–10 min., place on a steam-bath for 30 min. filter on paper after 12 hr., wash
P^{1c} (red)
F^{1c}
Fuse with $K_2S_2O_7$, add $(NH_4)_2C_2O_4$, etc., as above
P^2 (yellow; if orange-red, treat as P^{2a})
Filtrate
P^{2a} (if yellow add to P^2; if red, to P^{2b})
Filtrate
P^{2b} (red)
F^{2b}
Fuse with $K_2S_2O_7$, add 50–100 ml. $(NH_4)_2C_2O_4$ soln. etc.
P^3 (Repeat fractional pptn. until first ppt. remains yellow (Note 4))
Filtrate
P^{3a} (orange)
Filtrate
P^{3a} (orange-red)
F^{3b}
Fuse with $K_2S_2O_7$, etc.
P^4 (Note 5)
Filtrate
P^{4a} (pale orange)
F^{4a}
Ignite, add 2% HCl, filter on paper, wash, ignite, weigh, fuse with $K_2S_2O_7$, add $(NH_4)_2C_2O_4$, filter, wash with hot H_2O
Ignite
Boil, add 0·5–1 g. tannin, add NH_4OH, etc. Ignite the ppt.
Fuse with $K_2S_2O_7$, add $(NH_4)_2C_2O_4$, etc. (see left)
Ppt.
Ignite, weigh, treat with HF+ H_2SO_4, ignite, weigh SiO_2 (Note 6)
Filtrate
Det. Ti colorimetrically
Ppt.
Det. SiO_2
Filtrate
Add an equal vol. of satd. NH_4Cl then reagent, etc. Ignite the ppt. and weigh (Note 7)

For notes, see foot of p. 381.

Treat the filtrate with $KMnO_4$, filter, ignite and weigh as Nb_2O_5.

Phenylarsonic acid ppts. Nb and Ta.[39] Boil the 1*N* HCl soln. contg. tartaric acid, add 30–40 ml. 3% reagent, heat on a steam-bath, add paper pulp, filter on paper after 12 hr., and wash with 4% NH_4NO_3 contg. some HNO_3. Ignite, add 5% HNO_3, heat on a steam-bath for 5–10 min., and make alk. with NH_4OH. Filter on Whatman No. 40 paper, wash with 4% NH_4OH and ignite to $(Nb,Ta)_2O_5$. Det. Ti colorimetrically and correct the wt. of the oxides. The bulk of Ti can be removed with pyrogallol (see above). If H_2O_2 is added, the bulk of the Nb does not ppt.

(c) *N*-Benzoyl-*N*-phenylhydroxylamine also provides a good gravimetric method for Ta.[40] To 0·1 g. oxides in a Pt crucible, add 5 ml. HF and cover with a lid filled with H_2O. Warm for 15–20 min., cool, add H_2O and 3 ml. 50% v/v H_2SO_4, evap. to fumes, cool, add 2 ml. 4*M* HF and transfer to a polythene beaker contg. 185 ml. H_2O and 2 ml. 4*M* HF, rinsing the crucible twice with 0·5 ml. 4*M* HF and with H_2O. Add hot 0·4% reagent, cool rapidly and leave for 2·5 hr. The pH should be 1·0 ± 0·1 and the HF concn. 0·016–0·020*M*. Filter on Whatman No. 42 paper, wash 8 times with 0·06% reagent, ignite at 900°C for 2 hr. and weigh as Ta_2O_5.

NOTES. (1) No interference is caused by Fe, Ni, Co, Al, Cr^{3+}, Sn^{4+}, V^{4+}. Interferences are large amts. of Cl^- or $C_2O_4^{2-}$. If less than 10 mg. Nb_2O_5 is present, repptn. is needed; if over 10 mg. is present 3 pptns. are required. If much Mo or W is present, cool 150 ml. soln. obtained as above (except that the total vol. of 4*M* HF should be 2·5 ml.) to 0°C, adjust to pH 3–4 with 5 g. NH_4OAc, add ca. 50 ml. 0·2*M* cupferron, cool at 0°C for 2 hr., filter on Whatman No. 40 paper and wash 8 times with 0·02*M* cupferron and 5 times with 5% NH_4OH; ignite and then proceed as above.

(2) Nb and Ta can be pptd. separately with *N*-benzoyl-*N*-phenylhydroxylamine; the former is pptd. above pH 6·5 and the latter above pH 2·9.[41]

(3) Cupferron can be applied gravimetrically or colorimetrically. For gravimetry, see under Separation, p. 374. It is possible to ppt. Nb and Ti and sep. them from Ta at pH 4·5–5·5 in soln. contg. Sn^{2+} and Sn^{4+} by means of cupferron.[42] For colorimetry of 20 μg. Nb,[43] ext. with $CHCl_3$ from a soln. contg. 0·4% reagent, 0·64% $(NH_4)_2C_2O_4$ and 1*M* H_2SO_4. This gives a 75% recovery and other solvents are even less useful.

(d) Oxine can be applied gravimetrically or colorimetrically for detn. of Nb. For gravimetry,[44] fuse < 0·2 g. oxides with 8–10 g. $NaHSO_4$, add 50 ml. satd. tartaric acid soln., heat on a steam-bath for 30 min., add 100 ml. H_2O and 5 ml. NH_4OH and heat further. Filter if turbid, ignite, repeat the fusion, etc. Dil. the filtrate to 400 ml. with H_2O, add $(NH_4)_2$-tartrate to give a 2% w/v soln., add 8 g. NH_4Cl, adjust to pH 6·0, warm and add 5–10 ml. 4% oxine in ethanol. Digest for 30 min., add paper pulp, leave to cool for 10 min., filter on Whatman No. 42 paper and wash with a mixt. contg. 0·1% oxine, 1% NH_4Cl and 1% $(NH_4)_2$-tartrate adjusted to pH 6·0. Add 1–2 g. $H_2C_2O_4$, dry, ignite and weigh as Nb_2O_5. Reppt. if necessary and det. Ti colorimetrically, applying a correction.

NOTES. (1) Sn and Sb do not interfere. Ta can be detd. in the filtrate with tannin after sepn. of Sn and Sb with H_2S. Ti appears mainly in the filtrate, but a correction in the wt. of the ppt. is needed.

(2) In $(NH_4)_2C_2O_4$ soln. Ta is also pptd.[45] The Nb ppt. can be weighed as $Nb_2O_5(C_9{\cdot}H_7ON)_6$ (?) after drying at 110–135°C.[46]

(3) For colorimetry a 1 ± 0·01% oxine in $CHCl_3$ reagent is used.[47] After pyrosulfate hydrolysis, ignite the mixed oxides, fuse with 2·5 g. $KHSO_4$, cool, add 5 drops H_2SO_4, fuse, cool, add 10 ± 0·02 g. citric acid in 40 ml. hot H_2O, and dil. to 250 ml. with H_2O. Take a 15 ml. aliquot (36–360 μg. Nb), add 15 ml. 1*N* NH_4OH and 10 ml. reagent, shake for 3 min., sep. and measure the yellow complex at 385 mμ. Mn, Ti, Zr and Fe interfere but Ta, W, Mo, Sb, Sn and V do not.

(e) Pyrogallol allows colorimetric detn. of Nb or Ta.[48] Fuse 25 mg. mixed oxides with 0·5 g. $K_2S_2O_7$, add 3 drops H_2SO_4, fuse, cool, add 1 g. $(NH_4)_2C_2O_4$ and 10 ml. H_2O, warm and dil. to 25 ml. with H_2O. To det. Ta, treat a 5 ml. aliquot with 4 ml. 10% $K_2S_2O_7$ and 0·8 ml. 4% $(NH_4)_2C_2O_4$, dil. to 20 ml. with H_2O, add 2 ml. reagent soln. (10 g. in 2·5 ml. 1:1 H_2SO_4 and 35 ml. H_2O, dild. to 50 ml. with H_2O), dil. to 25 ml. with H_2O, and measure the yellow complex at 400 mμ. To det. Nb, treat a 1 ml. aliquot with 5 ml. 10% $K_2S_2O_7$, 20 ml. 4% $(NH_4)_2C_2O_4$ and 20 ml. reagent (1 g. in 30 ml. 20% Na_2SO_3, filtered and dild. to 25 ml. with Na_2SO_3), dil. to 50 ml. with H_2O and measure the yellow complex at 410 mμ.

NOTES. (1) The Ta method is suitable for 10–80 μg. Ta/ml. of final soln.; the Nb method for 0–1000 μg. Nb/ml. of final soln.

Zr and Sn do not interfere in the Ta method. Fe, W, Mo, V, Bi, Sb and F^- interfere; a correction can be applied for

---

NOTES. (1) Observe the color of the ppt. If yellow, over 1/3 of oxide is Ta_2O_5; continue addn. and stop while there is no color change, adding <50 ml. in total. If orange, Nb has copptd.; add 10 (for small Ta:Nb ratios)—20 ml. reagent, then 30 ml. satd. NH_4Cl and some NH_4OH, boil for 5 min. etc., then treat the resultant deep orange ppt. as for P1b.

(2) If the ppt. is orange, add NH_4OH and reagent to give a deep orange ppt. as described above and treat as for P1b.

(3) The optimum wt. is 0·01–0·02 g.

(4) Usually 2 pptns. suffice. P^3 is needed only when P^2 is orange.

(5) If P^4 is yellow, add it to Ta; if pale orange, add to Nb.

(6) Ti is then detd. colorimetrically. If Ti was previously sepd. by the oxalate–salicylate–$CaCl_2$ method, subtract only the amt. of SiO_2 and add 0·8 mg. Ta_2O_5/0·2 g. Ta_2O_5. Otherwise, subtract both SiO_2 and TiO_2.

(7) Ti is detd. colorimetrically and corrections are made as in Note 6, 2·4 mg. Nb_2O_5/0·2 g. Nb_2O_5 being added.

Nb; with Ti, the absorbance is read at 500 mμ and a correction made.

In the Nb method, Ti, Bi, W, Fe, V, Mo and F^- interfere; a correction can be made for Ta.

(2) $SnCl_2$ prevents Fe^{3+} interference; prep. a soln. contg. 200 g. pyrogallol, 100 ml. HCl and 10 ml. 2*M* $SnCl_2$/l., which is stable for 1 month. For <2 mg. Ta_2O_5 in soln.,[49] add 25 ml. 8*N* HCl and 10 ml. reagent followed by $(NH_4)_2C_2O_4$ soln. (12·5 g. and 50 g. $KHSO_4$/l.) to give a final concn. of 0·125 g. $(NH_4)_2C_2O_4$/50 ml. Dil. to 50 ml. with H_2O and measure at 325 mμ ($\epsilon = 4775$). Fe does not interfere; U, Mo, W, Sb, Ti, Nb, Sr, Cr, V, Bi, Cu, Pt, tartrate, F^- and oxidants interfere. The Ta absorbance increases with increasing acidity; Ti absorbance is minimum in 2·5–4·5*N* HCl and that of Nb is small at <5*N* HCl. Other interferences increase with increasing acidity. The Ta absorbance increases with increasing concns. of pyrogallol, but the blank also increases; the blank decreases with increasing amts. of $(NH_4)_2C_2O_4$. $KHSO_4$ has little effect. Corrections can be made for Ti, Nb and Zr. The method has been applied to detn. of Nb and Ta in steels with H_3PO_4-contg. solns.; corrections can be made on the basis of 10 mg. Nb = 0·1 mg. Ta, 0·1 mg. Ti = 0·2–0·3 mg. Ta and 1 mg. W = 0·05 mg. Ta.[50, 51] Ta can be detd. in Ti alloy after repeated sepn. with tannin.[52] Other methods have also been proposed.[53]

Various homologs of pyrogallol have been applied colorimetrically. Chromotropic acid in 40-fold excess is used in concd. H_2SO_4 soln. with measurement at 485 mμ for Nb ($\epsilon = 3500$) and 375 mμ for Ta ($\epsilon = 6600$).[54]

Pyrocatechol is useful for detn. of Ta.[55] Fuse 10–100 mg. mixed oxides with 3 g. $KHSO_4$, add 50 ml. $(NH_4)_2C_2O_4$ soln. and dil. to 100 ml. with H_2O. To an aliquot, add 5 ml. 10% reagent and dil. to 25 ml. with satd. $(NH_4)_2C_2O_4$ soln.; measure the yellow complex at 400–440 mμ. Nb can be reduced electrolytically and Ti with Zn–Hg, so that neither interferes.

Hydroquinone allows detn. of Nb in H_2SO_4 soln. contg. a little H_3PO_4 with measurement at 460 and 520 mμ, simultaneous detn. of Nb and W being possible.[50, 53, 56] The reagent contains 6·0 g. hydroquinone in 100 ml. H_2SO_4. Ti interferes. For < 0·7 mg. Ta in H_2SO_4 soln.,[57] add 3·0 ml. reagent, dil. to 10 ml. with H_2SO_4 and measure at 375 mμ. The only interferences are Nb, PO_4^{3-}, F^- and H_2O; Ti and Mo can be removed by double extn. with hexone. The method has been applied to U and Pu alloys.

Sulfosalicylic acid can be used for Nb detn.[58] Fuse the oxide with KOH, leach with H_2O, add reagent to give a final concn. of 2% and measure the yellow color at 370 mμ (for small amts. of Ta) or at 390 mμ (for large amts. of Ta). This is suitable for < 1 p.p.m. Nb in the final soln. Interferences are Ti, Mo, V, U, SO_4^{2-}, $C_2O_4^{2-}$, F^-, PO_4^{3-}, AsO_4^{3-} and tartrate.

Tiron is satisfactory for detn. of 2·5–8·5 mg. Nb in 50 ml. 5*N* HCl soln.[59] No interference arises from Ta, Fe, Sn in amts. up to 3–4 times that of Nb; V can be reduced with ascorbic acid.

Gallic acid in EtOH can be used for Ta detn.[60] Fuse the sample with $K_2S_2O_7$, add satd. $(NH_4)_2C_2O_4$ soln. and reagent and compare the yellow color. This is suitable for 2–40 μg. Ta/ml. of final soln.

(f) Miscellaneous gravimetric methods. Heating in H_2 reduces Nb_2O_5 but not Ta_2O_5. Heat 0·5 g. $(Nb, Ta)_2O_5$ at 800°C for 1 hr. in H_2, cool and weigh $NbO_2 + Ta_2O_5$; calc. Nb from the difference.[61]

Pyrosulfate hydrolysis can be applied gravimetrically.[8, 10, 53] Treat the mass from $K_2S_2O_7$ fusion with SO_2 water, boil, leave for 12 hr., etc. Pptn. is complete with Nb or with Nb + Ta, but not with Ta alone. The results depend strongly on the amt. and type of other elements present. Bicarbonate hydrolysis can be utilized similarly (see under Separation, p. 374).

(g) $KMnO_4$ titration is best used with ferroin indicator for detn. of Nb.[1, 8, 53, 62] For < 0·3 g. $(Nb, Ta)_2O_5$ in a SiO_2 crucible, fuse with 3–5 g. $K_2S_2O_7$, cool, transfer to a beaker, add 20 ml. H_2SO_4 and heat until clear. Cool, add 1–2 ml. 30% H_2O_2 and 100 ml. cold H_2O, rinse the crucible with H_2O, cool, add 20 ml. H_2SO_4 and dil. to 200 ml. with H_2O. Add 2 g. succinic acid, warm to about 60°C and pass the soln. through a Jones reductor (see Note 1) into 25 ml. ice-cold Fe^{3+} soln. (100 g. $Fe_2(SO_4)_3$ in 150 ml. H_3PO_4 and 20 ml. 1:1 H_2SO_4 mixed with 850 ml. H_2O). Cool the soln., add ferroin indicator and titrate with 0·1*N* $KMnO_4$ to pink. Deduct a blank value.

NOTES. (1) For the reductor, stir 1 kg. 20-mesh Zn with 500 ml. 2% $HgCl_2$ for 45–60 sec., decant and wash 5 times with H_2O. Mix with 500 ml. warm 1:99 H_2SO_4, decant and wash with H_2O. Prep. a 1 × 33 in. column for 0·5 g. Nb_2O_5 or a 1 × 18 in. column for < 0·175 g. Nb_2O_5, wash with hot 1:99 H_2SO_4, then with hot H_2O. Pass the sample soln. through at 60–70°C, wash with 150 ml. 1:4 H_2SO_4 contg. 1·5 g. succinic acid at 60–70°C, then wash 3 times with 50 ml. H_2O.

(2) Zn–Hg can also serve as reductant.[63] For < 100 mg. $(Nb, Ta)_2O_5$ in a SiO_2 crucible, fuse with 5 g. $K_2S_2O_7$ (if much Nb is present, heat to 500°C and if much Ta is present, to 800°C). Cool, add 0·6% H_2O_2 in 7*N* H_2SO_4, keep under CO_2 and treat with Zn–Hg for 30 min.; then heat to 50–60°C for 30 min. passing the evolved gases through boiled and cooled H_2O. Cool, sep. (with a little Zn–Hg in the receiver), add a known amt. of Fe^{3+} and H_3PO_4 and titrate with $KMnO_4$ or with Ti^{3+} in presence of KSCN. If <10 mg. Nb is present, reduce at room temp.; if <1 mg. Nb or if much Ta is present, add 6 mg. TiO_2 before the fusion.

(3) Electrolytic reduction has been investigated.[64]

(h) KSCN is satisfactory for colorimetric detn. of Nb.[14] Mix 10 ml. HCl, 1·00 ml. $SnCl_2$ soln. (112·9 g. in 250 ml. HCl), 5·00 ml. H_2O and 10·00 ml. Me_2CO. maintain at 20°C for 15 min., add 10 ml. KSCN soln, (291·5 g./l.) and then add 10·00 ml. sample soln. (< 3·5 μg. Nb/ml. of ca. 0·5*M* tartaric acid soln.). Dil. to about 50 ml. with H_2O, store at 20°C for 5 min., allow to cool, dil. to 50 ml. with H_2O and measure the yellow color at 385 mμ within 15 min. of the addn. of KSCN.

NOTES. (1) If preliminary sepn. with *n*-propylarsonic acid is done, very few elements interfere. No interference arises from Ta, Mo, W, Ti, V, U in amts. less than Nb, or from Fe and Cr in amts. below 10 times that of Nb.

(2) In 1·2M HCl medium contg. 60% Me_2CO, $\epsilon = 38\,000 \pm 400$; the color is absorbed by Dowex 2 resin.[65] The optimum concn. of KSCN is 0·3M.[66] The absorbance of Ti increases rapidly with increasing concns. of KSCN and Me_2CO; Nb can be calcd. from the absorbances at 360 mμ (Ti) and 400 mμ (Nb + Ti).[66] The color is most stable at 405 mμ.[67]

(3) The technique has been applied to detn. of Nb in minerals and steels,[68] and in Ti metal.[69] For analysis of steels,[19] mix 34 ml. HCl–Me_2CO soln. (147 ml. HCl and 58·8 ml. H_2O dild. to 500 ml. with Me_2CO; prepd. freshly), 5 ml. 0·05M tartaric acid sample soln., 0·5 ml. 2M $SnCl_2$ in HCl and 9 ml. 6M NH_4SCN (228 g./500 ml.) and dil. to 50 ml. with H_2O; measure after 5–10 min. at 385 mμ ($\epsilon = 11\,800$). This is suitable for 0–2 μg. Nb/ml.

(4) Extn. procedures may be advantageous. For 1–50 μg. Nb in 1–20 ml. 10% tartaric acid soln.,[70] add 5 ml. 20% KSCN, 2 ml. 15% $SnCl_2$ in 4M HCl and 1M tartaric acid, and 5 ml. 9M HCl in 1M tartaric acid; after 5 min. add 5 ml. Et_2O (previously shaken with a 1/10 vol. of $SnCl_2$), shake for 10 sec., sep. after 5 min., add 1 ml. 9M HCl, 0·7 ml. 50% KSCN and 5 ml. Et_2O and ext. again. Combine the extracts, dil. to 25 ml. with Et_2O, and measure at 385 mμ after 30 min. No interference occurs from Ta, Ti or U; interferences are V, W, Mo, Pt, $C_2O_4^{2-}$, F^-, PO_4^{3-}, AsO_4^{3-} and large amts. of NO_3^- and SO_4^{2-}. For analysis of rocks and soils,[71] fuse 0·2 g. 80-mesh sample contg. 50–2000 p.p.m. Nb with 4 g. $NaHSO_4$, add 10 ml. 1M tartaric acid; after 12 hr. pipet 1–2 ml. (contg. 20 μg. Nb). Add 5·0 or 5·6 ml. 9M HCl in 1M tartaric acid, cool, add 5 ml. 20% NH_4SCN and 5 ml. Et_2O and shake for 30 sec. Sep., shake 2–3 times with 2 ml. 10% $SnCl_2$ in 2M HCl, dil. to 10 ml. with Me_2CO and measure at 385 mμ. No interference is caused by 1 mg. Fe, Ti, Ta or U, 0·5 mg. V or 0·1 mg. W or Mo. Other modifications have been described.[72]

The color can be extd. with Et_2O, EtOAc, cyclohexanol, cyclohexanone but not with $CHCl_3$, CCl_4 or C_6H_6. A standard Nb soln. can be obtained by shaking Nb_2O_5 with HCl for several days; the soln. contains ca. 10 mg. Nb/ml.

(5) HCl forms a complex with <10 μg. Nb/ml. HCl soln., which absorbs at 281 mμ.[73] Co, Ni, Mn, Cd, Hg, Th, Si and Zr do not interfere. The wt. ratios of metal to Nb that cause interference are 0·04 for Cu, 0·06 Fe, 0·1 Cr, 0·15 Ti, 0·2 Pb or Mo, 0·6 V^{5+}, 3 W, 7 Bi or Sn^{4+} and 2 Ta (or 10 if 0·01M HF is added).

(i) H_2O_2 allows colorimetric detn. of < 1·25 mg. Nb in 50 ml. soln. contg. 5 ml. H_3PO_4 and 25 ml. H_2SO_4.[24, 74] Add 1 ml. 3% reagent and measure the yellow color at 342 mμ. Ti interferes; 0·5 mg. = 0·02–0·04 mg. Nb, and an equal amt. of Ti should be added to the standard. Other interferences are Ba, Pb, Sr, Zr, $Fe(CN)_6^{4-}$, SiO_2, F^-, V, W and Mo. No interference arises from 7·5 mg. Ta or from Ce, Co, Cu, Mn, Ni, Cr, U.

Simultaneous detn. of Nb and Ta is possible with measurement at 365 mμ for Nb and at 285 mμ for Ta.[75] Absorbance of Nb is at a max. and that of Ta is negligible at 363 mμ; absorbance of Ta is at a max. and that of Nb at a minimum at 287 mμ.[76] Nb can be measured at 365 mμ, and Ta at 285 mμ after 2 days.[77]

A detailed study of the reaction has been made.[78] In 50–100% H_2SO_4, the absorption max. occurs at 365 mμ, the complex contg. 2Nb:3H_2O_2; in 40–60% H_2SO_4, the max. occurs below 250 mμ, a 1:2 complex being formed; in < 40% H_2SO_4, the max. is at 263 mμ and the complex is 1:1.

The method can be applied to steels with measurement at 420 mμ.[79, 80]

(j) Na_2HPO_4 and molybdate permit colorimetric detn. of samples contg. ca. 2·5 mg. Nb.[81] Treat with 5 ml. HF and 5 ml. HNO_3, add 10 ml. 12·6N H_2SO_4, evap., fume for 5 min. and allow to cool. Add 10 ml. H_2O and 5 ml. 1:50 HF and, after at least 2 hr., dil. to 100 ml. with H_2O. Pipet 10·0 ml., add 10 ml. H_2O, 2 ml. 0·06% Na_2HPO_4 and 5 ml. 2% $(NH_4)_2MoO_4$, wait for 15 min., add rapidly 10 ml. 12·6N H_2SO_4, and after 30 sec., 3 ml. $SnCl_2$ soln. (125 g. in 500 ml. 1:1 HCl, pipet 10 ml., add 10 ml. 10N HCl and dil. with H_2O to 500 ml.). Dil. to 50 ml. with H_2O and measure the blue color at 715 mμ within 5 min.

NOTE. Interferences are Sb, As, Ba, Bi, Ce, Pb, Hg, Se, Sr, W, V, PO_4^{3-}. No interference occurs with 5 mg. Ti, 10 mg. Ta or Mo, 30 mg. Fe, 50 mg. Cu or with 100 mg. Al, Be, B, Cd, Ca, Cr, Co, Mg, Mn, Ni, K, Si, Na, Sn, Zn.

(k) Miscellaneous colorimetric methods. Addn. of Zn to a soln. of Nb and fluoride in HCl forms a blue color which can be measured.[8, 82]

Quinalizarin (0·01% in Me_2CO) is suitable for detn. of 10 μg. Nb in 5 ml. > 90% H_2SO_4 soln.[82] Ta interferes.

References

1. HILLEBRAND and LUNDELL, 463 (588); SCOTT and FURMAN, 331; KIMURA, 366; SCHOELLER and POWELL, 198; PIGOTT, 312, 469; FRESENIUS–JANDER, **Vb**, 299 (1957).
2. SCHOELLER, W. R., *The Analytical Chemistry of Tantalum and Niobium. The Analysis of their Minerals and the Application of Tannin in Gravimetric Analysis*, (1937).
3. BLEYENHEUFT, L., *Ingr. chimiste*, **20**, 165 (1936).
4. CHERNIKOV, YU. A., and GORYUSHINA, V. G., *Zavodskaya Lab.*, **11**, 875 (1945).
5. SLAVIN, M., *et al.*, *Brazil, Ministério agr., Dept. nacl. prod. mineral, Bol.*, No. 21 (1946).
6. FROMMES, M., *Z. anal. Chem.*, **99**, 205 (1934).
7. CUTTITTA, F., *U.S. Geol. Survey Bull.*, 1029-A (1957).
8. SCHOELLER, 37 ff.
9. SCHOELLER and POWELL, 198 ff.
10. KIMURA, 366, 468.
11. TSCHERNICHOW, J. A., and KARAJEWSKAYA, M. P., *Z. anal. Chem.*, **98**, 97 (1934).
12. ATKINSON, R. H., *et al.*, *Anal. Chem.*, **24**, 477, 480, 484 (1952); HISKEY, C. F., *et al.*, *ibid.*, 1988.
13. TREADWELL, W. D., *Helv. Chim. Acta*, **35**, 2248 (1952).
14. FREUND, H., and LEVITT, A. E., *Anal. Chem.*, **23**, 1813 (1951).

15. BERG, R., *Oxin*, 51 (1935).
16. HISKEY, C. F., and BATIK, A. L., *Anal. Chem.*, **25**, 823 (1953).
17. LESSNER, E., and WEISSER, H., *Z. anal. Chem.*, **157**, 343 (1957).
18. DAS, M. S., *et al.*, *Analyst*, **81**, 239 (1956).
19. BACON, A., and MILNER, G. W. C., *Anal. Chim. Acta*, **15**, 129 (1956).
20. WELCHER, **I**, 166.
21. BYKOVA, V. S., *Compt. rend. acad. sci. U.R.S.S.*, **18**, 655 (1938); WELCHER, **II**, 151.
22. ALIMARIN, I. P., and STEPANYUK, E. I., *Zavodskaya Lab.*, **22**, 1149 (1956).
23. ALIMARIN and GIBALO, I. M., *Doklady Akad. Nauk S.S.S.R.*, **109**, 1137 (1956).
24. HILLEBRAND and LUNDELL, 482 (605).
25. ALIMARIN, I. P., and BUROVA, T. A., *J. Applied Chem. (U.S.S.R.)*, **18**, 289 (1945); STOCKHAUSEN, C. J., and ZAIL, D. M., *Anal. Chem.*, **26**, 425 (1954).
26. ZAIKOVSKIĬ, F. V., *Zhur. Anal. Khim.*, **11**, 269 (1956).
27. GILLIS, J., *et al.*, *Mededeel. Koninkl. Vlaam. Acad. Wetenschap., Belg., Kl. Wetenschap.*, **6**, No. 10, 5 (1944).
28. JABOULAY, B. E., *Rev. Mét.*, **45**, 343 (1948).
29. CHAIGNEAU, M., *Compt. rend.*, **244**, 900 (1957).
30. WELCHER, **II**, 148.
31. WIRTZ, H., *Z. anal. Chem.*, **117**, 6 (1939).
32. WIRTZ, *Z. anal. Chem.*, **122**, 88 (1941).
33. SCHWARZ, V., *Z. angew. Chem.*, **47**, 288 (1934).
34. CHERNIKHOV, I. A., and KARSAEVSKA, M. P., *Z. anal. Chem.*, **99**, 398 (1934).
35. HAYASHI, S., and KATSURA, T., *J. Chem. Soc. Japan*, **70**, 437 (1949).
36. TOMÍČEK, O., and HOLEČEK, V., *Chem. listy*, **46**, 11 (1952).
37. ALIMARIN, I. P., *Zavodskaya Lab.*, **13**, 547 (1947).
38. DUPRAW, W. A., *Anal. Chem.*, **27**, 309 (1955).
39. ALIMARIN, I. P., and FRID, B. I., *Zavodskaya Lab.*, **7**, 913, 1109 (1938); *Trudy Vsesoyuz. Konf. Anal. Khim.*, **2**, 333 (1943); WELCHER, **IV**, 56.
40. MOSHIER, R. W., and SCHWARBERG, J. E., *Anal. Chem.*, **29**, 947 (1957).
41. MAJUMDAR, A. K., and MUKHERJEE, A. K., *Naturwissenschaften*, **44**, 491 (1957).
42. MAJUMDAR and CHOWDHURY, J. B. R., *Naturwissenschaften*, **44**, 420 (1957).
43. TROĬTSKIĬ, K. V., *Primenenie Mechenykh Atomov v Anal. Khim., Akad. Nauk S.S.S.R., Inst. Grokhim. i Anal. Khim. im V.I. Vernadskogo*, 184 (1955).
44. BELEKAR, G. K., and ATHAVALE, V. T., *Analyst*, **82**, 630 (1957).
45. WELCHER, **I**, 302.
46. KIBA, T., and IKEDA, T., *J. Chem. Soc. Japan*, **60**, 913 (1939).
47. KASSNER, J. L., *et al.*, *Anal. Chem.*, **37**, 492 (1955).
48. HUNT, E. C., and WELLS, R. A., *Analyst*, **79**, 345 (1954); see also GOTO, H., and KAKITA, Y., *Kinzoku-Gakkai-Shi*, **11**, (10), 33 (1948); *Sci. Repts. Research Insts. Tohoku Univ., Ser. A*, **2**, 249 (1950); WELCHER, **I**, 165; EDER, A., *Arch. Eisenhüttenw.*, **26**, 431 (1955); YANA, M., *et al.*, *Japan Analyst*, **4**, 499 (1955) (in steel).
49. DINNIN, J. I., *Anal. Chem.*, **25**, 1803 (1953).
50. IKENBERRY, L., and BOYER, W., *Anal. Chem.* **25**, 1340 (1953).
51. MARZYS, A. E. O., *Analyst*, **80**, 194 (1955).
52. NORWITZ, G., *et al.*, *Anal. Chim. Acta.*, **11**, 173 (1954).
53. A.S.T.M. 150.
54. BRANDT, W. W., and MEHRTENS, D. G., *Anal. Chem.*, **27**, 309 (1955).
55. TOMÍČEK, O., and JERMAN, L., *Chem. listy*, **46**, 144 (1952); also see SARMA, B., and GUPTA, J., *J. Indian Chem. Soc.*, **32**, 285 (1955).
56. JOHNSON, C. M., *Iron Age*, **157**, (14), 66; (15) 66 (1946).
57. WATERBURY, G. R., and BRICKER, C. E., *Anal. Chem.*, **29**, 1474 (1957).
58. DAS GUPTA, A. K., and DHAR, S. K., *J. Sci. Ind. Research (India)*, **12B**, 396 (1953).
59. FLASCHKA, H., and LASSNER, E., *Mikrochim. Acta*, 778 (1956).
60. FREUND, H., *et al.*, *U.S. Bur. Mines, Rept. Invest.*, 5242 (1956).
61. KRISHNASWAMI, K. R., and MURTHI, D. S., *J. Indian Inst. Sci.*, **18A**, 69 (1935).
62. KNOWLES, H. B., and LUNDELL, G. E. F., *J. Research Natl. Bur. Standards*, **42**, 405 (1949).
63. OKA, Y., and MIYAMOTO, M., *J. Chem. Soc. Japan*, **69**, 133 (1948); also see HAGIWARA, H., *ibid.*, 129.
64. TREADWELL, W. D., and NIERIKER, R., *Helv. Chim. Acta*, **25**, 474 (1942); SCHOELLER, W. R., *Analyst*, **67**, 321 (1942) (unreliable); TOMÍČEK, O., and SPURNÝ, K., *Chem. listy*, **46**, 6 (1952).
65. CROUTHAMEL, C. E., *et al.*, *Anal. Chem.*, **27**, 507 (1955).
66. MUNDY, R. J., *Anal. Chem.*, **27**, 1408 (1955).
67. MARZYS, A. E. O., *Analyst*, **79**, 327 (1954); **80**, 199 (1955).
68. MILNER, G. W. C., and SMALES, A. A., *Analyst*, **79**, 315, 425 (1954).
69. NORWITZ, G., *Anal. Chim. Acta*, **9**, 561 (1953).
70. BUKHSH, M. N., and HUME, D. N., *Anal. Chem.*, **27**, 116 (1955).
71. WARD, F. N., and MARRANZINO, A. P., *Anal. Chem.*, **27**, 1325 (1955).
72. LAW-ZECHA, A. B. H., *et al.*, *Anal. Chem.*, **24**, 1169 (1952); HASTINGS, J., and MCCLARITY, T. A., *ibid.*, **26**, 683 (1954).
73. KANZELMEYER, J. H., and FREUND, H., *Anal. Chem.*, **25**, 1807 (1953).
74. TELEP, G., and BOLTZ, D. F., *Anal. Chem.*, **24**, 163 (1952).
75. PALILLA, F. C., *et al.*, *Anal. Chem.*, **25**, 926 (1953).
76. LANGMYHR, F. J., *Tidsskr. Kjemi, Bergvesen Met.*, **13**, 164 (1953).
77. SCHÄFER, H., and SCHULTE, F., *Z. anal. Chem.*, **149**, 73 (1956).
78. ADLER, N., and HISKEY, C. F., *J. Am. Chem. Soc.*, **79**, 1827, 1831 (1957).
79. GELD, I., and CARROLL, J., *Anal. Chem.*, **21**, 1098 (1949).
80. See also PICKUP, R., *Colonial Geol. and Mineral Resources (Gt. Brit.)*, **3**, 358 (1953).
81. CLARK, J. R., and CHANG, S. M., *Anal. Chem.*, **26**, 1230 (1954); DAVYDOV, A. L., *et al.*, *Zavodskaya Lab.*, **13**, 1038 (1947); POPEL, A. A., and MAKSIMOVA, L. P., *Uchenye Zapiski, Kazan. Gosudarst. Univ. im V.I. Ul'yanova-Lenina*, **116**, No. 5, 86 (1956) (in steel).
82. SANDELL, 292.

52

THE ALKALINE EARTH METALS

The principal references for this chapter are mentioned in ref. 1. The analytical chemistry of the alkaline earths have been reviewed[2] and special studies have been made.[3]

It should be noted that these elements are partly or entirely lost when groups I to III are separated in presence of sulfate, phosphate, oxalate or fluoride; a hydroxide precipitate adsorbs the earths and must be reprecipitated in order to recover them. Barium and strontium remain as their sulfates in a silica residue. Excessive amounts of ammonium ions cause incomplete precipitation of group IV elements. It is usually advisable to determine barium in a separate sample.

In the following parts of this chapter, each alkaline earth is considered separately, after general methods of attack and separation have been discussed. Several general studies of flame photometric determination of the earths have been made and it is in order to mention those here.[4, 5] Further information is given for the separate metals at the appropriate places.

Attack

(a) Minerals, etc. Minerals are generally decomposed by treatment with HCl, or by fusion with Na_2CO_3 followed by extn. with HCl.

For carbonates, treat with HCl and a few drops of HNO_3; fuse any residue with Na_2CO_3 or $Na_2S_2O_7$. For barite, phosphates and molybdates, fuse with Na_2CO_3, ext. with H_2O, and treat the residue with HCl. Barite can also be decomposed with HI.

Fluorite is usually decomposed by fusion with Na_2CO_3 and quartz powder and extn. with H_2O, or by treatment with $HClO_4$. For further information, see Chapter 60, p. 448. In another method,[6] suitable for 0·1–0·2 g. fluorite, heat with 0·1*N* AcOH for 30 min. on a steam-bath, filter and det. sol. Ca in the filtrate. Ignite the residue, transfer to a beaker, add 5–10 ml. 2*N* HCl, 50 ml. H_2O and 1–2 g. $Be(NO_3)_2$, heat and filter. Treat the filtrate with NH_4OH until a ppt. appears, add hot dil. AcOH and $(NH_4)_2C_2O_4$, etc. Ignite the residue on the filter and weigh to det. insol. matter.

Separation

SEPARATION FROM OTHER GROUPS

H_2S pptn. from acidic soln. allows sepn. from group II elements; oxidants interfere in the sepn. of Ba or Sr.

Sepn. from Fe, etc. is possible by treatment with $(NH_4)_2S$. Group III elements are sepd. by repptn. 2 or 3 times with NH_4OH and NH_4Cl. In both these procedures, F^-, CO_3^{2-}, PO_4^{3-}, AsO_4^{3-} and SO_4^{2-} interfere. Oxine allows sepn. from Fe, Al, Cu, Ni, Zn, Cd, Mn. Electrolysis at the Hg-cathode gives sepn. from Fe, Cu, Zn, Cr, etc.

Sepn. from SO_4^{2-} and PO_4^{3-} is achieved by fusion with Na_2CO_3, extn. with H_2O and repeated fusion and extn. of the residue. Sepn. from PO_4^{3-} is also possible by treating the slightly acidic soln. with a 10-fold amt. of Fe^{3+} or Al^{3+} and boiling; or by treatment of the HNO_3-contg. soln. with $(NH_4)_2MoO_4$.

Ca can be sepd. from Fe, Al, Ti and PO_4^{3-} as follows: add NH_4OH to the slightly acidic soln. until a ppt. appears, clear the soln. with 7% citric acid, add 15 ml. in excess, dil. to 200 ml. with H_2O, heat and add $(NH_4)_2C_2O_4$.

$(NH_4)_2C_2O_4$ can also serve to sep. Ca and Sr from Mg in soln. contg. NH_4OH and NH_4Cl. On repptn. nearly all Ba passes into the filtrate along with a little Sr and a trace (< 0·5 mg.) of Ca. Sr is recovered from the filtrate by acidifying and adding Ca^{2+} and NH_4OH. Pptn. of Sr is almost complete from solns. contg. 20% v/v of 85% EtOH; Ba pptn. is almost complete from 33% v/v EtOH solns. Ca and Sr can be sepd. from Pb, Cu, etc. with $(NH_4)_2C_2O_4$ from acetate-buffered solns. contg. EDTA.[7]

$Mg_2P_2O_7$ ppts. contg. Ca and Sr are treated as follows for sepn. of small amts. of Ca and Sr. Dissolve the ppt. in H_2SO_4 using an excess of < 0·5 ml.; if dissoln. is difficult, boil with HNO_3, add H_2SO_4 and evap. to fumes. Then add 75% v/v EtOH (100 ml./0·3 g. $Mg_2P_2O_7$), leave for 12 hr., filter on paper and wash with 75% EtOH. Dry the ppt., add some HCl followed by NH_4OH, $(NH_4)_2C_2O_4$, etc. Treatment with 90% MeOH is also satisfactory.[8]

The alk. earths can be sepd. from large amts. of Mg as follows:[9] place the soln. contg. 1–2 g. Mg and no NH_4^+ in a 500 ml. measuring flask, dil. to 200 ml. with H_2O, add 1*N* NaOH until about 95% of the Mg ppts. and dil. to 500 ml. with H_2O. After 1–3 hr., pipet 250 ml. of supernate, add 5 ml. 6*N* HCl and 100 ml. 5% $(NH_4)_2C_2O_4$, etc.

Sepn. from Mg is also possible with H_2SO_4. Treat the neutral soln. with H_2SO_4, add 4 vols. EtOH, filter on paper after 12 hr. and wash with 75% EtOH. Ignite the ppt., fuse with Na_2CO_3, ext. with H_2O and add HNO_3. This procedure can be used after the filtrate from treatment with $(NH_4)_2C_2O_4$ has been evapd. to dryness.

Sepn. of Ba from Pb can be done as follows.[10] Acidify the EDTA-contg. soln. with H_2SO_4, dissolve the ppt. in EDTA and NH_4OH and reppt.; redissolve the ppt., add eriochrome black T indicator and back-titrate with Mg^{2+} soln.

Na-naphthylhydroxamate in solns. contg. NH_4OAc and NH_4OH allows sepn. of Ca from Mg.[11]

Ca can be sepd. from Mg in mixed oxides by extn. with 30% sucrose soln. Mannitol can also be applied:[12] to 10 ml. soln. add 20 g. mannitol, neutralize with 5*M* KOH, add 5 ml. in excess, filter and wash with a soln. contg. 25 g. mannitol and 10 ml. 5*M* KOH dild. to 500 ml. with H_2O; dissolve in 100 ml. H_2O contg. 5 ml. HCl, add 7–8 g. mannitol and reppt.

Ba can be concd. by copptn. with $PbSO_4$ or $PbCrO_4$ which is then dissolved, electrolyzed and the soln. extd. with dithizone.

SEPARATION OF ALKALINE EARTHS FROM EACH OTHER

The mutual sepn. of alk. earths is difficult. The methods of Ballczo and Doppler appear to be the most satisfactory.

(a) Method of Ballczo and Doppler.[2] This is given in Table 50. For an alternative procedure, boil the soln., add $(NH_4)_2C_2O_4$ and NH_4OH, leave for 4 hr., boil, add $(NH_4)_2SO_4$ and filter. Ignite, ext. with dil. HCl and weigh $BaSO_4$. Then det. Ca and Sr by pptn. with oxalate in the filtrate.

The sepn. of small amts. requires different methods. To sep. Ca from Sr, ppt. as CaC_2O_4 and $SrCO_3$, filter, evap. to dryness with HNO_3 twice and ext. with satd. $Sr(NO_3)_2$ in AcOH. Det. Sr by titration with EDTA.

To sep. < 0·3 mg. Ba from 1000-fold amts. of Ca and Sr, pass the neutral soln. contg. less than 200 μg. Sr, 150 μg. Ca and 100 μg. Mg/ml. through an alumina column at a rate of 3 ml./min., wash with 20 ml. H_2O and det. Ca and Sr by pptn. as oxalate as described above. Elute Ba with 6 ml. 2*N* HNO_3 and 30 ml. 0·1*N* HNO_3 and titrate with EDTA, masking Al with triethanolamine. For the column, boil 25 g. alumina with 50 ml. 1*N* HNO_3 for 20 min., decant, wash 5 times with H_2O, dry at 110–120°C for 3 hr., prep. a 16 × 50 mm column and wash with 400 ml. H_2O.

To sep. Ba and Sr from Ca, ppt. $BaCrO_4$ from EDTA-contg. soln., treat with H_2O_2 and heat to destroy EDTA; adjust to pH 8–9 and pass through an alumina column pretreated with 0·1*N* NaOH. Elute Sr (and a trace of Ba and Ca) with dil. HNO_3 and det. as above.

(b) HNO_3 separation method.[13] Evap. the nitrate (or chloride and perchlorate) soln. to dryness, add 10·0 ml. H_2O and 26·0 ml. 100% HNO_3 (prepd. from $NaNO_3$ and H_2SO_4) dropwise while stirring; after 30 min. filter on a Gooch crucible and wash 10 times with 1 ml. portions of 80% HNO_3. Dissolve in a little H_2O with 1–2 drops HNO_3, evap. and repeat. Dry at 130–140°C for 2 hr. and weigh as $Sr(NO_3)_2$; if < 25 mg. Ca is present, repptn. is unnecessary. The method allows sepn. of Sr from Ca, Mg, group V, NH_4^+, Al, Be, etc. A study of the sepn. of Sr from Ca has been made with radioactive tracers.[14]

Ba can be sepd. from Ca, etc. as follows. Evap. the nitrate soln. to dryness, add 5·0 ml. H_2O and 3 ml. 70% HNO_3 dropwise while stirring; then add 11·0 ml. 100% HNO_3, filter after 30 min. on a Gooch crucible, wash with 70% HNO_3, dry at 130–140°C for 2 hr. and weigh as $Ba(NO_3)_2$.

(c) Fresenius' method.[1] This is given in Table 51. Mn interferes by causing high results for Sr and low results for Ca.

If much Sr or Ba is present, heat at 130°C, ext. 5 times with 5 ml. portions of org. solvent and proceed as in Table 51. Possible solvents are AcOH, iso-BuOH, AmOH, Me_2CO[15] or butyl cellosolve.[16] Me_2CO is suitable for < 5% $Sr(NO_3)_2$ and butyl cellosolve for > 5%.

The optimum pH for pptn. of $BaCrO_4$ is 4·5. Homogeneous pptn. can be useful (see p. 392). After pptn. of $BaCrO_4$, Ca and Sr can be pptd. as oxalate, converted to the carbonates, heated at 800°C and the CO_2 evolved measured; this allows calcn. of Ca, and Sr is found by difference.[17]

(d) Method of Kallmann.[18] This is given in Table 52. Interferences are Pb, Na, K, large amts. of NH_4^+ and SO_4^{2-}. The filtrate from $SrCl_2$ may contain 0·1–0·3 mg. $CaCl_2$.

(e) Other methods. Ba is sepd. from Sr and Ca by extn. with 4:1 33% HCl–Et_2O from the chlorides dissolved in the min. amt. of H_2O.

Ca is sepd. from Ba by treating the sulfates with 30 ml. 30% $HClO_4$, evapg. to 10–15 ml., dilg. to 150 ml. with H_2O and filtering.[19] Ca is sepd. from Sr by treating the sulfates with 40 ml. 30% $HClO_4$, heating until crystals appear, cooling, dilg. to 200 ml. with hot H_2O, boiling for 5 min. with 10 ml. 18% H_2SO_4 and filtering after 2 hr.[19]

For the possibilities of ion exchange resins, see Chapter 13, Section 4.4.

Determination

The determination of calcium, barium and strontium in presence of each other is difficult. The methods listed above under Separation are generally used. In

TABLE 50. Separation of Alkaline Earths (Ballczo and Doppler Method)

Treat the soln. with 10 ml. 0·5M EDTA, adjust the pH to 4·5–5·0, dil. to 100 ml. with H_2O, boil, add dropwise 1–2 g. $(NH_4)_2Cr_2O_7$ in 10 ml. H_2O, filter after 30 min. and wash with cold H_2O

Ppt.
Dry at 180° and weigh
$BaCrO_4$

Filtrate
Acidify, boil, add 2 g. $(NH_4)_2C_2O_4$, adjust to pH 3·5–4 (methyl red) with NH_4OAc, filter after 4 hr. and wash with 1% $(NH_4)_2C_2O_4$ and once with 10 ml. H_2O

Ppt.
Heat with 20 ml. 0·1N $K_2C_2O_4$–0·2N K_2CO_3 soln. on a steam-bath for 30 min. and filter through the same filter

Ppt.
$(SrCO_3 +$ some $SrC_2O_4 + CaC_2O_4)$
Repeat the last step once

Filtrate
Add 4 ml. 1:4 H_2SO_4, titrate with 0·1–0·01N $KMnO_4$. Run a blank. Difference $= Sr$

Ppt.
Dissolve in 4 ml. 1:4 H_2SO_4 and H_2O, pass through the same filter and titrate with $KMnO_4$
Ca

Filtrate
Titrate as for the previous filtrate
Sr

TABLE 51. Separation of Alkaline Earths (Fresenius Method)

Evap. the nitrate soln. to dryness, heat at 150–160°C for 1 hr., add a 10-fold wt. of anhyd. EtOH, leave for 1–2 hr., add an equal vol. of anhyd. Et_2O and leave for 12 hr. Filter on a Gooch crucible, wash with 1:1 EtOH–Et_2O. If $Ca(NO_3)_2$ is $> 0·5$ g., ext. again

Residue
Wash with hot H_2O

Filtrate
Evap. to dryness, add H_2O and $(NH_4)_2C_2O_4$, etc.
Ca

Residue
Ignite, weigh and deduct if necessary

Filtrate
Dil. to 150 ml. with H_2O, add 10 ml. 30% NH_4OAc neutralized with NH_4OH, boil, add a 5 ml. excess of 10% $(NH_4)_2Cr_2O_7$, cool, filter on paper and wash with 20 ml. 3% NH_4OAc dild. to 1 l. with H_2O

Ppt.
Add dil. HNO_3, make turbid with NH_4OH, pour into 10 ml. 30% NH_4OAc, boil, cool and filter

Filtrate

Ppt.
$BaCrO_4$

Filtrate

Evap. with HNO_3, add NH_4OH and $(NH_4)_2CO_3$

Ppt.

Evap. with HCl and H_2SO_4, etc.

Ppt.
$SrSO_4$

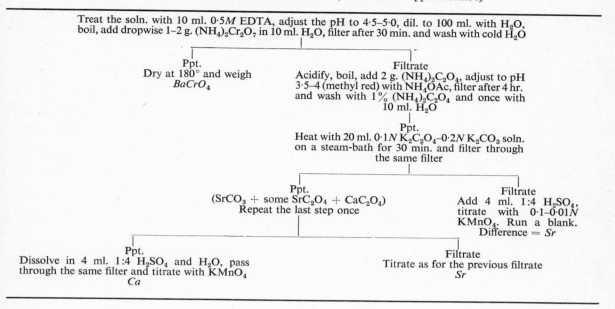

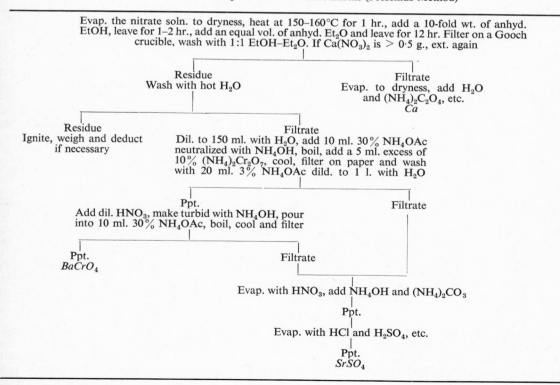

TABLE 52. Separation of Alkaline Earths (Kallmann Method)

Evap. the soln. to dryness with 5 ml. $HClO_4$ below 180°C, cool, add 10 ml. BuOH, heat, boil, add 10 ml. 20% HCl in BuOH dropwise, boil for 1 min., store at 50° for 15 min. and cool. Filter on a Gooch crucible, decant and wash 5–8 times with 1 ml. portions of 10% HCl in BuOH

→ **Ppt.**
Dry at 110° for 1 hr., ignite at 350° for 15 min. and weigh. Ext. with hot H_2O, dry at 110° and weigh. Difference = *(Ba, Sr)Cl₂*

→ → **Filtrate**
Evap. to dryness, add 5 ml. warm H_2O, 55 ml. 12*N* HCl and 15 ml. BuOH[a], heat at 75° and cool. Filter on a Gooch crucible, decant and wash 8 times with 1–2 ml. portions of 4:1 11*N* HCl–BuOH

→ → → **Ppt.**
Dry at 110° for 1 hr., heat at 350° for 15 min., weigh *$BaCl_2$*[b]

→ → → **Filtrate**
Evap. to dryness, add 5 ml. H_2O, 1 ml. HNO_3 and 3 ml. $HClO_4$, evap. to dryness below 180°, cool, heat with 5 ml. BuOH, boil, add dropwise 10 ml. 20% HCl in BuOH, boil for 30 sec. and cool. Filter on a Gooch crucible, wash twice with 1 ml. portions of 10% HCl in BuOH

→ → → → **Ppt.**
Dry for 1 hr. at 110°, heat at 350° for 15 min. *$SrCl_2$*

→ → → → **Filtrate** (combined with the first Filtrate)

→ **Filtrate**

Combined filtrates: Add 1/3 vol. of H_2O, evap. to dryness, add 10 ml. H_2O, 2 ml. HNO_3 and 10 ml. $HClO_4$, evap. to fumes, cool, add H_2O, $H_2C_2O_4$, etc.

→ **Ppt.**
CaC_2O_4

[a] If (Ba, Sr)Cl_2 is <250 mg., or $SrCl_2$ is <125 mg., half vols. of HCl and BuOH suffice.
[b] Corrections must be applied for $BaCl_2$. These are:

$BaCl_2$	<50 mg.	50–150 mg.	150–500 mg.
Correction	+2·0 mg.	+2·0 − 0·4 mg./100 mg. $SrCl_2$	+0·2 − 0·6 mg./100 mg. $SrCl_2$

recent years, titrimetric methods with EDTA and flame photometry have become widely adopted.

CALCIUM

The usual method involves pptn. as oxalate followed by weighing or titration. For small amounts, titration with EDTA is satisfactory. The best colorimetric methods are those with pyrogallolcarboxylic acid, murexide, phthalein complexone or plasmocorinth.

(a) $(NH_4)_2C_2O_4$ can be applied gravimetrically, titrimetrically or colorimetrically. For gravimetric detn.[1, 2] of < 0·1 g. Ca in 100–400 ml. soln. contg. a little NH_4OH and 5 g. NH_4Cl and < 1 mg. Ca/ml., boil, add hot 4% reagent until pptn. is complete, then add hot concd. reagent to give an excess of 1 g./100 ml. soln.; boil for 1–2 min., heat on a steam-bath for 30 min. and leave to cool for 1 hr. Filter on paper and wash with 0·1% reagent 5 times. Dissolve in 50 ml. 1:4 HCl, add H_2O and reagent as above followed by dropwise addn. of NH_4OH until alk. Filter on paper, wash, ignite at 1200°C and weigh as CaO after cooling over P_2O_5 or H_2SO_4 as desiccant.

NOTES. (1) Interferences are Sr, SiO_2, CO_3^{2-}, S, F^-, BO_2^- and large amts. of NH_4^+ or Mg. A yellow or green color indicates Mn contamination; other impurities may be Pt, Si, Al or rare earths.

(2) Repptn. gives complete sepn. from Mg and from a little Ba but up to 0·5 mg. CaO appears in the filtrate; this can be recovered from the $Mg_2P_2O_7$ ppt. (see under Separation, p. 385). The ppt. must be ignited in an elec. furnace; with gas heating up to 1% SO_3 is absorbed.[20]

(3) Other weighing forms, which have no special advantage, are $CaCO_3$ (heat at 460–660°C), $CaSO_4$ (add H_2SO_4 and heat at > 190°C), CaF_2 (add HF and heat at 400–950°C), or CaC_2O_4 (heat at 226–398°C). For small amts. of Ca, wash with EtOH and Et_2O, dry at 105–110°C and weigh as $CaC_2O_4 \cdot H_2O$.

(4) Several other procedures have been described. The following method gives a better sepn. from Mg and the ppt. is readily filtered.[21] To 100 ml. neutral soln. add methyl red, 2·4 ml. 1:1 HCl (to give pH 1·0), 15 ml. satd. reagent

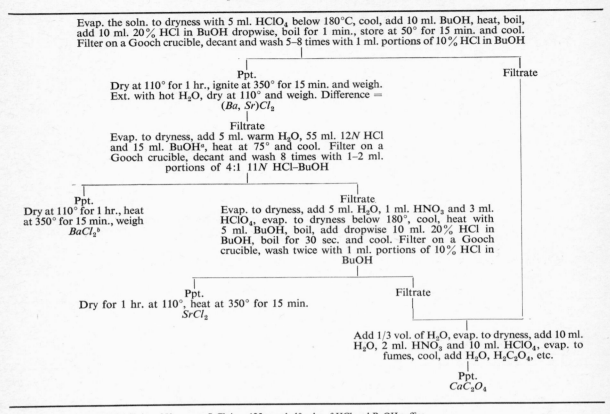

and 10 g. urea (the soln. should be clear); heat for 15 min. (to give pH 5·0), filter and apply a $KMnO_4$ titration.
Another method[1] is convenient when only Ca need be detd. To 150 ml. neutral soln. add 10 ml. HCl, heat to 50°C, add 2 drops methyl orange and neutralize with NH_4OH; add 1 ml. NH_4OH, neutralize with 10% $H_2C_2O_4$ and add 12 ml. in excess (to give pH 4; AcOH, citric acid or salicylic acid may be used here). Boil for 1–2 min., add 50 ml. satd. reagent soln., dil. to 250 ml. with H_2O, boil for 2 min. heat for 1 hr. on a steam-bath and leave to cool. Filter on paper, wash with a soln. contg. 2 g. $(NH_4)_2C_2O_4$ and 1 g. $H_2C_2O_4$/l. H_2O and ignite. Add H_2O and 40 ml. 1:4 HCl, dil. to 200 ml. with H_2O, add 5 mg. Fe as $FeCl_3$ soln., make slightly alk. with NH_4OH, add 10 ml. Br_2 water and maintain near boiling for 15 min. Add 5 ml. Br_2 water, heat for 15 min. on a steam bath, filter on paper and wash with a soln. contg. 10 ml. NH_4OH and 10 g. NH_4Cl/l. Treat the filtrate with HCl, boil, add some reagent and NH_4OH, etc. No interference arises from Fe, Al, Ti, Zr, Mg, Ba, PO_4^{3-} but Sr interferes.
In other modifications,[22] the ppt. is dissolved in hot strongly acidic soln. which is cooled rapidly and adjusted to pH 3·7 with formate buffer. The pH can also be adjusted to 3·5–4·5 with NH_4OH.

For a titrimetric finish,[1, 2] ppt. as described above, filter on a glass crucible and wash with satd. CaC_2O_4 soln. or with cold H_2O. Heat to 70°C with 100 ml. warm 1:10 H_2SO_4, dil. with H_2O and titrate with 0·1*N* $KMnO_4$. The method has been applied to Al and its alloys;[23] for the washing technique, see ref. 24. Other titrants, e.g. $KBrO_3$ soln.[25] and Ce^{4+} soln.,[26] are also suitable. In all cases the titrant should be standardized against $CaCO_3$; results are low with $Na_2C_2O_4$.

Ca as oxalate, and Mg as arsenate can be pptd. simultaneously:[27] dissolve the ppt. in 50 ml. 4*N* H_2SO_4, heat to 70°C and titrate with $KMnO_4$ soln. (Ca); then cool, add KI and H_2SO_4 and titrate with $Na_2S_2O_3$ (Mg).

Most of the colorimetric methods based on pptn. of CaC_2O_4 involve the decompn. of some oxidant. In all cases it is essential to treat the standard solns. in exactly the same way.

For 0·05–0·15 mg. Ca in 5 ml. neutral soln.[28] add 1–2 drops HCl, 1–2 drops methyl orange, 1 ml. satd. $H_2C_2O_4$ soln. and dil. NH_4OH to give pH 4·5. After 12 hr. centrifuge for 5 min., remove the supernate with a capillary leaving 0·2 ml., add 3 ml. H_2O, swirl, centrifuge and remove the supernate as before. Mix the ppt. with 1 ml. of 1:1:1 H_2O–EtOH–Et_2O, shake gently with 3 ml. H_2O, centrifuge, remove the supernate and repeat again. Dry at 100–110°C for 0·5–1 hr., dissolve in 2·0 ml. 0·5*N* H_2SO_4 by placing in hot H_2O for 5 min. and cool. Add 2·00 ml. 0·005*N* Ce^{4+} in 0·2*N* H_2SO_4; after 30 min. dil. to 20 ml. with H_2O, add 1·5 ml. 1% KI, dil. to 25 ml. with H_2O and measure at 400 mμ.

NOTES. (1) The final color can also be measured at 600 mμ after addn. of starch.[29] The degree of bleaching of Ce^{4+} can be measured at 390 mμ.[30] Bleaching of $KMnO_4$ measured at 520–550 mμ is suitable for 0·1–3·4 mg. Ca.[31] Ignition of the ppt. can be followed[32] by dissoln. in HCl and treatment with KI and KIO_3.
(2) Dissoln. of the ppt. in HCl and $FeCl_3$ soln. allows final detn. with sulfosalicylic acid,[33] salicylic acid[34] or thiocyanate;[35] the last is suitable for 0·05–0·6 mg. Ca. Diphenylamine can be utilized:[36] dry the ppt. from 0·02–0·5 mg. Ca, add 0·1 g. diphenylamine and 1 drop H_2SO_4, heat at 150°C for 15 min. and at 180°C for 10 min., add EtOH and measure at 509 mμ.
(3) For a nephelometric procedure, see ref. 37.
(4) Certain other org. acids can replace $H_2C_2O_4$. Racemic acid has been used gravimetrically.[38] Oxalohydroxamic acid serves to ppt. 1–50 mg. Ca; the ppt. is dissolved in AcOH and the purple color formed with Fe^{3+} is measured.[39] Some Sr can be tolerated.
Naphthylhydroxamic acid ppts. 60 μg. Ca from boiling soln. at pH 10; centrifuge, add EDTA in buffer pH 10 and measure the yellow–red color at 410 mμ.[40] A nephelometric method and a titrimetric method with periodatocuprate are also available.[41]

(b) EDTA titration has been applied with many indicators. Calcon is among the best available.[42] Treat the soln. with 5 ml. diethylamine, add 4 drops calcon soln. (0·02 g. in 50 ml. MeOH; stable for 5 months), adjust to pH 12·5 and titrate from red to blue. Then det. Ca + Mg in another portion using eriochrome black T indicator (see Chapter 53, p. 398). Mg, Sr and Ba do not interfere with the use of calcon.

NOTES. (1) In another method for $<$ 0·5m*M* Ca + Mg soln.,[43] adjust to pH 13 with NaOH, add 3 drops 10% KCN, 2 drops 1% gelatin and 3 drops calcon soln. and titrate to blue (Ca); then adjust to pH 10 with NH_4OH and NH_4Cl, boil, add eriochrome black T and titrate further to blue (Mg).
(2) Indicators with which Ca can be titrated without Mg interference are: murexide–naphthol green B (50 mg. MgO tolerated with addn. of 200 mg. tartaric acid; Fe and Al require addn. of triethanolamine and KCN),[44] calcein,[45] 2-hydroxy-1-(2-hydroxy-4-sulfo-1-naphthylazo)-3-naphthoic acid,[46] pyrogallolcarboxylic acid,[47] and varnish scarlet C with methylene blue.[48]
(3) Various other modifications are possible. With eriochrome black T indicator,[49] treat 100 ml. of almost neutral soln. with 2 ml. buffer pH 10, 1 ml. 0·1*M* Mg–EDTA and 2–4 drops indicator; titrate with 0·01–0·001*M* EDTA. KCN masks interference from Co, Ni, Cu, Zn, Cd, Hg and Pt-metals; dimercaptopropanol masks Bi, Pb, Zn, Cd, As, Sb, Sn, Fe, Al and Na_2S prevents interference from small amts. of Fe. Most masking agents have now been replaced by triethanolamine and KCN.
Phthalein complexone can be used in a similar method.[50] Titration with NaOH using methyl red indicator is possible after EDTA addn.[51] EDTA can be back-titrated with Cu^{2+} in $>$ 0·15*M* NH_4OH medium with a photometric endpoint at 630 mμ.[52]
Ca is titrated potentiometrically with EGTA without interference from Mg.[53]

(c) Pyrogallolcarboxylic acid provides a colorimetric detn. of 0·2–0·4 mg. Ca in 10 ml. soln.[28, 54] Add 1 ml. 2*N* NaOH and 2 ml. 2% starch, dil. to 50 ml. with satd.

reagent soln. and measure the blue-violet color at 570 mμ. Mg, Al, Zn can be tolerated but Sr, Ba, Sn^{2+}, PO_4^{3-}, F^-, $C_2O_4^{2-}$ and CO_3^{2-} interfere; Fe and Ti can be sepd. with NaOH.

Chloranilic acid is suitable for 1 mg. Ca.[55, 56] Add 10 ml. 0·1% reagent, dil. to 30 ml. with H_2O, shake occasionally for 1·5 hr., filter on paper, dil. to 50 ml. with H_2O and measure at 530 mμ. Interferences are Fe, Mg, Al, Sr, Ba and Mn. This acid can also be used gravimetrically. Bromanilic acid is less sensitive to Mg interference than the chloro analog[55] and is also used colorimetrically or gravimetrically.[57] Iodanilic acid hemiether has been utilized colorimetrically for 0·4–2 mg. Ca in 30 ml. soln. at pH 6·9–7·0;[58] add 10 ml. reagent, shake, dil. to 50 ml. after 4 hr., filter and measure at 530 mμ.

(d) Flame photometry[59] can be utilized by means of the bands at 554 and 622 mμ, or the line at 422·7 mμ. For the line measurement, internal standards are Mn (403·4 mμ) or Li (670·8 mμ). Interferences are Al, PO_4^{3-} and SO_4^{2-}. See also p. 385.

(e) Picrolonic acid can be used gravimetrically, titrimetrically or colorimetrically. For gravimetry of 35–800 μg. Ca in 2 ml. neutral soln.,[60] heat to 50°C, add reagent (2·7 g. picrolonic acid/l. H_2O heated on a steam-bath, left for 12 hr. to cool and filtered) until the ppt. becomes cryst., allow to cool, add $\frac{1}{2}$ the vol. of reagent previously added and store at 0°C for 12 hr. Filter on a glass filter, wash with 0·2 ml. portions of H_2O at 0°C, dry at 150–175°C for 30 min. and weigh as $Ca(C_{10}H_7N_4O_5)_2\cdot\frac{1}{2}H_2O$; or dry at 200–230°C and weigh as the anhyd. salt.

NOTES. (1) Fe and Al are masked by sulfosalicylic acid. Mg, Na and K in < 10-fold amts. and NH_4^+ in equal amts. do not interfere.
(2) For a colorimetric finish,[61] wash the ppt. from 20–150 μg. Ca with Et_2O, add hot H_2O and 1 drop Br_2 water, heat, add 10 ml. EtOH, allow to cool, add 2 ml. 2*N* NaOH and compare after 12 hr. The ratios of cations to Ca that do not interfere are Mg:K:Na:NH_4^+:Ca = 2:5:2:5:1. The ppt. can also be dissolved in 2*N* H_2SO_4, treated with $K_2S_2O_8$, extd. with $CHCl_3$ and measured; the color is pyrazole blue.[62]
(3) For a titrimetric detn., add Li-picrolonate and titrate the filtrate with methylene blue.[63]

(f) Na_2MoO_4 allows a simple and accurate gravimetric detn. of 0·1–1 mg. Ca in 6 ml. soln.[64] Place the soln. in a Pt dish, add 0·8 ml. 5% reagent (adjusted to pH 4 with HCl), adjust to pH 6–7 (methyl red) using NH_4OH, boil for 2–3 min., cool, filter on a filter stick after 15 min. and wash with a little hot H_2O. Heat the Pt dish and filter stick at 700°C for 5 min. (230–1000°C) and weigh as $CaMoO_4$.

NOTES. (1) Ba and Sr can be detd. in the same way; Mg does not interfere if repptn. is done.
(2) For colorimetric detn. of < 30 μg. Ca,[65] add 1 ml. Na_2MoO_4 (75 ml. 5% Na_2MoO_4 in 50% EtOH with 25 ml. pyridine), keep at 70°C for 30 min., cool, centrifuge and wash 3 times with 50% EtOH. Add to the ppt. 4 ml. hot 0·8% $SnCl_2$ in 4*N* HCl and wash with 4 ml. 4*N* HCl and then with H_2O. Then add 2·5 ml. 5% NH_4SCN and 5 ml. iso-AmOH, shake and sep., ext. with 3 ml. AmOH, dil. to 10 ml. with AmOH and measure. No interference arises from Fe, Cu, Al, Mg, Zn.
(3) Na_2WO_4 also permits gravimetric and colorimetric detns.[66, 67] Ppt. at pH 7–8 and at 80°C, dry at 110°C (< 400°C) and weigh; alternatively, centrifuge, add Ti^{3+} and measure colorimetrically. A large excess of Mg is tolerable. The gravimetric detn. is reported as poor and as excellent.[67]

(g) H_2SO_4 can be applied gravimetrically or titrimetrically. For gravimetric detn.[1, 66] treat the slightly acidic soln. with a 10-fold excess of dil. H_2SO_4, add 4 vols. EtOH, filter on paper after 12 hr. and wash with 75% EtOH; burn the paper and ppt. separately, heat to dull redness and weigh as $CaSO_4$. The method has been applied to Ni–Cr–Fe.[23]

Photometric titration with dil. H_2SO_4 soln. is suitable for 2–4 mg. Ca in alc. soln.[68]

(h) Ferron allows gravimetric and colorimetric detns. For gravimetry of 5–50 mg. Ca in 20 ml. soln.,[69, 70] add 1·5 ml. AcOH and 25 ml. reagent (7 g. ferron in 100 ml. 0·25*M* Li_2CO_3 filtered after several hr.); after 2 hr., filter on a G3 crucible, wash twice with EtOH and twice with Me_2CO, dry at 105°C for 30 min. and weigh as $3[Ca(C_9H_4NIOHSO_3)_2]\cdot 10H_2O$. The error is ±0·35%. Amts. down to 0·2 mg. Ca can be detd. as described in Note 2.

NOTES. (1) Interferences are Pb, Mn, I^- and As^{3+}; no interference is caused by K, NH_4^+, Mg, Na, Ni, citrate, tartrate, SO_4^{2-} or ClO_4^-.
(2) For colorimetric detn. of 21–212 μg. Ca in 1 ml. soln., add 1 drop 10% AcOH and 2 ml. reagent; filter after 2–6 hr., and wash with 1 ml. EtOH and 1 ml. Me_2CO. Add 10 ml. Fe^{3+} soln. (1·718 g. Fe-alum/l. 1*N* HCl) and measure at 625 mμ.
(3) Oxine is applied titrimetrically[71] or colorimetrically.[72] Heat the neutral or slightly acidic soln. to 60°C, add 5 ml. 2*N* NH_4OH and 3% oxine in EtOH, boil, cool to 40–50°C, filter on a glass crucible and wash with warm and then cold H_2O. Dissolve in HCl and titrate with $KBrO_3$–KBr soln., or dry at 90–290°C and weigh as $Ca(C_9H_6ON)_2$. Interferences are Mg, Sr and large amts. of NH_4^+; repptn. removes Sr. For colorimetry, Folin–Denis reagent is reduced with the ppt.

(i) $K_4Fe(CN)_6$ has been applied gravimetrically and titrimetrically.[73] Adjust the NH_4^+-free soln. to pH 8 with NaOH, add an equal vol. of EtOH, heat to 50°C and add satd. reagent soln. in 20% EtOH; filter on a glass crucible, wash with 50% EtOH, dry at 105°C and weigh as $K_2CaFe(CN)_6$. Alternatively, wash twice with Me_2CO, transfer to a beaker, dissolve the ppt. in 1 drop 1·8*N* H_2SO_4 and H_2O, dil. to 20 ml. with H_2O and titrate to setopaline indicator with $KMnO_4$ soln.; or dissolve the ppt. in 3·6*N* H_2SO_4 and titrate with

Ce^{4+} soln. with ferroin indicator. The latter is suitable for 0·05–2·5 mg. Ca.

(j) Miscellaneous titrimetric methods. NaF soln. may be used to titrate 50–100 mg. Ca in 10–20 ml. soln.[74] Add 0·1 ml. 0·1*M* $FeCl_3$ and 4 ml. 60% NH_4SCN as indicator, add an equal vol. of EtOH and titrate with 0·5*M* NaF to colorless.

K_2CrO_4 is used with magneson II as indicator[75] for 3–27 mg. Ca in soln. Add 1 ml. satd. magneson II in EtOH and 5 ml. 1:1 NH_4OH, dil. to 20 ml. with H_2O and titrate; 100 mg. Mg does not interfere.

(k) Murexide allows a rapid colorimetric detn. of Ca but the complex formed is not stable.[76, 77] The method is suitable for < 1·2 mg. Ca/l. of final soln. Add 0·1*N* NaOH to give a final pH of 11·3, dil. to 80 ml. with H_2O, add 10 ml. reagent (40 mg. murexide in 75 ml. H_2O, filtered and mixed with 175 ml. EtOH) and dil. to 100 ml. with H_2O; measure at 506 mμ within 5 min. Interferences are Cu, Ni, Co, Mn, Zn, Cd, Sn; no interference arises from 10 p.p.m. Mg, 1 p.p.m. Sr or Fe^{3+} and 5 p.p.m. Ba. The color is said to vary up to an Mg/Ca ratio of 40, but is then constant, hence Mg should be added if necessary.

(l) Phthalein complexone is suitable for 0·1 mg. Ca in neutral soln.[77] Add 25 ml. buffer pH 10·15 (0·75% NH_4Cl in 1:19 NH_4OH), dil. to about 90 ml. with H_2O, add 10·0 ml. 0·03% reagent, dil. to 100 ml. and measure at 575 mμ.

(m) Varnish scarlet C is suitable for colorimetric detn.[78] To 5 ml. soln. add 0·2 ml. 0·1% reagent and 0·1–0·2 ml. NaOH and measure at 480 mμ.

NOTES. (1) Co and PO_4^{3-} interfere. If Fe, Cu, Mg or Mn is present, treat 4 ml. soln. with 0·05 ml. Al soln. (K-alum to give 1 mg. Al/ml.), 0·05 ml. $BaCl_2$ soln. (1 mg. Ba/ml.) and 0·05 ml. Na_2S soln. (2 mg. H_2S/ml.), then add reagent, etc.

(2) Several analogous reagents can be applied similarly. For the use of eriochrome black T, see Chapter 53, p. 398. Plasmocorinth permits detn. of 0–50 μg. Ca/ml. soln.[79] Add 4 ml. 0·004% reagent and 5 ml. 2·1*N* NaOH and measure at 620 mμ. Mn interferes but Fe and Be do not. Ca can be detd. in Ti after extn. of the Ti–SCN^- complex with Et_2O.[80]

Tannin can also be used.[81]

(n) $K_4[Ni(NO_2)_6]$ can be used in colorimetric or titrimetric methods and in electrodeposition. For colorimetry,[82] treat 5 ml. soln. with 5 ml. Ni soln. (30 g. $Ni(NO_3)_2$ and 45 g. KNO_2/100 ml. H_2O); centrifuge after 1–2 hr. and wash with a satd. soln. of the ppt. in 25% KNO_2. Dissolve the ppt. in 5 ml. AcOH, dil. to 100 ml. with H_2O and take an aliquot contg. 0·1–0·5 mg. Ca. Add 1 ml. Br_2 water, remove the Br_2 color with NH_4OH, add 1 ml. NH_4OH in excess and 0·5 ml. 1% dimethylglyoxime in EtOH, and dil. to 25 ml. with H_2O. Compare after 15 min. For a titrimetric method, see Erdey.[39]

In an alternative procedure[83] treat the ppt. from 1 mg Ca with 7 ml. H_2O, 3 ml. 5% antipyrine and 1 ml. H_2SO_4 and compare the green color. Griess reagent can also be applied.[84]

Ca can also be detd. by electrolyzing the Ni in the ppt.[85]

(o) Miscellaneous colorimetric methods. Na_3PO_4 can be used to ppt. Ca after sepn. as oxalate, and the PO_4^{3-} detd. by a molybdenum blue method.[28, 66, 86] For 0·2–0·5 mg. Ca in 5–10 ml. soln., acidify to methyl red with HCl, heat almost to boiling, add 1 ml. 4% $(NH_4)_2C_2O_4$, make alk. with 1:1 NH_4OH, leave to cool for 1–2 hr., centrifuge and wash with 0·1% $(NH_4)_2C_2O_4$. Add 1:1 HCl, evap., add 0·5 ml. 30% H_2O_2, heat on a steam-bath for 30 min., dil. to 3–5 ml. with H_2O. Add 0·5 ml. 6*N* NaOH, leave for 2–3 min., add 0·5 ml. 1% Na_3PO_4, centrifuge after 1 hr. and wash thrice with 2 ml. portions of a mixt. of 58 ml. EtOH, 10 ml. AmOH, 32 ml. H_2O and 1 drop 6*N* NaOH. Add 0·5 ml. 2·5% $(NH_4)_2MoO_4$ in 6*N* H_2SO_4 and 1 ml. eiconogen reagent (0·25 g. in 100 ml. H_2O contg. 15 g. $NaHSO_3$ and 0·5 g. Na_2SO_3, shaken for 2–3 hr.). Dil. to 10·0 ml. with H_2O, place in the dark for 10 min. and compare. Hydroquinone reduction is also suitable.[86]

Alizarin is suitable for detn. of 2 μg. Ca in serum.[87] To 1·0 ml. H_2O, add 0·02 ml. serum, 2·0 ml. 1·0*N* triethanolamine and 3·0 ml. reagent (4 mg. alizarin/l. *n*-octanol), shake mechanically for 20 min. and centrifuge. Recentrifuge the upper phase, dil. to 5 ml. with *n*-octanol and measure at 560 mμ. Add to the standard an amt. of Mg equal to that in the sample. Sr and Ba interfere.

Oleate provides a nephelometric method for < 0·28 mg. Ca in 45 ml. soln.[28, 66, 88] For the reagent, mix 7·05 g. oleic acid in 5 ml. H_2O with 1·60 g. KOH, transfer to a flask with 50 ml. 70% EtOH, heat under reflux and dil. to 250 ml. with H_2O; mix this with 100 ml. 3% Duponol and filter or centrifuge after 12 hr. For a detn. make the soln. alk. to litmus with NH_4OH, add 1 ml. in excess, dil. to 50 ml. with H_2O, wait 15 min. and filter if necessary; pipet 5·00 ml. of filtrate, add 5·0 ml. reagent and measure at 420 mμ. No interference arises from 1000 p.p.m. Mg or from 500 p.p.m. Fe, Al, Mn, Cu, Zn, Pb. For a titrimetric detn. make the soln. alk. to phenolphthalein with NaOH, just acidify with 0·1*N* HCl, add 1 drop HCl and titrate with oleate soln. to red.

Other reagents which allow nephelometric detns. are stearate, palmitate, myristate, ricinoleate, sulforicinoleate;[89] for details, see ref. 66.

STRONTIUM

The only satisfactory methods are gravimetric determination as $SrSO_4$, titrimetric determination after precipitation with oxalate or fusion with boric acid, and flame-photometric determination. EDTA titration is reasonably accurate.

(a) H_2SO_4 provides the best gravimetric detn. of Sr.[1, 2] Add a 10-fold excess of dil. H_2SO_4 to the neutral soln. followed by an equal vol. of EtOH and leave for

12 hr. Filter on a Gooch crucible, wash with 50% EtOH contg. some H_2SO_4 and then with EtOH, ignite at dull redness (100–300°C) and weigh as $SrSO_4$. Interferences are Ba, Ca, etc.

(b) Fusion with H_3BO_3 can be followed by titration with 0·002–0·0002*N* borax with methyl red–methylene blue as indicator.[90] For 500 μg. Sr as nitrate, add a 30-fold amt. of H_3BO_3, evap. and fuse. Add 2 ml. 0·01*N* HCl, cover and heat. Transfer to a flask with hot H_2O, add 10 ml. MeOH and heat to remove most of the H_3BO_3. Repeat if necessary. Finally titrate.

(c) Flame photometry allows detn. of 100 μg. Sr/ml. by means of the line at 460·7 mμ or the band at 681 mμ[4, 91] (see also p. 385).

(d) $(NH_4)_2C_2O_4$ is applied in the same way as for Ca (see p. 388).[1, 2] Weigh the ppt. as SrO after ignition above 1170°C, or as $SrCO_3$ after ignition at 500–800°C, or as SrC_2O_4 after drying at 335–350°C. Alternatively, titrate the ppt. with $KMnO_4$. With small amts. of Sr, ferroin should be used as indicator.[2] The ppt. can be weighed[92] as $SrC_2O_4 \cdot H_2O$ after drying at 100–105°C. When Sr is recovered from a $Mg_2P_2O_7$ ppt., pptn. should be done from 1:5 EtOH medium.

(e) Miscellaneous gravimetric methods. $(NH_4)_2CO_3$ is used as follows.[66, 93] Treat the soln. with reagent and with NH_4OH, boil, filter on a Gooch crucible after 12 hr., wash, ignite at 500–800°C (410–1100°C) and weigh as $SrCO_3$; alternatively, titrate the ppt. with acid.

For the use of MoO_4^{2-}, see p. 390. For pptn. of $SrCl_2$ or $Sr(NO_3)_2$, see under Separation, pp. 386 and 388.

Picrolonic acid ppts. Sr from neutral soln.[94] Heat to 50–55°C, add dropwise a 100% excess of 0·01*N* reagent, cool to 0°C, filter on a glass crucible, wash with H_2O at 0°C or with CS_2, dry in air and weigh as $Sr(C_{10}H_7N_4O_5)_2 \cdot 8H_2O$.

KH_2PO_4 allows detn. of 35–200 mg. Sr in 40–60 ml. soln.[95] Add 10–20 ml. 0·5*M* reagent, boil, make turbid with 1*N* KOH, boil for 5–10 min. until the ppt. becomes crystalline. Make alk. to methyl orange with KOH, add 2–3 ml. in excess, heat for 15 min. and leave to cool for 1 hr. Filter, wash with a little H_2O, dry at 120–130°C for 1 hr. and weigh as $SrHPO_4$, or ignite and weigh as $Sr_2P_2O_7$. Interferences are Na and NH_4^+.

(f) EDTA titration is suitable for $< 0·005M$ Sr solns.[2, 50] To 100 ml. soln. add 10 ml. 0·1*M* Zn–EDTA, 5 ml. 1*M* NH_4Cl and ca. 7 ml. NH_4OH (to give a 1*M* soln.). Then add 2–4 drops eriochrome black T indicator and titrate with 0·01*M* EDTA. See also p. 389 and p. 393. Mg–EDTA can replace Zn–EDTA but the end-point is less satisfactory. Phthalein complexone can be used as indicator.

(g) Miscellaneous colorimetric methods. Chloranilic acid can serve for detn. of < 0·2 mg. Sr/ml.[96] Adjust the soln. to pH 5–7, place 5 ml. in a centrifuge tube, add 5·00 ml. 0·05% chloranilic acid, store at 0°C for 3–12 hr., centrifuge and measure at 530 mμ. Bromanilic acid is suitable for 0·4–3·2 mg. Sr.[97]

Murexide and phthalein may be used similarly to the methods for Ca (see p. 391).

BARIUM

Gravimetric determination as sulfate is generally used. For small amounts, titration with EDTA, or titration of the $BaCrO_4$ precipitate is satisfactory. The latter precipitate can also be determined colorimetrically. Flame photometry is quite satisfactory.

(a) H_2SO_4 allows gravimetric, titrimetric and nephelometric detns. For gravimetric detn.[1, 98] boil the soln. contg. < 1 ml. HCl/100 ml., add hot dil. H_2SO_4 dropwise to give an excess of < 5 ml./100 ml. soln., and heat on a steam-bath. Filter on paper, wash with hot H_2O contg. 2 drops H_2SO_4/l., then wash with a little hot H_2O. Ignite at 900°C (780–1000°C) and weigh as $BaSO_4$. Reheat after addn. of a drop of H_2SO_4 if necessary.

NOTES. (1) Interferences are Sr, Ca, Pb and large amts. of Al or Cl^-. VO_3^- can be removed by treatment with Al and NH_4OH. Large amts. of Fe^{3+} must be reduced with Zn or Al, or treated with a < 1·5% excess of NH_4SCN and boiled till colorless. EDTA prevents many interferences.[2]

(2) To remove impurities from the ppt., heat with 5 ml. H_2SO_4, cool, pour into 50 ml. H_2O, dil. to 100 ml. with H_2O and place on a steam-bath for 1 hr.; then filter, etc. $PbSO_4$ can be removed by treatment with 15% KI in AcOH (see Chapter 20, p. 157).

(3) Homogeneous pptn. can be done by means of sulfamic acid,[99] dimethyl sulfate,[100] or EDTA and $(NH_4)_2S_2O_8$.[101]

(4) Various titrimetric procedures are available (see also Chapter 58, p. 435). Tetrahydroxyquinone can serve as indicator;[102] for 10–50 mg. Ba in 20 ml. soln. at pH 4·0–5·0, add 20 ml. iso-PrOH and 0·2 g. indicator (1:300 tetrahydroxyquinone–KCl) and titrate with 0·025*M* K_2SO_4. Sr interferes but Ca, Mg, Ni, Co, Zn, Mn, Cr^{3+}, Hg^{2+}, PO_4^{3-} and small amts. of Fe, Ti, Cu, Pb, Al can be tolerated.

Na-rhodizonate is also suitable as indicator.[66] The benzidine method for SO_4^{2-} (see p. 436) can be applied to the filtrate obtained after addn. of excess H_2SO_4 to a soln. contg. 0·5–2 mg. Ba.[66, 103] Alizarin S is also useful with K_2SO_4 titrant (see Chapter 58, p. 435).

(5) Nephelometry is applicable[104] for 10^{-5} to 10^{-4} mg. Ba/l. contg. 0·096 or 0·192*M* $Pb(NO_3)_2$ and 1·74 or 3·48*M* NH_4OAc; add some 1*N* H_2SO_4 and compare after 40 min. See also Chapter 58, p. 436.

(b) $(NH_4)_2Cr_2O_7$ also allows gravimetric, titrimetric and colorimetric detns. of Ba. For the gravimetric procedure,[1, 2] see under Separation, p. 387; filter on a Gooch crucible, wash, heat below 300°C (> 60°C) and weigh as $BaCrO_4$. Homogeneous pptn. by means of urea is satisfactory for sepn. of 100 mg. Ba from 40 mg. Sr.[105]

The ppt. can be titrated in various ways. Addn. of excess 0·1*N* Fe^{2+} in dil. H_2SO_4 and back-titration with 0·1*N* $KMnO_4$ is satisfactory[106] and can be adapted for detn. of 1–10 mg. Ba.[2] Amperometric titration with Fe^{2+}

is suitable for < 100 μg. Ba.[90] For iodometric titration,[106] dissolve the ppt. in 50–100 ml. 1:10 HCl, add 2 g. KI and titrate with $0{\cdot}1N$ $Na_2S_2O_3$. Titration with As^{3+} soln. is suitable also (see Chapter 20, p. 159).

For direct titration[107] of neutral $0{\cdot}1M$ Ba soln., add 5 ml. EtOH/10 ml. soln. and 5 drops rosolic acid indicator and titrate with $0{\cdot}1N$ K_2CrO_4 to purple. For other titrimetric methods, see ref. 66.

For a colorimetric finish, centrifuge the ppt., dissolve in 1:1 HCl and measure with a blue filter.[28]

(c) Flame photometry can be applied by means of the bands at 515 and 873 mμ or the line at 535·4 mμ (which is weak).[4]

(d) Miscellaneous gravimetric methods. For gravimetric detn. as $BaCl_2$ or $Ba(NO_3)_2$, see under Separation, pp. 386 and 388.

H_2SiF_6 ppts. Ba from neutral or slightly acidic soln.[108] Add excess reagent and a 1/3 vol. of EtOH; after 12 hr., filter on a Munroe crucible, wash with 50% v/v EtOH, dry at 110°C and weigh as $BaSiF_6$. Ca and Sr do not interfere. $(NH_4)_2BeF_4$ ppts. Ba as $BaBeF_4$ which can be dried at 100°C; Pb does not interfere.[109]

$Na_2S_2O_3$ ppts. Ba from 70% EtOH soln.[110] Heat the soln. to 96°C, add EtOH to give a 70% v/v soln., then add a satd. soln. (at 96°C) of $Na_2S_2O_3$ in 70% v/v EtOH; filter on a glass crucible, wash with 70% EtOH at 96°C, dry in a desiccator (68–75°C) and weigh as $BaS_2O_3{\cdot}H_2O$. Alternatively, titrate the ppt. or the filtrate with $0{\cdot}1N$ I_2. Sr interferes but Ca does not.

$(NH_4)_2C_2O_4$ ppts. Ba from 50% EtOH soln. which is alk. to phenolphthalein;[111] the ppt. is dried at 105°C and weighed as $BaC_2O_4{\cdot}\frac{1}{2}H_2O$ or titrated with $KMnO_4$ soln.

(e) EDTA titration can be utilized with several indicators. For 0·5 g. $BaCl_2$ in 250 ml. soln.[112] add 2 drops AcOH, boil for 5 min., cool, add 10 ml. buffer (8·25 g. NH_4Cl and 113 ml. NH_4OH dild. to 1 l.) and 0·4 g. indicator (0·25 g. eriochrome black T in 25 g. NaCl) and titrate with EDTA reagent soln. For the reagent, dissolve 2·6 g. $MgCl_2{\cdot}6H_2O$, 1·9 g. $CaCl_2{\cdot}2H_2O$, 28·0 g. EDTA and 7·9 ml. 50% NaOH in H_2O and dil. to 1 l. An alternative reagent[113] contains 0·8 g. $ZnCl_2$, 1·0 g. $MgCl_2{\cdot}6H_2O$ and 7·0 g. EDTA/l. Photometric titration at 650 mμ is possible.[114]

Phthalein complexone can also be applied in photometric titration at 570 mμ.[115] For 0·05–12 mg. Ba, neutralize the soln. with NaOH, add 10 ml. buffer (10 g. NH_4Cl/l. of NH_4OH; 10 ml. dild. to 60 ml.), dil. to 60 ml. with H_2O, add 10 drops indicator (60 mg. in 60 ml. triethanolamine) and titrate. This indicator is suitable for back-titration with $BaCl_2$ soln.[50]

For detn. of 50 μg.–10 mg. Ba as sulfate,[2, 116] mix with 100 mg. $NaPO_3$, fuse at 1000°C for 15 min., cool, add H_2O and 1 ml. HCl and evap. to dryness. Repeat the addn. and evapn. Add dil. HCl and 30 mg. indicator (2:1:500 eriochrome black T–tropeolin OO–NaCl) per 25 ml. soln. Then add excess EDTA soln., adjust to blue-green with NH_4OH, add 1 ml. buffer (54 g. NH_4Cl and 350 ml. NH_4OH/l.) per 25 ml. soln. and titrate with 0·01–0·001M $MgCl_2$ to a red color. If Al is present, add triethanolamine.

(f) Miscellaneous titrimetric methods. Addn. of Na-lauryl sulfate and titration with a quaternary ammonium salt is feasible.[117] Palmitate, etc. have been used in the same way as for Ca (see p. 391).

Na_2HPO_4 with methyl red indicator may be used[118] to titrate neutral Ba soln. contg. 27·5% v/v EtOH after addn. of 1 drop $0{\cdot}1N$ HCl. Interferences are NH_4^+, Fe, etc.

Pptn. with KIO_3 is followed by iodometric titration.[119] For 60–300 mg. $BaCl_2$ in 20 ml. soln., boil, add 25 ml. 3·2% KIO_3 soln., boil, cool, dil. to 100 ml. with H_2O, take a 10 ml. aliquot and titrate.

(g) Molybdate can be used to ppt. Ba, the ppt. being evaluated colorimetrically, gravimetrically or titrimetrically. For a colorimetric finish[120] on the ppt. from 0–100 μg. Ba, dissolve in HCl, add 5% KSCN and $SnCl_2$ and ext. with Et_2O. Ca and Sr in amts. equal to Ba do not interfere. For the gravimetric finish, see p. 390. For the titration method,[121] dissolve the ppt. in 1:1 HCl, reduce with Zn–Hg, add excess $0{\cdot}1N$ NH_4VO_3 and 5 ml. H_3PO_4 and titrate with $0{\cdot}1N$ Fe^{2+} soln. using diphenylamine indicator.

(h) Miscellaneous colorimetric methods. Na-ethylmethylpicrate ppts. 2 mg. Ba/ml. soln.[122] Add 15 ml satd. reagent, filter through a filter stick after 1 hr. and wash with a satd. soln. of the ppt. in Et_2O; dissolve in 50 ml. warm H_2O, cool, dil. to 100 ml. with H_2O and measure at 390 mμ. Alternatively, dry the ppt. at 105°C and weigh as $Ba(C_9H_8N_3O_7)_2{\cdot}H_2O$. No interference arises from Ca, or from Sr or K if repptn. is done.

Na-rhodizonate allows detn. of 80–300 μg. Ba in neutral soln.[123] Place the soln. in a Nessler tube, add 0·5 ml. HCl, dil. to 10 ml. with H_2O and add 2 ml. $CHCl_3$ and 0·5 ml. satd. reagent soln. Shake, leave to stand and compare the color on the boundary of the phases. The error is ± 40 μg. No interference arises from 0·36–1·5 mg. Sr or from 0·98 mg. Ca.

$KMnO_4$ and K_2SO_4 are used as follows.[124] To 2 ml. 5% HNO_3 soln. add 100 mg. reagent mixt. (the 2 solids mixed 1:1 and sieved through 80 mesh); after 2 hr. add 30% tartaric acid in 20% H_2SO_4 to decomp. $KMnO_4$. Transfer part of the ppt. to CSS 598 confined spot test paper, dry and fix with paraffin in CCl_4. Compare with standards contg. 5, 10, 25, 50, 75 and 150 μg. Ba prepd. similarly. Mg does not interfere but Ca, Sr, Fe and Pb do.

Phthalein complexone can be used similarly to the method for Ca (p. 391).

References

1. HILLEBRAND and LUNDELL, 486 (611); SCOTT and FURMAN, 205, 899, 117; KIMURA, 523; FRESENIUS–JANDER, **IIa**, 208 (1940).
2. BALLCZO, H., and DOPPLER, G., *Z. anal. Chem.*, **151**, 26 (1956); **152**, 321 (1956).

3. DUPUIS, T., and DUVAL, C., *Bull. soc. chim. France*, 567 (1949).
4. HINSVARK, O. N., *et al.*, *Anal. Chem.*, **25**, 320 (1953).
5. VALLEE, B. L. and MARGOSCHES, M., *Anal. Chem.*, **28**, 175, 180 (1956) (Ca, Sr, Mg, Na, K); IKEDA, S., *J. Chem. Soc. Japan*, **76**, 783 (1955); **78**, 1428, 1431 (1957) (+ EtOH, Me_2CO); SUGAWARA, K., *et al.*, *Bull. Chem. Soc. Japan*, **29**, 679, 683 (1956) (+ tartaric acid).
6. FEIGL, F., and SCHAEFFER, A., *Anal. Chem.*, **23**, 351 (1951).
7. PŘIBIL, R., and FIALA, L., *Chem. listy*, **46**, 331 (1952).
8. CALEY, E. R., and ELVING, P. J., *Ind. Eng. Chem.*, *Anal. Ed.*, **10**, 264 (1938).
9. GREEAR, J. A., and WRIGHT, E. R., *Anal. Chem.*, **21**, 596 (1949).
10. BELCHER, R., *et al.*, *Chem. & Ind.* (*London*), 127 (1954).
11. FLASCHKA, H., and HUDITZ, F., *Radex Rundschau*, 181 (1952).
12. MURACA, R. F., and RETZ, M. T., *Chemist Analyst*, **43**, 73 (1954).
13. WILLARD, H. H. and GOODSPEED, E. W., *Ind. Eng. Chem.*, *Anal. Ed.*, **8**, 414 (1936).
14. MINAMI, E., and SASAKI, Y., *Japan Analyst*, **2**, 299 (1953).
15. STEWART, P. B., and KOBE, K. A., *Ind. Eng. Chem.*, *Anal. Ed.*, **14**, 298 (1942).
16. KOBE and MOTSCH, W. L., *Anal. Chem.*, **23**, 1498 (1951).
17. DREKOPF, K., and WINZEN, W., *Brennstoff-Chem.*, **38**, 208 (1957).
18. KALLMANN, S., *Anal. Chem.*, **20**, 449 (1948).
19. OSBORN, G. H., *Analyst*, **70**, 207 (1945).
20. IEVINŠ, A., *Latvijas Univ. Raksti*, *Chem. Ser.*, **2**, 465 (1935).
21. INGOLS, R. S., and MURRAY, P. E., *Anal. Chem.*, **21**, 525 (1949).
22. MCCOMAS, JR., W. H., and RIEMANN, W., III, *Ind. Eng. Chem.*, *Anal. Ed.*, **14**, 929 (1942); LINGANE, J. J., *et al.*, *ibid.*, **17**, 39 (1945).
23. A.S.T.M., 216 ff.
24. IEVINŠ, A., and OŠIS, F., *Z. anal. Chem.*, **120**, 401 (1940).
25. SZEBELLÉDY, L., and MADIS, W., *Z. anal. Chem.*, **114**, 347, 350 (1938).
26. KELLY, O. J., *et al.*, *Ind. Eng. Chem.*, *Anal. Ed.*, **18**, 319 (1946).
27. PROČKE, O., and MICHAL, J., *Collection Czechoslov. Chem. Communs.*, **10**, 20 (1938).
28. SANDELL, 243.
29. SENDROY, J., JR., and ALVING, A. S., *J. Biol. Chem.*, **142**, 159 (1942).
30. WEYBREW, J. A., *et al.*, *Anal. Chem.*, **20**, 759 (1948).
31. SCOTT, R. E., and JOHNSON, C. R., *Ind. Eng. Chem.*, *Anal. Ed.*, **17**, 504 (1945).
32. DE LUCA, H. A., *Can. J. Research*, **25B**, 449 (1947).
33. WELCHER, **II**, 138.
34. BURRIEL-MARTI, F., *et al.*, *Anal. Chem.*, **25**, 583 (1953).
35. WELCHER, **II**, 55; MCGREGOR, A. J., *Analyst*, **75**, 211 (1950).
36. DE LA RUBIA PACHECO, J., and LOPEZ-RUBIO, F. B., *Inform. quím. anal.* (*Madrid*), **6**, 40 (1952).
37. HUNTER, J. G., and HALL, A., *Analyst*, **78**, 106 (1953).
38. WELCHER, **II**, 115.
39. DHAR, S. K., and DAS GUPTA, A. K., *J. Sci. Ind. Research*, **11B**, 520 (1952); also see JANKOVITS, L., and ERDEY, L., *Acta Chim. Acad. Sci. Hung.*, **7**, 155 (1955).
40. AMIN, A. M., *Chemist Analyst*, **46**, 31, 33 (1957).
41. BECK, G., and BERLI, W., *Mikrochim. Acta*, 24 (1957); BECK, *Mikrochemie ver. Mikrochim. Acta*, **36/37**, 245 (1951).
42. HILDEBRAND, G. P., and REILLEY, C. N., *Anal. Chem.*, **29**, 258 (1957).
43. LOTT, P. F., and CHENG, K. L., *Chemist Analyst*, **46**, 30 (1957).
44. TIKHOMĬROVA, V., and ŠIMÁČKOVÁ, O., *Chem. listy*, **50**, 1925 (1956); also see CHENG, *et al.*, *Anal. Chem.*, **24**, 1640 (1952); ACONSKY, L., and MORI, M., *ibid.*, **27**, 1001 (1955) (photometric at 610 mμ).
45. DIEHL, H., and ELLINGBOE, J. L., *Anal. Chem.*, **28**, 882 (1956).
46. PATTON, J., and REEDER, W., *Anal. Chem.*, **28**, 1026 (1956.)
47. KOVAŘIK, M., and MOUČHA, M., *Z. anal. Chem.*, **150**, 416 (1956).
48. KUZNETSOV, V. I., and MIKHAĬLOV, V. A., *Zhur. Anal. Khim.*, **12**, 59 (1957).
49. BIEDERMANN, W., and SCHWARZENBACH, G., *Chimia* (*Switz.*), **2**, 56 (1948).
50. SCHWARZENBACH, *Die komplexometrische Titration*, 59 (1955).
51. RIO, A., and TODARO, M., *Ann. chim.*, **44**, 139 (1954).
52. RAMAIAH, N. A., *Anal. Chim. Acta*, **16**, 569 (1959).
53. SCHMID, R. W., and REILLEY, N., *Anal. Chem.*, **29**, 264 (1957).
54. PECH, J., *Chem. listy*, **43**, 8 (1949); also see OKÁČ, A., and PECH, *Collection Czechoslov. Chem. Communs.*, **13**, 403, 514 (1948); TSAO, M. U., *J. Biol. Chem.*, **199**, 251 (1952).
55. KUBO, S., and TSUTSUMI, C., *Rept. Food Research Inst.* (*Tokyo*), **2**, 145 (1949).
56. TYNER, E. H., *Anal. Chem.*, **20**, 76 (1948); GAMMON, N., JR., and FORBES, R. B., *ibid.*, **21**, 1391 (1949); FROST-JONES, R. E. U., and YARDLEY, J. T., *Analyst*, **77**, 468 (1952); BARRETO, A., *Rev. quím. ind.* (*Rio de Janeiro*), **4**, (108), 18 (1945).
57. ERDEY, L., and JANKOVITS, L., *Acta Chim. Acad. Sci. Hung.* **4**, 245 (1954).
58. JANKOVITS, *Acta Chim. Acad. Sci. Hung.*, **10**, 99 (1956).
59. CHEN, P. S., JR., and TORIBARA, T. Y., *Anal. Chem.*, **25**, 1642 (1953); KINGSLEY, G. R., and SCHAFFERT, R. R., *ibid.*, 1738; BAKER, G. L., and JOHNSON, H., *ibid.*, **26**, 465 (1954); CHOW, T. J., and THOMPSON, T. G., *ibid.*, **27**, 910 (1955); YOKOSUKA, S., *et al.*, *Japan Analyst*, **4**, 437 (1955); **5**, 71 (1956); IKEDA, S., *J. Chem. Soc. Japan*, **76**, 1258 (1955).
60. HECHT and DONAU, 221; WELCHER, **IV**, 41; KIBA, T., and IKEDA, T., *J. Chem. Soc. Japan*, **60**, 911 (1939); IMAI, H., *ibid.*, **78**, 188 (1957).
61. ALTEN, F., *et al.*, *Biochem. Z.*, **265**, 85 (1933); COHN, G., and KOLTHOFF, I. M., *J. Biol. Chem.*, **147**, 705 (1943); MACKERETH, F. J. H., *Analyst*, **76**, 482 (1951); also see KLEMENT, R., *Z. anal. Chem.*, **128**, 431 (1948) (with methylene blue).
62. ERDEY, L., and JANKOVITS, L., *Acta Chim. Acad. Sci. Hung.*, **4**, 235 (1954).
63. WELCHER, **IV**, 525.

64. MOSER, R., and ROBINSON, R. J., *Anal. Chem.*, **19**, 929 (1947); also see IEVINŠ, A., and GRINŠTEINS, V., *Z. anal. Chem.*, **127**, 20 (1944).
65. HARRISON, G. E., and RAYMOND, W. H. A., *Analyst*, **78**, 528 (1953).
66. FRESENIUS–JANDER, **IIa**, 208 ff (1940).
67. RINCK, E., and OSTERTAG, H., *Compt. rend.*, **224**, 1108 (1947); IEVINŠ and GRINŠTEINS, *Z. anal. Chem.*, **124**, 288 (1942); PELTIER, S., and DUVAL, C., *Anal. Chim. Acta*, **1**, 408 (1947).
68. BOBTELSKY, M., and EISENSTADTER, J., *Anal. Chim. Acta*, **14**, 89 (1956).
69. GILLIS, J., *et al.*, *Mikrochim. Acta*, 760 (1956).
70. WELCHER, **I**, 339.
71. BERG, R., *Oxin*, 40 (1935).
72. YOSHIMATSU, S., *Tôhoku J. Exptl. Med.*, **15**, 355 (1930).
73. FLASCHKA, H., and SPITZY, H., *Mikrochemie ver. Mikrochim. Acta*, **34**, 269 (1949); **35**, 306 (1950).
74. RINGBOM, A., and MERIKANTO, B., *Acta Chem. Scand.*, **3**, 29 (1949).
75. PASOVSKAYA, G. B., *Trudy Komissii Anal. Khim., Akad. Nauk S.S.S.R., Inst. Geokhim. i Anal. Khim.*, **7**, 272 (1956).
76. WILLIAMS, M. B., and MOSER, J. H., *Anal. Chem.*, **25**. 1414 (1953); also see OSTERTAG, H., and RINCK, E, *Compt. rend.*, **231**, 1304 (1950); **232**, 629 (1951); *Chim. anal.*, **34**, 108 (1952); TAMMELIN, L. E., and MOGENSEN, S., *Acta Chem. Scand.*, **6**, 988 (1952); WATSON, L. R., and SCOTT, A. B., *J. Chem. Phys.*, **24**, 619 (1956).
77. POLLARD, F. H., and MARTIN, J. V., *Analyst*, **81**, 348 (1956).
78. ASHIZAWA, T., *Repts. Balneol. Lab., Okayama Univ.*, **3**, 39 (1950); **6**, 15 (1952).
79. YANAGIZAWA, F., *Niigata-Igakukai-Zasshi*, **65**, 760 (1951); *J. Biochem.*, **42**, 3 (1955); KINGSLEY, G. R., and ROBNETT, O., *Am. J. Clin. Pathol.*, **27**, 223 (1957).
80. GOTO, H., and TAKEYAMA, S., *Sci. Repts. Research Insts. Tohoku Univ., Ser A.*, **9**, 138 (1957).
81. WELCHER, **II**, 171.
82. TSYVINA, B. S., *Zavodskaya Lab.*, **15**, 142 (1949); see also ERDEY.[39]
83. WELCHER, **III**, 108.
84. ZIMMER, H., *Z. anal. Chem.*, **155**, 337 (1957).
85. PELTIER, S., and DUVAL, C., *Anal. Chim. Acta*, **1**, 408 (1947).
86. WELCHER, **I**, 131, 231.
87. NATELSON, S., and PENNIAL, R., *Anal. Chem.*, **27**, 434 (1955); WELCHER, **IV**, 420.
88. SAIFER, A., and CLARK, F. D., *Ind. Eng. Chem., Anal. Ed.*, **17**, 757 (1945).
89. WELCHER, **II**, 45 ff; **IV**, 308.
90. BALLCZO, W., and SCHENK, W., *Mikrochim. Acta*, 163 (1954); BALLCZO and MUTHENTHALLER, H., *Mikrochemie ver. Mikrochim. Acta*, **39**, 152 (1952).
91. CHOW, TS. J., and THOMPSON, T. G., *Anal. Chem.*, **27**, 18 (1955); TAYLOR, A. T., and PAIGE, H. H., *ibid.*, 282; DIAMOND, J. J., *ibid.*, 913; IKEDA, S., *J. Chem. Soc. Japan*, **78**, 1225 (1957).
92. MATSUMOTO, T., *Bull. Chem. Soc. Japan*, **25**, 242 (1952).
93. SCOTT and FURMAN, 902.
94. PENCHEV, N. P., and NONNOVA, D. C., *Compt. rend. acad. bulgare sci.*, **7**, (1), 45 (1954).
95. DENK, G., *et al.*, *Z. anal. Chem.*, **152**, 31 (1956).
96. LUCCHESI, P. J., *et al.*, *Anal. Chem.*, **26**, 521 (1954).
97. ISHIBASHI, M., and HARA, T., *Technol. Repts. Dôshisha Univ.*, **5**, 154 (1954).
98. KARAOGLANOV, Z., and ZAGORCHEV, B., *Z. anal. Chem.*, **98**, 12 (1934).
99. WAGNER, W. F., and WUELLNER, J. A., *Anal. Chem.*, **24**, 1031 (1952).
100. ELVING, P. J., and VAN ATTA, R. E., *Anal. Chem.*, **22**, 1375 (1950).
101. HEYN, A. A., and SCHUPAK, E., *Anal. Chem.*, **26**, 1243 (1954).
102. DEAL, S. B., *Anal. Chem.*, **27**, 109 (1955).
103. KING, E. J., *Biochem. J.*, **26**, 586 (1932); WELCHER, **II**, 311.
104. SHINAGAWA, M., and MURATA, T., *J. Sci. Hiroshima Univ., Ser. A*, **18**, 429 (1955).
105. GORDON, L., and FIRSCHING, F. H., *Anal. Chem.*, **26**, 759 (1954).
106. SCOTT and FURMAN, 128.
107. NAZARENKO, V. A., *Zavodskaya Lab.*, **4**, 515 (1935).
108. WELCHER, **I**, 96.
109. GHOSH, A. K., and RAY, A. B., *Anal. Chim. Acta*, **14**, 112 (1956).
110. GASPAR Y ARNAL, T., and SANTOS, M., *Anales fís. y quím.* (*Madrid*), **40**, 660 (1944); BOSCH, F. DE A., and GÓMEZ, M. P., *Anales real soc. españ. fís. y quim.* (*Madrid*), **52B**, 187 (1956).
111. MATSUMOTO, T., *Bull. Chem., Soc. Japan*, **25**, 361 (1952).
112. MANNS, T. J., *et al.*, *Anal. Chem.*, **24**, 908 (1952).
113. UENO, K., and YAMAGUCHI, K., *Japan Analyst*, **3**, 331 (1954).
114. ROWLEY, K., *et al.*, *Anal. Chem.*, **28**, 136 (1956).
115. COHEN, A. I., and GORDON, L., *Anal. Chem.*, **28**, 1445 (1956).
116. BALLCZO, H., and DOPPLER, G., *Mikrochim. Acta*, 403 (1954).
117. GWILT, J. R., *J. Appl. Chem.* (*London*), **5**, 471 (1955).
118. RANDALL, M., and STEVENSON, H. O., *Ind. Eng. Chem., Anal. Ed.*, **14**, 620 (1942).
119. GUTHRIE, F. C., *J. Soc. Chem. Ind.*, **59**, 98 (1940).
120. NOZAKI, T., *J. Chem. Soc. Japan*, **74**, 796 (1953); **75**, 168 (1954); **77**, 1430 (1956).
121. HAGIWARA, K., and SUZUKI, H., *Bull. Osaka Ind. Research Inst.*, **6**, 58 (1955).
122. CALEY, E. R., and MOORE, C. E., *Anal. Chem.*, **26**, 929 (1954).
123. ISHIMORI, T., *J. Chem., Soc. Japan*, **72**, 988 (1951).
124. YAGODA, H., *J. Ind. Hyg. Toxicol.*, **26**, 224 (1944).

53

MAGNESIUM

The main sources for this chapter are mentioned in ref. 1. Methods of analysis for magnesium have been reviewed.[2]

Attack

The same methods as those described for Ca can be applied (see p. 385).

Separation

For the chief methods of sepn. see Chapter 52, p. 385.

Treatment with H_2S, NH_4OH and NH_4Cl, $(NH_4)_2S$, or $(NH_4)_2C_2O_4$ allows sepn. from groups I to IV resp. Sepn. from Mn is also possible with NH_4OH and $(NH_4)_2S_2O_8$.

Extn. with acetylacetone in CCl_4 (1:4) from soln. neutralized with $NaHCO_3$ seps. Mg from Al, Fe^{3+}, Ti, Mn, Cu, V, U, etc. Ext. 1–2 times with the reagent, wash with CCl_4, make slightly acidic, wash with CCl_4, sep., add Br_2 water and Na_2SO_3.

NaOH gives a sepn. from Al, Sn and Zn. If H_2O_2 is also added,[3] Mg is sepd. from large amts. of Ti. Mg is sepd. from Fe, Ni, Mn, Pb, Al, Sn, Zn by treatment with NaOH, tartrate and CN^-. Addn. of NaOH, triethanolamine and CN^- seps. Al, Fe, etc. (see p. 398). $(NH_4)_2HPO_4$ in citrate soln. seps. Mg from Al, Fe, Zn, Sn, etc.

Mg is sepd. from large amts. of Al by passing HCl gas through solns. contg. HCl and Et_2O.

Oxine seps. Mg from almost all elements (see below).

H_2SO_4 allows sepn. of Mg from Ba; Ca can also be sepd. (see Chapter 52, p. 386).

A little Mg is sepd. from much Ca by treatment of neutral soln. with 0·2–0·3 g. CaO; warm, filter (do not wash), add HCl, NH_4OH and $(NH_4)_2C_2O_4$.

A suspension of HgO seps. Mg from group IV elements. Evap. the neutral soln. to dryness along with the reagent, heat, add H_2O, etc. Ag_2O can be applied similarly.[4]

For sepn. with mannitol and KOH, see Chapter 52, p. 386.

$(NH_4)_2CO_3$ allows sepn. of Mg from Na and K; some Li coppts. For $< 0·4$ g. chlorides in 50 ml. soln., add 50 ml. EtOH, 50 ml. reagent soln. (18 ml. NH_4OH 75 ml. H_2O and 95 ml. EtOH, satd. with $(NH_4)_2CO_3$) then stir for 5 min. and leave for 15 min.

Sepn. from Na and K is also achieved by extn. of the dried chlorides with AmOH or with EtOH and Et_2O.

Determination

Precipitation with oxine is the most accurate method for 1–20 mg. of Mg; precipitation with $(NH_4)_2HPO_4$ is most suitable for macro amounts of Mg. In recent years EDTA titration has been very widely investigated. For colorimetric determination, the best reagents seem to be oxine or titan yellow and its analogs.

(a) Oxine acetate provides gravimetric or titrimetric detns.[1, 5, 6, 7] Many modifications of the colorimetric procedure are available. For detn. of < 20 mg. Mg in 50 ml. soln. of pH 9·5–12·7 ($NH_4OH + NH_4Cl$), heat to 60°C, add 2% oxine acetate soln., boil and allow to cool for 30 min.; filter on a G3 crucible, wash with hot H_2O contg. some NH_4OH, dry at 110°C and weigh as $Mg(C_9H_6ON)_2·2H_2O$. Alternatively, dry at 140–150°C and weigh as $Mg(C_9H_6ON)_2$, ignite with $H_2C_2O_4$ and weigh as MgO, or dissolve the ppt. from the sinter with dil. HCl and titrate with 0·1*N* $KBrO_3$–KBr soln.

NOTES. (1) No interference arises from K, Na, Li, PO_4^{3-}, $C_2O_4^{2-}$ or tartrate. It is recommended to add Me_2CO. If PO_4^{3-} is present, the soln. should be made alk. after addn. of reagent.

(2) Various sepn. methods are available. To sep. Mg from Ba, Sr and from Ca by repptn., add oxine to 100 ml. soln. contg. 5–10 g. NH_4OAc and a few ml. of NH_4OH. To sep. Mg from elements other than Cu, Cd and Zn, ppt. from 100 ml. soln. contg. 15–20 ml. 2*N* NaOH and 3 g. Na_2-tartrate. Sepn. from Fe, Al, etc. is possible with solns. contg. NaOAc and AcOH. Sepn. from Fe, Al, Mn, Zn, Cu is possible by extn. of the ppt. with EtOH contg. 8 ml. NH_4OH/l. Direct extn. with EtOH allows sepn. from Al, Zn, Mn, Cu. Sepn. from Fe is done by addn. of reagent to acidic (AcOH) soln. and extn. with $CHCl_3$.

(3) Detn. with oxine has been applied to steels, Al alloys, tc.[6]

(4) Titratio of the ppt. with Ce^{4+} soln. has advantages of speed and great sensitivity.[8] For > 5 μg. Mg, treat the oxine ppt. ith 0·05*N* $(NH_4)_2Ce(NO_3)_6$ in 2*M* $HClO_4$ at

95–100°C and back-titrate with $Na_2C_2O_4$ soln. using ferroin indicator. Modifications have been described.[9, 10]

Various colorimetric oxine methods have been described. For details see Chapter 8, Section 1.1 and Sandell.[11] For 0·05–0·55 mg. Mg,[12] add 1·0 ml. of a soln. contg. 3 g. $H_2C_2O_4$ and 25 g. tartaric acid/100 ml., add 1 drop bromothymol blue and dil. to 6 ml. with H_2O. Place in H_2O at 95°C for 1 min., adjust to slightly acidic with 10*N* NaOH or HCl, then make just alk. with 0·25*N* NaOH. Add 5 drops 5% KCN, 1·0 ml. 0·25*N* NaOH and 1·00 ml. 1% oxine in EtOH and leave for 1 hr. Alternative methods of completion are then available. If the ppt. is to be detd., wash the vessel wall with 1 ml. EtOH, centrifuge, remove the supernate, add 10 ml. wash soln. (500 ml. 10% NH_4OH and 50 ml. EtOH), stir, rinse the wall with 1 ml. EtOH, centrifuge and remove the supernate. Wash the ppt. into a 50 ml. flask with Fe^{3+} soln. (20 g. $FeCl_3 \cdot 6H_2O$ and 20 ml. AcOH/l.), dil. to 50 ml. with H_2O and measure the blackish green color after 30 min. at 650 mμ.

To complete the detn. on the supernate, dil. to 10 ml., centrifuge, pipet 1 ml. into a 100 ml. measuring flask, add 5 ml. 1*N* HCl, 55 ml. H_2O, 1 ml. sulfanilic acid soln. (1·72 g. in 60 ml. AcOH dild. to 200 ml. with H_2O), 1 ml. $NaNO_2$ soln. (1·452 g./500 ml.) and, after 15 min., 20 ml. 2*N* NaOH; dil. to 100 ml. with H_2O and measure at 425 mμ.

NOTES. (1) No interference arises from Fe, Al, Cu, etc. If Ca^{2+} is present, add 2 ml. Ca soln. (2·5 g. $CaCO_3$ in 100 ml. H_2O treated with 5 ml. HCl and dild. to 1 l. with H_2O) to the standard and proceed as above. In the coupling method the absorbance varies with the amt. of sulfanilic acid and $NaNO_2$ as well as with temp.[13] Coupling with 4-aminoantipyrine and oxidation with $K_3Fe(CN)_6$ in alk. soln. forms an orange-red complex.[14]

(2) For a simpler detn. of 0–80 μg. Mg, which can be applied to Ni metal,[15] add 2 ml. 1:1 HNO_3, dil. to 40 ± 2 ml. with H_2O, neutralize to congo red with NH_4OH, and add 5·0 ml. 50% v/v butyl cellosolve and 20·0 ml. 3% oxine in $CHCl_3$ (freshly prepd.). Shake for 1 min., pass through filter paper and measure at 400 mμ. Fe and Al must be previously pptd. with NH_4OH. Ni, Co, Zn, Mn, Pb, Cu are removed by treatment with $(NH_4)_2S$ followed by diethyldithiocarbamate. Ca is removed as oxalate.

(3) Treatment with 0·1% oxine in $CHCl_3$ of a soln. contg. 2% $BuNH_2$ at pH 10·5–13·6 followed by extn. allows measurement at 380 mμ.[16] No interference arises from Cr, Mo, W, As, Sb, Ca, Se, Be, Te, Re, Pt; over 5 mg. Sn interferes, U, V and Ti require addn. of H_2O_2, while Cu, Ag, Au, Ni, Pd can be masked with KCN. Fe can be detd. simultaneously from the absorbance at 580 mμ.

(4) 5–50 μg. Mg as oxinate can be detd. with Folin–Denis reagent. Dissolve the ppt. in 0·5 ml. 1*N* HCl, then add 5 ml. 25% Na_2CO_3 and 1 ml. Folin–Denis reagent (4 g. phosphomolybdic acid, 20 g. Na_2WO_4, 10 ml. 85% H_3PO_4 and 150 ml. H_2O boiled under reflux for 2 hr.); heat at 80°C for 30 min. and compare the blue color.

(5) It is possible to dissolve the ppt. in 0·1*N* HCl and det. the absorbance directly at 365 mμ.[17]

Reagents analogous to oxine are 8-hydroxyquinaldine and dimethyl-8-quinolinol. The latter can be used gravimetrically, titrimetrically or colorimetrically at pH 8·2–9·8 (see Chapter 22, p. 175). The former is used gravimetrically in the same way as oxine at pH above 9·3;[18] the ppt. is weighed as $Mg(C_{10}H_8ON)_2$ after drying at 88–300°C. Interferences are Al, > 2 mg. Ca, and tartrate.

(b) $(NH_4)_2HPO_4$ also provides gravimetric, titrimetric and colorimetric methods.[1, 19] For gravimetric detn., treat the acidic (HCl) soln. contg. 2·5 g. NH_4Cl/250 ml. with sufficient reagent to give an excess of 1 g./100 ml.; make the soln. alk. to phenolphthalein with NH_4OH, add 10 ml. NH_4OH/100 ml. soln. and leave for 12 hr. Filter on paper, wash 5–6 times with 5:95 NH_4OH, dissolve in 1:4 HCl, dil. to 50–150 ml. with H_2O, add 0·1–0·3 g. $(NH_4)_2HPO_4$, make alk. by slow addn. of NH_4OH and add 5 ml. NH_4OH/100 ml. soln. Filter on paper after 4 hr., wash and transfer to a Pt crucible. Heat very slowly in an electric furnace, carbonizing and ashing at a low temp.; then ignite at 1000–1100°C for 30 min. and weigh as $Mg_2P_2O_7$. (If the ppt. is heated for too long, some P_2O_5 may be lost.) If the amt. of Mg is small, filter on a glass crucible, wash with dil. NH_4OH and EtOH, dry in a vacuum desiccator over $CaCl_2$ and weigh as $MgNH_4PO_4 \cdot 6H_2O$.

NOTES. (1) Ba and Sr must be sepd. with H_2SO_4. Ca ppts. as $Ca_3(PO_4)_3$ and must be sepd. by methods for group IV (see p. 385). With Fe and Al, ppt. Mg from soln. contg. tartrate, citrate or sulfosalicylic acid; alternatively, dissolve the $Mg_2P_2O_7$ ppt. in HCl, make alk. with NH_4OH, acidify with AcOH, filter, ignite, weigh and deduct the correction. With Mn, ppt. from solns. contg. KCN; if the ignited ppt. is pink, det. Mn colorimetrically and deduct. Large amts. of Na and K interfere by copptn. of $MgKPO_4 \cdot 6H_2O$. Large amts. of NH_4^+ interfere. The method has been applied to a variety of metals and alloys.[6]

(2) For titrimetric detn.[1, 19] ppt. as above, filter on a glass crucible, wash and leave for 45 min. Add a known vol. of 0·1*N* H_2SO_4 and back-titrate with 0·1*N* NaOH using methyl orange indicator. Other titrimetric finishes involve iodometric detn. of excess acid after addn. of KIO_3 and KI, or titration of PO_4^{3-} in the ppt. with UO_2^{2+} soln. The ppt. can also be titrated with $BiOClO_4$ soln. after dissoln. in $HClO_4$ (see Chapter 23, p. 186).

(3) The PO_4^{3-} in the ppt. can be detd. colorimetrically as phosphomolybdate or as molybdenum blue after reduction with $SnCl_2$, hydroquinone, eiconogen, etc. The ppt. can also be evaluated with Nessler's reagent.[19]

(4) $(NH_4)_2HAsO_4$ allows gravimetric and titrimetric detns.[19] The procedure is similar to that given above; the ppt. is dried *in vacuo* and weighed as $MgNH_4AsO_4 \cdot 6H_2O$ or heated at 415–885°C and weighed as $Mg_2As_2O_7$. Titration with acid or UO_2^{2+} soln. or iodometric titration is again possible.

(c) Titan yellow is suitable for colorimetric detn.[11,19,20] For up to 25 μg. Mg in 5 ml. soln. add 3 ml. mixed compensating soln. (see Note 1), 1 ml. 0·5% titan yellow in 50% EtOH and, immediately, 2 ml. 10*N* NaOH. Measure after 10 min. at 550 mμ (green filter).

NOTES. (1) For the compensating soln. dissolve 1·40 g. $CaCl_2$, 0·37 g. $Al_2(SO_4)_3 \cdot 18H_2O$, 0·16 g. $MnSO_4 \cdot H_2O$, 0·70 g. $Na_3PO_4 \cdot 12H_2O$, 0·059 g. $CuSO_4 \cdot 5H_2O$ and 5 ml. HCl in H_2O and dil. to 1 l. For 2% polyvinyl alc. soln., dissolve 20 g. in 400 ml. H_2O at 90°C, cool, dil. to 1 l. and filter if necessary. Just before the detn. mix equal vols. of these 2 solns. and a 1% $NH_2OH \cdot HCl$ soln.
(2) No interference is caused by Fe, Al, Cu, Ca, PO_4^{3-}. Interference of Mn can be corrected for.

Many other azo compds. have been suggested for Mg colorimetry. Eriochrome black T allows simultaneous detn. of Ca and Mg.[21] For 50 ml. soln. contg. 0·3–6·0 p.p.m. Ca + Mg, add 25 ml. reagent soln. (100 mg. in 14 ml. H_2O mixed with buffer pH 11·7, dild. to 250 ml. with EtOH and shaken mechanically for 30 min.) and 5 ml. buffer pH 11·7 (see Note 1) or 10 ml. buffer pH 9·52 (see Note 1). Dil. to 100 ml. with H_2O and measure at 630 mμ. Calculations are done as follows: if Mg = x and Ca = y, then $\text{Abs.}_{9\cdot5} = 0\cdot120\,x + 0\cdot0133\,y - 0\cdot024$, and $\text{Abs.}_{11\cdot7} = 0\cdot152\,x + 0\cdot127\,y - 0\cdot026$. However, when $x < 1\cdot2$ or $y > 4\cdot0$, then $\text{Abs.}_{11\cdot7} = 0\cdot152\,x + 0\cdot1267\,y - 0\cdot026 + 0\cdot0216(1\cdot2 - x) - 0\cdot010(y - 4)$; when $x = 4\cdot0$, $\text{Abs.}_{9\cdot5} = (0\cdot0968 + 0\cdot00473\,x)x + 0\cdot0133y - 0\cdot025(x - y)^2$. The accuracy is ±0·12 p.p.m. for Ca and ±0·09 p.p.m. for Mg.

NOTES. (1) For buffer pH 11·7, dissolve 78 ml. piperidine in 300 ml. H_2O, add 8·5 ml. HCl, dil. to 500 ml. with H_2O and adjust the pH to 11·7. For buffer pH 9·52, mix 8·5 ml. HCl with 300 ml. H_2O, add 24 ml. NH_4OH, dil. to 500 ml. and adjust the pH to 9·52.
(2) Magneson II allows detn. of 10–100 μg. Mg.[22] Add 5 ml. 0·005% reagent, dil. to 40 ml. with H_2O, add 5 ml. 1*N* Na_2CO_3, dil. to 50 ml. with H_2O and measure at 650 mμ. Amperometric titration with magneson II is also possible.[23]
(3) Brilliant yellow is suitable for 0·1–1 mg. Mg.[11, 24] Add 1 ml. 0·03% v/v H_2SO_4, 20 ml. satd. $CaSO_4$, 5 ml. Al^{3+} soln. (0·309 g. $Al_2(SO_4)_3$/l.), 1 ml. 0·05% reagent, 4 ml. 20% NaOH and dil. to 100 ml. with H_2O. Measure the red complex after 5 min. at 560 mμ. No interference arises from Fe, Al, Ca or 250 p.p.m. Cl^-; Mn, Zn and 5 p.p.m. F^- or PO_4^{3-} interfere.
(4) Tropaeolin OO is satisfactory for 4 μg. Mg in 4 ml. soln.[25] Heat the soln. on a steam-bath, add 2 ml. satd. aq. reagent soln. and cool at 0°C for 1 hr. Centrifuge, wash 4 times with 4 ml. portions of H_2O, dissolve in 4 ml. H_2SO_4, dil. to 50 ml. with H_2O and compare the purple color. Ca interferes. The reagent can be used gravimetrically, the ppt. being dried at 103–358°C and weighed as $Mg(C_{18}H_{14}O_3N_3S)_2$.
(5) Solochrome cyanine RS may be applied colorimetrically.[26]
(6) Xylidine blue I is 100-fold as sensitive to Mg as titan yellow.[27] To 5 ml. reagent soln. (0·15 mg./ml. EtOH) add 5 ml. sample soln. contg. 0·5–10 μg. Mg and which is just acid to phenolphthalein. Add 0·5 ml. 0·08*M* borax, dil. to 25 ml. with EtOH and measure at 510 mμ after 30 min. Interferences are Cd, Ca, Co, Mn, Ni, Fe^{3+}, Cu, Zn, Fe^{2+}, Pb, Sr, Ba, Al, Be, Ce^{4+}, rare earths, Cr, Au, Mo, Nb, Pd, Tl and 1000 p.p.m. $C_2O_4^{2-}$. If Ca is in the range 0·4–12 p.p.m., measurements are made after 1 hr., because the color caused by Ca fades. Other interferences are avoided by extn. with oxine in $CHCl_3$ at pH 7. 0·1–0·4 p.p.m. Mg can be detd. at 505 or 535 mμ with xylidine blue II.
(7) Pontachrome violet SW can be used amperometrically for detn. of Mg.[28] To 10 ml. 0·5% dye soln., add 1·5 ml. piperidine and 2 ml. ethylenediamine, adjust to pH 11·0 with HCl, dil. to 20 ml. with H_2O and titrate with 0·001–0·01*M* Mg^{2+} soln.

(d) 2-Hydroxy-1-naphthaldehyde can be applied gravimetrically or titrimetrically.[29] For 2–6 mg. Mg in 50 ml. soln. add 100 ml. 1*M* reagent in EtOH, 5 ml. 10% NH_4Cl, heat to 60°C and add 5 ml. 25% NH_4OH. Filter on a G3 crucible, wash with 50% EtOH, dry at 125–130°C and weigh as $C_{22}H_{14}O_4Mg$. Alternatively, dissolve in 20 ml. 0·1*N* HCl and back-titrate with 0·1*N* NaOH.

(e) $(NH_4)_2C_2O_4$ can also be used gravimetrically or titrimetrically.[19, 30] For < 40 mg. Mg in 5 ml. soln., add 85 ml. AcOH and 10 ml. satd. reagent soln., place on a steam-bath for 0·5–1 hr., filter through a hard paper and wash with 85% AcOH. Dry, ignite above 480°C and weigh as MgO; alternatively, dissolve in dil. H_2SO_4, and titrate with 0·1*N* $KMnO_4$. Dried below 176°C, the ppt. can be weighed as $MgC_2O_4 \cdot 2H_2O$; or dried at 233–397°C, as MgC_2O_4.

NOTES. (1) If <25 mg. Mg is present, the above method is preferable to the $(NH_4)_2HPO_4$ method. If over 40 mg. Mg or if SO_4^{2-} is present, treat 5 ml. soln. with 1 g. $(NH_4)_2C_2O_4$ in 15 ml. AcOH and 10 ml. H_2O, add 70 ml. AcOH, etc. For detn. of Mg in the filtrate from the Ca detn. or for repptn., add 25 ml. HNO_3, evap. to dryness, add 2 ml. HNO_3 and 5 ml. $HClO_4$, evap. to dryness, add 5 ml. H_2O, etc.
(2) Naphthylhydroxamic acid can be applied nephelometrically (see Chapter 52, p. 389).

(f) KF has been used gravimetrically for up to 0·1 g. MgO as sulfate.[31] Add 10 ml. 7% KF, centrifuge, wash 5 times with 60% EtOH and 3 times with 80% EtOH, dry at 130° and then at 450–500°C and weigh as $KMgF_3$.

(g) EDTA now provides the best-known titrimetric method for Mg. With eriochrome black T as indicator,[32] almost neutralize 35 ml. soln. with NaOH or HCl, add 2–3 ml. buffer soln. (67·5 g. NH_4Cl and 570 ml. NH_4OH/l.) and 8 drops indicator soln. (0·15 g. erio T and 0·5 g. borax in 25 ml. MeOH) and titrate with 0·01*M* EDTA.

NOTES. (1) Interference of heavy metals is avoided by addn. a few drops of 5% Na_2S or KCN, or dimercaptopropanol; triethanolamine, KCN and $NH_2OH \cdot HCl$ may also be added. Large amts. of PO_4^{3-} must be sepd. by ion-exchange. If Ca is present, it can be detd. separately with murexide as indicator and a correction made, or it can be sepd. by ion exchange. The above titration has been applied to detn. of Mg in Al.[6, 33]

(2) Pyrocatechol violet is also a good indicator.[34] Chrome azurol S has been used for photometric titration of Mg in Al:[35] Carry out preliminary sepn. with triethanolamine, KOH and KCN; add HCl and NH_4OH–10% NH_4Cl (2:2, 6:5, 8:4, 14:5 or 20:6), followed by 5 ml. 10% triethanolamine and 10 mg. KCN. Add 1 ml. indicator and titrate with measurement at 580 mμ.

Bromothymol blue has been suggested as indicator.[36] Photometric titration at 220 mμ is possible.[37] For potentiometric titration, see Chapter 52, p. 389.

(3) If the concn. of Mg is very low, it is advisable to add 1 ml. 0·1*M* Mg–EDTA complex.

(4) EDTA can also be applied gravimetrically.[38] For 0·2–1·2 m*M* Mg in 10–15 ml. soln., add 25 ml. 0·1*M* EDTA, adjust to pH 3·6–3·8 with HCl or NaOH and leave for 48 hr. Filter on a glass crucible, wash with 10 ml. H_2O and 10 ml. Me_2CO, dry *in vacuo* over $Mg(ClO_4)_2$ and weigh. An empirical factor of 0·5832 is required. Interferences are Be, Al, Mn, PO_4^{3-}, citrate and tartrate. If Ca > Mg, repptn. is needed. Ba, Co, Ni, Zn, Cu, Cd, Th and Bi can be tolerated if more reagent is added.

(h) KI and hexamine are applicable for detn. of > 0·05 mg. Mg in 2 ml. soln.[39] Add 2·2 g. KI, 0·9 ml. reagent (15 g. KI in 30 ml. satd. hexamine soln.) and cool to 0°C for 30 min. Filter on a G4 crucible, covered with paper, and wash twice with a satd. soln. of the ppt. in Me_2CO, then thrice with a satd. soln. of the ppt. in $CHCl_3$; repeat the washing process. Wash the ppt. into 2 ml. 0·05*N* H_2SO_4, add 1 drop alizarin S indicator and some H_2O, place on a steam-bath for 10 min. and titrate with 0·01*N* NaOH.

NOTE. Group IV and V elements can be present but PO_4^{3-} interferes. The ppt. can be dried at room temp. and weighed as $MgI_2{\cdot}2(CH_2)_6N_4{\cdot}10H_2O$.[40]

(i) Li-picrolonate allows detn. of Mg by addn. of excess of 0·05*N* soln. to a hot neutral soln. and back-titration with 0·01*N* methylene blue soln.[41]

(j) Miscellaneous colorimetric methods. Quinalizarin is suitable for detn. of < 0·3 mg. Mg.[19, 41] Add 5 ml. 5% gum arabic soln., 5 ml. 0·01% reagent in EtOH, dil. to 35–40 ml. with H_2O, add 5 ml. 2*N* NaOH, dil. to 50 ml. with H_2O and measure the blue complex at 600 mμ. Al does not interfere if Al < 2Mg.

Curcumin allows detn. of 0·02–0·4 mg. Mg in 40 ml. neutral soln.[19, 41] Add 2 ml. starch–glycerol soln. (10 starch triturated with 20 ml. H_2O, poured into 70 ml. glycerol, heated below 144°C and stirred until clear; an aliquot is shaken with some H_2O and filtered). Then add 4 drops 1% curcumin in EtOH, 5 ml. 4*N* NaOH and dil. to 50 ml. with H_2O. Measure the yellowish color, or measure the reddish fluorescence under UV light. Fe and BO_2^- interfere; PO_4^{3-} requires addn. of an equal amt. to the standard.

$CaK_2Fe(CN)_6{\cdot}(CH_2)_6N_4{\cdot}6H_2O$ in 10% hexamine soln. can be applied colorimetrically or gravimetrically.[42] To prep. the reagent, dissolve 8·4 g. $K_4Fe(CN)_6{\cdot}3H_2O$ in 100 ml. H_2O, add 4·4 g. $CaCl_2{\cdot}6H_2O$ and 11·2 g. hexamine in 200 ml. H_2O, filter on a glass crucible after 1 hr., wash with EtOH and dry (yield 7 g.). Dissolve 0·5 g. of this reagent in 20 ml. 10% hexamine and filter. To det. up to 1 mg. Mg, evap. the soln. to dryness, add 2·5 ml. reagent soln., filter on a G4 crucible after 1 hr., wash 6 times with 1 ml. portions of 20% hexamine and 3 times with Me_2CO; suck the filter dry, add H_2O, 1 ml. 10% gum arabic soln. and 1 ml. 0·1% $FeCl_3$; compare the blue color.

The ppt. can be detd. gravimetrically as $[Fe(CN)_6CaMg]_3{\cdot}4(CH_2)_6N_4{\cdot}40H_2O$ after drying at room temp.

I_2 can be applied with I^- in alk. soln.[19] For 0·15–3 mg. Mg in 30–40 ml. neutral soln. add 5 ml. reagent soln. (3·17 g. I_2 and 17–20 g. KI in 250 ml. H_2O) and 7–8 ml. 1*N* NaOH, dil. to 50 ml. with H_2O and compare the brown color. It seems likely that the color is due to adsorbed I_2 on $Mg(OH)_2$ rather than $Mg(IO)_2$. Interferences are NH_4^+, Mn, Fe, Al and large amts. of group V elements.

(k) Flame photometry. Mg can be measured at 371, 383 mμ (band) or 285 mμ (line);[43] interferences are PO_4^{3-} and SO_4^{2-}. The technique is suitable for detn. of 0·4–2% Mg in Al after treatment with 15 ml. 1:1 HCl and some HNO_3 and diln. to 100 ml. with H_2O; a H_2–O_2 flame is used.[44] It is possible to det. 1–6 μg. Mg in 80% Me_2CO soln. using a multiple radiation buffer.[45]

References

1. HILLEBRAND and LUNDELL, 506 (632); SCOTT and FURMAN, 528; FRESENIUS–JANDER, **IIa**, 122 (1940); KIMURA, 268.
2. DUPUIS, T. and DUVAL, C., *Bull. soc. chim. France*, 567 (1949).
3. MOMOKI, K. and ARIMA, T., *Japan Analyst*, **4**, 581 (1955).
4. VALENTIN, F. and SUCHÁROVÁ, M., *Chem. zvesti*, **4**, 68 (1950).
5. HECHT and DONAU, 220; WELCHER, **I**, 271.
6. A.S.T.M., 148 ff.
7. ISHIMARU, S., *J. Chem. Soc. Japan*, **53**, 566 (1932).
8. GERBER, L., *et al.*, *Ind. Eng. Chem., Anal. Ed.*, **14**, 658 (1942); also see Chapter 8, Section 1.1.
9. KOBROVA, M., *Chem. listy*, **48**, 1167 (1954).
10. ISHIBASHI, M. and FUJINAGA, T., *Bull. Chem. Soc. Japan*, **23**, 27, 229 (1950).
11. SANDELL, 426.
12. WILSON, A. E., *Anal. Chem.*, **23**, 754 (1951).
13. YOKOUCHI, N., *Japan Analyst*, **3**, 3 (1954).
14. MCALLISTER, R. A., *Analyst*, **79**, 522 (1954).
15. LUKE, C. L. and CAMPBELL, M. E., *Anal. Chem.*, **26**, 1778 (1954); **28**, 1443 (1956).
16. UMLAND, F. and HOFFMANN, W., *Anal. Chim. Acta*, **17**, 234 (1957).
17. DETERDING, H. C. and TAYLOR, R. G., *Ind. Eng. Chem., Anal. Ed.*, **18**, 127 (1946).
18. WELCHER, **I**, 332.
19. FRESENIUS–JANDER, **IIa**, 122 ff.

20. Young, H. Y. and Gill, R. F., *Anal. Chem.*, **23**, 751 (1951); also see Challis, H. J. G. and Wood, D. F., *Analyst*, **79**, 762 (1954) (in Ti metal); Mitchell, J. A., *ibid.*, 280; Bussmann, A., *Z. anal. Chem.*, **148**, 413 (1945); Noddack, W., *et al.*, *ibid.*, **147**, 417 (1955) (in Ni metal; sepn. of Ni by extn. of diethyldithiocarbamate in $CHCl_3$); Wilson, A. E. and Wander, I. W., *Anal. Chem.*, **22**, 195 (1950); Drosdorff, M. and Nearpass, D. C., *ibid.*, **20**, 673 (1948); Kenyon, D. A. and Oplinger, G., *ibid.*, **27**, 1125 (1955).
21. Young, A., *et al.*, *Anal. Chem.*, **27**, 356, 418 (1955); also see Harvey, A. E., *et al.*, *ibid.*, **25**, 498 (1953); Pohl, H., *Z. anal. Chem.*, **155**, 263 (1957) (in Ni).
22. Farhan, F., *Mikrochemie ver. Mikrochim. Acta.*, **35**, 560 (1950); Umemoto, H., *Repts. Balneol. Inst.*, *Okayama Univ.*, **13**, 1 (1953).
23. Kostromin, A. I., *Uchenye Zapiski. Kazan. Gosudarst. Univ. im V.I. Ul'yanova-Lenina*, **115**, No. 3, 65 (1955).
24. Taras, M., *Anal. Chem.*, **20**, 1156 (1948); Andersson, K. G. K., *ibid.*, **24**, 1028 (1952); Edson, S. N. and Mills, R. H., *Chemist Analyst*, **46**, 4 (1957).
25. Welcher, **IV**, 571.
26. Bacon, A., *Metallurgia*, **44**, 207 (1951).
27. Mann, Ch. K. and Yoe, J. H., *Anal. Chem.*, **28**, 202 (1956); *Anal. Chim. Acta*, **16**, 155 (1957).
28. Dean, J. A. and Bryan, H. A., *Anal. Chim. Acta*, **16**, 180 (1957).
29. Gusev, S. I., *et al.*, *Zhur. Anal. Khim.*, **10**, 349 (1955).
30. Matsumoto, T., *Japan Analyst*, **3**, 307 (1954); Kawagaki, K., *J. Chem. Soc. Japan*, **78**, 1562 (1957).
31. Talipov, Sh. T. and Sofěikova, Z. T., *Trudy Sredneaziat. Gosudarst. Univ.* (*Tashkent*), **33**, No. 4, 95 (1952) (in Al alloy); Talipov and Tashkodzhaev, A. A., *ibid.*, **35**, No. 7, 141, 145 (1954) (as $NaMgF_3$).
32. Cheng, K. L., *et al.*, *Anal. Chem.*, **24**, 1640 (1952); Diehl, H., *et al.*, *J. Am. Water Works Assoc.*, **42**, 40 (1950); Schwarzenbach, G., *Die komplexometrische Titration*, 53 (1955).
33. Beranek, T. L., *Hutnické listy*, **12**, 434 (1957).
34. Malát, M., *et al.*, *Chem. listy*, **48**, 663 (1954).
35. Kanie, T., *Japan Analyst*, **6**, 711 (1957).
36. Hahn, F. L., *Anal. Chim. Acta*, **4**, 583 (1950).
37. Sweetser, P. B. and Bricker, C. E., *Anal. Chem.*, **26**, 195 (1954).
38. Bricker, C. E. and Parker, G. H., *Anal. Chem.*, **29**, 1470 (1957).
39. Welcher, **III**, 130.
40. Ishibashi, M. *et al.*, *J. Chem. Soc. Japan*, **61**, 128 (1940).
41. Welcher, **IV**, 43, 409, 457, 525.
42. Welcher, **III**, 127; **IV**, 131.
43. Kuemmel, D. F. and Karl, H. L., *Anal. Chem.*, **26**, 386 (1954).
44. Ikeda, S., *J. Chem. Soc. Japan*, **76**, 1122 (1955).
45. Manna, L., *et al.*, *Anal. Chem.*, **29**, 1885 (1957).

54

THE ALKALI METALS

The main sources for this chapter are given in ref. 1. A monograph on the production, properties and uses of sodium is available.[2] The purification, detection and determination of rubidium and cesium have been studied in detail.[3] Methods of determination for the alkali metals have been assessed[4] and the subject has been reviewed several times.[5]

In the later parts of this chapter, the determination of each of the alkali metals is treated separately. Some general remarks are in order here. The conversion of alkali metal sulfates to their halides is often needed. Two methods are available: in the first, the sulfate is evaporated repeatedly with hydriodic acid and then with chlorine water; in the other the sulfate is heated for 40 min. in a platinum crucible inside a porcelain crucible with 6–8 times its weight of 4:1 NH_4Br–NH_4I, and this is repeated 2–3 times.

The flame-photometric determination of these metals should also be mentioned in a general way, for this is one of the most satisfactory methods available. Na, K and Li are determined without difficulty.[6] Ca does not interfere with the determination of Na and K if Al is added.[7] Li and Na do not interfere with the method for K, Rb and Cs at 1000°C if N_2 is added to the H_2–O_2.[8] Studies of interferences have been made.[9, 10] Analysis of rocks[11] and of natural waters[12] has been studied.

Attack

(a) Lawrence Smith method. To 0·5 g. sample add 4 g. $CaCO_3$ (or more if much Fe is present) and 0·5 g. NH_4Cl, mix thoroughly, transfer to a Pt crucible, cover with a thin layer of $CaCO_3$ and heat slowly. Then heat at 800°C for 40–60 min. after there is no NH_3 odor. Cool, add hot H_2O and heat on a steam-bath until the fused mass disintegrates. Filter through paper, decant and wash 3–5 times with 50 ml. H_2O; if Mg is present, wash with hot satd. $Ca(OH)_2$ soln. Evap. the filtrate to 100 ml., filter on paper and wash with satd. $Ca(OH)_2$ soln. Combine the residues, dry, mix with NH_4Cl, heat, etc.; then treat the filtrate separately as described for the main filtrate. Heat the main filtrate, add $(NH_4)_2CO_3$ and NH_4OH, heat on a steam-bath, filter on paper and wash with hot H_2O. Dissolve the ppt. in HCl and reppt. Evap. the filtrate to dryness on a hot plate, stirring after crystals appear; then heat to dull redness. Add 25 ml. H_2O and 1–2 drops 10% $BaCl_2$, heat, filter on paper and wash with H_2O. Treat with $(NH_4)_2CO_3$ and NH_4OH as before and filter. Add a little $(NH_4)_2C_2O_4$ and a little oxine in EtOH and some NH_4OH, heat for 30 min. on a steam-bath, leave to cool, filter on paper and wash with 0·1% $(NH_4)_2C_2O_4$. Evap. the filtrate to dryness, heat to dull redness, add 1 drop HCl, heat at 110°C, cover with NH_4Cl, heat to dull redness, cool and weigh. Then add H_2O, filter on paper and wash with H_2O; ignite, weigh and obtain the weight of alkali chlorides by difference. Repptn. is necessary if Li is present.

Various modifications have been proposed. Sepn. from SO_4^{2-} and Mg is better as follows:[13] heat a 0·5 g. sample with 4 g. $CaCO_3$ and 1 g. $BaCl_2{\cdot}2H_2O$ to redness (a higher temp. than above), then proceed similarly to the Lawrence Smith method. In another method,[14] heat a 1 g. sample with 3·5–4 g. 2:1 CaO–$CaCl_2{\cdot}2H_2O$ (previously dried at 200–250°C) for 40 min. at 800–900°C. For analysis of alumina,[15] mix 0·5 g. intimately with 1–1·5 g. H_3BO_3 or 0·85 g. B_2O_3, heat gently for 5 min., ignite for 5 min., cool, boil with H_2O, add a few drops HCl, boil for 5 min., filter, etc. and finally apply flame photometry.

(b) Berzelius method. Heat the sample with 1·5 ml. 1:1 H_2SO_4 and 5–10 ml. HF, and evap. almost to dryness, whilst avoiding bumping. Add $BaCl_2$ soln., evap. to dryness, add some hot H_2O, make alk. with dil. $Ba(OH)_2$, evap. to dryness, add H_2O, filter on paper and wash with dil. $Ba(OH)_2$. Treat with $(NH_4)_2CO_3$ and NH_4OH, etc.

Again, many alternative procedures are available. For a 1 g. sample,[16] add a little H_2O (and some HCl if much carbonate is present), then 5 ml. 1:1 H_2SO_4 and 15 ml. HF; evap. to dryness, heat to dull redness for 20–30 min., cool, transfer to a 400 ml. beaker, dil. to 200 ml. with H_2O and heat for 30 min. Add 2–3 ml. 3% H_2O_2, boil out H_2O_2, add 2 drops methyl red, neutralize with dil. NH_4OH and boil for 1–2 min. Filter on Whatman No. 41 paper, wash with 2%

NH_4Cl, evap. to dryness and add 15 ml. H_2O, 85 ml. AcOH contg. 1 g. NH_4OAc, and 1·5 ml. ethyl oxalate. Heat near boiling for 1 hr., filter on Whatman No. 42 paper and wash with hot 85% AcOH. Evap. to dryness, add 10 ml. HNO_3 and 30 ml. HCl, evap. to dryness and repeat if necessary. Filter into a Pt crucible, add 1 drop dil. H_2SO_4, evap. to dryness, heat to dull redness and weigh.

In another method,[17] treat a 0·5 g. sample with a little H_2O and 10 ml. HF, evap. to dryness, add H_2O, pour into a Pt dish contg. 2 g. CaO and boil for 5 min. Filter on paper, wash with hot H_2O. Treat the filtrate with 25 ml. of soln. contg. 100 g. $(NH_4)_2CO_3$ and 80 ml. NH_4OH dild. to 500 ml., then evap. to dryness; add a little H_2O and 15 ml. of the above alk. soln., filter on paper after 15 min. and wash with cold H_2O. Add 4 drops satd. $(NH_4)_2C_2O_4$ soln. to the filtrate, heat on a steam-bath for 1 hr. and evap. to 50 ml. Filter on paper and wash with 1% $(NH_4)_2C_2O_4$. Acidify with HCl, evap. to dryness, heat to dull redness, etc.

For silicates,[18] treat with $HClO_4$ and HF, evap. to dryness, repeat and heat at 550°C for 30 min. Ext. with 1:30 NH_4OH, filter, add $(NH_4)_2C_2O_4$ and oxine, etc.

For analysis of borosilicate glass[19] treat with a little H_2O, 2 g. $H_2C_2O_4$ and 20 ml. HF, cover, evap. to dryness and heat at 150°C. Cool, add H_2O, a little $H_2C_2O_4$, evap. and heat and repeat. Then add hot H_2O and cool. Filter on paper and wash; treat the ppt. with HCl, $H_2C_2O_4$ and NH_4OH, and filter. Treat the combined filtrates with 5% oxine in EtOH, make alk. with NH_4OH, filter on paper after 1·5 hr. and wash with 1% NH_4OH contg. a little oxine. Treat the ppt. with HCl and reppt. Evap. the filtrates to dryness, heat to dull redness, add HCl, evap. and add H_2O. Filter on paper and wash. Then add some EtOH, evap., heat to dull red and weigh. It is possible to det. Pb, Al, Ca, Mg, etc. in one sample.

A shorter method is available.[20] Treat the sample with HF and H_2SO_4, ignite, leach with dil. NH_4OH, filter, add $(NH_4)_2C_2O_4$, oxine and NH_4OH, evap. the filtrate, ignite and weigh as mixed sulfates. Dissolve in H_2O, add a little HCl and 2% $BaCl_2$ (1 ml./10 mg. sulfate), filter, add $HClO_4$ and then det. K as perchlorate without removing Ba.

(c) Distn. method for Li.[21] Mix 1·000 g. sample (100 mesh) with 2·9 g. $CaCO_3$ and 0·56 g. $CaCl_2$, transfer to a Pt boat placed in a Pt vessel and heat for 30 min. at 1200°C *in vacuo*, then allow to cool to 700°C for 15 min., collecting in a Pyrex tube with a plug of pyrex glass wool, followed by a condenser.

Separation

(a) Li can be sepd. from Al by the basic acetate method or with oxine. Sepn. from alk. earths is obtained by repptn. with $(NH_4)_2CO_3$ and a considerable amt. of NH_4Cl. Sepn. from Mg is possible with $Ba(OH)_2$ or oxine.

(b) Sepn. of K, Rb and Cs from Na and Li. H_2PtCl_6 is probably the best reagent for this purpose. To the chloride soln. in a porcelain dish, add 10% reagent soln. in an amt. equiv. to the weighed chloride (regarded as NaCl). Heat on a steam-bath and add H_2O if needed to complete dissoln. Evap. to a syrupy consistency so that a solid mass results on cooling. Then add 80% v/v EtOH, filter on paper, decant and wash with 80% EtOH. Dissolve from the filter by passing through a little hot H_2O, collect in a Pt crucible, evap. to dryness, cover, heat at 135°C, remove the cover, dry at 130°C and weigh as K_2PtCl_6. NH_4^+ and SO_4^{2-} interfere. The reagent must be pure because Pt^{2+}, nitrosyl- or hydroxy-chloroplatinic acid, and free HCl interfere. The EtOH must be free from aldehydes; 100% EtOH ppts. Na. The ppt. should be golden yellow, an orange color indicating Na contamination. When Li is present, repptn. is needed. For recovery of Pt, see ref. 22. And for further details, see under Determination, p. 408. Mg and Na can be detd. in the filtrate: evap. in a 100 ml. flask, add H_2O and let stand under pressure of H_2 gas; filter through paper, wash with H_2O, evap., transfer to a Pt crucible, heat to dull red and weigh. Then det. Mg as phosphate and subtract.

$HClO_4$ is also useful. Treat the chloride soln. in a 150 ml. pyrex beaker with a 2–3-fold excess of reagent. Evap. to dryness below 350°C, cool, add 3–5 ml. H_2O, evap. again and cool. Add 10–20 ml. 1:1 anhyd. *n*-BuOH–EtOAc, heat for a few min. below b.p., leave to cool, filter on a Gooch crucible and wash 3 times with 5 ml. solvent. Treat the residue with a little hot H_2O, evap. to dryness, cool, add 10 ml. solvent, ext., etc. Filter through the same Gooch crucible (previously dried at 110°C) and wash several times with 0·5–1 ml. solvent (the total filtrate and washings must not exceed 55 ml.). Then dry at 110°C, heat at 350°C for 15 min. and weigh as $KClO_4$. Interferences are NH_4^+ and SO_4^{2-}; no interference arises from Ba, Ca, PO_4^{3-} or small amts. of Mg.

Na and Li can be detd. after the above sepn. Evap. the filtrates and washings to 20 ml. on a sand-bath, heat at 80–90°C, add 20% HCl in BuOH (2 ml. dropwise, then 6 ml. more rapidly), allow to cool, filter on a Gooch crucible and wash with 1–2 ml. 6–7% HCl in BuOH (the filtrate and washings must be < 50 ml.); dry at 110°C, ignite at 600°C for 5 min., cool and weigh, then add H_2O, dry at 110°C, weigh and measure NaCl by difference. Li can be detd. as sulfate after evapn. of filtrate and washings. See also ref. 23.

For a more direct pptn. method with $HClO_4$, evap. the chloride soln. to dryness with $HClO_4$, add 2–3 ml. hot H_2O and 65–100 ml. hot 0·5–1% $HClO_4$ in BuOH dropwise. Boil for 30 sec., leave to cool, filter on a Gooch crucible, etc. A correction of −0·2 mg. was needed for KCl and one of +6·0 mg. for NaCl in a test on a mixt. of 0·14 g. KCl and 0·16 g. NaCl.

Various solvents can replace *n*-BuOH–EtOAc in the above procedure. A mixt. of 970 ml. anhyd. EtOH, 10 ml. $HClO_4$ (s.g. 1·12) and 20 ml. H_2O can be applied. Others are 5% MeOH in anhyd. EtOH, EtOAc, AmOH, etc. Explosions may occur when filtrates are evapd. if the first two of these solvents are used.

A satd. soln. of HCl in 1:1 anhyd. EtOH–Et_2O provides another method. Dry the mixed chlorides at 140–150°C in a stream of HCl gas, cool, add 2–3 ml. reagent and filter after 12 hr. on paper moistened with reagent. Decant 3 times with reagent soln., treat the residue as above, combine the filtrates, add dil. H_2SO_4, etc. HCl gas is useful in the removal of large amts. of Na; repptn. is needed if Li is present.

For sepns. possible with hexyl or $Na_3Co(NO_2)_6$, see pp. 409 and 411; for those with $ZnH(UO_2)_3(AcO)_9$ and other triple acetates, see p. 407. Controlled potential electrolysis can be used.[24]

(c) Sepn. of Li from Na, K, etc. 20% HCl in *n*-BuOH is satisfactory (cf. the above sections); treat the chlorides with a little H_2O and 5 ml. $HClO_4$, evap. to dryness below 350°C, add 20 ml. anhyd. *n*-BuOH and 0·2 ml. $HClO_4$, boil, add 8 ml. reagent dropwise, allow to cool, filter on a glass crucible, wash, etc.

Anhyd. EtOH and Et_2O are also suitable. Treat 0·5 g. mixed chlorides with 1·5 ml. H_2O and 1 drop HCl followed by 20 ml. EtOH (added to the center of the vessel); stir, add 60 ml. Et_2O, stir, filter on a glass crucible after 5 min. and wash with 1:4–5 EtOH–Et_2O. Evap. the filtrate to dryness, add 10 ml. EtOH, heat to dissolve, add 50 ml. Et_2O and 1 drop HCl, filter on the same filter after 30 min., wash, heat and weigh as (Na,K)Cl.

Me_2CO may be used to sep. Li from Na, K, Rb, Cs, Ba, Sr, Mg but Ca interferes.[25] Treat the chlorides with 25 ml. solvent and 1 drop HCl, filter and repeat.

AmOH is utilized in Gooch's method. Evap. the soln. contg. $< 0·2$ g. chlorides almost to dryness in a flask, add 15–20 ml. AmOH and a Pt coil, and evap. to half the vol.; cool, add a few drops of HCl, boil and cool. Filter on a Gooch crucible and wash with anhyd. solvent. Repeat the whole process if > 10 mg. LiCl is present. When NaCl is present, add 0·41 mg. to the residue for each 10 ml. filtrate; likewise add 0·51 mg. for KCl and 0·92 mg. for NaCl + KCl. Hexyl alcohol is said to be better, because no corrections are needed.[26] Other possible reagents are 2-ethyl-1-hexanol,[26] *n*-BuOH,[27] iso-BuOH,[26] or dioxane.[26] The bromides can be extd. with AmOH also.[26]

Pyridine has also been employed in the sepn.; it must be dried with KOH and distd. at 114–116°C before use. Evap. the chloride soln. to dryness, add 2 drops HCl, evap. to dryness, add 25 ml. pyridine and boil for 5–10 min. Filter through paper and wash with 5 ml. hot pyridine. Treat the residue with H_2O and 1 drop HCl, evap. to dryness, etc. Combine the filtrates and washings, evap. to dryness, add dil. H_2SO_4, etc., and weigh as $LiSO_4$.

Other possible methods are treatment with 0·02*N* picrolonic acid with EtOH or AcOH; and extn. with dipivaloylmethane in Et_2O (see under Determination, p. 406).

(d) Sepn. of Rb and Cs from K. HCl in EtOH can be employed as in the method described under (f) below, as can 9-phosphomolybdic acid, phosphotungstic acid, hexyl salt with extn. by 2:2:4 dioxane–AmOH–xylene, and $SnCl_4$.

Na-silicomolybdate is also applicable. Heat the 3*N* HCl soln. to 65°C, add reagent, filter on a glass crucible and wash with 3*N* HCl; dry the ppt., heat in a Cl_2 stream and sep. from SiO_2, or boil with $Ba(OH)_2$ and then pass CO_2. For the reagent, dissolve 60 g. NaOH in 400 ml. H_2O, boil, add 172 g. MoO_3 gradually during 10–15 min., stop heating, add 500 ml. H_2O and then 350 ml. 5:2 HNO_3 slowly while stirring; add 28 g. $Na_2SiO_3·9H_2O$ in 25 ml. 2*N* NaOH slowly, evap. to 700–800 ml. and filter.

$NaNO_2$ and $Bi(NO_3)_3$ can be applied. To 1 ml. sample soln. add 10 ml. reagent (50 g. $NaNO_2$ and 15 g. $Bi(NO_3)_3·5H_2O$ in 100 ml. H_2O) and filter after 24 hr. Addn. of $AgNO_3$ allows more effective sepn.[28]

Fractional crystn. with $H_2C_2O_4$ serves to sep. Rb from K.[29]

(e) Sepn. of Cs from Rb and K. Silicotungstic acid, $SbCl_3$, and $SbCl_3$ with $FeCl_3$ can be applied as described below. Pptn. of $Cs_3Bi_2I_9$ can be used as for detn. (see p. 412).

(f) Sepn. of mixts. of alkali metals. The 4 principal methods are listed below.

(*i*) Method of Wells and Stevens[30] in which H_2PtCl_6 is the main reagent. The procedures are outlined in Table 53. For modifications involving hexyl salt, see ref. 31.

(*ii*) Method of O'Leary and Papish[32] in which 9-phosphomolybdic acid is applied. The method is given in Table 54. For the reagent, heat dodecaphosphomolybdic acid at 300–350°C with stirring until green, then cool, add H_2O and filter. Add a little Br_2 water, evap. very slowly and filter off the yellow prismatic crystals. Dissolve in H_2O to give a 20% soln.

NOTES. (1) The error is ±2%.

(2) K, Rb and Cs are sepd.[33] from Na and Li by means of $HClO_4$. The bulk of K and Rb is sepd. from Cs with NaH-tartrate, and the bulk of K from Rb with HCl. Rb is sepd. from K with phosphotungstic acid in 2–3% $HClO_4$ soln. The unsepd. fractions of K and Rb and all the Cs in the above sepns. can be recovered with $HClO_4$, Cs being sepd. from this K and Rb with phosphotungstic acid in 40% $HClO_4$ soln. K can be sepd. from Rb as in Table 54. Rb and Cs are detd. by acid–base titration (see p. 411); K is detd. by pptn. with $Na_3Co(NO_2)_6$ and $KMnO_4$ titration.
Na is sepd.[33] from Li by means of HCl and EtOH, Na being weighed as $Na_2CO_3·2MgO·2U_3O_8$ and Li as Li_2SO_4.

(*iii*) Method of Strecker, Diaz and Fresenius[34] in which HCl and EtOH treatment is followed by treatment with $SnCl_4$. This procedure is outlined in Table 55. In a similar method,[35] 10–12 g. chloride mixt. is treated with HCl to remove the bulk of K and Na,

TABLE 53. Method of Wells and Stevens[30]

The sample consists of chlorides in amts. normally found in rock analysis; RbCl is < 10 mg. and CsCl < 20 mg. Add H_2PtCl_6 and filter on a G4 crucible, etc.

- **Ppt.** Dry and weigh $(K, Rb, Cs)_2PtCl_6$. Evap. twice with HCOOH, filter, collect in 30 ml. stoppered flask, evap. to dryness, dry at 106°C, cool, add 0·4 ml. H_2O, warm, cool, sat. with HCl, add 10 ml. HCl in EtOH, filter on a glass crucible, wash with 2 ml. EtOH–Et_2O
  - **Residue** *KCl* (Add 0·6 mg. for each extn.)
  - **Filtrate** Evap. to dryness, heat and weigh; if the residue is <0·6 mg., Rb and Cs are absent; if >0·6 mg., proceed as below; repeat the above extn. if the residue is large. Add 0·1 ml. 5% $(NH_4)_2SO_4$, stir to dissolve, add 5 ml. satd. reagent (Note 1) dropwise while stirring, filter on a glass crucible after 30 min. and wash three times with 0·5 ml. wash soln. (Note 2). See Note 3
    - **Ppt.** Add H_2O, evap., dry, heat and weigh *Rb_2SO_4* Deduct an amt. equiv. to 0·6 mg. KCl
    - **Filtrate** Add a little $(NH_4)_2SO_4$, evap. until crystals appear, add a few drops EtOH, dry, add EtOH, dry and heat under radiant heat to moderate redness. Cool, weigh, r eheat and weigh *Cs_2SO_4*
- **Filtrate** Add some HCOOH, evap., add dil. HCOOH, evap. and filter. Evap. to dryness, add 0·4 ml. H_2O, 0·01 ml. HCl and 5 ml. EtOH, stir, add 15 ml. Et_2O, filter on a glass crucible after 15 min. and wash with 1:4 EtOH–Et_2O
  - **Residue** Dry and weigh *NaCl*
  - **Filtrate** Evap., add H_2O, H_2S, etc., heat and weigh *LiCl*

NOTES. (1) For the reagent, dissolve 1 g. $(NH_4)_2SO_4$ in 20 ml. H_2O, stir with 100 ml. 95% EtOH, filter and store.
(2) For the wash soln. dissolve 1 g. $(NH_4)_2SO_4$ and 0·16 g. NH_4Cl in 20 ml. H_2O and continue as in Note 1.
(3) Alternatively, remove K as follows and then proceed as before. Evap. the filtrate to dryness, add some H_2O and a small excess of H_2PtCl_6, evap. almost to dryness, add 5 ml. 15% EtOH, stir, filter through paper and wash with 95% EtOH. This method seps. Rb and Cs from small amts. of K.
(4) Anhyd. solvents must be employed.

Cs is pptd. with $SbCl_3$ in HCl, and Rb with $SnCl_4$ in HCl, and Li is extd. with AmOH after removal of Sb and Sn with H_2S. $SnBr_4$ can replace $SnCl_4$.[36]

(*iv*) For sepn. with ion exchange resins, see Chapter 13, Section 4.4.

Determination

The alkali metals can be weighed simultaneously as their mixed chlorides; they are then determined singly after separation by the above-mentioned methods. Most commonly, only determinations of Na and K are needed, in which case the metal present in the lesser amount is determined by any convenient method, the other metal being calculated. The flame-photometric procedure is probably the most convenient for routine analysis.

LITHIUM

Li is often weighed as the sulfate after extraction of the chlorides with an organic solvent. Nephelometric determination with stearate after extraction with amyl alcohol is convenient. The colorimetric methods involving oxine or thoron are usually preferable.

(a) H_2SO_4 is generally applied gravimetrically, though it can be used titrimetrically. For gravimetry[1] evap. the chloride soln., add dil. H_2SO_4, evap to dryness, ignite at 550–600°C (160–900°C) for 5–10 min. and weigh as Li_2SO_4. For titrimetry,[37] heat the Li_2SO_4 with 20 ml. 0·1*N* HCl, add a small excess of $BaCl_2$, then add NH_4OAc and excess $(NH_4)_2Cr_2O_7$; filter, add HCl and KI and titrate with $Na_2S_2O_3$.

(b) NH_4-stearate is applied nephelometrically.[38, 39] For 0·05–0·4 mg. Li in 2 ml. AmOH, add 5 ml. 2% reagent in AmOH and measure after 30 sec. Na and K do not interfere. For complete details, see ref. 39.

(c) Flame photometry is successful at 670·8 mμ. For full details see refs. 11 and 40.

(d) LiCl can be weighed after drying at 180–600°C,[41] but is hygroscopic.

(e) $ZnH(UO_2)_3(OAc)_9$ can be used gravimetrically for 0·6–10 mg. Li as the solid chloride.[41, 42] Add 10 ml. reagent (Note 2), stir for 15 min., leave for 15 min., filter on a glass filter contg. a thin layer of asbestos, and wash with five 2 ml. portions of reagent, then 5 times with a satd. soln. of the ppt. in EtOH, then 3 times with Et_2O. Dry at 40°C for 10 min., cool in a desiccator

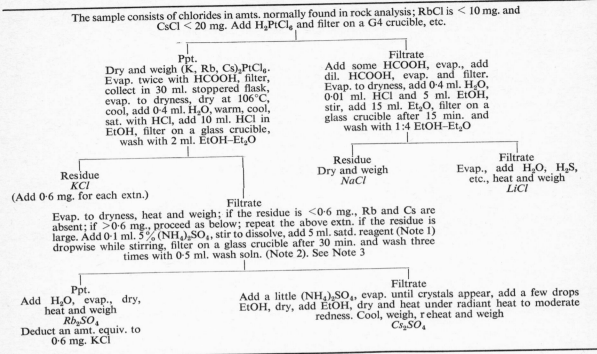

TABLE 54. Separation of K, Rb and Cs

The sample should consist of < 1·0 g. KCl and < 0·08 g. RbCl + CsCl. Evap. the chlorides several times with HNO_3. Boil with 100 ml. 1:3 HNO_3, add 20% 9-phosphomolybdic acid, filter on a Munroe crucible and wash with 1% $NaNO_3$

- **Ppt.** Dissolve in a min. amt. of dil. NaOH, pass H_2S, boil, just acidify with HNO_3, boil and filter
  - **Filtrate** Evap. to 20 ml., add 60 ml. EtOH, a small excess of 10% H_2PtCl_6 and 2–3 ml. Et_2O, filter on a Munroe crucible and wash with 80% EtOH
    - **Ppt.** Add a few ml. H_2O and several drops $N_2H_4{\cdot}H_2O$ soln., filter under suction and wash with H_2O
      - **Filtrate** Boil with a little aqua regia, evap. to dryness with HCl and repeat. Add 50–75 ml. 6*N* HCl and 0·5–1·0 g. silicotungstic acid in 2–3 ml. H_2O, filter on a Munroe crucible after 12 hr. and wash with 6*N* HCl
        - **Ppt.** Dissolve in the min. amt. of dil. NaOH, acidify slightly with HNO_3, dil. to 200 ml. with H_2O, add 10% $Hg_2(NO_3)_2$, filter on paper and wash with 1% $Hg_2(NO_3)_2$
          - **Filtrate** Add some aqua regia, evap. to 10 ml., add EtOH, etc. as for the Rb filtrate
            - **Ppt.** *Cs_2PtCl_6*
        - **Filtrate** Add some HNO_3, and 5 ml. H_2PtCl_6, evap. to 10 ml., add 3 vols. EtOH, a small excess of H_2PtCl_6 and a few ml. Et_2O. Filter on a Munroe crucible and wash with 80% EtOH
          - **Ppt.** *Rb_2PtCl_6*
- **Filtrate** *K*

TABLE 55. Method of Strecker, Diaz and Fresenius

Dissolve the chlorides in a min. amt. of H_2O, add 1:2 HCl–EtOH slowly, filter and wash with abs. EtOH

- **Ppt.** *KCl*
- **Filtrate** Boil, add boiling concd. $SnCl_4$ in 1:2 HCl–EtOH, cool for 4 hr., filter on a Gooch crucible and wash with abs. EtOH
  - **Ppt.** Dry at 110°C and weigh: *$(Rb,Cs)_2SnCl_6$*
    Add 5% tartaric acid and H_2S, filter; evap. to dryness, ignite carefully, add an equal wt. of $FeCl_3$, a min. amt. of H_2O and 50 ml. AcOH per g. of mixed chlorides. Heat, add 30–40% $SbCl_3$ in AcOH, heat on a steam-bath for 1 hr., cool, filter on a glass crucible after 12 hr. and wash with 5–10% $SbCl_3$ in AcOH. Reppt. if much Rb is present
    - **Ppt.** Add a little HCl, dil. with H_2O to give a soln. contg. 3 ml. HCl/100 ml., add H_2S, filter, evap. to dryness, add $HClO_4$, etc.
      - **Ppt.** *$CsClO_4$*
  - **Filtrate** Add H_2S, evap. to dryness, add $HClO_4$, etc.
    - **Ppt.** *$KClO_4$*

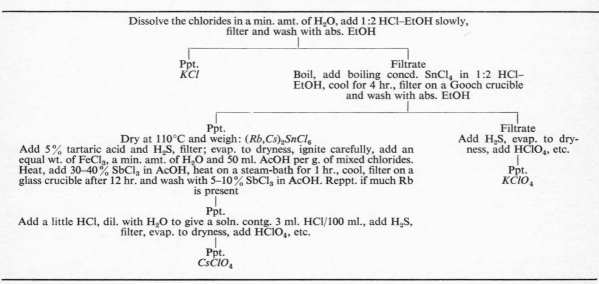

over $CaCl_2$ and weigh as $LiZn(UO_2)_3(OAc)_9 \cdot 6H_2O$; alternatively, dry at 125–162°C and weigh as the anhyd. salt or ignite at 497–1000°C and weigh as $Li_2O \cdot 2ZnO \cdot 2U_3O_8$.

NOTES. (1) Mg, Ca, Na interfere but can be sepd. with Me_2CO (see under Separation, p. 403).
(2) For the reagent, dissolve 125 g. $Zn(OAc)_2 \cdot 3H_2O$ in 600 ml. AcOH, dil. to 1 l. with H_2O, sat. with $UO_2(OAc)_2 \cdot 2H_2O$, add a little LiCl, allow to stand for at least 30 min. and filter just before use.
(3) The Ni salt can be used gravimetrically in a similar way and also colorimetrically.[43]

(f) Choline and H_3PO_4 are satisfactory gravimetrically[41, 44] or colorimetrically. For < 50 mg. Li in 17 ml. soln. or 50–150 mg. Li in 34 ml. soln., add 8 or 16 ml. reagent (4·5 ml. 85% H_3PO_4 and 100 ml. 25% choline) rapidly; for > 15 mg. Li in 25 ml. soln. add 25 ml. reagent slowly. Cover, heat on a steam-bath, add an equal vol. of 2-propanol 1 hr. after the ppt. appears, filter after 2 hr. on a medium porcelain crucible, and wash with not over 40 ml. of a satd. soln. of the ppt. in 50% 2-propanol. If over 10 mg. Na is present, add 2 ml. 4*M* HCl, suck dry after 30 sec. and repeat this twice. Then wash 4–5 times with H_2O, evap. the filtrate to 5 ml., add phenolphthalein, add 2*M* choline till a pink color appears, dil. with H_2O and reppt. Finally, ignite at 550–800°C and weigh as Li_3PO_4. Apply a correction of 0·3 mg. per 50 ml. soln. K and SO_4^{2-} do not interfere.

Colorimetry of 8 μg–2 mg. Li is satisfactory with a molybdenum blue finish.[45]

(g) Hexamine and $K_3Fe(CN)_6$ may be used gravimetrically or colorimetrically.[46] Dissolve the solid chloride in a mixt. of 100 ml. 30% hexamine, 105 ml. H_2O and 200 ml. Me_2CO (1 ml./5 mg. chloride). Pipet 1 ml., add 2 ml. reagent (50 ml. 30% hexamine, 50 ml. H_2O and 100 ml. 15% $K_3Fe(CN)_6$ heated to 35°C and mixed with 150 ml. Me_2CO); after 15 min., filter on a G3 crucible, and wash 5 times with 0·5 ml. portions of a mixt. of 100 ml. 30% hexamine and 110 ml. Me_2CO, 5 times with 1 ml. portions of 94% Me_2CO and then with Me_2CO. Dry at 50°C and weigh as $2Li_3Fe(CN)_6 \cdot K_3Fe(CN)_6 \cdot 5[(CH_2)_6N_4 \cdot 6H_2O]$.

NOTES. (1) For detn. of 15 μg. Li/ml., after washing with hexamine and Me_2CO, dissolve the ppt. in H_2O and measure with a violet filter.
(2) No interference arises from 5 mg. Na or NH_4^+/ml., 30 mg. K or Cs/ml., or 50 mg. Rb/ml.
(3) For <50 μg. Li, add 0·2 ml. solvent mixt. and 0·5 ml. reagent, filter on a glass crucible after 1 hr. and wash with 0·5 ml. solvent mixt. and then with 0·5 ml. of the above wash soln. 3 times. Dissolve the ppt. in 2 drops H_2O and 40 ml. EtOH, add 8 ml. leucomalachite green (0·5 g. warmed with Zn and HCl until colorless, dild. to 500 ml. with H_2O and decanted), dil. to 100 ml. with H_2O, and measure after 15 min. in a 2 cm. cell with an orange filter.

(h) Miscellaneous gravimetric methods. $NaAlO_2$ may be used for detn. of 3–4 mg. Li.[39] Add H_2O to give a final vol. of 40–50 ml., and 13 ml. reagent soln. (60 g. K-alum in 800 ml. H_2O mixed with 25 g. NaOH in 100 ml. H_2O, filtered after 12 hr.); adjust to pH 11–11·5 with 0·5*N* H_2SO_4. Filter on paper after 1–2 hr., wash with cold H_2O till there is no reaction with phenolphthalein. Ignite at 950–1000°C and weigh as $Li_2O \cdot 2Al_2O_3$. Na, K, etc. do not interfere. A method involving ignition at 470–900°C and weighing as $2Li_2O \cdot 5Al_2O_3$ has been proposed.[41]

NH_4F in NH_4OH can also be applied.[41] To a few ml. of sample soln. add 15 ml. reagent, filter on paper and wash with NH_4OH contg. some NH_4F. Ignite, add dil. H_2SO_4, heat above 400°C and weigh as Li_2SO_4. Alternatively, heat at 270–440°C and weigh as LiF. A correction of 1 mg. is needed for each 7 ml. filtrate and washings. The method is particularly inaccurate in dil. solns. Na and K do not interfere.

(i) Miscellaneous titrimetric methods. Dipivaloylmethane is utilized with a non-aqueous titration.[47] To 1 ml. soln. which is 0·5*N* in Li, 0·5*N* in Na and 1·0*N* in KOH, add 50 ml. 0·1*N* dipivaloylmethane in Et_2O and shake for 2 min. To a 25 ml. aliquot add 25 ml. AcOH and titrate with 0·1*N* $HClO_4$ in dioxane using methyl violet indicator. Deduct the titer obtained when a 4th ext. is titrated. Alternatively, to the aliquot add an equal vol. of H_2O, shake and titrate with 0·1*N* HCl using thymol blue indicator. K and Na do not interfere with the above correction.

The Volhard titration is applicable to the detn. of 1–50 mg. Li after extn. of the chloride with 10–15 ml. 2-ethylhexanol.[48] Add to the ext. 50 ml. EtOH, 2 ml. HNO_3, 2 ml. 20% Fe–alum, 1 ml. 0·1*N* KSCN and a 0·5 ml. excess of 0·1*N* $AgNO_3$. Stir vigorously, allow to settle, and back-titrate with 0·1*N* KSCN adding more EtOH if the phases sep.

(j) Thoron provides a good colorimetric detn. of 1–10 μg. Li/ml. soln.[49] Add 0·2 ml. 20% KOH, 7·0 ml. Me_2CO and 1 ml. 0·2% thoron, dil. to 10 ml. with H_2O and measure after 30 min. at 486 mμ. No interference is caused by 50-fold amts. of Na, or by 10-fold amts. of Ca and Mg after sepn. with KOH.

(k) Oxine is suitable for colorimetry of 10 μg. Li/ml. of EtOH soln. neutralized to methyl orange.[50] Add 3 ml. reagent soln. contg. 85 mg. oxine in 250 ml. redistd. EtOH and measure the green fluorescence under UV light.

NOTES. (1) Interference of Mg is avoided by addn. of 1 ml. satd. NaF in EtOH; Zn must be previously sepd. with oxine. 30 μg. Ca can be tolerated, as can 1 mg. NaCl or 1 g. KCl.
(2) Results are affected by the pH and by the amts. of H_2O and oxine present.
(3) For application to 1–3 g. of sample, sep. Li from the other elements by distn.[21] or with $HClO_4$,[23] add $H_2C_2O_4$, filter, add aqua regia and evap. to dryness. Add H_2O, 2 ml. 5% oxine in AcOH, and NH_4OH, heat and allow to cool for 2 hr.; filter on paper and wash with dil. NH_4OH. Treat the filtrate with aqua regia, evap. to dryness, treat

with HNO_3 and $HClO_4$, evap. to dryness and add a min. amt. of H_2O (<2 ml.). Add 1 drop HCl and 20 ml. anhyd. EtOH mixed with 60 ml. Et_2O, filter under suction after 5 min. and wash with 1:5 EtOH–Et_2O. Evap. to dryness. (If over 2 ml. H_2O was needed to dissolve the residue, treat it with 10 ml. EtOH, 50 ml. Et_2O and 1 drop HCl, and filter after 30 min.) Treat with 1 drop HCl, dissolve in EtOH, dil. to 100 ml. with EtOH and pipet out 25 ml. Add 0·01*N* KOH in EtOH (det. the requisite amt. by titrating a separate 5 ml. portion until neutral to methyl orange, after diln. to 15 ml.), then dil. to 50 ml. with EtOH, pipet 0·1 ml, and det. Li as described above, dilg. if necessary.

(l) K_2FeIO_6 can be applied colorimetrically or titrimetrically. For colorimetry of 20–100 μg. LiCl in soln.,[38, 51] evap. the soln. to dryness, dissolve in the min. amt. of H_2O, add 7–8 ml. anhyd. EtOH and 20 ml. Et_2O, filter on paper after 5 min. and wash with 5 ml. 1:4 EtOH–Et_2O. Evap. the filtrate to dryness, add 1 drop H_2O and 1 ml. 1*N* KOH, and heat to 90–100°C. Add 2·0 ml. hot reagent (mix 10 ml. 2*N* KOH and 2·3 g. KH_4IO_6 with 40 ml. H_2O, add dropwise 12 ml. 0·1*M* $FeCl_3$ in 0·2*N* HCl, dil. to 100 ml. with 2*N* KOH, filter and store in a paraffined bottle). Heat at 90–100°C for 5 min., place in cold H_2O for 5 min., filter on a porcelain filter and wash 4 times with 0·75–1 ml. portions of 1*N* KOH. Dissolve the ppt. in 10 ml. cold HCl, dil. to 25 ml. with H_2O, pipet 5 ml., dil. to 20 ml. with H_2O, add 3 ml. 2*N* KSCN, dil. to 25 ml. with H_2O and measure the red color.

NOTES. (1) Na, Ca and Mg interfere.

(2) For titrimetry,[52] dissolve the ppt. in dil. H_2SO_4, neutralize with KOH, add H_2SO_4 to clear the soln., add KI, wait for 5 min., add $NaHCO_3$ and titrate with As^{3+} or $Na_2S_2O_3$. Small amts. of Na do not interfere.

SODIUM

The zinc uranyl acetate method is the most reliable for small amounts; for semimicro determinations, the analogous magnesium triple salt procedure is better.

(a) NaCl can be utilized gravimetrically[1] after ignition at 450–700°C (407–700°C). To det. Na in the filtrate after pptn. of K_2PtCl_6, evap., add some H_2O, reduce with HCOOH and NH_4OAc or with H_2, etc.

(b) $ZnH(UO_2)_3(OAc)_9$ is applied gravimetrically, titrimetrically and colorimetrically. For gravimetric detn.[1, 53] of < 8 mg. Na/ml. soln., add 30 ml. reagent (Note 1) or enough to give a 10:1 vol. ratio of reagent to soln.; filter on a glass crucible after 1 hr. and wash with 2 ml. portions of reagent 5–10 times, then with a satd. soln. of the ppt. in EtOH 5 times and then 3 times with Et_2O. Dry at room temp. and weigh as $NaZn(UO_2)_3(OAc)_9 \cdot 6H_2O$. Alternatively, heat at 360–674°C and weigh as $Na_2O \cdot 2ZnO \cdot 2U_3O_8$.

NOTES. (1) For the reagent, dissolve 10 g. $UO_2(OAc)_2 \cdot 2H_2O$ and 6 g. 30% AcOH in 50 ml. H_2O by warming; dissolve 30 g. $Zn(OAc)_2 \cdot 3H_2O$ and 3 g. 30% AcOH in 30 ml. H_2O by warming. Mix the solns., leave to cool (if no ppt. appears, add a trace of NaCl), allow to stand and filter just before use.

(2) No interference arises from < 50 mg. KCl, NH_4^+, Ca, Ba, Mg or small amts. of PO_4^{3-}. Interferences are Li, Sr, org. compds., and K with PO_4^{3-} or SO_4^{2-}; citrate or tartrate prevents Mo interference. Large amts. of PO_4^{3-} may be removed with $ZnCO_3$. Na can be sepd. from Li, K and PO_4^{3-} as follows:[54] treat the ppt. with 12–30 ml. 21–23% HCl in BuOH (s.g. 0·91–0·93), stopper, place in the icebox for 1 hr., centrifuge, add H_2O, evap. and reppt.

(3) Methods involving this reagent have been reviewed.[55]

Many titrimetric finishes have been recommended for this pptn. method.[41, 53] For redox titrations, dissolve the ppt. in acid, reduce in a Jones reductor, or with Cd, Zn–Hg, etc., and then titrate with $KMnO_4$, with Ce^{4+} and ferroin indicator, or with $K_2Cr_2O_7$ and diphenylamine indicator, etc. Alternatively, dissolve the ppt., add a known excess of $TiCl_3$ and back-titrate with $FeCl_3$ using KSCN indicator. For details of such titrations, see Chapter 39, p. 300.

For titration with EDTA,[56] dissolve the ppt. by boiling with 3–5 ml. HCl and 50 ml. H_2O, add a small excess of 1*M* $(NH_4)_2CO_3$, 2 ml. of buffer pH 10 and eriochrome black T indicator and titrate with 0·01*M* EDTA.

For iodometric titration, treat the ppt. with H_2O, 5 g. $(NH_4)_2SO_4$, a few drops 5*N* H_2SO_4, 2 g. KI, starch indicator and $K_4Fe(CN)_6$ and titrate with $Na_2S_2O_3$ soln. (see Chapter 36, p. 281).

For acid–base titration, titrate the ppt. with 0·02*N* NaOH using phenolphthalein indicator, or dissolve the ppt. in tartaric acid, distil and titrate with 0·01*N* $Ba(OH)_2$.

For detn. of U^{6+}, treat the ppt. with 10–15 ml. H_2O, 3–20 ml. 0·05*M* Na_2HPO_4, boil, add 2 drops cochineal indicator (2 g. in 100 ml. H_2O and 50 ml. EtOH) and titrate with 0·05*M* $UO_2(OAc)_2$ from red to green.

It is also possible to dissolve the ppt. in NaOAc, ppt. U with oxine and titrate the ppt. bromometrically.

Several colorimetric finishes are also available.[41, 53] For treatment of the ppt. from 50 μg. Na, add 5 ml. H_2O and 5 ml. 1% $K_4Fe(CN)_6$ in 2% AcOH and measure the brown color. For the ppt. from 100–500 μg. Na, add H_2O, 5 ml. satd. $(NH_4)_2CO_3$ in 1*N* NH_4OH, 5 ml. 3% H_2O_2, dil. to 50 ml. with H_2O and measure at 520 mμ.[38] It is also possible to dissolve the ppt. in hot H_2O or 20% citric acid and measure the yellow color at 400–465 mμ. Other reagents are Na-salicylate, pyrocatechol, sulfosalicylic acid,[57] alizarin[58] and NH_4SCN.[59]

Other divalent metals can replace Zn in the reagent. The sensitivity decreases in the following order: Mg, Zn, Ni, Co, Cu, Mn, Fe, Cd, Hg. Interferences are fewer with the Ni or Co reagents.[60]

The Mg salt can be applied gravimetrically, titrimetrically and colorimetrically.[1] For the reagent, heat

90 g. $UO_2(OAc)_2$ and 60 ml. AcOH in 1 l. H_2O to 70°C; also heat 600 g. $Mg(OAc)_2{\cdot}4H_2O$ and 60 ml. AcOH with 1 l. H_2O to 70°C; mix equal vols of the solns., leave at 20°C for 2 hr. and filter. For gravimetric detn. of 0·5–25 mg. Na in < 5 ml. soln., add 100–250 ml. reagent (12·5 ml./mg. Na), maintain at 20°C for 30–45 min. with occasional shaking, filter on a glass crucible and wash with 5 ml. portions of a satd. soln. of the ppt. in EtOH. Dry at 105°C for 30 min. and weigh as $NaMg(UO_2)_3(OAc)_9{\cdot}5H_2O$; or heat at 360–745°C and weigh as $Na_2O{\cdot}2MgO{\cdot}2U_3O_8$. The ppt. is said[37] to be $Na_2CO_3{\cdot}2MgO{\cdot}2U_3O_8$ after ignition at 640–700°C. NH_4^+ does not interfere, nor does 1 mg. Li; up to 200 mg. Ca, Ba, Mg, K, Fe, Al, Cr can be present if the soln. is warmed and cooled before filtration. PO_4^{3-} can be removed with magnesia mixt. A colorimetric method based on detn. of Mg in the ppt. with titan yellow is possible[61] for 30–150 μg. Na/ml.

The Ni salt can be applied gravimetrically or colorimetrically;[62] dimethylglyoxime can be used to det. the Ni in the ppt. from < 100 μg. Na.[63] The Cu salt also allows colorimetric and gravimetric detns. For the former,[53, 64] evap. the soln. nearly to dryness, add 1–2 ml. reagent (*N* AcOH satd. with $Cu(OAc)_2$ and $UO_2(OAc)_2$), centrifuge after 1 hr. and wash with EtOH. Treat the ppt. with H_2O and NH_4OH, centrifuge, treat with AcOH and NH_4OH and centrifuge again. Combine the centrifugates and compare the Cu color with standards. The Cu salt is said[65] to be more sensitive and less subject to Li interference than the Zn method.

The Mn salt can be used to ppt. 8–10 μg. Na, the ppt. being treated with KIO_4 and the color of MnO_4^- being measured.[66]

(c) Flame photometry is applicable at 589 or 819 mμ[67] (see also p. 401).

(d) H_2SO_4 can be used gravimetrically.[1] Evap. NaCl soln. to dryness with dil. H_2SO_4, heat, add $(NH_4)_2CO_3$ and ignite above 750°C (90–878°C) to Na_2SO_4.

(e) K-dihydroxytartrate is suitable for gravimetric and titrimetric detns.[41] For 0·3 g. Na in 10 ml. soln., cool to 0°C, add 10 ml. reagent (0·5 g. in 10 ml. H_2O at 0°C, neutralized to phenolphthalein with 1*N* KOH), store at 5°C for 12 hr., filter on paper and wash with H_2O at 5°C. Dissolve the ppt. through the filter with dil. H_2SO_4 into a porcelain crucible, ignite to dull redness and weigh as Na_2SO_4. The error is −2%. Alternatively, titrate the ppt. with $KMnO_4$ soln.

(f) Resorcinol is utilized gravimetrically[68] for 0·1–0·2 g. NaCl in 100 ml. neutral soln. Add 5 ml. cold reagent (100 g. in 500 ml. H_2SO_4 heated for 1 hr. at 120–125°C), filter on a glass crucible after 15 min., wash with reagent soln., EtOH and Et_2O, dry and weigh as $C_6H_4(ONa)_2$.

(g) Mg-1,8-naphthylamine sulfonate can be applied gravimetrically or titrimetrically.[69] Evap. the soln. almost to dryness, add a 3-fold excess of 10% reagent soln. (7–8 ml./10 mg. Na) and an equal vol. of EtOH, stir, filter after 30–60 min. and wash with a satd. soln. of the ppt. in EtOH 6–7 times and then with EtOH. Dry at 105°C and weigh (conversion factor 0·09377). Alternatively, dissolve the ppt. in hot H_2O, dil. to 250 ml. with H_2O, take a 20 ml. aliquot, add 1 g. KBr, 5 ml. HCl, excess 0·1*N* $KBrO_3$ and after 15–25 min., 1 g. KI, and titrate with 0·1*N* $Na_2S_2O_3$. The error for the gravimetric method is ±0·5%, for the titrimetric ±0·8%. The ratios of ion to Na that do not interfere are 2·5 for K, 3 for Ca, 10 for Mg and 4–7 for SO_4^{2-}.

(h) $(NH_4)_3AlF_6$ allows gravimetric detn.[70] of 2–20 mg. Na. To the sample soln. add a 0·75 vol. of satd. reagent soln. (7·66 g./l. H_2O), centrifuge and wash 3–4 times with 0·5% reagent and then 2–3 times with 50% EtOH; dry at 120–130°C and weigh as Na_3AlF_6.

For a titrimetric detn. involving H_2SiF_6,[71] dissolve NaCl or $NaNO_3$ in H_2O, add a 3-fold amt. of SiO_2 gel and HF and evap. to dryness. Heat at 120°C, add 10 ml. warm H_2O and 10–25 ml. 4*N* $CaCl_2$ and titrate with NaOH using bromocresol purple or chlorophenol red indicator.

(i) K_2HSbO_4 is generally used titrimetrically though other finishes are also possible. For detn. of < 0·1 g. Na in concd. neutral or slightly alk. soln.,[41, 72] cool below 12°C, add 80 ml. reagent (Note 1), after 1 hr. add 40 ml. EtOH, and after 2 hr. filter on a glass crucible and wash with 25% EtOH once and 50% EtOH thrice. Dissolve the ppt. in hot H_2O and 40 ml. HCl (s.g. 1·19), dil. to 250 ml. with H_2O, add 1 g. Na_2SO_3 and boil for 20 min. Heat to 70–80°C, add methyl orange and titrate with 0·1*N* $KBrO_3$ to colorless. The factor must be detd. empirically.

NOTES. (1) For the reagent heat 324 g. Sb_2O_5 and 606 g. KNO_3, or 292 g. Sb_2O_3 and 808 g. KNO_3, to 500–600°C and ext. with H_2O at 80°C.

(2) For gravimetric detn., dry at room temp. and weigh as $Na_2H_2Sb_2O_7{\cdot}6H_2O$ or ignite at 600–950°C and weigh as $NaSbO_3$ (Duval). See also ref. 73. For nephelometry or colorimetry, dissolve the ppt. in HCl, add gelatin and H_2S or KI and shake with C_6H_6.

(j) Ball's reagent can be applied colorimetrically.[74] Na is pptd. as $Na_6Cs_9[Bi(NO_2)_6]_5$ and the ppt. is treated with α-naphthylamine and sulfanilic acid. The ppt. can also be weighed after drying at 160–670°C. Compare Chapter 52, p. 391.

POTASSIUM

Until recent years H_2PtCl_6 was considered much the best reagent for potassium; it has now been largely superseded by tetraphenylboron. Small amounts can be determined colorimetrically by means of H_2PtCl_6 or cobaltinitrite; the latter reagent also provides a satisfactory titrimetric determination.

(a) Weighing as KCl after ignition at 450–700°C (219–500°C) provides the simplest determination of K.[41]

(b) H_2PtCl_6 is applied gravimetrically, titrimetrically and colorimetrically. For gravimetric detn.[1, 75]

see under Separation (p. 402) for details of the pptn. method. Dry the ppt. at 130°C (54–270°C) and weigh as K_2PtCl_6.

NOTES. (1) The compn. of the ppt. does not correspond exactly to the above formula, but it is possible to use the theor. factor.
(2) In an alternative method,[1] ppt. with a small excess of H_2PtCl_6 from a soln. contg. 5 ml. HCl, proceed as before, then filter through paper and wash. Dissolve the ppt. by passing hot H_2O through the filter, collect in a beaker and add 0·5 g. Mg/0·2 g. K (press the Mg down with a glass rod to dissolve it quickly). After the reaction subsides, add 2 ml. dil. HCl, boil for 1 hr., add more HCl and boil further. Filter on paper, wash with H_2O, ignite and weigh as Pt. No interference arises from Mg, Fe, Al, group IV metals, Na, SO_4^{2-}, Cl^-, PO_4^{3-}, NO_3^-, BO_2^- or SiO_2. An electrodeposition finish is also possible (see Chapter 32, p. 242).
(3) In the Lindo–Gladding method,[1] ppt. as above, filter on paper, wash with 80% EtOH until colorless, then 6–8 times with 10% NH_4Cl soln., and finally with 80% EtOH; dry at 130°C and weigh as K_2PtCl_6. For the NH_4Cl wash soln., dissolve 100 g. NH_4Cl in 500 ml. H_2O, add 5–10 g. K_2PtCl_6, shake occasionally for 6–8 hr., leave for 12 hr. and filter. No interference is caused by Na, Mg, SO_4^{2-} or PO_4^{3-}.
(4) To det. a small amt. of K in presence of much Na, e.g. a little KCl in 1·48–1·63 g. NaCl,[76] add H_2O and a 2-fold equiv. amt. of $HClO_4$, evap. to dryness, cool, add H_2O, evap. to dryness, cool and dissolve in 95 ml. EtOH, warming if necessary. Add 0·2 g. H_2PtCl_6 in 5 ml. EtOH, stir and cool to 0°C for at least 1 hr. Filter on a glass crucible, wash once with 1 ml. EtOH and 9–10 times with 1 ml. portions of anhyd. EtOH, dry at 130°C and weigh as K_2PtCl_6. Li_2PtCl_6 is an easier reagent to handle than the acid.

For titrimetric finishes, dissolve the ppt. in hot H_2O, treat with Mg and titrate the filtrate with $AgNO_3$ using dichlorofluorescein indicator,[77] or apply Volhard's method, or treat the ppt. with KI and excess $Na_2S_2O_3$ soln. and back-titrate with I_2 soln.[78]

For colorimetry, dissolve the ppt. in HCl and measure at 410 mμ (for < 2m*M* K/l.) or at 470 mμ (for < 6m*M* K/l.).[79] If KI is also added, measurement is done at 490 mμ.[79, 80, 81] $SnCl_2$ can also be applied[81] (cf. Chapter 32, p. 241). To det. 2–12 μg. K, add a known excess of reagent, ext. with 1:1 EtOAc–BuOH and measure at 264 mμ.[82]

(c) Tetraphenylboron can be used as either the Na or the Li salt, and also provides satisfactory gravimetric, titrimetric and colorimetric procedures. The soly. of the K ppt. is less than that of AgCl. For gravimetric detn. of > 2 mg. K_2O in acidic (HCl) soln.[83, 84] add excess reagent (Note 1) and H_2O to give a final vol. of 50 ml. for 5–10 mg. K_2O and 100 ml. for 20 mg. K_2O, as well as a final concn. of 0·1*N* HCl. After 5 min. filter on a glass crucible, wash with a satd. soln. of the ppt. in H_2O contg. a little AcOH, dry at 120°C and weigh as $K[B(C_6H_5)_4]$.

NOTES. (1) For the reagent, dissolve 1·5 g. Na- or Li-tetraphenylboron in 250 ml. H_2O, stir for 5 min. with some $Al(OH)_3$, filter. Use 10 ml. reagent for 5 mg. K_2O. The reagent is stable for several days.
(2) Interferences are Rb, Cs, Hg^{2+} and Tl^+. NH_4^+ can be removed with HCHO. Fe^{3+} requires NaF addn. When Mn, Fe, Co, Ni, Cu or Al is present, boil the ppt. with Me_2CO and NaOH and reweigh. Na, Li, Ca, etc. do not interfere. If EDTA is added, $CaHPO_4$ does not interfere,[85] nor do Fe, Al, Ti, Ni, Co, Cr, Mn, As, Sb, Pb, Zn, Ca, etc.[86] Complete sepn. of K from NH_4^+ is possible after HCHO addn.[87]
(3) Other recommendations for pptn. conditions are pptn. from 0·2–0·6*N* HCl at 0°C,[88] and pptn. at pH 4–6 at 40–50°C.[89]

A variety of titrimetric finishes has been suggested. The ppt. can be heated[90] with Me_2CO at 92–97°C for 15 min. and then titrated with 0·025*N* Ce^{4+} in 2*N* $HClO_4$. For trace amts. of K, it is best to coppt. with NH_4^+, ignite to KBO_2, add excess HCl and back-titrate with NaOH using methyl red–methylene blue indicator.[91] To det. the ppt. from 2–10 mg. K,[91] wash the ppt. through the filter with three 5 ml. Me_2CO portions and two 10 ml. H_2O portions; collect in 5 ml. satd. $HgCl_2$ soln., add 10 ml. 0·1*N* NaOH, heat almost to boiling, add 5 ml. 10% KI and methyl red and titrate with 0·1*N* HCl. The reaction is $(C_6H_5)_4BK + 4HgCl_2 + 3H_2O = 4(C_6H_5)HgCl + KCl + 3HCl + H_3BO_3$.

Excess of reagent in the filtrate can be titrated potentiometrically with Tl^+ soln.[92] After dissoln. of the ppt. in Me_2CO and addn. of a mixt. of 4 ml. 2*N* AcOH, 1 ml. 0·1*N* KBr and 2 drops 1% eosin, it is possible[93] to titrate with $AgNO_3$ soln.; alternatively,[93] excess $AgNO_3$ is added and Volhard's method applied. Mohr's titration with 0·01*N* $AgNO_3$ has also been used.[94] The ppt. can be titrated with NaOH using methyl red–methylene blue indicator after passage through a cationite resin.[95] Titration with 2·5% cetyltrimethylammonium bromide using bromophenol blue indicator is feasible.[96] Conductometric titration has been proposed.[97]

For a colorimetric detn.,[98] treat the ppt. with 5 ml. 3:1 acetonitrile–H_2O, dil. to 25 ml. with this solvent and measure at 266 mμ ($\epsilon = 3225$).

(d) $Na_3Co(NO_2)_6$ is best applied colorimetrically though it has been often examined for gravimetric and titrimetric procedures. For colorimetry[41, 99] of 2 μg. K/ml. soln. add 1 ml. reagent (Note 1), store for 3 hr. at 0°C, centrifuge and wash with 5 ml. H_2O at 0°C, then with 60% v/v Me_2CO at 0°C, finally twice with 5 ml. Me_2CO at 0°C. Dissolve the ppt. in 1 ml. 0·1*N* AcOH by heating for 10–15 min. on a steam-bath, add 2 ml. 0·5% sulfanilic acid in 30% AcOH and 1 ml. 0·5% α-naphthylamine in 30% AcOH and measure the red color. The error is ±6% for 2–5 μg. K; if $AgNO_3$ is not added the error is ±3% for 0·05–0·15 mg. K.

NOTES. (1) For the reagent add 25 g. $Na_3Co(NO_2)_6$ to 50 g. $NaNO_2$ in 150 ml. H_2O, mix with 2 g. $AgNO_3$ in 50 ml. H_2O and dil. to 200 ml. with H_2O; add 2 ml. AcOH, pass

air for 5 min., store at 4–6°C for 12 hr., filter on a Whatman No. 42 paper, centrifuge just before use.
(2) For a comparison of methods involving $Na_3Co(NO_2)_6$, see refs. 41, 100. Many modifications have been suggested; the compn. of the ppt. varies with the conditions, particularly the temp., the amt. of EtOH added, and the concn. of the reagent (when Na:K exceeds 100, the ppt. is $K_2NaCo(NO_2)_6$). Thus the method is not reliable when applied gravimetrically and titrimetric procedures cannot be used for macro analysis; in all cases an empirical factor should be detd. in a parallel expt.[101] The sensitivity is increased when $AgNO_3$ is added.
The ppt. is difficult to filter; 0·1% $Al_2(SO_4)_3$ is said to be a satisfactory wash liquid.[102]
It may be possible to obtain a ppt. of definite compn., i.e. $K_3[Co(NO_2)_6]\cdot 2H_2O$, if the Li-salt is used as reagent.[103]
(3) For titrimetric detn. many variations have been proposed. Cerimetric titration is suitable for 0·1–0·2 mg. K/ml. soln.[104] Add 0·5 ml. 0·2*N* $AgNO_3$, 0·5 ml. 12·5% $Na_3Co(NO_2)_6$ dropwise and after 10–20 min. centrifuge for 15 min.; pipet the supernate leaving 0·3 ml. soln., add 0·5 ml. H_2O, centrifuge and repeat. Dissolve the ppt. in 1·5 ml. *N* NaOH by heating for 10 min. on a steam-bath; cool to 0°C, add 2·5 ml. 1*N* H_2SO_4 and 1 drop ferroin and titrate with 0·01*N* Ce^{4+} until the blue color remains for 2 min. A blank detn. is needed. Alternatively,[105] ppt. using the method given below, add excess Ce^{4+} and back-titrate with Fe^{2+} soln. using ferroin indicator.
Volhard's titration may be used for detn. of the ppt. from 0·15–2·0 mg. K;[106] ppt. similarly to the above method, dissolve the ppt. in 5 ml. 1:4 HNO_3, heat, cool, add 0·5 ml. satd. Fe-alum and titrate with 0·01*N* NH_4SCN.
For iodometric titration,[107] ppt. 0·02–0·1 mg. K in 0·5 ml. soln. with 0·5 ml. reagent (dissolve 25 g. $Co(NO_3)_2$ in 12·5 ml. AcOH and 50 ml. H_2O; dissolve 120 g. $NaNO_2$ in 180 ml. H_2O; add the latter to the former, pass air through, store in an icebox and filter just before use). Keep at 20–25°C for 1 hr., centrifuge for 10 min. and wash with four 5 ml. portions of H_2O, centrifuging well each time. Then add a small excess 0·01*N* Ce^{4+} (1 ml. for 0·06 mg. K), warm, cool, add 1% KI and titrate with 0·2*N* $Na_2S_2O_3$. The ppt. can also be dissolved in H_2SO_4 with excess $K_2Cr_2O_7$ before the iodometric finish.[107] Excess $K_2Cr_2O_7$ can also be titrated with Fe^{2+} soln. using diphenylamine indicator.[108]
For $KMnO_4$ titration,[41, 109] treat the ppt. with excess $KMnO_4$, acidify with H_2SO_4, add $H_2C_2O_4$ and titrate with $KMnO_4$ soln. Direct titration is also possible.[110] A method in which $KPbCo(NO_2)_6$ is pptd. has been described.[41]
For an acid–base titration,[111] treat the ppt. with excess urea soln. (1 g./l. 0·053*N* H_2SO_4) and titrate with 0·053*N* NaOH using bromothymol blue indicator.
EDTA titration has been applied with murexide or eriochrome black T indicator.[112]
(4) Several modifications of the colorimetric method are available. In general, $Na_3Co(NO_2)_6$ is satisfactory for > 80 μg. K/ ml. soln.; for smaller amts. it is better to add $AgNO_3$ as well.[99] Reagents which have been used to det. NO_2^- in the ppt. are sulfanilic acid with phenol, Na-naphthionate with β-naphthol,[113] novocaine with α-naphthylamine, phenoldisulfonic acid,[114] antipyrine,[115] indole,[115] *N*-(1-naphthyl)-ethylenediamine with sulfanilamide,[113] etc. For details of these methods, see Chapter 63, p. 466.
To det. Co in the ppt., available reagents are choline with $K_4Fe(CN)_6$,[116] NH_4SCN,[117] cysteine, nitroso-R salt or α-nitroso-β-naphthol,[118] dimethylglyoxime with Na_2S, $KHCO_3$ with H_2O_2, 27% HCl or oxine. In the oxine method,[119] the ppt. is treated with sulfamic acid and oxine, extd. with $CHCl_3$ and the color measured at 403 mμ. For further details, see Chapter 35, p. 270 et seq.
(5) It is possible to estimate (±10%) 1–2 mg. K by sepg. by paper chromatography and measuring the area of the $KPb[Co(NO_2)_6]$ spot.[120]
(6) Radiometric measurement as $K_2Na[Co(NO_2)_6]\cdot H_2O$ has been studied.[121]
(7) For gravimetric detn., the ppt. can be weighed as $K_2Na[Co(NO_2)_6]\cdot H_2O$ but the temp. of drying is undefined.[41, 122] 0·01–0·1 mg. K can be detd. as the Ag salt and 0·1–0·5 mg. as the Na salt.[123] The ppt. can[124] be dissolved in HCl and finally weighed as $KClO_4$.
(8) Some similar reagents have been examined. $K_2PbCu(NO_2)_6$ can be pptd. as follows.[125] To 0·1 g. nitrate soln. add 6·5 ml. reagent (6·6 g. $Cu(OAc)_2$ and 11·7 g. $Pb(OAc)_2$ in 100 ml.), then add $NaNO_2$, store at 0°C for 1 hr., filter on a G3 or 4 crucible, wash with EtOH and dry at 100°C. An empirical factor of 0·1331 is applied.
$Na_2Ca[Ni(NO_2)_6]$ has been used as reagent for K in slightly acidic soln.[126] For the reagent, dissolve 100 g. $CaCl_2\cdot 6H_2O$, 46 g. $Ni(NO_3)_2\cdot 6H_2O$ and 58 g. $NaNO_2$ in 100 ml. H_2O, add 5–6 mg. KCl and filter after 12 hr. For a detn., add reagent, heat for 1 hr. at 70–80°C, filter, wash with a satd. soln. of the ppt. in dil. EtOH, dry at 130°C and weigh as $K_2Ca[Ni(NO_2)_6]$.

(e) Flame photometry can be used at 768 and 404·6 mμ. For references see pp. 401 and 408. If a propane flame is used, Na and Ca do not interfere.[127]

(f) $HClO_4$ can be applied gravimetrically or titrimetrically.[1] For the pptn. procedure, see under Separation, p. 402. Dry the ppt. at 350–400°C (73–653°C) and weigh as $KClO_4$.

For titrimetry, treat the ppt. with H_2O and a known excess of methylene blue, filter, add $CHCl_3$ to the filtrate and titrate with picric acid soln. until the aq. layer is colorless. Alternatively, treat the ppt. with $N_2H_4\cdot H_2SO_4$, etc. and titrate with $AgNO_3$ soln., or reduce with $TiCl_3$ and titrate with $KMnO_4$ or with $FeCl_3$ using KSCN indicator.

Weighing as $KReO_4$ after drying at 54–220°C is said[128] to be more accurate.

$NaIO_4$ can also be used gravimetrically and titrimetrically.[129] To det. > 0·4 mg. K as nitrate in 5 ml. soln., add reagent (recrystd. from HNO_3; 1 g./3 ml. H_2O), and after 3–4 min. add 90 ml. 1:1 EtOH–EtOAc. Stir occasionally during 30 min. at 0°C, filter on a Gooch crucible and wash with EtOAc at 0°C; dry at 105°C (82–287°C) for 10 min, and weigh as KIO_4. Alternatively, dissolve the ppt. in 150 ml. H_2O contg. 5 g. B_2O_3 and 5 g. borax, add 3 g. KI and titrate with 0·1*N* As^{3+} using starch indicator. ($IO_4^- \rightarrow IO_3^-$). For the As^{3+} soln. dissolve 4·945 g. As_2O_3 and 10 g. $NaHCO_3$ in H_2O, heat to 50°C, sat. with CO_2, dil. to 1 l. with H_2O and standardize against $NaIO_4$ and KI. No interference occurs from Na in 70-fold amts., Mg, Ca, Li, Al, Zn, Ni, Co, or small amts. of SO_4^{2-}, BO_2^- or

PO_4^{3-}. Interferences are NH_4^+, Rb, Cs, Fe, Mn, Cr, Cl^-, NO_2^-, reductants, and Ca with SO_4^{2-}. Titrimetry is better when SO_4^{2-} is present. The EtOH used should be purified by distn. after heating 1 l. with 0·5 g. NaOH and 2·5 g. $AgNO_3$ under reflux for 2–3 hr. H_5IO_6 can also be utilized for a titrimetric procedure.[129]

(g) The hexyl salt of Ca, Mg or Na provides gravimetric, titrimetic and colorimetric procedures. For gravimetric detn.[1, 130, 131] of 0·4–8 mg. K in neutral or slightly alk. soln. in a micro beaker at 0°C, add 0·1*N* reagent to give an excess of 0·02–0·03*N* reagent in soln. in a total vol. of 10 ml. (< 5 ml. for < 1 mg. K). Store at 0°C for 3–5 hr. (12 hr. for < 1 mg.), filter on a filter stick and wash once with 0·3–0·5 ml. H_2O at 0°C, 3 times with 0·3–0·5 ml. portions of a satd. soln. of the ppt. in H_2O at 0°C and twice with H_2O at 0°C. Dry the beaker and stick at 105–110°C (50–200°C) and weigh as $KC_{12}H_4O_{12}N_7$.

NOTES. (1) Interferences are Rb, Cs, Tl^+, NH_4^+, Ba, Pb, Hg^{2+}, Cu, Ag, Bi, Sn, Sb, Fe, Al, UO_2^{2+}, Ti, Th, Zr, CO_3^{2-}; PO_4^{3-} does not interfere if the Na-salt is used. No interference arises from Sr, Cd, Ni, Co, Zn, Mn, SO_4^{2-}, etc., or from 5-fold amts. of Na or Li, 15-fold Mg or 8-fold Ca.

(2) If necessary repptn. can be done after dissoln. of the ppt. in Me_2CO and evapn. of the solvent. The hexyl compd. can be weighed after sepn. with HCl, or it can be titrated with alkali.[130] Amperometric titration is possible.[132]

(3) 10–100 μg. K can be detd. colorimetrically at 420–490 mμ.[130, 133]

(4) Other nitro compds. which have been utilized are α-hexyl, dihexyl, tetranitroacridone, etc. (see Chapter 11, Section 1.1).

A satd. soln. of picric acid in EtOH is suitable for pptn. of 10 mg. K in 2 ml. soln.[41, 134] Add 8 ml. reagent, store at 20°C for 1 hr., filter on a glass crucible, wash with Et_2O, dry at 110°C (54–217°C) and weigh as $C_6H_2O_7N_3K$. Alternatively, titrate with methylene blue soln. shaking with $CHCl_3$ between addns. until the aq. layer is colorless. For colorimetry, compare the yellow colors of the aq. soln.

Na-6-chloro-5-nitrotoluene-3-sulfonate (or the bromo compd.) allows detn. of 0·1–0·2 g. K in 100 ml. soln.[41, 134] Boil the soln., add 10% reagent, store below 5°C for 12 hr., filter on a glass crucible, wash with H_2O at 0°C, dry at 120°C (54–278°C) and weigh as $C_7H_5NO_5ClSK$. Alternatively, titrate with $TiCl_3$ or $SnCl_2$ soln. For colorimetry, reduce the ppt. to the amine, diazotize and couple. Naphthol yellow S can be utilized gravimetrically,[134] and dilituric acid gravimetrically or titrimetrically.[135]

(h) Miscellaneous gravimetric methods. Dil. H_2SO_4 can be used to form K_2SO_4 as a weighing form for KCl, ignition being done at above 750°C (408–880°C).[41]

HBF_4 ppts. K from 10 ml. soln.[136] Add 30 ml. reagent (0·5 g. NaCl in 40 ml. H_2O, 250 ml. 48–50% HBF_4, 500 ml. EtOH and 500 ml. MeOH, cooled to 3°C, filtered on a Gooch crucible and stored in a polyethylene bottle). Store at 3°C for 45–60 min., filter on a Gooch crucible (cooled), wash 3–4 times with 10 ml. portions of 1:1 MeOH–EtOH, dry at 105–110°C for 30 min. and weigh. The empirical factor is 0·3105. If over 0·5 g. Na is present, wash with 30 ml. MeOH–EtOH and reweigh; the change in wt. should not exceed 0·5 mg. Interferences are NH_4^+, F^-, SO_4^{2-} and Al + Ca. No interference arises from 0·5 g. NaCl or from Cd, Zn, Mg, Mn, Fe, Co, Ni, Al, Cu, Li, HNO_3 or H_3PO_4. HCl prevents Ca interference. For a titrimetric method involving SiO_2, HF, etc. see p. 452.

(i) Satd. 12-phosphomolybdic acid soln. can be employed to det. 0·1–2 mg. K in 1–20 ml. soln.[137] Add 5 ml. reagent, evap. until a turbidity appears, cool for 15 min. when solidification should have occurred, and add 20 ml. 2% HNO_3. Filter, wash with 2% HNO_3 and with satd. KCl soln. and titrate with 0·02*N* NaOH soln. Alternatively, weigh the Mo in the ppt. as $PbMoO_4$.

(j) Tartaric acid is employed titrimetrically.[41, 138] Dissolve the solid sample in a min. amt. of H_2O, make the soln. 50% in MeOH, add methyl orange and then add reagent (20 g. with 5 g. NaOAc in 500 ml. H_2O dild. to 1 l. with MeOH) dropwise until the color changes from red to yellow. After 1–2 hr., filter on paper and wash 3–4 times with MeOH. Dissolve the ppt. in 50 ml. H_2O which has been neutralized to phenolphthalein with NaOH and heated to 70–80°C, and titrate with NaOH soln. Mg and Na do not interfere.

(k) $CdSO_4$ and $Li_4Fe(CN)_6$ are applicable in conjunction with a $KMnO_4$ titration.[139] Add a known amt. of $CdSO_4$ and excess of $Fe(CN)_6^{4-}$, filter and titrate the ppt. with $KMnO_4$ soln. Up to 0·5 g. Na can be present. If $Na_4Fe(CN)_6$ is used as the reagent, the ppt. is dissolved in H_2SO_4, excess Zn^{2+} is added and back-titrated with $K_4Fe(CN)_6$ soln. using diphenylamine indicator.

RUBIDIUM AND CESIUM

Almost all the methods for K can be applied for these elements. A few specific methods exist for Cs, but there is none available for Rb. RbCl can be used as a weighing form after drying at 450–490°C (88–605°C) and CsCl after drying at 530–640°C (110–877°C).[41] Treatment with dilute H_2SO_4 permits weighing Rb_2SO_4 after ignition above 490°C (76–877°C), and Cs_2SO_4 after ignition at 480–870°C (105–876°C).[41]

(a) $HClO_4$ can be utilized in the same way as for K.[41] $RbClO_4$ is dried at 95–343°C and $CsClO_4$ at 70–611°C.

(b) H_2PtCl_6 is also applied as for K (p. 408),[41] the ppt. being weighed as such or converted to Pt.

$SnCl_4$ in EtOH ppts. Rb and Cs from concd. chloride solns.[41] Add 1:2 HCl–EtOH, boil, add hot reagent, filter on a glass crucible, wash with anhyd. EtOH, dry at 110°C and weigh as Rb_2SnCl_6 (70–407°C) and Cs_2SnCl_6 (130–344°C).

The corresponding $PbCl_6^{2-}$ salts can also be utilized gravimetrically.[41]

$SbCl_3$ is suitable for pptn. of Cs from 100 ml. AcOH soln.[140] Add a known vol. of 10% w/v $SbCl_3$ in AcOH, leave to stand, pipet the supernate, add 150 ml. H_2O, 10 ml. 1:1 H_2SO_4 and 10 ml. 1:1 HCl and titrate with 0·1*N* $KMnO_4$ soln. No interference occurs with Li, Na, K, Mg, Ca, Sr, NH_4^+ or from up to 50 mg. Rb. NO_3^- interferes.

$K_3Bi_2I_9$ can be used gravimetrically or colorimetrically. For the former,[141] treat the solid chloride with a min. amt. of AcOH or H_2O, add reagent (5 g. Bi_2O_3, 17 g. KI boiled with 50 ml. AcOH) and finally weigh as $Cs_3Bi_2I_9$. No interference occurs with Rb, K, NH^+, Li, Na, Mg, Ca, Fe, Al, SO_4^{2-}. The method may, however, not be very accurate.[141] In the colorimetric procedure, the ppt. from 0·5–50 μg. Cs is treated with dithizone.[142]

(c) **Flame photometry** allows detn. of Rb at 780·0 and 420·1 mμ, and detn. of Cs at 852·2 and 455·5 mμ.[11]

(d) **Na-tetraphenylboron** is used in the same way as for K.[87]

(e) **Hexyl salts** are also used in the same way as for K.[143] $RbC_{12}H_4O_{12}N_7$ is weighed after drying at 70–274°C.

(f) **$Na_3Co(NO_2)_6$** is also employed similarly as for K (p. 409).[41] Dry the Cs ppt. at 110°C and weigh as Cs_3-$Co(NO_2)_6$, or at 219–494°C and weigh as $CoO{\cdot}3CsNO_3$. Ignite the Rb salt and finally weigh as RbCl. Cs can be detd. colorimetrically with nitroso-R salt or Griess reagent.[144]

$Na_3La(NO_2)_6$ is another reagent.[145] Treat the soln. with 50% reagent soln., filter on a glass crucible, wash with MeOH, dry and weigh as $Cs_2NaLa(NO_2)_6$. Alternatively, titrate the ppt. with Ce^{4+} soln. No interference arises from 25-fold amts. of Rb or 100-fold amts. of K.

(g) **Phosphotungstic acid** is utilized gravimetrically, titrimetrically[146] and nephelometrically. Add reagent to the acidic ($HClO_4$) soln. to ppt. $(Rb,Cs)_2HPO_4{\cdot}12WO_3{\cdot}xH_2O$. Dissolve in excess alkali and back-titrate with HCl using phenolphthalein and thymolphthalein indicator, or ignite at 800–850°C for at least 2 hr. and weigh as $(Rb,Cs)_4P_2O_7{\cdot}24WO_3$.

NOTES. (1) For nephelometry, treat 5 ml. soln. at 20°C with reagent, and measure after 2 hr. for Rb or 1 hr. for Cs. The errors are ±5% for 2–50 μg. Rb and ±10% for 0·3–20 μg. Cs.

(2) Na-silicomolybdate allows colorimetric detn. Treat the Cs ppt. (see under Separation, p. 403) with 3 ml. H_2O, 2 ml. HCl and 1 ml. 50% $SnCl_2$ and measure the blue color.[147]

(3) Silicotungstic acid also permits colorimetric detns.[148] For 0·5–4·5 mg. Cs in 5 ml. 6*N* HCl soln., add 1·00 ml. 5% reagent in 6*N* HCl, pass air for 2 min. and leave for 35 min.; pipet 5 ml. of supernate, adjust to pH 0·2 with 8 ml. 3*N* NaOH, add 8 ml. Ti^{3+} soln. (1 ml. 20% $TiCl_3$ and 1 ml. HCl heated and dild. to 100 ml. with H_2O, freshly prepd.), dil. to 25 ml. with H_2O and measure at 725 mμ. Interferences are Al, Cr^{6+}, Fe^{3+}, Mn^{7+}, 0·5 mg. Rb, 1 mg. Cu^{2+}, F^-, MoO_4^{2-}, NH_4^+, NO_3^- or NO_2^-, 5 mg. Ni, 7·5 mg. K, 10 mg. Co, 20 mg. PO_4^{3-} and 25 mg. BO_2^-, Br^-, AcO^-, Cl^-, I^-, Ca, Li, Mg, Na, Sr or SO_4^{2-}.

(h) **Iodometric titration** is possible by utilizing the different stabilities of triiodides.[149] Treat the chloride soln. with $H_2C_2O_4$, evap. to dryness, ignite, add HI, evap. and add I_2 just before the mass is dry. Evap. to dryness, add more I_2, cover and heat for 5–10 min. Ext. with CCl_4 and wash with 0·004*N* I_2 in CCl_4. Add a suitable amt. of CCl_4 and titrate the solid (Cs) and liquid (Rb) phases separately with $Na_2S_2O_3$ soln. after addn. of KI. For details the original should be consulted. K does not interfere.

References

1. HILLEBRAND and LUNDELL, 517 (646); SCOTT and FURMAN, 861; FRESENIUS–JANDER, **Ia**, 1 (1940); KIMURA, 273; SCHOELLER and POWELL, 42, 48.
2. SITTIG, M., *Sodium: its Manufacture, Properties and Uses*, Reinhold, New York (1956).
3. MEIER, D., *Über die Anreicherung, den Nachweis und die Bestimmung von Rubidium und Caesium*, Univ. Wagner, Innsbruck (1949).
4. DUPUIS, TH., *Bull. soc. chim., France*, 327 (1949).
5. BELCHER, R., *Ind. Chemist*, **22**, 731 (1946); **23**, 33, 205 (Na), 673 (1947); **24**, 213 (1948) (K); ROBINSON, J., *Chem. Age*, **66**, 447, 467, 507, 573 (1952); YAMAGATA, N., *Japan Analyst*, **4**, 401 (1955) (Rb and Cs).
6. JENTZSCH, D., and JACOB, G., *Chem. Tech.*, **7**, 93 (1955).
7. SPECTOR, J., *Anal. Chem.*, **27**, 1452 (1955).
8. PUNGER, E., *et al.*, *Mikrochim. Acta*, 1247 (1956).
9. FUKUSHIMA, S., *et al.*, *Mikrochim. Acta*, 35 (1957).
10. IKEDA, S., *J. Chem. Soc. Japan*, **78**, 913 (1957).
11. HORSTMAN, E. L., *Anal. Chem.*, **28**, 1417 (1956).
12. SUGAWARA, K., *et al.*, *Bull. Chem. Soc. Japan*, **29**, 679 (1956).
13. STEVENS, R. E., *Ind. Eng. Chem., Anal. Ed.*, **12**, 413 (1940).
14. PUKALL, W., *Sprechsaal*, **66**, 231 (1933); also GEILMANN, W. and GÄNSSLE, A., *Glastechn. Ber.*, **28**, 16 (1955).
15. ARCHIBALD, K., and MCLEOD, M. E., *Anal. Chem.*, **24**, 222 (1952).
16. ELVING, P. J., and CHAO, P. CH., *Anal. Chem.*, **21**, 507 (1949).
17. KOENIG, E. W., *Ind. Eng. Chem., Anal. Ed.*, **7**, 314 (1935).
18. MARVIN, G. G., and WOOLAVER, L. B., *Ind. Eng. Chem., Anal. Ed.*, **17**, 554 (1945).
19. SMITH, R. D., and CORBIN, P., *Ind. Eng. Chem., Anal. Ed.*, **4**, 137 (1932).
20. KODAMA, K., *Research Repts. Nagoya Munic. Ind. Research Inst.*, No. 12, 78 (1954).
21. FLETCHER, M. H., *Anal. Chem.*, **21**, 173 (1949).
22. HILLEBRAND and LUNDELL, 39 (43).
23. KALLMANN, S., *Ind. Eng. Chem., Anal. Ed.*, **16**, 712 (1944).
24. PENTHER, C. J., and POMPEO, D. J., *Anal. Chem.*, **21**, 178 (1949); OKA, M., *et al.*, *J. Chem. Soc. Japan, Ind. Chem. Sect.*, **56**, 58, 838 (1953).
25. WELCHER, **I**, 395.
26. WELCHER, **I**, 75, 100, 106, 358.
27. HAGIWARA, K., and KATO, T., *Analysis and Reagent (Japan)*, **2**, 179 (1948).
28. ISHIBASHI, M., and HARA, T., *Japan Analyst*, **2**, 76 (1953).
29. D'ANS, J., *Angew. Chem.*, **62**, 118 (1950).

30. WELLS, R. C., and STEVENS, R. E., *Ind. Eng. Chem., Anal. Ed.*, **6**, 439 (1934); see also HILLYER, J. C., *ibid.*, **9**, 236 (1937); HILLEBRAND and LUNDELL (659); SCHOELLER and POWELL, 50.
31. SATO, S., *J. Chem. Soc. Japan*, **72**, 182, 185, 249, 289, 350, 420 (1951).
32. O'LEARY, W. J., and PAPISH, J., *Ind. Eng. Chem., Anal. Ed.*, **6**, 107 (1934); SCOTT and FURMAN, 894.
33. KATO, T., *J. Chem. Soc. Japan*, **56**, 373, 399 (1935).
34. STRECKER, W., DIAZ, F. O., and FRESENIUS, H., *Z. anal. Chem.*, **67**, 321 (1925/26); **86**, 182 (1931); HILLEBRAND and LUNDELL, 529.
35. IIMORI, S., and YOSHIMURA, J., *Bull. Inst. Phys. Chem. Research (Tokyo)*, **5**, 73 (1926).
36. FEL'DMAN, R. V., *J. Applied Chem. (U.S.S.R.)*, **11**, 1017 (1938).
37. KATO, T., *J. Chem. Soc. Japan*, **56**, 399 (1935).
38. SANDELL, 416.
39. KATO, T., and HAGIWARA, Z., *Technol. Repts. Tohoku Univ.*, **14**, No. 2, 10, 14, 21 (1950).
40. ELDESTAD, R. B., and HORSTMAN, E. L., *Anal. Chem.*, **27**, 1229 (1955) (in silicate); SYKES, P. W., *Analyst*, **81**, 283 (1956).
41. FRESENIUS–JANDER, **Ia**, 3.
42. SHIGEMATSU, T., *et al.*, *J. Chem. Soc. Japan*, **73**, 378 (1952); GRÜTTNER, B., *Z. anal. Chem.*, **133**, 36 (1951).
43. SHIGEMATSU, T., and KIMURA, K., *J. Chem. Soc. Japan*, **73**, 443 (1952).
44. CALEY, E. R., and SIMMONS, JR., G. A., *Anal. Chem.*, **25**, 1386 (1953); also see HACKL, O., *Z. anal. Chem.*, **118**, 1 (1939/40).
45. NOZAKI, T., *J. Chem. Soc. Japan*, **76**, 445 (1955).
46. FORSTER, C. F., *Analayst*, **79**, 629 (1954).
47. GUTER, G. A., and HAMMOND, G. S., *J. Am. Chem. Soc.*, **78**, 5166 (1956).
48. WHITE, J. C., and GOLDBERG, G., *Anal. Chem.*, **27**, 1188 (1955).
49. THOMASON, P. F., *Anal. Chem.*, **28**, 1527 (1956); see also NIKOLAEV, A. N., and SOROKINA, A. A., *Doklady Akad. Nauk S.S.S.R.*, **77**, 427 (1951).
50. WHITE, C. E., *et al.*, *Anal. Chem.*, **23**, 478 (1951).
51. NAZARENKO, V. A., and FILATOVA, V. YA., *Zhur. Anal. Khim.*, **5**, 234 (1950).
52. PROČKE, O., and ŠLOUF, A., *Collection Czechoslov. Chem. Communs.*, **11**, 273 (1939); ROGERS, L. B., and CALEY, E. R., *Ind. Eng. Chem., Anal. Ed.*, **15**, 209 (1943); BACON, F. R., and STARKS, D. T., *ibid.*, **17**, 230 (1945).
53. WELCHER, **II**, 8 ff.
54. SHELL, H. R., *Anal. Chem.*, **22**, 575 (1950).
55. COLLINS, JR., T. T., *Chem. Eng. News*, **21**, 1219 (1943).
56. SCHWARZENBACH, G., *Die komplexometrische Titration*, p. 53 (1955); SEN, B., *Z. anal. Chem.*, **157**, 1 (1957).
57. WELCHER, **II**, 140.
58. WELCHER, **IV**, 415.
59. KOVALENKO, P. N., and TEN'KOVTSEV, V. V., *Ukrain. Khim. Zhur.*, **20**, 411 (1954).
60. PALLA CARREIRO, A. A., *Rev. port. farm.*, **4**, 1 (1954).
61. KATO, T., *et al.*, *Japan Analyst*, **4**, 106 (1955).
62. SHIGEMATSU, T., and KIMURA, K., *J. Chem. Soc. Japan*, **73**, 117, 120 (1952); also see TSYVINA, B. S., *Zavodskaya Lab.*, **15**, 139 (1949).
63. KRUPKIN, A. I., and LORINA, G. A., *Zhur. Anal. Khim.*, **11**, 30 (1956).
64. KATO, T., *J. Chem. Soc. Japan*, **56**, 400 (1935).
65. CALEY, E. R., and ROGERS, L. B., *Ind. Eng. Chem., Anal. Ed.*, **15**, 32 (1943).
66. LEVA, E., *J. Biol. Chem.*, **132**, 487 (1940).
67. BIFFEN, F. M., *Anal. Chem.*, **22**, 1014 (1950); INMAN, W. R., *et al.*, *ibid.*, **23**, 483 (1951); BAUSERMAN, H. M., and CERNEY, JR., R. R., *ibid.*, **25**, 1821 (1953); BRUMBAUGH, R. J., and FANUS, W. F., *ibid.*, **26**, 463 (1954).
68. WELCHER, **I**, 180.
69. DRANITSKAYA, M. M., *Trudy Odessk. Univ., Sbornik Khim. Fakulteta*, **3**, 89 (1953).
70. TALIPOV, SH. T., and SOFEĬKOVA, Z. T., *Trudy Sredneaziat. Gosudarst. Univ. (Tashkent)*, **33**, (4), 91 (1952).
71. TREADWELL, W. O., and KÖNIG, W., *Helv. Chim. Acta*, **16**, 1201 (1933).
72. LEWIN, A. B., *Z. anal. Chem.*, **104**, 406 (1936); KATO, T., and OKINAKA, Y., *Analysis and Reagent (Japan)*, **3**, 78 (1949).
73. CHESHAEV, K. S., *Zhur. Anal. Khim.*, **9**, 239 (1954).
74. WELCHER, **II**, 408.
75. HECHT and DONAU, 227.
76. SMITH, G. F., and SHEAD, A. C., *J. Am. Chem. Soc.*, **55**, 3957 (1933).
77. BULLOCK, B., and KIRK, P. L., *Ind. Eng. Chem., Anal. Ed.*, **7**, 178 (1935).
78. MATSUI, H., *J. Chem. Soc. Japan*, **64**, 645 (1943).
79. ADAMS, M. F., and ST. JOHN, J. L., *Ind. Eng. Chem., Anal. Ed.*, **17**, 435 (1945).
80. YOE, 359.
81. SANDELL, 499.
82. ECKEL, R. E., *J. Biol. Chem.*, **195**, 191 (1952).
83. KOHLER, M., *Z. anal. Chem.*, **138**, 9 (1953); RAFF, P., and BROTZ, W., *ibid.*, **133**, 241 (1951); FLASCHKA, H., *ibid.*, **136**, 99 (1952) (39–395 μg K).
84. MANASEVIT, H. M., *Anal. Chem.*, **27**, 81 (1955); GLOSS, G. H., *Chemist Analyst*, **42**, 50 (1953).
85. BERKHOUT, H. W., *Chem. Weekblad*, **48**, 909 (1952).
86. CLULEY, H. J., *Analyst*, **80**, 354 (1955).
87. ENGELBRECHT, R. M., and MCCOY, F. A., *Anal. Chem.*, **28**, 1772 (1956).
88. SPOREK, K., and WILLIAMS, A. F., *Analyst*, **80**, 347 (1955).
89. GEILMANN, W., and GEBAUHR, W., *Z. anal. Chem.*, **139**, 161 (1953).
90. SPIER, H. W., *Biochem. Z.*, **322**, 467 (1952).
91. FLASCHKA *et al.*, *Z. anal. Chem.*, **138**, 161, 241 (1953); FLASCHKA and ABDINE, H., *ibid.*, **144**, 415 (1955).
92. SCHMIDT, H. J., *Z. anal. Chem.*, **157**, 321 (1957).
93. RÜDORFF, W., and ZANNIER, H., *Z. anal. Chem.*, **137**, 1 (1952); *Angew. Chem.*, **66**, 638 (1954).
94. BERKHOUT and JONGEN, G. H., *Chemist Analyst*, **45**, 1 (1956).
95. FLASCHKA and SADEK, F., *Chemist Analyst*, **45**, 20 (1956).
96. SCHALL, E. D., *Anal. Chem.*, **29**, 1044 (1957).
97. JANDER, G., and ANKE, A., *Z. anal. Chem.*, **158**, 8 (1957).
98. PFLAUM, R. T., and HOWICK, L. C., *Anal. Chem.*, **28**, 1542 (1956).
99. ROBINSON, R. J., and PUTMAN, G. L., *Ind. Eng. Chem., Anal. Ed.*, **8**, 211 (1936); WELCHER, **II**, 408.
100. TINSLEY, J., *Analyst*, **73**, 86 (1948).
101. ROBINSON, and HOUSSCHILDT, J. D., *Ind. Eng. Chem., Anal. Ed.*, **12**, 676 (1940).
102. THRUN, W. E., *Ind. Eng. Chem., Anal. Ed.*, **5**, 79 (1933).

103. DUPUIS, T., *Compt. rend.*, **237**, 256 (1953); *Anal. Chim. Acta*, **9**, 493 (1953); FERRARI, A., *et al.*, *Gazz. chim. ital.*, **85**, 273 (1955).
104. KLEIN, B., and JACOBI, M., *Ind. Eng. Chem.*, *Anal. Ed.*, **12**, 687 (1940).
105. BROWN, D. S., *et al.*, *Ind. Eng. Chem.*, *Anal. Ed.*, **10**, 653 (1938).
106. ISMAIL, A. M., and HARWOOD, H. F., *Analyst*, **62**, 443 (1937).
107. KAYE, I. A., *Ind. Eng. Chem.*, *Anal. Ed.*, **12**, 310 (1940); also see MAJAROFF, K. L., and MATZKIEWITSCH, W. B., *Zavodskaya Lab.*, **3**, 705 (1934).
108. BOURDON, D., *Chim. anal.*, **31**, 154 (1949).
109. HUBBARD, R. S., *J. Biol. Chem.*, **100**, 557 (1933); ISHIBASHI, M., and KAGI, K., *J. Chem. Soc. Japan*, **63** 1414 (1942).
110. KAWE, A., *Z. anal. Chem.*, **115**, 385 (1938/39).
111. PENG. C., *Science* (*China*), **17**, 542 (1933).
112. TAKETATSU, T., *J. Chem.*, *Japan*, **78**, 640 (1957); SEN, B., *Z. anal. Chem.*, **157**, 2 (1957).
113. WELCHER, **II**, 403, 418.
114. WELCHER, **I**, 258.
115. WELCHER, **III**, 109, 567.
116. WELCHER, **II**, 502.
117. CHENERY, E. M., *Analyst*, **77**, 102 (1952); **80**, 569 (1955).
118. WELCHER, **III**, 318, 334
119. BAAR, S., *Analyst*, **78**, 353 (1953).
120. BEERSTECHER, JR., E., *Anal. Chem.*, **22**, 1200 (1950).
121. ISHIMORI, T., and TAKASHIMA, Y., *Bull. Chem. Soc. Japan*, **26**, 481 (1953).
122. ISHIBASHI, M., and KAGI, K., *J. Chem. Soc. Japan*, **59**, 954 (1938).
123. KORENMAN, I. M., *et al.*, *Primenenie Mechenykh. Atomov v. Anal. Khim.*, *Akad. Nauk. S.S.S.R.*, *Inst. Geokhim. i Anal. Khim. im. V. I. Vernadskogo*, 29 (1955); *Ref. Zhur. Khim.*, 10,074 (1956).
124. KLÜGEL, C., and RITTER, A., *Z. anal. Chem.*, **97**, 314 (1934); HASLAM, J., and BEELEY, J., *Analyst*, **65**, 185 (1940).
125. BAGBANLY, I. L., and SELIMKHANOV, I. P., *Trudy Komissii Anal. Khim.*, *Akad. Nauk S.S.S.R.*, *Otdel. Khim. Nauk*, **5**, No. 8, 167, 173 (1954).
126. ALEKSANDROV, G. P., and LYUTAYA, M. D., *Ukrain. Khim. Zhur.*, **21**, 518 (1955).
127. MEHLICK, A., *J. Assoc. Offic. Agr. Chemists*, **39**, 330 (1956).
128. TALLERT, H., *Z. anorg. u. allgem. Chem.*, **204**, 140 (1932).
129. WILLARD, H. H., and BOYLE, A. J., *Ind. Eng. Chem.*, *Anal. Ed.*, **13**, 137 (1941); also see JENTOFT, R. E., and ROBINSON, R. J., *Anal. Chem.*, **28**, 2011 (1956).
130. SATO, S., *J. Chem. Soc. Japan*, **72**, 182, 185, 450, 488, 492, 593 (1951); **73**, 2 (1952).
131. HECHT and DONAU, 230; WELCHER, **IV**, 10.
132. SANDBERG, B., *Svensk Kem. Tidskr.*, **58**, 197 (1946).
133. SANDELL, 501; WELCHER, **IV**, 14; FABER, R., and DIRKSE, I. P., *Anal. Chem.*, **25**, 808 (1953).
134. WELCHER, **IV**, 2, 19, 28, 525.
135. DE GRAAFF, C. L., and NOYONS, E. C., *Chem. Weekblad*, **43**, 300 (1947); PRESS, R. E., and MURRAY, K. A., *J. S. African Chem. Inst.*, **6**, 17 (1953) ($CuSO_4$, iodometry).
136. MANASEVIT, H. M., *Anal. Chem.*, **27**, 81 (1955); RYSS, I. G., and NILUS, E. L., *Zhur. Anal. Khim.*, **12**, 64 (1957).
137. BELCHER, R., and ROBINSON, J. W., *Mikrochim. Acta*, 49 (1954); *Anal. Chim. Acta*, **8**, 239 (1953).
138. WELCHER, **II**, 178.
139. TANANAEV, I. V., and KOZLOV, A. S., *Zhur. Anal. Khim.*, **6**, 149 (1951); KOZLOV, *Zavodskaya Lab.*, **22**, 157 (1957).
140. KURODA, K., *Chem. and Chem. Ind.* (*Japan*), **1**, 103 (1948).
141. PLYUSHCHEV, V. I., and KORSHUNOV, B. G., *Zhur. Anal. Khim.*, **10**, 119 (1955); FEL'DMAN, R. V., *Z. anal. Chem.*, **102**, 102 (1935).
142. ISHIBASHI, M., and HARA, T., *Japan Analyst*, **2**, 300 (1953).
143. WELCHER, **IV**, 10.
144. DUVAL, C., and DOAN, M., *Mikrochim. Acta*, 200 (1953).
145. DUTT, N. K., *J. Indian Chem. Soc.*, **22**, 71 (1946).
146. KATO, T., *J. Chem. Soc. Japan*, **56**, 407 (1935).
147. BURKSER, E. S., and FEL'DMAN, R. V., *Zavodskaya Lab.*, **7**, 166 (1938).
148. KROCHTA, W. G., and MELLON, M. G., *Anal. Chem.*, **29**, 1181 (1957).
149. YAMADERA, H., *J. Chem. Soc. Japan*, **72**, 559 (1951); **74**, 491 (1953).

55

SILICON

The principal references for this chapter are given in ref. 1. A comparative study of the precision and accuracy of various methods for chemical analysis of silicate rocks has been carried out.[2] Methods for analysis of silicates by colorimetry and EDTA titrations have been compared.[3, 4] The colorimetry of silica has been reviewed.[5]

It should be noted that silica is found in the residue from acid treatments, in the precipitates formed with NH_4OH (this is usually less than 1 mg., but may be more if zinc is present), and, if the latter precipitate is small, in the precipitates formed with $(NH_4)_2C_2O_4$ and $(NH_4)_2HPO_4$.

It is essential to avoid contamination from glassware and from reagents; alkalies are especially prone to silica contamination.

Silicomolybdic acid is formed only in slightly acidic solutions; once formed, however, it is stable even in $2N$ acid solution. It is of interest that the reduction of molybdic acid is inhibited by an acidity of $1N$ H_2SO_4; that of vanadomolybdic acid is prevented by $1{\cdot}25N$ H_2SO_4, and that of arseno- or phosphomolybdic acid by $1{\cdot}5N$ H_2SO_4.

Attack

(a) Silicates are best decomposed by fusion with a 5-fold amt. of Na_2CO_3. Then heat with 150–200 ml. H_2O (less may cause peptization), add a little EtOH if a green color appears, add HCl, etc. See also Chapter 2, Section 3 and under Determination (p. 417). Berzelius' method[6] is used if F or B is present. For an improved procedure,[7] see Table 56. Less then 0·3% F does not interfere; for up to 10% F, add 4·5 g. $AlCl_3{\cdot}6H_2O$; Zr or Ti does not prevent F interference.[8]

Heating with $CaCO_3$ and NH_4Cl as in the Lawrence Smith method for alkali metals, followed by evapn. with $HClO_4$ can be applied.[9]

(b) Minerals, etc. For W, Nb or Ta minerals, fuse with K_2CO_3. For minerals contg. S, treat with HNO_3 and HCl, or with Br_2 and CCl_4 followed by HNO_3. For 0·5 g. cement, heat on a sand-bath with 5·5 ml. Ac_2O and 4·5 ml. H_2O, add up to 5 ml. 1:1 HCl, warm, add 10 ml. H_2O and filter. Alternatively, mix with 0·5 g. NH_4Cl in a 50 ml. beaker, cover, add 5 ml. HCl, stir, heat on a steam-bath for 30 min., add 10 ml. warm H_2O and filter.

(c) Fluorides. Berzelius' method or fusion with B_2O_3 is usually applied. With CaF_2, heat 0·5 g. slowly with 15 ml. satd. H_3BO_3 soln. in 20% $HClO_4$, fume for 5 min., cool, heat to fumes with 2–3 ml. H_2O, cool, heat with 75 ml. H_2O, filter, etc.[10, 11]

For cryolite,[12] heat 1 g. with 6 g. borax and 14 g. $KHSO_4$ slowly and fume for 30 min. Add 100 ml. H_2O and 2 ml. HCl, evap. to a syrup and heat at 100–105°C while crushing the residue. Leave to cool, add a few drops HCl, heat for 2–3 min, add hot H_2O, heat, filter, etc.

(d) Steels, alloys, etc. For steels, warm with 5–10 ml. HCl and 5–10 ml. 1:3 HNO_3, or with 60 ml. 1:1 HNO_3; add 30–50 ml. $HClO_4$, evap. and fume for 15 min., and add hot H_2O (especially if much Cr is present). Alternatively, evap. to fumes with 20 ml. 50% H_2SO_4, add dil. HCl, etc.

For Fe–W, heat with 40 ml. 2:1 H_3PO_4–$HClO_4$, add 30 ml. $HClO_4$, heat and fume for 10 min.; this allows detn. of Si only. For detn. of Si and W, heat with 50 ml. HCl, add 10 ml. HNO_3 slowly, evap. almost to dryness and cool. Then add 30 ml. HCl and 20 ml. H_2O or 70 ml. 40% tartaric acid, heat, filter, ignite, etc. Alternatively, after dissoln. in HCl, evap. to fumes with 30 ml. H_2SO_4 and HNO_3, cool, add 5 ml. HCl and 100 ml. H_2O and heat. In either case, filter on paper, wash with 1:1 HCl and hot H_2O alternately 4 times and then wash 4 times with hot H_2O. Finally, ignite, etc.

In another method,[13] treat 0·5 g. 150-mesh Fe–W with 20 ml. 30% H_2O_2, 15 ml. H_2O and $H_2C_2O_4$ and heat gently; add 20 ml. $HClO_4$ and 10 ml. H_3PO_4 and heat again. Fume for 10 min., dil. to 100 ml. with H_2O, etc.

Heat-resistant alloys are decomposed similarly:[13] heat 1 g. with 30 ml. 30% H_2O_2, 5 ml. H_2O, 10 ml. HCl and 3 g. $H_2C_2O_4$, then add $HClO_4$, etc. as above. For Fe–Si–Mn,[13] heat 0·5 g. with 20 ml. 30% H_2O_2, 20 ml. HCl and 40 ml. H_2O, adding more H_2O_2 if necessary; then add $HClO_4$, etc.

Fe–Si can be decomposed by treatment with 1:10 Br_2–HBr, with $HClO_4$ as above, with 1:2 HCl, or by fusion with Na_2CO_3 and KNO_3.

TABLE 56. Analysis of Silicates Containing Fluorine

Fuse 0·5 g. 200 mesh sample with 1·0 g. ZnO and 5 g. Na_2CO_3 for 20 min. Ignite at 1050–1100°C for 20 min. and transfer to a 500 ml. stainless steel beaker. Dissolve in 200 ml. H_2O, add 20 ml. ZnO soln. (1·0 g. ZnO, 1·3 g. $(NH_4)_2CO_3$ and 2 ml. NH_4OH dild. to 25 ml.), boil for 8–10 min., filter after 5 min. on Whatman No. 40 paper and wash twice with hot H_2O. Wash the residue back into the beaker, add 60–70 ml. hot H_2O, heat, filter and wash 5 times with hot H_2O

- **Residue**: Ash at 650°C in a Pt dish, wash the steel beaker with 25 ml. H_2O contg. 4 ml. HCl, combine, add 20 ml. HCl, etc.
  - **Residue**: *SiO_2*
  - **Filtrate**: Add 3–5 ml. HNO_3 and 20 ml. $HClO_4$, evap. to fumes, cover, heat for 20 min., etc.
    - **Ppt.**: *SiO_2*
- **Filtrate**: Collect in a 500 ml. measuring flask and dil. to the mark
  - Pipet 25 ml. into 70 ml. H_2O, adjust to pH 1·3 with 1:1 HCl, add molybdate, eiconogen, etc. (see p. 418) *SiO_2*
  - Evap. the rest of the soln. to <75 ml., transfer to a distn. flask, add 150 mg. 300 mesh silica sand, glass beads, and 25 ml. $HClO_4$, heat to 123°C, and then steam-distil at 140°C at 5–7 ml./min. Collect ca. 500 ml. For large F amts., pipet 100 ml. and titrate. For small amts. add 3 NaOH pellets, evap. to 100 ml., add alizarin S and titrate with Th^{4+} soln. at pH 3·0–3·05 checked by a glass electrode *F*

Fe–W, Fe–Cr (C > 1%), Fe–V (Si > 5%), Fe–Ti, Si–Mn or Si–C are decomposed as follows. Mix 0·5 g. in an Fe crucible with 5 g. Na_2O_2, cover with Na_2O_2, heat slowly at first, then heat for 1·5 hr. in the semisolid state; finally raise the temp. slowly during 1·5 hr. Alternatively, fuse with KOH in a Ni crucible.

Fe–Mn, Mn, Fe–Cr (C < 1%), Fe–V (Si < 5%) and Fe–Mo can be decomposed by digestion with H_2SO_4 and dil. HNO_3.

For Al metal and light alloys, evap. to fumes with 35 ml. mixed acids (450 ml. H_2O, 150 ml. H_2SO_4, 300 ml. HCl and 100 ml. HNO_3), cool, add 10 ml. 1:3 H_2SO_4 and 100 ml. H_2O and heat; filter, fuse the residue with Na_2CO_3, treat with HCl, etc. Alternatively, place the sample in a Ni or Monel beaker, add 15 ml. 35% NaOH, evap. to 5 ml. and, when dark, add a few ml. 3% H_2O_2. Pour into a mixt. of 65 ml. 1:1 H_2SO_4 and 20 ml. $HClO_4$, evap. to fumes; or neutralize with HCl, add 20 ml. $HClO_4$, evap. to fumes, etc.

Separation

Acid treatment allows sepn. from many elements (see under Determination, below, and Chapter 2, Section 3). As little as 0·1 mg. can be sepd.[14] with $HClO_4$.

Sepn. from B is obtained with HCl and MeOH. Sepn. from large amts. of F^- is achieved with H_3BO_3 in HCl and H_2SO_4 or $HClO_4$, or by fusion with Na_2CO_3 as in Berzelius' method, or by fusion with Na_2CO_3 and borax. Fusion with B_2O_3 is satisfactory for sepn. small amts. of F^-.

Sepn. from W is possible by treatment with HF and H_2SO_4 followed by heating below 850°C, or by heating at 700°C in a stream of HCl gas. The latter method also allows sepn. from Sb, Nb, Ta, Sn, Ge, Mo, V. Evapn. with H_2SO_4 and H_3PO_4 gives sepn. from W; H_3PO_4 alone yields incomplete sepn.[15]

Si can be sepd. from Sb, Sn, Ge by evapn. with Br_2–HBr, H_2SO_4 or $HClO_4$. Evapn. with $HClO_4$, or evapn. with H_2SO_4 and extn. of the residue with NH_4OAc, yields sepn. from Pb.

Fusion with $K_2S_2O_7$, and extn. with $H_2C_2O_4$ or tartaric acid, seps. Si from Nb and Ta (see p. 373).

Electrolysis at the Hg-cathode yields sepn. from Fe, etc.

Extn. with cupferron in $CHCl_3$ allows sepn. from Sb, Bi, Fe, Mo, Nb, Ta, Sn, Ti, W, V, and partly from Cu.

For sepns. with ion exchange resins, see Chapter 13, Section 2.

Determination

The usual gravimetric method involves ignition and weighing of the residue from the acid treatment; this is reweighed after treatment with HF and H_2SO_4, and the difference represents SiO_2. Small amounts of Si are determined gravimetrically or titrimetrically after precipitation with an organic base molybdate. Colorimetry can be done with molybdate alone or by a molybdenum blue method.

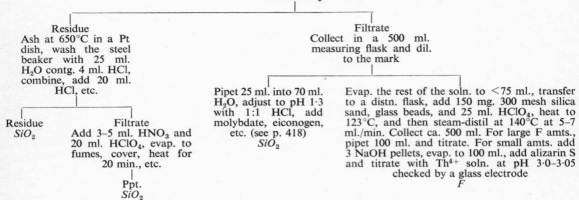

(a) Acid treatment, followed by gravimetry, forms the classical method.[1] Evap. the HCl soln. to dryness, heat for 1 hr. on a steam-bath, add 2 ml. HCl and 50 ml H_2O, filter on Whatman No. 41 paper and wash with hot 5:95 HCl and then with H_2O. Evap. to dryness, heat for 2 hr. as above, add 2 ml. HCl and 50 ml. cold H_2O, filter on Whatman No. 42 paper and wash with cold 5:95 HCl and H_2O. Combine the residues, ignite in a Pt crucible at 1200°C (> 358°C), and weigh. Add carefully a little H_2O, 5 ml. HF, 2 drops 1:1 H_2SO_4, then evap. to dryness, ignite and weigh. The difference corresponds to SiO_2.

NOTES. (1) The method has been applied to many steels, metals, alloys, etc.[16]

(2) About 1 mg. SiO_2 passes into the filtrate and can be recovered from the ppt. formed with NH_4OH (see Chapter 43, p. 320). Evapn. with H_2SO_4 or $HClO_4$ is better than HCl; HNO_3 is rarely used. If the residue is ignited too rapidly, some SiC may be formed and this is difficult to ignite completely. If Ti or Al is present, $H_2C_2O_4$ is preferable to H_2SO_4 in the treatment with HF.

(3) Shorter methods are possible. For example,[17] evap. the HCl soln. to dryness, heat for 1 hr. at 130°C, add 15 ml. AcOH, place on a steam-bath, add H_2O to give a vol. of 60–70 ml., heat at 70°C, stir and leave to cool; filter on Whatman No. 42 paper, etc.

Another procedure[18] involves the melt after fusion with Na_2CO_3. Treat with HCl or H_2SO_4 to give a 10% soln., heat at 60–70°C, add 2% gelatin (0·1 g./0·1 g. SiO_2) and filter after 5 min. Glycerol may also be added:[19] evap. with HCl almost to dryness, add 15 ml. glycerol, heat to boiling, heat at 150–170°C for 5 min., cool, add 2–3 ml. HCl and 30 ml. hot H_2O and filter. Fusion with $K_2S_2O_7$, removal of SO_3 by heating at 800°C for 3–4 min., cooling and treatment with 1:2 HCl or dil. H_2SO_4 is also satisfactory.[19]

(4) If B is present, some is found in the residue and is volatilized by the HF treatment. If W is present, heat the residue at 1200°C, weigh, heat with HF and H_2SO_4 below 850°C and reweigh; det. W in a separate sample. If the residue from the HF treatment exceeds 1 mg., presence of Nb, Ta, Ti, Zr, W, Ba, Sr, Ca, Sb, Bi, Sn, etc., is suspected.

(b) Molybdate methods are used for gravimetric, titrimetric and colorimetric detns. For classification, see Chapter 57, p. 428.

(*i*) Gravimetric methods. *A*. $(NH_4)_2MoO_4$ alone has not been used gravimetrically. Oxine and molybdate allow detn. of 0·5–10 mg. Si in 50 ml. slightly acidic soln.[20] Add 12·5 ml. 1:1 HCl, 50 ml. H_2O and 15 ml. 20% $(NH_4)_2MoO_4$, heat at 75 ± 3°C for 10 min. and cool. Then add 21·5 ml. 1:1 HCl and 25 ml. oxine soln. (14 g. in 20 ml. 1:1 HCl dild. to 1 l. with H_2O), heat at 65 ± 5°C for 10 min., cool and dil. to 250 ml. with H_2O. Filter on a glass crucible, wash with a soln. contg. 200 ml. oxine soln. and 50 ml. HCl/l., dry at 110–120°C, ignite at 500°C (593–813°C) for 1 hr. and weigh as $SiO_2 \cdot 12MoO_3$. Alternatively, dry at 140°C (160–200°C), cool in a vacuum desiccator and weigh as $(C_9H_7ON)_4H_4[Si(Mo_{12}O_{40})]$.

NOTES. (1) Interferences are P, V, Ge, As; F^- interference is prevented by addn. of 8 g. H_3BO_3/0·8 g. HF.

(2) Better results are obtained with a special wash soln.[21] Boil some ppt. with a mixt. of 12 ml. AcOH and 143 ml. HCl dild. to 1 l. with H_2O, under reflux for 10 min.; leave for at least 12 hr. and filter just before use.

B. 2,4-Dimethylquinoline and molybdate can be used for 2–4 mg. silicate.[22] Fuse with 25 mg. Na_2CO_3 in a 1 ml. Pt crucible, add H_2O, heat and cool; add 0·5 ml. 10% $(NH_4)_2MoO_4$ and 0·45 ml. 6·0*N* HCl, dil. to 12–13 ml. with H_2O, leave for 5 min., heat to 75°C for 3–4 min., add 1·55 ml. 6·0*N* HCl and 1·5 ml. base soln. (2 g. in 100 ml. 0·25*N* HCl), etc.

Quinoline,[23] 5,6-benzoquinaldine or 8-hydroxyquinaldine[24] may also be used.

C. Pyramidone is suitable for 0·3 mg. SiO_2 in 100 ml. soln.[25] Add 5 ml. 5% $(NH_4)_2MoO_4$ and 2·5 ml. 10*N* H_2SO_4, heat on a steam-bath for 5 min., cool and add 3 ml. 0·1*M* pyramidone. Filter on a glass crucible, wash with 0·1*N* HCl at 0°C, dry at 75–90°C and weigh as $(C_{13}H_{17}N_3O)_3H_8Si(Mo_2O_7)_6 \cdot 6H_2O$. It is reported that the tetrahydrate is formed on drying at 80–100°C.

D. Hexamine and molybdate are used[26] at pH 3; the ppt. is dried at 80–150°C and weighed as $(C_6H_{12}N_4)_4Si(Mo_{12}O_{38})$, or heated at 473–840°C and weighed as $SiO_2 \cdot 12MoO_3$. Antipyrine, urea, coniine and cobaltiammine can be applied but are less satisfactory.[26]

(*ii*) Titrimetric methods. *A*. Pptn. with $(NH_4)_2MoO_4$ can be followed by a neutralization or a redox titration.[27] For 3–30 mg. SiO_2 in 5 ml. soln., add H_2O, 0·5–2·0 ml. 50% $(NH_4)_2MoO_4$ in 1:3 NH_4OH, 1–5 ml. 13·4*N* HNO_3 (s.g. 1·379; 1 ml./0·5 ml. molybdate) and 5 g. NH_4NO_3; the total vol. should be 20 ml. Heat at 70°C for 1 hr., filter on a glass crucible and wash with 15% NH_4NO_3 contg. 0·02% HNO_3. Dissolve the ppt. in 0·1*N* NaOH and titrate with acid. Alternatively, evap. the titrated soln. to 10 ml., heat to fumes with 6–10 ml. H_2SO_4, add 50 ml. H_2O, reduce with Zn–Hg and titrate with 0·1*N* $KMnO_4$. In another method,[28] treat the ppt. with KI, ext. with iso-BuOH and titrate iodometrically.

B. Oxine can be used to ppt. silicomolybdate as above and a bromometric titration applied.[20] Ppt. as above but use only 10 ml. molybdate soln. Filter on dry double Whatman No. 42 paper. To a 100 ml. aliquot of filtrate, add 50 ml. 8% $H_2C_2O_4$, 100 ml. 1:1 HCl, 100 ml. H_2O, 50 ml. 20% KBr, some 0·1% methyl red, excess of 0·2*N* $KBrO_3$–KBr, and leave for 1–2 min.; add 5 ml. 10% KI and 5 ml. 0·5% starch and titrate with 0·1*N* $Na_2S_2O_3$.

After pptn. with hexamine at pH 3, the ppt. can be treated with dil. HCl and excess $NaHSO_3$ and titrated iodometrically.[26, 29]

Neutralization titrations can be used after pptn. with pyridine[30] or quinoline[31] and molybdate.

(*iii*) Colorimetric methods. *A*. $(NH_4)_2MoO_4$ alone can be used to det. 1–5 p.p.m. SiO_2 (in the final soln.).[32] Add 5 ml. 5% reagent and 2 ml. $HClO_4$, dil. to 75 ml. with H_2O, and, after 30 min., add 4 ml. 20% tartaric acid; dil. to 100 ml. with H_2O and measure at 332 mμ after 15 min.

NOTES. (1) PO_4^{3-} does not interfere. The method has been applied[16] to Cu, Al, Mg and their alloys. Simultaneous detn. of P is possible.[33]

(2) The optimum pH is 1·1–1·2. The color of the Si complex is virtually unaffected by tartaric acid, though it is

slightly affected by citric acid and greatly affected by $C_2O_4^{2-}$; tartaric acid completely prevents formation of the As complex and almost completely prevents formation of the P complex. For a method involving comparison of the yellow color (which can also be measured at 420 mμ) against picric acid, see ref. 10.

(3) In aq. soln. ionic or molecular silica reacts with the reagent but colloidal silica does not; the latter can be converted to a reactive form by boiling with alkali.[34]

(4) For extn. methods which allow successive detn. of P, As, Ge and Si, see Chapter 57, p. 430. For an ext. method,[35] in which As and P do not interfere and which is applicable to Ni, add 2 ml. 10% $(NH_4)_2MoO_4$ to 40 ml. of warm 0·05–0·3*N* HNO_3 sample soln. and heat at 50°C for 10 min.; add 5 ml. 7*N* HNO_3 and ext. with 10 ml. AmOH. Shake the org. phase with 10 ml. borax buffer (pH 11–11·5), sep. and measure the aq. phase at 340 mμ.

B. Reduction to molybdenum blue has been much more frequently applied. Many reductants have been examined.

(1) Eiconogen is suitable for < 0·25 mg. SiO_2 in 50 ml. neutral (to litmus) soln.[7, 36] Dil. to 94 ml. with H_2O, add 1 ml. molybdate (18·8 g. $(NH_4)_2MoO_4$ and 23 ml. H_2SO_4 dild. to 250 ml.), wait for 5 min., and add 4 ml. 10% tartaric acid and 1 ml. eiconogen soln. (0·2 g. in 25 ml. 8% anhyd. Na_2SO_3 mixed with 200 ml. 12·5% $NaHSO_3$ and dild. to 250 ml. with H_2O). Dil. to 100 ml. with H_2O (pH 1·6) and measure after 20 min. at 820 mμ (for traces) or at 660 mμ.

(2) $SnCl_2$ can be applied for 10–40 μg. Si in 10 ml. neutral soln.[37] Add 5 ml. 1*N* HCl, 5 ml. 8% $(NH_4)_2MoO_4$ and, after 10–15 min., 10 ml. HCl (s.g. 1·18); after a few min., add 2 ml. $SnCl_2$ soln. (1 g. in 2 ml. HCl (s.g. 1·18) dild. to 100 ml. with H_2O), dil. to 50 ml. with H_2O and measure at 650 mμ. Interference from 3 mg. Fe^{3+} is avoided by reduction with an Ag reductor; V, Mo, Cu, Ni are removed by extn. with diethyldithiocarbamate in $CHCl_3$. P interference is slight if $H_2C_2O_4$ is present.[38] SnC_2O_4 can be used as the reductant (see Chapter 57, p. 430).

(3) Metol is satisfactory for < 60 μg. Si in 20 ml. soln.[39] (see also Chapter 57, p. 431). For the reagent, shake 5 g. metol and 3 g. Na_2SO_3 with 240 ml. H_2O, filter, mix 100 ml. filtrate with 60 ml. 20% $H_2C_2O_4$, cool, add 120 ml. 1:4 H_2SO_4 and dil. to 300 ml. with H_2O. For a detn. treat the sample soln. with 3 ml. molybdate soln. (2 g. $(NH_4)_2MoO_4$ in 70 ml. H_2O contg. 6 ml. HCl, dild. to 100 ml. with H_2O and filtered); after 10 min. add 15 ml. reductant, dil. to 50 ml. with H_2O and measure at 812 mμ after 3 hr. Ge interferes; $NH_2OH{\cdot}HCl$ prevents Fe^{3+} interference, $C_2O_4^{2-}$ that of P or V, and BO_2^- that of F^-, while corrections are applied for Cl^-. Few other ions interfere. The color formed with metol is said to be most stable;[39] unstable colors are formed with $SnCl_2$; and hydroquinone, amidol and eiconogen are not entirely satisfactory.

(4) Na_2SO_3 has been used for < 125 μg. Si in 50 ml. neutral soln.[20, 21, 33] Add 25 ml. 1*N* HCl, 25 ml. 10% $(NH_4)_2MoO_4$ and, after 2 min., 5 ml. 17% Na_2SO_3; after 7 min. measure at 715 mμ. PO_4^{3-} does not interfere, nor does F^- if H_3BO_3 is added.

(5) $(NH_4)_2Fe(SO_4)_2$ is applicable for 8–260 μg. Si in 25 ml. soln.[40] Add 10 ml. 2·5% $(NH_4)_2MoO_4$, wait for 20 min., add 10 ml. 4% $H_2C_2O_4$ and 5 ml. Fe soln. (6 g. $(NH_4)_2Fe(SO_4)_2$ in 50 ml. H_2O contg. 1 ml. 5% H_2SO_4, dild. to 100 ml. with H_2O); measure at 610 or 810 mμ. P and As do not interfere.

(6) Hydroquinone allows detn. of 0·5–40 mg. Si in 200 ml. soln. contg. 15 ml. AcOH.[41] Add 20 ml. 13% $(NH_4)_2MoO_4$, after 20 min., add 20 ml. 10% $H_2C_2O_4$, and after 10 min., add 10 ml. reductant (0·75 g. hydroquinone and 10 g. Na_2SO_3 in 100 ml. H_2O). Heat for 30 min., dil. to 500 ml. with H_2O and compare.

(7) *p*-Hydroxyphenylglycine may be used for 1–10 μg. Si in 5 ml. neutral soln.[42] Add 4 ml. 2·5% $(NH_4)_2MoO_4$ in 0·1*N* H_2SO_4, after 10 min., add 30 ml. H_2O and 2 ml. 0·05% reductant in 2·5% Na_2SO_3, dil. to 50 ml. with H_2O and compare.

(8) Other reductants. Pyrrole can be used but the color fades.[43] For a procedure with ascorbic acid, see Chapter 28, p. 210. Reduction with KI can be followed by extn. of the I_2 formed with iso-BuOH and colorimetry.[28]

C. Formation of silicovanadomolybdate is possible.[44] For 0·05–0·7 mg. SiO_2 in 30 ml. soln. add 5 ml. 1% citric acid and 5 ml. 5% $(NH_4)_2MoO_4$ (contg. 3% v/v H_2SO_4); after 5 min., add 7 ml. 4% H_2SO_4, 2 ml. 1% $NaVO_3$ and 2 ml. 5% $Na_2S_2O_3$; after 15 min., add 35 ml. glycerol soln. (60 g. Na_2CO_3 in 600 ml. H_2O mixed with 100 ml. glycerol). Dil. to 100 ml. with H_2O, stopper and compare the blue color after 2 hr. No interference arises from 2 mg. PO_4^{3-}, 5 mg. As or from Fe, Al, Ca or Mg.

D. Cocaine and molybdate allow detn. of 0·3 μg. Si in 6 ml. soln. by simple addn. of 4 ml. reagent contg. 4·3 ml. 5% Na_2MoO_4, 4·3 ml. 2·5% cocaine-HCl and 11·4 ml. 96% AcOH.[45]

(c) HF-KCl treatment can be followed by alkali titration.[16, 46] Treat the soln. with HF, KCl and paper pulp, filter and wash with satd. KCl soln. at 0°C; titrate the ppt. with NaOH using phenolphthalein indicator.

(d) H_2TiF_6 and H_2O_2 are used colorimetrically for 2–14 mg. SiO_2 in soln.[47] Add 2 ml. 10*N* H_2SO_4 and 4 ml. reagent (1·04 g. Na_2TiF_6, 0·82 g. NaF and 0·55 ml. 30% H_2O_2 in 100 ml. H_2O, filtered); dil. to 20 ml. with 0·1*N* H_2SO_4 and measure at 420 mμ.

References

1. Hillebrand and Lundell, 536 (671); Scott and Furman, 794; Kimura, 293; Pigott, 419.
2. Schlecht, W. G., *Anal. Chem.*, **23**, 1568 (1951).
3. Fowler, R. M., *et al.*, *Anal. Chem.*, **24**, 196 (1952).
4. Corey, R. B., and Jackson, L., *Anal. Chem.*, **25**, 624 (1953).
5. Tarutani, T., *Japan Analyst*, **6**, 396 (1957).

6. Hoffman, J. I., and Lundell, G. E. F., *J. Research Natl. Bur. Standards*, **20**, 621 (1938).
7. Shell, H. R., and Craig, R. L., *Anal. Chem.*, **26**, 996 (1954).
8. Shell, *Anal. Chem.*, **27**, 2006 (1955).
9. Meier, F. W., and Stuckert, L., *Z. anal. Chem.*, **101**, 81 (1935).
10. Scott and Furman, 794 ff.
11. Lamure, J., *Chim. anal.*, **33**, 320 (1951).
12. Spielhaczek, H., *Z. anal. Chem.*, **119**, 4 (1940).
13. Kawamura, K., *Japan Analyst*, **2**, 418 (1953).
14. Potter, G. V., *Anal. Chem.*, **22**, 927 (1950).
15. Bogdachenko, A. G., *Zavodskaya Lab.*, **7**, 1425 (1938).
16. A.S.T.M., 94 ff.
17. Goto, H., *J. Chem. Soc. Japan*, **59**, 919 (1938).
18. Jenkins, M. H., and Webb, J. A. V., *Analyst*, **75**, 481 (1950).
19. Liteanu, C., *et al.*, *Acad. rep. populare Romîne, Studii cercetări chim.*, **3**, 55, 61 (1955).
20. McHard, J. C., *et al.*, *Anal. Chem.*, **20**, 325 (1948).
21. Brabson, J. B., *et al.*, *Anal. Chem.*, **20**, 504 (1948).
22. Miller, C. C., and Chalmers, R. A., *Analyst*, **78**, 24 (1953).
23. Armand, M. and Berthoux, J., *Anal. Chim. Acta*, **8**, 510 (1953).
24. Majumdar, A. K., and Banerjee, S., *Sci. and Culture (Calcutta)*, **19**, 265 (1953); *Anal. Chim. Acta*, **13**, 424 (1955).
25. Hecht and Donau, 244; Welcher, **III**, 115.
26. Duval, C., *Compt. rend.*, **218**, 119 (1944).
27. Kitajima, S., *Bull. Chem. Soc. Japan*, **10**, 341 (1935).
28. Veĭtsman, R. M., *Zavodskaya Lab.*, **23**, 153 (1957).
29. Duval, C., *Anal. Chim. Acta*, **1**, 33 (1947).
30. Welcher, **III**, 37.
31. Wilson, H. N. and Redman, H. N., *Analyst*, **74**, 243 (1949).
32. De Sesa, M. A., and Rogers, L. B., *Anal. Chem.*, **26**, 1278 (1954); Case, O. P., *Ind. Eng. Chem., Anal. Ed.*, **16**, 309 (1944) (400 mμ, Cu and its alloys); Narita, K., *J. Chem. Soc. Japan*, **77**, 270 (1956) (410 mμ, in steel).
33. Yoe, 369.
34. Iwasaki, I., *et al.*, *Bull. Chem. Soc. Japan*, **24**, 226 (1951); *J. Chem. Soc. Japan*, **74**, 857 (1953); **75**, 79 (1954); Okura, T., *ibid.*, 915, 918; *Japan Analyst*, **4**, 173, 175 (1955); Tarutani, T., *J. Chem. Soc. Japan*, **77**, 743, 1324 (1956); Chow, D. T. W., and Robinson, R. J., *Anal. Chem.*, **25**, 646 (1953).
35. Yokosuka, S., *Japan Analyst*, **5**, 282 (1956).
36. Boltz, D. F., and Mellon, M. G., *Anal. Chem.*, **19**, 873 (1947); Kenyon, O. A., and Bewick, H. A., *ibid.*, **25**, 145 (1953); Codell, M., *et al.*, *ibid.*, 1432; Codell and Norwitz, G., *Anal. Chim. Acta*, **16**, 327 (1957) (in Ti); Menis, O., and Manning, D. L., *ibid.*, 67 (in Th); Narita, K., *J. Chem Soc. Japan*, **78**, 1367 (1957) (in steel); Blasius, E. and Czekay, A., *Z. anal. Chem.*, **147**, 1 (1955).
37. Abbeg, S., *Anal. Chem.*, **20**, 633 (1948); Luke, C. L., *ibid.*, **25**, 148 (1953) (metals); also see Woods, J. T., and Mellon, M. G., *Ind. Eng. Chem., Anal. Ed.*, **13**, 760 (1941).
38. Jensen, K. J., and Rodden, C. J., *Natl. Nuclear Energy Ser., Div. VIII*, Vol. I, 221 (1950).
39. Mullin, J. B., and Riley, J. P., *Anal. Chim. Acta*, **12**, 162 (1955); *Analyst*, **80**, 73 (1955).
40. Andrew, T. R., and Gentry, C. H. R., *Analyst*, **81**, 339 (1956); Chalmers, R. A., *ibid.*, **78**, 32 (1953); Saunders, W. F., and Cramer, C. H., *Anal. Chem.*, **29**, 1139 (1957) (in steel, + NaF).
41. Gettler, A. O., and Umberger, C. J., *Am. J. Clin. Path., Tech. Sect.*, **9**, 1 (1945); also see Pavelka, F., and Morth, H., *Mikrochemie*, **16**, 239 (1935).
42. Welcher, **III**, 391.
43. Welcher, **III**, 573.
44. A. Němec, J. Laník and A. Koppová, *Z. anal. Chem.*, **83**, 428 (1931); *cf.* V. N. Galakhova, *Zhur. Anal. Khim.*, **12**, 499 (1957).
45. Welcher, **IV**, 237.
46. Vandall, C., and Jehenson, P., *Ind. chim. belge*, **20**, Spec. No., 435 (1955).
47. Fukamauchi, H., *et al.*, *Japan Analyst*, **6**, 229, 303 (1957).

56

TUNGSTEN

The main sources for this chapter are given in ref. 1. A monograph on the chemistry of tungsten is available.[2] Several detailed studies and reviews of the analytical chemistry of tungsten have been published.[3–6]

It should be noted that tungstic oxide is volatile above 850°C; it should always be heated in an electric furnace and not with gas.

Attack

(a) Ores, etc. Scheelite and hübnerite (ferberite) are best decomposed with HCl and HNO_3 (see p. 421).

With wolframite, fuse with an 8-fold amt. of Na_2CO_3, ext. with H_2O contg. a little EtOH and repeat the fusion and extn. Fe, Zr, Mn, etc. are found in the residue; W, Mo, V, As, P, Cr and partly Si, Al, Sb, Sn, Nb, Ta appear in the filtrate.

In another method, which is suitable for Chinese ores,[2] mix 1 g. wolframite in a Ni crucible with a 10-fold amt. of Na_2O_2, cover with Na_2O_2, heat slowly and swirl when fused; heat to dull redness for 5 min., cool and tap on an Fe plate to detach the fused mass. Transfer to a beaker, rinse the crucible with warm H_2O, acidify with HCl, add 20 ml. HCl and dil. to 250 ml. with H_2O. Boil for 5–6 min., add 10 ml. cinchonine soln. (see under Separation) and filter pulp, dil. to 500 ml. with H_2O, leave on a steam-bath for 4–6 hr., etc. Fusion with NaOH and Na_2O_2 is generally better for low-grade ores.[7] Fusion with $Na_2S_2O_7$ and extn. with hot 5% tartaric acid is also applicable to wolframite.

(b) Steels. Heat 2–5 g. with 50–75 ml. HCl, oxidize by heating with HNO_3, add cinchonine, etc. If little W is present, leave for 12 hr.; if much Mo is present, leave for 36 hr. Contamination with V can be minimized by oxidation of the HCl soln. with H_2O_2 at 70°C.

(c) Fe–W, W-metal, etc. For Fe–W, W-metal or W–C,[8] treat a 1 g. sample with 5 ml. HF and dropwise addn. of HNO_3. Warm, add 15 ml. $HClO_4$ or 1:1 H_2SO_4, evap. to fumes, cool, transfer to a beaker with H_2O and wipe with paper. Rinse with 1:1 NH_4OH, H_2O and 1:1 HCl and dil. to 150 ml. with H_2O. Add 10 ml. HCl, dil. to 450 ml. with H_2O, add 10 ml. cinchonine soln. (see under Separation), maintain at 10–15°C for 30–40 min. with occasional stirring, add 5 ml. 3% cupron in Me_2CO, stir for a few min., filter, etc.

In another method for Fe–W,[9] add satd. $H_2C_2O_4$ or citric acid, heat to 80°C and add 1·5 ml. 30% H_2O_2 for each 0·1 g. sample; after 30–35 min., evap. to dryness, add 100 ml. 1:4 HCl and 7–8 ml. cinchonine and complete as before.

(d) Tungsten bronze. Place 0·5 g. in a porcelain crucible, add 2 g. $(NH_4)_2SO_4$ and 2 ml. H_2SO_4, and evap. to fumes. Cool, transfer to a porcelain dish with H_2O, add 50 ml. HNO_3, heat on a steam-bath for 3–4 hr., cool and filter.

Separation

Cinchonine is applied for sepn. of W from many elements.[1, 8] A detailed procedure is given in Table 57; the reagent used contains 12·5 g. cinchonine/l. 1:1 HCl. Large amts. of group V elements interfere as do NH_4^+, P, Mo, As, V, F^- and org. compds.; SiO_2, Sn, Sb, Nb, Ta, Fe and Cr interfere to some extent. Further details are given on p. 422. The method has been applied to steels,[8] to Fe–W in conjunction with cupron[8] and to Co–W.[10] Mo and Fe retard the pptn. of W; if much of these metals is present, the ppt. must be allowed to stand for 30–40 hr. Corrections for impurities can be made (see Table 58).[8] If Ag is present, ext. with NH_4OH, ppt. Ag in the filtrate with $(NH_4)_2S$ and treat the residue and the filtrate in the usual way. Other methods for correction have been proposed.[7, 10]

Sepn. of small amts. of W from SiO_2 is possible as follows: treat with HCl, digest the residue with HF and H_2SO_4 and ignite at 700°C. Treat the filtrate with cinchonine, ignite the ppt. and combine with the first ignited residue. Fuse with Na_2CO_3, add HCl and cinchonine, leave for 12 hr. etc.

Sepn. from large amts. of SiO_2 is done by evapn. at 205°C with 5 ml. H_3PO_4, 80 ml. H_2SO_4 and 10 ml. $HClO_4$, or with $HClO_4$ alone, or with H_2SO_4 and H_3PO_4.

Heating of mixed oxides at 450°C in a stream of air and CCl_4 seps. W from SiO_2, Ta, Ti, Zr, Th, Al. Other gas mixts. which have been applied similarly are HCl + O_2, Cl_2 + S_2Cl_2, CCl_4 + O_2, $CHCl_3$ + air; HCl gas or

TABLE 57. Analysis of W Minerals

Use a 1 g. sample of <200 mesh in a 400 ml. beaker; stir with 5 ml. H_2O and 100 ml. HCl, heat at 60° for 1 hr., boil to 50 ml., add 40 ml. HCl and 15 ml. HNO_3, boil to 50 ml., add 5 ml. HNO_3, break up the cake, evap. to 10–15 ml., add 150 ml. hot H_2O and place on a steam-bath for 30 min. Add 5 ml. cinchonine soln. and filter pulp, heat for > 30 min. on a steam-bath, filter on Whatman No. 40 paper with filter pulp, decant 3 times and wash with a hot soln. contg. 25 ml. reagent and 30 ml. HCl/l., then with 1% HCl

- **Ppt.**
  Return to the beaker with <25 ml. H_2O, add 6 ml. NH_4OH, warm, and pass through the original paper; wash 10 times with warm 1% NH_4Cl in 1:9 NH_4OH
  - **Residue B**
    Ext. with 1:9 HCl, filter and wash with hot 0·5% HCl and the above NH_4Cl soln. alternately
    - **Residue D**
      Ash in a porcelain crucible at low temp., transfer to a Pt crucible, add HF and H_2SO_4, ignite, fuse with Na_2CO_3, add H_2O and filter
      - **Filtrate**
        Boil with HCl, add 5 ml. cinchonine, heat on a steam-bath and leave for 12 hr.
        - **Ppt.** (→ combined ppts.)
    - **Filtrate**
      Add HCl, HNO_3, reagent, etc.
      - **Ppt.** (→ combined ppts.)
  - **Filtrate**
    Boil to 10 ml., add 20 ml. HCl and 10 ml. HNO_3, evap. to 10–15 ml., add 150 ml. hot H_2O, some filter pulp and 10 ml. reagent; heat for >30 min. on a steam-bath, filter on paper and wash with the above reagent wash soln.
    - **Ppt.** (main WO_3) (→ combined ppts.)
    - **Filtrate C**
      Add reagent, etc.
      - **Ppt.** (→ combined with Ppt. from Filtrate A)
- **Filtrate A**
  Add reagent, etc.
  - **Ppt.**

Ppt. from Filtrate C and Ppt. from Filtrate A: Filter through the original paper, ext. with NH_4OH, add HCl and HNO_3, add reagent, etc.
- **Ppt.** (→ combined ppts.)

Combined ppts.: Heat very slowly in a Pt crucible to 700°, add HF and H_2SO_4, heat to 750–850° and weigh. The WO_3 may contain Mo, Ag, Fe, P, V, Nb, Ta which must be corrected for (see Table 58)

TABLE 58. Corrections for Impurities in WO_3

Fuse the WO_3 with 4 g. Na_2CO_3, add 100 ml. H_2O, filter and wash with 1% Na_2CO_3

- **Residue**
  Ignite, fuse with 1 g. Na_2CO_3, add 25 ml. H_2O, etc.
  - **Residue**
    Ignite and deduct correction
    Fe, Ti, Zr and part of Nb, Ta
  - **Filtrate** (→ combined with Filtrate below)
- **Filtrate**

Combined filtrates: Evap. to 100 ml.; if yellow, det. *Cr* colorimetrically. Divide into 3 parts
- Treat with KSCN and $SnCl_2$
  Mo
- Add 5 ml. excess H_3PO_4, and if Cr is present add an equal amt. to the standard
  V
- Acidify, add excess NH_4OH, boil, filter, wash and ignite
  Sn, Nb, Ta

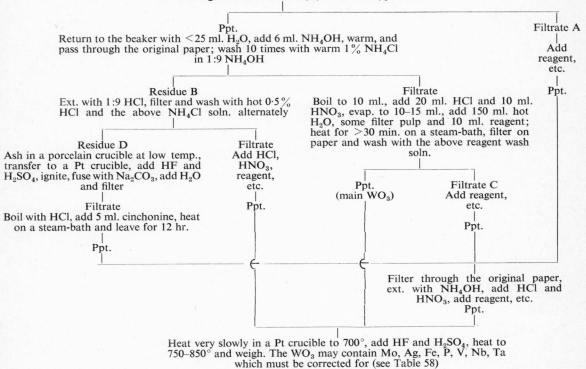

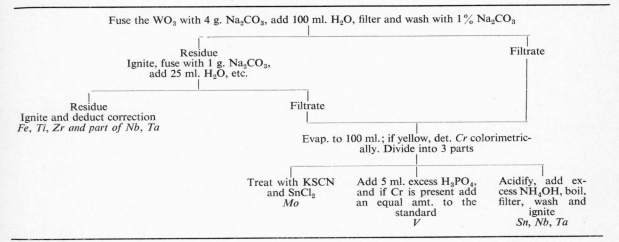

Cl_2 is also suitable. The volatilized W is collected in 15 ml. HNO_3 and 150 ml. H_2O. Fe is retained in the residue if heating is done at 400°C in presence of KCl. Sepn. of (volatile) Mo from W is done by heating in a HCl stream at 250–270°C. Heating at 300°C with 1 g. NH_4Cl and 1 g. NH_4Br allows sepn. from Fe. Sepn. from Sn is obtained by heating with a 15-fold amt. of NH_4I at 425–475°C, or by heating 3–4 times with NH_4Cl (see p. 206).

Sepn. of W from Mo, Sb, As, Sn is possible with H_2S. Add 6 g. tartaric acid/100 ml. soln., make alk. with NH_4OH, pass H_2S, acidify and pass more H_2S. Pptn. directly from acidic soln. is less satisfactory. If only traces of Mo are present, add some Sb^{5+} or Cu (see also Chapter 29, p. 213).

Treatment with $(NH_4)_2S$ allows sepn. from Ag, Fe, etc. Copptn. with Mn should be noted.

$SnCl_2$ allows sepn. from Mo. Treat 0·25 g. alkali salts in 60–300 ml. soln. with 20 ml. reagent (50 g./200 ml. HCl) for each 0·15 g. WO_3, boil for 5 min., filter on paper and wash with hot 1:20 HCl.

Sn and Sb can be sepd. from W by fusion of the oxides with a 12–15-fold amt. of KCN and leaching with H_2O. Sepn. from Sn can be done by fusion of mixed oxides in a porcelain crucible with $Na_2S_2O_3$, extn. with hot H_2O, diln. to 700 ml., addn. of up to 20 ml. 1*N* acid, or of NH_4NO_3 and boiling. Alternatively, the oxides are ignited with a 2-fold amt. of Zn for 15 min., cooled and dil. HCl is added; after addn. of $KClO_3$ and 1·5 vols. H_2O, the ppt. is filtered after 12 hr.

Sepn. of W from Sn is also possible by electrolysis of the soln. contg. Na_2S and NaOH at 50–60°C for 4 hr. with 0·5–1·7 amp. and 1·7–2·3 v.

A silica gel column is also suitable.[11] Treat the alk. (NaOH) soln. with 10 ml. 0·1*M* EDTA, neutralize to methyl red with H_2SO_4, dil. to 200 ml. with H_2O, make 0·2*M* in $(NH_4)_2SO_4$, adjust to pH 9 with NH_4OH and pass through the column (1–1·4 cm. × 10–15 cm.) at a rate of 5 ml./min. Elute W with 200 ml. H_2O, add 6 ml. HCl and elute Sn with 70 ml. H_2O.

$MgSO_4$ allows sepn. of W from P and As. Treat 100 ml. soln. contg. 15 ml. NH_4OH and some $(NH_4)_2$-tartrate with 2 g. $MgSO_4$ in 10 ml. H_2O at 0°C; add 4–5 glass beads, shake mechanically for 10 min. and store at 0°C for 12 hr. If As is present, do not wash the ppt.; repptn. is essential. Large amts. of Na interfere; Fe^{3+} requires SO_2 addn. Sepn. of 0·2 g. WO_3 from 0·2 g. P_2O_5 is possible as follows.[4] Treat the acidic (HCl) soln. with 25 ml. 20% NH_4Cl, neutralize to methyl orange with 6*N* NH_4OH, add 5 ml. in excess and dil. to 200 ml. with H_2O. Boil, add magnesia mixt. at a rate of 80–100 drops/min., to give a 10 ml. excess, add 5 ml. NH_4OH, leave for 12 hr. and reppt.

Treatment with tannin and cinchonine gives a sepn. from P (see under Determination, below); P cannot be detd. in the filtrate.

The best method of sepn. of W from As involves evapn. of the HCl-contg. soln. with SO_2 or HBr.[4]

Incomplete sepn. of W from Mo is obtained by extg. the freshly pptd. oxides with dil. H_2SO_4.

Extn. of the freshly pptd. oxides with dil. NH_4OH allows sepn. of W from small amts. of Sn, Nb, Ta. Even 0·2 mg. W can be sepd. from 10 g. Fe, Ti, etc. by adding the nearly neutral sample soln. to boiling 20% NaOH dropwise, then boiling for 30 min., adding H_2O, filtering and repptg.

Sepn. of W from Zr, Th, rare earths, Fe and Be is achieved by fusion with Na_2CO_3, extn. with H_2O, addn. of filter pulp and filtration;[12] sepn. of Sn, Nb and Ta is incomplete. Fusion with Na_2CO_3 and extn. with concd. NaOH soln., etc. allows sepn. from Ti (see p. 361). Fusion with K_2CO_3 and addn. of magnesia mixt. or NaCl gives a sepn. from Nb and Ta (see p. 374).

Addn. of HCl to the tartaric acid soln. followed by the pyrosulfate method with tannin and cinchonine allows sepn. from V (see Chapter 51, p. 378).

Treatment of the dil. H_2SO_4 soln. contg. HF with cupferron allows sepn. of W from Nb, Ta, Zr, Ti, etc.

Extn. with dithiol in AmOAc from 3·7*N* HCl soln. contg. NH_2OH allows sepn. from Mo (see under Determination, p. 424).

W is sepd. from U by extn. of the HNO_3 soln. with Et_2O (see p. 298). Many elements can be sepd. from W by the following extn. Treat the HCl soln. with $SnCl_2$ and KSCN and ext. with Et_2O. Evap. the org. phase to 5–10 ml., add HCl, blow air through to remove Et_2O, add 30% H_2O_2 and H_2SO_4, etc. Extn. of a dil. H_2SO_4 soln. contg. thioglycolic acid with BuOAc seps. Mo from W which appears in the aq. phase.

Various concn. methods are applicable. Boiling with Fe^{3+} and NH_4OH or with Al^{3+} and $NaHCO_3$ is satisfactory. Treatment with Sb^{5+} and rhodamine B can also be used. The best method for carbon steels[8] involves cupron and Mo: warm a 5 g. sample contg. <0·2% W with 75 ml. 1:6 H_2SO_4 and add 1:1 HNO_3 until the oxidation of Fe and carbide is complete. Add 5 mg. Mo in soln., dil. to 150 ml. with H_2O, cool to 5°C, add cupron, etc. Ignite below 525°C, add NH_4OH and filter; ignite the residue and deduct a correction. Det. W with cinchonine, or det. Mo with H_2S or colorimetrically and calc. W.

Determination

Several org. bases have been proposed for gravimetric detn. but cinchonine is commonly used. Redox titrations are convenient because PO_4^{3-} does not interfere. The best colorimetric methods are those with thiocyanate or dithiol.

(a) Cinchonine has been used gravimetrically[1, 7, 8, 10] and also titrimetrically. The method of pptn. has been described on p. 420; the ppt. is weighed as WO_3 after ignition at 750–850°C (>1014°C).

NOTES. (1) Traces of W appear in the filtrate, especially if large amts. of group V elements are present; this can be prevented by addn. of tannin. Sepn. from PO_4^{3-} is also possible.[4, 7, 12, 13] For < 0·2 g. WO_3 in 100 ml. alk. soln., add 50 ml. 20% NH_4Cl, dil. to 200 ml. with H_2O, heat to 50°C and add 0·5–2 g. tannin in a few ml. of H_2O; acidify to litmus with 1:1 HCl, add 5 ml. HCl in excess followed by filter pulp and 5 ml. 5% cinchonine in 1:3 HCl dropwise. After 12 hr. filter on Whatman No. 41 paper, wash with 5% NH_4Cl contg. 0·5 g. tannin, ignite at 550–835°C and weigh as WO_3. If WO_3 exceeds 0·2 g., evap. the sample soln. to 30–40 ml., add an equal vol. of HCl, boil until the ppt. turns yellow, dil. to 300 ml. with hot H_2O, add 0·5 g. tannin and continue as above, filtering through Whatman No. 40 paper with filter pulp.

(2) The best results are said to be obtained[14] with cinchonine, antipyrine and tannin.

(3) For a titrimetric finish for small amts. of the cinchonine ppt.,[15] filter on paper and wash with cinchonine soln. and then with 2% KNO_3; suspend the ppt. in 10 ml. H_2O, dissolve in excess 0·02*N* NaOH, add phenolphthalein and titrate with 0·02*N* HCl.

Numerous org. bases have been suggested to replace cinchonine. Tannin used with antipyrine is suitable for <0·15 g. WO_3 in 150–250 ml. slightly alk. (NH_4OH) soln.[4, 7, 12, 16] Add a few ml. H_2SO_4 and 5–8 g. $(NH_4)_2SO_4$/100 ml. soln., boil, add a 3–4-fold excess of 10% tannin and boil gently for 5–10 min.; add 10–15 ml. 10% antipyrine after cooling; filter on paper and wash with a soln. contg. 5 ml. H_2SO_4, 50 g. $(NH_4)_2SO_4$ and 2 g. antipyrine/l. Ignite above 987°C and weigh as WO_3. The method may not always be satisfactory.[4]

Brucine can also be applied.[17] To 300 ml. 0·6*N* HCl soln., add 5 ml. 10% brucine in 3*N* HCl, place on a steam-bath for 20 min., leave to cool for 4 hr., filter on paper and wash with a 1:1:100 mixt. of reagent soln., HCl and H_2O. Add NH_4OH, evap., add 20 ml. HNO_3, evap. to dryness, add 35 ml. 2·5*N* HCl, place on a steam-bath for 20 min., dil. to 200 ml. with H_2O, add reagent, etc.; finally ignite above 818°C and weigh as WO_3.

Benzidine is suitable for 0·2 g. W in 200 ml. neutral soln.[18] Add 10 ml. 0·1*N* H_2SO_4, boil, add 15 ml. 2% benzidine in 1% HCl, leave to cool, filter on paper and wash with a 1:30 mixt. of reagent and H_2O; ignite and weigh as WO_3, or titrate with 0·1*N* NaOH using phenolphthalein indicator, or det. the ppt. colorimetrically by diazotization and coupling with phenol. P and As do not interfere, but large amts. of Fe do interfere.

Various benzidine derivs. have been studied for W detn. 1-Amino-4-(*p*-aminophenyl)-naphthalene is said to be best because Mo does not interfere;[19] pptn. is done with 1% reagent in 0·7*N* HCl from a 0·7*N* HCl medium. For other derivs., see ref. 20. Reduction with $SnCl_2$ can precede pptn.[21] *o*-Dianisidine has also been suggested.[22]

Other org. reagents which may be used are totaquine,[23] phenylhydrazine-HCl,[24] rhodamine B,[25] tetrabase,[25] *o*-tolidine,[24] quinine,[25] α-naphthylamine,[24] cumidine,[24] tetramethyl-4,4′-diamidobenzophenone,[24] β-naphthoquinoline,[26] dianisalacetoneoxime,[26] cinnamalanisalacetone oxime,[26] *anti*-1,5-di-(*p*-methoxyphenyl)-5-hydroxamino-3-oximino-1-pentene,[27] nitron,[26] cupron,[26] nemadine,[28] worcine,[29] pyramidone,[30] 6- or 8-toluquinaldine,[31] rivanol,[32] 4,4′-diaminotriphenylmethane.[33] With cupron[26] pptn. is complete almost immediately but Mo interferes (see Chapter 29, p. 216).

Rhodamine B can be applied colorimetrically for 0·23 μg. W/ml. soln.[34] Add 5 ml. 1*N* NaCl, dil. to 30 ml. with H_2O, add 5 ml. 0·1*N* HCl and 5 ml. 0·1% reagent and dil. to 50 ml. with H_2O; measure the decrease in fluorescence after 60 min. Interferences are Fe, Al, Tl, V, Hg, Mo, As, Cr^{6+}, F^-, PO_4^{3-}, $C_2O_4^{2-}$.

Methyl violet also allows a colorimetric detn.[35] Make the soln. neutral to phenolphthalein, add 0·5 ml. 0·5*N* HCl, wait for 10 min., add 1·2 ml. 0·01% reagent, shake, dil. to 5 ml. with H_2O and compare. The method is suitable for 1–36 μg. W/ml. of final soln.

(b) Reduction with Pb–Hg can be followed[36] by titration with 0·1*N* $K_2Cr_2O_7$. For a soln. contg. 30–160 mg. W, evap. to the appearance of crystals, add a few drops of H_2O and 75 ml. hot HCl, boil for 2 min. and cool to 70–80°C. Transfer to the reductor with HCl, pass CO_2 for a few min., add Pb-Hg (40 g. Pb in 100 g. Hg) and shake for at least 15 min. until the deep yellow W^{3+} color appears. Sep. the amalgam; add excess of Fe^{3+} (10% Fe-alum in 2·5% H_3PO_4), 70 ml. H_2O, 40 ml. H_3PO_4 and 8 drops Ba-diphenylamine sulfonate indicator, while passing CO_2. Then titrate rapidly until the green color starts to fade and titrate slowly to violet.

NOTES. (1) Interferences are Mo, V, Fe, etc. The method is not recommended for detn. of W in mixts.[37]

(2) For 3–10 mg. W, 50 ml. HCl and 0·05*N* titrant should be used.

(3) Various other reductants can replace Pb–Hg. With Zn–Hg, reduction can be followed by titration with $KMnO_4$, with Ce^{4+} using diphenylamine indicator, or with Fe^{3+} using 0·5% cacotheline indicator.[38] Treat 50 ml. soln. contg. 50 mg. W, 10 ml. 3*N* H_3PO_4, 10 ml. 6*N* H_2SO_4 and 10 ml. HCl, with 15 ml. of nearly satd. Zn–Hg. Pass CO_2 and shake for 7–8 min. until blackish green. Sep. the amalgam, and titrate. The optimum concn. for reduction is 1·8–2·6*N* HCl and 1·3–2·6*N* H_2SO_4.

If HCl solns. are used under CO_2, Bi–Hg gives reduction to W^{5+} and Pb–Hg or Cd–Hg to W^{3+}; titration with $KMnO_4$ soln. follows addn. of H_2SO_4 and $MnSO_4$.[39] Pb–Hg reduction can be used with $CuSO_4$ titration.[39] Reduction to W^{4+} with Cd–Hg in 4–6*N* HCl soln. allows final titration with Fe^{3+} soln. using KSCN indicator.[39]

(c) $SnCl_2$ and KSCN are suitable for colorimetry of 0·1–1·5 mg. W in 15 ml. soln.[40, 41] Add 10 ml. H_2SO_4, cool, add 20 ml. HCl and 5 ml. 2*M* $SnCl_2$ (112·9 g. in 250 ml. HCl), place in boiling H_2O for 5 min. and then in running H_2O at 10–15°C for 3 min. Add 10 ml. KSCN (20 g. in 80 ml. H_2O) soln., dil. to 100 ml. with H_2O and measure the yellow color at 400 mμ after 15 min.

NOTES. (1) No interference arises from Fe, Ag, Nb, Ta, Mo, PO_4^{3-}, F^-, Cl^- or tartrate. Interferences are Hg, Au, Pt, Cr, Ni, Co, As, V and > 10 mg. Ti.

(2) Reduction with Sn–Hg[42] or with $TiCl_3$ [43] is also applicable. Extn. with cyclohexanone gives 99·2% recoveries; other org. solvents are less satisfactory.[44]

(3) Heating the soln. is unnecessary if the acidity exceeds 10*M* and the Cl^- concn. exceeds 8*M*. Several variations are possible.[45] Evap. the soln. with H_2SO_4 to 0·5 ml., add 2 ml. 10% $SnCl_2$ in HCl (or 2 ml. HCl and 0·1 ml. Hg) and, after 30 min., add 15 ml. 1·0*M* NH_4SCN in Me_2CO; dil. to 25 ml. with H_2O and measure at 398 mμ after 15 min. (ϵ = 17 600). Alternatively, after 30 min., add 5 ml. 3·0*M* NH_4SCN, ext. with 10 ml. Et_2O, repeat this process, dil. to 25 ml. with Et_2O and measure at 405 mμ (ϵ = 18 300). Alternatively, add 5 ml. 3·0*M* NH_4SCN, dil. to 25 ml. with H_2O and measure at 398 mμ (ϵ = 13 800); In these methods, Mo does not interfere; in the last method Ti, Nb, Co and V do not interfere.

For < 2 mg. W in soln.[46] add 10 ml. H_2SO_4 and 2 ml. H_3PO_4, evap. and fume for 2–5 min.; add 8–10 ml. H_2O, cool, add 20 ml. HCl and 2–3 g. $SnCl_2$; after 5–10 min., add 15 ml. 6·6% KSCN, cool, dil. to 90 ml. with H_2O, cool, dil. to 100 ml. with H_2O, etc.

(d) Dithiol allows a colorimetric detn. of W in the aq. phase (20 ml.) after detn. of Mo.[47] Add 20 ml. HCl and 0·2 g. Ti sponge, warm until the soln. is purple, add 10 ml. 0·5% w/v dithiol in AmOAc and heat at 80–90°C for 20 min. with occasional shaking. Cool, transfer to a separatory funnel, discard the aq. phase and dil. to 20 ml. with AmOAc; wash twice with 15 ml. 4:1 HCl, pass through Whatman No. 41 paper, wash once or twice with 1–2 ml. AmOAc, dil. to 25 ml. with AmOAc and measure the grey-blue color at 600 mμ. The method is suitable for 0·01–0·20 mg. W in the final soln.

(e) Oxine can be used gravimetrically or titrimetrically for 5–40 mg. W in weakly alk. or neutral soln.[48] Heat to 40–60°C, add excess 4% reagent in EtOH, boil, adjust to pH 3·3–3·5 with AcOH and boil; filter on a G4 crucible, wash with warm H_2O, dry at 120°C and weigh as $WO_2(C_9H_6ON)_2$; ignite above 674°C and weigh as WO_3.

NOTES. (1) No interference is caused by group IV and V elements or by PO_4^{3-}. If Sn is present, add 5 g. $H_2C_2O_4$ and 5 g. NH_4OAc to 150–200 ml. soln., neutralize to methyl orange with NH_4OH, heat to 60–70°C, add 2 ml. oxine soln. (20 g. in 50 ml. AcOH) and heat for 1–2 hr. on a steam-bath. Filter on paper and wash with a mixt. of 5 g. $(NH_4)_2C_2O_4$, 5 g. NH_4OAc and 1 ml. reagent in 300 ml. cold H_2O. Finally add $H_2C_2O_4$ and ignite to WO_3. If EDTA is added, the only interferences are Mo, U and partly Ti.[49]

(2) For a titrimetric finish, dissolve the ppt. in hot 4*N* NaOH, add 10–20 ml. 15% $H_2C_2O_4$, HCl, $KBrO_3$ soln. etc.[49]

(f) TlOAc allows a gravimetric detn. as Tl_2WO_4; the procedure is the same as that for Mo (see p. 216).

Several other inorg. reagents may also be applied. With $Pb(NO_3)_2$, adjust the soln. to pH 6·0–6·5 with 1*N* AcOH, add reagent, dry above 100°C and weigh.[50] Titration with $Pb(NO_3)_2$ is possible with a potentiometric[50] or a visual (adsorption indicator, see Table 10) end-point.

Pptn. with satd. $Hg(NO_3)_2$ can be followed[51] by ignition below 800°C and weighing as WO_3. $Hg_2(NO_3)_2$ has also been utilized.[52]

$BaCl_2$ is suitable for 0·2 g. WO_3 in 250 ml. neutral soln.[53] Boil, add 0·316 g. reagent in 10 ml. H_2O, allow to cool, filter on a porcelain crucible, wash with H_2O, ignite at 750°C (>1011°C) and weigh as $BaWO_4$. Pptn. can also be done from alk. soln.

$CaCl_2$ allows a titrimetric procedure.[54] To 200 ml. soln. at pH 8–9, add 20–25 ml. satd. $CaCl_2$, filter after several min. and wash with hot H_2O; dissolve the ppt. by heating with 20–25 ml. 1:1 HCl, filter, wash, adjust to pH 12–13 with NH_4OH, add murexide indicator and titrate with EDTA soln.

$CuSO_4$ provides a colorimetric procedure for 0·028–0·28 mg. W/ml. of neutral soln.[55] Add 2 ml. 0·1*N* $CuSO_4$, dil. to 10 ml. with H_2O, heat at 75°C for 30 min., cool to 10°C, filter and wash with 80% EtOH; dissolve the ppt. in 10 ml. 28% HCl and compare.

Chloropurpureocobaltic salts allow[56] pptn. and weighing of $[CoCl(NH_3)_5]_2O{\cdot}2{\cdot}4\,WO_3$.

(g) Vanadophosphoric acid can be utilized colorimetrically for 10–120 p.p.m. W in soln.[57] For the reagent, dissolve 0·8 g. $NaVO_3$ in 50 ml. dil. NaOH, neutralize with HCl, dil. to 80 ml. with H_2O, add 20 ml. 85% H_3PO_4, cool and dil. to 100 ml. with H_2O. For a detn. add 2·5 ml. reagent, dil. to 50 ml. with H_2O and measure at 360–460 mμ (ϵ = 621). Interferences are Bi, Pb, Th, Zr, Fe, Cr^{6+}, Mn^{7+}, $S_2O_3^{2-}$, oxidants, $C_2O_4^{2-}$, citrate, AsO_4^{3-}, GeO_3^{2-}.

(h) Miscellaneous colorimetric methods. Cochineal provides a fluorimetric method for 2–50 μg. W in neutral soln.[58] Add 2·0 ml. 0·2*M* AcOH–NaOAc (1:1), dil. to 5 ml. with H_2O, add 1·5 ml. satd. cochineal in EtOH, dil. to 10 ml. with H_2O, and measure the red fluorescence under UV light.

Hydroquinone is suitable for 50–150 μg. W in 2 ml. H_2SO_4 soln.[41, 59] Add 3·0 ml. reagent (10 g. hydroquinone in 100 ml. H_2SO_4, filtered on a glass crucible; the reagent is stable for 2 days); dil. to 10 ml. with H_2SO_4 and measure the red color at 478 mμ. Interferences are Cl^- and NO_3^-, 5-fold amts. of Mo, Ti, Fe, V, Ru, As, Ce^{3+}, Ni, Cr, 10-fold amts. of Cu, Sn, Mn^{7+} and 30-fold amts. of Mn^{2+}, Hg, Zn, Co.

$TiCl_3$ can be applied as follows.[60] To 40 ml. of slightly acidic soln. add 5 ml. reagent (1 ml. ≡ 2 mg. Fe), dil. to 50 ml. with H_2O and compare.

Ti^{3+} and malachite green can serve in a catalytic method for analysis of steels.[61] For a 1 g. sample contg. 0·3–0·7% W, digest with 1:9 H_2SO_4 and 0·5–1 ml. 1:1 HNO_3; add 50 ml. H_2O, adjust to pH 3·0–3·4 with NH_4OH, dil. to 100 ml. with H_2O, cool to 15°C and add 1 ml. $CuSO_4$ soln. (1 mg./ml.), 3 ml. 20% $Na_2S_2O_3$, 1 ml. 0·05% malachite green and Ti^{3+} soln. (9·3 mg./ml.). Measure the time interval until decolorization is complete. 0·1 mg. Mo or V interferes but 7 mg. Cr, 10 mg. Mn, 40 mg. Ni or Co and 50 mg. P do not interfere.

$K_4Fe(CN)_6$ provides a colorimetric method for 10–250 mg. WO_4^{2-} in soln.[62] Add 6 g. reagent and 1·5 g. $H_2C_2O_4$, dil. to 100 ml. with H_2O and measure at 480 mμ after 90 min. Interferences are MoO_4^{2-}, CrO_4^{2-}, PO_4^{3-}, AsO_4^{3-} and SiO_3^{2-}. At 377 mμ, 0·5–0·9 mg. W can be measured.[63]

References

1. HILLEBRAND and LUNDELL, 547 (683); SCOTT and FURMAN, 1001; KIMURA, 355; SCHOELLER and POWELL, 277; PIGOTT, 499.
2. LI, K. C., and WANG, C. Y., *Tungsten*, 3rd ed., Reinhold, New York (1955).
3. SCHOELLER, W. R., *Analysis of Tungsten Ores, Sands, Clays and Minerals*, **2**, 67 (1934).
4. LAMBIE, D. A., *Analyst*, **68**, 74 (1943); **70**, 124 (1945); **74**, 405 (1949).
5. CHERNIKOV, YU. A., and GORYUSHINA, V. G., *Zavodskaya Lab.*, **12**, 517 (1946).
6. BUSCARÓNS, F., *et al.*, *Anales fís. y quím.* (*Madrid*), **41**, 498 (1945).
7. SCHOELLER and POWELL, 277 ff.
8. A.S.T.M., 116, 180.
9. GUSEV, S. I., and KUMOV, V. I., *Zhur. Anal. Khim.*, **3**, 373 (1948); also see KAWAMURA, K., *Japan Analyst*, **2**, 420 (1953).
10. TOUHEY, W. O., and REDMOND, J. C., *Anal. Chem.*, **20**, 202 (1948).
11. ZEZÁČ, Z., and ROUBAL, M., *Chem. listy*, **51**, 884 (1957).
12. SCHOELLER, 92.
13. WELCHER, **II**, 158; **IV**, 229.
14. OATS, J. T., *Eng. Mining J.*, **144**, (4), 72 (1943).
15. Chemists of U.S. Steel Corporation, *Sampling and Analysis of Carbon and Alloy Steels*, 239 (1938).
16. WELCHER, **II**, 158; **III**, 107.
17. GRIMALDI, F. S., and DAVIDSON, N., *U.S. Geol. Survey Bull.*, No. 950, 135 (1946).
18. WELCHER, **II**, 313.
19. BELCHER, R., and NUTTEN, A. J., *J. Chem. Soc.*, 1516 (1951).
20. HOVORKA, V., *Collection Czechoslov. Chem. Communs.*, **10**, 518 (1938); **13**, 520 (1948); *Chem. listy*, **36**, 113 (1942).
21. POTREPPE, C., *Bull. soc. chim. Belges*, **38**, 375 (1929).
22. BUSCARÓNS, F., *et al.*, *Anales fís y quím.* (*Madrid*), **41**, 249 (1945); **43**, 979 (1947).
23. PHILIPP, P., *Anais assoc. quím. Brasil*, **6**, 161 (1947).
24. WELCHER, **II**, 335 ff.
25. WELCHER, **IV**, 257 ff.
26. WELCHER, **III**, 59 ff.
27. YOE, J. H., and JONES, L., *Ind. Eng. Chem., Anal. Ed.*, **16**, 45 (1944).
28. GLEASON, K. H., *Eng. Mining J.*, **145**, (8), 79 (1944).
29. GOTO, H., *Analysis and Reagent* (*Japan*), **3**, 130 (1950).
30. GUSEV, S. I., and KUMOV, V. I., *Zhur. Anal. Khim.*, **3** 373 (1948).
31. GOLUBTSOVA, R. B., and SHEMYAKIN, F. M., *Trudy Komissii Anal. Khim., Akad. Nauk S.S.S.R., Otdel· Khim. Nauk*, **3**, 241 (1951).
32. GOLUBTSOVA, *Zhur. Anal. Khim.*, **8**, 105 (1953).
33. LUCENA CONDE, F., and ZATO, J., *Anales real soc. españ, fís. y quím.* (*Madrid*), **51**B, 605 (1955).
34. MURATA, A., and YAMAUCHI, F., *J. Chem. Soc. Japan*, **77**, 1259 (1956).
35. NEMIROVSKAYA, A. F., and PETRASHEN, V. I., *Nauch. Trudy, Novocherkasskiĭ Politekh. Inst. im S. Ordzhonikidze*, **26**, 237 (1955).
36. HOLT, M. L., and GRAY, A. G., *Ind. Eng. Chem., Anal. Ed.*, **12**, 144 (1940).
37. HILLEBRAND and LUNDELL (689).
38. SHIOKAWA, T., *J. Chem. Soc. Japan*, **70**, 415 (1949); **67**, 58 (1946).
39. ISHIMARU, S., *Kagaku-Zikken-Gaku*, X, 39 (1942).
40. FREUND, H., *et al.*, *Anal. Chem.*, **23**, 78 (1951); also see UZUMASA, Y., and DOI, K., *J. Chem. Soc. Japan*, **62**, 496 (1941); SANDELL, E. B., *Ind. Eng. Chem., Anal. Ed.*, **18**, 163 (1946) (in rock).
41. SANDELL, 584.
42. GENTRY, C. H. R., and SHERRINGTON, L. G., *Analyst*, **73**, 57 (1948).
43. FERNJANČIČ, S., *Z. anal. Chem.*, **97**, 332 (1934).
44. TROĬTSKIĬ, K. V., *Primenenie Mechenykh Atomov v Anal. Khim.*, **1**, 133 (1955).
45. CROUTHAMEL, C. E. and JOHNSON, C. E., *Anal. Chem.*, **26**, 1284 (1954).
46. NISHIDA, H., *Japan Analyst*, **3**, 25 (1954); **4**, 523 (1955); **6**, 299 (1957).
47. SHORT, H. G., *Analyst*, **76**, 710 (1951); GREENBERG, P., *Anal. Chem.*, **29**, 896 (1957) (in Ti, Ta, Zr); also see BAGSHAWE, B. and TRUMAN, R. T., *Analyst*, **72**, 189 (1947); BICKFORD, C. F., *et al.*, *J. Am. Pharm. Assoc., Sci. Ed.*, **37**, 255 (1948); SANDELL, 586; MACHLAN, L. A. and HAGUE, J. L., *J. Research Natl. Bur. Standards*, **59**, 415 (1957) (in steel, Ti).
48. WELCHER, **I**, 299; ISHIMARU, S., *J. Chem. Soc. Japan*, **55**, 201 (1934); **56**, 73 (1935).
49. PŘIBIL, R. and SEDLÁR, V., *Collection Czechoslov. Chem. Communs.*, **16**, 69 (1951).
50. CARRIÈRE, E. and BERKEM, R., *Bull. soc. chim. France*, **4**, 1907 (1937) (gravimetric); NODA, I., *J. Electrochem. Soc. Japan*, **8**, 184, 319 (1940) (potentiometric).
51. BLUMENTHAL, H., *Metall u. Erz*, **39**, 253 (1942).
52. CLOKE, F., *Mining J.*, **70**, 314 (1944).
53. WHITE, M. C. DE, *Rec. trav. chim.*, **62**, 134 (1943); also see BUSCARÓNS, F., *et al.*, *Anales fís y quím.* (*Madrid*), **42**, 1139 (1946).
54. DE SOUSA, A., *Anal. Chim. Acta*, **10**, 517 (1954).
55. SYSOEV, V. A., *Trudy Moskov. Technol. Inst., Leghoĭ Prom. im L. M. Kaganovicka*, No. 3, 169, 179 (1941).
56. DUPUIS, T., *Mikrochim. Acta*, 851 (1955).
57. GULLSTROM, D. K. and MELLON, M. G., *Anal. Chem.*, **25**, 1809 (1953).
58. GOTO, H., *J. Chem. Soc. Japan*, **60**, 939 (1939).
59. BRICKER, C. E. and WATERBURY, G. R., *Anal. Chem.*, **29**, 1093 (1957); WELCHER, **I**, 134.
60. YOE, 387; also see MILOSLAVSKIĬ, N. M. and GUREVICH, A. B., *Zavodskaya Lab.*, **5**, 1170 (1936) ($SnCl_2$).
61. SHIOKAWA, T., *J. Chem. Soc. Japan*, **71**, 3 (1950); GOTO, H. and IKEDA, S., *ibid.*, **73**, 654 (1952).
62. D'AMORE, G., *Ann. chim.* (*Rome*), **45**, 759 (1955).
63. LARUMBE, F. H., *Anales asoc. quím. Arg.*, **45**, 52 (1957).

57

PHOSPHORUS

The principal sources for this chapter are mentioned in ref. 1. Complete schemes have been described for the analysis of apatite rocks[2] and phosphate rocks.[3]

In the full schedule of analysis, phosphorus remains in the residue from treatment with acid, as phosphates of tin, titanium, zirconium, and thorium. If the residue is treated with HF and H_2SO_4, and ignited, some phosphorus is lost. Loss of phosphorus may also occur when an H_2SO_4 solution is evaporated to fumes; if $HClO_4$ is present, a lower temperature is possible and losses are avoided. Coprecipitation of various types may also cause losses of phosphate. In general it is advisable to determine phosphorus on a separate sample.

Attack

(a) Rocks, etc. Treat the sample with HNO_3, fuse the residue with Na_2CO_3 and then evap. to dryness with HNO_3, Treat with dil. HNO_3, filter, etc.

For silicates, treat with HNO_3 and dil. with H_2O; alternatively, fuse with Na_2O_2 or $Na_2S_2O_7$ (a low temp. is needed with the latter melt).

(b) Steels, etc. Treat the steel sample with 1:1 HNO_3, add $KMnO_4$ until the soln. is slightly pink, boil and add 2% Na_2SO_3 or $(NH_4)_2C_2O_4$ until MnO_2 dissolves. Boil, add H_2O (if V is present, add 5 ml. 10% $FeSO_4$), then 2–3 drops H_2SO_3 and $(NH_4)_2MoO_4$, etc.

With Fe–Cr or acid-resistant steel, treat a 2 g. sample with 30 ml. 1:2 HCl-HNO_3 and 30–40 ml. $HClO_4$, boil to fumes, cool and add 50 ml. H_2O. Filter, add SO_2, boil, add $(NH_4)_2MoO_4$, etc. Treat the residue from the acid treatment with HF and H_2SO_4, evap. to dryness, fuse with Na_2CO_3, etc.

For rustless steels, warm 2 g. steel with 20 ml. $HClO_4$, boil for 20–30 min., filter; add NH_4OH to the filtrate until a ppt. appears, then add 20–30 ml. HNO_3 (s.g. 1·20) and NH_4HSO_3, boil, etc. Treat the residue with HF and H_2SO_4 as above.

For steels contg. high proportions of Si, W, Ti, U, Zr, Nb or Ta, treat a 2 g. sample with HCl, HNO_3 and $HClO_4$, evap. to fumes and add H_2O. Filter on paper, wash with hot H_2O, then add HCl, etc. If W is present, evap. the HCl–HNO_3 soln. to dryness, add 20 ml. 1:1 HCl, dil. to 100 ml. with hot H_2O, filter on paper and wash with hot H_2O. Then add 30 ml. HCl, evap. to a syrup and repeat. Finally treat with 50 ml. HNO_3 (s.g. 1·20), filter on paper, wash with hot H_2O, add $(NH_4)_2MoO_4$, etc. For recovery of P from the residue, proceed as follows. If WO_3 predominates in the residue, transfer to a beaker with H_2O, wash the paper with 25 ml. hot 1:4 NH_4OH contg. 0·5 g. citric acid, then wash twice with hot H_2O and 3–4 times with hot 1:20 HCl. Collect the washings in the beaker, heat and acidify with HCl, keeping the vol. below 75 ml. If the residue is appreciable and contains much SiO_2, ignite gently, moisten with 1:1 HCl, add HF and evap. to dryness. Fuse with Na_2CO_3, leach with H_2O, acidify with HCl, add 2–3 ml. NH_4OH and 0·5 g. citric acid and acidify with HCl again, keeping the vol. below 75 ml. Add 25 ml. acidic magnesia mixt. to either of these solns., cool to 0°C and add some glass beads and a 10 ml. excess of NH_4OH. Shake mechanically for 1 hr. and store below 5°C for 12 hr. Filter on paper, wash with dil. NH_4OH 3–4 times, dissolve the ppt. in 1:4 HCl, add magnesia mixt., etc.

For Fe–Mn, treat with dil. HNO_3, add 65% $HClO_4$ and evap. to fumes. Cool, evap. with HF, fume for 20–30 min. and cool. Add 50 ml. H_2O, 10 ml. HNO_3 and a few drops of 2% $KMnO_4$ and boil; add SO_2, boil, etc.

With Fe–Si, Fe–V or Fe–W, heat with HNO_3, add HF dropwise followed by $HClO_4$, fume, etc.

With Fe–Mo, treat with HCl and HNO_3, add H_2SO_4, evap., etc.

For Fe–Si or Fe–P, fuse with a 2:1 mixt. of Na_2CO_3 and KNO_3 or MgO, dissolve in HCl, add HNO_3, evap. to dryness, etc.

(c) Organic compounds. Digest with $HClO_4$, HNO_3 and HI.[4] Many variations are possible. Alternatively, heat with Mg, treat with dil. H_2SO_4 and absorb the PH_3 evolved in Br_2 water; then add MoO_4^{2-}, ext. with EtOAc, etc.[5]

Separation

Pptn. with $(NH_4)_2MoO_4$ is the main method of sepn. from many elements.[1] For 0·1 g. P_2O_5 in 50 ml. of neutral or slightly acidic (HNO_3) soln. add 30 ml.

34% NH_4NO_3 and 10–20 ml. 25% HNO_3 (s.g. 1·53) and heat to 50°C. Add reagent dropwise at 50°C using a freshly prepd. 3% soln. (see below for the amts.).

P_2O_5	(mg.)	100	10	5	2	1
$(NH_4)_2MoO_4$	(ml.)	120	15	15	10	10
NH_4NO_3	(ml.)	20	20	20	15	15
HNO_3	(ml.)	19	10	10	5	5

Stir for 5–10 min. and allow to cool for several hr. with occasional stirring. Filter on paper, decant once and then wash with a soln. contg. 50 g. NH_4NO_3 and 40 ml. HNO_3 (s.g. 1·53)/l. Dissolve the ppt. in 10 ml. 8% NH_4OH. If a turbidity appears, acidify with HNO_3, add some citric acid and more NH_4OH; if the turbidity persists, follow the treatment for Ti and Zr given below. Then add 20 ml. 34% NH_4NO_3, 30 ml. H_2O and 1 ml. 3% $(NH_4)_2MoO_4$. Heat to 60°C, add dropwise 20 ml. hot HNO_3 and leave for 2–12 hr. Filter on paper, wash, dissolve in 1:1 NH_4OH and wash with hot H_2O, dil. HCl and dil. NH_4OH. Then add magnesia mixt. etc.

Large amts. of NH_4^+ interfere, as do acids in excess of 1:9 HCl, 1:20 H_2SO_4 or 1:20 HF; H_3BO_3 prevents HF interference. These acids require addn. of more reagent and NH_4NO_3. V^{4+}, V^{5+}, Ti, Zr, Se, Te, W and SiO_2 interfere. As^{5+} interferes, but small amts. can be tolerated if pptn. is done at a low temp. $C_2O_4^{2-}$ and org. compds. generally retard pptn. and more reagent is needed.

If much P is present, V^{5+} coppts. completely but V^{4+} does not ppt. at room temp.; to avoid interference treat the soln. with NH_4NO_3 and HNO_3, cool to 10–15°C, add 5 ml. 40% $FeSO_4$, stir, add several drops SO_2 water and 1 g. Fe as $Fe(NO_3)_3$ (if Fe was absent from the soln.), add 75 ml. $(NH_4)_2MoO_4$ soln., stir for 10 min., leave for over 4 hr., etc.

To overcome interference from Ti or Zr, treat the first ppt. with NH_4OH and $(NH_4)_3$-citrate, filter on paper and wash; ignite, fuse with Na_2CO_3, ext. with H_2O and repeat the ignition and fusion. Alternatively, treat the residue from the NH_4OH treatment twice with HF and then with dil. NaOH alternately. Treat the filtrate from either of these treatments with HNO_3, boil, add NH_4OH and combine with the main soln. If Ti is below 10 mg./100 ml. soln.,[6] sepn. is possible with 10–15 ml. HNO_3 and 5–10 g. NH_4NO_3.

SiO_2 can be sepd. by prior evapn. with HNO_3. Fe interference is avoided by addn. of tartaric acid to give a 6% soln. For sepn. of W, see Chapter 56, p. 422.

The optimum conditions for the sepn. as phosphomolybdate are 0·7–1·3*N* HNO_3 and a MoO_4^{2-}:PO_4^{3-} ratio of 1·5–3·0. In most cases, repptn. is not necessary. $HClO_4$ solns. can be used if HNO_3 is added. Creeping of the ppt. can be prevented by addn. of a little 10% aerosol to the wash soln.[7]

Sepn. of P from large amts. of group IV elements and from Cu, Ni, Cr, Mo, W, etc. is achieved by treatment with Fe^{3+} or Al^{3+} and NH_4OH. This can also be used for concn. purposes.

$ZrOCl_2$ allows sepn. of P from nearly all other elements. Treat the HCl soln. with reagent, evap. to dryness, boil with 30 ml. HCl and 10 ml. HBr and evap. to dryness. Heat on a sand-bath, evap. with dil. HCl, dil. to 500 ml. with H_2O and heat to 50°C. Filter on paper, wash, ignite, fuse with Na_2CO_3, and leach with boiling H_2O contg. a little Na_2O_2.

P, As, V, etc. can be sepd. from Fe, Ni, Co, Ti, Zr and partly from Cr^{3+} by pptn. with dil. NaOH, or by repeated fusion with Na_2CO_3 or Na_2O_2 followed by leaching with H_2O.

H_2S in acidic soln. seps. P from group II elements; sepn. from Mo is incomplete. In alk. soln. H_2S gives a sepn. from Fe, Co, Zn, etc. but group IV elements interfere. Sepn. from Mo is achieved by H_2S treatment of the alk. soln., acidification and further treatment with H_2S.

Sepn. from As is possible by evapn. of an acidic soln. contg. KI. Evapn. with HF, HCl and HBr allows[8] sepn. from As, Ge and SiO_2.

Magnesia mixt. yields almost complete sepn. from W, Mo or V when solns. contg. NH_4OH and $(NH_4)_2$-tartrate are treated (see Chapter 56, p. 422).

Electrolysis at a Hg-cathode in dil. H_2SO_4 soln. seps. P from Fe, Co, Ni, Cr, Mn, etc.

Cupferron allows sepn. from Fe, Zr, Ti, etc. Oxine seps. P from Mg, Al, Zn, Fe, Mn, Ni, Co, Cu, Cd, Bi, Th, Ti, V, U, W and Mo.[9] Evap. the filtrate to 10 ml., add HNO_3 and 80 ml. satd. $KMnO_4$, boil for 30 min. and if still yellow, add more $KMnO_4$; then boil with H_2O_2, add $(NH_4)_2MoO_4$, etc.

Extn. with Et_2O allows sepn. from Fe and Mo.

F^-, etc. can also be sepd. by ion exchange (see Chapter 13, p. 109).

Determination

Phosphorus is generally determined as pyrophosphate after precipitation with magnesia mixture. For small amounts, a molybdate method is usually preferable. The number of proposed modifications is extremely large; colorimetry as phosphomolybdate or as phosphovanadomolybdate, or the titrimetric method involving quinoline phosphomolybdate is satisfactory for milligram amounts of P. For microgram amounts, a 'molybdenum blue' procedure with N_2H_4, Fe^{2+}, metol or hydroquinone as reductant, or with an extraction step, is more successful. For gravimetric determination, it seems preferable to precipitate the Mo of the phosphomolybdate precipitate either as $PbMoO_4$ or as the oxinate.

(a) Magnesia mixture. This can be applied for gravimetric and titrimetric finishes.[1] For the reagent, dissolve 50 g. $MgCl_2{\cdot}6H_2O$ and 100 g. NH_4Cl in H_2O, make alk. with NH_4OH to phenolphthalein and leave for several days; filter, acidify with HCl, dil. to 1 l. with H_2O and make yellow to *p*-nitrophenol (pH 5–6) with HCl.

For detn. of <100 ml. of slightly acidic soln., add

0·5 g. citric acid, adjust with NH_4OH until pale yellow to *p*-nitrophenol and add 10 ml. reagent (an excess of 0·1 ml./mg. P). Add 2·5% NH_4OH slowly so as to complete the pptn. within 5–6 min. Then make alk. to phenolphthalein, add a 1/7th vol. of 20% NH_4OH and leave for a few hr., or for 12 hr. if the amt. of P is small or the amt. of foreign salt is large. Filter on paper, decant and wash thrice with 1:20 NH_4OH. Dissolve the ppt. in 25 ml. 1:1 HCl, wash the paper with 1:20 HCl and dil. to 50–100 ml. with H_2O. Then add 1–2 ml. reagent, NH_4OH, etc. Filter on paper, wash, dry and heat very slowly until ashing is complete. Finally ignite at 1000–1050°C (>477°C) and weigh as $Mg_2P_2O_7$.

NOTES. (1) If As^{5+} is present, dissolve the first ppt. in HCl and treat the soln. with H_2S (for large amts.) or with 1–2 g. NH_4Br followed by evapn. to 5–10 ml. (for small amts.). If Se or Te is present, add 1 g. citric acid for the first pptn. With Fe, Al, V, Zn, Sn, Ti, Zr, add 3–5 g. citric acid and a 50-fold excess of reagent for the first pptn., and leave for 1–2 days; for the second pptn. add 0·2–0·5 g. citric acid and 3–4 ml. reagent and leave for over 6 hr. V interference is also prevented by reduction with SO_2. EDTA prevents interference of Ca, Ba, Sr, Ni, Cu, Zn, Cd and Pb.
The method has been used for detn. of P in steels.[10]
(2) Some P_2O_5 is lost above 1100°C. Results tend to be high if only one pptn. is made. If necessary, ignite the filter paper from the first pptn., fuse with Na_2CO_3, ext. with H_2O, acidify and combine with the main soln.
(3) The ppt. can be weighed without ignition.[11, 12] Ppt. as above, filter on a porcelain crucible and wash with 1·5% NH_4OH and then with Me_2CO thrice, or wash with 1% NH_4OH and then with MeOH. Dry in a desiccator at 100 mm. Hg for 10 min. or dry in air and weigh as $NH_4MgPO_4{\cdot}6H_2O$. Apply an empirical factor of 0·2788 in the former case.
(4) For a titrimetric finish[13] dissolve the ppt. in 1:2 HCl, dil. to 80 ml. with H_2O, add a small excess of EDTA, make alk. with NH_4OH and add pH 10 buffer (67·5 g. NH_4Cl and 570 ml. NH_4OH/l.); titrate with Mg^{2+} soln. using eriochrome black T indicator at 30–40°C.
(5) A colorimetric finish is based on the bleaching of the color formed by Mg with quinalizarin.[14]

Various other metals can be used to ppt. PO_4^{3-} in gravimetric, titrimetric or colorimetric procedures. None of these methods has been widely applied.

$Bi(NO_3)_3$ ppts. PO_4^{3-} from 1*N* HNO_3 soln.;[15] add reagent to the hot soln. followed by an equal vol. of hot H_2O, dry the ppt. at 119–961°C and weigh as $BiPO_4$. No interference arises from Mg, Zn, Mn, Ni, Co. For a titrimetric detn.[16] of 10–100 mg. P_2O_5, heat the sample to fumes with $HClO_4$, dil. to 30 ml. with H_2O, add some $Bi(ClO_4)_3$ followed by NaOH until a ppt. appears, and then add 0·5 ml. 20% $HClO_4$ and 1 ml. 1% KI and boil. Then titrate with $Bi(ClO_4)_3$. Thiourea can be used as indicator in titration of PO_4^{3-} with Bi^{3+} soln.[17] A nephelometric procedure has been suggested.[18]

$UO_2(OAc)_2$ is applied gravimetrically as follows.[19] Treat the acidic (AcOH) soln. with 2 g. NH_4OAc (pH 5; just pink to methyl red), boil, add reagent and leave for 12 hr. Filter on Whatman No. 40 paper, wash, ignite at 673–946°C and weigh as $(UO_2)_2P_2O_7$. Large amts. of Ca interfere but Ba and group V elements do not. For a colorimetric or titrimetric finish,[20] dissolve the ppt. in dil. H_2SO_4, reduce with Zn–Hg and titrate with $KMnO_4$ soln. Alternatively, treat the ppt. with 5 ml. 5% CCl_3CO_2H and 2 ml. 0·5% $K_4Fe(CN)_6$ and compare the color after 5 min. Amperometric titration is also possible.[21]

$ZrOCl_2$ ppts. PO_4^{3-} from acidic (HCl) soln.[22] Evap. the mixt. to dryness, heat to 130°C, add 6*N* HCl, filter on paper, wash with 1:10 HCl, ignite at 1000°C (>586°C) and weigh as $2ZrO_2{\cdot}P_2O_5$.

TlOAc is used in conjunction with $AgNO_3$ for 50–180 mg. $Na_2HPO_4{\cdot}12H_2O$ in 25 ml. soln.[23] Neutralize the soln. to methyl orange with KOH, acidify with HNO_3, boil, neutralize with NH_4OH and reboil. Add 6–12 ml. 4% TlOAc and 10–20 ml. 0·1*N* $AgNO_3$ dropwise; filter on a glass crucible, wash with 71% EtOH, then twice with abs. EtOH and 5–6 times with Et_2O. Dry *in vacuo* (20–720°C) and weigh as Ag_2TlPO_4. The Volhard titration can be applied to the filtrate (see p. 196).

$ZnCl_2$ can be used gravimetrically,[24] the ppt. being ignited above 610°C and weighed as $Zn_2P_2O_7$.

A possible titrimetric method involves $MnCl_2$ and $KMnO_4$.[24] PO_4^{3-} can be titrated with Pb^{2+} soln. in presence of several adsorption indicators (see Table 10).

A colorimetric procedure depends on the Fe^{3+}–SCN^- color being bleached.[25]

(b) Formation of phosphomolybdate. This can be applied in many different forms and is treated below under Gravimetry, Titrimetry and Colorimetry.

(*i*) *Gravimetry. A.* $(NH_4)_2MoO_4$ is the classical pptg. reagent.[1, 12, 26] For up to 7 mg. P in <90 ml. soln., add 8 ml. HNO_3, dil. to 100 ml. with H_2O, heat to 50 ± 1°C and add 50 ml. reagent dropwise during 7–10 min. (For the reagent, dissolve 30 g. $(NH_4)_2MoO_4$ in 100 ml. 1:1 NH_4OH, pour into 168 ml. HNO_3 in 360 ml. H_2O, leave for 24 hr., dil. to 900 ml. with H_2O, filter and store in a polythene bottle). Digest the ppt. for 75 min. with occasional stirring, leave to cool for 1 hr., filter on a Gooch crucible and wash by decantation with 15 ml. portions of a soln. contg. 20 g. $NaNO_3$ and 12·5 ml. HNO_3 in 2·5 l. H_2O. Wash with two 15 ml. and two 10 ml. portions by decantation, then wash the ppt. 6 times with the wash soln. and once with 0·15*N* HNO_3. Dry at 130–140°C (180–410°C) and weigh as $(NH_4)_3PO_4{\cdot}12MoO_3$, or ignite at 470–550°C (812–850°C) and weigh as $P_2O_5{\cdot}24MoO_3$. With an empirical factor of 0·0163, the ppt. can be weighed after drying for 1 hr. at 110°C (Pigott[1]).

It may be preferable to dissolve the ppt. and weigh the Mo contained in it after pptn. as $PbMoO_4$ or as oxinate; such methods are considered on p. 432.

B. Me_2CO treatment of the ppt. yields a different weighing form.[27] To 10 ml. slightly acidic (H_2SO_4)

soln. add 40 ml. mixed acids (1 l. 1:2 HNO_3 and 30 ml. H_2SO_4), boil, remove from the heat, shake and add 50 ml. reagent (150 g. $(NH_4)_2MoO_4$ in hot H_2O, cooled, poured into a mixt. of 50 g. $(NH_4)_2SO_4$ and 400 ml. HNO_3 (s.g. 1·4), cooled, dild. to 1 l. with H_2O and filtered; the soln. is stable for 2 days). Shake vigorously for 5 min., leave for 3–4 hr., filter on a G4 crucible and wash 5 times with 2% NH_4NO_3. Fill the crucible with Me_2CO, leave to drain, half-fill the crucible and leave to drain again. Place *in vacuo* for 1 hr. and weigh as $[(NH_4)_3PO_4 \cdot 12MoO_3]_8 \cdot [(NH_4)_4Mo_9O_{29}] \cdot 40H_2O \cdot 2Me_2CO$. The compn. of the ppt. seems uncertain.[27]

C. Oxine ppts. phosphomolybdate from slightly acidic soln.[12, 28] For <10 mg. P in 100 ml. soln., heat to 70°C, and add 30 ml. reagent (5 g. oxine in 100 ml. 5:95 HCl; mix 16 ml. with 42 ml. HCl and 42 ml. 10% $(NH_4)_2MoO_4$). After 12 hr., filter on a glass crucible, wash with a min. amt. of 1% NH_4NO_3, dry at 115–135°C and weigh as $(C_9H_7ON)_3 \cdot H_7[P(Mo_2O_7)_6] \cdot 2H_2O$. Alternatively, dry at 176–225°C and weigh as $(C_9H_7ON)_6 \cdot P_2O_5 \cdot 24MoO_3 \cdot 12H_2O$, or dry at 235–250°C and weigh as the anhyd. salt, or dry at 480–550°C (800–852°C) and weigh as $P_2O_5 \cdot 24MoO_3$.

Interferences are F^-, As^{5+}, SeO_3^{2-}, and SiO_2 (if $>P_2O_5$); Al, Fe, Ca, Mg, Ni, Co, Zn, Mn, Cu and citrate do not interfere.

D. Strychnine ppts. 0·02–0·5 mg. P_2O_5 as phosphomolybdate in 10 ml. neutral soln.[29] Add 3 ml. reagent soln. (1·5% strychnine nitrate mixed with a soln. of 84 g. $(NH_4)_2MoO_4$ in 600 ml. NH_4OH in a 1:3 ratio just before use). Filter on a glass crucible after 1–2 hr., wash with H_2O at 0°C, dry at 110°C (154–225°C) and weigh as $(C_{21}H_{22}O_2N_2)_3 \cdot H_3PO_4 \cdot 12MoO_3$.

E. Quinoline can be applied gravimetrically but is much better used titrimetrically (see below).[30, 31]

F. $[Co(NH_3)_5NO_3](NO_3)_2$ can be used to det. 0·6–16 mg. P in neutral soln.[32] Add 6 ml. 6*N* H_2SO_4, evap. to 6–8 ml. and add 1 ml. Na_2MoO_4 soln. (0·2 mg. MoO_3/ml. slightly acidic (H_2SO_4) soln.) for each mg. P, and 0·85% Co-complex soln. until the test soln. becomes pink. Then add 3–5 ml. Co-complex soln., stir, digest at 90°C for 5 min. and evap. to 18–20 ml. if necessary. Filter on a glass crucible, and wash with 0·3*N* HNO_3 until no SO_4^{2-} remains, once with H_2O, 3 times with 5 ml. portions of EtOH and twice with 5 ml. portions of Et_2O. Dry *in vacuo* for 30 min. and weigh as $[Co(NH_3)_5NO_3]H_3(PMo_{12}O_{41})$. This method cannot be used to det. As or Ge.

(*ii*) *Titrimetry. A.* $(NH_4)_2MoO_4$ pptn. of PO_4^{3-} is generally followed by dissoln. of the ppt. in excess NaOH and back-titration with acid.[1, 33] Certain redox titrations are also applicable.

For 0·5–5 mg. P, ppt. as described above except that pptn. is done at 35–40° instead of 50°C. Filter on paper and wash the beaker and filter 15 times with 1% KNO_3; then wash the filter 5 times. Return the ppt. to the beaker, add a 2 ml. excess of 0·1*N* NaOH and 25 ml. CO_2-free H_2O, shake, add 6 drops phenolphthalein indicator and titrate with 0·1*N* H_2SO_4 until colorless. Finally titrate to pink with 0·1*N* NaOH. (1P = 23 NaOH.)

NOTES. (1) Interferences are CO_2, Se, Te, etc. (see under Separation, p. 427). The method has been recommended for steels, brasses, etc.[10]
(2) SO_4^{2-} must be present in order to obtain a constant P:Mo ratio. H_2O is said to be better than KNO_3 for washing because K^+ may replace NH_4^+ in the ppt.[33] Other suggested wash liquids are 2:10 000 HNO_3 and 1% $MgSO_4$. If much P is present, 1:1 bromophenol blue–phenol red is a better indicator than phenolphthalein.
(3) For titration with $KMnO_4$, wash the ppt. on the paper with a soln. contg. 25 ml. H_2SO_4 and 15 ml. NH_4OH/l. Add 50 ml. dil. NH_4OH and 10 ml. H_2SO_4 and pass through a Jones reductor. Collect in Fe^{3+}-alum soln. and titrate with 0·1*N* $KMnO_4$.[34] Methylene blue can also serve as titrant.[34] Titration with Ce^{4+} soln. using ferroin indicator,[35] or oxidation with NaOBr and iodometric titration[36] (see p. 463) are other possibilities.

B. Me_2CO addn. to the ppt. can also be utilized titrimetrically, leading to a reaction where 1P = 29 NaOH. Pptn. is carried out as on p. 428 and titration as above.

C. Oxine can be used with a bromometric titration.[37] For 5 mg. P in 150 ml. soln. contg. 35 ml. HCl, add 20 ml. $(NH_4)_2MoO_4$ soln. (10 ml. 10% soln. poured into 35 ml. 30% HNO_3) and 20 ml. oxine soln. (6 g. in 10 ml. HCl, dild. to 1 l. with H_2O); place on a steam-bath for 30 min., cool, filter on a glass crucible and wash with a soln. contg. 3 ml. HCl and 3 g. NaCl/l. Dissolve in 10 ml. HCl, 20 ml. EtOH and 20 ml. H_2O, heat to 70–80°C and dil. to 100 ml. with H_2O. Add 10 ml. 0·1*N* $KBrO_3$–KBr, wait 30 min., add 5 ml. 10% KI and titrate with 0·1*N* $Na_2S_2O_3$. No interference is caused by As, Si or Fe.

D. Strychnine can be used as described above to ppt. phosphomolybdate and the ppt. can be dissolved in NaOH which is back-titrated with HCl soln. (1P = 20 NaOH).

E. Quinoline ppts. phosphomolybdate and the ppt. is dissolved in NaOH which is back-titrated.[30, 31, 38] This is the best titrimetric method for P. To 100 ml. hot acidic soln. add 20% NaOH until a ppt. appears, followed by 2 drops HCl, 1 g. citric acid and 50 ml. molybdate soln. (see Note 1). After 3 min., add 25 ml. quinoline soln. (Note 1), boil for 1–2 min., maintain near boiling for 5 min. and cool. Filter, wash with H_2O and dissolve the ppt. in excess 0·5*N* CO_2-free NaOH and 50 ml. H_2O. Titrate with 0·5*N* HCl using 3:2 thymol blue–phenolphthalein indicator.

NOTES. (1) For the molybdate soln. dissolve 54 g. MoO_3 in 200 ml. H_2O contg. 11 g. NaOH, pour into a mixt. of 120 g citric acid, 140 ml. HCl and 250–300 ml. H_2O, cool, filter, dil. to 1 l. and add some 0·5% $KBrO_3$ if blue. For quinoline soln. add 50 ml. distd. quinoline to a warm mixt. of

60 ml. HCl and 300 ml. H_2O, dil. to 1 l. with H_2O and filter.
(2) No interference arises from SiO_2 if citric acid is present. As interferes.
(3) Cinchonine and pyridine are not suitable to replace quinoline.[30]

(*iii*) *Colorimetry and nephelometry*. Very many modifications have been proposed.

A. $(NH_4)_2MoO_4$ can be used alone for detn. of <0·5 mg. P in 25 ml. neutral soln.[39] Add 5 ml. 2·5*N* HNO_3 or $HClO_4$, 14 ml. H_2O and 5 ml. 10% reagent and dil. to 50 ml. with H_2O. Measure the yellow color at 380 (for 1–15 p.p.m.), 400 or 420 mμ. SiO_2, As^{5+} and Fe interfere.

An extn. procedure may be better.[40] Ext. 25 ml. soln., which is 0·96*N* in HCl and 0·025*M* in Na_2MoO_4, twice with 10 ml. portions of 1:4 *n*-BuOH–$CHCl_3$. Measure at 310 mμ (ϵ = 24 400). No interference is caused by 4 mg. As, 5 mg. Si, 1 mg. Ge or by Fe. Octanol extn. is suitable for detn. of 0·002–3 μg. P (Schaffer[40]).

Successive extn. of P, As, Si and Ge is possible.[41] To the soln. add 5 ml. molybdate (40 mg. MoO_3/ml.) and 2 ml. $HClO_4$, dil. to 150 ml. with H_2O and measure at 332 mμ; this gives the total amt. (0·5–2 p.p.m. P, 3·0–9·0 p.p.m. As and 1·0–3·0 p.p.m. Si). Shake for 2 min. with 20 ml. iso-AmOAc and measure at 330 mμ (P). Adjust the soln. to contain 17% EtOH, add 20 ml. iso-AmOAc, shake for 2 min. and measure at 323 mμ (As).

In another procedure[42] extract P from 0·14 ±0·03*N* HNO_3 soln. with 2:3 iso-BuOH–$CHCl_3$; then extract As from 0·7*N* HNO_3 soln. once with 1:1 EtOAc–*n*-BuOH and twice with $CHCl_3$; finally extract Si and Ge 3 times from 1*N* HNO_3 soln. with *n*-BuOH. For another modification, see ref. 43.

A reduced molybdate reagent[44, 45] is suitable for detn. of <160 μg. P_2O_5. For the reagent, dissolve 8·15 g. $(NH_4)_2MoO_4$ in 60 ml. H_2O; to a 25 ml. aliquot add 12·5 ml. HCl, dil. to 50 ml. with H_2O and shake vigorously with 10 ml. Hg for 5 min.; filter. Mix 30 ml. of the first molybdate soln., 50 ml. HCl, 56 ml. H_2SO_4 and 40 ml. reduced soln., dil. to 200 ml. with H_2O. The soln. is stable for 6 months and contains Mo^{6+}: Mo^{5+} = 3:2.

For a detn., add 1·5 ml. reagent, dil. to 30 ml. with H_2O, place on a steam-bath for 15 min., cool, dil. to 50 ml. with H_2O and measure at 840 mμ. Interferences are Ba, W, As^{5+}, Pb, Fe, Sb^{3+}, Bi, Ge, 20 p.p.m. NO_3^- and 100 p.p.m. SiO_3^{2-} or $C_2O_4^{2-}$.

B. Molybdenum blue is formed by reduction of phosphomolybdate complexes. Many reductants have been used. In general, care must be taken with dilution because the color depends on pH.

(i) $SnCl_2$ is suitable in the detn. of <30 μg. P in 30 ml. soln.[46] Add 5 drops quinaldine red and adjust with HCl or NH_4OH to a pink color; dil. to 35 ml. with H_2O and add 10 ml. molybdate soln. (15·0 g. $(NH_4)_2MoO_4$ in 300 ml. H_2O at 50°C, filtered, cooled, mixed with 350 ml. 10·0*N* HCl and dild. to 1 l.) and 5 ml. $SnCl_2$ soln. (10 g. in 25 ml. HCl; 1·0 ml. added to 332 ml. H_2O). Measure at 820 mμ within 4–20 min.

NOTES. (1) Interferences are Ba, Pb, Hg, Ag, Sr, Zr, Sb, Bi, Cd, Cr, Cu, Fe^{3+}, Zn, Ce^{4+}, Co, Ni, U^{6+}, SiO_2, WO_4^{2-}, $P_2O_7^{4-}$, citric acid, etc. F^- interference is prevented by H_3BO_3. No interference arises from Al, Ca, Mg, or 100-fold amts. of Fe^{2+}. Up to 600 p.p.m. SO_4^{2-}, 50 ClO_4^- and 25 NO_3^- can be tolerated. Cl^- does not interfere. Fe^{3+}, As^{5+} and NO_3^- do not interfere if $Na_2S_2O_5$ is added to a dil. H_2SO_4 soln.[45]
The method has been used after concn. with $Mg(OH)_2$[47] and to det. P in GeO_2.[48] SnC_2O_4 can replace $SnCl_2$ as reductant.[49]
If much Fe is present, it can be reduced by the Jones reductor, or masked by NaF addn.[50] To minimize any effect of excess $SnCl_2$, 1 ml. 4% $KClO_3$ can be added.[51]
(2) A permanent color standard can be prepd. by mixing suitable vols. of solns. contg. 8·83 g. Cu (as sulfate)/ml. and 0·010% bromophenol blue dild. with pH 4·35 buffer.[52]
(3) The color is more stable and interferences are reduced if the phosphomolybdate is reduced after extn.[53] For 10–60 μg. P, add 5 ml. 72% $HClO_4$, dil. to 45 ml. with H_2O (to give 0·5–1·4*N* acid), add 5 ml. 10% Na_2MoO_4 and mix. After several min., ext. with 40 ml. iso-BuOH, sep. and wash twice with 25 ml. H_2O. Add 25 ml. 0·2% $SnCl_2$ (2·38 g. $SnCl_2 \cdot 2H_2O$ in 170 ml. HCl, dild. to 1 l. with H_2O and stored over Sn), shake for 15 sec., sep., dil. to 50 ml. with iso-BuOH and measure at 725 mμ within 15 min. (ϵ = 22 700). Interference of As or Ge is avoided by addn. of 5 ml. 35% NaBr and 5 ml. $HClO_4$ and evapn.; that of 30 p.p.m. Si is avoided by evapn. with $HClO_4$ without filtration. Other interferences are Ce^{4+}, Au, $S_2O_3^{2-}$, Sn^{2+}, V, W, and moderate amts. of Hg^+, Sn^{4+}, As^{3+}, I^- and Hg^{2+}; 50 mg. amts. of most other elements can be tolerated. This method has been used for plain carbon steel.
For detn. of P in Ni,[54] ext. 2–3 times with 10 ml. 1:3 *n*-BuOH–$CHCl_3$ from 0·9*N* HNO_3 soln.; combine the org. phases, shake with 10 ml. 1% $SnCl_2$ in 0·4*N* HCl and measure at 725 mμ (P). Then adjust to 1·8*N* in HNO_3, ext. As twice with 20 ml. 1:1 *n*-BuOH–EtOAc, sep., reduce twice with 15 ml. $SnCl_2$ soln. and measure at 725 mμ (As). Si and Ge do not interfere.
Iso-AmOH,[55] EtOAc[56] and Et_2O have also been used for extn.

(ii) $N_2H_4 \cdot H_2O$ can be used in a single soln. with molybdate.[57] To prep. the reagent, mix 10 ml. 0·15% $N_2H_4 \cdot H_2O$ and 25 ml. 2·5% $Na_2MoO_4 \cdot 2H_2O$ in 10*N* H_2SO_4 and dil. to 100 ml., just before use.

For detn. of <0·1 mg. P in 25 ml. soln. which is neutral to litmus, add 20 ml. reagent soln., dil. to 50 ml. with H_2O, place in boiling H_2O for 10 min., cool, dil. to 50 ml. with H_2O (to give a 1*N* H_2SO_4 soln.) and measure at 830 mμ.

NOTE. Interferences are Sn^{2+}, As^{5+}, NO_3^-, 200 p.p.m. Fe^{3+}, 10 p.p.m. WO_4^{2-}, and Pb, Bi, Ba, Sb^{3+}. No interference is caused by Al, Fe^{2+}, Cr, Cu, Co, Mn, Ni, Mg, Zn, Cl^- Br^-, AcO^-, SiO_3^{2-}, VO_3^-, F^-, BO_2^-, citrate.

(iii) Hydroquinone can be applied in detn. of 2–200 μg. P in 30 ml. neutral soln.[58, 59] Add 10 ml. molybdate (5% $(NH_4)_2MoO_4$ in 1*N* H_2SO_4) and 10 ml. reductant (100 ml. 0·5% hydroquinone contg. 1 drop H_2SO_4), dil. to 100 ml. with H_2O and measure at 700 mμ after 30 min.

NOTES. (1) Interferences are Al, Ce^{4+}, Fe^{3+}, Pt, VO_3^-, and large amts. of Cr^{3+}, Cu^{2+}, ClO_3^-, Ni, As^{5+}, BO_2^-, ClO_4^- and WO_4^{2-}.
(2) Reduction with pyrogallol is possible.[60]
(3) Again, extn. can precede reduction.[61] For 25–125 μg. P in 10 ml. soln. add 5 ml. 0·2*N* H_2SO_4 (if As, Si or F is present, use 1–2*N*), 2 (or 5) ml. 5% $(NH_4)_2MoO_4$ and after 1 min., 7–8 ml. BuOH. Shake for 1 min., discard the aq. phase (and add 5 ml. H_2O, shake and sep.); add 15 ml. H_2O, shake, add 1 ml. 2% hydroquinone, shake, leave for 5–6 min., add 1 ml. sulfite (95 ml. 15% $NaHSO_3$ and 5 ml. 20% Na_2SO_3), shake, leave for 5–6 min., sep., dil. to 25 ml. with H_2O and measure at 720 mμ.

(iv) Eiconogen can be used in detn. of 0·3 mg. P_2O_5 in 10 ml. soln.[59, 62] Add 1 ml. 5% $(NH_4)_2MoO_4$, 1 ml. 33% H_2SO_4 and 1 ml. reductant (0·5 g. eiconogen, 195 ml. 15% $Na_2S_2O_5$ and 5 ml. 20% Na_2SO_3); measure the blue color after 10 min.

(v) Metol is suitable for detn. of 0·5–2·5 mg. P_2O_5 in 50 ml. soln.[63] To prep. the reagent, dissolve 1 g. metol, 150 g. $Na_2S_2O_5$ and 5 g. Na_2SO_3 in H_2O and dil. to 500 ml. For a detn. add 5 ml. reagent soln. and 10 ml. molybdate soln. (50 g. $(NH_4)_2MoO_4$ in 500 ml. 10*N* H_2SO_4 soln. dild. to 1 l. with H_2O); after 10 min. add 20 ml. NaOAc soln. (1 l. 5*N* NaOH neutralized with AcOH and dild. to 2 l.), dil. to 100 ml. with H_2O and measure the blue color.

NOTES. (1) No interference is caused by small amts. of Fe, SiO_2 or NO_3^-. SiO_2 does not interfere at all if citric acid is added but a large excess of citric acid bleaches the color.[64] The color formed with metol is more stable than that given with eiconogen or $SnCl_2$.[64]
(2) Reduction with amidol has been proposed.[65]
(3) For an extn. method,[66] treat the soln. with 1·5 ml. 0·6*M* molybdate and 0·6 ml. 2*N* HCl, dil. to 50 ml. with H_2O and ext. with a 30 ml. and a 20 ml. portion of iso-BuOH; combine the extracts, add metol and Na_2SO_3 and measure at 730 mμ (P). Then add 10 ml. HCl, ext. with BuOH after 25 min. and measure the Si content.

(vi) Benzidine-HCl is suitable for detn. of 0·1 mg. P in 10 ml. slightly acidic soln.[67] Add 0·2 ml. 50% $(NH_4)_3$-citrate, 0·25 ml. 7·5% $(NH_4)_2MoO_4$ in 3*N* HNO_3 and 0·2 ml. 0·25% benzidine-HCl in 2% AcOH, dil. to 50 ml. and measure. Interferences are As^{5+}, SiO_2, H_2O_2 and SO_4^{2-}.

(vii) Fe^{2+} allows detn. of >0·1 μg. P in 0·2 ml. soln.[68] Add 9 ml. molybdate soln. (25 ml. 6·6% $(NH_4)_2MoO_4$ and 200 ml. H_2O mixed gradually with 25 ml. 7·5*N* H_2SO_4) followed by 0·8 ml. Fe soln. (5 g. $FeSO_4·7H_2O$ and 1 ml. 7·5*N* H_2SO_4 dild. to 50 ml.) and measure at 720 mμ. Up to 200-fold amts. of Si can be present.

(viii) Ascorbic acid is a suitable reductant for concentrations of >0·5 μg. P/ml. of final soln.[69] To 10 ml. soln., add 20 ml. 1*N* H_2SO_4, 5 ml. 2% $(NH_4)_2MoO_4$ and 10 ml. 0·1*N* ascorbic acid, dil. to 50 ml. and measure at 820 mμ after 15 min.

(ix) $Na_2S_2O_3$ can be applied[70] in conjunction with sulfite for concentrations of <8 μg. P/ml. of final soln. To the sample add 7 ml. 1:9 H_2SO_4, 5 ml. soln. contg. 5 g. Na_2SO_3 and 150 g. $NaHSO_3$/500 ml., followed by 2 ml. 6% $Na_2S_2O_3$ and 5 ml. 5% $(NH_4)_2MoO_4$; after 15 min. add 10 ml. 34% NaOAc, dil. to 50 ml. with H_2O and measure.

(x) Thiourea can also serve as the reductant.[71]

C. Organic bases can be used in colorimetric methods as in other procedures.

(i) Oxine allows detn. of 2–10 μg. P in 5 ml. soln.[72] For the oxine reagent mix 0·5 g. oxine in 5*N* HCl with 4·2 g. $(NH_4)_2MoO_4$ in 5*N* HCl and dil. to 100 ml. with 5*N* HCl. For a detn., add 1 ml. oxine soln., heat at 60°C for 30 min., centrifuge, add 5 ml. H_2O at 0°C and centrifuge again. Then add 5 ml. 0·1*N* NaOH, 0·5 ml. phenol reagent (see Note) and 2 ml. 10% Na_2CO_3. Mix, heat at 40°C for 10 min. and measure the blue color.

NOTE. For the phenol reagent (Folin–Ciocalteu's reagent) dissolve 50 g. $(NH_4)_2WO_4$ and 12·5 g. $(NH_4)_2MoO_4$ in 350 ml. H_2O, add 25 ml. 85% H_3PO_4 and 50 ml. HCl and boil for 10 hr. under reflux. Add 75 g. Li_2SO_4, 25 ml. H_2O and a few drops Br_2, boil out the Br_2, cool, dil. to 500 ml. with H_2O and filter if turbid. Store in a brown bottle.

(ii) Strychnine molybdate is suitable for detn. of 0·1–7 μg. P in org. samples.[73] Digest with 1·5 ml. H_2SO_4 (s.g. 1·262) at 150°C for 5 hr., then at 210–220°C for 2 hr. adding 30% H_2O_2 dropwise every 30 min. Cool, add 31·34 ml. reagent (7·5 g. molybdic acid in 60 ml. H_2SO_4 (s.g. 1·78) dissolved by heating, cooled, poured into a soln. of 2 g. strychnine-HNO_3 in 900 ml. H_2O and dild. to 1 l. with H_2O), then shake for 3 hr. under H_2O at 20°C, and compare the colors. SiO_2 does not interfere.

Antipyrine[74] and quinine[75] have also been proposed for nephelometry.

(iii) Methyl violet can ppt. phosphomolybdate, the ppt. being dissolved in Me_2CO and the colors compared.[76]

D. Vanadomolybdate reagent can be employed to det. 0·1–1 mg. P in slightly acidic soln.[77] For the reagent, dissolve 1·0 g. NH_4VO_3 in 300 ml. H_2O, add 200 ml. HNO_3, mix with 50 g. $(NH_4)_2MoO_4$ in 400 ml. H_2O and dil. to 1 l. with H_2O. For a detn. dil. the soln. to 50 ml. with H_2O, add 25 ml. reagent, dil. to 100 ml. with H_2O, and measure the yellow color after 2 min. at 400 mμ.

NOTES. (1) Interferences are Cr^{6+}, Mn^{7+}, Ce^{4+}, Sn^{4+}, Ag, I^- 10 p.p.m. Cr^{3+}, 50 p.p.m. F^- or Cl^-, 100 p.p.m Th,

As^{5+} or Co, and 400 p.p.m. Bi. Other ions do not interfere, but if large amts. of Fe, Cu or Ni are present, measurement should be done at 450–470 mμ.

(2) The method can be used in $HClO_4$ solns.[78, 79] For 0·3–2 mg. P_2O_5 in 100 ml. final soln.,[79] treat the initial soln. contg. 5% v/v $HClO_4$, with 10 ml. 0·020*M* NH_4VO_3 in 0·4*M* $HClO_4$ and 20 ml. 0·20*M* $(NH_4)_2MoO_4$.

(3) The method has been applied to steels (SO_4^{2-} is said to stabilize the color),[80] to rocks[81] and to Cu and brazing alloys.[10]

(4) The method is said to be more sensitive at 315 mμ.[82]

(5) The complex can be extd. from 1·3*N* HNO_3 soln. with 10:1 EtOH–BuOH.[83]

E. Silicotungstate reagent provides a detn. of 20–80 μg. P in 15 ml. soln.[84] For the reagent, mix 5·7 g. $Na_2SiO_3·H_2O$, 79·4 g. $Na_2WO_4·2H_2O$, 500 ml. H_2O and 15 ml. H_2SO_4, boil for 5 hr., cool and dil. to 1 l. with H_2O. For a detn., add 25 ml. 1:1 iso-BuOH–C_6H_6, 5 ml. silicotungstate reagent and 5 ml. molybdate reagent (50 g. $(NH_4)_2MoO_4$ in 400 ml. 10*N* H_2SO_4 dild. to 1 l. with H_2O); shake for 15 sec. and pipet out 10 ml. of solvent phase. Wash the pipet with a soln. of 20 ml. H_2SO_4 in 980 ml. anhyd. EtOH. Dil. to 45 ml. with wash soln., add 1 ml. $SnCl_2$ (10 g. $SnCl_2·2H_2O$ in 25 ml. HCl; 1 ml. dild. with 200 ml. 1*N* H_2SO_4 just before use), dil. to 50 ml. with wash soln., mix and compare the colors. No interference is caused by Fe or by proteins.

(c) Oxine can be used to det. the Mo in an ammonium phosphomolybdate ppt.[85] Dissolve the ppt. in 20 ml. 6*N* NH_4OH contg. 5 g. NH_4OAc, dil. to 200 ml. with H_2O and add excess 5% oxine in Me_2CO and 20–30 ml. AcOH. Warm, boil out the Me_2CO, cool, filter on a glass crucible, dry at 140°C and weigh as $MoO_2(C_9H_6ON)_2$. The method is rapid and accurate.

(d) $Pb(NO_3)_2$ can also serve to ppt. the Mo from a phosphomolybdate ppt.[86, 87] Dissolve the ppt., which has been washed with 1:50 HNO_3, in 15 ml. 1:2 NH_4OH, and wash with H_2O. Collect the soln. in the original beaker and pass the ext. through the filter, washing with H_2O. Boil, add 10 ml. HCl (s.g. 1·16) and 10 ml. 4% $Pb(NO_3)_2$, and clear the soln. with dil. HCl if necessary. Pour this soln. into a boiling mixt. of 50 ml. 25% NH_4Cl and 50 ml. 10% NH_4OAc, rinse with hot H_2O, boil and leave to settle for a few min. Filter on paper and wash with hot H_2O. Heat slowly in a porcelain crucible, ignite at 550–600°C and weigh as $PbMoO_4$.

NOTES. (1) HCOOH-buffered solns. can also be used.[87]

(2) With $Pb(OAc)_2$ as pptg. agent,[86] dissolve the phosphomolybdate ppt. in 15 ml. 1:1 NH_4OH, wash with some tepid H_2O, and pass the soln. through the filter, washing with warm H_2O. Dil. to 300 ml. with H_2O, boil, add 50 ml. 3% reagent slowly, boil, digest for a few min., filter and wash with 8% AcOH 12 times. Ignite below 600°C and weigh as $Pb_3(PO_4)_2·24PbMoO_4$.

(e) Benzidine can be used to ppt. PO_4^{3-}, the detn. being finished alkalimetrically.[88] For <0·1 g. P_2O_5 in 50–150 ml. soln. contg. <0·4% AcOH, add 30 ml. 1% benzidine in 10% AcOH for each 150 ml. soln.; filter after 10–15 min. and wash with H_2O. Suspend in CO_2-free H_2O and titrate with 0·1*N* NaOH using phenolphthalein indicator.

(f) Flame photometry[89] can be applied to det. 0·005–0·013*M* PO_4^{3-} by means of the decrease in luminosity of 1000 p.p.m. Ca^{2+}.

References

1. HILLEBRAND and LUNDELL, 556 (694); SCOTT and FURMAN, 689; KIMURA, 304; PIGOTT, 381; FRESENIUS–JANDER, **Va** β (1953).
2. HARVEY, C. O., *Analyst*, **61**, 817 (1936).
3. HOFFMAN, J. I. and LUNDELL, G. E. F., *J. Research Natl. Bur. Standards*, **20**, 607 (1938).
4. KAHANE, E. and KAHANE, M., *Compt. rend.*, **198**, 372 (1934).
5. JUREČEK, M. and JENÍK, J., *Chem. listy*, **51**, 1312 (1957).
6. HØRGÅRD, C., *Z. anal. Chem.*, **95**, 329 (1933).
7. APPLETON, L., *Chemist Analyst*, **32**, 65 (1943).
8. LEVINE, H., *Anal. Chem.*, **27**, 258 (1955).
9. ISHIMARU, S., *J. Chem. Soc. Japan*, **55**, 732 (1934); **56**, 62 (1935).
10. A.S.T.M., 83 ff.
11. LEDERLE, P., *Z. anal. Chem.*, **121**, 241 (1941).
12. HECHT and DONAU, 251.
13. KATO, T., *et al.*, *Japan Analyst*, **4**, 84 (1955); HUDITZ, F., *et al.*, *Z. anal. Chem.*, **135**, 333 (1952).
14. WELCHER, **IV**, 457.
15. KEŠANS, A., *Z. anal. Chem.*, **128**, 215 (1948); **125**, 6 (1943).
16. RATHJE, W., *Angew. Chem.*, **51**, 256 (1938).
17. SALMON, J. E. and TERRY, H., *J. Chem. Soc.*, 2813 (1950).
18. CHEPELEVETSKIĬ, M. L., *Zavodskaya Lab.*, **11**, 498 (1945).
19. LEWIS, P. T., *Analyst*, **65**, 560 (1940).
20. SAITO, S., *Sci. Repts. Fac. Sci., Tohoku Univ.*, **16**, 739 (1927).
21. KOLTHOFF, I. M. and COHN, G., *Ind. Eng. Chem., Anal. Ed.*, **14**, 412 (1942).
22. STUMPER, R. and METTELOCK, P., *Compt. rend.*, **224**, 122 (1947).
23. SPACU, G. and DIMA, L., *Z. anal. Chem.*, **120**, 317 (1940).
24. ISHIBASHI, M., *Mem. Coll. Sci., Kyoto Imp. Univ.*, **A12**, 39, 49 (1929).
25. SZABÓ, Z. G. and BECK, M. T., *Anal. Chem.*, **25**, 103 (1953).
26. THISLETHWAITE, W. P., *Analyst*, **72**, 531 (1947); JØRGENSEN, G., *Z. anal. Chem.*, **108**, 190 (1937).
27. SPENGLER, W., *Z. anal. Chem.*, **110**, 321 (1937); **124**, 241 (1942).
28. KIBA, T. and IKEDA, T., *J. Chem. Soc. Japan*, **60**, 913 (1939); also see BRABSON, J. A. and EDWARDS, O. W., *Anal. Chem.*, **28**, 1485 (1956).
29. MYRBÄCK, K., *Z. physiol. Chem.*, **148**, 197 (1925).
30. WILSON, H. N., *Analyst*, **76**, 65 (1951); **79**, 535 (1954).
31. FENNELL, T. R. F. W., *et al.*, *Analyst*, **82**, 639 (1957).
32. FURMAN, N. H. and STATE, H. M., *Ind. Eng. Chem., Anal. Ed.*, **8**, 420 (1936).
33. GISIGER, L., *Z. anal. Chem.*, **115**, 15 (1938/39).
34. SCOTT and FURMAN, 699.
35. BIRNBAUM, N. and WALDEN, G. H., *J. Am. Chem. Soc.*, **60**, 66 (1938).
36. FRODL, F., *Chemiker-Ztg.*, **50**, 825 (1926).

37. Welcher, **I**, 311.
38. Fernlund, U., *et al.*, *Z. anal. Chem.*, **138**, 41 (1953); **146**, 111 (1955).
39. Boltz, D. F. and Mellon, M. G., *Anal. Chem.*, **20**, 749 (1948); Yoe, 336.
40. Wadelin, C. and Mellon, *Anal. Chem.*, **25**, 1668 (1953) (in steel); also see Schaffer, F. L., *et al.*, *ibid.*, 343.
41. DeSesa, M. A. and Rogers, L. B., *Anal. Chem.*, **26**, 1381 (1954).
42. Kiba, T. and Ura, M., *J. Chem. Soc. Japan*, **76**, 520 (1955).
43. Alekseev, R. I., *Zavodskaya Lab.*, **11**, 122 (1945).
44. Lucena-Conde, F. and Pratt, L., *Anal. Chim. Acta*, **16**, 473 (1957).
45. Zinzadze, C., *Ind. Eng. Chem.*, *Anal. Ed.*, **7**, 227, 320 (1935).
46. Dickman, S. R. and Bray, R. H., *Ind. Eng. Chem.*, *Anal. Ed.*, **12**, 665 (1940); also see Woods, J. T. and Mellon, M. G., *ibid.*, **13**, 760 (1941); Fontaine, T. D., *ibid.*, **14**, 77 (1942); Robinson, R. J. and Wirth, H. E., *ibid.*, **7**, 147 (1935).
47. Ishibashi, M. and Tabushi, M., *Japan Analyst*, **6**, 7 (1957).
48. Ishihara, Y. and Taguchi, Y., *Japan Analyst*, **6**, 724 (1957).
49. Ingamells, C. O., *Chemist Analyst*, **45**, 10 (1956).
50. Hill, U. T., *Anal. Chem.*, **23**, 1496 (1951).
51. McClelland, J. A. C. and Hardwick, P. J., *Analyst*, **69**, 305 (1944).
52. Parry, E. P. and McClelland, A. L., *Anal. Chem.*, **27**, 140 (1955).
53. Lueck, C. H. and Boltz, D. F., *Anal. Chem.*, **28**, 1168 (1956).
54. Yokosuka, S., *Japan Analyst*, **5**, 395 (1956).
55. Rainbow, C., *Nature*, **157**, 268 (1946).
56. Stoll, K., *Z. anal. Chem.*, **112**, 81 (1938).
57. Boltz, D. F. and Mellon, M. G., *Anal. Chem.*, **19**, 873 (1947); see also Luke, C. L. and Campbell, M. E., *ibid.*, **25**, 1588 (1953) (in Ge metal); Hahn, F. L. and Luckaus, R., *Z. anal. Chem.*, **149**, 172 (1956).
58. Kitson, R. E. and Mellon, M. G., *Ind. Eng. Chem.*, *Anal. Ed.*, **16**, 466 (1944).
59. Yoe, 346 ff; Welcher, **I**, 123 ff.
60. Kato, T., *Technol. Repts. Tohoku Univ.*, **15**, 70 (1950).
61. Ging, N. S., *Anal. Chem.*, **28**, 1330 (1956).
62. Bose, H. L. and Jones, E. B., *Nature*, **138**, 644 (1936); Woods, J. T. and Mellon, M. G., *Ind. Eng. Chem.*, *Anal. Ed.*, **13**, 760 (1941).
63. Scheel, K. C., *Z. anal. Chem.*, **105**, 256 (1936); Bamann, E., *et al.*, *Chem. Ber.*, **8**, 438 (1948).
64. Holmes, W. L. and Matzok, I., *Sci. Agr.*, **27**, 245 (1947).
65. Müller, E., *Z. physiol. Chem.*, **237**, 35 (1935).
66. Ruf, E., *Z. anal. Chem.*, **151**, 169 (1956).
67. Welcher, **II**, 295.
68. Rockstein, M. and Herron, P. W., *Anal. Chem.*, **23**, 1500 (1951); also see Summer, J. B., *Science*, **100**, 413 (1944); Bacon, A., *Analyst*, **75**, 321 (1950); Kajanne, P. *Suomen Kemistilehti*, **30B**, 101 (1957) (EDTA).
69. Erdey, L., *et al.*, *Acta Chim. Acad. Sci. Hung.*, **5**, 65 (1954); Chen, P. S., *et al.*, *Anal. Chem.*, **28**, 1756 (1956); Welcher, **I**, 81.
70. Ikeda, S., *J. Chem. Soc. Japan*, **72**, 23 (1951); **73**, 549, 662 (1952).
71. Meshcheryakov, A. M., *Pochvovedenie*, No. 3, 88 (1956).
72. King, E. J. and Delory, G. F., *Biochem. J.*, **31**, 2046 (1937).
73. Bergold, G. and Pister, L., *Z. Naturforsch.*, **3B**, 332 (1948); Welcher, **IV**, 261.
74. Gusev, S. I., *Trudy Komissii Anal. Khim.*, *Akad. Nauk S.S.S.R.*, **3**, 215 (1951).
75. Welcher, **IV**, 254; Yoe, 343.
76. Imai, K., *J. Biochem.*, **20**, 18 (1948).
77. Barton, C. J., *Anal. Chem.*, **20**, 1068 (1948); Hill, U. T., *ibid.*, **19**, 318 (1947) (Na-salts are preferred to NH_4-salts); Kitson, R. E. and Mellon, M. G., *Ind. Eng. Chem.*, *Anal. Ed.*, **16**, 379 (1944); also see Ma, T. S. and McKinley, J. D., *Mikrochim. Acta*, 4 (1953).
78. Racicot, E. L., *Anal. Chem.*, **23**, 1873 (1951).
79. Quinlan, K. P. and DeSesa, M. A., *Anal. Chem.*, **27**, 1626 (1955).
80. Baghurst, H. C. and Norman, V. J., *Anal. Chem.*, **27**, 1070 (1955).
81. Sandell, E. B., *Anal. Chim. Acta*, **11**, 183 (1954).
82. Michelson, O. B., *Anal. Chem.*, **29**, 60 (1957).
83. Kinnunen, J. and Wennerstrand, B., *Chemist Analyst*, **40**, 73 (1951).
84. Martin, J. B. and Doty, D. M., *Anal. Chem.*, **21**, 965 (1949).
85. Ishimaru, S., *J. Chem. Soc. Japan*, **55**, 735 (1934).
86. Pigott, 396 ff.
87. Bagshawe, B. and Pill, A. L., *Metallurgia*, **54**, 251 (1956).
88. Welcher, **II**, 294.
89. Dippel, W. A., *et al.*, *Anal. Chem.*, **26**, 553 (1954).

58

SULFUR

The main sources for this chapter are given in ref. 1. A bibliography of analytical methods for sulfur has been published which contains 3400 references.[2] The analytical chemistry of the various sulfur oxides has been reviewed.[3] Texts on organic analysis should be consulted.

For general analysis of sulfur-containing materials, it should be noted that sulfur is found in the residue from acid treatments when the material contains Ba, Sr, Pb or Ca. Loss of sulfide may occur if sulfide minerals are ground for too long in a mortar, owing to oxidation. Care must be taken in all cases to avoid contamination from gas burners.

Attack

(a) Minerals. A general method is to heat with fuming HNO_3 in a sealed tube.

With pyrites, treat 1·3736 g. of 80-mesh sample in a 300 ml. covered beaker with 4 ml. Br_2 and 6 ml. CCl_4. After 15 min. add 15 ml. HNO_3, wait for 15 min. and remove Br_2 by heating on an asbestos plate on a steam-bath. Remove the cover, evap. to dryness on a steam-bath, add 10 ml. HCl, evap. to dryness and dry at 100°C for 12 hr. Add 4 ml. HCl and 100 ml. H_2O, washing the cover and the beaker walls. Boil for 5 min., leave to cool for 5 min., cover and add 0·2–0·3 g. Al granules. Filter on paper and wash with hot H_2O. To the filtrate, add 6 ml. HCl, dil. to 1·6 l. with H_2O, add $BaCl_2$, etc.

In an alternative method, treat 0·5 g. pyrites in a 250 ml. beaker with 12 ml. 3:1 HNO_3–HCl and 4–5 drops Br_2. Cover for 30 min., heat on a steam-bath and rinse the cover after effervescence stops. Evap. to dryness, add 5 ml. HCl, cover, heat, remove the cover and evap. to dryness. Then add 20 ml. hot H_2O, electrolyze at the Hg-cathode, etc.

Alternatively, heat the pyrites with H_3PO_4 and H_3PO_2 and titrate the H_2S evolved.[4]

For analysis of stibnite, treat with 10 ml. 10% Br_2 in CCl_4, add 5 ml. of Br_2 and after 1 hr. add 15 ml. HNO_3 at 0°C. After 30 min., add 15 ml. HCl and after 30 min. heat very slowly until a syrup is obtained. Add 10 ml. HCl and evap., add 20 ml. HCl and transfer to an Erlenmeyer flask (the total vol. of soln. should be <100 ml.). Add 5 g. Fe powder, filter on paper after 1 hr. and wash. Dil. to 1·6 l. with H_2O, add 125 ml. 6% $BaCl_2$ at a rate of 5 ml./min. and filter on a Gooch crucible after 12 hr.

For minerals contg. little S, fuse with 12:1 Na_2CO_3–KNO_3 and leach with H_2O contg. 1–2 drops EtOH; filter and add HCl and $BaCl_2$, etc. Alternatively, fuse with 4:1 ZnO–Na_2CO_3, ext. with H_2O, treat with Br_2 and HCl, boil, add $BaCl_2$, etc.

Minerals contg. W or Mo are best decomposed by heating at 1000°C in a stream of H_2 which has been bubbled through HCl. Even $BaSO_4$ is converted to H_2S by this method.

(b) S can be dissolved with HNO_3 and $KClO_3$.

(c) Insol. metal sulfates. Fuse $BaSO_4$ with Na_2CO_3 and leach with H_2O; sepn. from Mg and group IV elements is obtained if this process is repeated at least thrice. With Pb, Sr or Ca sulfate, boil with Na_2CO_3 soln.

(d) Conversion of SO_4^{2-} to H_2S. (i) Mix solid sulfates with 5:2:1 $NaHCO_3$–Al–C, heat and add HCl; collect the H_2S in $Cd(OAc)_2$ soln.

(ii) Heat sulfate solns. with 15 ml. reducing soln. (mix 160 ml. HI (s.g. 1·70), 45 ml. 50% H_3PO_2 and 160 ml. HCl (s.g. 1·19) for 1 hr. under reflux in a stream of N_2 or CO_2) pass N_2 through, and collect in $Cd(OAc)_2$ or NaOH soln.[5]

(iii) Heat the sulfate soln. with reducing reagent (200 g. H_3PO_4 dehydrated at 300°C, mixed with 20–80 g. $SnCl_2{\cdot}2H_2O$, heated at 300°C under CO_2 until no more HCl is evolved, then cooled and stored in a desiccator) for 15 min. under CO_2 at 300°C. Sweep with CO_2 and collect in $Zn(OAc)_2$ soln.[6] Org. compds. can be decomposed by heating with the dehydrated H_3PO_4 and $K_2Cr_2O_7$ and proceeding as above.[6]

(e) Steels. Treat 5 g. with 5 ml. HNO_3 and 1 ml. Br_2; if the reaction is slow, add HCl dropwise at intervals. Then add 0·5 g. $NaNO_3$, evap. to 10 ml., cool, add 10 ml. HCl, evap. to dryness, add 30 ml. HCl and evap. until crystals appear. Alternatively, heat with $HClO_4$ to remove HNO_3. If much W is present, dissolve in HNO_3 (and HCl and HF if needed), add HCl, evap.

and repeat; then filter, evap. with HCl, add 1:1 HCl and cinchonine, etc.[7]

Combustion and evolution methods are also suitable (see p. 438).

For Fe–Cr, heat with 60% H_3PO_4 at 320–340°C and titrate the H_2S evolved.[8]

Separation

Fe, etc. can be removed by adding a 5–10 ml. excess of NH_4OH to the acidic (HCl) soln. followed by repptn. Large amts. of NH_4Cl can be removed by heating with HNO_3 and then with HCl.

Electrolysis at the Hg-cathode at 0·8–1 amp. for 5–6 hr. in dil. acid soln. allows sepn. of Fe, Cu, Cr, Mo, Ni, etc.

Treatment with Al, Zn or Fe of acidic solns. gives sepn. from Pb, Sb and allows reduction of Fe^{3+}.

Fusion with Na_2CO_3 and leaching with H_2O seps. S from group IV elements and Mg (see above). Treatment with H_2S in acidic soln. allows sepn. from group II elements; Se and HNO_3 interfere.

Ion exchange resins allow sepn. from Fe, etc. (see Chapter 13, Section 2.1). Sepn. from Fe, etc. is also obtained on a 10–20 ml. column of activated alumina followed by elution with 0·1*M* NH_4OH.[9]

Determination

The commonest method of determination is the gravimetric procedure as $BaSO_4$. For mg. amounts of SO_4^{2-}, a titrimetric finish after precipitation with benzidine, $BaCl_2$ or $BaCrO_4$ is often applied. Methods involving conversion to H_2S are generally less accurate, but are often convenient for small amounts of sulfur. High-temperature combustion processes are now often applied in metal analysis and in silicate analysis.

(a) $BaCl_2$ can be applied in gravimetric, titrimetric and nephelometric procedures. For gravimetric detn.[1, 10] of <25 mg. S in 100 ml. neutral soln., add 1 ml. HCl, boil and pour into boiling reagent soln. contg. a 7–9 ml. excess of 10% $BaCl_2$ dild. to 100 ml. with H_2O. Place on a steam-bath for 0·5–12 hr., filter on Whatman No. 42 paper and wash with hot H_2O until the filtrate is Cl^--free. Ignite below 900°C (>800°C) and weigh as $BaSO_4$.

NOTES. (1) Interferences are Fe^{3+} (see Note 2), large amts. of Al or Cr, KNO_3, ClO_3^- and PO_4^{3-}. For details of interfering elements and impurities in the ppt. see ref. 10. The method has been applied to steels:[7] for the most accurate analysis treat the filtrate from the $BaSO_4$ pptn. and the washings with 2 ml. 10% $BaCl_2$, evap. just to dryness, add 2 ml. 1:1 HCl and 25 ml. warm H_2O and digest at 60–70°C for several hr.; then filter, ignite and apply a correction. Ni and Ni–Cu can also be analysed.[7] For analysis of Ni–Cr or Ni–Cr–Fe,[7] dissolve a 5 g. sample in 250 ml. soln. contg. 30% $K_2CuCl_4{\cdot}2H_2O$ and 7·5% v/v HCl with mechanical stirring, filter and treat the residue with HNO_3, etc.

(2) If much Fe is present,[1] treat the soln. contg. 4 ml. HCl/100 ml. with 0·2 g. Al granules, filter on paper and wash. Collect the filtrate in a 2·5 l. beaker, dil. to 1·6 l. with H_2O, add 10 ml. HCl and 125 ml. 5% $BaCl_2$ at a rate of 5 ml./min., stir and leave for 12 hr. Filter on a Gooch crucible, etc. Reduction with Zn is usual in ferrous analysis. If little SO_4^{2-} is present, add 10·0 ml. 0·1% K_2SO_4 (Pigott[1]) or 10·0 ml. Na_2SO_4 soln. contg. 0·1 g. S/l.[7] The filter paper should be washed with 1:1 HCl and with H_2O before the filtration, because some Ba^{2+} can be adsorbed.[11]

Direct titration of SO_4^{2-} with Ba^{2+} solns. can be done with tetrahydroxyquinone, rhodizonate, alizarin S or thoron as indicator; indirect titration with $BaCl_2$ and EDTA is now most often applied.

Tetrahydroxyquinone is suitable in titrations with 0·02*N* $BaCl_2$ for detn. of 5 mg. S in 15 ml. soln. at pH 6·5–7·5.[12] Add 80 mg. indicator (Na-salt) and 15 ml. EtOH and titrate to orange-red. The end-point is not sharp and a comparison soln. is essential. At least 3 ml. $BaCl_2$ soln. must be used. Light transmitted through a Wratten No. 45 filter may help detection of the end-point. Further details of this method and that with rhodizonate have been examined.[13]

With Na-rhodizonate as indicator,[14] adjust the soln. to pink to phenolphthalein, add an equal vol. of EtOH and half the required amt. of 0·01*N* $BaCl_2$; then add 0·2–0·4 g. of indicator and titrate to a red color. Fe, Ca, etc. can be removed by ion exchange.[15]

Pptn. with excess $BaCl_2$ and back-titration with EDTA using cresolphthalein complexone indicator is suitable for detn. of 20–50 mg. SO_4^{2-} in slightly acidic (HCl) soln.[16] Heat, add a small excess of 0·01*M* $BaCl_2$, heat on a steam-bath, cool, neutralize with 1*N* NaOH and dil. to 100 ml. with H_2O. Add a few drops of indicator, 5–10 ml. NH_4OH and 100 ml. MeOH and titrate with 0·01*M* EDTA to the color change from red to almost colorless; for a better end-point, add a 1–2 ml. excess of EDTA and back-titrate with Ba^{2+} soln. Back-titration of excess EDTA is possible with Zn^{2+} in presence of Mg–EDTA and eriochrome black T indicator.[17] If interfering elements are present (e.g. in steels), it is better to filter $BaSO_4$, dissolve in excess 0·02*M* EDTA and 5 ml. 9*M* NH_4OH, and back-titrate with 0·01*M* Mg^{2+} with eriochrome black T indicator.[18] A similar method is possible with cresolphthalein complexone indicator.[19]

$BaCl_2$ or $Ba(ClO_4)_2$ soln. is suitable for direct titration with alizarin S or thoron indicator.[9, 20, 21] For 0·2–0·8m*M* SO_4^{2-} in 10 ml. soln. or 2–4m*M* SO_4^{2-} in 45 ml. soln., add 10 or 40 ml. MeOH, EtOH or iso-PrOH and adjust to pH 3–3·5 with $HClO_4$ or $Mg(OAc)_2$. Titrate rapidly with 0·1*M* $Ba(ClO_4)_2$ or $BaCl_2$, add 1 or 5 drops 0·2% alizarin S and complete the titration. Interferences are Fe, Cr, etc. and moderate amts. of most anions. Thoron is a better indicator for small amts. and is suitable after sepn. on alumina or Dowex 50 resin.[9] Other suggested indicators are 1-(4-nitro-2-sulfophenylazo)-2-hydroxy-3,6-disulfonaphthalene and methylene blue,[22] and stilbnaphthazo;[23] see Table 10 for other adsorption indicators.

$BaCl_2$ can be used in conjunction with Na-palmitate.[24] For 1–10 mg. SO_4^{2-} in 100 ml. soln., add 20·00 ml. 0·005*M* $BaCl_2$, evap. almost to dryness, add 50·00 ml. 0·005*N* Na-palmitate and digest on a steam-bath. Filter, wash with warm EtOH and titrate with 0·0246*N* H_2SO_4 to dinitrophenol indicator or a potentiometric end-point. Lauryl sulfate can be applied rather similarly (see Chapter 52, p. 393).

SO_4^{2-} can be titrated directly with $BaCl_2$ using $Hg(NO_3)_2$ as external indicator.[25]

Pptn. with $BaCl_2$ can be followed by addn. of $Na_2S_2O_3$ and iodometric titration (see Chapter 52, p. 393).

For a nephelometric detn. of 4–80 μg. SO_4^{2-} in 1·0 ml. soln.,[26] add 1 ml. 0·1*N* HCl, 25 ml. EtOH, 15 ml. H_2O, 2 ml. 0·05% gelatin and 2 ml. 0·12*N* $BaCl_2$; the error is ±8% for 4–20 μg. SO_4^{2-} and ±4% for 20–80 μg. No interference is caused by 0·03*M* NaCl, 0·004*M* KCl, 0·12*M* NH_4Cl, 0·002*M* $MgCl_2$, $CaCl_2$ or Na_2HPO_4, or by 0·003*M* $NaHCO_3$.

(b) $BaCl_2$ and K_2CrO_4 are frequently applied in titrimetric or colorimetric detns. For titration of 1 mg. S in 10 ml. soln. in a 25 ml. measuring flask,[27] add 2 ml. 0·2*N* HCl and 2 ml. 0·025*M* $BaCl_2$; after 5 min. add 3 ml. buffer (530 g. NaOAc and 6 g. AcOH/l.) and after a few min., add 5 ml. 0·1622*M* K_2CrO_4 and dil. to 25 ml. with H_2O. Filter on a dry Whatman No. 42 paper and pipet out 20 ml. Add 10 ml. 2*N* H_2SO_4 and 10 ml. 10% KI and place in darkness for 15 min. Titrate with 0·0075*M* $Na_2S_2O_3$ (standardized against 0·02*N* KIO_3 on the same day) using starch indicator. Det. a blank.

NOTES. (1) Interferences are PO_4^{3-}, NO_3^-, Pb, etc.
(2) 0·05–0·3 mg. S can be detd. by scaling the above amts. down to 1/5 th. The theor. factor cannot be applied when $BaCrO_4$ is pptd. from alk. soln.[1]
(3) Titration with Fe^{2+} soln. can replace the iodometric method.[28] Boil the 0·1*N* HCl sample soln. and add dropwise a known excess (about 5 ml.) of 0·025*M* $BaCl_2$; after digestion for 2 hr. add 6*N* NH_4OH (CO_2-free) until slightly alk., and 1 ml. 0·1*N* $K_2Cr_2O_7$ slowly. Cool, filter with an Emich filter stick and wash with three 5 ml. portions of H_2O. Dissolve the ppt. by warming with 2*N* HCl, cool and titrate with 0·025*N* Mohr's salt using 0·1 ml. 0·2% Ba-diphenylamine sulfonate indicator.
(4) Various colorimetric methods are based on the same reaction. For 50–70 ml. soln. contg. 2–120 μg. S/ml.,[29] add 2 ml. 4*N* AcOH–1*N* NaOAc and 3 ml. $BaCrO_4$ soln. (20 g./l. 5% $HClO_4$); shake for 2 min., neutralize with 4*N* NH_4OH (orange-yellow to yellow) and dil. to a definite vol. after 5 min. Filter and measure in a 2 cm. cell at 366 mμ (for 2–17 μg./ml.) or 405 mμ (for 10–120 μg./ml.). In a more sensitive method,[30] treat 2 ml. soln. with 5 ml. $BaCrO_4$ soln. (1·2670 g./100 ml. 1*N* HCl dild. to 1 l. with H_2O); after 15–20 min. add 1 ml. NH_4OH (100 ml. 1:3 NH_4OH and 0·25 g. CaO), dil. to 10 ml. with H_2O, shake for several min. and centrifuge. Pipet 2 ml. of the supernate, add 2 ml. diphenylcarbazide (0·5 g. warmed with 30 ml. EtOH, cooled and dild. to 50 ml. with EtOH) and dil. to 25 ml. with 0·1*N* H_2SO_4. Measure the blue-violet complex after 10 min. at 540 mμ.
(5) Ba-chloranilate can be used in a similar method.[31] For <40 mg. SO_4^{2-} in soln. of pH 4, add 10 ml. 0·05*M* KH-phthalate buffer and 50 ml. EtOH, dil. to 100 ml. with H_2O and shake for 10 min. with 0·3 g. reagent (1 l. 0·1% chloranilic acid and 1 l. 5% $BaCl_2$; decant after 12 hr., wash with H_2O till Cl^--free, thrice with EtOH and then with Et_2O; dry for 1 hr. *in vacuo*). Then centrifuge and measure the supernate at 530 mμ. Cations can be removed by ion exchange.

(c) Benzidine has been applied titrimetrically, gravimetrically and colorimetrically. For detn. of 20–300 μg. S in 50 ml. soln.[32] acidify with HCl to bromophenol blue, adjust to pH 2·75 ± 0·3, add 2 ml. benzidine soln. (4 g. in 250 ml. 0·2*N* HCl) and, after 2 min., 4 ml. 95% Me_2CO. After over 10 min. filter on a filter stick contg. filter pulp and wash 3 times with 1 ml. 95% Me_2CO and once with 5 ml. Transfer the ppt. to a large test tube with H_2O, heat, add 2 drops 0·05% phenol red and about half the required amt. of 0·01*N* NaOH; boil and complete the titration.

NOTES. (1) PO_4^{3-} interferes. Fe^{3+} must be reduced with $NH_2OH·HCl$; Fe^{2+}, Cu, Co, Ni, Mn, Al do not interfere.
(2) Potentiometric titration of the ppt. with 0·1*N* KNO_2 is possible.[33]
(3) Colorimetric methods generally involve reaction with the ppt. For 10–240 μg. S in 2 ml. soln.,[34] ppt. as above and suspend the ppt. in H_2O; add 1 ml. buffer (1 g. borax/100 ml. 0·1*N* NaOH), dil. to 7 ml. with H_2O and add 1 ml. 0·15% Na-β-naphthoquinone-4-sulfonate. After 5 min. add 2 ml. Me_2CO and after 5 min. measure the red color.
Other possible colorimetric finishes involve dissoln. of the ppt. from 1–25 μg. S in 1·2*N* HCl and measurement at 250 mμ,[35] coupling with phenol or thymol,[36] coupling with *N*-(1-naphthyl)-ethylenediamine,[37] formation of a yellow color with HCHO,[38] treatment with H_2O_2 and $FeCl_3$,[39] or reaction with phosphotungstic acid.[40]
(4) Gravimetric detn. is possible[41] for 0·5–10 mg. S with an error of ±0·05 mg.
Various derivs. of benzidine have been examined; the best is 4-chloro-4′-aminodiphenyl which is used titrimetrically.[42] Absorptiometric detn. is possible for 30–120 μg. SO_4^{2-}, the supernate being measured at 254 mμ.[43]

(d) $[Co(NH_3)_6]Br_3$ can be employed gravimetrically, titrimetrically or colorimetrically.[44] Treat the neutral or slightly acidic soln. with reagent soln. (1·5 g. and 250 mg. NH_4Br in 100 ml. 0·1*N* HCl) and add 2 vols. MeOH or Me_2CO. Filter, dry at 80°C (< 56°C) and weigh as $[Co(NH_3)_6]BrSO_4$. Alternatively, dissolve in H_2O and titrate with $AgNO_3$ soln., or compare the color with standard Co solns.

Octammino-μ-nitroaminodicobaltic nitrate is suitable for gravimetry of 1–15 mg. SO_4^{2-} at pH 7.[45] Add 0·3 ml. 1% reagent/mg. SO_4^{2-} and add Me_2CO to give a concn. of 25% in a total vol. of < 20 ml. After 4 hr., filter on a glass crucible and wash with 25% Me_2CO and then with Me_2CO. Dry in air and weigh as $[(NH_3)_4CoNH_2NO_2Co(NH_3)_4](SO_4)_2·2H_2O$. EDTA prevents interference of Al and Fe; 1 ml. 0·2*N* HCl prevents PO_4^{3-} interference.

(e) $Pb(NO_3)_2$ is suitable for absorptiometric detn. and can also be used titrimetrically. For analysis of 1–3 mg. rubber,[46] add 0·25 ml. 10% $Pb(NO_3)_2$, 1 ml. satd. Br_2 in HNO_3 and 3 drops $HClO_4$. Heat for 30–60 min. until a paste is obtained, cool, mix with 10 ml. Me_2CO and heat at 50–60°C for 10–15 min. Centrifuge, remove the supernate and wash twice with 10 ml. Me_2CO. Add 2 drops H_2O, evap. to dryness, cool, shake with 10·0 ml. 50% v/v HCl, shake and measure at 270 mμ.

Erythrosine can serve as indicator in titration of 50–100 mg. SO_4^{2-} in 50 ml. soln. (neutral to phenolphthalein).[47] Add 16 ml. EtOH and 14 drops 1% erythrosine and titrate with 0·1*M* $Pb(NO_3)_2$ to violet. Cl^- interferes; if present, titrate with $AgNO_3$ using fluorescein indicator, filter and proceed as above. For other adsorption indicators, see Table 10.

Dithizone is used as indicator in titration with 0·02*N* Pb^{2+} in 80% Me_2CO media at pH 4.[48] Pb^{2+} can be added in excess and titrated with K_2CrO_4 soln. using siloxene indicator.[49] Amperometric titration is possible.[50]

(f) Th^{4+}, borate and amaranth allow colorimetry of 0–400 p.p.m. S at 521 mμ.[51] F^- interferes; PO_4^{3-} can be removed by La^{3+} addn. and HCO_3^- by Amberlite IRC-50 in the RH-form.

(g) Infrared spectroscopy with a KBr disk is suitable for detn. of 30–80 μg. SO_4^{2-} with an error of ±2–3%.[52]

HYDROGEN SULFIDE DETERMINATION

(a) Redox titrations. Treatment with excess KIO_3 and iodometric titration is suitable for 2·5 mg. S^{2-} in 10 ml. soln.[53, 54] Add 15 ml. 0·1*N* KIO_3 and 10 ml. 10*N* NaOH, boil gently for 10 min., cool, add 20 ml. 8*N* H_2SO_4 and 5 ml. 5% KI and titrate with 0·1*N* $Na_2S_2O_3$.

For steels,[7] treat a 5 g. sample with 80 ml. 1:1 HCl; use 2:1 HCl or concd. HCl (and 0·5 ml. HF if much Si is present) and provide a condenser when alloy steels are analyzed. Heat until dissoln. is complete and boil for 30 sec. Absorb in 200 ml. H_2O contg. 15 ml. 10% $ZnSO_4$ in 1:1 NH_4OH. Add 2 ml. starch soln. (5 g. sol. starch in 25 ml. H_2O added to 500 ml. boiling H_2O, cooled and mixed with a cold soln. of 5 g. NaOH in 50 ml. H_2O and 15 g. KI). Then add 40 ml. 1:1 HCl and titrate with 0·03*N* KIO_3 to a blue color.

NOTES. (1) Annealing may be needed for high-S or high-C steels. For Ni–Cr or Ni–Cr–Fe, treat with HCl in a stream of H_2 and absorb in 25 ml. of a soln. of 25 g. $CdCl_2$ in 1 l. 3:2 NH_4OH; filter, etc. Treatment of the residue may be needed. For Ni, use $CdSO_4$ if S <0·01% and $ZnSO_4$ if S >0·01%. For brasses and bronzes, add a crystal of $SnCl_2$ in 75 ml. HBr for dissoln., with a stream of N_2; if the sample is difficult to dissolve, add 2 ml. 2% $SbCl_3$ in 1:1 HCl. Sb,[7] Ni, and Ti[55] can also be analyzed.
(2) KIO_3 can be used with a $CHCl_3$ indicator.[53]
(3) I_2 may replace KIO_3. For a 0·5–1 g. sample,[53, 56] boil for 20 min. with 100 ml. 1:1 HCl (add 0·5–1 g. Zn for sulfides); absorb in 50 ml. $CdSO_4$ soln. (70 g. in 500 ml. mixed with 1·2 l. NH_4OH and dild. to 2·5 l. with H_2O), dil. to 500 ml. with H_2O, neutralize with 1:1 HCl and add 5 ml. starch soln. Titrate with 0·1*N* I_2 adding HCl occasionally until a blue color remains for 5 min. If much S is present, filter, suspend in H_2O, add excess 0·1*N* I_2, starch and HCl and back-titrate with $Na_2S_2O_3$. If Cd^{2+} is used the soln. must be protected from light. Other absorbents are KOH, or Na_2HAsO_3; absorption in excess I_2–KI is possible.[56]
(4) Hypohalite oxidation is useful for small amts.[53, 54, 57] For NaOBr soln. add 100 g. Br_2 to 60 g. NaOH in 1·6 l. H_2O while cooling. For NaOCl, pass Cl_2 into 90 g. NaOH in 1·5 l. H_2O until the wt. has increased by 35 g. For a detn., treat the alk. sample soln. with a 30% excess of hypohalite, add 2–3 g. KI after 3–5 min. and dil. to 4–5 times the original vol. Add a 3–5 ml. excess of HCl and titrate with $Na_2S_2O_3$ using starch indicator. For analysis of steels,[58] absorb H_2S in 25 ml. 0·1*N* NaOCl and 25 ml. H_2O, boil for 5 ± 1 min., cool, add 10 ml. 10% KI and 20 ml. 2*N* HCl and titrate with 0·05*N* $Na_2S_2O_3$.
(5) $KMnO_4$ is applicable in alk. soln.[53] Add 25 ml. 0·1*N* $KMnO_4$ to 5–10 ml. 4*N* NaOH and add 10 ml. 0·1*N* S^{2-}; after 5 min., acidify, add KI and titrate with 0·1*N* $Na_2S_2O_3$. Alternatively,[56] absorb H_2S in KOH, pour into an acidic Fe^{3+} soln. and titrate with $KMnO_4$ soln.
(6) $K_2Cr_2O_7$ is suitable[59] for absorption of H_2S if a known excess is used with 60 ml. 13·5*N* H_2SO_4 and 7 ml. 20% NaCl; back-titration is done with Fe^{2+}.
(7) $K_3Fe(CN)_6$ can be used in direct titration.[53] Mix 20 ml. buffer (70 ml. NH_4OH and 50 g. NH_4Cl/l.) and a few drops of indicator (4–5 ml. satd. dimethylglyoxime in EtOH mixed with 1 ml. 0·02*N* $FeSO_4$ and 0·5 ml. NH_4OH); pass H_2 for 5 min., add the sample soln. and titrate with 0·1*N* $Fe(CN)_6^{3-}$. Excess of $Fe(CN)_6^{3-}$ can be added and back-titrated with $VOSO_4$ soln. Na-nitroprusside may serve as indicator in direct titrations.[60]
(7) Other possibilities are absorption of H_2S in neutral $CdSO_4$ and titration with KOH soln.,[56] absorption in $AgNO_3$ in NH_4OH, filtration and Volhard's titration,[56] and titration with $KBrO_3$ or Br_2 soln.[53]
(8) NaN_3 can be added to the I_2 soln. for titration.[61] For the reagent, mix 1·27 g. I_2 and 3·00 g. NaN_3 with 100 ml. H_2O and dil. 100-fold just before use. For detn. of 1–10 ml. ca. $10^{-4}M$ S^{2-} soln., dil. to 15 ml. with H_2O, add 0·5 ml. starch and titrate to a blue color.

(b) *p*-Amino-*N*,*N*-dimethylaniline-HCl in conjunction with $FeCl_3$ provides the colorimetric 'methylene blue' method.[62] For 5–100 μg. S in 10 ml. soln., add 1·5 ml. 6*N* H_2SO_4, dil. to 50 ml. with H_2O and add 0·1 ml. 2% amine soln., and 0·05 ml. 5% $FeCl_3$; measure at 668 mμ.

(c) $Bi(NO_3)_3$ allows colorimetric detn. of 6–40 μg. S as H_2S.[63] Add 10 ml. 6% NaOH and an equal vol. of reagent soln. (42·8 g. $Bi(NO_3)_3$ in 3 l. AcOH and 15 l. H_2O), and pass N_2 gas for 30 sec. Measure the color after 5 min.

Various similar methods have been suggested. For detn. of 30–200 μg. S as H_2S, add 6% NaOH to a vol. of 70 ml., pass N_2 gas, add 70 ml. reagent soln. (44·4 g. $UO_2(NO_3)_2$ and 31·4 g. $Cd(OAc)_2$ in 20 l. H_2O and 4 l. AcOH), pass N_2 for 3 min. and compare the colors.[63]

With $Pb(NO_3)_2$ as reagent,[64] convert S^{2-} to sulfate, reduce with HI and H_3PO_2 and absorb H_2S in 1 ml. reagent (5 g. $Pb(NO_3)_2$ in 50 ml. H_2O mixed with 20 g.

citric acid and dild. to 100 ml. with H_2O) and 20 ml. 1:2 NH_4OH. Measure at 370 mμ; the method is suitable for 3–100 μg. S in the final aliquot. An apparatus similar to that used in the Gutzeit method for As has been described.[56]

Other tests based on similar reactions involve As_2O_3 paper[65] or Ag-dithizonate (see Chapter 59, p. 443).

$Hg(SCN)_2$ can be applied with Fe–alum.[66] For 10 ml. soln. contg. 0·05–10 mg. S/l., add 1 ml. 0·3% w/v $Hg(SCN)_2$ in EtOH and after 5 min. add 2 ml. 6% Fe–alum in 6*N* HNO_3 and 1 ml. CCl_4; after 5 min. centrifuge and measure at 460 mμ. AgSCN is applicable similarly.

Dithizone can serve[67] as indicator in direct titration with Hg^{2+} or Cd^{2+}. A gravimetric or titrimetric Volhard method can be used for 0·5–50 mg. S^{2-} or 1–25 mg. S^{2-} if Hg^{2+} or Ag^+ is used resp.[68]

S^{2-} can be pptd. with Cu^{2+}, excess being titrated with EDTA.[69] To a mixt. of 25 ml. 0·05*M* $Cu(ClO_4)_2$ and 15 ml. buffer contg. 0·67*M* AcOH and 0·33*M* NaOAc, add 10–40 ml. 0·02*M* S^{2-} soln., filter on a G4 crucible, and wash with 20–30 ml. H_2O. To the filtrate add 2–3 ml. NH_4OH, dil. to 100–200 ml. with H_2O, add 3–6 drops of satd. murexide soln. in H_2O, and titrate with 0·05*M* EDTA.

(d) $(NH_4)_2MoO_4$ and H_3PO_4 can be applied colorimetrically.[70] Collect the H_2S in 10 ml. 5% $Zn(OAc)_2$ contg. 1% NaOAc, and add 2·5 ml. 10% $(NH_4)_2MoO_4$ and 6 ml. 2·75*M* H_3PO_4. Dil. to 50 ml. with H_2O and measure the blue color at 770 mμ within 20–50 min.

NOTES. (1) Na_2WO_4 can replace molybdate.[71] To 10 ml. soln. add 5 ml. reagent soln. (25 g. Na_2WO_4, 20 g. H_3PO_4 (s.g. 1·71) and 75 g. tartaric acid dild. to 500 ml.) and 3·5 ml. 4*N* NaOH. Compare the blue color after 3 min.
(2) Mo^{6+} can also be used with KSCN in HCl soln. with addn. of Me_2CO or EtOH.[72]
(3) Fe^{3+}-dimethylglyoxime has been applied colorimetrically.[73]

(e) Direct combustion method.[56] Combustion is carried out at 1425–1525°C and is followed by titration with KIO_3. The method has been used for steels, Ni–Cu, brasses and bronzes.[7] It can also be followed by a neutralization titration.[74] A colorimetric finish with $K_2Cr_2O_7$ and diphenylcarbazide has also been proposed.[75]

References

1. HILLEBRAND and LUNDELL, 570 (711); SCOTT and FURMAN, 903; KIMURA, 312; PIGOTT, 422.
2. SCHOLL, A. W., and YOUNG, R. L., *Sulfur*, A. W. Scholl, Huntington, W. Va., U.S.A. (1954).
3. KURTENACKER, A., *Chem. Anal.*, **38** (1938).
4. HORAK, O., *Z. anal. Chem.*, **139**, 196 (1953).
5. KREIDER, R. E., and FOULDS, J. G., *Anal. Chem.*, **26**, 1983 (1954); BETHGE, P. O., *ibid.*, **28**, 119 (1956); VANDEEL, C., and ALLARD, E., *Ind. chim. belge*, **20**, Spec. No., 435 (1955); also JOHNSON, C. M., and NISHITA, H., *Anal. Chem.*, **26**, 1008 (1954) (HI + red P + HCOOH).
6. KIBA, T., *et al.*, *Bull. Chem. Soc. Japan*, **28**, 641 (1955); **30**, 44, 482 (1957).
7. A.S.T.M., 91 ff.
8. HORAK, O., *Z. anal. Chem.*, **140**, 255 (1953); **137**, 245 (1952).
9. NYDAHL, F., *Anal. Chem.*, **26**, 580 (1954); FRITZ, J. S., *et al.*, *ibid.*, **29**, 158 (1957).
10. FALES, H. A., and THOMPSON, W. S., *Ind. Eng. Chem., Anal. Ed.*, **11**, 206 (1939); SCHROEDER, W. C., *ibid.*, **5**, 403 (1933); KARAOGLANOV, Z., *Z. anal. Chem.*, **106**, 129 (1936); BALAREW, D., *ibid.*, **115**, 112 (1938/39).
11. SCHLEICHER, A., *Z. anal. Chem.*, **121**, 90 (1941).
12. OGG, C. L., *et al.*, *Anal. Chem.*, **20**, 83 (1948); BOVEE, H. H., and ROBINSON, R. J., *ibid.*, **29**, 1353 (1957).
13. MUTSCHIN, A., and POLLACK, R., *Z. anal. Chem.*, **106**, 385 (1936); **107**, 18 (1936); **108**, 8, 309 (1937).
14. ALICINO, J. F., *Anal. Chem.*, **20**, 85 (1948); MUKOYAMA, T., *Japan Analyst*, **4**, 558 (1955) (rhodizonate paper).
15. ISAGAI, K., *Japan Analyst*, **4**, 171 (1955).
16. ANDEREGG, G., *et al.*, *Helv. Chim. Acta*, **37**, 113 (1954).
17. UENO, K., and YAMAGUCHI, Y., *Japan Analyst*, **3**, 331 (1954).
18. BELCHER, R., *et al.*, *Chem. & Ind.* (*London*), 850 (1954); *Analyst*, **80**, 751 (1955).
19. MUKAI, K., and GOTO, K., *Japan Analyst*, **6**, 732 (1957).
20. FRITZ, J. S., and FREELAND, M. Q., *Anal. Chem.*, **26**, 1593 (1954); FRITZ and YAMAMURA, S. S., *ibid.*, **27**, 1461 (1955).
21. GEYER, R., *Z. anal. Chem.*, **146**, 174 (1955).
22. KUZNETSOV, V. I., *Doklady Akad. Nauk S.S.S.R.*, **77**, 61 (1951).
23. MARKOVA, L. V., *Ukrain. Khim. Zhur.*, **23**, 89 (1957).
24. NAKATA, H., and KUSAKA, Y., *Japan Analyst*, **4**, 621 (1955); also see DAVEY, W., and GWILT, J. R., *J. Appl. Chem.* (*London*), **5**, 474 (1955).
25. DAMERELL, V. R. and STRATER, H. H., *Ind. Eng. Chem., Anal. Ed.*, **6**, 19 (1934).
26. TAKIYAMA, K., and SUITO, E., *Japan Analyst*, **3**, 292 (1954); also see TOENNIES, G., and BAKAY, B., *Anal. Chem.*, **25**, 160 (1953) (0·01–100 p.p.m., 40% dipropylene glycol + EtOH); KELLY, H. J., and ROGERS, L. B., *ibid.*, **27**, 759 (1955) (2% EtOH soln. at pH 1).
27. JOSEPHSON, B., *Analyst*, **64**, 181 (1939).
28. BELCHER, R., and GODBERT, A. L., *Analyst*, **66**, 289 (1941).
29. KATO, T., *et al.*, *J. Chem. Soc. Japan*, **76**, 373 (1955); also see EGAMI, F., and TAKAHASHI, N., *Bull. Chem. Soc. Japan*, **30**, 442 (1957).
30. URBACH, C., *Mikrochemie*, **14**, 321 (1934); WELCHER, **III**, 443; also see IWASAKI, I., *et al.*, *J. Chem. Soc. Japan*, **74**, 400 (1953).
31. BERTOLACINI, R. J., and BARNEY II, J. E., *Anal. Chem.*, **29**, 281 (1957).
32. TANAKA, N., *J. Chem. Soc. Japan*, **64**, 443 (1943); WELCHER, **II**, 298; KOLTHOFF and STENGER, *Volumetric Analysis*, Vol. II, 163 (1947) (details).
33. KELLER, R. E. and MUNCH, R. M., *Anal. Chem.*, **26**, 1518 (1954).
34. TANAKA, S., *J. Biochem.*, **28**, 37 (1938); WELCHER, **II**, 307.
35. ANDERSEN, L., *Acta Chem. Scand.*, **7**, 689 (1953).
36. CUTHBERTSON, D. P., and THOMPSETT, S. L., *Biochem. J.*, **25**, 1237 (1931).

37. Welcher, **II**, 418.
38. Welcher, **I**, 385.
39. Hubbard, R. S., *J. Biol. Chem.*, **88**, 663 (1930).
40. Wu, H., *J. Biol. Chem.*, **43**, 1890 (1920).
41. Gottschalk, G., and Dehmel, P. *Z. anal. Chem.*, **155**, 251 (1957).
42. Belcher, R., *et al.*, *J. Chem. Soc.*, 1334 (1953); *Analyst*, **81**, 4 (1956); Wilkinson, H. C., *ibid.*, 9 (in coal).
43. Jones, A. S., and Letham, D. S., *Analyst*, **81**, 15 (1956).
44. Mahr, C., and Krauss, K., *Z. anal. Chem.*, **128**, 477 (1948).
45. Belcher, R., and Gibbons, D., *J. Chem. Soc.*, 4216 (1952).
46. Kress, K. E., *Anal. Chem.*, **27**, 1618 (1955).
47. Burg, W. V., *Ind. Eng. Chem.*, *Anal. Ed.*, **11**, 28 (1939); also see Ricci, J. E., *ibid.*, **8**, 130 (1936) (eosin).
48. Archer, E. E., *Analyst*, **82**, 208 (1957).
49. Kenney, F., *et al.*, *Anal. Chem.*, **29**, 543 (1957).
50. Gordon, B. E., and Urner, R. S., *Anal. Chem.*, **25**, 897 (1953).
51. Lambert, J. L., *et al.*, *Anal. Chem.*, **27**, 800 (1955).
52. Tai, H., and Underwood, A. L., *Anal. Chem.*, **29**, 1430 (1957).
53. Kolthoff and Belcher, *Volumetric Analysis*, Vol. III.
54. Bethge, P. O., *Anal. Chim. Acta*, **9**, 129 (1953); **10**, 113, 310 (1954).
55. Luke, C. L., *Anal. Chem.*, **29**, 1227 (1957) (in Ni); Codell, M., *et al.*, *ibid.*, 1496 (Ti).
56. Scott and Furman, 991.
57. Dunicz, B. L., and Rosenqvist, T., *Anal. Chem.*, **24**, 404 (1952).
58. Kitchener, J. A., *et al.*, *Analyst*, **76**, 509 (1951).
59. Radmacher, W., and Mornhauser, P., *Z. anal. Chem.*, **141**, 419 (1954).
60. Kiboku, M., *Japan Analyst*, **6**, 491 (1957).
61. Suzuki, S., and Kawagoe, S., *Japan Analyst*, **1**, 87 (1952).
62. Diemair, W., *et al.*, *Z. anal. Chem.*, **116**, 385 (1939); Yoe, 373, 375; Welcher, **II**, 253; also see Budd, M. S., and Bewick, H. A., *Anal. Chem.*, **24**, 1536 (1952); Polson, D. S. C., and Strickland, J. D. H., *Anal. Chim. Acta*, **6**, 452 (1952); Oka, Y, and Matsuo, S., *J. Chem. Soc. Japan*, **74**, 618 (1953); Johnson and Nishita.[5]
63. Field, E., and Oldach, C. S., *Ind. Eng. Chem.*, *Anal. Ed.*, **18**, 665 (1946); Treiber, E., *et al.*, *Mikrochem. ver. Mikrochim. Acta*, **40**, 32 (1952) (also Ag, Pd, Cu salts).
64. Luke, C. L., *Anal. Chem.*, **21**, 1369 (1949); Čůta, F., *et al.*, *Chem. listy*, **50**, 320 (1956).
65. Yoe, 375.
66. Utsumi, S., *J. Chem. Soc. Japan*, **74**, 301, 358 (1953).
67. Archer, E. E., *Analyst*, **81**, 181 (1956).
68. Dick, J., and Bica, V., *Acad. rep. populare Romîne, Baza cercetări ştiinţ. Timişora, Studii cercetări ştiinţ.*, **2**, 103 (1955).
69. Kivalo, P., *Anal. Chem.*, **27**, 1809 (1955).
70. Bethge, P. O., *Svensk Kem. Tidskr.*, **64**, 177 (1952).
71. Lapin, L. N., and Hein, W. O., *Z. Hyg. Infektionskrankh.*, **114**, 605 (1933).
72. Nazarenko, V. A., and Shusotva, M. B., *Zhur. Anal. Khim.*, **11**, 489 (1956).
73. Charlot, G., *Bull. soc. chim. France*, **7**, 144 (1940).
74. Pigott, 459.
75. Sakihama, A., *Japan Analyst*, **6**, 439, 487 (1957).

59

CHLORINE, BROMINE AND IODINE

The main sources for this chapter are Hillebrand and Lundell,[1] Scott and Furman[2] and Kimura.[3] Micro methods for these halogens have been reviewed,[4] as have more general procedures.[5]

Attack

(a) AgCl and rocks. Fuse with Na_2CO_3 and leach with H_2O (and with EtOH for rocks). Treat with HNO_3, leave for 12 hr. if turbid, add a slight excess of NH_4OH, filter on paper and wash with hot H_2O.

$PbCl_2$ is decomposed by digestion with $NaHCO_3$; and Hg_2Cl_2 and $HgCl_2$ by digestion with NaOH and Na_2CO_3 resp.

(b) Glasses. Evap. to fumes with HF, $HClO_4$ and Ag_2SO_4; cool, add H_2O, filter on paper, treat the ppt. with NH_4OH and then HNO_3.

(c) Organic compounds. Very many methods are available. Combustion in oxygen is most satisfactory. See textbooks of organic analysis for details.

Separation

CHLORINE

$AgNO_3$ seps. Cl from many elements; interferences are I^-, Br^-, CN^-, SCN^-, Sb^{5+}, Sn^{4+}, Pt^{4+}, Cr^{3+}, Hg^{2+}.

Sepn. from Sn is obtained by neutralization to methyl orange with dil. NH_4OH, addn. of NH_4NO_3 and boiling. Treatment with NH_4OH (and if necessary repptn. after dissoln. in dil. HNO_3) allows sepn. from Al and Cr.

Evapn. to dryness with Na_2CO_3, heating just to fusion and extn. with H_2O seps. Cl^- from Pt. Boiling with Na_2CO_3 allows sepn. from heavy metals.

Hg and Sb are sepd. by treatment with H_2S, filtration, removal of H_2S by passing CO_2; the soln. is then made alk. with NaOH, boiled with H_2O_2 and made just acid with HNO_3.

Treatment with Zn and H_2SO_4 seps. Cl from Ag and AgCN.

Cl^- can be sepd. from I^- with Fe-alum. Treat the sample with 400 ml. H_2O and 10 ml. 1:1 H_2SO_4, add 2 g. Fe-alum and 3 ml. HNO_3 and boil. If I is to be detd., steam-distil it into 2–3 flasks contg. 50 ml. 5% NaOH and 50 ml. 3% H_2O_2, combine the contents of the flasks, add 50 ml. H_2O_2, boil, cool, acidify with H_2SO_4, add a few drops SO_2 water, etc. $NaNO_2$ can replace Fe-alum.

Cl^- is sepd. from Br^- by H_2TeO_4; treat $< 0{\cdot}5$ g. sample with 40 ml. H_2O, 10 ml. 1:1 H_2SO_4 and 1 g. reagent, and distil while passing CO_2, until 17–18 ml. of soln. remains.

Small amts. of Cl^- can be sepd. from much Br^- by treatment with $KH(IO_3)_2$ as shown below:

KCl present (%)	5–10	1·5–5	0·25–1
Sample (g.)	0·6	1·8	3·6
0·2*N* $KH(IO_3)_2$ added (ml.)	36	96	186
2*N* HNO_3 added (ml.)	20	26	35

These vols. refer to 200–250 ml. soln.

BROMINE

Br^- can be sepd. from I^- by treatment with H_2TeO_4 or $NaNO_2$. Sepn. from Cl^- is obtained by treatment with CrO_3 in 1:3 H_2SO_4 soln. with passage of air. Distn. as BrCN is also possible (see p. 444). Sepn. from Cl^- and I^- is possible with $KMnO_4$;[2, 6] treat 40 ml. soln. with 2 ml. 1*N* reagent and 5 ml. 1:4 H_3PO_4 while passing air at a rate of 3–4 bubbles/sec. for 30 min., and collect Br_2 in 1% KI.

IODINE

I^- can be sepd. from Cl^- and Br^- in several ways. For the method involving $PdCl_2$, see under Determination, p. 446. Treatment with $AgNO_3$ followed by H_2SO_4 and CrO_3 is feasible. Another method is to add 5 ml. H_3PO_4 and 10–20 ml. H_2O_2 to 50 ml. soln. and distil.

SEPARATION OF 3 HALOGENS FROM EACH OTHER

(*i*) Treatment with oxidants allows eventual detn. of each halide as its Ag^+ salt.[1, 2] Treat a sample contg. $< 0{\cdot}25$ g. of each halide with 700–750 ml. H_2O, 5 ml. 1:5 H_2SO_4 and 2 g. $NaNO_2$ and steam-distil for 30–45 min. until the residual soln. is reduced to 500–600 ml. Collect the distillate in 1:1 5% NaOH–3% H_2O_2; then warm with more H_2O_2, boil, cool, acidify with H_2SO_4, and if I_2 seps., add SO_2 water and boil; finally add $AgNO_3$ to ppt. AgI. Treat the 500–600 ml.

residual soln. with NaOH until slightly alk., evap. to 50 ml. and transfer to a 750 ml. flask; cool, neutralize with 1:1 AcOH, add 65 ml. AcOH and 1–1·5 g. $KMnO_4$ and steam-distil slowly for 60–65 min. Treat this distillate in the same way as above and ppt. AgBr. Make the second residual soln. alk. with NaOH, warm, add EtOH, filter and wash with 1% $NaNO_3$; treat the filtrate with HNO_3 and $AgNO_3$ to ppt. AgCl.

NOTE. For micro sepn.[7] treat 5 ml. soln. with 1 ml. 30% $NaNO_2$ and 1 ml. AcOH and pass air through for 30–45 min.; then add 1 ml. 30% $NaNO_2$ and 8 ml. 6·6*N* HNO_3 and pass air through for 30–40 min. Collect the distillate in 4 absorbers contg. 6·6*N* HNO_3 (Cl), one contg. 10 ml. 10% Na_2SO_3 (Br), and one contg. 10 ml. 10% NaOH (I).

(*ii*) $AgNO_3$ can be used as follows.[1, 2] Divide the sample soln. into 2 parts. In one aliquot ppt. all 3 halides as their Ag salts. To the other aliquot, add $AgNO_3$ and treat the ppt. with 2 g. $K_2Cr_2O_7$ in 30 ml. H_2SO_4 for 30 min. at 95°C, passing air near the end of the period. Dil. to 300–400 ml. and filter. To the filtrate add concd. Na_2SO_3 dropwise until an SO_2 smell appears. The ppt. formed is AgI; filter and treat the filtrate with KI to ppt. Ag, which is equiv. to Br^-.

NOTE. In another method,[8] divide the sample into 2 parts. In one part, ppt. Ag(Cl, Br, I), weigh, mix with NH_4I, heat slowly to 400°C and just fuse; weigh as AgI. To the other part, add 25 ml. Me_2CO, adjust to 2–2·5*N* in H_2SO_4, add KIO_3 until colorless, dil. to 350 ml. and add $AgNO_3$. Filter and wash with H_2O and Me_2CO and then with H_2O. Weigh as Ag(Cl, Br), convert to AgI in the same way as above and weigh as AgI. The 3 halides can then be calcd. Ag(Cl, Br) can be converted to AgBr by heating with NH_4Br.
Simultaneous detn. of the 3 halogens by coulometric[9] or amperometric[10] titration with $AgNO_3$ is possible.

(*iii*) $KBrO_3$ titrations and iodometric titrations can be joined to give simultaneous detns. of halogens[1] (see also under Determination, p. 443).

(*iv*) Ion exchange resins allow sepns. as described in Chapter 13, section 4.4.

(*v*) $PdSO_4$ is used colorimetrically in simultaneous detn. of the 3 halides.[11] Several steps are involved. First, to the soln. add 0·4 ml. 5*N* H_2SO_4, dil. to 5–8 ml. with H_2O, add 0·4 ml. $PdSO_4$ soln. (1·4 mg. Pd/ml. 1·5*N* H_2SO_4), dil. to 10 ml. with H_2O and measure against H_2SO_4 and $PdSO_4$ as reference, taking the absorbance at 230 mμ (A_1) and 390 mμ (A_2). This gives the total absorbance. Second, to 5 ml. soln. add 0·2 ml. 5*N* H_2SO_4 and 40 mg. MnO_2, heat at 70–80°C for 25 min., cool, decant, add 0·2 ml. H_2SO_4, $PdSO_4$, etc.; the absorbance due to $Cl^- + Br^-$ is measured at 230 mμ (A_3) and 390 mμ (A_4). Third, to 5 ml. soln. add 0·2 ml. H_2SO_4 and 40 mg. PbO_2, etc.; measure the absorbance due to Cl^- at 230 mμ (A_6) and also against H_2O as reference (A_5). For calculation, $Cl^- = A_5 - A_6$, $Br^- = A_3 - A_5$, and $I^- = A_2 - A_4$. The method is suitable for final concns. of 2–25 μg. Cl/ml., 0·5–7 μg. Br/ml. and 1–6 μg. I/ml.

Concentration[12]

I^- can be concd. with AgBr, Br^- with AgCl, and Cl^- with Ag_2CrO_4.

Determination

If a simultaneous determination of all 3 halogens is required, one of the above methods should be applied. Chloride can be readily determined by the Volhard or Fajan method, and iodide and bromide can be previously separated without difficulty. The gravimetric and nephelometric silver methods for chloride have been well studied. For bromide, the permanganate or hypochlorite method is to be recommended. Iodide can be determined, even in presence of bromide and chloride, by oxidation with hypochlorite or bromine and iodometry, or by Fajan's method. For small amounts of chloride or bromide colorimetric methods based on reaction with Hg or Ag thiocyanate are best; for iodide, the color of iodine, with or without starch, or a catalytic method is to be preferred.

CHLORINE

(a) $AgNO_3$ is used in the classical ; imetric, titrimetric and nephelometric techniques.

(*i*) For gravimetric detn.[1, 2, 3, 13] of < 0·1 g. Cl^- in 200 ml. soln. contg. 1–2 ml. HNO_3, add 5% $AgNO_3$ (contg. 1 ml. HNO_3/l.) dropwise until the ppt. coagulates. Heat to 60–70°C and place in the dark for 5–12 hr. Filter on a glass crucible, wash with 0·005% $AgNO_3$, 1:100 HNO_3 and then twice with H_2O, dry at 130°C (70–600°C) and weigh as AgCl. If necessary Cl^- in the filtrate can be detd. nephelometrically. Adsorption of Ag^+ on the ppt. can be prevented[14] by addn. of NH_4NO_3.

(*ii*) Volhard's method.[1, 2, 3] For < 0·1 g. Cl^- in 100 ml. 1:99 HNO_3 soln., add a 1–3 ml. excess of 0·1*N* $AgNO_3$, filter and wash with 1:99 HNO_3. Treat the filtrate with 5 ml. satd. Fe-alum soln. and titrate with 0·1*N* NH_4SCN.

NOTES. (1) Interferences are Br^-, I^-, CN^-, SCN^-, Hg^{2+}, Pd, NO_2^- and Tl^{3+}. No interference is found from Cu, As, Sb, Cd, Bi, Pb, Zn, Fe, Mn, Co, Al.
(2) Adsorption of Ag^+ on the ppt. can cause results 0·7% high; this can be prevented by addn. of 2 g. NH_4NO_3/100 ml. of final vol.[14] Filtration is unnecessary if the ppt. is shaken with a suitable org. solvent before back-titration; nitrobenzene (1 ml./50 mg. Cl^-) is best[2, 15] but thymol (4 g./10 ml. EtOH or Et_2O/100 ml. of final vol.),[14] toluene, xylene, C_6H_6 (10 ml.),[16] or $CHCl_3$[17] can also be used. The last 4 reagents are not very satisfactory.[17]
(3) Filtration can also be avoided if the conditions are closely controlled.[18] For 70–140 mg. Cl^- in 30 ml. soln. contg. 100m*M* HNO_3, add 10 ml. 0·2*M* $Fe(NO_3)_3$ and 1·00 ml. 0·01*N* KSCN and titrate with 0·1*N* $AgNO_3$ using a comparison soln. In an alternative method for the same amt. of Cl^- in 30 ml. soln., add 17 ml. 6*N* HNO_3 and

0·1N $AgNO_3$ until the supernate is clear, followed by 1–2 ml. in excess (if possible, add $AgNO_3$ before HNO_3); then add 10 ml. 2M $Fe(NO_3)_3$ and 1N KSCN to give a pink color and titrate with 0·1N $AgNO_3$.

(*iii*) Potentiometric titration[18, 19] is accurate to ±0·1% for 0·02M Cl^-. The error is below ±1% for $10^{-4}M$ Cl, $10^{-5}M$ Br^- or $10^{-6}M$ I^- in acetate-buffered soln. contg. liquid nonionic detergent. The error is said[20] to be ±1% for $10^{-4}M$ Cl^- down to 1 μg. Cl^-. See also above (p. 441) and below.

(*iv*) Mohr's method.[1, 2, 3] Adjust the soln. to pH 6·5–10·5 with NH_4OAc, $NaHCO_3$ or borax, add 1–2 ml. 5% K_2CrO_4/100 ml. soln. and titrate with 0·1N $AgNO_3$. Bleach the red color with 0·01N NaCl and deduct a correction.

NOTES, (1) Interferences are Br^-, I^-, CN^-, SCN^-, $S_2O_3^{2-}$, PO_4^{3-}, CO_3^{2-}, S^{2-}, org. compds., Pb, Bi, Ba, Fe; NH_4^+ interferes if the pH exceeds 7·2. If SO_4^{2-} exceeds 0·2 g., add an equal vol. of EtOH.[21]
(2) The end-point can be made sharper by addn. of 5–10 ml. 0·1% agar-agar.[22]

(*v*) Fajan's method.[2] To 10 ml. soln. at pH 4–7 add 2 drops 0·1% dichloro-R-fluorescein indicator (in 60–70% EtOH, or in H_2O with the Na-salt), and titrate dropwise with $AgNO_3$ soln. using vigorous stirring, to the color change from yellow-green to red-orange. The error is < ±2% in detn. of 0·0005N Cl^-.

NOTES. (1) Br^- and I^- interfere, but Cu, Zn, Mg, Ni, Al, Ca, Sr, Ba do not.
(2) Other indicators are mentioned in Table 10. Eosin is used at pH 0·5–2·0.[23] The end-point with fluorescein is sharper if a surface-active agent such as Tween 80 is added.[24]

(*vi*) Other titrimetric methods. Back-titration with KI soln. using starch and Ce^{4+} as indicator has been proposed.[25] To 30 ml. soln. contg. 5 ml. 6N HNO_3 add excess 0·1N $AgNO_3$, filter and wash with 1N HNO_3. Add 3 ml. 0·5% starch and 0·1 ml. 0·1N $(NH_4)_2Ce(SO_4)_3$ and titrate with 0·1N KI to a blue color; det. a blank. Cu^{2+} and Fe^{3+} do not interfere.

p-Dimethylaminobenzilidenerhodanine can be used as external indicator in direct titration.[26] For 0·02–0·2 mg. Cl^-, add 2 ml. 2N HNO_3, dil. to 5 ml. with H_2O and titrate with 0·01N $AgNO_3$ until a brown spot is obtained on filter paper treated with a satd. soln. of reagent in Me_2CO, dried and stored in the dark. The error is ±8 μg.

In other methods, the AgCl ppt. is dissolved in NH_4OH and titrated with KCN soln. using KI indicator, or dissolved in $Ni(CN)_4^{2-}$ in NH_4OH and titrated with EDTA. See p. 146, for details.

(*vii*) Nephelometry and colorimetry. Nephelometry is suitable for 20 ml. soln. contg. 0·01–3 mg. Cl^-/l.;[27] add 2 ml. $10^{-3}M$ $AgNO_3$ contg. $2 \times 10^{-2}M$ $Pb(NO_3)_2$, place in the dark for 20 min. and compare. For a classical study, see ref. 28. Treatment with 0·01N $AgNO_3$ of solns. contg. 90 ml. EtOH/110 ml. is also satisfactory.[29]

For colorimetry,[30] dissolve the AgCl ppt. from 25–350 μg. Cl^- in 2–3 ml. 1:1 NH_4OH, wash with 2–3 ml. H_2O, dil. to 8 ml. with H_2O, add 1 ml. 0·01M Na_2S, dil. to 10 ml. with H_2O and measure the yellow-brown color with a blue filter.

(*viii*) Cl^- can be detd. by the potential difference of an Ag–AgCl cell.[31]

(b) $Hg(SCN)_2$ and Fe-alum allow colorimetry of 0·05–5 p.p.m. Cl^- in 5 ml. soln. or 3–8 p.p.m. Cl^- in 2·5 ml. soln.[32] For detn. add 1 ml. Fe-alum soln. (8 g./100 ml. 6N HNO_3) and 0·5 or 3 ml. 0·1% $Hg(SCN)_2$ in dioxane and EtOH (2:1 or 9:1). After 10 min. measure at 460 mμ.

NOTES. (1) No interference is caused by Na, K, Mg, Ca, Al, SO_4^{2-}, Cu, Cr, Co, or 100 mg. Fe/l. Interferences are Br^-, I^-, CN^-, S^{2-}, $S_2O_3^{2-}$, $Fe(CN)_6^{4-}$, $Fe(CN)_6^{3-}$ and > 10 p.p.m. F^- or PO_4^{3-}. NO_2^- is removed by addn. of excess $KMnO_4$ and removal of excess with H_2O_2.
(2) Hg-chloranilate is suitable[33] for < 1 mg. Cl^- in 40 ml. soln. at pH 7. Add 5 ml. 1N HNO_3 and 50 ml. methyl cellosolve, dil. to 100 ml. with H_2O and add 0·2 g. reagent (5% $Hg(NO_3)_2$ in 2% HNO_3 added dropwise to 0·1% chloranilic acid at 50°C, decanted, washed 3 times with EtOH and once with Et_2O and dried at 60°C *in vacuo*). Shake for 15 min., filter and measure at 530 mμ. The error is ±1% for < 10 p.p.m. Cl^- and ±0·1% for > 10 p.p.m. Cl^-. Cations must be removed by ion exchange. Br^-, I^-, SCN^- and F^- interfere but SO_4^{2-}, AcO^-, $C_2O_4^{2-}$ and citrate do not.

(c) $AgIO_3$ or $Hg_2(IO_3)_2$ reacts with Cl^- to release IO_3^- which can be detd. iodometrically.[34] For 1–5 ml. 0·02N Cl^- soln., add 1 ml. 1N HNO_3, dil. to 50 ml. with H_2O, add 70–100 mg. metal iodate and shake for 3 min. Wash the vessel wall with 1 ml. 2:1 EtOH, filter on a Pregl filter and wash with 1:2 EtOH. Then add 10 ml. 1N H_2SO_4 and 0·2 g. KI and titrate with 0·02N $Na_2S_2O_3$.

NOTE. In another procedure,[35] treat the soln. contg. < 0·17N H_3PO_4 (pH 2·0–3·0) with 10 mg. $AgIO_3$/ml. soln. and centrifuge. Then for solns. contg. $3–12 \times 10^{-3}M$ Cl^-, add 2 ml. N_2H_4 soln. (equal vols. of satd. $N_2H_4 \cdot H_2SO_4$ and 40% w/v NaOH satd. with air) and measure the vol. of N_2 evolved. For larger amts. of Cl^-, use the iodometric finish; colorimetry using KI and starch is also possible for > 0·6 μg. Cl^-. Colorimetric detn. based on this reaction is also suitable for 0–180 p.p.m. Cl^-, CdI_2 and linear starch being used with measurement at 615 mμ.[36]

(d) $KMnO_4$ allows detn. of Cl^- in a Conway diffusion cell.[37] Place 1 ml. 20% KI in the inner compartment of the cell, and 1 ml. soln., 0·2 g. $KMnO_4$ and 1 ml. 24–30% v/v H_2SO_4 in the outer compartment. Cover, mix and leave for 1·5–2 hr. Titrate with 0·005N $Na_2S_2O_3$ for >35 μg. Cl^-. For 7–35 μg., compare the color at 464 mμ; for <7 μg., compare after addn. of 0·5 ml. 0·2% starch.

NOTES. (1) After distn. colorimetry of Cl_2 (0·1–2·5 μg.) is possible with tolidine[38] at pH 1·6 and 438 mμ; 0·3–3 μg. Cl_2 can be detd. with Fast green FCF.[39]
(2) Treatment with $KBrO_3$ can be followed by iodometry.[40] To 20–30 ml. soln. in a glass-stoppered flask, add 2–15 ml. 1*N* KCN, enough 1:1 H_2SO_4 to give a 30% v/v soln., and an 8–10-fold excess of 1*N* $KBrO_3$. Leave to cool for 45–90 min. and add the soln. in a thin stream to a mixt. of 50–100 ml. 10% $PhNH_2·HCl$, 10 ml. 1*N* KBr and 20 ml. HCl or 1:1 H_2SO_4. After 0·5–1 hr. add KI to give a 1% soln. and titrate with $Na_2S_2O_3$ soln. Br^- and I^- interfere but simultaneous detns. are possible.

(e) $Hg(NO_3)_2$ can be applied titrimetrically or colorimetrically. Diphenylcarbazone is the best indicator. For titration of <25 mg. Cl^- in 100 ml. soln.[41] add 5 drops indicator mixt. (0·5 g. diphenylcarbazone and 0·05 g. bromophenol blue in 75 ml. EtOH dild. to 100 ml. with H_2O), adjust the color to just yellow with 0·05*N* HNO_3 or 0·025*N* NaOH and add 1 ml. 0·05*N* HNO_3; titrate with 0·025–0·1*N* $Hg(NO_3)_2$ to blue-violet.

NOTES. (1) For the Hg^{2+} soln. dissolve the necessary amt. of $Hg(NO_3)_2$ in 100 ml. H_2O contg. 1–1·5 ml. HNO_3 for 0·1*N* soln., or 0·25–0·40 ml. HNO_3 for more dil. solns., and dil. to 1 l. with H_2O.
(2) Interferences are Fe^{3+}, CrO_4^{2-}. No interference arises from NO_3^-, SO_4^{2-}, PO_4^{3-}, Mg, Ca, Al in moderate amts., from 100 p.p.m. Zn, Pb, Fe^{2+}, Ni or Cr, and from 50 p.p.m. Cu.
(3) Other indicators proposed are diphenylcarbazide disodium disulfonate,[42] Na-nitroprusside,[43] and 2-nitroso-1-naphthol.[44]
(4) Colorimetry is suitable for < 30 p.p.m. Cl^- in 50 ml. soln.[41] Add 5 drops 1% diphenylcarbazone in EtOH, make orange with 0·025*N* NaOH and yellow with 0·05*N* HNO_3, then add 1 ml. 0·05*N* HNO_3. Add 1 ml. 0·014*N* $Hg(NO_3)_2$ and compare the blue-violet color. If Cl^- is > 8 p.p.m. more Hg^{2+} is needed.
(5) Addn. of Hg(OH)CN to neutral Cl^- soln. can be followed by titration with 0·01*N* H_2SO_4 with methyl red–methylene blue as indicator.[45]

(f) $Hg_2(NO_3)_2$ is used titrimetrically with bromophenol blue as indicator.[46] For other indicators, see Table 10. Amperometric[47] and coulometric[48] titrations are possible. Other indicator systems are NH_4SCN with $Fe(NO_3)_3$,[49] or titan yellow.[50]

(g) $K_2S_2O_5$ and KIO_3 can be applied in a catalytic method as for Br^- (see p. 444).

(h) Ag_2CrO_4 and diphenylcarbazide provide a colorimetric method for 0·2–0·3 ml. 0·1–0·7% NaCl soln.[51] Place the soln. in a capillary tube, add Ag_2CrO_4, centrifuge, add diphenylcarbazide soln. (0·5 g. in 70 ml. EtOH, mixed with 25 ml. AcOH and dild. to 100 ml. with H_2O). Compare the color with standards.

NOTES. (1) In an alternative method,[52] filter off Ag_2CrO_4, treat the filtrate with $Na_2S_2O_4$ and measure with a red filter. Treatment of the filtrate with NH_4OH allows measurement at 366 mμ for 1–25 μg. Cl^-/ml., or at 405 mμ for 50–80 μg. Cl^-/ml.[52] In air, > 10^{-12} g. Cl^- can be estimated[53] by microscope measurement of the colorless circular area formed with gelatin impregnated with Ag_2CrO_4.
(2) Ag-dithizonate is suitable for detn. of < 5 μg. Cl^- in 0·02 ml. soln.[54] Add 5 ml. EtOAc and 2 ml. reagent (100 mg./100 ml. $CHCl_3$, shaken several times with 0·1*N* AcOH), dil. to 10 ml. with EtOAc and measure at 598 mμ. Up to 12 μg. Br^- and 19 μg. I^- can be detd. similarly.

(i) $Fe(ClO_4)_3$ allows colorimetric detn. of <50 p.p.m. Cl^-.[55] For the reagent, mix 20–30 g. $Fe(ClO_4)_3$ with $HClO_4$ and decant until no further yellow color is obtained; filter on a glass filter. Dissolve 8 g. purified material in 1 l. 70% $HClO_4$ contg. a few ml. H_2O. For a detn. add 2·5 ml. sample soln. to 7·4 ml. reagent soln., dil. to 10 ml. with H_2O, cool and measure at 353 mμ. The flasks must be protected from light. Blanks must be detd.

NOTES. (1) No interference arises from NO_3^-, AcO^-, Cr^{3+}, Co, Pb, Ni, Mn, Al, Ba, Ca, Na, K. Interferences are Hg, 2 p.p.m. SCN^-, 16 p.p.m. SO_4^{2-}, 20 p.p.m. I^-, PO_4^{3-}, 40 p.p.m. Br^-, F^-.
(2) Less interference is found with a reagent contg. 120 g. $Fe(ClO_4)_3$ in 540 ml. 60% $HClO_4$ and 460 H_2O. To 4·9 ml. reagent, add 5 ml. sample contg. < 100 p.p.m. Cl^-, dil. to 10 ml. with H_2O and measure at 348 mμ.
(3) For the use of $PdSO_4$, see p. 441.

(j) Flame photometry can be used with $Cu(NO_3)_2$ added.[56] The decrease in the measurement of Ag at 328 mμ allows detn. of 0·07–0·2 meq. Cl^-/l. with an error of ±5%.[57]

BROMINE

(a) $AgNO_3$ is applied gravimetrically and titrimetrically by methods similar to those outlined for Cl^- (p. 441). For gravimetry, the ppt. is dried at 70–946°C and weighed as AgBr;[1, 2, 3, 13] the diln. of the soln. should be greater and protection from light more stringent than in the case of AgCl.

Filtration is unnecessary in Volhard's method when applied to Br^-. Mohr's method, potentiometric titration, the use of KI–Ce^{4+}–starch indicator, and dissoln. in $Ni(CN)_4^{2-}$ with EDTA titration can be utilized in the same way as for Cl^- (see also under Separation).

Fajan's method is generally applied with eosin as indicator. For 10 ml. soln. contg. 0·0005–0·1*N* Br^- and slightly acidic in AcOH (0·1*N* HNO_3 medium is possible), add 1–3 drops 0·5% Na-eosin and titrate with vigorous shaking to a purple color. The error is ±0·05% for 0·1*N* Br^-, ±0·5% for 0·01*N* and ±1% for 0·0005*N*. Dichloro-(R)-fluorescein (see p. 442) and other adsorption indicators (Table 10) can also be used.

(b) Oxidation methods. (*i*) Oxidation to Br_2 is best done with $KMnO_4$ (Goda[6]). Distil the Br_2 (see under Separation, p. 440) into 5 ml. 0·1*N* KOH, rinse the condenser with H_2O, dil. to 50 ml. with H_2O, add 0·2–0·3 g. KI and 10 ml. 1*N* HCl, place in the dark for

15 min. and titrate with 0·01*N* $Na_2S_2O_3$. $KBrO_3$ and $K_2Cr_2O_7$ are also applicable as oxidants. The distillate can be collected in KI, As^{3+} or N_2H_4, or extd. into CCl_4.

(*ii*) Oxidation to BrO_3^- is effected with NaOCl.[58] To 25 ml. neutral soln. add 1 g. $NaH_2PO_4 \cdot 2H_2O$, 10 g. NaCl (but not if Br^- is < 2 mg.) and 5 ml. 1*N* NaOCl. Heat just to boiling, add 5 ml. 50% HCOONa, cool, dil. to 150 ml. with H_2O, add 1 g. KI, 25 ml. 6*N* H_2SO_4 and 1 drop 0·5% $(NH_4)_2MoO_4$ and titrate with 0·1*N* $Na_2S_2O_3$. Interferences are I^- and large amts. of Ca and Mg.

Oxidation to OBr^- is possible.[59]

(*iii*) Oxidation to BrCN is done with Cl_2 water in presence of KCN.[60] Place 10 ml. neutral soln. contg. 20–250 μg. Br^- in a 50 ml. glass-stoppered flask, add 8–16 drops satd. Cl_2 water, shake and add 4–8 drops 5% KCN; shake several times with loosening of the stopper, then add 10–15 drops 10% HCl, 3–4 drops 20% KI and 2 drops 1% starch and titrate after 10 min. with 0·002*N* $Na_2S_2O_3$.

In another method,[40] treat 50–60 ml. soln. with 10 ml. 1*N* KCN, enough HCl to give a 10–15% soln., and 0·1*N* $KBrO_3$ until no yellow color remains. Then add 20 ml. 10% $PhNH_2 \cdot HCl$, 10 ml. 0·1*N* KBr and, after 0·5–1 min., 1 g. KI and titrate with 0·1*N* $Na_2S_2O_3$.

$KMnO_4$ and KIO_3 can be used also in this method.

(*iv*) Colorimetric methods. Oxidation to BrO_3^- can be followed by reaction with bromide and rosaniline.[61] For <5 μg. Br^-, add the soln. to 1 ml. buffer (10 vols. 40% $NaH_2PO_4 \cdot 2H_2O$, 7 vols. 2*N* KOH and 5 vols. H_2O), dil. to 4·5 ml. with H_2O, add 0·25 ml. 1*N* NaOCl in 0·1*N* NaOH and place in a boiling water-bath for 10 min. Add 0·25 ml. 50% HCOONa, place in the bath for 5 min., cool, dil. to 5 ml. with H_2O and pipet 1 ml. of soln. into 0·1 ml. molybdate (0·15 g. KBr and 3·0 g. $(NH_4)_2MoO_4$/100 ml.) and rosaniline soln. (for each μg. Br^-, add 0·1 ml. of a soln. contg. 6 mg. rosaniline in 100 ml. 2*N* H_2SO_4). Then add 0·4 ml. H_2O, and 0·4 ml. 14*N* H_2SO_4, maintain at 20–30°C for 3 min., add add 2 ml. tert-BuOH and 1 ml. 14*N* H_2SO_4 and measure at 570 mμ. Methyl orange can replace rosaniline.[62] Oxidation with $Ca(OCl)_2$ in borax medium can be followed by reaction with phenol red.[2]

For detn. of 1–20 μg. Br^- in 2–5 ml. 1*N* H_2SO_4, add 3 ml. 6·5% KCN and 2–5 ml. CrO_3 soln. (150 g./80 ml.) and heat for 8 min. in a water-bath under a stream of N_2 at 75 ml./min. Collect the BrCN in 4 ml. satd. benzidine–HCl soln., 1 ml. pyridine and 1 ml. 96% EtOH, dil. to 50 ml. with 50% EtOH and measure at 580 mμ within 20 min.[63] 10 mg. Cl^- and I^- can be tolerated.

Treatment of dil. H_2SO_4 soln. and 10 ml. CCl_4 with Cl_2 water can be followed by extn. of Br_2 into the org. phase.[64] Other possible reagents are fuchsine with iso-AmOH extn.[65] or chloramine T.[65] Chloramine T and fluorescein can be used in acetate buffer.[65] Fast green FCF is suitable after $KMnO_4$ oxidation.[39]

(c) $Hg(NO_3)_2$ titration with diphenylcarbazone indicator is applied as for Cl^-. The end-point is sharper if the indicator is added 2–3 ml. before the end-point; the final 65 ml. soln. should contain 6 ml. 0·2*N* HNO_3 and 8 ml. dioxane.[66]

(d) Miscellaneous titrimetric methods. $AgIO_3$ can be used in the same way as for Cl^- detn. (p. 442). For coulometric titration with Hg^+, see p. 443. A method involving pptn. with ferroin of $[Fe(C_{12}H_8N_2)_3](HgBr_3)_2$ can be applied (see p. 153).

A chronometric titration is possible as follows.[67] Mix 5 ml. 0·001*M* $K_2S_2O_5$, 5 ml. sample and 1 ml. 5% starch, pipet 1 ml. soln. add 1 drop 0·1*M* KIO_3 in 0·05*N* H_2SO_4 and measure the time till the blue color appears.

(e) AgSCN with Fe^{3+} provides a colorimetric method for 0·3–40 mg. Br^-/l.[68] To 10 ml. soln. add 10 mg. AgSCN, 1 ml. EtOH and 2 ml. 6% Fe^{3+}-alum in 6*N* HNO_3, shake for 1 min., leave for 5 min., shake for 30 sec. and repeat 4 times; centrifuge and measure at 460 mμ within 30 min.

NOTES. (1) Up to 20 mg. Cl^-/l. can be tolerated.
(2) $Hg(SCN)_2$ and Fe^{3+} allow detn. of 0·1–40 mg. Br^-/l. (see p. 442).
(3) The Ag-dithizonate method can be applied as for Cl^- (p. 443).

(f) $NaAuCl_4 \cdot 2H_2O$ (0·4 ml. of 0·5% soln.) forms a yellow-brown color with 2 ml. Br^- soln. contg. CCl_3COOH.[69] For the use of $PdSO_4$, see p. 441.

(g) Flame photometry can be used[57] in the same way as for Cl^-.

IODINE

(a) $AgNO_3$ methods are available as for Cl^- and Br^-. For gravimetric detn.[1, 2, 3, 13] treat ammoniacal soln. with 0·05*N* $AgNO_3$, adjust to 1% v/v in HNO_3, filter on a glass crucible and wash with 1% HNO_3 and with H_2O. Dry at 130°C (60–900°C) and weigh as AgI. The ppt. is extremely sensitive to light so that the method is seldom used.

In Volhard's method (p. 441) filtration is unnecessary; the Fe-alum indicator must be added after pptn. of AgI.[1, 2, 3]

In Fajan's method, dimethyl(R)-diiodo(R)-fluorescein serves as indicator.[2] Add indicator to 100–200 ml. soln. contg. 5 ml. 0·5*N* $(NH_4)_2CO_3$ and titrate from orange to blue-red using a comparison soln. The error is ±1% for 0·001*N* I^-. Up to 1 g. KCl can be tolerated. See Table 10 for other indicators.

$AgNO_3$ can also be used with Fe^{3+} or IO_3^- and starch as indicator.[70] To 10 ml. 0·1*N* I^- soln. add 1–2 drops satd. $Fe_2(SO_4)_3$, several drops 4*N* H_2SO_4, 2 ml. starch and 5–10 ml. 2*N* $(NH_4)_2CO_3$ and titrate with $AgNO_3$ from violet through orange to yellow.

Potentiometric titration is used as for Cl^- (p. 442), also the $Ni(CN)_4^{2-}$–EDTA method (see p. 442).

Cinchonine–Bi^{3+} can serve as indicator in direct titration with $AgNO_3$ (see Table 11).

(b) Oxidation methods.[71] (*i*) Oxidation to I_2 is done with Fe-alum in H_2SO_4 soln.[2] followed by distn. (see under Separation, p. 440). Absorb in KI soln. and titrate with $Na_2S_2O_3$, or absorb in $NaHCO_3$ and titrate with As^{3+}. Alternatively, ext. with $CHCl_3$, add 1 ml. H_2SO_4 and 50 ml. 20% NH_4HF_2 and titrate with $Na_2S_2O_3$.

NOTES. (1) Cl^- and Br^- do not interfere. If small amts. of I^- are to be detd.,[72] absorb in Br_2 water, boil while passing air, add KI and titrate with $Na_2S_2O_3$.
(2) For more direct titration of I^-, add excess 0·1*N* KIO_3, HCl and calcite, boil off I_2, add KI and titrate with $Na_2S_2O_3$.[2] In another method, add excess KIO_3 and tartaric acid, wait for some min., add Na_2HPO_4 and titrate.[2]
I_2 can also be extd. with CS_2 after treatment of the I^- soln. with $NaNO_2$ and H_2SO_4; the extract is then titrated.[2]
(3) For analysis of table salt,[73] dissolve 5–10 g. in 50 ml. H_2O, add 5 ml. 0·01*N* $K_2Cr_2O_7$ and 10 ml. 20% AcOH followed by 2 ml. 0·1*N* $Na_2C_2O_4$ (or NaF or Na_2HPO_4); after 10–15 min. add 6 ml. 0·01*N* Mohr's salt and some 0·1*N* KI and titrate with 0·002*N* $Na_2S_2O_3$.
(4) Coulometric titration[74] with Ce^{4+} and oxidation with $KMnO_4$ are also possible.

(*ii*) Oxidation to IO_3^- is best done with OCl^-.[75] For 25 ml. 0·02*N* I^- soln. add 5 ml. 4*N* H_3PO_4 and 5% $Ca(OCl)_2$ until colorless. Add 5 ml. 10% phenol, wait for 5–10 min., add 5 ml. 1*N* KI and titrate with 0·1*N* $Na_2S_2O_3$. Cl^-, Br^- and Fe^{3+} do not interfere.

NOTES. (1) Addn. of a slight excess of reagent, using starch indicator can be followed by back-titration with 0·02*N* KI to an amber color.
(2) Cl_2- or Br_2-water is also satisfactory. For the former[76] treat 200 ml. soln. with 1 drop methyl red, acidify with HCl, add 15 ml. satd. Cl_2 water, and after a few min. add boiling stones and evap. to 100 ml. Cool, add 1 ml. H_3PO_4 and 0·2–0·5 g. KI, place in the dark for 5 min. and titrate with 0·01*N* $Na_2S_2O_3$.
With Br_2 as oxidant,[77] add excess, leave for 5 min., add HCOOH and H_2SO_4 and titrate with $Na_2S_2O_3$; $KMnO_4$ and KIO_4 are also applicable. NaOCl can be used in excess, or for direct titration.

(*iii*) Oxidation to ICl. Add an equal vol. of HCl to the soln. and 5 ml. $CHCl_3$ and titrate with 0·1*N* KIO_3 till the org. phase is colorless.[2] For micro application, see ref. 78. $KMnO_4$, NH_4VO_3 and chloramine T can be used similarly.

NOTES. (1) For titration with 0·01*N* $KBrO_3$, treat 10 ml. soln. contg. 2–10 mg. I^-, with 1 g. KBr, 2 ml. CCl_4 and 5 ml. HCl and titrate.[79]
(2) KCN is used in oxidn. to ICN. To 60–70 ml. soln. add 5–10 ml. 1*N* KCN and H_3PO_4 to give a 30% soln. (or H_2SO_4 to 15%, or HCl to 5–10%). Titrate with 0·1*N* $KBrO_3$ using starch indicator, or add excess and back-titrate with $Na_2S_2O_3$. Titration of Br^- can follow immediately. See also Chapter 5, Section 7·3.
(3) Coulometric titration with Br_2 is suitable[80] for detn. of 13–2000 μg. I^-.
(4) Oxidation to iodoacetone is also possible.[81] To the soln. add 25 ml. Me_2CO and 10 ml. 1:1 H_2SO_4, dil. to 100 ml. with H_2O and titrate with Ce^{4+} soln. using ferroin indicator. KIO_3, etc. can also be used.

(*iv*) Oxidation to IO_4^- is done with $KMnO_4$ in alk. soln.[82] Mix 1·5 g. KOH and 5 ml. H_2O, cool, add 20 ml. 0·1*M* $KMnO_4$ and 10 ml. of ca. 0·0125*M* I^-. After 1 min. add 5–7 ml. satd. $BaCl_2$ and 10 drops 1% $Ni(NO_3)_2$ if a large amt. of green ppt. appears; titrate with 0·05*M* NaOOCH to colorless. Oxidation with O_3 in dil. NaOH soln. followed by iodometric titration is possible.[83]

(*v*) Colorimetric methods can be based on extn. or on the color formed with starch. For <0·2 μg. I^- in 0·2 ml. soln.[84] in a 5 ml. centrifuge tube with a mark at 2 ml., add 0·1 ml. 1% NaOH and 0·1 ml. 1% $KMnO_4$ and place in boiling H_2O for 30 min. Leave to cool, cool further in an ice-box, and add 6% H_2O_2 (cooled with ice and NaCl) to remove the pink color. Store at 37°C for 1 hr. or at 18°C for 12 hr., dil. to 2 ml. with H_2O, shake and centrifuge for 15 min. Pipet 1·5 ml. into another tube with a silicone-greased stopper. Add 0·1 ml. 1% KI, 0·2 ml. 5% H_2SO_4 and 1·8 ml. toluene, shake for 10 min., centrifuge for 5 min. and measure at 311 mμ. Alternatively, after H_2SO_4 addn. as above, shake for 10 min. with 1·8 ml. $CHCl_3$, centrifuge, pipet 1·5 ml. of the $CHCl_3$ phase, add 1·5 ml. 5% KI, shake for 10 min., centrifuge, pipet out the upper layer and measure at 352 mμ. Extn. with xylene and measurement at 494 mμ is suitable for 0·03–0·1 mg. I^-.

NOTES. (1) The color of the $CHCl_3$ or CCl_4 extract is deepened by addn. of KI in EtOH.[85]
(2) Alternative reagents are HNO_3 with dioxane,[86] CCl_4,[86] or $NaNO_2$ and HCl with $CHCl_3$.[87]
(3) 0·2–12 p.p.m. I_2 can be detd. with 1% variamine blue at pH 3·0 (acetate buffer).[88]

Linear starch can be applied for 10–30 μg. I^- in 20 ml soln.[89] For the reagent, dissolve 2·5 g. linear starch in 990 ml. boiling H_2O, cool, add 0·40 g. KIO_3 and 1·0 g. $Cd(OAc)_2$ and dil. to 1 l. with H_2O; filter through several thicknesses of paper under suction. For a detn. add to the test soln. 1·0 ml. 100% HCOOH and 1·0 ml. reagent and measure at 625 mμ after 10 min. Interference are Br^-, SO_3^{2-}, S^{2-}, $S_2O_3^{2-}$, As^{3+}.

(c) Catalysis of the Ce^{4+}–As^{3+} reaction can be used for detn. of 0·1–1 μg. I^- in 8 ml. soln.[90] Maintain at 20±0·2°C, add 0·5 ml. 0·1*N* As^{3+} in 0·01*N* H_2SO_4 and 0·5 ml. 60% H_2SO_4, and leave for 20 min. Add 1 ml. 0·02*N* $(NH_4)_2Ce(SO_4)_3$ in 1·6*N* H_2SO_4, leave for 8 min. ±5 sec., add 1 ml. 1·5% $(NH_4)_2Fe(SO_4)_2$ in 0·6% H_2SO_4 and 1 ml. 4% KSCN and compare. For 0·01–0·1 μg. I^-, maintain at 30 ±0·2°C, add Ce^{4+}, leave for 20 ±5 sec. and add Fe^{2+}, etc.

KSCN and KNO_2 can also be utilized.[91] To 10 ml. soln. contg. 0·5–10 mg. I^-/l., add 1 ml. reagent ($3 \times 10^{-3}M$ KSCN + $3 \times 10^{-4}M$ KNO_2) and keep at 25°C for several min. Add 2 ml. 6% w/v Fe-alum in 5·7*N* HNO_3, keep at 25°C for 20 min. and measure at 460 mμ. For 0·05–0·8 mg. I^-/l. use more dil. SCN^- and keep at 30°C for 30 min. For 0·002–0·05 mg./l. keep at 45°C for 30 min. and for 0·0002–0·0015 mg./l. keep at 70°C for 30 min.

Other methods are based on the use of ferroin.[92] or on decolorization of methylene blue in presence of SO_2.[93] For other modifications, see ref. 94.

(d) Miscellaneous gravimetric methods. $PdCl_2$ ppts. I^- from 1% v/v HCl soln.[1, 2] Add reagent, etc. (see p. 245), filter on a Gooch crucible, wash with warm H_2O and some EtOH, dry at 90–95°C (84–365°C) and weigh as PdI_2.

Treatment with $CuSO_4$ and SO_2 water followed by drying at 100–200°C allows weighing as CuI.[95]

Bi-2-mercaptothiazoline ppts. 5–500 mg. I^- on shaking with the reagent soln.[96] Filter on a Gooch crucible, wash with reagent soln., H_2O and EtOH, and dry *in vacuo* over H_2SO_4. The error is −6%. Cl^- does not interfere but NO_2^-, S^{2-}, SO_3^{2-}, $S_2O_3^{2-}$, IO_3^-, IO_4^-, BO_2^-, CrO_4^{2-} do. For the reagent, shake 0·305 g. $BiONO_3$ with 3·6 ml. H_2SO_4, dil. to 100 ml. gradually with H_2O, add 0·238 g. 2-mercaptothiazoline, stir and filter.

(e) Miscellaneous titrimetric methods. Titration with $Hg(NO_3)_2$ with diphenylcarbazide indicator is satisfactory in media contg. dioxane or pyridine[66, 97] (see also p. 443). $HgCl_2$ can be used with starch indicator;[98] for 3 ml. 0·01*N* I^-, add 1 ml. 0·5% starch and 3 drops 0·02% I_2 and titrate with 0·001*M* $HgCl_2$ to colorless.

$AgIO_3$ can be used as for Cl^- (p. 442.)

Hg^+ soln. is applicable with several adsorption indicators (Table 10) and in amperometric and coulometric methods (see p. 443).

(f) Miscellaneous colorimetric methods. $PdSO_4$ is used as described under Separation. AgSCN with Fe^{3+} is suitable for 0·5–60 mg. I^-/l. (see p. 444). $Hg(SCN)_2$ can replace AgSCN in the same range.[99] For the method with Ag-dithizonate, see p. 443.

Sulfanilic acid in conjunction with α-naphthylamine allows detn. of 1–10 μg. I^- in 1 ml. soln.[100] Add 4 ml. H_2O, 0·1 ml. AcOH and 3 drops Br_2 water, boil for 1 min., cool, add 3 drops 0·1*N* KI and distil for 2 min. Absorb in 5 ml. 0·01*N* NaOH, add 1 ml. AcOH and 2 ml. sulfanilic acid reagent (105 ml. 0·04*N* sulfanilic acid, 15 ml. 1*N* $NH_2OH{\cdot}H_2SO_4$ and 30 ml. AcOH). After 8–10 min. add 1 ml. amine reagent (3 g. α-naphthylamine boiled for a few min. with 100 ml. hot H_2O), wait for 15 min., dil. to 15 ml. with H_2O and measure with a green filter.

(g) Flame photometry can be applied as for Cl (see ref. 57).

References

1. Hillebrand and Lundell, 583 (724).
2. Scott and Furman, 263 (Cl), 189 (Br), 448 (I).
3. Kimura, 325.
4. Beaucourt, J. H., *Metallurgia*, **38**, 353 (1948).
5. Goncharova, I. A., *Gidrokhim. Materialy*, **20**, 101 (1953).
6. Edwards, F. W., *et al.*, *Analyst*, **61**, 743 (1936); Goda, S., *Bull. Shanghai Sci. Inst.*, **8**, 233 (1939).
7. Kahane, E., and Kahane, M., *Compt. rend.*, **237**, 1244 (1953); *Bull. soc. chim. France*, 396 (1954).
8. Burger, K., *Z. anal. Chem.*, **92**, 19 (1933).
9. Tutundzic, P. S., *et al.*, *Anal. Chim. Acta*, **12**, 481 (1955); Lingane, J. J., *Anal. Chem.*, **26**, 622 (1954).
10. Laitinen, H. A., *et al.*, *Ind. Eng. Chem.*, *Anal. Ed.*, **18**, 355 (1946).
11. Chapman, F. W., Jr, and Sherwood, R. M., *Anal. Chem.*, **29**, 172 (1957).
12. Ballczo, H., and Mondl, G., *Mikrochemie ver. Mikrochim Acta*, **39**, 247 (1952).
13. Hecht and Donau, 238.
14. Bitzkei, J., *Z. anal. Chem.*, **118**, 64 (1940).
15. Welcher, **IV**, 23.
16. Stschigol, S., *Z. anal. Chem.*, **91**, 182 (1932).
17. Welcher, **I**, 61, 68.
18. Swift, E. H., *et al.*, *Anal. Chem.*, **22**, 306 (1950).
19. Shiner, V. J., Jr., and Smith, M. L., *Anal. Chem.*, **28**, 1043 (1956); Kolthoff, I. M., and Kuroda, P. K., *ibid.*, **23**, 1304, 1306 (1951) (also amperometric); Kolthoff and Stock, J. T., *Analyst*, **80**, 860 (1955) (+ gelatin).
20. Ramsay, J. A., *et al.*, *J. Exptl. Biol.*, **32**, 822 (1955).
21. Ikeda, N., and Komooka, H., *J. Chem. Soc. Japan*, **74**, 473 (1953).
22. Lottermoser, A., and Lorenz, W., *Kolloid.-Z.*, **68**, 201 (1934).
23. Uzumasa, Y., and Ogura, K., *J. Chem. Soc. Japan*, **59**, 1253 (1938).
24. Nogami, H., *et al.*, *J. Pharm. Soc. Japan*, **74**, 1402 (1954).
25. Reber, L. A., and McNabb, W. M., *Ind. Eng. Chem.*, *Anal. Ed.*, **9**, 529 (1937); also see Christy, R. K., and Robson, W., *Biochem. J.*, **22**, 571 (1928) (KIO_3).
26. Hirano, S., *J. Soc. Chem. Ind. Japan*, **45**, 1204 (1942).
27. Kitano, Y., and Tsubota, H., *J. Chem. Soc. Japan*, **75**, 931 (1954).
28. Kolthoff, I. M., and Yutzy, H., *J. Am. Chem. Soc.*, **55**, 1915 (1933).
29. Luce, E. N., *et al.*, *Ind. Eng. Chem.*, *Anal. Ed.*, **15**, 365 (1943).
30. Kuroda, P. K., and Sandell, E. B., *Anal. Chem.*, **22**, 1144 (1950) (in rock).
31. Malmstadt, H. V., *et al.*, *Anal. Chem.*, **28**, 1878 (1956).
32. Iwasaki, I., *et al.*, *Bull. Chem. Soc. Japan*, **29**, 860 (1956); also see Utsumi, S., *J. Chem. Soc. Japan*, **73**, 835 (1952); Iwasaki, *et al.*, *Japan Analyst*, **5**, 275 (1956) (in Ti); Zall, D. M., *et al.*, *Anal. Chem.*, **28**, 1665 (1956) (use of $HClO_4$ and perchlorate); Bergmann, J. G., and Sanik, Jr., J., *ibid.*, **29**, 241 (1957); Swain, J. S., *Chem. & Ind.* (*London*), 418 (1956).
33. Barney, II, J. E., and Bartolacini, R. J., *Anal. Chem.*, **29**, 1187 (1957).
34. Belcher, R., and Goulden, R., *Mikrochim. Acta*, 290 (1953).

35. SENDROY, JR., J., *J. Biol. Chem.*, **120**, 335, 405, 419 (1937).
36. LAMBERT, J. L., and YASUDA, S. K., *Anal. Chem.*, **27**, 444 (1955).
37. CONWAY, E. J., *Biochem. J.*, **29**, 2221 (1935); also NAYLOR, H., *J. Textile Inst.*, **46**, T576 (1955) (As^{3+}).
38. WELCHER, **II**, 462.
39. GORDON, H. T., *Anal. Chem.*, **24**, 857 (1952).
40. BERG, R., *Z. anal. Chem.*, **69**, 1, 342 (1926).
41. CLARKE, F. E., *Anal. Chem.*, **22**, 553, 1458 (1950).
42. PARSONS, J. S., and YOE, J. H., *Anal. Chim. Acta*, **6**, 217 (1952).
43. GEYER, E., and ROTSCH, A., *Z. anal. Chem.*, **98**, 382 (1934).
44. BADWA, T. I., *Gidrokhim. Materialy*, **21**, 139 (1953).
45. VIEBOCK, F., *Ber.*, **65B**, 493, 586 (1932).
46. KOLTHOFF, I. M., and LARSON, W. D., *J. Am. Chem. Soc.*, **56**, 1881 (1934).
47. KOLTHOFF and MILLER, C. S., *J. Am. Chem. Soc.*, **63**, 405 (1941).
48. DEFORD, D. D., and HORN, H., *Anal. Chem.*, **28**, 797 (1956); PRZYBYLOWICZ, E. P., and ROGERS, L. B., *ibid.*, 799.
49. STSCHIGOL, M., *Ann. chim. anal. et chim. appl.*, **18**, No. 3, 61 (1936).
50. VOROBEICHIKOV, V. A., *Zavodskaya Lab.*, **22**, 645 (1956).
51. WELCHER, **III**, 444.
52. BOSCH, F. DE A., and RUBIA PACHECO, J. DE LA, *Anales real soc. españ. fíz. y quím. (Madrid)*, **B47**, 419 (1951); KATO, T., and SHINRA, K., *J. Chem. Soc. Japan*, **77**, 245 (1956).
53. FARLOW, N. H., *Anal. Chem.*, **29**, 883 (1957).
54. KIRSTEN, W. J., *Mikrochim. Acta*, 1086 (1955/56); also see IWANTSCHEFF, G., *Angew. Chem.*, **62**, 361 (1950).
55. WEST, P. W., and COLL, H., *Anal. Chem.*, **28**, 1834 (1956).
56. HONMA, M., *Anal. Chem.*, **27**, 1656 (1955).
57. MENIS, O., *et al.*, *Anal. Chem.*, **29**, 76 (1957).
58. KOLTHOFF, I. M., and YUTZY, H., *Ind. Eng. Chem., Anal. Ed.*, **9**, 75 (1937); also see WILLARD, H. H., and HEYN, A. H., *ibid.*, **15**, 321 (1943) (acetate buffer); SZABÓ, Z. G., and CSANYI, L., *Anal. Chim. Acta*, **6**, 208 (1952) (theory).
59. FARKAS, L., and LEWIN, M., *Anal. Chem.*, **19**, 665 (1947).
60. SCHULEK, E., and PUNGOR, E., *Anal. Chim. Acta*, **5**, 137 (1951); SCHULEK, *et al.*, *Z. anal. Chem.*, **134**, 161 (1951).
61. HUNTER, G., and GOLDSPINK, A. A., *Analyst*, **79**, 467 (1954).
62. TARAS, M., *Anal. Chem.*, **19**, 342 (1947).
63. VAN PINXTEREN, J. A. C., *Analyst*, **77**, 367 (1952).
64. WELCHER, **I**, 66; YOE, 137.
65. WELCHER, **IV**, 498, 491, 546.
66. MCCLEARY, H. R., *Ind. Eng. Chem., Anal. Ed.*, **14**, 31 (1942).
67. NIKITIN, E. K., and PONOMAREVA, E. N., *Trudy Komissii Anal. Khim., Akad. Nauk S.S.S.R., Inst. Geokhim. i. Anal. Khim.*, **7**, 234 (1956).
68. UTSUMI, S., *J. Chem. Soc. Japan*, **74**, 35 (1953).
69. BARBOUR, R. F., *Brit. Med. J.*, No. 2, 957 (1936).
70. CHIRNOAGĂ, E., *Z. anal. Chem.*, **102**, 339 (1935).
71. KOLTHOFF and BELCHER, *Volumetric Analysis*, Vol. III (1957).
72. BRATTON, A. C., *et al.*, *Ind. Eng. Chem., Anal. Ed.*, **10** 600 (1938).
73. RAMANJANEYULU, J. V. S., and SHUKLA, B. K., *Z. anal. Chem.*, **151**, 31, 34, 184 (1956).
74. LINGANE, J. J., *et al.*, *Anal. Chim. Acta*, **16**, 165 (1957).
75. YNTEMA, L. F., and FLEMING, T., *Ind. Eng. Chem., Anal. Ed.*, **11**, 375 (1939).
76. GODA, S., *Bull. Shanghai Sci. Inst.*, **8**, 235 (1939).
77. SPITZER, L., *Ind. Eng. Chem., Anal. Ed.*, **8**, 465 (1936).
78. KORENMAN, I. M., and AMBROCH, Z. A., *Mikrochemie*, **21**, 60 (1936).
79. WINKLER, L. W., *Z. anal. Chem.*, **87**, 116 (1932).
80. WOOSTER, W. S., *et al.*, *Anal. Chem.*, **21**, 1457 (1949).
81. LEWIS, D., *Ind. Eng. Chem., Anal. Ed.*, **8**, 199 (1936).
82. STAMM, H., *Z. angew. Chem.*, **47**, 791 (1934).
83. WILLARD, H. H., and MERRITT, L. L., *Ind. Eng. Chem., Anal. Ed.*, **14**, 489 (1942).
84. CUSTER, J. J., and NATELSON, S., *Anal. Chem.*, **21**, 1005 (1949); also see MENSCHENFREUND, D., *J. Assoc. Offic. Agr. Chemists*, **39**, 523 (1956).
85. OVENSTON, T. C. J., and REES, W. T., *Anal. Chim. Acta*, **5**, 123 (1951).
86. SEIFER, A., and HUGHES, J., *J. Biol. Chem.*, **118**, 241 (1937); BOSE, A. C., and BOGCHI, K. N., *Analyst*, **60**, 81 (1935).
87. MAJAROFF, K. L., and MATSKIEWITSCH, W. B., *Mikrochemie*, **13**, 376 (1933).
88. ERDEY, L., and SZABADVÁRY, F., *Magyar Kém. Folyóirat*, **61**, 341 (1955).
89. LAMBERT, J. L., *Anal. Chem.*, **23**, 1251 (1951); also see HOUSTON, F. G., *ibid.*, **22**, 493 (1950).
90. ROGINA, B., and DUBRAVČIC, M., *Analyst*, **78**, 594 (1953); DUBRAVČIC, *ibid.*, **80**, 146 (1955) (in NaCl).
91. UTSUMI, S., *J. Chem. Soc. Japan.*, **74**, 298 (1953); IWASAKI, I., *et al.*, *ibid.*, **78**, 474 (1957); *Bull. Chem. Soc. Japan*, **26**, 108 (1953).
92. SANDELL, E. B. and KOLTHOFF, I. M., *Mikrochim. Acta*, **1**, 9 (1937).
93. LUNDGREN, H. P., *J. Am. Chem. Soc.*, **59**, 413 (1937).
94. CHANEY, A. L., *Ind. Eng. Chem., Anal. Ed.*, **12**, 179 (1940); DECKER, J. W., and HEYDEN, H. S., *Anal. Chem.*, **23**, 798 (1951); LEIN, A., and SCHWARTZ, N., *ibid.*, 1507; LACHIVER, F., *Ann. chim.*, **10**, 92 (1955).
95. MATSUURA, K., *J. Chem. Soc. Japan*, **52**, 731 (1931); FUKAMAUCHI, H., *J. Pharm. Soc. Japan*, **75**, 1070 (1955).
96. BARAKAT, M. Z., *et al.*, *Analyst*, **82**, 192 (1957).
97. JÍLEK, A., and KOUDELA, *Collection Czechoslov. Chem. Communs.*, **9**, 265 (1937).
98. KORENMAN, I. M., *Mikrochemie*, **14**, 181 (1934).
99. UTSUMI, S., *J. Chem. Soc. Japan*, **74**, 32 (1953).
100. ENDRES, E., and KAUFMANN, L., *Z. physiol. Chem.*, **243**, 144 (1936); *Angew. Chem.*, **49**, 535 (1936); ROGINA, B., and URCH-HORVAT, M., *Arkiv. Kem.*, **20**, 130 (1948).

FLUORINE

The main sources for this chapter are given in refs. 1 and 2. Several comprehensive reviews on the determination of fluorine and fluorides have been published;[3, 4, 5] shorter reviews are also available.[6] Several comparative studies of various types of fluorine analysis have been carried out.[4, 7]

Attack

(a) Berzelius method. Mix 0·5 g. sample with 3 g. $NaKCO_3$; if little silica is present, add quartz powder and if S^{2-} is present add KNO_3. Fuse and leach with hot H_2O. Boil the residue with H_2O contg. 2 g. Na_2CO_3 and combine the filtrates (ca. 300 ml.). Boil with 0·5 g. ZnO in $HClO_4$ soln., filter on paper and wash with hot H_2O. Evap. to 200 ml. and make just acid to methyl orange with HCl. Add 0·3 g. ZnO and 0·5 g. $(NH_4)_2CO_3$ in 10 ml. H_2O contg. 0·5 ml. NH_4OH and evap. to 100 ml. Filter, wash, evap. to 25 ml. and distil.

(b) Fluorite. To 1 g. sample add 25 ml. 3:2 $HClO_4$ and distil almost to dryness by heating in an oil bath; add 20 ml. 1:1 $HClO_4$ and distil again, then add 10 ml. 1:1 $HClO_4$ and distil further.

In another method,[8] fuse 0·5 g. sample with 0·5 g. TiO_2 and 5 g. $NaKCO_3$, leach with H_2O and filter. Add phenolphthalein and evap. to dryness, adding drops of NH_4OAc if the soln. turns pink. Add H_2O, boil and filter. Add 0·25*N* $Ca(OAc)_2$, boil, cool, transfer to a measuring flask and dil. to 500 ml. with H_2O. Filter on paper, pipet 100 ml. filtrate, det. Ca in this aliquot and calc. F.

For simultaneous detn. of SiO_2, fuse 0·5 g. fluorite with 1·5 g. $Na_2HPO_4{\cdot}12H_2O$ and 5 g. $NaKCO_3$, leach with warm H_2O and proceed as above. Combine the residues and det. SiO_2.

Fluorite is also decomposed by fusion with K_2CO_3 and a 2·5-fold amt. of quartz powder.

(c) Organic compounds. Fusion with alk. metal in a bomb is most effective; for details, see refs. 3, 4, 5. For plant materials, mix with $Mg(OAc)_2$, heat, cool and distil.[9] $Ca(OH)_2$, Na_2CO_3, etc. can also be used. After ignition of org. materials,[10] fuse with NaOH and distil with $HClO_4$; otherwise CaF_2 may be formed and not decomposed by $HClO_4$. For other methods, see refs. 3, 5.

Separation

The Berzelius method (see above) allows sepn. from SiO_2 and PO_4^{3-}.

Distn. as H_2SiF_6 is most widely applied.[3, 5, 11] Add $HClO_4$ and glass beads to 25 ml. soln. in a 50 ml. flask and steam-distil at 130–140°C. Collect 200–500 ml. distillate. Make alk. to phenolphthalein with dil. NaOH, evap. to dryness in a Pt dish, add H_2O, etc. Cl^- interference is prevented by $AgClO_4$ or Ag_2SO_4; $KMnO_4$ prevents interference from S^{2-} or org. compds. Colloidal silica and large amts. of Al or PO_4^{3-} interfere.

In the above procedure, silica deposits on the neck and side-arm of the flask must be removed with concd. NaOH.

Distn. from H_2SO_4 soln. at 145–155°C with steam passing over as well as through the soln. is said[12] to be better than distn. from $HClO_4$. H_2O_2 should be added if MnO_2 is present.[13]

95% Recoveries are reported for distn. from H_2SO_4 contg. quartz; 2 g. 75% Fe–C per 0·1 g. F is said to be better than quartz.[14] If distn. is done from H_3PO_4, Fe and Al do not interfere.[15] Distn. from H_2SO_4 or H_3PO_4 at 170–180°C in a stream of air has been recommended.[16] With any procedure, precise attention to detail is essential.

Distn. as BF_3 has been suggested.[17] For 2 g. phosphate rock, add 1 g. B_2O_3 and 100 ml. 1:2 H_2SO_4 and distil until H_2SO_4 begins to collect in the condenser. Add H_2O and distil further, add 1:3 H_2SO_4 and distil again. Repeat these addns., etc., twice more, collecting a total distillate of 400 ml. Titrate a 200 ml. aliquot with Th^{4+} soln. using alizarin indicator.

In a polyethylene microdiffusion app. HF can be distd. at 60°C.[18]

$AgNO_3$ allows sepn. of F^- from PO_4^{3-}; Al interferes. Transfer the alk. soln. to a 300 ml. measuring flask, neutralize with HNO_3, add a small excess of $AgNO_3$, dil. to the mark and filter on dry paper. Discard the first 10–15 ml. and pipet 25 ml. into a 300 ml. measuring flask; add NaCl, dil. to 300 ml. with H_2O, filter on dry paper, discard the first 15 ml., pipet 200 ml. of filtrate and det. F^-.

$CaCl_2$ seps. F^- from B. Boil the alk. soln., add excess reagent, filter on paper and wash with hot H_2O.

Ignite gently, evap. to dryness with dil. AcOH, add dil. AcOH, filter through paper and wash with dil. AcOH.

Ion exchange resins allow sepn. of F^- from PO_4^{3-} and SO_4^{2-} (see Chapter 13, Section 2.2).

Determination

Determination of fluoride is difficult, for there is a lack of really satisfactory methods. Macro amounts are usually determined gravimetrically as CaF_2, or titrimetrically as PbClF. Triphenyltin chloride seems the most promising gravimetric reagent for mg. amounts, but is expensive; methods involving $Th(NO_3)_4$ require experience and strict adherence to controlled conditions. Colorimetric methods are always based on bleaching of a lake, e.g. Al-hematein, Zr-alizarin S, or a colored complex, e.g. Fe^{3+}–SCN^-.

(a) $CaCl_2$ is used in the classical Berzelius gravimetric method.[1, 2, 3] Titrimetric and nephelometric methods are also available. For gravimetry, add 1 ml. 2*N* Na_2CO_3 to 100 ml. slightly alk. (Na_2CO_3) soln., heat and add 20% $CaCl_2$ dropwise to give a 2–3 ml. excess. Heat almost to boiling for several min., cool, filter on paper and wash with hot H_2O. Dry at 110°C, ignite the ppt. and paper separately, ignite below 800°C and cool. Add 10 ml. H_2O and some 10% AcOH, evap. to dryness, heat for 30 min. on a hot plate, cool and add 10 ml. H_2O. Filter on paper and wash with H_2O until there is no turbidity with NaF. Sep. the ppt., ash the paper, ignite together at 450–800°C and weigh as CaF_2. Results tend to be low. In an alternative finish, evap. to fumes with dil. H_2SO_4, add $(NH_4)_2CO_3$, ignite at 400–950°C and weigh as $CaSO_4$.

NOTES. (1) B does not interfere, but NH_4^+, SiO_2, PO_4^{3-}, VO_3^-, CrO_4^{2-}, Al, etc. interfere.

(2) Good results are obtained by compensation of error. An easily filterable ppt. is obtained by slow addn. of hot $CaCl_2$ to hot soln. contg. AcOH and NaOAc.[19] Filtration is also aided by addn. of filter pulp[19] or of 15 ml. 10% gelatin.[20]

(3) Various titrimetric procedures are described. For 5–65 mg. F^- in 50 ml. soln. at pH 4–4·5,[21] add 20 ml. 0·1–0·2*N* $CaCl_2$, boil for 5 min. and filter after 12 hr.; titrate the filtrate with EDTA using eriochrome black T indicator. Moderate amts. of other halogens and SO_4^{2-} can be tolerated.

For 0·019–1·9 mg F^- in 2 ml. soln.,[22] heat to 70–80°C, add excess 0·0943*M* $Ca(NO_3)_2$, cool and add an equal vol. of EtOH, 1 drop 0·01% $K_3Fe(CN)_6$ and solid NH_4Cl. Titrate potentiometrically with 0·05*M* $K_4Fe(CN)_6$.

After treatment with cation exchange resin,[23] reflux to remove CO_2, add 15 ml. neutral 4*N* $CaCl_2$, boil for 1–2 min. and rinse the wall; add bromocresol purple indicator and titrate with 0·1*N* NaOH. The sample is pretreated by fusion with Na_2CO_3, K_2CO_3 and SiO_2, leaching with hot H_2O, filtration etc. (see Chapter 13, Section 2.3).

(4) Nephelometry is suitable for 2 mg. F^- in 25 ml. soln. which is neutral to methyl red.[24] For the reagent, dissolve 20 g. $CaCl_2$ in H_2O, neutralize to methyl red with 0·1*N* HCl, add 2 ml. 0·1*N* HCl, dil. to 100 ml. with H_2O and filter on Whatman No. 42 paper. For a detn. treat the sample soln. with 1 ml. 5% gelatin, 10 ml. EtOH and 5 ml. reagent and measure after 15 min.

(b) $Pb(NO_3)_2$ and NaCl are generally used in conjunction with a final Volhard titration.[1, 2, 3, 25] For 0·03–0·1 g. F^- in 200 ml. neutral soln. add 3 ml. 10% NaCl, dil. to 250 ml. with H_2O, and make acid to bromophenol blue with HNO_3; make alk. with NaOH, add 2 ml. 1:1 HCl and add 5 g. $Pb(NO_3)_2$ (recrystd. from 2:100 HNO_3 and dried over H_2SO_4) in small portions. Place on a steam-bath, add 5 g. NaOAc, stir (pH = 4·6–4·7) and heat on the bath for 30 min. After 12 hr. at <15°C, filter on Whatman No. 42 paper and wash once with cold H_2O, 5 times with satd. PbClF soln. and once with H_2O). Return the ppt. and paper to the beaker, dissolve in 100 ml. 5:95 HNO_3 by warming, add a small excess of 0·1*N* $AgNO_3$, heat on the steam-bath for 30 min., cool, filter on paper and wash. Add Fe-alum and titrate with 0·1*N* NH_4SCN.

NOTES. (1) Interferences are 0·5 mg. Al or Fe, 10 mg. PO_4^{3-}, SO_4^{2-}, CrO_4^{2-}, AsO_4^{3-} or SiO_2, 50 mg. B, 0·5 g. NH_4^+, and 10 g. Na or K salts.

(2) Many modifications are described. If a known amt. of NaCl is used for pptn., excess can be titrated in the filtrate with $AgNO_3$ using fluorescein indicator.[26] Diphenylamine blue indicator[19] or amperometric titration[27] can also serve in back-titration of Cl^-. PbClF ppts. from 0·2–2 mg. F^- can be dissolved in HNO_3 and titrated with 0·01*M* EDTA using eriochrome black T indicator after addn. of NaK-tartrate, NH_4OH and KCN.[28] Pyrocatechol violet or xylenol orange can replace eriochrome T.[29]

(3) For gravimetric detn. of 50 mg. F^- in 100 ml. soln.,[2, 30] neutralize to methyl orange with 0·5*N* HNO_3 and add a few drops in excess (pH 3·6–5·6); add 200 ml. reagent (20·5 g. $Pb(NO_3)_2$ and 15 g. KCl/l.) and leave for 1 hr. Filter on a glass crucible, wash with 30–50 ml. satd. PbClF soln., dry at 150°C (66–538°C) and weigh as PbClF. $PbCl_2$ is also a satisfactory pptant.[31] For 10–30 mg. F^- in < 80 ml. soln.[32] add 1 ml. 30% AcOH, heat, add 50 ml. hot reagent (10·5 g. $PbCl_2$ and 13 g. $Pb(NO_3)_2$/l.), filter on a glass crucible after 12 hr., wash with satd. PbClF soln. and Me_2CO and dry at 110°C.

(4) Pptn. as PbBrF can be followed by detn. of Br^- in the filtrate.[2, 33]

(c) Triphenyltin chloride allows gravimetric detn. of 0·1–50 mg. F^- in 20–100 ml. soln. at pH 4–9.[1, 34] Add a 2·5–3·5-fold excess of reagent dissolved in 20–100 ml. $CHCl_3$ satd. with the ppt.; cover and stir vigorously for 1·5 hr. adding more $CHCl_3$. Filter on a glass crucible, wash with H_2O and with satd. soln. of the ppt. in $CHCl_3$, dry at 100–110°C for 30 min. (<158°C) and weigh as $(C_6H_5)_3SnF$. No interference arises from Al, Fe, PO_4^{3-} or BO_2^-, but CO_3^{2-}, SiO_2, Se, Be and Zr interfere.

(d) $Th(NO_3)_4$ is generally used titrimetrically with alizarin S indicator, or colorimetrically by means of the bleaching effect of F^- on a Th-dye lake. Gravimetry is seldom used.

For <50 mg. F^- in up to 100 ml. soln.,[1, 2] add 8 drops 0·05% alizarin S, adjust to yellow with NaOH or HCl and add 1 ml. buffer (9·448 g. CH_2ClCO_2H and 2·00 g. NaOH/100 ml.) to give pH 2·9–3·1 and titrate with 0·1*N* Th^{4+} to a red color. PO_4^{3-}, SO_4^{2-}, Cl^-, etc. and large amts. of Na interfere.

NOTES. (1) Many modifications have been described.[3, 5, 35] The end-point of the above procedure is said to be sharper if 10 ml. 5% starch is added per 100 ml. soln.[36] In all cases the $Th(NO_3)_4$ must be standardized under the conditions used. Amperometric titration is possible.[37] The method has been applied to rocks after fusion with Na_2CO_3 and ZnO.[38]

Micro procedures are satisfactory[19] for 0·06–3·2 mg. F^-. The error is ±5 μg. for 50–100 μg. F^-.[39] A color standard contg. 1·236 g. $Co(NO_3)_2 \cdot 6H_2O$ and 0·093 g. K_2CrO_4/l. with 4 ml. 0·05*N* NaF and 4 ml. 0·05*N* $Th(NO_3)_4$ may be useful.[40] 50% EtOH media improves titration of 2–50 μg. F^-.[41] Photometric titration has been recommended.[42]

(2) Many indicators have been studied to replace alizarin. Alizarin S can be screened with methylene blue.[43] Two-color indicators, in order of preference,[44] are purpurin sulfonate, alizarin S, eriochrome cyanine R, 2,3-dicyano-quinalizarin, solochrome brilliant blue BS; mono-color indicators are quercetin and morin. Fluorescent indicators are morin, quercetin, ferron, 8-hydroxyquinoline-5-sulfonic acid, or kaempferol.[44] For SNADNS, etc., *cf* Chapter 46, p. 341.[45] 1–100 μg. F^- can be titrated using SPADNS indicator.[46] Photometric titration using SPADNS indicator is suitable for <70 μg. F^- in rock.[47] Other proposed indicators are chrome azurol S[48] and eriochrome azurol B.[49] Order of preference is said[49] to be eriochrome cyanine R, alizarin S, chrome azurol S and eriochrome azurol B.

Many colorimetric methods are available. Thoron forms a lake with Th, which can be used[38, 50] in detn. of <100 μg. F^-. Make the soln. alk. to phenolphthalein with NaOH, add 0·2 ml. $HClO_4$, 1 ml. 10% $NH_2OH \cdot HCl$, 2 ml. $Th(NO_3)_4$ (50 μg. Th/ml.) and 2 ml. 0·1% thoron, and dil. to 25 ml. with H_2O. After 15 min. measure in a 2 cm. cell at 545 mμ.

Neothoron is applicable for < 50 μg. F^- at pH 2·1–2·4.[51] Add 1 ml. 0·05% neothoron, 1 ml. $Th(NO_3)_4$ (110 μg. Th/ml.) and 1 ml. 1% $NH_2OH \cdot HCl$, dil. to 50 ml. with H_2O and measure at 570 mμ. Interferences in p.p.m. are 0·5 Al, 1·5 PO_4^{3-}, 5 Fe^{3+}, 100 SO_4^{2-}, 300 Ca and 400 Mg.

Chrome azurol S allows detn. of 5–90 μg. F^- in 20 ml. soln.[52] Add 2 drops 1% *p*-nitrophenol, acidify with 0·1*N* $HClO_4$, add 5 ml. 5*M* $NaClO_4$ and 10 ml. buffer (100 g. *o*-toluidine and 50 ml. $HClO_4$ dild. to 2 l.; decant after several hr., add 100 ml. H_2O and 10 ml. $HClO_4$ and adjust to pH 4·0). Then dil. to 40 ml. with H_2O, add 5 ml. dye soln. (40 mg. chrome azurol S, 50 mg. thymol and 5·0 g. gum arabic/l.) and 5 ml. Th^{4+} soln. (0·100 g. $Th(NO_3)_4 \cdot 4H_2O$/l. of 0·001*N* $HClO_4$), leave for 2 hr. and measure at 605 mμ. The error is ±10%. 0·1 μg. F^- can be detd. with 5 cm. cells.

N-[4-(*o*-Arsenophenylazo)-1-naphthyl]ethylenediamine–Th^{4+} is suitable for 0–0·6 μg. F^-/ml. of final soln.[53] To prep. the reagent, dissolve 0·1 g. dye in 100 ml. H_2O, add 3 ml. 1:10 HCl and 3 ml. Th soln. (6·96 g. $Th(NO_3)_4 \cdot 4H_2O$ in 20 ml. H_2O), dil. to 1 l. with H_2O and leave for 3 hr. For a detn. treat the soln. with 0·5 ml. buffer (94·45 g. $CH_2ClCOOH$ and 30·0 g. NaOH/l.) and 0·5–3·0 ml. reagent, dil. to 100 ml. with H_2O and measure the red color after 3 min.

Alizarin S–Th reagent is used[2, 54] for 0–50 μg. F^-. For the reagent, mix 10 ml. 0·1*N* HCl, 10 ml. 1% $NH_2OH \cdot HCl$, 40 ml. 0·1% alizarin S and 40 ml. 0·5% $Th(NO_3)_4$. For detn., neutralize the sample soln. to *p*-nitrophenol with 0·05*N* KOH, add 10 ml. reagent, dil. to 50 ml. with H_2O, and measure at 525 mμ after 2 hr. A differential method[55] is accurate to ±1% for 50–200 μg. F^-/50 ml., and to ±2% for 25–50 μg. F^-. For the modifications, see ref. 56.

Th^{4+} with amaranth paper[57] and Th^{4+} with the diphenylguanidine salt of chromotrope 2B[58] have also been recommended; the latter is used as a suspension in an org. medium with measurement at 515 mμ.

Gravimetric detn. is possible[59] by conversion of the ppt. to ThO_2 above 700°C.

(e) Zr and alizarin S can be applied colorimetrically or titrimetrically. For colorimetric detn. of 0–100 μg. F^- in 50 ml. soln.,[2, 60, 61] add 5 ml. reagent (40 ml. H_2SO_4, and 300 ml. H_2O, cool, add 120 ml. HCl, cool, add 0·30 g. $ZrOCl_2$ and 0·35 g. alizarin S, filter and dil. to 1 l. with H_2O). Dil. to 100 ml. with H_2O, and measure after 2 hr., in a 5 cm. cell at 525 mμ against 250 μg. F^- and 50 ml. reagent as reference.

NOTES. (1) Interferences are org. compds., Al, Fe, PO_4^{3-}, SiO_2, B and large amts. of CO_3^{2-}, SO_4^{2-}, Cl^-, Ca, Mg, Mn, Na, Cu.

(2) For titrimetric detn.[62] of 1–40 mg. F^-, make alk. with NH_4OH, add 10 ml. AcOH, dil. to 100 ml. with H_2O and place in a buret. With vigorous shaking, add 2 ml., then 0·5 and 0·1 ml. increments to a mixt. of 10 ml. reagent (see below), 5 ml. AcOH and 5 ml. H_2O until the color matches that of a mixt. of 10 ml. reagent, 5 ml. AcOH and 5 ml. H_2O to which 8 ml. 0·01*N* NaF is added in 2 ml. increments. For the reagent, prep. soln. A from 25 g. $Zr(NO_3)_4$ in 75 ml. HCl and 300 ml. H_2O heated at 80°C for 30 min., boiled for 5 min., cooled and dild. to 500 ml. with H_2O; prep. soln. B from 2·5 g. alizarin S in 30 ml. H_2O, heated at 80°C for 1 hr. and dild. to 500 ml. with H_2O. Mix 50 ml. of A and 50 ml. of B, leave for 30 min., dil. to 1 l. with H_2O and leave for 2 hr. PO_4^{3-}, AsO_4^{3-}, SeO_3^{2-} and large amts. of SO_4^{2-} and HCl interfere in the above method.

(3) Many reagents can replace alizarin S in the colorimetric method. For alizarin itself, see ref. 61. Quinalizarin is suitable for 20–200 μg. F^- in 100 ml. soln.[2, 61] For the reagent, mix 2·5 ml. 0·14% quinalizarin in 0·3% NaOH with 2·5 ml. 0·87% $Zr(NO_3)_4$ in H_2O and dil. to 100 ml. For a detn. add 5 ml. 2% $BaCl_2$, leave for 6 hr., filter and pipet out 50 ml. Add 3 ml. 1:1 HCl and 5 ml. reagent and measure after 20 min. Interferences are Al, Fe, PO_4^{3-} and SO_4^{2-}.

Purpurin is used for 10–50 μg. F^- in 2 ml. HCl

soln.[2, 61, 63] Add this to 10 ml. reagent and compare with standards. For the reagent, dissolve 300 mg. purpurin in 1 l. EtOH and 0·8 g. Zr as $ZrOCl_2\cdot 8H_2O$ in 1 l. 10*N* HCl and mix. Purpurin sulfonic acid allows detn. of $<1\cdot4$ μg. F^-/ml.[64]

Eriochrome cyanine R is satisfactory for <70 μg. F^- in 50 ml. soln.[65] Add 5 ml. dye soln. (1·8 g./l.), maintain at 22 ± 2°C, add 5 ml. Zr soln. (0·265 g. $ZrOCl_2$ or 0·220 g. $Zr(NO_3)_4$ in 50 ml. H_2O mixed with 700 ml. HCl and dild. to 1 l. with H_2O). Measure at 527·5 mμ within 5 min. PO_4^{3-} and SO_4^{2-} interfere; Al interference is avoided by reading after 2 hr. SO_4^{2-} interference is overcome by adding $BaCl_2$ to a mixed reagent.[66] The max. absorbancy differs with different sources of reagent.[66]

Pyrocatechol violet can be used to det. 10 μg. F^- at pH 1 (in HCl) in presence of 0·05 mg. Zr/ml. with measurement at 525 mμ.[67]

Hematoxylin can be used for 5 μg. F^- in 50 ml. soln.[68] Add 6 ml. Zr soln. (1·7 ml. 0·87% $Zr(NO_3)_4$, 50 ml. 1*N* H_2SO_4 and 50 ml. 1*N* HCl) followed by 1 ml. hematoxylin soln. (0·020 g. in 100 ml. H_2O used after standing for several days) and compare after 4 hr.

Pararsonic acid is suitable[69] for <1 p.p.m. F^-. For the reagent, pour 40 ml. pararsonic acid soln. (0·2 g. in 100 ml. 6*N* HCl) into 40 ml. Zr soln. (0·1 g. $ZrOCl_2\cdot 8H_2O$ in 100 ml. 6*N* HCl), centrifuge after 30 min., wash with 2*N* HCl and suspend in 200 ml. 2*N* HCl. For a detn., shake 10 ml. soln. with 10 ml. 6*N* HCl and 1 ml. reagent, leave for 1 hr., filter and measure at 500 mμ; the error is $\pm0\cdot05$ p.p.m. Interferences are 2 p.p.m. $S_2O_3^{2-}$ or S^{2-}, 5 p.p.m. NO_2^-, CN^- or CrO_4^{2-}, 10 p.p.m. SO_4^{2-}, MnO_4^- or Al, and 50 p.p.m. BO_2^-, Sb, Sn, Cd, Fe.

KH-phthalate may be used to det. 10–70 p.p.m. F^- (in the final soln). Add 10 ml. Zr soln. (3 g. $ZrOCl_2\cdot 8H_2O$/l. 2·5*N* HCl) and 10 ml. phthalate soln. (7 g./l. 0·25*N* HCl), dil. to 100 ml. with H_2O and measure at 430 mμ (see Chapter 49, p. 355).

Phenylfluorone is satisfactory for <6 μg. F^-/ml., with measurement at 530–550 mμ in 0·05*N* HCl soln.[70]

(f) Al^{3+} and hematein are used for colorimetric detn. For the reagent[71] mix 100 ml. Al^{3+} soln. (0·05 mg./ml.), 850 ml. H_2O, 25 ml. satd. $NaHCO_3$ and 15 ml. hematein soln. (0·1 g. hematoxylin dissolved in 55 ml. 0·09*N* HCl at 60°C, adjusted to red with 0·02*N* NaOH, mixed with 3 ml. 3% H_2O_2 and 100 ml. 1% AcOH and left for 1 hr.); after 1 hr. add 10 ml. 1:2 AcOH and leave for 48 hr. before use. The reagent is stable for 9 days. For detn. of 0–140 μg. F^- in 100 ml. soln. add 10 ml. reagent (pH 4·6), leave for 4 hr. and measure at 550 mμ.

NOTES. (1) 1000 p.p.m. SO_4^{2-} corresponds to 0·2 p.p.m. F^-; PO_4^{3-} interference depends on the amt. of F^- present.

(2) Again, many modifications have been described. Morin is useful in detn. of 0·005–0·08 μg. F^- in 0·25 ml. soln.[72] For the reagent, mix 0·1 ml. Al soln. (0·4749 g. alum/l.), 0·1 ml. 0·1% morin in EtOH, 0·1 ml. buffer (19 g. CH_2ClCO_2H, 12 g. AcOH and 10 g. NaOH, dild. to 100 ml. and adjusted to pH 4·4) and 2 ml. EtOH and dil. to 15 ml. with H_2O. For a detn. add 1·2 ml. reagent, dil. to 10 ml. with H_2O after 5 min., and measure the fluorescence under UV light. Up to 8 μg. F^-/ml. can be measured at 420 mμ in 40% EtOH media.[73]

Eriochrome red B or superchrome garnet Y can be used for fluorimetric detn. of 0–50 μg. F^-.[74] Amperometric titration is possible using the latter indicator.[75]

Aluminon is suitable for detn. of 0–500 μg. F^-.[2, 76] Add 5 ml. soln. contg. 40 μg. Al^{3+}, 8 ml. 1*N* HCl, 5 ml. 3*N* NH_4OAc, 5 ml. 0·1% aluminon and 0·5 ml. 6*N* $(NH_4)_2CO_3$; dil. to 100 ml. with H_2O (pH 4·6), maintain at 30°C for 45 min. and compare. Interferences are 0·18 mg. SiO_2/100 ml., 0·1 mg. $C_2O_4^{2-}$, 1·51 mg. Cr, 4·2 mg. BO_2^- and 7 mg. SO_4^{2-}. Cr^{3+} can be removed by ion exchange for detn. of F^- in chrome-plating baths.

Eriochrome cyanine R,[77] chrome azurol S[78] and oxine with $CHCl_3$ extn.[44] are also applicable.

Al^{3+} soln. can also be used for titration of F^-. Eriochrome cyanine R is the best indicator for 20 mg. F^- in 20 ml. soln.[79] Neutralize the soln. to phenolphthalein, add 10 g. NaCl and 4 drops 0·1% indicator, boil gently, and make yellow (if necessary) by addn. of 0·1*N* HCl or NaOH; titrate with 0·2*N* $AlCl_3$ to pink.

NOTES. (1) Interferences are CO_3^{2-}, SO_4^{2-}, SiO_2, Pb, Ni, Cr, etc. The method has been applied for org. analysis (Gilbert and Saylor[77]).

(2) Potentiometric titration is suitable[80] for 0–14 μg. F^-. Methyl red–methylene blue can be used with alum titrant.[81] For other modifications, see ref. 2.

(g) $(NH_4)Fe(SO_4)_2$ is generally applied colorimetrically; titrimetric detn. is also possible. For colorimetry of 100 μg. F^- in 100 ml. soln.,[2, 82] add 1·0 ml. 1*N* $HClO_4$, 1·0 ml. Fe^{3+} soln. (0·15 mg. Fe/ml. 0·01*N* $HClO_4$), 1·0 ml. NH_4SCN (10 mg. SCN^-/ml. adjusted to pH 7·5–8·0 with NH_4OH) and 1·0 ml. H_2O; measure at 460–490 mμ against the above mixt. with addn. of 1·0 ml. H_2O contg. 3 mg. $ZrOCl_2$.

NOTES. (1) Many reagents can replace SCN^- in the above method. Resacetophenone is said to be the most sensitive.[83] Mix 1 ml. 10% resacetophenone in Me_2CO (or 1% 5-phenylsalicylic acid in EtOH) with 40 ml. EtOH and Fe^{3+} soln. to give a final concn. of 10 (or 5) p.p.m. Fe. Add the sample soln., dil. to 100 ml. with 0·1*M* acetate buffer pH 2, and measure at 465 mμ (or 575 mμ). The method is suitable for 0–6 p.p.m. F^- in the final soln. Interferences are Al, Ca, Mg, Ni, Co, SO_4^{2-} and PO_4^{3-}.

Salicylic acid is applicable for 0–400 μg. F^- soln.[84] Add the sample to 10 ml. reagent (0·16 g. Na-salicylate and 50 ml. Fe soln. contg. 5·406 g. $FeCl_3$/l. 1*N* HCl adjusted to pH 3·0) and dil. to 50 ml. with H_2O; measure at 530 mμ after 30 min. Sulfosalicylic acid can be used for 0·8–4 p.p.m. F^- at pH 3·0 and at 520 mμ.[85] It is better than salicylic acid (Sen[7]).

Ferron allows detn. of 0·1–0·5 mg. F^- in 25 ml. soln.[2, 86] Add 2·0 ml. reagent soln. (90 ml. satd. ferron, 10 ml. 1·0*N* $FeCl_3$ in 2*N* HCl and 100 ml. H_2O) and compare with standards.

Acetylacetone is also serviceable.[2, 87] For the reagent, mix just before use, 5 ml. $Fe(NO_3)_3$ (0·2 mg. Fe/ml.) soln. in 0·02*N* HNO_3, 3 ml. 0·05% acetylacetone and 2 ml. of

soln. contg. 29·2 g. NaCl and 30·1 g. $MgSO_4$/l. For detn. of <0·5 mg. F^- in 100 ml. soln., acidify to *p*-nitrophenol with 1*N* HNO_3, add 0·5 ml. in excess, boil for 2 min., cool, make just alk. with CO_2-free 0·5*N* NaOH, neutralize with 0·1*N* HNO_3 and add 1 drop in excess; dil. to 110 ml. with H_2O, add 10 ml. reagent and measure at 361 mμ after 10 min. The error is $\pm$0·01 mg.
Tiron is satisfactory (Sen[7]). Satd. NaBr soln. with Fe^{3+} allows detn.[88] of 1–5 mg. F^-.

Fe^{3+} soln. is also applied titrimetrically, usually with SCN^- as indicator.[2] For 50 ml. neutral soln.[89] add 10 ml. 10% KSCN and enough NaCl to saturate the soln. and to leave solid NaCl during the titration; titrate with $FeCl_3$ soln. (12–12·5 g./l. filtered after 12 hr.) to a yellow color, add 10 ml. 1:1 AmOH–Et_2O and titrate to red. Amperometric titration of 9–18 mg. F^- is possible in 50% EtOH soln. at pH 3.[90]

(h) Benzidine and Hg-succinimide allow gravimetric detn. of < 40 mg. F^- in 10 ml. of slightly acidic (AcOH) soln.[2, 91] Heat to 50°C, add reagent (1·84 g. benzidine in AcOH, dild. to 500 ml. with H_2O and mixed with 500 ml. 0·02*N* Hg-succinimide), heat on a steam-bath for 10 min., filter on a glass crucible, wash with cold H_2O, dry at 50°C *in vacuo* and weigh as $C_{24}H_{28}N_4F_6Hg$. Interferences are SO_4^{2-}, PO_4^{3-} and oxidants.

(i) $Bi(NO_3)_3$ ppts. BiF_3 from soln. at pH 6·5; the ppt. is dried at 50–93°C and weighed.[2, 92] Very many elements interfere.

(j) Distn. of H_2SiF_6 can be followed by titration with 0·1*N* NaOH using phenolphthalein indicator.[1, 2, 93] Treat 0·1–0·2 g. CaF_2 with 25 ml. H_2SO_4, a 10-fold amt. of SiO_2 and 1 g. anhyd. $CuSO_4$. Distil at 220°C for 30 min. while passing air. Stop heating but continue passing air. Finally titrate.

NOTES. (1) H_2O interferes in the distn. In an alternative procedure,[94] add 98·5% H_2SO_4 and glass beads, heat at 140–150°C for 1·5 hr. and then at 175°C for 1·5 hr., etc.
(2) For gravimetric detn.,[95] absorb in NaF and weigh as Na_2SiF_6.

(k) Na_2SiO_3 and KCl are used in titrimetric detn.; gravimetry is also possible.[2, 3] For analysis of 0·5 g. cryolite,[96] add 1·25 g. quartz powder and 6 g. Na_2CO_3 or K_2CO_3 and fuse; leach with 200 ml. hot H_2O, transfer to a 300 ml. measuring flask, add 20 g. $(NH_4)_2CO_3$, heat at 40°C for 1 hr., cool and dil. to 300 ml. with H_2O. After 12 hr., filter on dry paper and pipet out 200 ml. of filtrate. Evap. to 30–40 ml., cool, add 2 g. KCl and 10–15 ml. Na_2SiO_3 soln. (0·01 g. SiO_2/ml.); add methyl orange indicator, acidify with 1:1 HCl, add a few drops in excess and add EtOH to give a 50% w/w soln. After 1 hr., filter on paper and wash with a soln. contg. 2 g. KCl in 100 ml. 50% EtOH. Return the ppt. and paper to the original beaker, add 100 ml. hot CO_2-free H_2O, titrate with 0·1*N* NaOH using phenolphthalein indicator, boil and complete the titration. A correction is applied for the vol. of mother liquor (ml $\times$ 0·0023 $\times$ 10^{-2}) and for the number of washings (ml. $\times$ 10^{-5}).

NOTES. (1) After sepn. by distn. H_2SiF_6 can be absorbed in 10 ml. satd. KCl soln. in 50% EtOH and a few drops methyl orange, before the final titration.[97] For other modifications, see refs. 2, 3, 98.
(2) Gravimetric detn. as K_2SiF_6 is possible[59] after drying at 150–500°C.

(l) $CeCl_3$ is satisfactory for 1–10 mg. F^- in 50 ml. soln. with murexide as indicator.[2, 99] Neutralize to bromophenol blue with NaOH, make just acid with 0·1*N* HCl, add an equal vol. of MeOH and a few drops 0·5% indicator and titrate with 0·05*N* $CeCl_3$. Use a comparison soln. contg. $CoCl_2$.

NOTES. (1) Interferences are SO_4^{2-}, PO_4^{3-}, CO_3^{2-}, and AcO^-.
(2) $Y(NO_3)_3$ can also serve as titrant.[100] For the reagent, boil 16 g. $Y(NO_3)_3{\cdot}4H_2O$ with 1 l. H_2O, leave for 1 hr. and filter. For detn. of 0·05–0·1 g. F^- in neutral soln. (phenolphthalein), add 3–4 drops methyl red and titrate.
(3) $La(NO_3)_3$ allows gravimetric, titrimetric and nephelometric detns. For gravimetry,[2, 101] treat the neutral soln. with 1 g. NH_4OAc, 0·6 ml. AcOH and 2% $La(NO_3)_3$ (total vol. $\not>$100 ml.); leave for 12 hr., and weigh as $2LaF_3{\cdot}La(OAc)_3$ or ignite at 495–946°C and weigh as $LaF_3{\cdot}La_2O_3$. Alternatively,[102] ppt. 10–100 mg. F^- from acetate-buffered soln. at pH 2·0–2·5 with a known excess of La^{3+}; ppt. La in the filtrate with cupferron, ignite and weigh. Potentiometric titration with La^{3+} is possible;[37] for visual indication[103] 3:5 0·1% bromocresol green—0·2% methyl red is used with 0·05*N* La^{3+}.

(m) $U(SO_4)_2$ is suitable for potentiometric titration of < 0·2 g. F^- in 50 ml. acidic (H_2SO_4) soln.[2, 104] Add 50–150 ml. satd. sulfanilic acid soln. in 0·5*N* K-sulfanilate, then add 2–3 g. sulfanilic acid and titrate under CO_2, with 0·5*M* $U(SO_4)_2$ in 0·4*N* H_2SO_4 (prepd. by passing UO_2SO_4 soln. through a Jones reductor). The ppt. is KUF_5.

NOTE. Interferences are Ca, Al, Fe^{3+} and PO_4^{3-}. No interference is caused by Fe^{2+}, Zn, Cd, Si, NH_4^+, Na or K.

(n) $Ti(SO_4)_2$ and H_2O_2 provide a colorimetric method for 0·05–12 mg. F^- in 1 g. sample.[1, 2, 105] Fuse with 8 g. Na_2CO_3 and K_2CO_3, leach with hot H_2O, add 3–4 g. $(NH_4)_2CO_3$ and heat to decompose the latter. Filter on paper and wash with H_2O. Add 4 ml. 3% H_2O_2 and 10 ml. $Ti(SO_4)_2$ soln. contg. 1 mg. Ti/ml. Make orange with 4 ml. H_2SO_4, then add Na_2CO_3 until the color starts to fade. Add H_2SO_4 (3 ml. for < 2·5 mg. F^- and 12 ml. for 2·5–12 mg. F^-), dil. to 100 ml. with H_2O and compare with standards or measure at 440 mμ.

NOTES. (1) Al, PO_4^{3-} and large amts. of alkali sulfates interfere.
(2) Ascorbic acid can replace H_2O_2 for detn. of 0–50 p.p.m. F^- at pH 4·2 (biphthalate buffer) with measurement at 360 mμ.[106] Chromotropic acid is used with Ti^{4+} at pH 1·4 with measurement at 460 mμ (Sen[7]).

(o) Miscellaneous colorimetric methods. $(NH_4)_2MoO_4$ can be applied with hydroquinone and sulfite.[107] Neutralize 10 ml. SiF_4 distillate collected in NaOH, with dil. H_2SO_4; add 1 ml. molybdate (50 g. $(NH_4)_2MoO_4$/l. 1*N* H_2SO_4), 1 ml. hydroquinone soln. (20 g./l. H_2O contg. 1 ml. H_2SO_4) and 3 ml. sulfite (500 ml. 15% Na_2SO_3 mixed with 2 l. 20% Na_2CO_3), and measure the blue color. Arsenomolybdate or phosphomolybdate are less satisfactory reagents.[108]

The catalytic action of F^- on the reaction between Ce^{4+}, CdI_2 and linear starch can be used to det. 0·3–0·9 p.p.m. F^- by measuring the time required to attain a certain color.[109]

F^- can be detd. by its effect on the Ce^{3+}–Ce^{4+} equilibrium; Ce^{3+} is labelled with ^{144}Ce and a final β-count is made after sepn.[110]

(p) Miscellaneous methods. The amt. of etching on a glass plate can be utilized;[1, 2] heat a 1 g. sample in a Pb crucible with 12 ml. H_2SO_4 for 45 min. at 165°C covered with a glass plate.

0·05–1 μg. F^-/ml. soln. can be detd. by the effect of F^- on phosphatase;[5, 111] the error is $\pm$0·01–0·1 μg.

An electrometric method using a Zr–Pt electrode is suitable for detn. of $<$ 2·5 mg. F^-/l. (see Chapter 49, p. 358).

Flame photometry can be applied by means of the CaF_2 band at 529·0 mμ.[112]

References

1. HILLEBRAND and LUNDELL, 594 (737); SCOTT and FURMAN, 399; KIMURA, 341.
2. FRESENIUS–JANDER, **VIIa**α, 132 (1950).
3. MCKENNA, F. E., *Nucleonics*, **8**, No. 6, 24 (1951); **9**, No. 1, 40 (1951); **9**, No. 2, 51 (1951).
4. BUSCH, G. W., *et al.*, *Natl. Nuclear Energy Ser., Div. VIII*, Vol. I, 226–270 (1950).
5. SIMONS, J. H., *Fluorine Chemistry*, Vols. I–II, Academic, New York (1950/51).
6. WILSON, H. N., *Ann. Repts. on Progr. Chem.* (*Chem. Soc. London*), **41**, 283 (1944); FROMMES, M., *Z. anal. Chem.*, **99**, 301 (1934); TADA, Y., *Japan Analyst*, **3**, 170 (1954); KRAMER, H. P.· *et al.*, *J. Am. Water Works Assoc.*, **48**, 573 (1956).
7. RINCK, E., *Bull. soc. chim. France*, 305 (1948); GEYER, R., *Z. anorg. Chem.*, **252**, 42 (1943); FUNASAKA, W., *et al.*, *Japan Analyst*, **2**, 368 (1953); **4**, 607 (1955); SEN, B., *Z. anal. Chem.*, **153**, 168 (1956).
8. TSUBAKI, I., *J. Soc. Chem. Ind. Japan*, **47**, 504 (1944).
9. CRITCHFIELD, JR., E., *Ind. Eng. Chem.*, *Anal. Ed.*, **14**, 57 (1942).
10. REMMERT, L. F., *et al.*, *Anal. Chem.*, **25**, 450 (1953).
11. DAHLE, D. and WICKMANN, H. J., *J. Assoc. Offic. Agr. Chemists*, **19**, 313 (1936); **20**, 297 (1937); ARMSTRONG, W. D., *Ind. Eng. Chem.*, *Anal. Ed.*, **8**, 384 (1936) (minute amt.); GILKEY, W. K., *et al.*, *ibid.*, 150; EBERZ, W. F., *et al.*, *ibid.*, **10**, 259 (1938) (app.); ESTILL, W. B. and MOSIER, L. C., *Anal. Chem.*, **27**, 1669 (1955) (app.).
12. SMITH, O. D. and PARKS, T. D., *Anal. Chem.*, **27**, 998 (1955).
13. DEUTSCH, S., *Anal. Chem.*, **27**, 1154 (1955).
14. HERLEMONT, H. and DELABRE, J., *Compt. rend.*, **196**, 1502 (1933).
15. BRUNISHOLZ, G. and MICHOD, J., *Helv. Chim. Acta*, **37**, 874 (1954).
16. TIEDEMANN, E., *Z. anal. Chem.*, **146**, 415 (1955).
17. MAKSIMYCHEVA, Z. T. and TALIPOV, SH. T., *Trudy Sredneaziat. Gosudarst. Univ. in V. I. Lenina, Khim. Nauki*, **35**, No. 7, 129 (1954); FASANO, H. L., *Anales soc. cient. Arg.*, **144**, 473 (1947).
18. SINGER, L. and ARMSTRONG, W. D., *Anal. Chem.*, **26**, 904 (1954).
19. GEYER, R., *Z. anorg. Chem.*, **252**, 42 (1943).
20. MIKHAILOVA, W. F., *Zavodskaya Lab.*, **6**, 1154 (1937).
21. BELCHER, R. and CLARK, S. J., *Anal. Chim. Acta*, **8**, 222 (1953); HENNART, C. and MERLIN, E., *ibid.*, **17**, 463 (1957).
22. TALIPOV, SH. T. and SHESTAKOVA, N. P., *Trudy Sredneaziat. Gosudarst. Univ.* (*Tashkent*), **33**, No. 4, 83 (1952).
23. SHEHYN, H., *Anal. Chem.*, **29**, 1466 (1957).
24. STEVENS, R. E., *Ind. Eng. Chem.*, *Anal. Ed.*, **8**, 248 (1936).
25. SPECHT, F. and HORNIG, A., *Z. anal. Chem.*, **125**, 161 (1943); SPECHT, F., *Z. anorg. u. allgem Chem.*, **231**, 181 (1937).
26. TANANAEFF, I., *Z. anal. Chem.*, **99**, 21 (1934).
27. PETROW, H. G. and NASCH, L. K., *Anal. Chem.*, **22**, 1274 (1950).
28. LASZLOVSKY, J., *Magyar Kém. Folyóirat*, **60**, 209 (1954).
29. VŘEŠTÁL, J., *et al.*, *Chem. listy*, **51**, 1677 (1957).
30. FISCHER, J. and PEISKER, H., *Z. anal. Chem.*, **95**, 225 (1933).
31. BELCHER, R. and TATLOW, J. C., *Analyst*, **76**, 593 (1951).
32. BELCHER, R. and MACDONALD, A. M. G., *Mikrochim. Acta*, 510 (1957).
33. VASIL'EV, A. A., *J. Applied Chem.* (*U.S.S.R.*), **9**, 747 (1936); CH'EBURKOWA, E. E., *Zavodskaya Lab.*, **16**, 1009 (1950); EHRLICH, P. and PIETZKA, G., *Z. anal. Chem.*, **133**, 84 (1951); *Angew. Chem.*, **65**, 131 (1953).
34. BALLCZO, H. and SCHIFFNER, H., *Z. anal. Chem.*, **152**, 3 (1956); *Mikrochim. Acta*, 1829 (1956).
35. ROWLEY, R. J. and CHURCHILL, H. V., *Ind. Eng. Chem.*, *Anal. Ed.*, **9**, 551 (1937); REYNOLDS, D. S. and HILL, W. L., *ibid.*, **11**, 20 (1939); CLIFFORD, P. A., *J. Assoc. Offic. Agr. Chemists*, **23**, 303 (1940); **24**, 350, 356 (1941); **25**, 396 (1942); **27**, 90, 246 (1944); SHELL, H. R. and CRAIG, R. L., *Anal. Chem.*, **26**, 996 (1954).
36. STROSS, W., *Metallurgia*, **36**, 346 (1947).
37. LANGER, A., *Ind. Eng. Chem.*, *Anal. Ed.*, **12**, 511 (1940).
38. GRIMALDI, F. S., *et al.*, *Anal. Chem.*, **27**, 918 (1955).
39. MCCLURE, F. J., *Ind. Eng. Chem.*, *Anal. Ed.*, **11**, 171 (1939).
40. EBERZ, W. F., *et al.*, *Ind. Eng. Chem.*, *Anal. Ed.*, **10**, 259 (1938).
41. HAMOND, J. W. and MACINTIRE, W. H., *J. Assoc. Offic. Agr. Chemists*, **23**, 398 (1940).
42. GWIRTSMAN, J., *et al.*, *Anal. Chem.*, **29**, 140, 887 (1957).
43. BALLCZO, H. and KAUFMAN, O., *Mikrochemie ver. Mikrochim. Acta*, **38**, 237 (1951).
44. WILLARD, H. H. and HORTON, C. A., *Anal. Chem.*, **22**, 1190, 1194 (1950).
45. DATTA, S. K., *Z. anal. Chem.*, **149**, 333 (1956).
46. BANERJEE, G., *Anal. Chim. Acta*, **13**, 409 (1955).
47. HOLLINGSWORTH, R. P., *Anal. Chem.*, **29**, 1130 (1957).
48. MILTON, R. F., *Analyst*, **74**, 54 (1949).

49. LONGO, R. E., *Publs. inst. invest. microquím., Univ. nacl. litoral* (*Rosario, Arg.*), **16**, No. 16, 11 (1952).
50. HORTON, A. D., *et al.*, *Anal. Chem.*, **24**, 548 (1952).
51. EMI, K. and HAYAMI, T., *J. Chem. Soc. Japan*, **76**, 1291 (1955); **77**, 1656 (1956) (in plant materials).
52. REVINSON, D. and HARLEY, J. H., *Anal. Chem.*, **25**, 794 (1953).
53. LIDDELL, H. F., *Analyst*, **78**, 494 (1953).
54. ICKEN, J. M. and BLANK, B. M., *Anal. Chem.*, **25**, 1741 (1953); SALSBURY, J. M., *et al.*, *ibid.*, **23**, 603 (1950).
55. LOTHE, J. J., *Anal. Chem.*, **28**, 949 (1956).
56. SAMACHSON, J., *et al.*, *Anal. Chem.*, **29**, 1888 (1957); TALVITIE, N. A., *Ind. Eng. Chem., Anal. Ed.*, **15**, 620 (1943).
57. LAMBERT, J. L., *Anal. Chem.*, **26**, 558 (1954).
58. LIDDELL, H. F., *Analyst*, **79**, 752 (1954).
59. MATSUURA, K., *J. Chem. Soc. Japan*, **52**, 730 (1931).
60. BUMSTED, H. E. and WELLS, J. C., *Anal. Chem.*, **24**, 1595 (1952); ARNOLD, E. A. and LEVITIN, M. A., *ibid.*, 605; SHAW, W. M., *ibid.*, **26**, 1212 (1954); FUWA, K., *Japan Analyst*, **3**, 98 (1954); RICHTER, F., *Z. anal. Chem.*, **124**, 161 (1942).
61. WELCHER, **IV**, 414, 427, 467.
62. NÖLKE, F., *Z. anal. Chem.*, **121**, 81 (1941); also see ZEPPELIN, H. v., *Angew. Chem.*, **63**, 281 (1951); ZEPPELIN, and FUCHS, J., *ibid.*, **64**, 223 (1952); UGNYACHEV, N. YA. and BILENKO, E. A., *Ukrain. Khim. Zhur.*, **12**, 34 (1937).
63. JAKI, F., *Mikrochemie*, **32**, 195 (1944).
64. WAKIMOTO, S., *J. Chem. Soc. Japan*, **77**, 1489 (1956).
65. MEGREGIAN, S., *Anal. Chem.*, **26**, 1161 (1954).
66. THATCHER, L. L., *Anal. Chem.*, **29**, 1709 (1957).
67. KRAHULEC, L., *Československ. hyg. epidemiol. mikrobiol. imunol.*, **4**, 376 (1955).
68. GAD, G. and NAUMANN, K., *Gas- u. Wasserfach*, **8**, 183 (1938).
69. KUMADA, M., *et al.*, *Bull. Chem. Soc. Japan*, **28**, 148 (1955); also see FEIGL, F. and RIJMAN, E., *Mikrochemie*, **12**, 133 (1933).
70. SANO, H., *Japan Analyst*, **5**, 289 (1956).
71. PRICE, M. J. and WALKER, O. J., *Anal. Chem.*, **24**, 1593 (1952); also see HUNTER, G. J., *et al.*, *Anal. Chim. Acta*, **8**, 351 (1953); MACNULTY, B. J. and HUNTER, *ibid.*, **9**, 426 (1953) ($\pm 10\%/0{\cdot}05$ p.p.m. F^-); BEVERIDGE, J. S., *ibid.*, 330; OKUNO, H., *J. Chem. Soc. Japan*, **63**, 23 (1942) (hematoxylin).
72. BOUMAN, J., *Chem. Weekblad*, **51**, 33 (1955); also see BUSCH, G. W., *et al.*, ref. 4; WILLARD, H. H. and HORTON, C. A., *Anal. Chem.*, **24**, 862 (1952); SZABÓ, Z. G. and BECK, M. T., *Acta Chim. Acad. Sci. Hung.*, **4**, 211 (1954).
73. BECK, M. T., *Acta Chim. Acad. Sci. Hung.*, **4**, 223 (1954).
74. POWELL, W. A. and SAYLOR, J. H., *Anal. Chem.*, **25**, 960 (1953).
75. CASTOR, C. R. and SAYLOR, *Anal. Chem.*, **24**, 1369 (1952).
76. HIGASHINO, T. and MUSHA, S., *Japan Analyst*, **4**, 3 (1955); also see OSCHERVICH, R. E., *Zavodskaya Lab.*, **7**, 934 (1938); WELCHER, **II**, 102.
77. RICHTER, F., *Chem. Tech.* (*Berlin*), **1**, 84 (1949); GILBERT, M. J. and SAYLOR, J. H., *Anal. Chem.*, **22**, 196 (1950); THRUN, W. E., *ibid.*, 918; MACNULTY, B. L., *et al.*, *Anal. Chim. Acta*, **14**, 368 (1956) ($\pm 0{\cdot}6\mu$g for 20μg F).
78. MACNULTY and WOOLLAND, L. D., *Anal. Chim. Acta*, **14**, 452 (1956).
79. SAYLOR, J. H. and LARKIN, M. E., *Anal. Chem.*, **20**, 194 (1948).
80. BAKER, B. B. and MORRISON, J. D., *Anal. Chem.*, **27**, 1306 (1955).
81. SCHLIEBS, R., *Z. anal. Chem.*, **150**, 322 (1956).
82. INGOLS, R. S., *et al.*, *Anal. Chem.*, **22**, 799 (1950); also see FOSTER, M. D., *Ind. Eng. Chem., Anal. Ed.*, **5**, 234 (1933); OKUNO, H., *J. Chem. Soc. Japan*, **60**, 1154 1158 (1941); SOMMER, L., *Chem. listy*, **47**, 906 (1953).
83. NICHOLS, M. L. and CONDO, JR., A. C., *Anal. Chem.*, **26**, 703 (1954); also see MADER, C., *Chemist Analyst*, **44**, 86 (1955).
84. KORTÜM-SEILER, M., *Angew. Chem.*, **A59**, 159 (1947); RICHARD, R. R., *et al.*, *Anal. Chem.*, **23**, 919 (1951); BATLET, J. C. and CHAPMAN, R. A., *ibid.*, **25**, 522 (1953) (good reproducibility).
85. LACROIX, S. and LABALADE, M., *Anal. Chim. Acta*, **4**, 68 (1950); MONNIER, D., *Helv. Chim. Acta*, **29**, 421 (1946).
86. WELCHER, **I**, 339; URECH, P., *Helv. Chim. Acta*, **25**, 1115 (1942); LIANG, SH. CH. and CH'ENG, CH. Y., *Sci. Sinica* (*Peking*), **6**, 259 (1957).
87. WILCOX, L. V., *Ind. Eng. Chem., Anal. Ed.*, **6**, 167 (1934); ARMSTRONG, W. D., *ibid.*, **5**, 300 (1933).
88. ERLER, K., *Z. anal. Chem.*, **131**, 103 (1950).
89. SPIELHACZEK, H., *Z. anal. Chem.*, **118**, 161 (1939/40).
90. MUSHA, S. and HIGASHINO, T., *J. Chem. Soc. Japan*, **77**, 128 (1956).
91. MILLER, C. F., *Chemist Analyst*, **26**, 35 (1937); WELCHER, **II**, 315; also see PERTUSI, C., *Atti III. congr. naz. chim.*, 573 (1929).
92. DOMANGE, L., *Compt. rend.*, **213**, 31 (1941); *Bull. soc. chim. France*, **9**, 96 (1942).
93. GEFFCKEN, W. and HAMANN, H., *Z. anal. Chem.*, **114**, 15 (1938).
94. ARMSTRONG, W. D., *Ind. Eng. Chem., Anal. Ed.*, **5**, 315 (1933).
95. SHINKAI, S., *J. Soc. Chem. Ind. Japan*, **39**, 162B (1936).
96. WASSILIEFF, A. A. and MARTIANOFF, N. N., *Z. anal. Chem.*, **103**, 107 (1935).
97. RASANOW, S. N., *Z. anal. Chem.*, **102**, 328 (1935).
98. TALIPOV, SH. T., *et al.*, *Trudy Sredneaziat. Gosudarst. Univ.*, (*Tashkent*), **33**, No. 4, 75 (1952).
99. BRUNISHOLZ, G. and MICHOD, J., *Helv. Chim. Acta*, **37**, 598, 874 (1954); also see BATCHELDER, G. and MELOCHE, V. W., *J. Am. Chem. Soc.*, **53**, 2131 (1931); **54**, 1319 (1932) (methyl red, ampho-magenta); NICHOLS, M. L. and OLSEN, J. S., *Ind. Eng. Chem., Anal. Ed.*, **15**, 342 (1943) (methyl red or glass electrode).
100. FRERE, F. J., *Ind. Eng. Chem., Anal. Ed.*, **5**, 17 (1933).
101. PERRIER, C. and GIAMMARINO, G., *Bull. R. Ufficio geol. Italia*, **51**, No. 16, 19 (1926); FISCHER, J., *Z. anal. Chem.*, **104**, 344 (1936); GIAMMARINO, *ibid.*, **108**, 196 (1937).
102. POPOV, A. I. and KNUDSON, G. G., *Anal. Chem.*, **26**, 892 (1954).
103. YAMASHITA, M., *Repts. Govt. Ind. Research Inst., Nagoya*, **4**, 73 (1955).
104. FLATT, R., *Helv. Chim. Acta*, **20**, 894 (1937); *Angew. Chem.*, **50**, 329 (1937).
105. YOE, 186; HACKL, O., *Z. anal. Chem.*, **116**, 93 (1939); SCHUMB, W. C. and RADIMER, K. J., *Anal. Chem.*, **20**, 871 (1948); HILL, H. J. and REYNOLDS, C. A., *ibid.*, **22**, 448 (1950).

106. SCHALL, E. D. and WILLIAMSON, H. G., *J. Assoc. Offic. Agr. Chemists*, **38**, 454 (1955).
107. MAYRHOFFER, A. and WASITZKY, A., *Mikrochemie*, **20**, 29 (1936); also see CURRY, R. P. and MELLON, M. G., *Anal. Chem.*, **28**, 1567 (1956); **29**, 1632 (1957) (eiconogen, 0·1–2·0 mg. F^-); PEREGUD, E. A. and BOĬKINA, B. S., *Zavodskaya Lab.*, **22**, 287 (1956) (ascorbic acid).
108. BERGAMINI, C., *Anal. Chim. Acta*, **4**, 153 (1950).
109. LAMBERT, J. L., *Anal. Chem.*, **25**, 271 (1953).
110. ARMSTRONG, W. D. and SINGER, L., *Anal. Chem.*, **26**, 1047 (1954).
111. STETTER, H., *Chem. Ber.*, **81**, 532 (1948).
112. ISHIDA, R., *J. Chem. Soc. Japan*, **77**, 241 (1956).

61

BORON

The main references for this chapter are given in ref. 1. The analytical chemistry of boron has been reviewed.[2]

It should be noted that boric acid volatilizes when acidic solutions are heated on a steam-bath. Most types of glass apparatus contain boron, hence it is advisable to use platinum or silica vessels during the procedures.

Attack

(a) Borax, etc. can be dissolved in H_2O.

(b) Ulexite, colemanite, etc. require heating with HCl under reflux.

(c) Silicates, enamels, B–C. Fuse with Na_2CO_3 weighed to the nearest mg., add an equiv. amt. of HCl at 15–30°C, cover and heat gently to remove CO_2. If much B is present, add SiO_2.

For silicates contg. Fe,[3] fuse a 0·1–0·25 g. sample (contg. < 0·2 g. SiO_2 and < 0·1 g. Fe) with a 4–5-fold amt. of Na_2CO_3; if much Fe is present, use an 8–10-fold amt. Ignite for 3–4 min., cool, warm with 5–6 ml. H_2O and transfer to a Kjeldahl distn. flask. The total vol. should be < 12 ml.; if it is more, gelatinous silica adsorbs B_2O_3. Add 15 ml. H_2SO_4 and 200 ml. MeOH, moisten the joint with H_2SO_4 and distil slowly until no further SO_3 fumes are evolved. If much Fe is present, add an extra 100 ml. MeOH and 0·1–0·2 g. $CaCO_3$ before distn. Collect the distillate in a 200 ml. Ag dish contg. 10 ml. 1*N* NaOH, and 1–2 drops 30% H_2O_2 (P_2O_5-free). Evap. to dryness, fuse with a little KOH, add a few ml. H_2O after cooling, etc.,

(d) Minerals. Fuse 2 g. anhyd. Na_2HPO_4 and 1 g. HPO_3 in a Pt crucible, add 0·5 g. mineral, cover and heat (with a blast lamp if necessary). Drop into ice water while hot, transfer to a distg. flask, heat the crucible with H_3PO_4 and combine. Add a few porcelain chips and 10 ml. H_3PO_4, reflux until clear, add MeOH and distil, etc.

(e) B and borides. Fuse B with KOH. For metal borides,[4] fuse a 100 mg. sample with 1 g. Na_2CO_3 for 5 min., cool while swirling, add 100–200 mg. $NaNO_3$, fuse for 20 min., cool, add 50 ml. 1:1 HCl and dil. to 200 ml. with H_2O. Add 20 ml. 1:2 NaOH and 10 g. $BaCO_3$ powder (if Cr is present, add also 10 ml. 10% $BaCl_2$), heat slowly to b.p., boil for 5 min. and let cool for 30 min. Filter under suction and wash with hot H_2O.

With B, or a sample contg. much B, use a 20-fold excess of Na_2CO_3. With Al–B or Cr–B, use Na_2CO_3 and $NaNO_3$. With Nb–B or Ta–B, fuse with K_2CO_3 and KNO_3, and ext. with H_2O. With W–B or V–B, fuse with Na_2CO_3 and KNO_3, and ext. with H_2O; add $FeCl_3$ if V is present.

(f) Steels.[5] Heat 5 g. steel with 25 ml. HCl in a 300 ml. flask fitted with a 14 cm. × 0·6 cm. diam. glass tube. Cool, add 10 ml. 15% H_2O_2, warm, cool, add 20 g. $CaCl_2$ and MeOH and distil. H_3PO_4 can also be used.

(g) Mineral waters. Evap. to 1/6–1/10 of the original vol., filter if necessary and evap. to a syrup. If the residue is large, acidify with HCl, add anhyd. EtOH, filter after 10–15 hr. and wash with EtOH. Add H_2O and 10 ml. 10% NaOH, evap. to dryness and ignite gently. Add H_2O, acidify with AcOH and distil.

(h) Org. compds. and graphite. Mix 0·2–2 g. graphite with 2 ml. 3% $Ca(OH)_2$, dry and burn in O_2 at 900°C. For org. compds.[6] add 2 ml. H_2SO_4 and 10 mg. $Ca(OH)_2$, heat gently until the soln. begins to darken, cool, add 1 drop 90% H_2O_2, heat gently and then to fumes, cool and repeat the H_2O_2 addn., etc. If the sample is dry-ashed, even in presence of $Ba(OH)_2$, some B may be lost.

In an alternative process for org. compds.,[7] warm a 0·2 g. sample with 2 ml. H_2SO_4, add 30% H_2O_2 and then 90% H_2O_2, warming between addns.; then add 2 drops satd. $FeSO_4$ in 0·1*N* H_2SO_4 and 40 ml. abs. MeOH, distil, add another 40 ml. MeOH and distil again. Collect the distillate in 10 ml. satd. $Ca(OH)_2$ soln. cooled in ice.

Separation

Distn. of the methyl ester from acidic soln. contg. MeOH allows sepn. from many elements. Details are given in Table 59 as well as above under Attack. For small amts. of B, distn. from soln. contg. MeOH and H_3PO_4 is preferable. $AlCl_3$ should be added if F^- is present.[8] A detailed study of the distn. has been made (Roth and Beck[8]).

Extn. with ether seps. B from SiO_2, Ca, Mg, Ba, Al,

TABLE 59. Distillation of Boric Acid

Heat a 1 g. sample with 10 ml. 1:1 HCl at 90°C for 1 hr.

Residual soln.
Cool, add 10 g. anhyd. CaCl₂ and 40 ml. MeOH,
distil until a syrup is obtained, and repeat the
MeOH addn. and distn. twice

Distillate

Residual soln.
Add H₂O and filter

Distillate

Residue
Ignite, fuse with Na₂CO₃,
add H₂O, transfer to a
flask with a condenser,
add HCl, boil, distil, add
MeOH and CaCl₂ and
distil

Collect in 15% CO₂-free
NaOH, and titrate

Distillate
Treat as for the other
distillates

Fe, Zn and Pb in glasses.[9, 10] If F⁻ is present (< 500 µg.),[10] add 15 g. AlCl₃, 20 ml. H₂O and 10 ml. 12M HCl, stir mechanically, add 30 ml. EtOH and 60 ml. Et₂O and shake for 5 min.; the partition coeff. is 0·59 ± 0·02. B can be sepd. from large amts. of SiO₂ by adding 60 ml. MeOH and 20 ml. iso-Pr₂O to 50 ml. soln. at pH 2–3 and extg. by the 'perforator' method.[11]

Extn. with CHCl₃ of tetraphenylarsonium fluoborate seps. B from U and Be.[12, 13] For 0·01–1 µg. B in 5 ml. 0·8M F⁻ soln. at pH < 3·2, add 5 ml. tetraphenylarsonium chloride in CHCl₃ (1·046 g./250 ml.), stir for 30 min., centrifuge, add 10 ml. H₂O, stir and sep.

Oxine can be used to sep. B from Al, Fe, Ti, Zr, Pb, Zn, Ni, etc. For 50 ml. of slightly acidic soln. at 60°C, add a small excess of oxine (7·5 g. in 50 ml. 1N NaOH, warmed and dild. to 200 ml. with H₂O), make alk. to bromocresol purple, warm for 5 min., add 5 ml. 1M MgCl₂, warm for 5 min., filter on a glass crucible and wash with H₂O. Make the filtrate just acid to methyl red, add 0·5 g. active charcoal, filter on paper after 5 min. and wash with H₂O. Finally boil the filtrate under reflux, cool and titrate.

Electrolysis at a Hg-cathode seps. B from Fe, Ni, Cu, Co, etc.

B can be sepd. from Al, Fe, PO₄³⁻, etc. by addn. of Pb(NO₃)₂ to the acidic soln. followed by NaHCO₃ until a ppt. appears; heat, neutralize to bromothymol blue with NaHCO₃, dil. to 250 ml. with H₂O, filter on a dry paper, etc.

B can be sepd. from PO₄³⁻ with AgNO₃; neutralize the soln. to bromocresol purple, add reagent, filter on paper, wash, add NaCl and mannitol, etc. Alternatively, CaCl₂ can be employed; make the soln. alk. to phenolphthalein, add 0·5 g. CaCl₂ and 25 ml. satd. Ca(OH)₂ soln., dil. to 100 ml. with H₂O, filter on dry paper, etc.

NH₄Cl has been used to sep. B from SiO₂. Add 3 g. NH₄Cl to 10–15 ml. alk. soln., neutralize after 5 min. with 6N HCl, add 10 drops in excess, boil and place on a steam-bath for 10 min. Filter on paper and wash with 0·01N HCl. Add excess NaOH to the filtrate with 5 ml. 1M MgCl₂, evap. to 30 ml., acidify with HCl, boil and titrate. If < 50 mg. SiO₂ is present, direct titration is feasible.

For sepns. with ion exchange resins, see Chapter 13, Sections 2.1 and 2.3.

The removal of large amts. of B can be accomplished by heating with HF or with HF and H₂SO₄.

Determination

The only satisfactory method for the determination of large amounts of B is the titrimetric procedure with mannitol. 1,1′-Dianthrimide and its analogs seem to be the best colorimetric reagents; curcumin is also satisfactory.

(a) **Mannitol addn.** followed by titration with NaOH soln. is the classical method (Chapin's method).[1] For a MeOH distillate contg. < 0·1 g. B₂O₃, add twice the amt. of 0·1–0·5N NaOH which is required by titration between the p-nitrophenol and phenolphthalein endpoints. Evap. to 25 ml. on a steam-bath, transfer to a flask, add 1:1 CO₂-free HCl until the indicator is colorless, warm under suction and adjust to yellow with 0·5N NaOH and then to faintly yellow with 0·1N NaOH. Add 1 g. mannitol and titrate with 0·1N NaOH until brown-red. Add another 1 g. mannitol and titrate further if the color fades.

NOTES. (1) Interferences are CO₃²⁻, WO₄²⁻, large amts. of F⁻ and As³⁺; the last interference can be prevented by addn. of H₂O₂ after the alkali. B in Ti metal is detd.[14] by dissoln. in HCl and HNO₃, passage through a cationite resin and sepn. with CaCO₃ before titration. Modifications of the

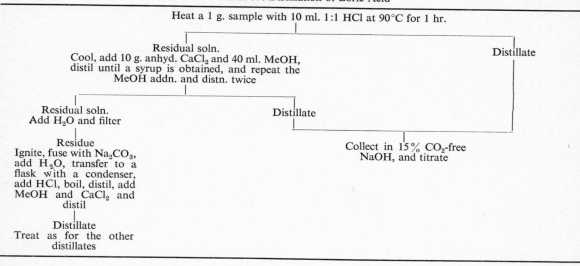

titration have been described.[15] Heavy metals and alk. earths can be masked with EDTA.[16]
(2) Various polyhydroxy compds. have been suggested to replace mannitol. Glycerol, glucose, fructose, invert sugar, sorbitol[17] and Ca-gluconate[18] are among those proposed.
(3) Indicators suggested to replace phenolphthalein are bromocresol purple (blue); α-naphtholphthalein (green); bromothymol blue + phenol red (see Table 8); 0·4% Safrol red No. 1 in EtOH; 1% methyl red in 50% EtOH; Kato's universal indicator (see Table 9; yellow, blue).
(4) Sorbitol can be used colorimetrically as a spot test;[19] it is said to be more sensitive than mannitol.

(b) 1,1′-Dianthrimide is probably the best colorimetric reagent for B.[6, 20] For 0·5–7·5 μg. B in 2·5 ml. soln., add 12·5 ml. H_2SO_4 and 5 ml. reagent soln. (1 g. in 2 l. H_2SO_4 stored in an ice-box) and maintain at 70°C for 5 hr. Measure the blue complex in a 2 cm. cell at 615 mμ.

NOTES. (1) Interferences are NO_3^-, NO_2^-, CrO_4^{2-}, IO_4^- and ClO_4^-.
(2) 1,1′-Dianthrimide is the best of some 60 reagents tested;[6] see also below and Chapter 12, Section 2. With quinalizarin the color produced is partially masked by the reagent itself.
(3) The vessels used should be of porcelain or Corning alkali-resistant glass. Evelyn colorimetric tubes are not suitable; Pt vessels cause a darkening of the color.
(4) With 1,1′-dianthrimide as well as with the other reagents mentioned below, H_2SO_4 can be replaced by AcOH and $(Ac)_2O$.[21]

Several other anthraquinone derivs. have been examd. Diaminochrysazine is suitable for < 5 μg. B in 2 ml. H_2SO_4 soln.[7] Add 1·00 ml. reagent soln. (0·3 mg./ml. H_2SO_4), wait for 15 min., add H_2SO_4 to a vol. of 10 ml., and measure after 10–15 min. at 525 mμ.

NOTES. (1) Interferences are Ti, Cr^{6+}, NO_3^- and F^-. No interference arises from Al, Ba, Ca, Co, Cr^{3+}, Cu, Fe^{3+}, Mg, Mn, Ni, Pb, Zn, Na, K, Cl^- or PO_4^{3-}. The concn. of acid is important; the reagent is twice as sensitive in 98% acid as in 95% acid. The color is affected by the temp. and the time of standing.
Tribromoanthrarufin is the most sensitive of the anthraquinone derivs. Tetrabromochrysazine[22] and various dianthrimide derivs.[23] have been studied.
(2) Quinalizarin is suitable for 0–8 μg. B/ml. soln.[24] Add 10 ml. reagent soln. (45 mg./l. H_2SO_4) and measure the purple color at 620 mμ. Interferences are 3 μg. F^-, 10-fold amts. of Ge, and oxidants.
(3) Carmine allows detn. of 0·1–24 μg. B in 2 ml. soln.[10, 25] Add 2 drops HCl and 10 ml. H_2SO_4, cool, add 10 ml. 0·025% carmine in H_2SO_4 and measure after over 45 min. at 585 mμ.
Other reagents proposed include alizarin S (measurement at 560, 345 or 480 mμ after 24 hr.),[26] 4,4′-diamino-1,1′-dianthraquinonylamine (measurement at 620 mμ after 30 min. at 150°C),[27] waxoline purple AS[28] and alizarin blue S.[29]

(c) Curcumin is a satisfactory colorimetric reagent for up to 20 μg. B.[5, 12, 30] Evap. the soln. in a porcelain crucible with 0·1 g. Na_2CO_3, heat at 110–130°C and cool. Add 1 drop phenolphthalein, neutralize with 1:4 HCl, add 0·5 ml. HCl in excess, 0·5 ml. 5% $H_2C_2O_4$ and 3 ml. reagent (62·5 mg. in 5 ml. carbitol, dild. to 500 ml. with Me_2CO) and evap. at 55 ± 3°C. Bake for 30 ± 5 min. at the same temp., cool, add Me_2CO, filter on a small filter and wash with Me_2CO. Collect the filtrate in a 25 ml. flask, dil. to 25 ml. with Me_2CO and measure at 535 mμ at 20–25°C.

NOTE. Interferences are heavy metals. NO_3^- and F^-. B in graphite can be detd. after calcining with CaO and passage through Amberlite IR-120 resin.[12]

(d) Miscellaneous gravimetric methods. Distn. from MeOH soln. and absorption in CaO soln. form the basis of Gooch's method.[31] Evap. the AcOH-contg. soln. to dryness, add 10 ml. MeOH, evap. to dryness and repeat 3 times. Then add a few drops of AcOH and more MeOH, etc. and repeat thrice again. Collect all the distillate in a soln. contg. a known amt. of CaO, leave for at least 1 hr. and evap. to dryness. Ignite above 700°C and weigh. The difference between the known wt. of CaO and the final wt. corresponds to B_2O_3. Some bumping may occur. Another absorbent is Na_2WO_4 with a little WO_3.

$BaCl_2$ and tartaric acid can be used to ppt. 10–200 μg. B from ammoniacal soln.[32] The ppt. is filtered on a glass crucible, washed with 2:1:1 NH_4OH:H_2O:MeOH, dried at 110°C and weighed as $Ba_5B_2C_{12}H_8O_{24}·4H_2O$; alternatively it is dissolved in HCl, Ba pptd. as $BaCrO_4$ and the ppt. titrated iodometrically.

Nitron allows pptn. of BF_4^-. For 125–250 mg. H_3BO_3 in 60 ml. soln.[33] add 15·0 ml. nitron soln. (37·5 g. in 250 ml. 50% v/v AcOH) and 1·0–1·3 g. 48% HF; leave for 10–20 hr. and cool at 0°C for 2 hr. Filter on porcelain, wash with a satd. soln. of the ppt., dry at 105–110°C for 2 hr. and weigh as $C_{20}H_{16}N_4·HBF_4$. Interferences are NO_3^-, ClO_4^-, IO_3^-, SCN^-, CrO_4^{2-}, ClO_3^-, Br^- and NO_2^-.

Extn. of methylene blue fluoborate with $(CH_2Cl)_2$ allows a colorimetric detn. at 645 mμ.[34]

(e) Chromotrope 2B provides a colorimetric method for < 4 μg. B in oxides.[35] Add 2 ml. 85% AcOH, 1 drop of a mixt. of 5 g. NH_2OH and 5 g. $N_2H_4·H_2O$ in 100 ml. AcOH, and 2 ml. reagent soln. (25 mg. in 100 ml. H_2SO_4, dild. to 200 ml. with AcOH). After some min. add 7 ml. 1:1 AcOH–Ac_2O; after 30 min. measure at 620–630 mμ.

NOTES. (1) Interferences are NO_3^-, VO_3^-, PO_4^{3-}, F^-, Fe^{3+} and Al^{3+}.
(2) Chromotropic acid can be used for detn. of up to 120 μg. B in 15 ml. soln. at pH 4·5–6·5.[36] Add 25 ml. 0·00028*M* reagent and 10 ml. 2*M* NaOAc (pH 7), dil. to 50 ml. with H_2O and measure at 361·5 mμ. SiO_2 interferes.

(f) Miscellaneous colorimetric reagents. Benzoin can be used for fluorimetric detn. of 1–25 μg. B in 1 ml. soln.[37] Add 0·5 ml. H_2O, add 0·5 ml. buffer (450 ml. 0·4% w/v NaOH and 50 ml. of a soln. of 7·505 g. glycine and 5·85 g.NaCl/l.); add 15 ml. EtOH and 3 ml. 0·5% benzoin in EtOH, dil. to 25 ml. with EtOH, and measure the fluorescence within 5–25 min. using a Hg-lamp with a Corning No. 5860 filter and a Wratten B2 or 2A filter as secondary filter.

B in neutral soln. can be detd. by its lowering of the bleaching effect of F^- on the Fe^{3+} complex with sulfosalicylic acid.[38]

Pentamethylquercetin forms a yellow color with 0·4–15 mg. H_3BO_3; the error is ±15%.[39] Morin is also applicable.[40]

I_2 and polyvinyl alc. allow detn.[41] of H_3BO_3. To 2 ml. 1% polyvinyl alc., add 2·5 ml. neutral sample soln. contg. 0·75–2·5 mg. B, 4·0 ml. 15% H_2SO_4, H_2O to give a vol. of 8 ml., 0·50 ml. 0·02*N* I_2; dil. to 10 ml. with H_2O and measure the blue color after 1 hr. at 565 mμ. Many ions interfere; no interference arises from PO_4^{3-}, SO_4^{2-} or Cl^-, from 1 mg. Al, Hg^{2+} or Sb^{3+}, or 2 mg. As^{5+}, NH_4^+, Sn^{4+}, $C_2O_4^{2-}$, AcO^-, tartrate or citrate.

(g) Flame photometry. The methyl ester can be used with measurement at 427 or 518 mμ.[42]

References

1. Hillebrand and Lundell, 609 (749); Scott and Furman, 162; Kimura, 345; Pigott, 103.
2. Muraki, I., and Hiiro, K., *Japan Analyst*, **6**, 319 (1957).
3. Schulek, E., and Vastagh, G., *Z. anal. Chem.*, **84**, 167 (1931); **87**, 165 (1932).
4. Blumenthal, H., *Anal. Chem.*, **23**, 992 (1951).
5. A.S.T.M., 132.
6. Ellis, G. H., *et al.*, *Anal. Chem.*, **21**, 1345 (1949).
7. Cogbill, E. C., and Yoe, J. H., *Anal. Chem.*, **29**, 1251 (1957).
8. Gaestel, C., and Hure, J., *Bull. soc. chim. France*, 830 (1949); Roth, H., and Beck, W., *Z. anal. Chem.*, **141**, 404 (1954).
9. Glaze, F. W., and Finn, A. N., *J. Research Natl. Bur. Standards*, **16**, 42 (1936); **27**, 33 (1941).
10. Ross, W. J., *et al.*, *Anal. Chem.*, **29**, 810 (1957).
11. Pohl, F. A., *Z. anal. Chem.*, **157**, 6 (1957).
12. Coursier, J., *et al.*, *Anal. Chim. Acta*, **13**, 379 (1955).
13. Ducret, L., and Seguin, P., *Anal. Chim. Acta*, **17**, 207 (1957).
14. Codell, M., and Norwitz, G., *Anal. Chim. Acta*, **11**, 233 (1954).
15. Luke, C. L., *Anal. Chem.*, **27**, 1150 (1955) (pH meter); Wilcox, L. V., *Ind. Eng. Chem., Anal. Ed.*, **12**, 341 (1940) (B < 2 mg.); Ruehle, A. E., and Shock, A., *ibid.*, **17**, 453 (1945) (potentiometric).
16. Přibil, R., and Wünsch, L., *Chem. listy*, **46**, 337 (1952).
17. Welcher, **I**, 102; **IV**, 281, 283.
18. Oehme, F., *Chem. Tech.* (*Berlin*), **3**, 171, 178 (1951).
19. Burkhalter, T. S., and Van Tuyl, D. P., *Anal. Chem.*, **26**, 1851 (1954).
20. Baron, H., *Z. anal. Chem.*, **143**, 339 (1954); Roth, H., and Beck, W., *ibid.*, **141**, 404, 414 (1954); Brewster, D. A., *Anal. Chem.*, **23**, 1809 (1951) (in Al); Codell, M., and Norwitz, G., *ibid.*, **25**, 1446 (1953) (in Ti).
21. Martin, G., and Maës, H., *Bull. soc. chim. biol.*, **34**, 1178 (1952).
22. Yoe, J. H., and Grob, R. L., *Anal. Chem.*, **26**, 1465 (1954).
23. Yoe, J. H., and Grob, R. L., *Anal. Chim. Acta*, **14**, 253 (1956).
24. MacDougall, D., and Biggs, D. A., *Anal. Chem.*, **24**, 566 (1952); Jones, A. H., *ibid.*, **29**, 1101 (1957) (in high-temp. alloys); Newstead, E. G., and Gulbierz, J. E., *ibid.*, 1673; Johnson, E. A., and Toogood, M. J., *Analyst*, **79**, 493 (1954); Kruger, A., *Z. anal. Chem.*, **141**, 209 (1954) (in AcOH–$(Ac)_2O$ medium).
25. Hatcher, J. T., and Wilcox, L. V., *Anal. Chem.*, **22**, 567 (1950); Smith, W. C., *et al.*, *ibid.*, **27**, 294 (1955); Colkins, R. C., and Stenger, V. A., *ibid.*, **28**, 399 (1956) (in Ti); Kawaguchi, H., *Japan Analyst*, **4**, 307 (1955).
26. Fernández-Cellini, R., and Alvarez-Gonzáles, F., *Anales real soc. españ. fis. y quím.* (*Madrid*), **B50**, 59 (1954).
27. Welcher, **II**, 336.
28. Higgins, D. J., *J. Sci. Food Agr.*, **2**, 498 (1951).
29. Brandt, W. W., and Garrett, J. E., *Anal. Chem.*, **26**, 1667 (1954).
30. Silverman, L., and Trego, K., *Anal. Chem.*, **25**, 1264 (1953); also see Dible, W. T., *ibid.*, **26**, 418 (1954) (in soil); Josephrynasiewicz, M. P., and Ryan, J. W., *ibid.*, 935 (in Na metal); Luke, C. L., *ibid.*,, **27**, 1150 (1955) (in Si, Ge metal; as above, EtOH extn.); Muraki, I., and Hiiro, K., *J. Chem. Soc. Japan*, **78**, 845, 850 (1957) (EtOH extn.; in graphite); A.S.T.M. 132 (in steel).
31. Hillebrand and Lundell, 617 (761).
32. Gautier, J. A., and Pignard, P., *Mikrochemie ver. Mikrochim. Acta*, **36**/**37**, 793 (1951).
33. Lucchesi, C. A., and DeFord, D. D., *Anal. Chem.*, **29**, 1169 (1957).
34. Ducret, L., *Anal. Chim. Acta*, **17**, 207 (1957).
35. Martin, G., *Bull. soc. chim. biol.*, **36**, 719 (1954); also see Henly, W. B., *Anal. Chem.*, **23**, 1716 (1951); Welcher, **IV**, 539.
36. Kuemmel, D. F., Mellon, M. G., *Anal. Chem.*, **29**, 378 (1957).
37. White, C. E., *et al.*, *Anal. Chem.*, **19**, 802 (1947); **29**, 1105 (1957); Parker, C. A., and Barnes, W. J., *Analyst*, **82**, 606 (1957) (detailed study).
38. Monnier, D., *et al.*, *Anal. Chim. Acta*, **1**, 13 (1947).
39. Neelakantam, K., and Rangaswami, S., *Proc. Indian Acad. Sci.*, **18A**, 171 (1943).
40. Jewsbury, A., and Osborn, G. H., *Anal. Chim. Acta*, **3**, 481 (1949).
41. Muraca, R. F., and Jacobs, E. S., *Chemist Analyst*, **44**, 14 (1955).
42. Dean, J. A., and Thompson, C., *Anal. Chem.*, **27**, 43 (1955); also see Stahl, V., *Z. anal. Chem.* **101**, 348 (1935).

CARBON AND HYDROGEN

The main sources for this chapter are given in ref. 1. In general, the methods of decomposition and determination differ widely with the type of sample for analysis.

Attack

C and H in org. compds. are normally detd. after decomposition of the sample by combustion in O_2. Very many modifications of the basic procedure have been recommended and books on org. analysis should be consulted.

(a) Steels.[1] Heat ordinary steels above 1100°C in a combustion tube through which O_2 is passed. For alloy steels, add Sn or open-hearth iron. For high Cr or Ni steels, heat above 1250°C. For high Si samples, e.g. Fe–Si, add 1 g. CaO and 1–2 g. ingot iron. Similar processes have been applied to a wide variety of steels and other metals and alloys.[2]

(b) Carbonates.[1, 3] Treat with HCl, HCl and HF, or $HClO_4$.

(c) Rocks.[4] Fuse with 10:1 $PbCrO_4$–K_2CrO_4.

Methods for other samples are given below.

Determination

CARBON

(a) Gravimetry as CO_2 is the commonest method. From the gas stream, remove H_2O and absorb CO_2 in a suitable vessel contg. askarite, soda-lime, KOH or $Ba(OH)_2$.

(b) Titration with HCl and phenolphthalein indicator is useful after absorption in a known amt. of $Ba(OH)_2$ soln. Reaction with $Ba(OH)_2$ can also be employed nephelometrically. Titration with $H_2C_2O_4$ has been recommended.[5] Ethylenediamine is said[6] to be a better absorbent than $Ba(OH)_2$, since it can be readily purified by distn. Absorption in pyridine, acetone, or NaOAc in MeOH is feasible.[7] Change of conductivity on absorption in $Ba(OH)_2$ can be used to det. C.[8] For small amts. of CO_2, the change in pH of a $NaHCO_3$ soln. can be measured.

(c) Gas-volumetric measurement is simple.[1, 2] Measure the vol. of the gases present, pass through KOH and remeasure. The difference corresponds to CO_2. Direct measurement of CO_2 vol. is possible after HCl treatment of silicate rocks.[9] Traces of C in steel can be detd. by combustion, freezing out CO_2 with liquid air and evapn. into a manometer.[10]

(d) Direct neutralization titrations are generally applied after wet combustion processes. For detn. of C in graphite,[11] coal, bitumen, shale, etc., add 40 ml. H_3PO_4, heat and det. CO_2 (carbonate); then add 4 g. CrO_3 and heat while passing air through. Pass the evolved gases through a gently boiling mixt. of 40 ml. H_3PO_4, 4 g. CrO_3, 0·1 g. HgO and H_2SO_4 and absorb in sofnolite. In other procedures[1, 12] H_2SO_4 is used with $K_2Cr_2O_7$ or CrO_3 for digestion. KIO_3 and H_3PO_4 (preheated at 300°C and cooled) can also be applied;[13] the I_2 evolved is collected in As^{3+} soln. which is then titrated with I_2 soln.

For a direct titration of CO_2, titrate the aq. soln. with 0·1*N* HCl using phenolphthalein indicator (pH ca. 8) (= x ml.), then add methyl orange and titrate further (pH ca. 4) (= y ml.) using a comparison soln. to detect the end-point. The amts. of OH^-, CO_3^{2-} and HCO_3^- can then be calcd. as follows:

	OH^-	CO_3^{2-}	HCO_3^-
$x = 0$	0	0	y
$x < \frac{1}{2}y$	0	$2x$	$y - 2x$
$x = \frac{1}{2}y$	0	$2x$	0
$x > \frac{1}{2}y$	$2x - y$	$2(y - x)$	0
$x = y$	y	0	0

NOTES. (1) Interferences are PO_4^{3-}, SiO_3^{2-}, S^{2-}, AsO_4^{3-}, etc.

(2) Many other indicators or mixed indicators have been suggested to replace methyl orange. A 1:1 0·1% methyl orange–0·25% indigocarmine soln. (10 drops/100 ml.) changes from green through grey at pH 4·1–4·0 to violet. With 3 drops of a soln. contg. 0·02 g. methyl red and 0·10 g. bromocresol green/100 ml. EtOH, in 150–250 ml. of test soln., the color changes from pink at pH 4·6 to pale pink–grey-blue at pH 4·8, to blue-grey at pH 5·0, to green-blue at pH 5·2.[14] If the proportions of methyl red and bromocresol green are 1:1, the color changes from yellow at pH 4·2 to blue at 4·7.[15]

(3) Covering the test soln. with C_6H_6, gasoline or paraffin oil[16] protects it from atmospheric CO_2.

(4) Distn. methods and micro-diffusion procedures are available.[1, 17] Special app. has been described for micro amts.:[18] to 100 ml. sample, add 5 g. Zn and 5 ml. 1:1 H_2SO_4– 1% $CuSO_4$, pass the CO_2 into 0·05*N* $Ba(OH)_2$ at 70–80°C and titrate with 0·05*N* HCl using phenolphthalein indicator.

(e) Colorimetry can be used to det. C in cast iron.[19], For the reagent, mix 100 ml. H_2SO_4 with 500 ml. H_2O. cool, add 50 ml. 88% H_3PO_4 and 350 ml. HNO_3. For detn. place a 0·8 g. sample in a 125 ml. Erlenmeyer flask, add 25 ml. reagent, heat on a steam-bath and cool rapidly immediately the sample has dissolved. Filter, dil. to 100 ml. with H_2O and measure with a blue filter.

HYDROGEN

H is nearly always detd. as H_2O. For indirect detn. of H_2O— in rocks, heat the sample at 105° and det. the loss in wt.[1] For H_2O + (Penfield method), heat the sample in a glass tube and weigh the condensed H_2O evolved.[1] Heating in a combustion tube or a Gooch apparatus can be followed by absorption in a desiccant and weighing. Desiccants which have been applied are $CaCl_2$, $CaSO_4$ (Drierite), $Mg(ClO_4)_2$ (Anhydrone), silica gel, etc. (see Table 6).

H in iron and steels is generally detd. by a vacuum fusion process.[20]

Org compds. and steels are decomposed by combustion in a stream of O_2 (see p. 460).

The detn. of H_2O has been subjected to critical review.[21]

(a) Karl Fischer method is the most widely applied titration for H_2O.[22] For detn. of 10–100 mg. H_2O in a sample, add excess of Karl Fischer reagent (see Note 1) and back-titrate with methanol of known H_2O content from brown to yellow, or titrate directly with the reagent to a brown color. Indicators may be used but potentiometric titration is most common. If the sample is insol. in the reagent, dissolve in anhyd. MeOH, $CHCl_3$, etc.; or remove the H_2O by heating and titrate the amt. evolved after absorption.

NOTES. (1) To prep. the reagent, mix 269 ml. pyridine, 667 ml. MeOH and 84·7 g. I_2, cool in ice and add slowly 64 g. liquid anhyd. SO_2. Leave for 1–2 days before use and store in an automatic buret fitted with a desiccant tube. Many modified prepns. have been proposed.[22] Standardize the reagent against H_2O, $(COONH_4)_2 \cdot 2H_2O$ or $CH_3COONa \cdot 3H_2O$.

(2) Interferences are group IV and V elements, Cu^{2+}, Zn, Ag, Hg^{2+}, oxides, hydroxides, oxy-acid salts, oxidants, reductants, mercaptans and H_2S.

(b) α-Naphthoxydichlorophosphine reacts with H_2O to liberate HCl.[23] Treat the sample with reagent soln. in C_6H_6, sweep with dry air, collect the HCl in H_2O and titrate. Acetylpyridinium chloride, cinnamoyl chloride[24] and other similar compds. can be applied similarly. Modified procedures with Ac_2O or benzoic anhydride are also available.[24]

(c) $CoCl_2$ allows colorimetric detn.[25] Dissolve the sample in EtOH, add reagent and measure at 655 mμ. The error is about ±0·5% for 1–5% H_2O.

(d) Treating with CaH_2, CaC_2 or Na and measuring the evolved gas is suitable for small amounts of H_2O.[26]

(e) Mg-nitride evolves NH_3 with H_2O; the NH_3 is detd. with Nessler reagent.[27]

References

1. HILLEBRAND and LUNDELL, 621 (766); SCOTT and FURMAN, 218, 442; KIMURA, 352; PIGOTT, 110.
2. A.S.T.M. 76 ff.
3. HECHT and DONAU, 245.
4. HILLEBRAND and LUNDELL, 623 ff.
5. LINDSLEY, C. H., and YOE, J. H., *Anal. Chem.*, **21**, 513 (1949).
6. SWICK, R. W., *et al.*, *Anal. Chem.*, **24**, 2000 (1952).
7. BLOM, L., and EDELHAUSEN, L., *Anal. Chim. Acta*, **13**, 120 (1955).
8. IVEKOVÍC, H., and POLAK, V., *Monatsh.*, **86**, 485 (1955).
9. SHAPIRO, L., and BRANNOCK, W. W., *Anal. Chem.*, **27**, 1796 (1955).
10. SMILEY, W. G., *Anal. Chem.*, **27**, 1098 (1955); HOLT, B. D., *ibid.*, 1500; GOTO, H., *et al.*, *Japan Analyst*, **6** 650 (1957); also see KAMADA, H., *et al.*, *ibid.*, 146 (mass-spectrometer).
11. DIXON, B. E., *Analyst*, **54**, 739 (1934).
12. VAN SLYKE, D. D., *Anal. Chem.*, **26**, 1706 (1954); CHEN, S. L., and LAUER, J. H., *ibid.*, **29**, 1225 (1957).
13. KIBA, T., *et al.*, *Japan Analyst*, **2**, 446 (1953).
14. COOPER, S. S., *Ind. Eng. Chem.*, *Anal. Ed.*, **13**, 466 (1941).
15. HÖPPNER, K., *Deut. Zuckerind.*, **4**, 316 (1936).
16. ČŮTA, F., and KÁMAN, K., *Chem. listy*, **38**, 28 (1939).
17. SARUHASHI, K., *Japan Analyst*, **4**, 337 (1955).
18. KOYAMA, T., *J. Earth Sci.*, *Nagoya Univ.*, **1**, 107 (1953).
19. JAMIESON, A., *Foundry*, **83**, No. 10, 132 (1955); PIGOTT, 125.
20. PIGOTT, 207; A.S.T.M. 259.
21. *Anal. Chem.*, **23**, 1058 (1951).
22. MITCHELL, J., and SMITH, D. M., *Aquametry*, Interscience, New York (1948); WIBERLY, J. S., *Anal. Chem.*, **23**, 656 (1951); MITCHELL, *ibid.*, 1069; JONES, J. G., *Analyst*, **76**, 5 (1951); IZAWA, M., *J. Japan Chem.*, **4**, 188 (1950); EBERIUS, E., *Wasserbestimmung mit Karl-Fischer-Lösung*, Verlag Chemie, Weinheim (1954); KOLTHOFF and BELCHER, *Volumetric Analysis*, Vol. III, 409 (1957).
23. WELCHER, **IV**, 324.
24. WELCHER, **II**, 231 ff.
25. AYRES, G. H., and GLANVILLE, B. V., *Anal. Chem.*, **21**, 930 (1949).
26. PERRYMAN, P. W., *Analyst*, **70**, 45 (1945).
27. ŠINGLIAR, M., and ZUBÁCK, J., *Chem. průmysl*, **6**, 426 (1956).

63

NITROGEN

The principal sources for this chapter are given in ref. 1. The analytical chemistry of ammonium ion[2] and that of nitrate and nitrite[3] have been considered in detail. Texts on organic analysis must be consulted.

The methods of determination vary widely, depending not only on the type of sample but also on the type of nitrogen linkage. Accordingly, after a consideration of the 4 main techniques for decomposition of nitrogen-containing samples, especially organic compounds, the principal types of nitrogen-containing ions are dealt with in turn. NH_3 is generally determined by titration or by colorimetry with Nessler's reagent after distillation from strong alkali. NO_3^- can be converted to NH_3, or determined gravimetrically with nitron or by some colorimetric procedure. NO_2^- is determined colorimetrically with Griess reagent or by oxidimetric titration. CN^- can be titrated with $AgNO_3$ solution (Liebig–Denigès method) or determined colorimetrically. Micro-diffusion methods are available for NH_4^+, NO_3^- and NO_2^- in water. Nitrogen in irons and steels can be determined by vacuum fusion methods.

Kjeldahl's method.[1, 2, 3] Place the sample in a 550 ml. Kjeldahl flask, add 0·1–0·2 g. Se (SeO_2 in 1:1 H_2SO_4), 0·7 g. HgO (or Hg), 10 g. K_2SO_4 and 20–30 ml. H_2SO_4 and heat gently to slow boiling. Boil for 0·5–1 hr. until pale yellow or colorless, boil for another 1 hr. and cool. Add 200 ml. H_2O, 50 mg. Zn and 25 g. NaOH and 1 g. Na_2S in 75 ml. H_2O. Steam-distil and collect in a known vol. of 0·1*N* H_2SO_4; add methyl red and back-titrate with 0·1*N* NaOH. Alternatively, collect in satd. H_3BO_3 soln., add methyl red and titrate with 0·1*N* H_2SO_4. For further details, see refs. 4 and 5.

NOTES. (1) Boiling for 30 min. suffices if 6 g. $Fe_2(SO_4)_3$ is added.[5] Rapid oxidation is also obtained by heating with H_2SO_4 and Se and then adding $HClO_4$;[6] or by digesting with H_2SO_4, H_3PO_4 and $K_2S_2O_7$.[7]

(2) If NO_3^- is present, shake the sample with 30–35 ml. H_2SO_4 and 1 g. salicylic acid for 5–10 min., add 5 g. $Na_2S_2O_3$, heat for min., cool, add HgO, etc. Special treatment is required for azo or hydrazine compds.

(3) For detn. of N in steel,[10] use a 2 g. sample if N > 0·1% or 5 g. if N < 1%; if Cr exceeds 0·5 g. add some boiling stones and use a 2 g. sample. Place the sample in a 800 ml. Kjeldahl flask, add 0·2 g. Se and 50 or 70 ml. acid mixt. (300 ml. H_2SO_4, 90 ml. H_3PO_4 and 1 l. H_2O), and, if Si exceeds 4%, add 50 ml. H_2O. Heat and evap. rapidly to fumes; rinse with 10 ml. H_2SO_4, boil gently for 2–4 hr., cool slightly, add 200 ml. H_2O, stir and heat to dissolve the salts. If the sample does not dissolve with this treatment, dissolve in HCl and proceed as above. Samples contg. much Co may require stronger treatment of the residue: heat with 50 ml. 3:2 $HClO_4$ on a steam-bath, add 50 ml. H_2O, filter and wash with 1:99 HCl; place in a flask, add 10 g. K_2SO_4, 1 g. $CuSO_4$ and 20 ml. H_2SO_4, heat until colorless, boil for 15–20 min., cool and combine with the first soln.

Transfer the digest to a 800 ml. Kjeldahl flask contg. 125 or 150 ml. 33·3% NaOH through a separatory funnel, add 75 ml. H_2O and distil.

For detn. of N in Ti and its alloys,[10] heat a 0·5–1 g. sample with 25 ml. 1:1 HCl and 2–3 ml. 48% HBF_4; if a residue remains, decant, add a Se crystal, heat to fumes with 5 ml. 1:1 H_2SO_4 and combine. Cool, add to NaOH, etc.

(4) Methyl red–bromocresol green is said to be better than methyl red alone.[8] Absorption of NH_3 in HIO_3–KIO_3 soln. followed by iodometric titration is accurate for 0·1–1·4 mg. N.[7].

Dumas' method. Heat the sample with CuO in an atmosphere of CO_2, sweep through Cu and CuO and measure the vol. of N_2 after absorption of CO_2, etc. in KOH soln.[1, 3] Very many modifications have been described.

Ter Meulen's method.[3] Mix 20–50 mg. org. sample with 1–2 g. Ni catalyst in a SiO_2 tube, heat in a stream of H_2 passing the pyrolysis products over a 25 cm. layer of Ni catalyst at 250°C, absorb the NH_3 in acid and back-titrate.

Heating with strong H_3PO_4 and HIO_3 followed by azotometry, allows analysis of org. samples (p. 465).[9]

AMMONIUM

(a) Distillation and neutralization titration have been described under Kjeldahl's method. Titration with 0·005*N* HCl or H_2SO_4 is possible with methyl red–methylene blue indicator. For detn. of N in steel or in Ti and its alloys,[10] collect the distillate in 1% H_3BO_3 and titrate with 0·007*N* H_2SO_4 soln. using methyl purple indicator.

For the possibilities of micro-diffusion analysis, see ref. 11.

(b) Nessler's reagent provides the classical colorimetric method.[1, 2, 12] To prep. the reagent, dissolve 45·5 g. HgI_2 and 34·9 g. KI in the min. amt. of H_2O, add 112 g. KOH in 140 ml. H_2O, dil. to 1 l. with H_2O, leave for several days and decant. For a detn., treat 90 ml. soln. with 5 ml. reagent, dil. to 100 ml. and measure the yellow-brown color after 30 min. at 400–425 mμ (for trace amts.) or at 525 mμ (for mg. amts.).

NOTES. (1) Interferences are org. amines, aldehydes, ketones, alcohols, chloramines, Mg, Mn, Fe and S^{2-}.
(2) For titrimetric detn. of < 1 mg. N,[13] add reagent, centrifuge, wash with 0·1*N* NaOH; to the ppt. add 2 ml. 0·1*N* NaOH, 5 ml. HCHO and a few ml. of EtOH, mix and leave for 15 min. Centrifuge and wash with H_2O. Add 2 ml. 0·2*N* KIO_3 and KI to the pptd. Hg, shake and back-titrate with 0·01*N* $Na_2S_2O_3$.
(3) For another method based on a similar principle,[14] use Graves' reagent (40 g. NaCl in 750 ml. H_2O mixed with 3·5 g. $HgCl_2$ and dild. to 2 l. with H_2O). To 10 ml. reagent and 0·5 ml. 1% gum arabic soln., add 10 ml. sample soln. contg. 0–20 p.p.m. N. After 15 min. measure at 425 mμ (blue filter).

(c) Miscellaneous gravimetric methods. Na-tetraphenylboron is used by pptn. of NH_4^+ along with K^+; weigh the ppt., dissolve in Me_2CO, boil with NaOH, filter and weigh.[15] See Chapter 54, p. 409, for details.

H_2PtCl_6 ppts. NH_4^+ from neutral soln.[2] Evap. the soln. with the reagent to dryness, add anhyd. EtOH, filter on a Gooch crucible, wash with EtOH, dry at 130°C (<181°C) and weigh as $(NH_4)_2PtCl_6$. Alternatively, ignite and weigh as Pt.

(d) Miscellaneous titrimetric methods. HCHO addn. allows final titration with 0·2*N* NaOH.[16] To 50 ml. soln. at pH 6·8, add 12 ml. HCHO soln. (36–38% soln. mixed with an equal vol. of H_2O and neutralized with 0·1*N* NaOH using 2 drops phenolphthalein indicator); after 10 min., titrate with 0·2*N* NaOH to pH 9.

Copptn. with K using $Na_3Co(NO_2)_6$ can be followed by $KMnO_4$ titration.[17] For 3–25 μg. NH_3, add a known amt. of KCl, ppt. with the reagent, filter on a glass crucible, wash with EtOH, dry, dissolve in dil. H_2SO_4 and titrate.

A sample ext. may be used to titrate pptd. $CuCO_3$.[18] Treat the sample with dil. H_2SO_4, filter, add excess anhyd. Na_2CO_3 and filter through cotton into a buret. Titrate a mixt. of 1 ml. 10% Na_2CO_3 and 0·25, 0·5 or 1·0 ml. of $CuSO_4$ soln. (3·3 g./100 ml.) to a blue endpoint. Det. the NH_3 content from standard curves. A colorimetric method can be based on the same reaction.[18] To 10 ml. 4% Na_2CO_3 and 2 ml. 10% $CuSO_4$, add 1 ml. sample soln., 1 ml. 22% $Ca(NO_3)_2$ and dil. to 50 ml. with H_2O. Measure at 700 mμ. The method is suitable for <1·2 mg. NH_3/100 ml. final soln.

(e) HOCl can be used colorimetrically or titrimetrically. Colorimetry with OCl^- and phenol is suitable for <1·4 μg. NH_3 in 10 ml. soln.[2, 19, 20] Add 1 ml. HOCl soln. (Cl_2 passed into H_2O at 0°C to give a soln. >0·08*M*; standardized iodometrically); after 5 min. add 1 ml. Na-phenate soln. (16·7 g. phenol and 7·2 g. NaOH in 300 ml.) and 1 drop 0·003*M* $MnCl_2$ soln. and compare after 3 min. NaOCl can replace HOCl.[20]

NOTES. (1) Interferences are Fe, Cr, Cu, oxidants, amino acids and nicotine.
(2) The sensitivity of the method is improved if MeOH is added.[21] To 10 ml. soln. add 4 ml. phenol soln. (62·5 g. phenol in MeOH, add 18·5 ml. Me_2CO, dil. to 100 ml. with MeOH; mix 20 ml. with 20 ml. 27% NaOH and dil. to 100 ml. with H_2O). Then add 3 ml. NaOCl soln. (0·9% available Cl_2), dil. to 25 ml. with H_2O and measure after 20 min.
(3) Other reagents may replace OCl^- or phenol. Chloramine T and thymol are suitable for 0·02–1 mg. NH_3/ml. soln.[22] Add 0·5 ml. 10% thymol in EtOH, 1·5 ml. 2*N* NaOH and 1·0 ml. 6·3% chloramine T; attach a condenser, heat for 5 min. on a steam-bath, cool and compare the blue color. Reaction with NaOBr and thymol with Et_2O or xylene extn. is also possible.[23]
Chloramine T can also be combined with a pyrazolone deriv. in pyridine.[24] For the reagent, dissolve 0·63 g. 3-methyl-1-phenyl-5-pyrazolone in 250 ml. H_2O at 75°C, and prep. 0·1% bis-(3-methyl-1-phenyl-5-pyrazolone) in pyridine; mix the 2 solns. in a 5:1 ratio just before use. For a detn., adjust 50 ml. sample soln. to pH 3·7, add 10 ml. buffer pH 3·7 (NaOAc and AcOH) and 0·9 ml. 3% chloramine T; after 90 sec. add 30 ml. pyrazolone soln. After 1 min. ext. with two 20 ml. (for < 0·1 p.p.m. NH_3) or 50 ml. (for > 2 p.p.m. NH_3) portions of CCl_4, filter through cotton and measure the green color at 450 mμ. Interferences are OCN^-, CN^-, SCN^-, which can be removed by ion exchange; and Zn, 1 p.p.m. Ag or Cu, 10 p.p.m. Co or Fe, 100 p.p.m. Al or Ni, and 500 p.p.m. Hg^{2+}. The method has been applied to steels.[25, 26] Substituted pyridines have no advantage and the reaction mechanism is uncertain.[25]

NaOCl or $Ca(OCl)_2$ solns. can be used in a titrimetric detn.[27] For 5–25 mg. NH_3 in 25 ml. soln., add 1 g. KBr and 0·5 g. $NaHCO_3$ followed by excess 0·1*N* OCl^- soln. After 5 min., add 10 ml. 0·01*N* As^{3+} and titrate with the OCl^- soln. using bordeaux or tartrazine indicator. Coulometric titration with Br_2 at pH 8·5 is suitable[28] for 14–230 μg. NH_3. For an azotometric method, see ref. 29.

(f) Tannin and $AgNO_3$ are suitable for colorimetry of 0·25–2 mg. NH_3 in 50 ml. soln.[2, 30] Add 2 drops 5% tannin and 1 drop 20% $AgNO_3$ and measure the yellow-orange color after at least 4 min.

NITRATE

(a) Nitron is the best available gravimetric reagent.[1, 3, 31] For <0·1 g. NO_3^- in 80–100 ml. soln., add 10 drops 2*N* H_2SO_4 or 1 ml. AcOH, heat on a steam-bath and add 10–12 ml. reagent (10 g. in 100 ml. 5% AcOH). Cool at 0°C for 2 hr., filter on a glass crucible, wash 5 times with 2 ml. portions of H_2O at 0°C, dry at 110°C (20–240°C) for 1 hr. and weigh as $C_{20}H_{16}N_4 \cdot HNO_3$. The results tend to be slightly low.

NOTES. (1) Interferences are Br^-, I^-, NO_2^-, CrO_4^{2-}, ClO_3^-, IO_3^-, ClO_4^-, ReO_4^-, SCN^-, $Fe(CN)_6^{4-}$, $Fe(CN)_6^{3-}$, $C_2O_4^{2-}$, picric acid, peptone and large amts. of Cl^-. No interference is found from dextrin, gelatin, sucrose, Al, Mg, NH_4^+, K, Mg, SO_4^{2-}, PO_4^{3-}, BO_2^-, $HCOO^-$, AcO^-, tartrate or benzoic acid.
(2) Similar reagents have been proposed but none seems advantageous. Di(1-naphthylmethyl)-amine is suitable for 5–25 ml. 0·1*N* NO_3^- soln.[3, 30] Dil. to 50 ml. with H_2O, add 2–10 ml. 2*N* H_2SO_4, boil, add 10 ml. 10% reagent in 50% AcOH and leave for 12 hr. Filter on a glass crucible, wash with cold H_2O, dry at 110°C for 1 hr. and weigh as $(C_{10}H_7CH_2)_2NH \cdot HNO_3$. Interferences are NO_2^-, ClO_3^-, ClO_4^-, etc.
Cinchonamine has been tested but is less satisfactory.[3, 32] *p*-Tolylisothiourea acetate is suitable for 0·15 g. KNO_3 in 10 ml. H_2O.[3] Add 10 ml. 2*N* H_2SO_4, 20 ml. reagent (1 g. in 50 ml.), cool at 0°C for 30 min., filter on a glass crucible and wash with dil. reagent soln., once with H_2O and once with EtOH. Dry at 110–120°C and weigh. Interferences are halides, NO_2^-, ClO_3^-, MnO_4^- and SCN^-. No interference arises from PO_4^{3-} or CN^-.

(b) Reduction with Devarda's alloy allows distn. and titration of NH_3 formed.[1, 3] For 1 g. sample, add 100 ml. H_2O, 5 ml. EtOH, 25 ml. 20% KOH and 3 g. alloy (45 Al:50 Cu:5 Zn). After a few min., heat very slowly and distil for 30 min. while passing air. Collect in a known amt. of 0·1*N* H_2SO_4 and back-titrate with 0·1*N* NaOH with methyl red indicator.

NOTES. (1) The optimum conditions for 1 g. nitrate are said to be 3 g. alloy and 2 g. NaOH in 250 ml. soln.[33] Other reductants which have been used are Mg with NaOH, Al powder with NaOH, Arndt's alloy (60 Cu: 40 Mg) in almost neutral soln.[3] The technique can be applied in microdiffusion analysis (Saruhashi[11]).
(2) The above distillate can also be analysed with Nessler's reagent.[34]
(3) A more direct method involves reduction with a known excess of Fe^{2+} soln. in 3% NaOH soln. with ammoniacal Ag_2SO_4 catalyst; after acidification with H_2SO_4, excess Fe^{2+} is titrated with KMnO soln.[35] Other reductants which can reduce NO_3^- to NH_3 under appropriate conditions are Cr^{2+},[36] Sn^{2+} and V^{2+}.[3]

(c) Reduction with N_2H_4 allows colorimetric detn. with Griess reagent.[3, 37] For the reductant, mix 25 ml. of soln. contg. 1·20 g. $N_2H_4 \cdot H_2SO_4$ in 250 ml. H_2O, with 5 ml. of a soln. contg. 39·3 mg. $CuSO_4 \cdot 5H_2O$ in 100 ml. H_2O, and dil. to 500 ml. with H_2O.

For analysis of sea water,[37] treat 40 ml. with 2 ml. phenate buffer pH 9·6 (9·4 g. phenol/200 ml. filtered and dild. to 250 ml. with H_2O; a 50 ml. aliquot of this is treated with 16 ml. 1·0*N* NaOH and dild. to 100 ml. with H_2O). Then add 1 ml. freshly prepd. reductant soln., leave for 24 hr., add 2 ml. Me_2CO, wait for 2 min., add 2 ml. sulfanilic acid soln. (0·30 g. and 12·9 ml. HCl dild. to 100 ml.) and 1 ml. α-naphthylamine-HCl soln. (0·60 g. and 1 ml. HCl dild. to 100 ml.) and shake. Add 1 ml. 2*M* NaOAc, dil. to 50 ml. with H_2O and measure at 540 mμ after 15 min. This method is suitable for <0·6 μg. N as NO_3^- per ml. in the final soln.

NOTES. (1) Reduction can be done with Zn mixed with the reagent.[3, 38] For 50 ml. soln. contg. > 0·1 μg. NO_3^-/ml., add 0·2 g. reagent mixt. (1 g. α-naphthylamine, 10 g. sulfanilic acid, 88 g. tartaric acid and 1–1·5 g. Zn powder) and measure the pink color. NO_2^- is removed with NaN_3 and AcOH.
(2) Aniline and α-naphthylamine can also be used[39] for the color reaction.
(3) Reduction with nitrate reductase[3] can be followed by color development with *N*-(1-naphthyl)-ethylenediamine and sulfanilic acid[40] or with α-naphthylamine and sulfanilic acid.[41]

(d) 3,4-Xylenol provides[3, 42] a colorimetric detn. of 0·1–0·35 mg. N as NO_3^-. Place the soln. in a 250 ml. distn. flask, evap. almost to dryness, cool and add 1 ml. reagent (2% in Me_2CO) and 15 ml. 80% w/w H_2SO_4. Swirl gently for 10 min., leave for at least 20 min., add 150 ml. H_2O and a boiling chip, and steam-distil. Collect 70–80 ml. distillate in 5 ml. 2% NaOH, cool, dil. to 100 ml. with H_2O, filter through cotton and measure at 432 mμ. Interferences are Cl^-, NO_2^- and H_2O_2.

NOTES. (1) Various similar reagents have been proposed. Amidol allows detn. of 0·2 mg. NO_3^- in 0·1 ml. soln.[43] Add 0·4 ml. H_2O, pour into 2 ml. reagent (0·5 g. amidol in 100 ml. H_2SO_4) and measure the red color. NO_2^- can be removed with urea and H_2SO_4; Cl^-, etc. interfere.
(2) Chloranil is suitable[44] for detn. of 50 μg. KNO_3. Evap. the soln. several times with AcOH to remove NO_2^-; add a little H_2O and 10–20 ml. reagent (10 g. chloranil in 500 ml. AcOH and 100 ml. H_2SO_4) and measure the yellow-red color.
(3) Other reagents[3, 44] are 2,4-xylenol, pyrogallol, phenol, resorcinol (see p. 467), salicylic acid.

(e) 1,2,4-Phenoldisulfonic acid is used colorimetrically for 0·02–0·15 mg. N as $NaNO_3$ solid.[3, 44, 45] Add 2 ml. reagent (25 g. phenol, 150 ml. H_2SO_4 and 75 ml. fuming H_2SO_4 heated at 100°C for 2 hr.); warm if necessary, add 20 ml. H_2O and 6–7 ml. NH_4OH and filter if turbid. Dil. to 100 ml. with H_2O and measure the yellow color at 400–425 mμ.

NOTES. (1) Interferences are CO_3^{2-} (which can be neutralized with H_2SO_4), large amts. of Cl^- (remove by centrifugation after addn. of 1 ml. Ag_2SO_4 soln. (contg. 4·397 g./l.) per mg. Cl^-); NO_2^- is oxidized to NO_3^- with H_2O_2 or $KMnO_4$ in soln. contg. 1 ml. *N* H_2SO_4/100 ml., and detd. simultaneously. Org. compds. interfere.
(2) α-Naphtholsulfonic acid is used for 0·05–1 mg. N as NO_3^- in solids.[3, 44] Add 2 ml. reagent (200 ml. H_2SO_4 heated for 30 min. on a steam-bath, mixed with 20 g. α-naphthol, heated for a further 1·5 hr. and cooled); stir for 15 min., add 8 ml. 10*N* KOH, dil. to 250 ml. with H_2O and measure the yellow color.

(3) Other reagents proposed[3, 44] are phenolsulfonic, sulfosalicylic, hydroquinonesulfonic, and pyrogallolsulfonic acids. Chromotropic acid (0·025*M* in 75% H_2SO_4) is suitable for 0·1–7 p.p.m. NO_3^- with measurement at 416 mμ.[46]

(f) Dicyclohexylthallic sulfate or acetate is applied in gravimetric and titrimetric procedures.[3, 47] For 50–100 mg. NO_3^- in 50–100 ml. soln., boil, add 50–100 ml. 0·05*M* reagent, cool, filter on a glass crucible and wash with 100 ml. H_2O at 0°C. Dry below 150°C and weigh as $C_{12}H_{22}TlNO_3$. Apply a correction of 1 mg. for each 150 ml. of filtrate and washings. For a titrimetric finish, treat the filtrate with a known excess of $H_2C_2O_4$, filter and titrate with $KMnO_4$ soln.

NOTE. Interferences are Ag, Cl^-, Br^-, I^-, CN^-, OCN^-, SCN^-, $Fe(CN)_6^{3-}$, $Fe(CN)_6^{4-}$; CO_3^{2-}, $C_2O_4^{2-}$, S^{2-}, SO_3^{2-}, NO_2^-, CrO_4^{2-}, MoO_4^{2-} and tartrate do not interfere in strong acid solns.

(g) Reduction with Fe^{2+} forms NO and excess Fe^{2+} can be titrated with $Cr_2O_7^{2-}$ soln.[3, 48] To 0·1–0·2 g. sample add 20–50 ml. 0·18*N* Fe^{2+} in 1N H_2SO_4 soln. (at least a 50% excess); then add 70 ml. HCl and 3–5 g. $NaHCO_3$ in small portions and attach a valve contg. satd. $NaHCO_3$ soln. to the flask. Boil for 3 min., add 3 ml. 1% $(NH_4)_2MoO_4$, boil for 10 min., replace the valve and cool. Add 35 ml. 6*N* NH_4OAc for each 50 ml. soln., add 3–5 ml. H_3PO_4 and 6–8 drops diphenylamine sulfonic acid indicator and titrate with 0·1*N* $K_2Cr_2O_7$.

NOTES. (1) The boiling time can be reduced for small amts. of NO_3^- if Cl^- is added; ferroin can also be used as indicator.[48]

(2) Other redox titrations are also applicable.[3, 48] Neutral NO_3^- soln. can be titrated with $TiCl_3$ with alizarin S indicator.[49] In the above procedure, the Fe^{3+} formed can be titrated:[50] pass CO_2 through the soln. contg. 60 mg. HNO_3, add 20 ml. 0·1*N* $FeSO_4$ and 70 ml. HCl and boil for 5 min. Cool and titrate with 0·1*N* $SnCl_2$ from yellow to pale green-blue. Prep. the $SnCl_2$ soln. in 3*N* HCl and store under liquid paraffin.

$Na_2S_2O_3$, $Hg_2(NO_3)_2$, Ti^{3+} and U^{4+} are also suitable for titration of the Fe^{3+} formed.

$KMnO_4$ may be employed[51] for back-titration of excess Fe^{2+}. For < 0·30 g. NO_3^- in 25 ml. soln. add 25·00 ml. Fe^{2+} soln. (270 g. $FeSO_4 \cdot 6H_2O$ in H_2O with some H_2SO_4, add 40 g. NaCl and 100 ml. HCl and dil. to 1 l. with H_2O); then add slowly 20 ml. H_2SO_4. Boil for 3–5 min., pour into 1 l. cold H_2O, rinse and titrate with 0·5*N* $KMnO_4$.

Iodometric titration is not very accurate.[3, 48] For 0·2 g. samples, add 20 ml. satd. $MnCl_2$ in HCl, heat almost to dryness with CO_2 passing and collect the distillate in KI soln. Titrate with $Na_2S_2O_3$. Variations of this method are possible with $K_4Fe(CN)_6$ and $KMnO_4$.

Direct titration with Fe^{2+} soln. in strong H_2SO_4 media is not very satisfactory.[48]

(3) For a colorimetric detn. of NO_3^- based on the same principle,[52] treat the solid sample with 20 ml. Fe^{2+} reagent (0·5 g. $FeSO_4 \cdot 7H_2O$ in 25 ml. H_2O mixed gradually with 75 ml. H_2SO_4 while cooling), stopper and shake occasionally during 30 min.; measure at 525 mμ.

(h) Azotometry can be applied[53] to det. 6–12 mg. NO_3^-. Treat the sample with 1·5–2·0 ml. H_2SO_4 and 70 mg. salicylic acid, warm, add 50 mg. $Na_2S_2O_3$, heat to fumes, add 5 ml. strong H_3PO_4 and cool. Add 1·5 g. KIO_3, pass CO_2 through the soln. to remove air, then heat at 200–250°C while passing CO_2 and measure the nitrogen vol.

NOTES. (1) Measurement of NO formed is suitable[1, 3] for detn. of < 0·3 g. KNO_3. Add 15 ml. H_2SO_4 and Hg and measure; corrections for temp. and press. are needed. $FeCl_2$ with HCl, and Cu with H_2SO_4 serve the same purpose.

(2) N_2O is formed by reaction with HCOOH, and N_2 by treatment with H_3PO_3 and NH_4Cl (for details, see ref. 3).

(i) Indigo carmine can be used titrimetrically for detn. of solns. contg. 2·7–115 mg. N_2O_5/l.[3, 54, 55] For the reagent, heat 0·32 g. indigo with 100 ml. H_2SO_4 for 30 min., cool and leave for 1 day; filter and dil. to 1 l. with H_2O. For a detn. treat 5 ml. soln. with 1 drop $HgCl_2$ soln. (5 g. $HgCl_2$ and 5 g. NaCl in 100 ml. H_2O) and 6 ml. H_2SO_4 and titrate until a blue-green color remains for 5 min.; not more than 3 ml. reagent should be used. Carbazole[56] may be used similarly.

(j) Miscellaneous colorimetric methods. Na-diphenylaminesulfonate allows detn. of 1–50 μg. N in 10 ml. soln.;[1, 3, 57] add 10 ml. H_2SO_4 and 0·1 ml. 0·006*M* reagent and measure the blue-violet color. Diphenylbenzidine or diphenylamine are less satisfactory.[3, 57]

Brucine is suitable for 2–70 μg. N in 10 ml. neutral soln.;[3, 58] add 0·20 ml. 5% brucine in $CHCl_3$ followed by 20 ml. H_2SO_4. After 5–10 min., dil. to 50 ml. with H_2O, cool rapidly, readjust the vol. and measure the yellow color at 410 mμ. Interferences are NO_2^- and ClO_4^-.

Hydrostrychnine or narcotine can be applied similarly.[3, 58]

Strychnidine allows colorimetric detn. of 0·1–1 p.p.m. N.[59] To 5 ml. soln. add 0·40 ml. sulfanilic acid soln. (0·6 g. in 70 ml. hot H_2O and 20 ml. hot HCl, dild. to 100 ml. with H_2O); after at least 10 min., add 5·4 ml. reagent (0·320 g. strychnidine in 1 l. H_2SO_4) and measure at 540 mμ (filter) after 20 ± 1 min.

β-Methylumbelliferone provides a detn. of 0·5 μg. NO_3^- in 0·3 ml. soln.[60] Add 0·6 ml. reagent, boil for 3–5 min., add H_2O, make alk. with NH_4OH, add H_2O and compare the yellow color.

Phenarsazinic acid may be used for NO_3^- in neutral or slightly alk. soln.[61] Evap. the soln. to dryness, add 1 ml. 0·3% reagent and 1 ml. H_2SO_4, heat for 10 min. on a steam-bath, add 20 ml. 30% NaOH, leave for 10 min., dil. to a definite vol. with H_2O and measure the red color with a blue filter in a 100 ml. cuvette. The aliquot used should contain <200 μg. NO_3^-. Interferences are IO_3^-, ClO_3^-, BrO_3^- and VO_3^-.

The absorbance of NO_3^- itself can be utilized.[62] Up to 0·6 mg. NO_3^- in 100 ml. can be measured at 203 or 210 mμ, and 1·4 mg. NO_3^- at 220 mμ. Small amts. of AcO^-, Cr^{3+}, ClO_3^- and Mn^{2+} can be tolerated, as well as moderate amts. of Co, Zn, PO_4^{3-}, Cl^-, SO_4^{2-}; Ca, Ba, Sr, Mg, Na, Ni, Al and NH_4^+ do not interfere.

NITRITE

(a) $KMnO_4$ titration provides a rapid method for NO_2^- detn.[1, 3, 48] Pour 50 ml. sample soln. slowly into excess of 0·2*N* $KMnO_4$ (10 ml. more than was required by a preliminary test) mixed with 10 ml. 1:4 H_2SO_4. Heat to 70–80°C, add 25 ml. 1:4 H_2SO_4, titrate with 0·2*N* $Na_2C_2O_4$ till colorless, add 5 ml. in excess and back-titrate with $KMnO_4$ soln.

Many other redox reagents can be applied for detn. of NO_2^- (for details, see refs. 3, 48; see also Chapter 54. p. 410).

(b) α-Naphthylamine-HCl and sulfanilic acid form the well-known Griess reagent, which is suitable[3, 63] for detn. of <7 μg. NO_2^-. To prep. the reagents, dissolve 0·6 g. of the amine in 100 ml. H_2O contg. 1 ml. HCl; and dissolve 0·6 g. sulfanilic acid in 70 ml. H_2O, cool, add 20 ml. HCl and dil. to 100 ml. with H_2O.

For a detn. treat 50 ml. soln. at pH 6·5–7·5 with 1·0 ml. sulfanilic acid soln., wait for 3–5 min., check the pH (pH 1·4), add 1·0 ml. amine soln. and 1·0 ml. 2*M* NaOAc, and measure the reddish-purple color at 520 mμ after 10–30 min.

NOTES. (1) Interferences are strong reductants and oxidants, Ag, Hg, Cu, Bi, Sb, VO_3^-, WO_4^{2-}, Au^{3+}, Pt^{4+}, 100 p.p.m. CN^- or Co, 200 p.p.m. SiO_2, AcO^- or CO_3^{2-}, and 40 p.p.m. Cr^{3+} or Sn^{4+}.

(2) An alternative reagent[64] contains 10 g. sulfanilic acid, 1 g. α-naphthylamine and 89 g. tartaric acid mixed. Add 0·3 g. of this mixt. to 50 ml. soln. and measure after 20 min.

(3) Other amines and/or acids can replace either of the components of the Griess reagent; for details, see ref. 3. Sulfanilamide (0·5% in 1:5 HCl) and 0·3% *N*-(1-naphthyl)-ethylenediamine-2HCl in 1% HCl provide a more sensitive method than the above.[65] For 0·001–0·015 p.p.m. N as NO_2^- in 50 ml. neutral soln., add 2 ml. amide soln., wait for 3 min., add 1 ml. amine soln. and measure the red color after 15 min. at 550 mμ.

α-Naphthylamine and phenoldisulfonic acid also allow a very sensitive detn.[66] For 0·005–0·2 p.p.m. N in 10 ml. soln. add 2 ml. amine soln. (0·2 g. in 14·7 g. AcOH and 20 ml. H_2O), heat for 2–5 min. in boiling H_2O and add 0·2 ml. phenoldisulfonic acid soln. (for prepn. see p. 464); after 10 min. measure the violet color in a 2 cm. cell at 560 mμ. NO_3^- does not interfere but Fe^{2+}, SiO_3^{2-}, Cu, Al, Pb and S^- interfere. The sensitivity is decreased when the reagents are added in the reverse order. For detn. of 0·1–1 p.p.m. N, treat 10 ml. soln. with 0·3 ml. acid and 1 ml. amine at 10–23°C for 15 min. or at 30°C for 5 min.; measure in a 2 cm. cell at 350 mμ.

Many combinations of reagents are possible. Dimethyl-α-naphthylamine and sulfanilic acid are suitable for 1–4 μg. N in 50 ml. soln.[3, 67] Dimethylaniline and sulfanilic acid are satisfactory for 1–10 p.p.m. N.[3, 67] Dimethylaniline alone can be used.[68] Phenol can be applied with aniline or with sulfanilic acid.[69]. β-Naphthol is suitable with xylidine,[69] benzidine[69] or Na-naphthionate.[3, 69] α- or β-Naphthol is satisfactory with sulfanilic acid.[3, 69] α-Naphthylamine is applicable with tartaric acid,[3, 68] novocaine,[3, 70] or aniline.[71] *m*-Phenylenediamine,[67, 69] *o*-dianisidine[67] and procaine[72] are other suggestions.

(4) *p*-Sulfanilic acid alone is applicable for colorimetry of 3–50 μg N.[73] Adjust to pH 1·4 with HCl, add 1·0 ml. reagent (0·60 g. in 50 ml., warmed, cooled and dild. to 100 ml. with H_2O), dil. to 100 ml. with H_2O and measure at 270 mμ within 3–15 min.

(5) Chloro-*p*-phenylenediamine (0·01*M* in 1:7 HCl) allows detn. of 10–50 μg. NO_2^- in 40 ml. soln. at pH 5–7.[74] Add 5 ml. reagent, dil. to 50 ml. with H_2O and measure at 354 mμ after 10 min.

(6) Nitrition B may be used gravimetrically for detn. of NO_2^- at pH 1·5–2·8.[75] Add reagent, filter, wash with 0·1*M* H_2SO_4 and with H_2O, and dry at 75°C. Hg and Ag interfere.

(c) $AgBrO_3$ provides a gravimetric detn. of 1 g. $NaNO_2$ in 200 ml. soln.[3] Add the sample soln. dropwise to 1·5 g. $AgBrO_3$ in 100 ml. H_2O and 110 ml. 2*N* AcOH; then add 30 ml. 1:4 H_2SO_4, heat to 85°C, filter on a Gooch crucible and wash with hot H_2O. Dry at 130°C and weigh as AgBr. Cl^- interferes but can be detd. separately and a correction made. An iodometric finish is also possible.[48]

$KClO_3$ can be applied similarly, in conjunction with a Volhard titration.[3]

(d) Iodometric titration is satisfactory for 0·05–0·5 mg. N as NO_2^- in 20 ml. soln.[3, 48, 76] Add 4 g. $NaHCO_3$ and 5 ml. 10% KI, pass CO_2 through the soln. for 10 min., add 10 ml. 5*N* H_2SO_4 (free of O_2) and titrate with 0·002*N* $Na_2S_2O_3$. NO_2^- can also be detd. by addn. of Br_2 and back-titration with As^{3+} soln. using starch-I_2 indicator.[77]

For a colorimetric method on this principle,[3, 78] suitable for $>0·25$ μg. NO_2^- in 50 ml. soln., add 2 ml. 6*N* H_2SO_4 and 4 ml. reagent and compare the blue color. For the reagent, boil 20 g. $SnCl_2$ and 5 g. starch with 100 ml. H_2O for several hr. adding H_2O occasionally; then add 2 g. ZnI_2, dil. to 1 l. with H_2O, leave for 1–2 weeks and decant.

(e) Hydrazine sulfate addn. can be followed by titration of the NH_3 formed.[3, 79] For 6 mg. NO_2^- in 20 ml. soln. which is neutral to neutral red indicator, pour the sample soln. into 40 ml. reagent (0·05*M*), heat on a steam-bath for 20 min., cool and add 15 ml. neutral 40% HCHO soln. Add 0·2 ml. phenolphthalein and titrate with 0·1*N* NaOH. Other neutralization methods are also available.[3] Reduction with Devarda's alloy is also satisfactory (see p. 464).

(f) Azotometry is possible after treatment of a neutral soln. of NO_2^- with 0·3 g. sulfamic acid.[3, 80] Conversion to N_2 is also feasible with NH_4Cl, urea, NaN_3 or HCHO. Thiourea converts NO_2^- to N_2 in AcOH soln. and to NO in HCl soln.[81] NO is also obtained by treatment with $K_4Fe(CN)_6$.

Nephelometric detn. has been proposed involving treatment with sulfamate and addn. of $BaCl_2$.[82] Gravimetric detn. is also feasible.[83]

(g) Miscellaneous colorimetric methods. Rivanol is satisfactory for 0–60 μg. $NaNO_2$ in soln.[3, 84] Add 10 ml. 0·05% rivanol and 15 ml. 6*N* HCl, dil. to 50 ml. with H_2O and measure at 525 mμ.

Indole is suitable for 0·01–0·36 mg. NO_2^- in soln.[3, 85] Add 1 ml. reagent (0·15 g. indole in 10 ml. EtOH, dild. to 100 ml. with H_2O) and 1 ml. 1:1 H_2SO_4, dil. to 100 ml. with H_2O and compare the red color after 5 min.

Antipyrine forms a green color with 50 ml. sample contg. 50 p.p.m. NO_2^- on addn. of 5 ml. reagent (1% antipyrine in AcOH, prepd. from 10% soln. immediately before use).[3, 86] Interferences are HCl, H_2SO_4 and Fe^{3+}.

Resorcinol allows detn. of 10–30 μg. NO_2^-/ml. soln.[87] Add 2 ml. H_2O, 0·5 ml. 1% reagent mixed with 5 drops H_2SO_4; add 10 drops H_2SO_4 and heat for 30 min. on a steam-bath. For NO_3^- detn. proceed as for NO_2^-, then add 10 drops H_2SO_4 and 1 drop HCl and heat further.

Thioglycolic acid can be used for $<$10 mg. NO_2^- in neutral soln.[88] Add 5 ml. 4% reagent, shake, add 1 ml. AcOH and 1 ml. Me_2CO, dil. to 100 ml. with H_2O and measure the yellow-red color at 355 mμ.

CYANIDE

(a) $AgNO_3$ is generally used titrimetrically, but gravimetry is also possible. The Liebig–Denigès method is the best known; Volhard's titration and various adsorption indicator methods are also applicable. For the Liebig–Denigès titration,[1, 89] treat the soln. with 5–8 ml. 6*N* NH_4OH and 0·2 g. KI, dil. to 100 ml. and titrate with 0·1*N* $AgNO_3$ until a turbidity appears. Ni-dimethylglyoxime can also serve as indicator. Amperometric titration[90] is applicable for 0–14 μg. CN^-.

For Volhard's titration,[89] add excess 0·1*N* $AgNO_3$ to the neutral soln., make slightly acidic with HNO_3 and filter through dry paper. Pipet an aliquot of the soln., add Fe^{3+}-alum and titrate with 0·1*N* NH_4SCN.

With diphenylcarbazone as indicator,[91] add 4–5 drops 0·3% indicator in EtOH to the soln. at pH 9–10 and titrate with $AgNO_3$ soln. to a reddish color. See Table 10 for other adsorption indicators.

p-Dimethylaminobenzylidenerhodanine is another possible indicator for direct titration.[92]

Gravimetric detn. is less satisfactory, the ppt. being dried below 237°C and weighed.[93]

(b) Chloramine T used in conjunction with pyrazolone derivs. in pyridine allows detn. of 0·05–1·0 p.p.m. CN^- colorimetrically.[92, 94] To 20 ml. soln., add 10 ml. buffer pH 6·8 (KH_2PO_4 and Na_2HPO_4), 0·25 ml. 1% chloramine T and wait for 1 min. Then add 15 ml. pyrazolone soln. (a 1:5 mixt. of 0·1% bis(1-phenyl-3-methylpyrazolone) in pyridine and 0·25% 1-phenyl-3-methyl-5-pyrazolone in H_2O) and measure the blue color at 620 mμ after 30 min.

NOTES. (1) Fe and other ions interfere but methods are available for overcoming the interferences.[94]

(2) Br_2 water can be used in conjunction with benzidine in pyridine in a similar procedure.[95] For 0·03–2·0 μg. CN^- in 1·0 ml. blood serum, add 5·0 ml. 20% CCl_3CO_2H and pass air through for 15 min. Collect the CN^- evolved in 0·5 ml. 0·1*N* NaOH and then add 0·50 ml. 20% CCl_3CO_2H, 1 drop Br_2 water, 0·20 ml. As^{3+} soln. (2 g. As_2O_3 in 100 ml. H_2O heated under reflux) and 3·6 ml. benzidine–pyridine soln. (4% benzidine–HCl mixed 1:5 with a mixt. of 1 l. 60% w/v pyridine and 100 ml. HCl just before use). Measure the red color at 532 mμ.

(3) Chloramine T can also be applied fluorimetrically with nicotinamide.[96] For 0·3–6 μg. CN^- in 1 ml. soln., add 4 ml. 0·5*N* KOH, 4 ml. 2*N* $KHCO_3$, 2 ml. 25% nicotinamide and 1 ml. 10% chloramine T. Dil. to 20 ml. with H_2O, add 4 ml. 6*N* KOH after 4 min. and measure the fluorescence under UV light.

(4) Formation of BrCN is also utilized in iodometric titrations.[48] For detn. of 0·04–0·1 g. HCN, add 5 ml. 20% H_3PO_4, Br_2 water to give a yellow color, and 2 ml. 5% phenol. After 15 min. add 0·5 g. KI and titrate with 0·01–0·1*N* $Na_2S_2O_3$ after 3–5 min. No interference arises from Cl^-, Br^-, S^{2-}, SO_3^{2-} and $S_2O_3^{2-}$.

(c) α-Furildioxime, $PdCl_2$ and $Ni(NO_3)_2$ provide[97] a colorimetric method for 0–3 p.p.m. CN^-. To 100 ml. soln. add 5 ml. of Pd–α-furildioxime soln. (0·01 g. dioxime in 25 ml. EtOH mixed with 0·3 ml. 5% $PdCl_2$, filtered, washed with EtOH; the ppt. is dissolved in 5% KI). Then add 3 ml. satd. NaOAc and 0·5 ml. 5% $Ni(NO_3)_2$ and compare the color within 10 min. The color varies from green–violet (with 0·5 p.p.m.) through violet to pink (with 3 p.p.m.).

NOTES. (1) Interference of S^{2-} is prevented by $Cd(NO_3)_2$ addn. and filtration; 2 p.p.m. Cl^- and 20 p.p.m. PO_4^{3-} interfere. Al and Fe can be masked by citrate or tartrate or sepd. by ion exchange.

(2) α-Nitroso-β-naphthol can replace α-furildioxime.[98] For detn. of 0·5–10 μg. CN^-/ml. (of the final measured soln.), treat 40 ml. soln. with 3 ml. buffer pH 10 (67 g. NH_4Cl and 500 ml. NH_4OH/l.), add 20 mg. Pd–α-nitroso-β-naphthol, dil. to 50 ml. with H_2O, shake for 3 min., filter and measure at 366 mμ.

(3) CuSCN and Fe-alum provide a colorimetric detn. for $>$ 0·05 mg. CN^-/l.[99] To 10 ml. soln. add 1 ml. buffer soln. (50 ml. 0·1*M* KH_2PO_4 and 29·6 ml. 0·1*N* NaOH) and 15 mg. CuSCN, shake for 1 min., keep at 20°C for 5 min., shake for 30 sec., and repeat the CuSCN addn. and shaking once more. Filter on a micro sinter G4 filter, add Fe^{3+}-alum, etc. P.p.m. of Cl^-, Br^- and I^- which can be tolerated are resp. 500, 100 and 5. $Hg(SCN)_2$ can be applied similarly.[99]

(4) Ni solns. are suitable for titrimetric detns. of CN^-. With dimethylglyoxime as indicator,[100] make 100 ml.

CN^- soln. alk. with NH_4OH and add 1 ml. in excess; then add 0·5 ml. 1% indicator in EtOH and titrate with Ni^{2+} soln. to a red color. For Ni^{2+} soln. use 19·75 g. $(NH_4)_2Ni(SO_4)_2·6H_2O$ and 2 ml. H_2SO_4/l. Resacetophenoneoxime can also serve as indicator (see Chapter 34, p. 267).

In an alternative method,[101] mix 50 ml. 0·01*M* $NiSO_4$, 10 ml. 1*N* NH_4Cl and 10 ml. NH_4OH, add the sample soln. contg. 40 mg. CN^-, and murexide indicator and titrate with 0·01*M* EDTA.

(5) Titration with Cu^{2+} is feasible (Scott and Furman[1]). For a 0·5 g. sample add 100 ml. H_2O and 5 ml. NH_4OH and titrate with Cu soln. (25 g. $CuSO_4·5H_2O$ in 500 ml. H_2O; add NH_4OH until the ppt. dissolves and dil. to 1 l.).

(6) CN^- can also be titrated with 0·01–0·1*M* $Hg(NO_3)_2$ using as indicator 0·1% 4,4′-bis(dimethylamino)-thiobenzophenone in Me_2CO (see Chapter 19, p. 151). Diphenylcarbazone is another suitable indicator (see p. 443). Addn. of excess $Hg(NO_3)_2$, and titration with NH_4SCN using Fe^{3+} indicator is said[102] to be better than $AgNO_3$ methods.

(7) *p*-Dimethylaminobenzilidenerhodanine allows colorimetric detn. of < 9 μg. CN^- in 3 ml. soln.[103] Place the soln. in a Conway cell, add 1 ml. satd. tartaric acid soln. and leave for 2 hr. at 27°C or for 1 hr. at 38°C, absorbing the CN^- in 3 ml. Hg soln. (18·7 μg. Hg^{2+} as nitrate/ml. of 0·005*N* HNO_3). Take a 2 ml. aliquot, add 41 ml. H_2O, 5 ml. 0·8*N* HNO_3 and 2 ml. reagent (75 mg. in 500 ml. abs. EtOH), and place in the dark for 20 min.; measure at 470 mμ.

(d) Miscellaneous colorimetric methods. Satd. picric acid soln. allows detn. of 40–110 μg. HCN/ml.[104] Add 3 ml. satd. picric acid and 1 ml. 5% Na_2CO_3, heat on a steam-bath, cool, dil. to 25 ml. with H_2O and measure the red color at 520 mμ. Interferences are H_2S and SO_3^{2-}. Over 2 μg. CN^- can be detected with Na-picrate paper.

$FeCl_3$ can be applied in conjunction with $FeSO_4$ or K_2S. With $FeSO_4$ the method is suitable for >0·2 mg. HCN in 8 ml. soln.[105, 106] Add 0·1 ml. 1% NaOH and 1 ml. 0·1% $FeSO_4$, warm for 5 min., add 0·25 ml. 0·1% $FeCl_3$ and 1 ml. 1% HCl and measure the blue color. With K_2S, 0·1–8 mg. KCN in 50 ml. alk. soln. can be detd.[106] Add 5 ml. 4% K_2S, evap. to dryness, add 10 ml. Me_2CO, decant and repeat the decantation twice. Then evap. to dryness, cool, dil. to 50 ml. with H_2O, add 2 ml. 0·5% $FeCl_3$ and measure the red color.

Bromate titration can follow treatment with $(NH_4)_2S$.[107]

Hydrolysis of CN^- with HCl at 140–145°C under press. can be followed by detn. with Nessler's reagent.[108]

Benzidine is used in conjunction with Cu^{2+} soln.[109] The leuco-bases of *o*-cresolphthalein or fluorescein and phenolphthalin have been employed.[110]

$HgCl_2$, PhNO and $K_4Fe(CN)_6$ allow detn. of 1–8 × 10^{-5}*M* CN^- solns.[111] Mix a soln. to be 40 × 10^{-6}*M* in $HgCl_2$, 6 × 10^{-4}*M* in PhNO and 4 × 10^{-2}*M* in acetate buffer pH 3·5–6·2, at the final measurement. Add the sample soln., make the soln. 8 × 10^{-4}*M* in $K_4Fe(CN)_6$ and measure the violet color after 20 min.

References

1. Hillebrand and Lundell, 633 (779); Scott and Furman, 629; Kimura, 352; Pigott, 320.
2. Fresenius–Jander, **Ia**, 267 (1940).
3. Fresenius–Jander, **Va**α (1957).
4. Kirk, P. L., *Anal. Chem.*, **22**, 354 (1950).
5. Stubblefield, F. M., and de Turk, E. E., *Ind. Eng. Chem., Anal. Ed.*, **12**, 396 (1940).
6. Mallol, A., *Farm. nueva* (*Madrid*), **11**, (108), 7 (1946).
7. Ballentine, R., and Gregg, J. R., *Anal. Chem.*, **19**, 281 (1947).
8. Kaye, I. A., and Weiner, N., *Ind. Eng. Chem., Anal. Ed.*, **7**, 397 (1935); Ogg, C. L., *et al.*, *Anal. Chem.*, **20**, 83 (1948).
9. Ohashi, S., *Bull. Chem. Soc. Japan*, **28**, 177, 537 (1955).
10. A.S.T.M., 130 ff.
11. Saruhashi, K., *Japan Analyst*, **4**, 337 (1955); Kuck, J. A., *et al.*; *Anal. Chem.*, **22**, 604 (1950); Kirk, P. L., *ibid.*, 611; Mayer, S. W., *et al.*, *ibid.*, **27**, 837 (1955).
12. Vanselow, A. P., *Ind. Eng. Chem., Anal. Ed.*, **12**, 376 (1940); Batmanova, O. Ya, *Gigiena i sanit.*, No. 7, 43 (1953) (solid reagent); Sarkar, P. B., and Ghosh, N. N., *Anal. Chim. Acta*, **14**, 209 (1956); for details see Am. Public Health Assoc., *Standard Methods for Examination of Water, etc.*, 10th ed., pp. 142–148 (1955).
13. Lestra, H., and Roux, G., *Compt. rend.*, **233**, 1453 (1951).
14. Wolf, B., *Anal. Chem.*, **19**, 334 (1947).
15. Kohler, G. M., *Z. anal. Chem.*, **138**, 9 (1953).
16. Welcher, **I**, 377; Adams, C. I., and Spaulding, G. H., *Anal. Chem.*, **27**, 1003 (1955) (after Kjeldahl digestion).
17. Hurka, W., and Ruždič, I., *Mikrochemie ver. Mikrochim. Acta*, **31**, 9 (1943).
18. Blinn, R. C., and Gunther, F. A., *Anal. Chem.*, **29**, 1882 (1957).
19. Scheurer, P. G., and Smith, F., *Anal. Chem.*, **27**, 1616 (1955).
20. Yoe, 307; Welcher, **I**, 189.
21. Crowther, A. B., and Large, R. S., *Analyst*, **81**, 64 (1956); also see Takei, S., *Japan Analyst*, **5**, 261 (1956) (EtOH).
22. Machida, Y., *J. Chem. Soc. Japan*, **68**, 52, 84 (1947).
23. Welcher, **I**, 187; Pigott, 337.
24. Kruse, J. M., and Mellon, M. G., *Anal. Chem.*, **25**, 1188 (1953).
25. Lear, J. B., and Mellon, *Anal. Chem.*, **29**, 293 (1957).
26. Kamada, H., and Saito, K., *Japan Analyst*, **6**, 150 (1957).
27. Kolthoff, I. M., and Stenger, V. A., *Ind. Eng. Chem., Anal. Ed.*, **7**, 79 (1935); Kolthoff, and Belcher, *Volumetric Analysis*, Vol. III, 582 (1957).
28. Arcand, G. M., and Swift, E. H., *Anal. Chem.*, **28**, 440 (1956).
29. Iwasaki, K., *J. Japan Biochem. Soc.*, **23**, 207 (1951).
30. Welcher, **II**, 173, 354.
31. Welcher, **III**, 138; Heck, J. E., *et al.*, *Analyst*, **59**, 18 (1934).
32. Welcher, **IV**, 224.
33. Donald, M. B., *Analyst*, **61**, 249 (1936).
34. Sallinger, H., and Hwang, Y., *Z. anal. Chem.*, **115**, 174 (1938/39).
35. Szabó, Z. G., and Bartha, L., *Nature*, **166**, 309 (1950).
36. Lingane, J. J., and Pecsok, R. L., *Anal. Chem.*, **21** 622 (1949).

37. MULLIN, J. B., and RILEY, J. P., *Anal. Chim. Acta*, **12**, 464 (1955).
38. MATSUI, H., *J. Chem. Soc. Japan*, **64**, 809 (1943).
39. KATO, T., *Japan Analyst*, **3**, 231 (1954).
40. GARNER, B., *et al.*, *Anal. Chem.*, **28**, 1589 (1956).
41. EGAMI, F., *et al.*, *Bull. Chem. Soc. Japan*, **27**, 623 (1954).
42. HOLLER, A. C., and HUCH, R. V., *Anal. Chem.*, **21**, 1385 (1949); JONES, G. B., and UNDERDOWN, R. E., *ibid.*, **25**, 806 (1953).
43. CERNĂTESCU, R., and GHELLER, E., *Z. anal. Chem.*, **101**, 402 (1935); WELCHER, **I**, 239.
44. WELCHER, **I**, 147 ff; BARNES, H., *Analyst*, **75**, 388 (1950) (2,4-xylenol).
45. TARAS, M. J., *Anal. Chem.*, **22**, 1020 (1950).
46. SWINEHART, B. A., and BRANDT, W. W., *Proc. Indiana Acad. Sci.*, **63**, 133 (1953); also see KATO, T., *Japan Analyst*, **3**, 229 (1954).
47. HARTMANN, H., and BÄTHGE, B., *Angew. Chem.*, **65**, 107 (1953).
48. KOLTHOFF and BELCHER, *Volumetric Analysis*, Vol. III, 182 ff (1957).
49. WELLINGS, A. W., *Trans. Faraday Soc.*, **28**, 665 (1932).
50. MURAKAMI, T., *Japan Analyst*, **4**, 630 (1955).
51. ENGELBRECHT, R. M., and MCCOY, F. A., *Anal. Chem.*, 1619 (1956).
52. SWANN, M. H., and ADAMS, M. L., *Anal. Chem.*, **28**, 1630 (1956).
53. OHASHI, S., and MAKISHIMA, H., *Bull. Chem. Soc. Japan*, **29**, 700 (1956).
54. MAYER, O., *Z. Untersuch. d. Lebensm.*, **66**, 193 (1933).
55. UNGAR, J., *J. Appl. Chem.* (*London*), **6**, 245 (1956); WELCHER, **IV**, 509.
56. WELCHER, **III**, 557.
57. WELCHER, **II**, 362 ff.
58. WELCHER, **IV**, 208 ff.
59. WESTLAND, A. D., and LANGFORD, R. R., *Anal. Chem.*, **28**, 1996 (1956).
60. WELCHER, **I**, 215.
61. PIETSCH, R., *Mikrochim. Acta*, 1672 (1956).
62. BASTIAN, R., *et al.*, *Anal. Chem.*, **29**, 1795 (1957).
63. RIDER, B. F., and MELLON, M. G., *Ind. Eng. Chem., Anal. Ed.*, **18**, 96 (1946); WELCHER, **II**, 405.
64. MACHIDA, Y., *J. Chem., Soc. Japan.*, **69**, 176 (1948).
65. SHINN, M. B., *Ind. Eng. Chem., Anal. Ed.*, **13**, 33 (1941); KERSHAW, N. F., and CHAMBERLAIN, N. S., *ibid.*, **14**, 312 (1942); BARNES, H., and FOLKARD, A. R., *Analyst*, **76**, 599 (1951).
66. ATO, S., and AOKI, H., *Repts. Sci. Research Inst.* (*Tokyo*), **30**, 329 (1954).
67. WELCHER, **II**, 343 ff.
68. YOE, 309.
69. WELCHER, **I**, 142 ff.
70. WELCHER, **IV**, 250.
71. KATO, T., *et al.*, *Japan Analyst*, **3**, 231 (1954).
72. JAMBOR, B., *Agrokémia és Talajtan*, **1**, 51, 67 (1951).
73. PAPPENHAGEN, J. M., and MELLON, M. G., *Anal. Chem.*, **25**, 341 (1953).
74. KUEMMEL, D. F., and MELLON, *Anal. Chem.*, **28**, 1675 (1956).
75. KOMER, N. P., and MARTYCHENKO, I. U., *Zhur. Anal. Khim.*, **11**, 259 (1956).
76. RAO, G. G., and PANDALAI, K. M., *Analyst*, **59**, 99 (1934); also see LANG, F. M., and AUNIS, G., *Chim. anal.*, **32**, 139 (1950).
77. KELLNER, A., *Z. anal. Chem.*, **157**, 13 (1957).
78. YOE, 313.
79. STEMPEL, B., *Z. anal. Chem.*, **91**, 412, 413 (1933).
80. LUTSENKO, YU. S., *J. Applied Chem.* (*U.S.S.R.*), **10**, 948 (1937).
81. WELCHER, **IV**, 187.
82. HILL, W. H., and HATCH, T. F., *Anal. Chem.*, **24**, 606 (1952).
83. BAUMGARTEN, F., and MARGGRAFF, I., *Ber.*, **63**, 1019 (1930); HERNANDEZ-GUTIERREZ, F., *Anales real soc. españ. fís. y quím.* (*Madrid*), **47B**, 649 (1951).
84. SVACH, M., and ZÝKA, J., *Z. anal. Chem.*, **148**, 1 (1955); WELCHER, **II**, 377.
85. WELCHER, **III**, 566.
86. YOE, 311; WELCHER, **III**, 108.
87. SÁNCHEZ, J. A., *Rev. asoc. bioquím. Arg.*, **16**, (64), 3 (1949).
88. ZIEGLER, M., and GLEMSER, O., *Z. anal. Chem.*, **144** 187 (1955).
89. KOLTHOFF and STENGER, *Volumetric Analysis*, Vol. II, 282 (1947).
90. BAKER, B. B., and MORRISON, J. D., *Anal. Chem.*, **27**, 1306 (1955).
91. RIPAN-TILICI, R., *Z. anal. Chem.*, **118**, 305 (1939/40).
92. LUDZACK, F. J., *et al.*, *Anal. Chem.*, **26**, 784 (1954).
93. TREADWELL and HALL, *Analytical Chemistry*, Vol. II, 338 (1935).
94. KRUSE, J. M., and MELLON, M. G., *Anal. Chem.*, **25**, 446 (1953); EPSTEIN, J., *ibid.*, **19**, 272 (1947).
95. BRUCE, R. B., *et al.*, *Anal. Chem.*, **27**, 1346 (1955); ALDRIDGE, W. N., *Analyst*, **69**, 262 (1944); **70**, 474 (1945).
96. HANKER, J. S., *et al.*, *Anal. Chem.*, **29**, 879 (1957).
97. BROOKE, M., *Anal. Chem.*, **24**, 583 (1952).
98. KATO, T., and SHINRA, K., *J. Chem. Soc. Japan*, **77**, 885 (1956).
99. UTSUMI, S., *J. Chem. Soc. Japan*, **74**, 32, 479 (1953).
100. URUSOVSKAYA, L. G., and ZHILINA, P. I., *Zavodskaya Lab.*, **15**, 740 (1949).
101. SCHWARZENBACH, G., *Die komplexometrische Titration*, 81 (1955); also see VŘEŠTÁL, J., and HAVÍŘ, J., *Chem. listy*, **50**, 1321 (1956) (pyrocatechol violet).
102. KOLTHOFF and STENGER, *Volumetric Analysis*, Vol. II, 339 (1947).
103. OHLWEILER, O. A., and MEDITSCH, J. O., *Anal. Chim. Acta*, **11**, 111 (1954).
104. WELCHER, **IV**, 31; also see FRANÇOIS, M. T., and LAFFITTE, N., *Bull. soc. chim. biol.*, **17**, 1088 (1935).
105. CHILDS, A. E., and BALL, W. C., *Analyst*, **60**, 294 (1935).
106. YOE, 154.
107. SHAW, J. A., *et al.*, *Ind. Eng. Chem., Anal. Ed.*, **16**, 550 (1944).
108. GALES, N., and PENSA, A. J., *Ind. Eng. Chem., Anal. Ed.*, **5**, 80 (1933).
109. WELCHER, **II**, 316.
110. WELCHER, **IV**, 482 ff.
111. KRALJÍC, I., and MATE, M., *Croat. Chem. Acta*, **28**, 249 (1956).

GENERAL INDEX

ORGANIC REAGENT INDEX